Upwelling Systems:
Evolution Since the Early Miocene

Geological Society Special Publications
Series Editor J. BROOKS

GEOLOGICAL SOCIETY SPECIAL PUBLICATION NO 64

Upwelling Systems:
Evolution Since the Early Miocene

EDITED BY

C. P. SUMMERHAYES
Institute of Oceanographic Sciences
UK

W. L. PRELL
Brown University
USA

K. C. EMEIS
Universität Kiel
Germany

1992

Published by

The Geological Society

London

THE GEOLOGICAL SOCIETY

The Society was founded in 1807 as the Geological Society of London and is the oldest geological society in the world. It received its Royal Charter in 1825 for the purpose of 'investigating the mineral structure of the Earth'. The Society is Britain's national learned society for geology with a Fellowship of 7000.

Fellowship is open to those holding a recognized honours degree in geology or cognate subject and who have at least two years relevant postgraduate experience, or have not less than six years relevant experience in geology or a cognate subject. A Fellow who has not less than five years relevant postgraduate experience in the practice of geology may apply for validation and subject to approval will be able to use the designatory letters C. Geol. (Chartered Geologist). Further information about the Society is available from the Membership Manager, Geological Society, Burlington House, London, United Kingdom W1V 0JU.

Published by the Geological Society from:
The Geological Society Publishing House
Unit 7
Brassmill Enterprise Centre
Brassmill Lane
Bath
Avon BA1 3JN
UK
(*Orders*: Tel. 0225 445046)

First published 1992

Distributors

USA
  AAPG Bookstore
  PO Box 979
  Tulsa
  Oklahoma 74101−0979
  USA
  (*Orders*: Tel: (918)584−2555)

Australia
  Australian Mineral Foundation
  63 Conyngham St
  Glenside
  South Australia 5065
  Australia
  (*Orders*: Tel: (08)379−0444)

British Library Cataloguing in Publication Data
A catalogue record for this book is available from the British Library

ISBN 0−903317−78−8

Contents

The geological record of upwelling evolution

Evolution of upwelling systems since the Early Miocene

C. P. SUMMERHAYES[1], W. L. PRELL[2] & K-C. EMEIS[3]

[1] *Institute of Oceanographic Sciences Deacon Laboratory, Brook Road, Wormley, Godalming, Surrey GU8 5UB*
[2] *Department of Geological Sciences, Brown University, Providence, RI, USA*
[3] *Geologisch-Paläontologisches Institut, Universität Kiel, Olshausenstrasse 40/60, 2300 Kiel, Germany*

This volume contains data on recent advances in the understanding and applications of the evolution of upwelling systems since the Early Miocene. The primary objectives of the volume are to identify the sedimentary expressions of coastal upwelling, to identify features common to sedimentary deposits in upwelling centres and to trace the evolution of these sensitive recorders of climatic and oceanographic change since the establishment of modern global circulation systems in the Miocene. The authors deliberately focus on results from deep ocean drilling expeditions, particularly Ocean Drilling Project (ODP) Legs 108 off NW Africa, 112 off Peru, and 117 off Arabia, and Deep Sea Drilling Project (DSDP) Leg 75 off SW Africa, in an effort to make these results more accessible and meaningful to the wider community. The editors hope that this volume will be a first step to encourage construction of meaningful syntheses which identify and explain the causes and characteristics of persistent upwelling systems over time, how these upwelling systems respond to climatic forcing, and what global teleconnections exist between different upwelling centres.

A previous major publication on upwelling in the geological record was *Coastal Upwelling: Its Sediment Record* (Suess & Thiede 1983; Thiede & Suess 1983), the proceedings of a NATO meeting in Portugal in 1981. Since then, significant new data have been obtained on the process and history of upwelling, especially through ODP and DSDP drilling. Syntheses of these new results could provide us with a unique opportunity to reconstruct the temporal and spatial palaeoenvironmental patterns associated with upwelling systems since the Early Miocene. These patterns should provide new insights on the forcing and feedback mechanisms that connect changes in climate, ocean circulation and marine productivity. The earlier publication described individual systems and their processes. We hope the present one will encourage syntheses that will contribute to the understanding of the global-scale history and evolution of upwelling environments and their response to climatic forcing.

Background and goals

A wide variety of environmental responses is encoded in the sedimentary sequences that lie under continuous or seasonal upwelling systems. The long-term (>1 Ma) persistence and trends of these upwelling systems as well as their short-term variability reflect changes in climate, tectonics and oceanic circulation. Thus a wide variety of mechanisms and processes must be explored to explain the variability observed in sedimentary upwelling records. For example researchers on previous ODP Legs (Ruddiman, Sarnthein *et al.* 1987; Suess, von Huene *et al.* 1988; Prell, Niitsuma *et al.* 1989) have suggested the following explanations for the variability of specific upwelling systems.

(1) Changes in the strength or direction of the local or regional wind fields: e.g. the Arabian Sea and NW African upwelling systems.

(2) Changes in the origin and composition of the intermediate waters that upwell in boundary current systems: e.g. the Peru and Benguela systems.

(3) Changes in nutrient availability of upwelled waters, which may affect primary productivity, the source of most organic components preserved in the sediments.

(4) Changes in the strength of oxygen minimum zones related to the biogenic oxygen demand, and the advection of bottom waters to slope and shelf depositional centres.

(5) Changes in clastic inputs from winds and rivers.

A better understanding of the diverse upwelling processes and their associated sediment variability will advance a primary goal of the ODP as set by its conferences on Scientific Ocean Drilling (COSOD I and II), namely, to

From SUMMERHAYES, C. P., PRELL, W. L. & EMEIS, K. C. (eds), 1992, *Upwelling Systems: Evolution Since the Early Miocene*. Geological Society Special Publication No 64, pp 1–5.

understand the causes of long-term changes in the atmosphere, oceans, cryosphere and biosphere. The depositional systems associated with persistent upwelling are extremely sensitive to changes in climatic and oceanographic patterns. The sediments beneath upwelling systems contain high-resolution, multicomponent records of oceanic responses that can be used to assess the importance of processes such as the orbital forcing of the Earth's climate system. The sedimentary records now available from the major upwelling systems provide us with material to identify changes in regional and possibly global oceanic circulation and biological productivity since the Early Miocene (i.e. over about the past 15 Ma). Thus, syntheses of the sedimentary records of upwelling history should yield crucial information about interoceanic variability, global atmospheric patterns, oceanic current systems and the causal mechanisms that link the different centres in time and space.

A second goal that the scientific community identified during both COSOD I and II was to understand the origin and evolution of marine sedimentary sequences. Specific goals included understanding the response of marine sedimentation to sea-level fluctuations, understanding sedimentation in oxygen deficient environments, and establishing global mass balances of sedimentary organic matter. These goals support and are inter-twined with the climatic and palaeoceanographic goals listed by COSOD I and II, because sedimentation associated with upwelling systems commonly occurs in oxygen-deficient environments that are rich in organic matter.

Thus far, ODP Legs 108, 112 and 117 (Ruddiman, Sarnthein *et al.* 1987; Suess, von Huene *et al.* 1988; Prell, Niitsuma *et al.* 1989) and DSDP Leg 75 (Hay, Sibuet *et al.* 1984) have successfully recovered high-quality, continuous sediment records that extend to the Middle Miocene in low-latitude upwelling areas. By the autumn of 1990, most of the shore-based research for the ODP Scientific Results volumes was complete. We considered it timely, therefore, to appraise the emerging new data sets and the models and concepts used to explain them. We hoped that a scientific conference dedicated to evaluating the geological record of upwelling on a global scale would facilitate the reconstruction of coherent patterns in global oceanic and atmospheric circulation for the last 10–15 Ma. A goal of the conference was to urge researchers to go beyond local/regional inventories and to question whether the environmental events and trends recognized in individual upwelling systems are synchronous and if they can be causally related on a global scale.

During the past decade, a wide variety of studies has linked global climate changes (on both short and long time scales) to changes in the CO_2 composition of the atmosphere. These CO_2 changes implicate the oceans and their organic-rich and carbonate-rich sediments as an important link and feedback in the carbon system. The exact role of upwelling systems in removing carbon and nutrients from the oceanic system is unknown, but is a critical process that must be better evaluated. Thus sedimentary records of the global upwelling systems offer the potential to estimate the role of upwelling in the carbon budget of the earth.

Sediments deposited beneath upwelling systems also have the potential to provide detailed information about diagenetic processes, because the abundance of organic matter may exaggerate diagenetic trends. The supply of reactants into the diagenetic zones can cause extreme environments to develop within the sediment column. Bacteria in these environments may persist to depths of 200 m beneath the seabed. As a result, a wide range of mineral formation reactions take place in the sediments of upwelling zones. Many of these phenomena may be better understood by evaluating their occurrence in the context of upwelling zones of differing chemical and sedimentological characteristics.

Studies of sediments associated with upwelling zones may also provide information about the hydrogeology of continental margins. At least three drilling Legs in upwelling areas (ODP 112 and 117, and DSDP 75) discovered previously unknown de-watering systems in the subsurface of shelf and slope basins. Naturally these systems further influence the diagenetic environment.

Our goals were to establish a framework in which the following three topics could be addressed and discussed by the authors.

1. **Criteria and methods to identify and explain simultaneous upwelling events in Cenozoic sediments**

   Under this heading we solicited papers on the:
   (a) faunal and floral indicators of upwelling,
   (b) sedimentary geochemical indicators of upwelling,
   (c) isotopic records of upwelling sequences since the Miocene,
   (d) organic carbon accumulation rates since the Miocene,
   (e) molecular stratigraphy.

2. **Establish and explain the historical sequence**

of simultaneous upwelling events in the Neogene

Under this heading we solicited contributions to examine:

(a) the onset of intense coastal upwelling systems in the modern oceans,

(b) the character, timing and causes of changes in upwelling sedimentation,

(c) the impact of glacial/interglacial climatic variability on upwelling sedimentation and productivity,

(d) the implications for oceanic circulation and climatic history.

3. **Diagenetic conditions in sediments of upwelling zones**

Under this heading we solicited papers to examine:

(a) pore water chemistry,

(b) bacterial activity deep in the sediment column,

(c) minerological and chemical markers of input and diagenesis.

Findings and recommendations for understanding the evolution and global significance of upwelling systems since the Miocene

The thematic groups and their areas of discussion are:

Group 1. Upwelling systems and criteria

This group considered how our understanding of the oceanography of modern upwelling systems should influence the study of palaeo-upwelling systems. It also focussed on the assumptions and criteria (sedimentary, biogenic, and chemical) that are used to identify past upwelling systems and their variability as well as on the chronology needed to accomplish global correlations of upwelling systems.

Group 2. Upwelling evolution, timing and modelling

This group examined the status of our knowledge about the character and evolution of individual upwelling systems, their scales of variability and relation to other climatic/oceanic events, and our ability to correlate events and trends between upwelling systems and oceans.

Group 3. Diagenesis

This group surveyed our knowledge of changes in the geochemical environments associated with upwelling systems and how they are preserved (or modified) in the sedimentary column.

Each thematic group was asked to evaluate the status of data sets, methodologies, concepts, and models in their respective areas ('Findings') and to recommend actions needed to advance our understanding of upwelling systems and how to model them ('Recommendations'). These recommendations were discussed in a plenary session and are presented here as a summary of the conference discussions:

1. Finding: To more accurately interpret the sediment record in terms of oceanographic processes, we need to better understand the extent of variability in modern upwelling systems and the variability of the flux of biogenic and other components into the sediments.

Recommendation: Sediment traps need to be deployed in upwelling areas to obtain seasonal fluxes of sedimentary components. Multi-level and spatial arrays of sediment traps would provide one means of assessing near-bottom, lateral sediment flux and the lateral advection of particulates on mid-water density surfaces (which spreads the upwelling signal). The scope of these experiments requires a sedimentological equivalent to the Coastal Upwelling Experiment and must include a systematic program of long-term satellite measurements for the study areas. Satellite measurements of the variability and productivity of modern upwelling systems, such as the EOS system, must be an integral part of these studies. More extensive use could be made of archives of Coastal Zone Color Scanner (CZCS) satellite data to study long-term variability in the 1980s.

2. Finding: We need to improve our understanding of the spatial dimensions of upwelling systems and how these dimensions change with time and major oceanographic/climatic variations. Long-term records of upwelling indices cannot be properly interpreted without a framework of more recent spatial and temporal changes of the system. At present, this knowledge does not exist for some major systems.

Recommendation: Networks of piston cores must be acquired or compiled to define the spatial dimensions for relatively recent times, backed up with networks of ODP hydraulic piston core (HPC) holes for longer, continuous records. These data would enable detailed CLIMAP-style mapping of specific time horizons, e.g. at 18 000 years, to establish how an entire upwelling system behaved at one time.

3. Finding: We need to improve our understanding of how oceanographic signals become recorded in sediment. One limitation on this goal is the poor recovery of the sediment–water interface during most coring operations.

Recommendation: Efforts are needed to develop an improved means of sampling the sediment–

water interface and more coring effort is needed to give adequate spatial and depth constraints on upwelling sediments.

4. Finding: The conference reached no general consensus on the priority of geographical areas for future ODP drilling; each area had its proponents. Of the areas most discussed (Benguela, Peru, Somalia, California, North West Africa) the Benguela system had the most support because it is currently the least well known. Consideration was also given to examining equatorial upwelling (recent ODP Leg 138) and upwelling around Antarctica. To understand the influence of gateways on continental margin upwelling records, a study of the western Australian margin was proposed to identify how sedimentation changed in response to the collision of Australia and Indonesia.

Recommendation: The proponents of Benguela drilling should cooperate to submit a preliminary proposal to ODP for the upcoming Atlantic campaign.

5. Finding: The nature of and changes in the feedstock water which upwells in these systems must be established to differentiate this source of variability from changes in simple physical forcing (e.g. winds). Thus there is a definite need to sample 'upstream' from as well as 'within' upwelling centres.

Recommendation: We do not know well how modern upwelling systems are fed at depth, so a combination of modern oceanographic studies and palaeoceanographic studies is needed to address this difficult problem of feedwater composition. Possible geochemical tools which help interpret water composition include: carbon isotopes ($\delta^{13}C$); Be and Nd isotopes; and elemental ratios, such as Cd/Ca in planktonic organisms and their remains.

6. Finding: The stratigraphic and especially the chronological framework for upwelling sediments is weak. Many studies have inadequate age models to ascertain the appropriate scales of variability and causal mechanisms. Likewise, the ability to correlate accurately between upwelling systems is very poor.

Recommendation: Studies of upwelling sediments should utilize isotopic and other stratigraphic tools to generate high resolution age models for correlation within upwelling systems and for the calculation of accumulation rates of biogenic and sedimentary components.

7. Finding: The regional patterns of sediment accumulation and budgets of important biogenic

and sedimentary fluxes are poorly known and are not well constrained by available samples or site survey data in most upwelling systems. These budgets are critical to understanding the links between primary productivity and sedimentary fluxes, and the global importance of productivity and carbon sequestering in upwelling systems.

Recommendation: Effort is needed to acquire or compile arrays of piston and box cores to provide better spatial and depth constraints on the sedimentary variability of regional upwelling systems. Placed within the context of high resolution site survey geophysical data and an adequate chronological framework, these arrays will enable calculation of regional budgets of important sedimentary components.

8. Finding: Comparison between (and even within) upwelling systems is difficult because few studies measure the same variables. Some faunal/floral measures are available for some systems but not others. Even similar studies ofen use different methodologies so that their results cannot be simply compared. This lack of 'systematic' or integrated study is a major hindrance to the global comparison and understanding of upwelling systems.

Recommendation: Encourage new studies to generate standard data sets as well as specific new data so that comparisons and syntheses can be made with confidence.

9. Finding: The sensitivity of upwelling systems to major changes in boundary conditions, such as wind fields, bathymetry, or ocean structure and currents, is poorly known from a theoretical or experimental standpoint. A knowledge of these sensitivities is important to interpreting the significance and causes of past variability in the upwelling record.

Recommendation: Theoretical studies are needed to relate the sensitivity of upwelling systems to the full range of climate and boundary condition changes that may have occurred during the Neogene. These studies should incorporate all types of models from local/regional to general circulation models of both the atmosphere and the oceans.

10. Finding: A major limitation to the understanding and modelling of geochemical processes in upwelling systems is the availability of material for the study of sediment−water interface processes.

Recommendation: The acquisition of large volume box cores at each potential drilling site is needed as part of the spatial and bathymetric array to provide constraints on the local and regional patterns of sediment accumulation (see Recommendations 2 and 7).

11. Finding: Coastal upwelling takes place in complex settings where continental margin processes (river input, windblown dust, subsurface hydrological processes) may confuse or alter diagenetic signals. Despite the problems in unravelling diagenetic signals in continental margin settings, these environments are nevertheless valuable for studying diagenesis because of their high rates of sediment supply and the resulting high temporal resolution.
Recommendation: Collect samples in less complex settings (e.g. equatorial upwelling zones) in order to calibrate geochemical tools.

12. Finding: Organic geochemistry offers considerable potential for reconstructing productivity from biomarker signals and for reconstructing ocean temperature history, especially in sediments where skeletal remains of plankton are not available.
Recommendation: Efforts to coordinate studies of upwelling systems with biogeochemical measurements of the environment should be encouraged and supported by funding agencies.

13. Finding: Our knowledge of past redox states and redox history in upwelling sediments is inadequate. The identification and understanding of these past redox states is critical to the proper interpretation of the organic fluxes and environmental history of upwelling systems.
Recommendation: Additional effort is needed to advance the use of inorganic tracers, e.g. Ce and U anomalies, Br/I ratios, as indicators of the past redox environment in sediments.

14. Finding: Coastal upwelling systems have great advantages over all other naturally occurring depositional environments because they permit studies of extreme diagenetic environments in the marine realm (due to high organic carbon concentrations) and provide unparalleled temporal resolution (due to very high sedimentation rates).
Recommendation: To advance our knowledge about early diagenesis of organic matter, neoformation of diagenetic minerals and organic molecules, and the formation of gas hydrates, diagenetic processes in upwelling sediments must be key targets of present and future research.

15. Finding: Too little effort has been put into microbiological studies that cover the entire depth interval of early diagenesis in upwelling sediments, even though unsystematic first attempts have yielded evidence that microbial activity is encountered to several hundred metres depth in the sedimentary column.
Recommendation: We need to pursue interdisciplinary efforts that involve microbiologists and geochemists alike in the study of organic matter degradation and diagenesis in upwelling sediments. Prerequisites are the successful development and application of in situ sampling devices that ensure recovery of deep sediment sections under ambient pressure and temperature conditions and that minimize risk of contamination.

Closing remarks

We hope that the findings and recommendations of this volume will assist in the design of experiments, surveys and models of upwelling systems in the future, especially those involving costly deep ocean drilling. Clearly, advances on many levels, from modern to ancient systems, are required to further advance our understanding of these complex systems.

This volume demonstrates the need to take a multidisciplinary, integrated approach to planning research on upwelling systems. Certainly, modern oceanographic process studies, together with flux studies and sediment studies now seem essential for documenting, understanding and modelling the behaviour and history of upwelling systems.

Finally, the editors and contributors proposed that the 'upwelling community' needs to keep in touch through regular get-togethers, e.g. by arranging an annual symposium at AGU and other national and international meetings.

Support for this volume came from the United States Science Advisory Committee (USSAC), the Royal Society, BP, Mobil and Chevron. We are grateful to the staff of the Geological Society for their support of the working groups. Special thanks are due to Jane Donnelly (Brown University) and Valerie West (IOSDL) for their editorial and secretarial assistance.

In accordance with the instructions for Contributors to the Proceedings of the Ocean Drilling Program (published by the Ocean Drilling Program in 1985) some authors use the term Ma or ka when referring to a specific date or interval (e.g. 15–20 Ma), but use My or ky when a general number of years is referred to (e.g. 4 m/ky). It is standard practice to use ka when discussing ages and ky when referring to cycle intervals.

Modern upwelling systems and
palaeo-upwelling criteria

Coastal upwelling in the modern ocean

ROBERT L. SMITH

College of Oceanography, Oregon State University, Corvallis, Oregon 97331−5503, USA

Abstract: During the past decade several major physical oceanographical experiments were performed over the continental margins along the ocean's eastern boundaries. The studies extended farther seaward than the continental shelf and extended over the seasons. As a result, our understanding of the processes and phenomena associated with coastal upwelling and affecting the ocean farther seaward has increased. The Coastal Ocean Dynamics Experiment investigated the dynamics controlling the currents over a continental shelf exposed to strong upwelling favourable winds; the experiment was more intensive and completely instrumented than any previous shelf experiment. The Coastal Transition Zone experiment investigated the cool 'filaments' conspicuous in satellite images of SST off northern California during the coastal upwelling seasons. Associated with the cool filaments are jets along the boundary between the cooler recently upwelled water and the warmer adjacent ocean water; as the jets meander equatorward and offshore (several hundred km), the upwelled water extends over greater distances offshore than previously thought likely. One experiment (SuperCODE) looked at the large alongshore scale, from 35°N to 50°N off the west coast of north America, defined the seasonal cycle, and found that the tendency for subsurface poleward flow over the continental shelf and slope increased at lower latitudes in spite of the increased equatorward mean wind. The ubiquitous poleward currents, usually subsurface over the inner slope and outer shelf, have been observed in all the experiments off the west coasts of the Americas, in spite of equatorward winds. Unlike the jets of the coastal transition zone, the poleward undercurrents are trapped to the continental slope and shelf. The Leeuwin Current Interdisciplinary Experiment took place off Western Australia, the only major eastern boundary without coastal upwelling in spite of strong equatorward winds. The alongshore pressure gradient along the west coast of Australia is large, perhaps because of the free connection to the western Pacific, and dominates the opposing equatorward wind stress, suppressing upwelling and causing poleward flow (the Leeuwin Current) at the surface over the slope and outer shelf.

In the modern ocean, sustained upwelling of subsurface water into the surface layer generally occurs where the wind-stress causes a divergence in the near-surface currents. A modern estimate of the distribution of the wind-stress over the world ocean is shown in Fig. 1 (from Hellerman & Rosenstein 1983). As has been understood since the early years of this century (Ekman 1905), wind stress on the oceans causes a net (vertically integrated) transport in a direction 90° to the right/left of the wind in the northern/southern hemisphere. The Ekman transport is restricted to a surface layer of thickness $O(10-100 \text{ m})$, roughly the same thickness as the surface mixed layer, and has a magnitude (per unit width) equal to the wind stress divided by the Coriolis parameter (f). In the modern ocean there are three regions where a divergence in the Ekman transport occurs over a sufficient scale $(O[10^4 \text{ km}^2])$ and with sufficient duration (season) to make upwelling a dominant process in the oceanography, the ecology and, ultimately, the geology. Along most of the ocean's eastern boundaries, the mean winds are equatorward at low and mid-latitude $(<45°)$ for a season or longer and the Ekman transport is away from the boundary causing coastal upwelling (Wooster & Reid 1963; Barber & Smith 1981). Along the equator, the Ekman transport, resulting from the climatological mean westward trade winds, is directed away from the equator in both hemispheres and equatorial upwelling occurs (Vinogradov 1981; Halpern *et al.* 1989). In regions of strong cyclonic wind-stress curl, the Ekman transport increases in the direction of the transport and causes divergence and upwelling (Yoshida & Mao 1957; Chelton 1982), as in the Arabian Sea during the southwest monsoon (Luther *et al.* 1990).

The focus of this paper is on the upwelling along the ocean's eastern boundaries. The circulation patterns in these coastal upwelling regimes had been reviewed (Smith 1983) at a previous conference on coastal upwelling and its sediment record. The focus of that review, as of the extensive studies during the Coastal Upwelling Ecosystems Analysis program (1972−1977), was on the continental shelf. The

From SUMMERHAYES, C. P., PRELL, W. L. & EMEIS, K. C. (eds), 1992, *Upwelling Systems: Evolution Since the Early Miocene.* Geological Society Special Publication No 64, pp 9−28.

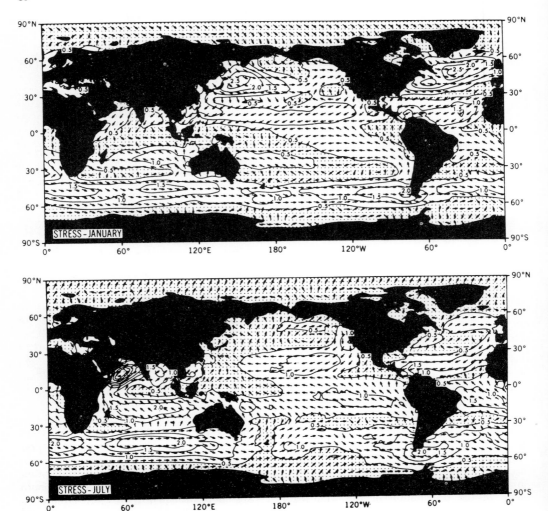

Fig. 1. Wind stress fields over the world ocean (from Hellerman & Rosenstein 1983). Arrows indicate direction of wind stress vectors and contours the magnitude in dynes cm^{-2} (shading indicates wind stress <0.5 dynes cm^{-2}).

purpose of this paper is to review results, some very preliminary, from field studies during recent years (1981–1988) that have expanded the view farther seaward, and to different regions. These results have caused the physical oceanographers to think anew about coastal upwelling regions and, in particular, about the interactions between the coastal ocean and the larger ocean seaward of the continental shelf. They should be important for the interpretation of the sediment record, which is usually obtained seaward of the continental shelf.

Coastal upwelling along the ocean's eastern boundaries

The intensity and persistence of coastal upwelling follows that of the coastal winds. All the eastern boundary regions where the wind stress (see Fig. 1) is nearly equatorward for part of the year are major upwelling regions, except the west coast of Australia (which provides an enlightening exception). Coastal upwelling is seasonal in most of the regions. Off the west coast of North America a relatively abrupt 'spring transition' to persistent coastal upwelling occurs as the North Pacific atmospheric pressure system strengthens and moves to the north, resulting in southward winds along the west coast of North America (Strub *et al.* 1987*b*; Lentz 1987). The divergence resulting from the offshore directed Ekman transport in the presence of a coastal boundary causes coastal upwelling. The cross-shelf scale over which active upwelling into the surface layer occurs is the baroclinic Rossby radius of deformation (Gill 1982). It is the fundamental horizontal scale at which rotation (f) becomes as important as buoyancy (the stratification) and at which the ocean can adjust to wind stress; it is O[10–50 km], roughly the width of the continental shelf. Over the past two decades substantial progress has been made in understanding the wind-driven circulation over the shelf proper (Allen *et al.* 1983; Brink 1987) and coastal upwelling in particular (Smith 1981, Brink 1983 and other papers in those volumes). The Coastal Ocean Dynamics Experiment (CODE), which occurred during the summers of 1981 and 1982 in a coastal upwelling region with strong winds (northern California at 38°N; see Fig. 1), studied the dynamical processes on the continental shelf more intensively and in greater detail than before or since (e.g. Winant *et al.* 1987 and other papers in the same issue).

The redistribution of mass during coastal upwelling, with denser upwelled water accumulating along the coast as the winds transport the surface water offshore, results in an alongshore geostrophic current that flows in the direction of the wind. The observed alongshore flow over the continental shelf is in geostrophic balance, as the ubiquitous findings of significant statistical correlation between the alongshore velocity component and sea level (or bottom pressure) show (Brink 1987). The alongshore correlation scales for the alongshore component of the velocity often exceed 100 km and even approach 1000 km off Peru (Brink *et al.* 1983). This is largely due to the wave guide nature of the continental shelf and slope; this wave guide can propagate an upwelling response (Gill & Clarke 1974). Coastal trapped wave theory has shown the importance of non-local winds in predicting the pressure (sea level) and along-shelf velocity response at timescales of the weather (Denbo & Allen 1987), intra-seasonal variability (Enfield 1987), the seasons (Pares-Sierra & O'Brien 1989) and interannual variations such as El Niño (Johnson & O'Brien 1990*a*). The 'trapping width' of the wave guide for these baroclinic Kelvin waves is the baroclinic Rossby radius of deformation; Rossby waves may slowly extend low-frequency (periods > annual) signals seaward (Johnson & O'Brien 1990*b*).

The cross-shelf transport in the surface layer over the continental shelf has been shown to be in good agreement with the Ekman transport estimates based on local wind stress wherever adequate measurements were available, e.g. Oregon, Peru and Northwest Africa (Smith 1981) and Northern California (Lentz 1987). The thickness of the Ekman layer is slightly greater than the mixed layer, but both are O[10 m]. The cross-shelf velocity is less than the geostrophic alongshore velocity by a factor of 2 to 10, but it is the divergence in the cross-shelf Ekman transport, imposed by the coast, that dominates the upwelling process. Figure 2a (from Lentz 1987) shows the response of both the cross-shelf and alongshore components of velocity on the Northern California shelf to the local wind stress. Figure 2b shows the cross-shelf flow at several locations under strong wind-stress during the spring transition (the period of wind-stress > 1 dyne cm^{-2} in Fig. 2a); this is an upwelling event with strong offshore flow (of the order of 0.1 to 0.2 m s^{-1}) in the upper 15–25 m, a net offshore Ekman transport of about 1 m^3 s^{-1} per alongshore m, and an equatorward alongshore jet with near-surface velocity of 0.5 m s^{-1}.

Below the Ekman layer, the onshore cross-shelf velocity is close to the measurement accuracy of the instrumentation, and the dynamics involve the alongshore pressure gradient and, probably, the curl of the wind-stress, which are difficult to measure with the required accuracy. A mass balance between the offshore directed Ekman transport and the return, or compensatory, subsurface flow is generally not obtainable locally but only over spatial scales of O[100 km], i.e., a balance is obtained only as an alongshore average. Both the observations and our understanding of the cross-shelf transport, especially in the larger fraction of the water column below the surface Ekman layer, are insufficient. Partly because of this, the processes that mediate the transition from the continental shelf to the open ocean, and control the flux (or exchange) between the coastal and open ocean, are not yet understood. To paraphrase Davis (1985*b*), recent observations off northern California suggest the processes are vastly more complex than imagined in models of wind-forced coastal trapped waves and broad scale upwelling forced by Ekman transport, with horizontal eddy fluxes representing the exchanges of substances and momentum between the coastal and open ocean.

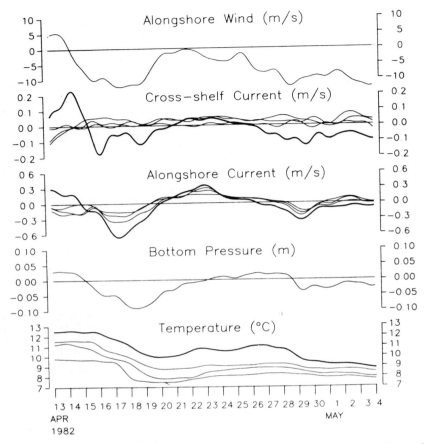

Fig. 2 (a). Time series of the wind, current and water temperature at 10 m, 35 m, 55 m, 75 m and bottom pressure at mid-shelf off northern California during CODE 1982 (C3 mooring in 90 m near 38.5°N). Heaviest line represents 10 m data. Poleward is positive alongshore; shoreward is positive cross-shelf.

The coastal transition zone

The boundary between upwelled water and the warmer lighter water, previously on the surface and farther seaward, is often sharp. This upwelling front may be over the shelf or farther seaward, depending in part on the duration and intensity of the upwelling. Because of the strong density gradient across the front, a strong geostrophic current sets up along the front (Mooers *et al.* 1976). This 'coastal jet' flows roughly parallel to the coast and in the direction of the upwelling favourable wind. The coastal jet might act either as a boundary restricting the exchange between the coastal and open ocean, or a vehicle for the exchange. As Sverdrup *et al.* (1942, p 501; and Rudnick & Davis 1988) pointed out: "It is probable that the tendency of the current is to break up in eddies, and that the forced vertical circulation limits the development of the current." Indeed, something like the upwelling front and coastal jet breaking up in eddies seemed to be a likely explanation of the structure observed in the satellite SST (Fig. 3) and colour imagery of the ocean off the west coast of North America. Kosro *et al.* (1991) gives an excellent summary of the motivation to study the transition zone between the coastal upwelling region and the adjacent ocean, which I have modified for this paper:

Over the past decade, in-situ and satellite observations of the waters off northern California have revealed the inhomogeneous nature of the transition zone between coastal and offshore waters during the spring–summer upwelling season. During the upwelling

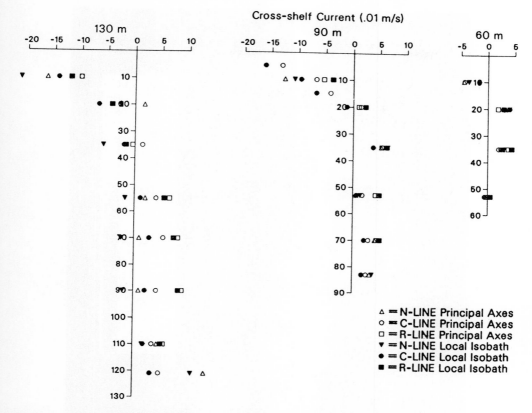

Fig. 2 (b). Time average of cross-shelf current (15 to 20 April 1982) for several shelf moorings within 25 km of C3 (open circles indicate C3 data). Source: Lentz (1987). Shoreward is positive.

season, coastal waters lying over the continental shelf and upper slope of northern California are cold, high in salinity (Huyer & Kosro 1987), and generally high in nutrients (Traganza *et al.* 1980); coastal currents respond rapidly to the local wind stress which varies on time scales of days (Winant, Beardsley & Davis 1987). Offshore, surface waters are warm and relatively fresh (Robinson 1976); they flow generally southward in an eastern boundary current (most often sampled south of 38°N) which contains mesoscale eddies (Lynn & Simpson 1987).

Satellite images of the transition zone have shown long tongues or filaments of cold or high chlorophyll water extending from the coastal zone to more than 200 km from shore (Bernstein *et al.* 1977; Abbott & Zion 1985). At least some of these cold tongues and filaments are associated with strong (>0.5 m s^{-1}), narrow ($\sim$30 km) seaward currents (Davis 1985*a*; Kosro 1987; Rienecker *et al.* 1985; Flament *et al.* 1985; Kosro & Huyer 1986).

Surface drifters deployed over the shelf near Pt. Arena (Davis 1985*a*) suggested that freshly upwelled waters may 'squirt' directly offshore, after undergoing little or no alongshore displacement. Other obser-

vations, including a May 1977 survey of northern California slope waters (Freitag & Halpern 1981) and a July 1982 survey of waters offshore of Pt. Arena (Kosro & Huyer 1986), suggested that the seaward jet off Point Arena is a continuation of a strong along-shore 'coastal jet' that flows generally southward along the upwelling front between warmer offshore waters and cold, freshly-upwelled coastal waters; this view is supported by the track of a drifter which moved rapidly southward at about 125°W between 45°N and 35°N in August and September 1984 (Thomson and Papadakis 1987) and it is implicit in the Ikeda & Emery (1984) model of California Current meanders. Still other observations (e.g. Mooers & Robinson 1984; Rienecker & Mooers 1989) suggested that pairs of oppositely-rotating eddies might interact to produce intense current jets and to extract filaments of cold coastally upwelled water out to sea (i.e. the eddies might act as roller bearings extracting filaments of cold water seaward from the continental margin).

The Coastal Transition Zone (CTZ) program was initiated with the explicit purpose of study-

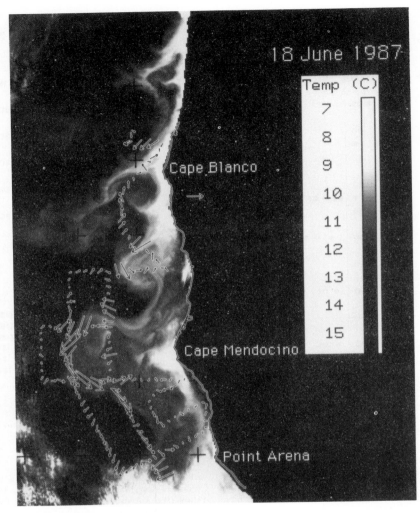

Fig. 3. Satellite sea surface temperature (SST) and shipborne acoustic doppler current measurements at 25 m during CTZ experiment 12–18 June 1988. Arrow below Cape Blanco represents 0.5 m s⁻¹, crosses indicate 1 degree latitude/longitude grid (cross just offshore of Cape Blanco is at 43°N, 125°W; cross just offshore of Point Arena is at 39°N, 124°W). Data and figure provided by P. M. Kosro & P. T. Strub.

ing the structure and dynamics of the transition region, and the characteristic 'filaments', 'squirts', and 'jets' that lie within it (Coastal Transition Zone Group 1988). The region chosen for the CTZ experiment was centered off northern California at about 39°N, offshore of the site of the CODE experiment discussed above and in the region used by OPTOMA (Ocean prediction through observation, modelling and analysis; Rienecker & Mooers 1989). The CTZ experiments took place during the summers of 1987 and 1988 (CTZ Group, 1988;

Strub *et al.* 1991), the season when the alongshore wind-stress exceeds 1 dyne cm⁻² (Fig. 1) and the resulting seaward Ekman transport exceeds 1 Sv (i.e. 10⁶ m³ s⁻¹) per 1000 km.

The 1987 experiment looked at the larger scale (42 to 37°N) and provided the evidence that the structures seen in the satellite images were not simply upwelling 'squirts' or a field of oceanic mesoscale eddies interacting with the coastal ocean, but the result of a strong alongshore jet meandering equatorward, perhaps starting as a coastal jet and eventually meandering as far as 300 km seaward. The jet flowed along the front separating the cool, productive, recently upwelled water from the warmer, relatively barren waters offshore (Kosro et al. 1991; Hood et al. 1990). Figure 3 shows a satellite image of SST upon which near-surface (25 m depth) currents, measured with ship-borne ADCP, have been overlaid. Figure 4 shows the sections normal to the coast at 43°, 41.5°, and 40°N of the alongshore velocity, temperature and salinity at the time of the image. The section at 43°N is shows a 'classic' coastal jet and upwelling front (cf. Mooers et al. 1976). This jet, and the front, meandered farther seaward as the two southern sections show. The two southern sections had additional measurements that support the interpretation that the jet and front are the boundary between water upwelled at the coast and oceanic water (Fig. 5, based on Hood et al. 1991). The jet and front continued equatorward to at least 37°N; maps of various properties, including satellite and ship SST, dynamic topography, and chlorophyll concentration, are given in CTZ Group (1988) and Hood et al. (1990, 1991).

The 1988 experiment looked in detail at a smaller region (37.5 to 39.5°N), confirming that the jet flows along the front, then 100−200 km seaward of the shelf break, separating upwelled water from the nutrient-poor water seaward (Huyer et al. 1991; Chavez et al. 1991). The jet is narrow, 30−75 km, rapid (at times >1 m s^{-1}) at the surface, and extending to >200 m, although with diminished velocity (10 cm s^{-1}). Since the jet flows rapidly equatorward, it efficiently advects water with upstream properties. Off northern California the jet itself carries water of lower salinity than that present either offshore or onshore at that latitude (Huyer et al. 1991). Indeed, the large volume of water transported within the jet (3−5 Sv) suggests that it may be a major constituent of the California Current. Satellite SST images are not useful in determining whether the current velocity structure is seasonal, since the cold upwelled water which serves as a 'dye' or tracer is only present during seasons of coastal upwelling. These strong narrow currents seem, on the basis of limited winter cruises, to occur only during the seasons of persistent coastal upwelling, i.e. strong equatorward winds (Kosro et al. 1991).

The results of the CTZ program show that the upwelling front may advance seaward a couple of hundred km beyond the continental shelf as the jet continues to flow equatorward for several hundred km without breaking up. The jet itself is not a region of abundant nutrients and phytoplankton (Chavez et al. 1991).

The jet and front remain a boundary, albeit an active one with some exchange across the front, perhaps by upwelling and downwelling along the jet's edges. Clearly, as the upwelling front meanders much farther seaward, the upwelling 'signal' extends much farther seaward than earlier thought likely.

Poleward undercurrents

During the past two decades, the use of moored current meters has provided direct evidence of the ubiquity of poleward 'undercurrents', flowing counter to the prevailing wind, over the continental shelves and slopes of the major coastal upwelling regions. A collection of papers from a workshop on the topic of poleward flows along eastern ocean boundaries has recently been published (Neshyba et al. 1989). All five of the ocean's eastern boundaries at the latitudes of the atmosphere's semi-permanent high pressure systems, of which the mid-latitude equatorward coastal winds are part, show evidence of subsurface poleward flow over the continental margin. The earlier evidence was from the water properties and the ecology (Wooster & Reid 1963). Subsurface poleward flow was observed, using moored current meters, in the three upwelling regions studied during the Coastal Upwelling Ecosystems Analysis program (Smith 1983). With the exception of the studies off Oregon (Huyer et al. 1978), the measurements were not long enough to confidently discuss a long-term mean or seasonal cycle of the poleward flow. Recent studies off the west coast of north America (Strub et al. 1987a; Lentz & Chapman 1989) and off Peru (Huyer et al. 1991), have provided long time series of currents over the shelf and slope at several latitudes.

An experiment (SuperCODE) to investigate the seasonal difference in the response of the currents on the continental shelf to the wind along the north American coast from 34° to 48°N was carried out simultaneously with the Coastal Ocean Dynamics Experiment at 38°N. The winds along the Pacific coast of north America vary with latitude. The annual mean wind stress is equatorward along the coast south of about 42°N, with the strongest seasonal cycle between 38° and 42°N; during summer the mean wind stress is equatorward along the entire coast, with the seasonal duration of the equatorward wind increasing at lower latitudes until 35°N, where the winds are equatorward during all seasons. Figure 6 (based on Strub et al. 1987a) shows the seasonal behaviour of the subsurface currents on the shelf and the wind-stress at several latitudes. The mean nearer-

(a)

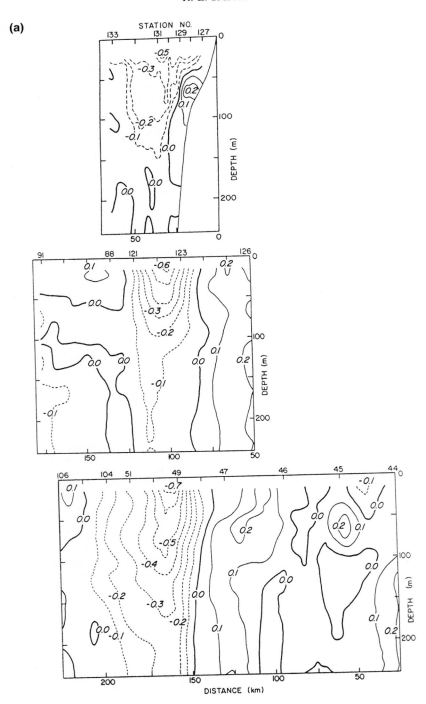

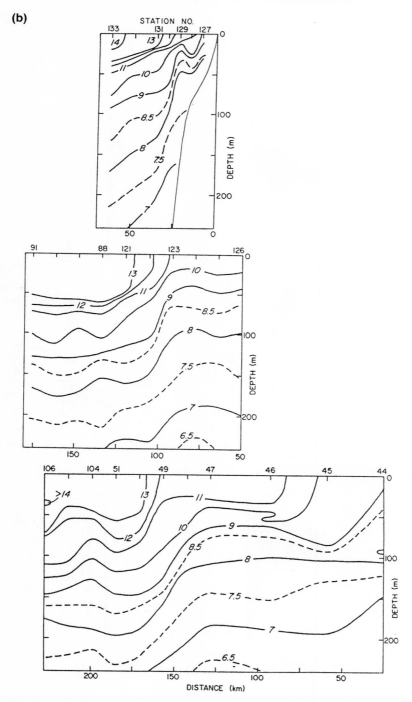

Fig. 4. Sections normal to the coast at about 43°, 41.5°, and 40°N (see Fig. 3) showing (a) alongshore velocity (poleward is positive, units are m s^{-1}) from acoustic doppler current profiler (ADCP) and (b) temperature from CTD stations. Distances are from the coast; the innermost stations of the southern two sections are seaward of the shelf break. Note the similarity of the equatorward velocity structure (jet) in the vicinity of the front (13°C).

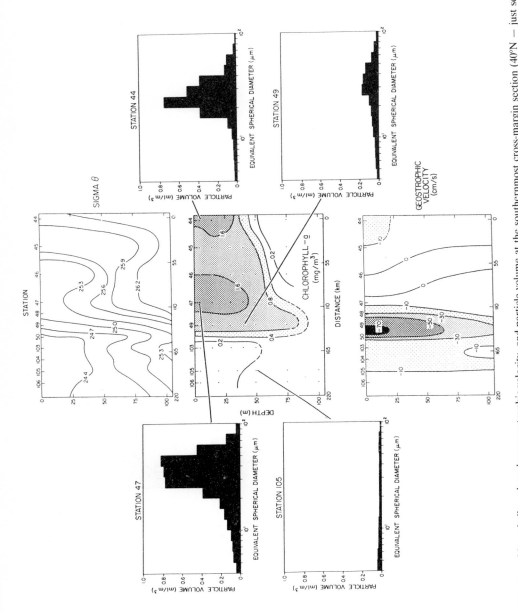

Fig. 5. Potential density, chlorophyll-a, alongshore geostrophic velocity, and particle volume at the southernmost cross-margin section (40°N — just south of Cape Mendocino) shown in Figs 3 & 4; station numbers as in Figs 3 & 4; station numbers as in Fig. 4 but distance scale in Fig. 5 is relative to most inshore station. Figure is adapted from Hood et al. (1991).

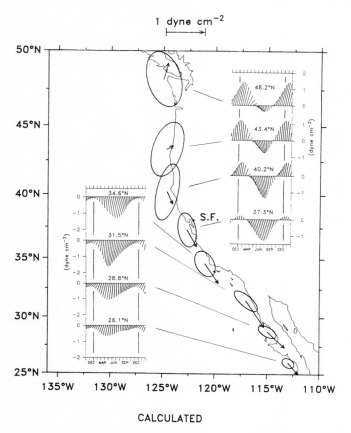

Fig. 6 (a). Annual cycles of wind stress over the continental shelf (vector time-series are relative to alongshore/cross-shelf direction). Figure from Strub *et al.* (1987*a*).

surface currents at the shelf-break are equatorward at latitudes north of about 42°N, but the means become increasingly poleward with depth and at lower latitudes, i.e. as one goes south, the winds are increasingly equatorward but the mean currents are more strongly poleward. During the height of the coastal upwelling season, May–July, when the winds are equatorward along the entire coast, the mean subsurface alongshore currents at midshelf and at the shelf break tend to flow poleward from 34° to 48°N, unless they are overridden near the surface by sufficiently strong equatorward winds (Denbo & Allen 1987). Denbo & Allen comment that 'the dynamical reasons for the tendency toward poleward mean flow are not totally understood and need theoretical explanation'. It should be pointed out that the paradoxical 'response' of the subsurface shelf currents to the wind occurs for the mean; the seasonal and

higher frequency variability of the currents over the shelf is strongly related to that of the alongshore component of the wind-stress (Huyer *et al.* 1978; Denbo & Allen 1987).

The current measurements at 38°N during CODE extended over the slope, and closer to the surface than at the other shelf locations shown in Fig. 6. Although only 20 km seaward of the mid-shelf mooring, and in water depth of 500 m, the currents measured over the slope were not correlated with either the shelf currents or the local wind-stress during any season (Lentz and Chapman 1989). The profiles for the alongshore current over the slope are shown in Fig. 7 (from Huyer *et al.* 1989). These profiles show that the flow below 100–150 m is poleward during all seasons but strongest during the spring and summer, when the coastal winds are most strongly equatorward and coastal upwelling is strongest. Unlike the jets of the coastal tran-

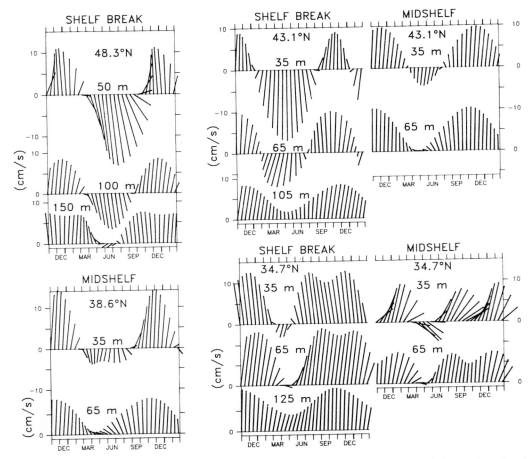

Fig. 6 (b). Annual cycles of currents over the continental shelf (vector time-series are relative to alongshore/ cross-shelf direction). Figure from Strub *et al.* (1987*a*).

sition zone, the poleward flow is trapped over the slope and shelf; the undercurrent is not observed in measurements >100 km from the shelf-edge (Stabeno & Smith 1987). The poleward undercurrent was clearly observed during the CTZ surveys of summer 1988, adjacent to the continental slope but not offshore under the jet, with core velocities up to 20 cm s^{-1} at 150–200 m (Huyer *et al.* 1990). The transport ranged from about 0.5 Sv to >1 Sv. Other studies tend to support the evidence of strongest poleward undercurrent during the summer (Chelton *et al.* 1988), although there is a tendency for poleward flow at all depths over the slope and shelf during winter along the north American coast at latitudes >32°N (Hickey 1979; Chelton 1984). It remains unclear whether the poleward flowing surface 'countercurrents' observed along the eastern boundaries during some seasons

are simply the surfacing of the poleward 'undercurrent'.

Along the Peru coast, at latitudes between 5 and 15°S, the winds are persistently equatorward and vary little with weather or season (Brink *et al.* 1983). The alongshore currents, below the shallow Ekman layer (O[10–20 m]), measured over the shelf between 10° and 15°S during the CUEA program were poleward in the mean but highly variable (Brink *et al.* 1983); most of the variability is attributable to remote forcing and propagates into the region via coastal trapped waves (e.g. Enfield *et al.* 1987). The structure and variability of the undercurrent over the continental margin of Peru was the focus of a study during 1981–1985, which serendipitously encompassed El Niño 1982–1983 (Huyer *et al.* 1991, 1987). The Peru undercurrent displayed variability at all timescales but the mean profile

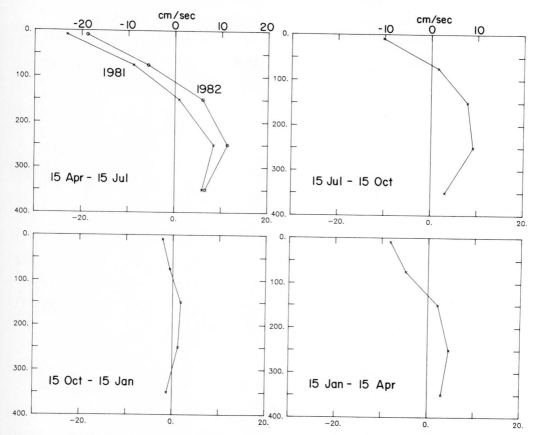

Fig. 7. Vertical profiles of the three-month average alongshore currents at slope mooring off northern California (500 m water depth) during CODE (from Huyer *et al.* 1989). Poleward is positive.

over the slope (Fig. 8; from Huyer *et al.* 1991) was similar to that of the undercurrent off northern California (Fig. 7). The Peru undercurrent flows poleward over the inner slope and outer shelf with a well defined core near 150 m, where the O[100 day] mean speed is O[10 cm s^{-1}] with periods of several days to two weeks during which sustained poleward flow exceeds 25 cm s^{-1}. The cross-margin section based on observations after El Niño (Fig. 9) is similar to that observed in other regions (e.g. Hickey 1979; Mittelstaedt *et al.* 1983; Chelton *et al.* 1988). The poleward surface flow at the offshore edge (seaward of 175 km from the coast) of Fig. 9 may be the Peru surface counter-current. The transport in the Peru undercurrent (within 125 km of the coast) is about 1 Sv at 10°S and has the proper depth, location and magnitude to supply the coastal upwelling to a least 15°S. There is no observable seasonal

cycle to the undercurrent off Peru; the mean alongshore velocity sections for 4 months during an austral fall and winter resemble those on twice the record-length, as well as the mean geostrophic velocity based on data from 4 surveys from a period spanning 18 months.

The dynamics governing the poleward flow over the continental margins in the coastal up-welling regions is not yet understood, although a number of recent theoretical studies have been published (see articles in Neshyba *et al.* 1989, and the review of that volume by Warren 1990). A venerable hypothesis (first articulated by Munk 1950) is that poleward flows in these regions are the result of the cyclonic wind-stress curl, which is a characteristic feature of these regions (Bakun & Nelson 1991). The alongshore pressure gradient is also a likely candidate. It is thought by some that the surface counter-currents, often observed in the same upwelling

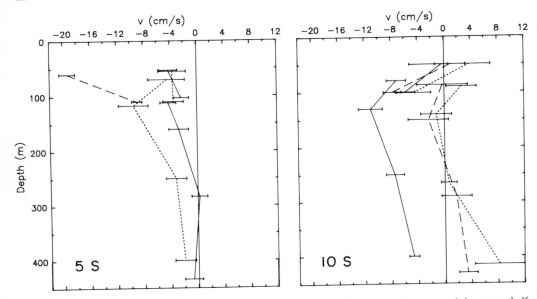

Fig. 8. Vertical profiles of 200-day average alongshore currents over the continental slope and the outer shelf off Peru at 5° and 10°S before (dashed), during (dotted) and after (solid line) El Niño of 1982–1983 (Huyer et al. 1991). The 95% confidence limits are shown. Poleward is negative.

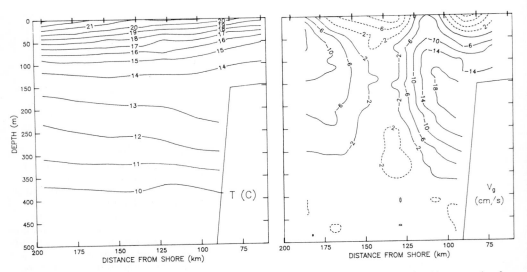

Fig. 9. Sections of temperature and alongshore geostrophic flow relative to 500 db obtained by averaging four sections at 10°S made after El Niño. Station positions are indicated by ticks at top; distance is from coast. Figure from Huyer et al. (1991). Poleward is negative.

regions outside of the upwelling season, are also part of the same phenomenon, as if the strong equatorward coastal winds have caused the poleward flow to submerge, becoming an undercurrent. It is usually assumed that the poleward subsurface flow over the slope and at mid-shelf are the same phenomenon, but this is not certain. The poleward flow is clearly trapped to the continental margin and not part of the larger-scale offshore oceanic flow. It also seems clear that poleward undercurrents are not necessarily linked to the coastal upwelling process — the poleward subsurface flow over the slope is less seasonal and generally uncorrelated with the local wind. As Warren (1990) writes: 'The (poleward) undercurrents are so widespread and persistent that one feels intuitively that they must embody some common physics or express a single archetype. Clearly that has not emerged yet. They are a most intriguing geophysical phenomenon...'

The west coast of Australia

The southeast Indian Ocean off western Australia is geographically and topographically the analogue of the other eastern boundary current regions. As in these regions, the winds off Western Australia are predominantly equatorward, and one might expect to find broad equatorward flow and upwelling along the coast. However, the ocean off Western Australia behaves quite unlike the other eastern boundary regions. There is no regular, continuous equatorward flow within 1000 km of the coast and no evidence of coastal upwelling. The reason for the absence of coastal upwelling in the presence of strong equatorward winds was puzzling (Wooster & Reid 1963). The evidence from fauna, ships' drift and water properties indicated warm water flowing poleward, against the prevailing wind, along the western coast of Australia from North West Cape (22°S) to Cape Leeuwin (34.5°S). Cresswell & Golding (1980), using satellite-tracked drifters, found that the poleward flow of warm water was fast (often >0.5 m s^{-1}) and continued eastward around Cape Leeuwin into the Great Australian Bight. They named the poleward surface flow the Leeuwin Current after a Dutch ship that explored eastward into the Bight in the early 17th Century.

The first large-scale study of the Leeuwin Current was conducted between North West Cape (22°S) and the southwestern corner of Australia (35°S) from September 1986 to August 1987 (Smith et al. 1991). As part of this Leeuwin Current Interdisciplinary Experiment (LUCIE), current meters were deployed along the shelf-edge (from 22° to 35°S) and across the shelf and upper slope (at 29.5° and 34°S). The mean wind and current vectors for March–May 1987, when the Leeuwin Current is maximum, are shown in Fig. 10. Figure 11 shows sections made during LUCIE at 29.5°S. Note the bending down of isotherms near the coast, the opposite of the behaviour in coastal upwelling (cf. Fig. 9), and the poleward geostrophic flow extending from the surface to 200 m and hugging the continental margin.

Except for about one month (January), the flow at 29.5°S between the surface and 250 m was strongly poleward within 100 km of the shelf-edge, with a poleward transport of about 5 Sv. The 325-day mean currents at the shelf-edge were poleward at about 10 cm s^{-1}, opposing a mean equatorward wind stress of 0.3 dynes cm^{-2}. The monthly mean current over the upper slope exceeded 50 cm s^{-1} poleward at times and had a 325-day mean of 30 cm s^{-1}; an equatorward undercurrent existed below 300 m with a 325-day mean of 10 cm s^{-1} at 450 m.

There is general agreement (see Batteen & Rutherford 1990) that the Leeuwin Current is generated by the alongshore pressure gradient, i.e. the gradient of geopotential anomaly at the sea surface. This gradient has a value greater than 2×10^{-6} m s^{-2}, i.e. an alongshore slope upward toward the equator of about 20 cm per 1000 km, which is anomalously large compared to other eastern boundary regions. The observations made during LUCIE generally confirmed the hypothesis (Thompson 1987) that the onshore geostrophic transport in balance with this alongshore pressure gradient exceeded the offshore Ekman transport induced by the equatorward wind stress. The cross-shelf flow was presumably balanced over the upper slope and outer shelf by the offshore bottom Ekman transport under the Leeuwin Current. One consequence of this momentum balance is the diminution or suppression of coastal upwelling under the equatorward winds. The onshore geostrophic flow near the surface is sufficient to overwhelm the offshore-directed Ekman transport: The onshore geostrophic transport in the upper 50 m was 1.4 m^3 s^{-1} per alongshore meter; the Ekman transport, using the average wind stress 0.3 dyn cm^{-2}, is -0.4 m^3 s^{-1} per alongshore meter. The CTD data during LUCIE indicate that the surface layer over the outer shelf and upper slope is nearly homogeneous to a depth of at least 30 m in summer (January/February) and to more than 100 m in winter (September, June and August). Even if the Ekman transport was concentrated in a shallower layer (20 m), the onshore geostrophic transport in this shallower layer would be enough (0.6 m^3 s^{-1} m^{-1}) to suppress any net offshore transport in the surface layer, and hence coastal upwelling, except during high wind stress (>1 dyn cm^{-2}). Thus the alongshore pressure gradient is the cause of the lack of coastal upwelling along the western Australia coast. Suppression of upwelling due to an alongshore pressure gradient is unusual in other

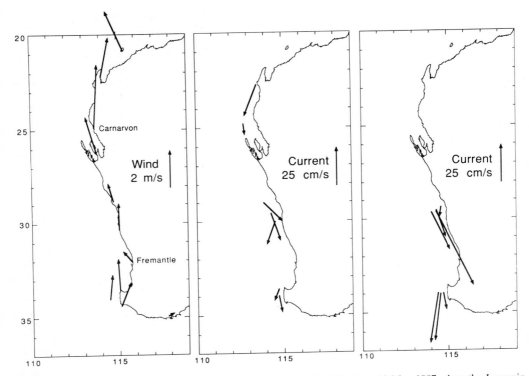

Fig. 10. Mean current and wind vectors for the 72-day period of 1 March to 12 May 1987 when the Leeuwin Current has its seasonal maximum strength. Left: winds at coastal stations and the meteorological buoy. Middle: currents 15 m above the bottom at the shelf-break moorings. Right: currents at the shallowest current deeper than 25 m on the moorings off Dongara (29.5°S) and Cape Mentelle (34°S). Scales such that 2° latitude equals 2 m s^{-1} for wind and 25 cm s^{-1} for current. Figure from Smith *et al.* (1991).

eastern boundary regions, but has also been observed off Peru during El Niño (Huyer *et al.* 1987). The seasonal variation in the strength of the Leeuwin Current seemed to be the result of variations in the wind stress and not in the alongshore pressure gradient, which had little seasonal dependence.

The cause of the anomalously large alongshore pressure gradient probably lies in the existence of the free passage from the western equatorial Pacific Ocean to the eastern equatorial Indian Ocean through the Indonesian Archipelago (Godfrey & Weaver 1991). The eastern boundary of the south Indian Ocean is the only eastern boundary that has a direct connection to the adjacent ocean's western equatorial region. As Weaver (1990) has said: 'In a sense...the Leeuwin Current can be thought of as being driven by equatorial Pacific winds which pile up warm water in the western equatorial Pacific'. The warm western equatorial Pacific waters flow through the Indonesian

Archipelago and maintain the very high geopotential anomalies (sea level) off northwestern Australia, but the magnitude of the throughflow is apparently not crucial to driving the Leeuwin Current. If the large alongshore pressure gradient is the result of the free connection of the eastern equatorial Indian Ocean to the western Pacific, the pressure gradient and the Leeuwin Current would be especially vulnerable to the interannual variability of El Niño. On an even longer timescale, Weaver (1990) suggests that an opening of the Isthmus of Panama (as was the case prior to 3.2 million years ago) would produce analogous climatic effects in the eastern Pacific, suppressing coastal upwelling and causing a large oceanic transport of heat poleward in the coastal regions.

Summary

During the past decade several major physical oceanographical experiments occurred over the

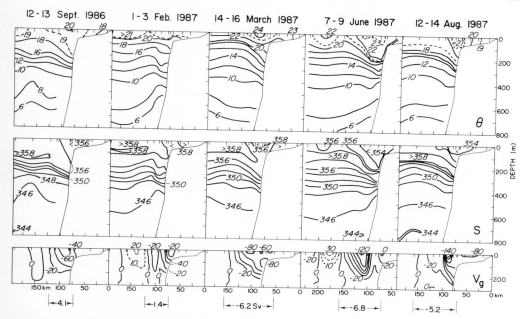

Fig. 11. Vertical sections of potential temperature, salinity, and alongshore component of geostrophic velocity (cm s^{-1}, relative to 300 dbar) off Dongara (29.5°S), for the five LUCIE cruises (Smith *et al*. 1991). The alongshore geostrophic transport (Sv) between 75 and 155 km from shore (relative to 300 dbar) is indicated at the bottom. Poleward is negative.

continental margins along the ocean's eastern boundary. As a result, our understanding of the processes and phenomena associated with coastal upwelling has increased. The Coastal Ocean Dynamics Experiment investigated the dynamics of a small region of the continental shelf in a coastal upwelling region with more extensive instrumentation than ever before. The experiment, which took place off northern California, observed that the cross-shelf transport in the surface mixed layer does agree with the Ekman transport inferred from the local wind stress. It also showed that the flow patterns could be much more complex, especially in the alongshore direction, than inferred during earlier studies of coastal upwelling. The companion experiment, SuperCODE, looked at the large alongshore scale, from 35°N to 50°N, defined the seasonal cycle, and found that the tendency for subsurface poleward flow over the continental shelf was ubiquitous; the mean poleward flow actually increased at lower latitudes in spite of the increased equatorward mean wind. During El Niño of 1982–1983, which was observed in studies along the equator, and off Peru and Oregon, changes in the equatorial ocean clearly propagated to the mid-latitude coastal oceans and persisted for months. Re-

mote forcing of shelf currents, via the mechanism of coastal trapped waves, can be an important factor at all timescales.

The Coastal Transition Zone experiment, motivated in part by the results from CODE, investigated the cool 'filaments' that are so conspicuous in satellite images of SST within a couple of hundred kilometres off the coast of northern California. The studies showed that these filaments are not simply coastal upwelling 'squirts' or the result of the oceanic eddy field impinging on the continental margins but are associated with geostrophically balanced jets. The 'jets' are along the boundary between the adjacent ocean water and recently upwelled water; the jet itself is transporting water with upstream properties. It appears that the upwelling front and its associated jet meander quasi-continuously equatorward and offshore, allowing the upwelled water to extend much farther seaward (by almost an order of magnitude) than the shelf width. This is evident off northern California, a region of strong equatorward winds favourable for coastal upwelling. Although evidence of similar features is seen in the satellite images of other coastal upwelling regions, field studies have not yet been made in those regions to determine whether the features are superficial or have sufficient depth to be a major influence on the effect of coastal upwelling on the surrounding ocean.

The ubiquitous poleward currents, usually subsurface over the inner slope and outer shelf, have been observed in all the experiments in spite of equatorward winds. Unlike the jets of the coastal transition zone, the poleward undercurrents are trapped to the continental margin. The timescale of the undercurrents variability over the slope is greater than that of typical shelf currents responding to the local wind. There is not yet a satisfactory model for poleward undercurrents, nor a comprehensive study of their alongshore continuity.

The west coast of Australia had long been a puzzle to oceanographers because of the absence of coastal upwelling or evidence of equatorward currents in spite of strong equatorward winds along the coast. The first major study of the region, the Leeuwin Current Interdisciplinary Experiment, showed that the current within 100 km of the shelf-edge was strong and poleward from the surface to about 300 m, in spite of persistent equatorward winds. The alongshore pressure gradient off western Australia is very large, perhaps because of the free connection to the western Pacific. It dominates the equatorward wind stress, suppressing upwelling and causing the poleward Leeuwin Current at the surface over the slope and outer shelf. Would (did) a free connection through the Isthmus of Panama cause a similar effect in the eastern Pacific?

The Office of Naval Research Coastal Sciences Program Grant Number N00014−92-J-1177 and National Science Foundation Grants OCE-8709930 and OCE-9103034 have supported the author's recent studies in coastal oceanography.

References

ABBOTT, M. R. & ZION, P. M. 1985. Satellite observations of phytoplankton variability during an upwelling event, *Continental Shelf Research*, **4**, 661−680.

ALLEN, J. S., BEARDSLEY, R. C., BLANTON, J. O., BOICOURT, W. C., BUTMAN, B., COACHMAN, L. K., HUYER, A., KINDER, T. H., ROYER, T. C., SCHUMACHER, J. D., SMITH, R. L., STURGES, W. & WINANT, C. D. 1983. Physical oceanography of continental shelves, *Reviews of Geophysics and Space Physics*, **21**, 1149−1181.

BAKUN, A. & NELSON, C. S. 1991. The seasonal cycle of wind stress curl in subtropical eastern boundary current regions, *Journal of Physical Oceanography*, **21**, 1815−1834.

BARBER, R. T. & SMITH, R. L. 1981. Coastal upwelling ecosystems. *In*: LONGHURST, A. R. (ed.) *Analysis of Marine Ecosystems*, Academic, London, 31−68.

BATTEEN, M. L. & RUTHERFORD, M. J. 1990. Modelling studies of eddies in the Leeuwin Current: The role of thermal forcing. *Journal of Physical Oceanography*, **20**, 1484−1520.

BERNSTEIN, R. L., BREAKER, L. & WHRITNER, R. 1977. California Current eddy formation: ship, air and satellite results, *Science*, **195**, 353−359.

BRINK, K. H. 1983. The near surface dynamics of coastal upwelling, *Progress in Oceanography*, **12**, 223−257.

—— 1987. Coastal ocean physical processes, *Review of Geophysics*, **25**, 204−216.

——, HALPERN, D. HUYER, A. & SMITH, R. L. 1983. The physical environment of the Peruvian upwelling system, *Progress in Oceanography*, **12**, 285−305.

CHAVEZ, F. P., BARBER, R. T., HUYER, A., KOSRO, P. M., RAMP, S., STANTON, T. & DE MENDIOLA, B. R. 1991. Horizontal transport and the distribution of nutrients in surface waters in the coastal transition zone off northern California: Effects on primary production, phytoplankton biomass and species composition, *Journal of Geophysical Research*, **96**, 14833−14848.

CHELTON, D. B. 1982. Large-scale response of the California current to forcing by the wind stress curl, CalCOFI Rep., Vol XXIII, 130−148.

—— 1984. Seasonal variability of alongshore geostrophic velocity off central California, *Journal of Geophysical Research*, **89**, 3473−3486.

——, BERSTEIN, R. L., BRATKOVICH, A. & KOSRO, P. M. 1988. Poleward flow off central California during the spring and summer of 1981 and 1984, *Journal of Geophysical Research*, **93**, 10604−10620.

Coastal Transition Zone Group 1988. The Coastal Transition Zone Program, EOS, *Transactions of the American Geophysical Union*, **69**(27), 698−699.

CRESSWELL, G. R. & GOLDING, T. J. 1980. Observations of a south-flowing current in the southeastern Indian Ocean. *Deep-Sea Research*, **27**, 449−466.

DAVIS, R. E. 1985*a*. Drifter observations of coastal surface currents during CODE: the method and descriptive view, *Journal of Geophysical Research*, **90**, 4741−4755.

—— 1985*b*. Drifter observations of coastal surface currents during CODE: the statistical and dynamical views, *Journal of Geophysical Research*, **90**, 4756−4772.

DENBO, D. W. & ALLEN, J. S. 1987. Large-scale response to atmospheric forcing of shelf currents and coastal sea level off the west coast of North America: May−July 1981 and 1982. *Journal of Geophysical Research*, **92**, 1757−1782.

EKMAN, V. W. 1905. On the influence of the earth's rotation in ocean currents, *Arch. Math. Astron. Phys.*, 2, No. 11.

ENFIELD, D. B. 1987. The intraseasonal oscillation in eastern Pacific sea levels: How is it forced?, *Journal of Physical Oceanography*, **16**,

1038–1054.

——, CORNEJO-RODRIGUES, M. P., SMITH, R. L. & NEWBERGER, P. A. 1987. The equatorial source of propagating variability along the Peru coast during the 1982–1983 El Niño, *Journal of Geophysical Research*, **92**, 14335–14346.

FLAMENT, P., ARMI, L. & WASHBURN, L. 1985. The evolving structure of an upwelling filament, *Journal of Geophysical Research*, **90**, 11765–11778.

FREITAG, H. P. & HALPERN, D. 1981. Hydrographic observations off northern California during May 1977, *Journal of Geophysical Research*, **86**, 4248–4252.

GILL, A. E. 1982. *Atmosphere-Ocean Dynamics*, Academic, New York.

—— & CLARKE, A. J. 1974. Wind-induced upwelling, coastal currents, and sea-level changes, *Deep-Sea Research*, **21**, 325–345.

GODFREY, G. S. & WEAVER, A. 1991. Is the Leeuwin Current driven by Pacific heating and winds?, *Progress in Oceanography*, **27**, 225–272.

HALPERN, D., KNOX, R. A., LUTHER, D. S. & PHILANDER, G. G. H. 1989. Estimates of equatorial upwelling between 140° and 110°W during 1984. *Journal of Geophysical Research*, **94**, 8018–8020.

HICKEY, B. M. 1979. The California current system — Hypotheses and facts. *Progress in Oceanography*, **8**, 191–279.

HELLERMAN, S. & ROSENSTEIN, M. 1983. Normal monthly wind stress over the world ocean with error estimates. *Journal of Physical Oceanography*, **13**, 1093–1104.

HOOD, R. R., ABBOTT, M. R. & HUYER, A. 1991. Phytoplankton and photosynthetic light response in the coastal transition zone off northern California in June, 1987. *Journal of Geophysical Research*, **96**, 14769–14780.

——, ——, —— & KOSRO, P. M. 1990. Physical and biological structure along an upwelling front off northern California: surface patterns in temperature, flow, phytoplankton biomass and species composition, *Journal of Geophysical Research*, **95**, 18081–18094.

HUYER, A. 1984. Hydrographic observations along the CODE Central Line off northern California, 1981, *Journal of Physical Oceanography*, **14**(10), 1647–1658.

——, KNOLL, M., PALUSKIEWICZ, T. & SMITH, R. L. 1991. The Peru Undercurrent: A study in variability. *Deep-Sea Research*, **38**, Suppl. 1, S247–S271.

—— & KOSRO, P. M. 1987. Mesoscale surveys over the shelf and slope near Point Arena, California, *Journal of Geophysical Research*, **92**, 1655–1681.

——, ——, FLEISCHBEIN, J., RAMP, S. R., STANTON, T., WASHBURN, L., CHAVEZ, F. A., COWLES, T., PIERCE, S. D. & SMITH, R. L. 1991. Currents and water masses of the coastal transition zone off northern California, June to August 1988, *Journal of Geophysical Research*, **96**, 14809–14831.

——, ——, LENTZ, S. & BEARDSLEY, R. 1989. Pole-ward flow in the California current system. *In*: NESHYBA, S. J., *et al.* (eds.) *Poleward flows along eastern ocean boundaries*, Springer, New York.

——, SMITH, R. L. & PALUSKIEWICZ, T. 1987. Coastal upwelling off Peru during normal and El Niño times, 1981–1984, *Journal of Geophysical Research*, **92**, 14297–14307.

——, ——, SOBEY, J. C. & SMITH, R. L. 1978. Seasonal differences in low-frequency current fluctuations over the Oregon continental shelf, *Journal of Geophysical Research*, **83**, 5071–5089, 1978.

——, SOBEY, J. C. & SMITH, R.L. 1979. The spring transition in currents over the Oregon continental shelf, *Journal of Geophysical Research*, **84**, 6995–7011.

IKEDA, M. & EMERY, W. J. 1984. Satellite observations and modeling of meanders in the California Current system off Oregon and northern California, *Journal of Physical Oceanography*, **14**, 1434–1450.

JOHNSON, M. A. & O'BRIEN, J. J. 1990a. The northeast Pacific Ocean response to the 1982–1983 El Niño, *Journal of Geophysical Research*, **95**, 7155–7166

—— —— 1990b. The role of coastal Kelvin waves on the northeast Pacific, *Journal of Marine Systems*, **1**, 29–38.

KOSRO, P. M. 1987. Structure of the coastal current field off northern California during the Coastal Ocean Dynamics Experiment, *Journal of Geophysical Research*, **92**, 1655–1681.

—— & HUYER, A. 1986. CTD and velocity surveys of seaward jets off northern California., July 1981 and 1982, *Journal of Geophysical Research*, **91**, 7680–7690.

——, ——, RAMP, S. R., SMITH, R. L., CHAVEZ, F. P., COWLES, T. J., ABBOTT, M. R., STRUB, P. T., BARBER, R. T., JESSEN, P. & SMALL, L. F. 1991. The structure of the transition zone between coastal waters and the open ocean off northern California, Winter and Spring 1987, *Journal of Geophysical Research*, **96**, 14707–14730.

LENTZ, S. J. 1987. A description of the 1981 and 1982 spring transitions over the northern California shelf, *Journal of Geophysical Research*, **92**(C2), 1545–1567.

—— & CHAPMAN, D. C. 1989. Seasonal differences in the current and temperature variability over the northern California shelf during the Coastal Ocean Dynamics Experiment, *Journal of Geophysical Research*, **94**, 12571–12592, 1989.

LUTHER, M. E., O'BRIEN, J. J. & PRESS, W. L. 1990. Variability in upwelling fields in the northwestern Indian Ocean, I: Model experiments for the past 18000 years, *Paleoceanography*, **5**, 433–445.

LYNN, R. J. & SIMPSON, J. J. 1987. The California current system: The seasonal variability of its physical characteristics, *Journal of Geophysical Research*, **92**, 12947–12966.

MITTELSTAEDT, E. 1983. The upwelling area off Northwest Africa — a description of the phenomena related to coastal upwelling, *Progress in*

Oceanography, **12**, 307−331.

MOOERS, C. N. K., COLLINS, C. A. & SMITH, R. L. 1976. The dynamic structure of the frontal zone in the coastal upwelling region off Oregon, *Journal of Physical Oceanography*, **6**, 3−21.

—— & ROBINSON, A. R. 1986. Turbulent jets and eddies in the California Current and inferred cross-shore transports, *Science*, **223**, 51−53.

MUNK, W. H. 1950. On the wind-driven ocean circulation, *Journal of Meteorology*, **7**, 72−93.

NESHYBA, S. J., MOOERS, C. N. K., SMITH, R. L. & BARBER, R. T. (eds) 1989. Poleward flows along eastern ocean boundaries, *Coastal and Esturarine Studies* **34**, Springer, New York.

PARES-SIERRA, A. & O'BRIEN, J. J. 1989. The seasonal and interannual variability of the California Current system: A numerical model, *Journal of Geophysical Research*, **94**, 3159−3180.

RIENECKER, M. M. & MOOERS, C. N. K. 1989. A summary of the OPTOMA programs mesoscale ocean prediction studies in the California Current system, *In*: NIHOUL, J. C. J. & JAMART, B. M. (eds) *Mesoscale/synoptic coherent structures in geophysical turbulence*. Elsevier, Amsterdam, 519−548.

——, ——, HAGA, D. E. & ROBINSON, A. R. 1985. A cool anomaly off northern California: an investigation using IR imagery and in situ data, *Journal of Geophysical Research*, **90**, 4807−4818.

ROBINSON, M. K. 1976. *Atlas of North Pacific Ocean: monthly mean temperatures and mean salinities of the surface layer*, Ref. Publ. 2, Naval Oceanographic Office, Washington, D.C.

RUDNICK, D. L. & DAVIS, R. E. 1988. Mass and heat budgets on the northern California continental shelf, *Journal of Geophysical Research*, **93**, 14013−14024.

SMITH, R.L. 1981. A comparison of the structure and variability of the flow fields in three coastal upwelling regions: Oregon, Northwest Africa, and Peru, *In*: RICHARDS, A. E. (ed.) *Coastal Upwelling*, American Geophysical Union, 107−118.

—— 1983. Circulation patterns in upwelling regimes, *In*: SUESS, E. & THIEDE, J. (eds) *Coastal Upwelling: Its Sediment Record*, Plenum, New York, Part A, 13−35.

——, HUYER, A., GODFREY, J. S. & CHURCH, J. A. 1991. The Leeuwin Current off Western

Australia, 1986−1987, *Journal of Physical Oceanography*, **21**, 323−345.

STABENO, P. J. & SMITH, R. L. 1987. Deep-sea currents off northern California, *Journal of Geophysical Research*, **92**, 755−771.

STRUB, P. T., ALLEN, J. S., HUYER, A. & SMITH, R. L. Large-scale structure of the spring transition in the coastal ocean off western North America, *Journal of Geophysical Research*, **92**(C2), 1527−1544.

——, ——, ——, —— & BEARDSLEY, R. C. 1987a. Seasonal cycles of currents, temperatures, winds and sea level over the northeast Pacific continental shelf: 35° to 48°N, *Journal of Geophysical Research*, **92**, 1507−1526.

—— et al. 1991. The nature of the cold filaments in the California Current system. *Journal of Geophysical Research*, **96**, 14743−14768.

SVERDRUP, H. U., JOHNSON, M. W. & FLEMING, R. H. 1942. The Oceans: their physics, chemistry and generaly biology, Prentice-Hall, New York.

THOMSON, R. E. & PAPADAKIS, J. E. 1987. Upwelling filaments and motion of a satellite-tracked drifter along the west coast of North America. *Journal of Geophysical Research*, **92**, 6445−6461.

TRAGANZA, E. D., NESTOR, D. A. & McDONALD, A. K. 1980. Satellite observations of a nutrient upwelling off the coast of California, *Journal of Geophysical Research*, **85**, 4101−4106.

VINOGRADOV, M. E. 1981. Ecosystems of equatorial upwellings, *In*: LONGHURST, A. R. (ed.) *Analysis of Marine Ecosystems*, Academic, London, 69−93.

WARREN, B. A. 1990. Book review of Neshyba et al. (eds) (1989). *Limnology and Oceanography*, **35**, 1219−1220.

WEAVER, A. J. 1990. Ocean currents and climate, *Nature*, **347**, 432.

WINANT, C. D., BEARDSLEY, R. C. & DAVIS, R. E. Moored wind, temperature, and current observations made during the Coastal Ocean Dynamics Experiment, *Journal of Geophysical Research*, **92**, 1569−1604.

WOOSTER, W. S. & REID, J. L. Jr., Eastern boundary currents. *In*: HILL, M. N. (ed.) *The Sea*, Interscience, New York, 253−280.

YOSHIDA, K. & MAO, H. L. 1957. A theory of upwelling of large horizontal extent. *Journal of Marine Research*, **16**, 40−57.

Can sediment geochemistry record changes in coastal upwelling palaeoproductivity? Evidence from northwest Africa and the Arabian Sea

GRAHAM B. SHIMMIELD

Marine Geosciences Unit, Department of Geology and Geophysics, University of Edinburgh, West Mains Road, Edinburgh EH9 3JW, UK

Abstract: The causes and consequences of organic carbon (C_{org}) burial in sediments underlying regions of coastal upwelling are of profound importance to studies of palaeoceanography and palaeoclimatology alike. The primary control on coastal upwelling, wind stress and resulting Ekman transport, is linked intimately to variation in the Earth's insolation record via a variety of feedback mechanisms. In comparison, the nutrients required to sustain productivity, and the factors affecting the C_{org} content of the sediment, are related to variation in global glacial boundary conditions. Using a variety of geochemical indicators, it is apparent that the record of upwelling off northwest Africa, driven by the northeast trade winds, is characterized by arid glacial conditions and high wind stress sustaining elevated euphotic zone productivity. The resulting C_{org} accumulation record reflects higher palaeoproductivity during glacial episodes. In contrast, the Arabian Sea upwelling is seasonal. Faunal and geochemical (Ba/Al, U/Th ratios) indicators suggest strong interglacial (23 ka) cyclicity in the Southwest Monsoon. The C_{org} record is spatially and temporally consistent, but in disagreement with other palaeoproductivity indicators. These results point to the decoupling of surface ocean productivity in areas of coastal upwelling from deep-ocean circulation and nutrient supply. This result has important consequences for driving atmospheric pCO_2 changes on timescales less than that of oceanic mixing. Further applications of geochemical tracers to areas of coastal upwelling, such as northwest Africa and Peru, are needed urgently.

Over the past decade there has been considerable interest in the causes and consequences of organic carbon burial in sediments underlying upwelling areas, both in areas of high coastal productivity (eastern boundary currents) and along the equatorial divergence zone. Studies from the northwest African margin (Müller *et al.* 1983; Zahn *et al.* 1986), the equatorial Atlantic (Morris *et al.* 1984) and the eastern equatorial Pacific (Adelseck & Anderson 1978; Pedersen 1983; Lyle *et al.* 1988; Pedersen *et al.* 1988) have shown a consistent pattern of elevated organic carbon accumulation rates during the last glacial period (Isotope Stage 2). These authors have concluded that the pattern of accumulation is a reflection of enhanced surface productivity during the last glacial cycle (rather than low concentrations of oxygen in bottom waters and accompanying enhanced preservation, as suggested by Emerson 1985). Recently, our knowledge of the geographical distribution of palaeoproductivity has significantly advanced with the publication of large synoptic data sets (Sarnthein *et al.* 1988; Sarnthein & Winn 1990) aimed at assessing glacial/interglacial differences in productivity and the resulting impact on the carbon cycle and the

atmospheric CO_2 budget. In these studies, and the earlier work of Newell & Hsiung (1984) and Flohn (1982), the role of low-latitude upwelling in lowering sea surface temperatures, increasing productivity and organic carbon flux, and thereby influencing atmospheric pCO_2, is seen as pivotal. Indeed, Sarnthein *et al.* (1988) observed a marked increase in biological productivity at low- and mid-latitude upwelling areas during the last glacial maximum (LGM) which they argue was due to elevated wind stress associated with meridional surface winds. They argue that this resulted in an increase in annual global transfer of particulate organic carbon of about $2-4$ Gt C through the thermocline, resulting in significant changes in both atmospheric (lower pCO_2) and deep-ocean chemistry (increase in $CaCO_3$ dissolution and alkalinity) as elaborated in recent models by Berger & Kier (1984) and Boyle (1988).

Consideration of the influence of wind-driven upwelling and associated productivity on atmospheric and ocean chemistry requires an appreciation of the uneven distribution of such upwelling zones. Productivity maps by Koblentz-Mischke *et al.* (1970), from which one can estimate new production ('export pro-

From SUMMERHAYES, C. P., PRELL, W. L. & EMEIS, K. C. (eds), 1992, *Upwelling Systems: Evolution Since the Early Miocene*. Geological Society Special Publication No 64, pp 29–46.

29

duction'; Sarnthein *et al.* 1988) suggests that 85% of the annual total occurs in the narrow, high-productivity belts along the equator, subpolar divergence zones and along continental margins. Clearly, factors affecting coastal productivity, particularly windstress and intermediate water nutrient supply (Codispoti 1981), require careful study. The role of coastal upwelling therefore appears to be critical in ocean/atmosphere chemistry models.

Recent studies from one such area, the northwest Arabian Sea (Clemens & Prell 1990; Shimmield *et al.* 1990), have highlighted the importance of regional climatology and meteorology (the Southwest Monsoon) in affecting upwelling. As a result, studies of new production budgets in such areas should be linked to other parameters ('proxy indicators') sensitive to external forcing of the Earth's orbital parameters which in turn govern meridional surface wind gradients through feedback mechanisms of changing ice volume, continental aridity, latent heat transfer and albedo. Such proxy indicators (see below) indicate that simple glacial/interglacial contrasts (with approximate 100 ka periodicity) cannot account for the total variance in the intensity of coastal upwelling observed (Clemens & Prell 1990). Indeed, Sarnthein *et al.* (1988) remarked on the importance of the possible decoupling of surface ocean productivity in upwelling areas from deep-ocean circulation and the consequence of this decoupling for driving atmospheric pCO_2 changes on time scales less than that of oceanic mixing. So, whilst a broad picture of elevated new production during glacial time (specifically the LGM) is widely recognized, the details of coastal upwelling and its response to external (Croll-Milankovitch) forcing are only now being evaluated.

In order to reconstruct the history of coastal upwelling under such conditions, a variety of proxy indicators relating to continental aridity, wind strength and source, oxygen minimum zone (OMZ) intensity and intermediate water nutrient supply and circulation, need to be addressed. This paper discusses some of the inorganic chemical tracers that can help to identify these processes. Unfortunately, the available geochemical database which can be used to address these processes is rather limited. In previous work (e.g. Müller & Suess 1979), the record of C_{org} accumulation in the sediment has been used to infer past variations in palaeoproductivity. By using a variety of geochemical tracers, the full complexity of coastal upwelling, and the resulting sedimentary record, is revealed. Indeed, the record of C_{org} accumulation

in the Arabian Sea does not support the interpretation of palaeoproductivity variation suggested by faunal and geochemical studies (see below). This paper emphasises the need to consider the decoupling of the processes driving coastal upwelling (primarily wind stress and resulting Ekman transport), from those responding to changes in ocean chemistry and circulation. The sedimentary column contains an integrated record of palaeoproductivity response to these processes and requires appropriate deconvolution.

After initially reviewing the pattern, and suggested controls, on late Pleistocene organic matter accumulation off northwest Africa (*Meteor* core 12392 and ODP Leg 108, Site 658; see Table 1 for locations and water depths), a more detailed study of upwelling sediments from the northwest Arabian Sea (ODP Leg 117, Sites 721 and 724; *Darwin* core 17−30) is presented. The northwest African upwelling regime is a 'classical' eastern boundary current system driven by persistent, large-scale interactions of ocean and atmosphere circulation. In contrast, the Arabian Sea upwelling system is driven by a seasonally reversing atmospheric phenomenon: the Monsoon. This region of high productivity occurs in a cul-de-sac with respect to oceanic circulation.

Northwest Africa

Off northwest Africa, the sedimentary record is influenced profoundly by both biogenic sedimentation stimulated by the northeast trade winds, and terrigenous sedimentation resulting from (i) aeolian dust supply, (ii) fluvial sedimentation during humid climate phases and (iii) turbidites and other mass flow deposits (Tiedemann *et al.* 1989). The biogenic record is characterized by a dramatic glacial (Stage 2) increase in C_{org} content described from the *Meteor* core 12392−1 (Müller & Suess 1979; Müller *et al.* 1983; Fig. 1). Using data from several oceanic areas with different primary productivity values, Müller & Suess (1979) constructed an empirical relationship to describe the variation in palaeoproductivity at this site (based on measurements of the primary production, sedimentation rate, C_{org} content, porosity and sediment density)[1]. Müller & Suess

---

[1] Recently, Sarnthein *et al.* (1987, 1988) have modified this relationship based on the positive non-linear relationship between total primary production and new production (Eppley & Peterson 1979), and the addition of 29 data points to the sediment trap inventory.

Table 1. Locations and depths of stations and sites.

Site	Latitude	Longitude	Depth (m)	Reference
Northwest Africa				
M12392−1	25°10'N	16°51'W	2575	Müller & Suess (1979)
Site 658	20°44.95'N	18°34.85'W	2263	Tiedemann *et al.* (1989)
Peru				
Site 688	11°32.26'S	78°56.57'W	3820	von Breymann *et al.* (1989)
Site 682	11°15.99'S	79°3.73'W	3788	von Breymann *et al.* (1989)
Site 685	9°06.78'S	80°35.01'W	5070	von Breymann *et al.* (1989)
Site 680	11°03.90'S	78°04.67'W	250	von Breymann *et al.* (1989)
V19−29	3°35.0'S	83°56.0'W	3070	Boyle (1983)
Northwest Arabian Sea				
Site 722	16°37.3'N	59°47.8'E	2028	Prell *et al.* (1991)
Site 724	18°27.7'N	57°47.1'E	593	Prell *et al.* (1991)
Site 728	17°40.8'N	57°49.5'E	1428	Prell *et al.* (1991)
RC 27−61	16°37.5'N	59°51.7'E	1890	Clemens & Prell (1990)
CD 17−30	19°55.6'N	61°42.9'E	3580	Shimmield *et al.* (1990)
Baja California				
TGT145−17	23°45.0'N	111°00.0'W	200	Shimmield (1985)
TGT163−5	26°30.6'N	113°27.3'W	71	Shimmield (1985)
TGT163−8	25°22.5'N	112°47.2'W	311	Shimmield (1985)
TGT163−12	25°02.2'N	112°20.6'W	75	Shimmield (1985)
TGT163−11	24°58.8'N	112°45.9'W	262	Shimmield (1985)
TGT163−7	24°54.8'N	113°25.0'W	3168	Shimmield (1985)
TGT163−14	24°49.4'N	113°44.8'W	3168	Shimmield (1985)
TGT163−10	24°41.7'N	114°04.0'W	3482	Shimmield (1985)
TGT163−9	24°16.0'N	115°03.7'W	3685	Shimmield (1985)

(1979) showed that primary production rates from Stages 2, 3 and 6 must have been 2−3 times higher than the modern value to explain the C_{org} contents at the prevailing accumulation rates. They suggested that either the upwelling centre shifted farther offshore during glacial times (lower sea level), or that coastal upwelling was generally higher as a result of stronger northeast trade winds. Subsequently, Müller *et al.* (1983) have shown that the $\delta^{13}C$ values and C/N ratio of the organic fraction in this core attest to a marine plankton origin, rather than the terrigenous input of land plant detritus, for this C_{org} maximum. In their review of palaeoproductivity reconstruction over the last 30 ka, Sarnthein & Winn (1990) point to the northwest African margin as a type example of the 'polarized' productivity pattern at the LGM, whereby increased new production in upwelling zones (by about 150% in this area), whilst central oceanic gyres became less productive. Faunal transfer function analysis by the CLIMAP group also suggests increased upwelling resulting in a lowering of sea surface temperature (by about 6°C) off northwest Africa at the LGM, although

displacement of assemblages in the Canary Current should also be considered (Mix 1989).

More recently, studies from ODP Leg 108 (Ruddiman *et al.* 1989) and, in particular, Site 658 (Tiedemann *et al.* 1989), have shown that the sedimentary record from the northwest African margin contains information on the climatic evolution of North Africa over the last 8 Ma. During the Pleistocene there appears to have been a general drift towards more arid conditions over the Saharan region (Ruddiman *et al.* 1989). Figure 2 illustrates the interdependence of $CaCO_3$ and terrigenous contents at Site 658 (data from Tiedemann *et al.* 1989) for the late Quaternary. The mass accumulation rate (MAR) is derived from an age model based on $\delta^{18}O$ stratigraphy of planktonic foraminifera (Sarnthein & Tiedemann 1989). The terrigenous content record suggests that this was the predominant component during episodes of high accumulation rate. The trend towards more arid conditions is also supported by the pollen data of Dupont *et al.* (1989). Tiedemann *et al.* (1989) believe that the late Pleistocene dust flux has components of both glacial ice boundary

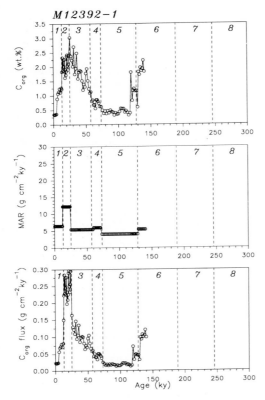

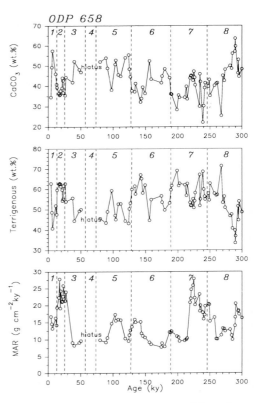

Fig. 1. Organic carbon (C_{org}, wt%), mass accumulation rate (MAR, g cm^{-2} ka^{-1}) and organic carbon flux (C_{org} flux, g cm^{-2} ka^{-1}) in *Meteor* core 12392−1 (Müller & Suess 1979) *versus* age (ka). Chronology (this and following figures) from oxygen isotope stratigraphy; stages indicated by italicized numbers. Note the strong influence of the age model on MAR, and the effect of C_{org} flux.

Fig. 2. Calcium carbonate ($CaCO_3$, wt%), terrigenous component (wt%) and mass accumulation rate (MAR, g cm^{-2} ka^{-1}) *versus* age (ka) at ODP Site 568, northwest Africa (Tiedemann *et al.* 1989). Isotope stratigraphy from Sarnthein & Tiedemann (1989).

conditions (125 ka periodicity) and strong coherence with equatorial sea-surface temperature records at the precessional (19- and 23-ka cycles) band suggesting an important link between aridity and the evaporational regime of the equatorial Atlantic. Ruddiman *et al.* (1989) argue for the importance of the Tibetan uplift as a major control on aridification of the central Sahara inducing stronger summer trade winds and aridity along the northwest African margin. Stein *et al.* (1989) and Tiedemann *et al.* (1989) show that the biogenic signal of upwelling is rather complex. Opal fluxes in the late Pleistocene display high-amplitude pulses apparently linked to warm, humid climatic conditions. These opal pulses are also associated with influxes of freshwater diatoms (Stabell 1989),

suggesting that interglacial productivity may be fed by fluvial discharge of nutrients during short-lived, but important, run-off maxima from the major rivers in the central Sahara. Examination of Fig. 1 indicates the strong dependence of the Stage-2 C_{org} flux on the MAR. The age model for this core was established using foraminiferal $\delta^{18}O$ stratigraphy (Müller *et al.* 1983) and displays the characteristic sharp transitions at stage boundaries. The use of $\delta^{18}O$ stratigraphy is ubiquitous in palaeoceanography, but the standard technique of matching stage boundaries with the SPECMAP $\delta^{18}O$ curve often results in an age model that has little resolution *during* isotope stages. New statistical techniques have been advocated to try to remove some of the inherent uncertainty in determining sedimentary fluxes in these records (i.e. 'sequence slotting', Thompson & Clark 1989). To some extent, the rapid decrease in C_{org} flux at the State 2/3 boundary is due to artifacts in the age model. In addition, Fig. 2 indicates a high terrigenous content and MAR during the Stage 2/3 C_{org} content maximum (if the M12392−1 C_{org} record is representative of northwest African margin). Allowing for uncertainties in the age models, the same may be true for the Stage 5/6 transition.

Thus, the geochemical record of northwest African upwelling is beguiling: apparently short-lived, nutrient-fed events during humid inter-glacials, succeeded by arid glacial conditions when increased wind stress sustained Ekman transport and coastal upwelling, produced the classic C_{org} profile of M12392−1. Ruddiman et al. (1989) concluded that the late Pleistocene record is one of intensification of both Saharan/Sahelian aridity and winter/summer dust plumes, whilst the development of a strong Sahelian moisture gradient resulted in extremes of wet and dry climate. The implication of the importance of external forcing and the orographic effect of Tibetan plateau uplift (Ruddiman & Kutzbach 1989) is clearly identified in their work. However, it should be noted that this interpretation of climatic history and upwelling response is based on numerous faunal, sedimentological and geochemical parameters, each of which responds to different aspects of the marine upwelling system.

Northwest Arabian Sea

The biogeochemical sedimentary record in the Arabian Sea is largely the history of Monsoon-induced upwelling. Prell (1984), Kutzbach (1981) and Clemens & Prell (1990) have all described the Indian Ocean Monsoon in some detail, drawing particular attention to the in-fluences on monsoon strength (a function of the pressure gradient between the Indian Ocean and the Asian continent) over the Pleistocene. The seasonal distribution of solar insolation, global ice volume, sea surface temperature, albedo of the Asian continent, and Himalayan uplift are all considered to be important. As such, parallels may be drawn with the northwest African upwelling system.

Here, the use of several key geochemical indicators to elucidate the history and controls on the coastal upwelling system off Arabia is described. Three cores collected from the Oman margin (ODP Site 724), Owen Ridge (ODP Site 722) and Indus abyssal plain (CD17−30; Table 1) have been chosen as representing sedimentation in, just below and well below the OMZ, respectively. In addition, C_{org} data from RC27−61 (the site survey core for Site 722) are also used as this is a high resolution record (courtesy of Dr D. Murray). Some of these data have been previously reported (Khan 1989; Shimmield & Mowbray 1991a, b); Shimmield et al. 1990; Murray 1991; Zahn & Pedersen 1991; Murray, this volume).

Organic carbon distribution and accumulation rate

Figure 3 illustrates the late Pleistocene record of C_{org} content off the Arabian margin. These profiles are particularly striking for two reasons: (1) the age/depth distribution is remarkably similar, with high C_{org} contents at 260, 140, 30−40, 20 and 0.8 ka BP, (2). The cores are situated in three, very different, depositional environments (continental slope, ridge and abyssal plain) but the historical record appears to be

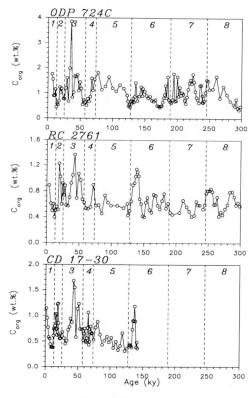

Fig. 3. C_{org} (wt%) contents with age (ka) in Hole 724C (Oman Margin; Zahn & Pedersen 1991) and RC 2761 (Owen Ridge; Murray this volume), and core CD 17−30 (Indus Fan abyssal plain; Khan 1989).

both well preserved and highly correlated. Figure 4 displays the change in C$_{org}$ flux over this same time period (derived from an age model based on foraminiferal δ^{18}O stratigraphy). Clearly, the slope location within the OMZ, Hole 724C, has a higher C$_{org}$ flux than the two deeper locations. However, the deepest site, CD17−30, has higher glacial fluxes than the ridge site. Hence, the record of C$_{org}$ accumulation off the Arabian margin does not follow a simple glacial/interglacial signal with high glacial contents. Instead, there appears to be a coherent signal across the marginal transect, which could be interpreted as being the result of changes in palaeoproductivity. In their regional compilations, Sarnthein et al. (1988) and Sarnthein & Winn (1990) remarked on the small or no productivity increase of the Arabian Sea upwelling at the LGM. In addition, they record a 30−60% short-term decrease in new production at about 15 ka BP. They concluded that the pattern of productivity in the Arabian Sea is complex and that this reversed

trend in palaeoproductivity, compared with the situation off northwest Africa, is not quantitatively important for the global biogeochemical budget.

However, Prell (1984), Ruddiman et al. (1989) and Clemens & Prell (1990) have shown that the key to understanding climate change and upwelling history lies in reconstructing the role of dynamic ocean−continent−atmosphere interactions (such as the Southwest Monsoon), rather than examining single proxy indicator records of palaeoproductivity. Previous studies (Prell & Curry 1981; Prell 1984, Prell & Kutzbach 1987; Clemens & Prell 1990) have documented the importance of precessional (19−23 ka cycles) insolation changes as a major driving force for the Indian Ocean Monsoon. Below, the use of inorganic geochemical proxy-indicators as a means of identifying both the history and interaction of the Southwest Monsoon on coastal upwelling and associated productivity, is outlined. Changes in continental aridity affecting the supply and source of wind-blown material, the intensity of palaeoproductivity and the severity of the resulting OMZ, and intermediate water nutrient supply and circulation are each addressed.

Continental aridity

Nair et al. (1989), using samples collected from sediments traps, have shown that the settling lithogenic material in the western Arabian Sea is of aeolian origin. The greatest flux of this material to the seafloor occurs during the summer Southwest Monsoon months. In addition, Sirocko & Sarnthein (1989) used satellite data to estimate the dust flux to the northwest Arabian Sea from the continent. They showed the strong seasonality in the dust plume and its significant contribution to the sediment record. By examining the record of lithogenic and CaCO$_3$ content of sediments from the Owen Ridge, a time-series record of lithogenic input to the western Arabian Sea may be constructed (Fig. 5). As pointed out by Clemens & Prell (1990), the elevated position of the Owen Ridge precludes downslope mass-flow deposition from the adjacent continental slope, or the Indus fan to the east, and lies well above the regional calcite lysocline. Hence, the Owen Ridge may be considered as a sediment trap, effectively recording the aeolian input rather than bottom sediment redistribution. Figure 5 shows that high CaCO$_3$ occurs during interglacial periods. As the MAR at Hole 722B (defined from δ^{18}O stratigraphy of planktonic foraminifera: Murray & Prell 1991) increases during glacial time, the

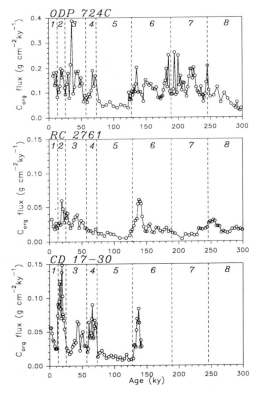

Fig. 4. Organic carbon fluxes (C$_{org}$ flux, g cm^{-2} ka^{-1}) at Hole 724C, RC 2761 and CD 17−30.

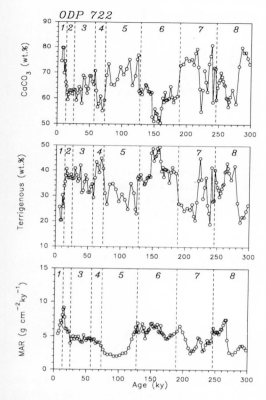

Fig. 5. CaCO$_3$ (wt%), terrigenous (lithogenic) component (1-CaCO$_3$; wt%) and mass accumulation rate (MAR; g cm^{-2} ka^{-1}) at the Owen Ridge site, Hole 722B.

variations in the CaCO$_3$ record are due largely to dilution by the lithogenic terrigenous component (Clemens & Prell 1990). This situation is analogous to that off northwest Africa (Fig. 2) and confirms the importance of terrigenous lithogenic supply in modulating the sedimentary record of these two upwelling regimes.

The variation of CaCO$_3$ content in the frequency domain (Fig. 6) is dominated by periodicity at the 100 ka cycle with some variance at 41 and 23 ka periods. This frequency distribution is matched by the proxy-global ice volume curve (the SPECMAP δ^{18}O variation), with the CaCO$_3$ signal being in phase and coherent with glacial boundary conditions (see Weedon & Shimmield 1991 for further details). We interpret the record of CaCO$_3$ dilution by terrigenous material as being a clear indicator of continental aridity with high lithogenic fluxes occurring during glacial periods characterized by increased

aeolian deflation and decreased vegetation cover over north and east Africa (Street & Grove 1979; Van Campo *et al*. 1982; Ruddiman *et al*. 1989; Clemens & Prell 1990; Weedon & Shimmield 1991).

Wind strength

Prell & Curry (1981) used the inverse correlation between sea surface temperature (SST) and the percentage abundance of the planktonic foraminifer *G. bulloides*, and the relationship between SST and wind-induced upwelling (Prell & Streeter 1982), to produce a palaeo-Monsoon upwelling index. This index appeared to be linked to solar radiation at the precessional (23 ka) cycle. Clemens & Prell (1990) went on to argue that the grain size distribution in RC27–61 (located at ODP Site 722 on the Owen Ridge) is closely paralleled by the *G. bulloides* record with coherent power and zero phase difference at the precision band. Hence, they proposed that lithogenic grain size is an indicator of wind strength of the monsoon winds, which transported material from the surrounding deserts, and stimulated wind-induced upwelling.

Titanium is known to be concentrated in the coarser sediment fraction (Schmitz 1987*a*), particularly in the heavy mineral assemblage which often contains ilmenite, rutile, titanomagnetite and augite. Boyle (1983) used the ratio of Ti/Al (i.e. the heavy mineral content of the lithogenic sediment fraction) as an indicator of fluctuations in the intensity of aeolian transport associated with glacial/interglacial cycles in the eastern Pacific. Donnelly (1982) has shown that basaltic volcanic ash may be responsible for elevated Ti/Al ratios. However, examination of the mineralogy sedimentology of cores from the Arabian Sea do not reveal evidence of volcanic ash. In Fig. 7 the time distributions of Ti/Al off Peru (Boyle 1983) and Arabia (Hole 722B, CD17–30) are shown. Off Peru the Ti/Al record is influenced by trade wind velocities modulated by glacial boundary conditions; in the Arabian Sea the frequency distribution appears to be only weakly controlled by glacial/interglacial conditions. Taking the data for the Owen Ridge core, 722B, Fig. 8 indicates that although all three Milankovitch frequencies are present, the precessional (23 ka) cycle dominates. The record is coherent with ice volume (SPECMAP δ^{18}O curve) at the 100 and 41 ka periods but not at 23 ka cycle. Given our knowledge of Monsoon wind strength based on faunal (*G. bulloides*) and pollen (Prell & Van Campo 1986) indices,

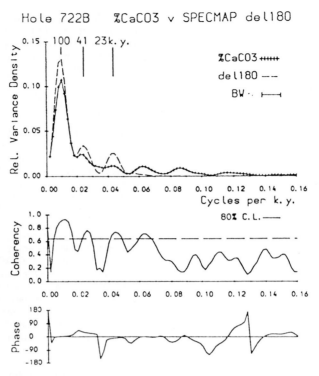

Fig. 6. (a) Relative variance density and cross-spectral analysis of CaCO₃ against the SPECMAP $\delta^{18}O$ profile in Hole 722B. (b) The statistically significant coherence (80% confidence level) between the spectra is given by the horizontal line. (c) Phase angle *versus* frequency plot. Significant coherence occurs at the major orbital frequency bands of 100 ka, 41 ka and 23 ka.

Weedon & Shimmield (1991) and Shimmield *et al.* (1990) infer that the Ti/Al record is a useful proxy-indicator for palaeo-wind strength.

Palaeoproductivity and oxygen minimum zone intensity

Despite the fact that no causal relationship between Ba and productivity has been established, the association of Ba, opal and biogenic sedimentation has been commented on by several workers since the early work of Revelle *et al.* (1955). Dehairs *et al.* (1980) and Bishop (1988) showed that barite (BaSO₄) was precipitated in decaying suspended marine particulate matter (particularly diatoms) in oceanic waters. Recently, measurements of Ba in the tests of foraminifera (Lea & Boyle 1989) and corals (Lea *et al.* 1989) have been used as an indicator of deep-ocean nutrient status and local upwelling intensity, respectively. In Fig. 9, the data of Von Breymann *et al.* (1990) from the

Peru margin (ODP Leg 112), together with measurements made by Shimmield (1985) in the Baja California upwelling system, are shown (Th and Al are both taken as indicators of terrigenous detritus). Both Site 680, and stations 145–17, 163–58, 163–8; 163–11, and 145–12 off Baja California, have low, shale-like, ratios of Ba/Th and Ba/Al. In contrast, deeper water core sites have large excesses of Ba, above any possible terrigenous contribution. The excess Ba is probably due to the 'dissolution residue' (*sensu* Dymond 1981) resulting from upwelling productivity. Schmitz (1987b), Shimmield & Mowbray (1991a) and Shimmield *et al.* (1990) suggest that down-core records of excess Ba may be used to identify palaeoproductivity pulses. Additionally, Shimmield (1985) suggested that barite-secreting organisms may be confined to a rather discrete zone within the upwelling productivity belt, seaward of the shelfbreak (under a different nutrient regime), and as a consequence shallow-water, organic-rich sediments receive little biogenic Ba. A

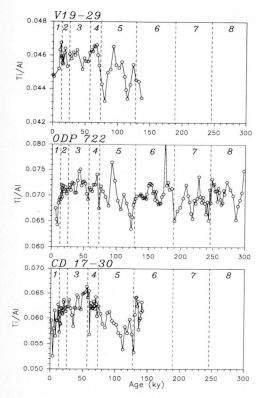

Fig. 7. High precision Ti/Al (weight ratio) profiles with age (ky) in V19−29 (Boyle 1983), Hole 722B, and in core CD 17−30. Note the cyclic periodicity that is particularly evident in Hole 722V (dominant 23 ka periodicity, Weedon & Shimmield 1991, and Fig. 8).

similar distribution of Ba was noted by Calvert & Price (1983) in their work off Namibia. Consequently, the sediments from nearshore shelf settings found at Site 680 (Peru) and Site 724 (Oman margin) are deficient in Ba despite the high organic matter content recorded in the sediment. Also, Von Breymann et al. (1990) point out that in very organic-rich sediments with shallow sulphate-reduction zones, Ba diagenesis probably removes the productivity signal. In sediments where sulphate-reduction is minimal, the 'dissolution residue' (Dymond 1981) high in Ba offers the potential of tracing past patterns of palaeoproductivity when both C_{org}, opal and $CaCO_3$ patterns have become modified by dissolution. Schmitz (1987b), for example, used Ba contents in sediments from the Indian Ocean to trace plate movement below the equatorial upwelling zone on a time scale of

millions of years. However, it should be noted that our knowledge of the Ba/C_{org} ratio in biogenic detritus is poor, as there is probably a gradient in the ratio from hemipelagic to coastal sediments. The enormous potential of Ba as a palaeoproductivity indicator relies on our ability to determine this relationship using sediment traps and cores from a range of oceanographic regimes.

Off Arabia (Fig. 10), the record of palaeoproductivity appears to be well preserved on the Owen Ridge and abyssal plain, but not in the highly-reducing sediments of the continental shelf (Site 724). There is a striking correspondence between the Ba/Al profile and the planktonic $\delta^{18}O$ record at the deep-water sites, with elevated Ba occurring during interglacial stages. The variation in Ba content at the deeper sites due to changes in the aluminosilicate contribution (see discussion above) is minimal (<10% of the signal in Hole 722B). Clearly, the signal at the Owen Ridge and abyssal plain contains important palaeoproductivity information, but rather different from the C_{org} records (Figs 3 & 4).

When Hole 722B is considered in the frequency domain, the clear correspondence between Ba/Al and the ice volume $\delta^{18}O$ record is apparent (Fig. 11). Spectral power, coherence and phase are similar to proxy-ice volume at eccentricity and obliquity frequencies. Since upwelling of nutrient-rich water depends on wind strength (Prell 1984), it might be expected that the Ba/Al palaeoproductivity record would be dominated by 23 ka precessional variation. Instead, the record is closely linked to the global ice volume signal. In Weedon & Shimmield (1991) and Shimmield et al. (1990) we suggest that intermediate water circulation and the position of a deep hydrological front (Kallel et al. 1988) strongly influence nutrient supply and resulting palaeoproductivity. From foraminiferal isotope data Kallel et al. (1988) suggested that intermediate water circulation and Antarctic bottom water flow were intensified during interglacial periods. Thus, hole 722B and core CD17−30 record the influence of global ice volume on nutrient supply to the northern Indian Ocean (see below for further discussion). It should also be noted that humid interglacial episodes probably promote increased nutrient run-off into the Arabian Sea thereby enhancing coastal productivity. The opal record at Site 722 (D. Murray, pers. comm.) displays rapid pulses of opal deposition, analogous to the northwest African margin (see above). It is possible that opal records from the Arabian Sea also record pulsed fluvial discharge.

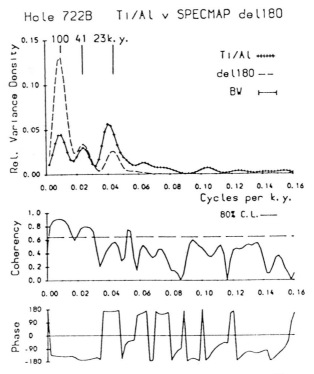

Fig. 8. Relative spectral density and coherence between Ti/Al and SPECMAP $\delta^{18}O$ for Hole 722B (see Fig. 6 caption for explanation). Note the strong 23 ka power in the Ti/Al signal and the coherency with ice volume at the eccentricity and tilt cycles.

Redox-sensitive metals such as Mo and U are known to accumulate preferentially in organic-rich, reducing sediments (Bertine 1972; Veeh, 1967; Pedersen et al. 1988; Anderson et al. 1989). The process of enrichment may either be due to diagenetic enrichment (often associated with a manganese oxyhydroxide pump; Pedersen et al. 1988; Shimmield & Pedersen 1990) or organic matter complexation, or both. Post-depositional relocation of U is known to occur in organic-rich turbidites (Colley et al. 1989) when downward diffusing O_2 creates an oxidation front remobilizing the reduced U. In the Panama Basin, the lack of Mo enrichment during Stage 2 was used by Pedersen et al. (1988) to argue that bottom sediments remained oxygen-replete during the burial of the high glacial C_{org} event. Off the Oman Margin, only sediments accumulating within the present day OMZ (e.g. Site 724) have Mo enrichments; Mo is undetectable at the Owen Ridge (Hole 722B) and at the abyssal plain (CD17−30). Despite the present depth of the base of the OMZ at

180 m (Shimmield et al. 1990) defined by oxygen concentrations <0.5 ml/l, it appears that the OMZ did not expand to intersect the ridge crest at Site 722 during the last 300 ka. Alternatively, the position of a hydrological front (Kallel et al. 1988) and/or intermediate water circulation (see below) sustained well-oxygenated water at the sediment−water interface. At the continental slope (Hole 724C) there is a strong correlation between Mo and C_{org} content (Fig. 12). This distribution suggests a less intense OMZ at Termination 1, Stage 4 and Stage 6.

In contrast, the distribution of U (normalized to Th measured by the same α-spectrometry technique: Shimmield & Mowbray 1991b), displays a trend that is more similar to the Ba palaeoproductivity signal especially at site 722B (Fig. 13). Specifically, the U content is highest during interglacial episodes, with a progressive decrease in signal amplitude away from the centre of upwelling. Since there is an association between redox state and organic matter content of the sediment, and U is often bound to organic

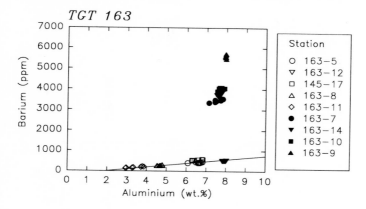

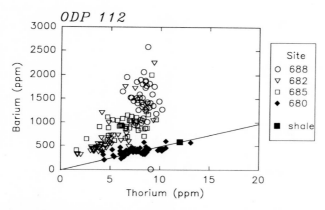

Fig. 9. Barium *versus* lithogenic indicators (Al, wt%; Baja California, TGT 163 and Th, ppm; Peru margin). Data from stations and sources listed in Table 1. Clear Ba enrichment above average shale values (indicated by the diagonal line) occurs in the hemipelagic sediments. Organic-rich shelf sediments undergoing complete sulphate reduction may have barite dissolution occurring (see text for further details.)

matter (see Shimmield & Pedersen 1990 for a review), the strong correlation between U/Th and other palaeoproductivity indicators (e.g. Ba/Al) might be expected. The high input of phytodetritus also drives the U-redoxcline within the sediment closer to the seawater interface, allowing substantial U fixation (perhaps as U^{4+}) within the sediment (Anderson *et al.* 1989). Once the U has become fixed there appears to be little evidence of post-depositional remobilization. Thus, the U/Th distribution has the potential of recording palaeoproductivity variations in a similar way to Ba (Fig. 11), but without the disadvantage of the subsequent mobility of Ba due to diagenesis in highly reducing sediments.

Intermediate water nutrient supply and circulation

Studies of the distribution of excess ^{230}Th $(^{230}$Th$_{xs})$ in marine sediments have focussed on the ability to predict the activity of the nuclide based on the assumption of vertical scavenging from the overlying water column following decay from its parent ^{234}U (Cochran & Osmond 1976; Mangini & Diester-Haass 1983; Francois *et al.* 1990; Yang *et al.* 1990). This prediction relies on an independent assessment of age and sediment accumulation rate, usually obtained by δ^{18}O stratigraphy. With a knowledge of radionuclide activity (A), accumulation rate (S) and the dry bulk density (ρ), the flux of ^{230}Th$_{xs}$

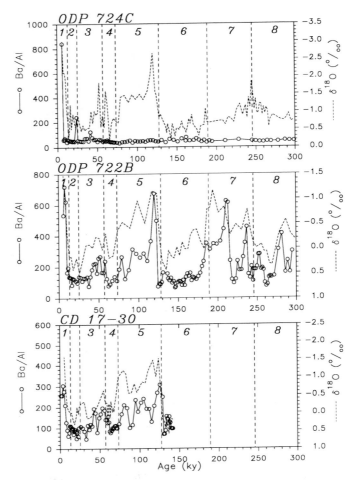

Fig. 10. Age profiles of $\delta^{18}O$ (‰, vs PDB) and Ba/Al ($\times 10^{-4}$) in Holes 724C, 722B and CD 17–30 in the northwest Arabian Sea. Note the extremely good agreement between the two records in Hole 722B and CD 17–30, and the scale change for Ba/Al. Isotope data from Zahn and Pedersen (1991), Murray & Prell (1991) and Shimmield *et al.* (1990), Ba/Al data in CD 17–30 from Khan (1989).

(F_{meas}) may be calculated and compared to the predicted flux (F_{pred}) to give an indication of the variability ($\Delta^{230}Th_{xs}$) in water column scavenging processes (Mangini & Diester-Haass 1983) or bottom sediment reworking (Cochran & Osmond 1976). Hence:

$$F_{pred} = 2.3\ D$$
$$F_{meas} = A(^{230}Th_{xs}) \times S \times \rho$$
$$\Delta^{230}Th_{xs} = F_{pred} - F_{meas}.$$

Figure 14 illustrates the distribution of both enhanced and deficient $^{230}Th_{xs}$ activity in Hole 722B and CD17–30 (see Shimmield & Mowbray 1991b for further details). With depth and age

the propagation of analytical errors and uncertainty of the age models limits accuracy to ±20%. Clearly, there is a deficit in $^{230}Th_{xs}$ on the Owen Ridge at mid-Stage 5, decreasing towards the present day. Figure 14 also presents the foraminiferal fragmentation index (Steens *et al.* 1991) for Site 728 on the Owen Ridge. The similarity of these two records indicates that during interglacial Stage 5 vigorous intermediate water circulation resulted in bottom sediment winnowing at the Owen Ridge crest, removing ^{230}Th associated with the finest particulate phases and fragmenting deposited foraminifera, but supplying nutrients to sustain the euphotic zone productivity. The predominant influence

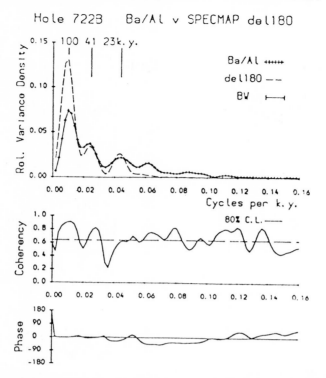

Fig. 11. Relative spectral density and coherence between Ba/Al and the SPECMAP $\delta^{18}O$ stack for Hole 722B (see Fig. 6 caption for explanation). Ba/Al is in phase with the global climate signal ($\delta^{18}O$) at the three main Milankovitch frequencies.

on this process is deep water formation (specifically Antarctic Bottom Water) and water column stratification, which in turn are linked to ice volume and ice sheet extent at high latitudes (Boyle 1988).

Conclusions

Coastal upwelling off Arabia is predominantly due to wind stress resulting from the influence of the Southwest Monsoon. Proxy indicators of wind strength, such as Ti/Al and lithogenic grain size, reveal the strong precessional insolation forcing acting on the Monsoon (Clemens & Prell 1990). However, the sedimentary record reveals that changes in glacial boundary conditions impact both the terrestrial climate (i.e. aridity, indicated by terrigenous flux) and oceanic nutrient supply (sustaining euphotic zone productivity resulting in Ba and U sequestration). The record of C_{org} accumulation is influenced by remineralization, preservation by varying sediment accumulation rate, local

variation in upwelling productivity and bottom sediment redistribution. Nevertheless, a coherent pattern of C_{org} accumulation is traceable across the Oman margin. Using sedimentary Mo content as an indicator of low oxygen fugacity in bottom waters, the intensity of the OMZ can be identified. $^{230}Th_{xs}$ and foraminiferal fragmentation index provide tracers of intensity of bottom-water flow. At the depth of the Owen Ridge, the record obtained reveals changes in intermediate water circulation linked to glacial boundary conditions.

At present, our knowledge of the scale of interaction of these factors on the historical C_{org} record is poorly known. However, it is clear that in the Arabian Sea, the geochemical (especially the Ba/Al ratio) and faunal (i.e. % *G. bulloides*; Prell 1984; Clemens & Prell 1990) records are at variance with the C_{org} distribution and traditional interpretation. This conundrum will require further study, with the application of geochemical palaeoceanography to other areas such as the northwest African margin.

Sarnthein *et al.* (1988) stated:

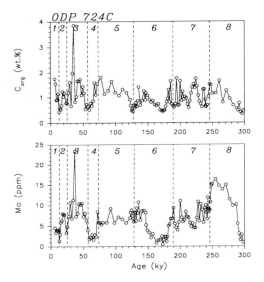

Fig. 12. Profiles of organic carbon (C$_{org}$, wt%) and molybdenum (Mo, ppm) in the slope sediments of Hole 724C situated within the oxygen minimum zone of the Oman margin. C$_{org}$ data from Zahn & Pedersen (1991).

'. . . low-latitude upwelling and its associated pulsating export productivity must be considered as a strong additional factor, if not the major agent, in changing ocean and atmospheric chemistry during Terminations I and II'

With studies of the palaeoceanographic history of coastal upwelling has come a realization of the complexity of interaction between the ocean−continent−atmosphere climate system. In order to reconstruct past changes in ocean and atmosphere chemistry we require a detailed knowledge of the behaviour and response of these upwelling systems. On a broad scale, the glacial-interglacial shifts in palaeoproductivity are now recognized, resulting in the transfer of some extra 2−4 Gt C/a to the deep ocean during the LGM (Sarnthein & Winn 1990). Similarly, external forcing (solar insolation and resulting feedbacks) and orographic factors (Tibetan uplift) drive a variety of meteorological processes, such as the Indian Ocean Monsoon, which impact on coastal upwelling and productivity (Ruddiman & Kutzbach 1989; Clemens & Prell 1990). Consequently, our understanding of the time-dependent behaviour of coastal upwelling, and its major contribution to global carbon cycling, requires evaluation of a variety of forcing mechanisms operating with different periodicities. Studies of the northwest

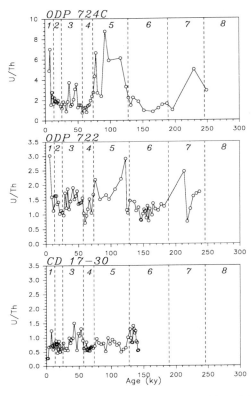

Fig. 13. Profiles of U normalized to Th (weight ratio) in the northwest Arabian Sea. Note the elevated U contents nearest the margin were organic matter fluxes and redox diagenesis were at a maximum. High U/Th ratio occur during high productivity episodes identified by proxy-indicators such as Ba/Al (Fig. 10).

African upwelling system and the Arabian Sea point to common features of the African climate change, with modulation by the Southwest Monsoon in the case of the latter. In the Arabian Sea, a host of proxy indicators ranging from faunal and floral species abundance and diversity to inorganic geochemical parameters allow detailed, high-resolution reconstruction of the late Pleistocene history. Inorganic geochemistry provides a relatively rapid estimation of a variety of proxy-palaeoceanographic indicators, both of controls on coastal upwelling productivity (wind stress, nutrient supply) and the preservation of the biogenic signal (bottom water chemistry, sediment winnowing).

The officers and crew of the RRS *Charles Darwin* and *JOIDES Resolution* provided the opportunity to undertake this study. Many people assisted me, particularly Steve Mowbray, Frances Lindsay, Athar Khan and Brian Price. Tom Pedersen commented on

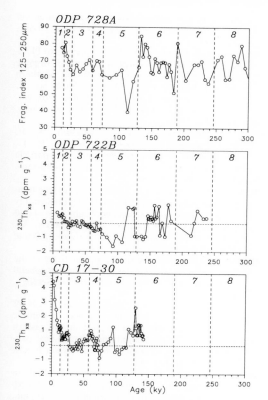

Fig. 14. Foraminiferal fragmentation index (whole#/(whole# + fragment#) × 100) in the 125–250 μm size range; Steens *et al.* 1991) for ODP Site 728 on the Oman margin compared to Δ^{230} Th$_{xs}$ (dpm g^{-1}) (see text for details of calculation) in Hole 722B and core CD 17–30. High and positive Δ^{230} Th$_{xs}$ values are linked to episodes of increased productivity and resulting particulate flux, whilst the deficit (particularly at the ridge site) may be due to bottom-currents causing foraminifera fragmentation, sediment winnowing and erosion.

an earlier draft of the manuscript. Two anonymous reviewers are thanked for their helpful contributions. Support by NERC (Grant GST/02/315) under the ODP Special Topic fund is acknowledged gratefully.

References

ADELSECK, C. G. Jr. & ANDERSON, T. F. 1978. The late Pleistocene record of productivity fluctuations in the eastern equatorial Pacific Ocean. *Geology*, **6**, 388–391.

ANDERSON, R. F., FLEISHER, M. Q. & LeHURAY, A. P. 1989. Concentration, oxidation state, and particulate flux of uranium in the Black Sea. *Geochimica et Cosmochimica Acta*, **53**, 2215–2224.

BERGER, W. H. & KEIR, R. S. 1984. Glacial-Holocene

changes in atmospheric CO_2 and the deep-sea record. *In*: HANSEN, J. E. & TAKAHASHI, T. (eds) *Climate Processes and Climate Sensitivity*. American Geophysical Union, Washington, DC., Geophysical Monograph, **29**, 337–351.

BERTINE, K. K. 1972. The deposition of molybdenum in anoxic waters. *Marine Chemistry*, **1**, 43–53.

BISHOP, J. K. B. 1988. The barite-opal-organic carbon association in oceanic particulate matter. *Nature*, **332**, 341–343.

BOYLE, E. A. 1983. Chemical accumulation variations under the Peru Current during the past 130 000 years. *Journal of Geophysical Research*, **88**, 7667–7680.

—— 1988. Vertical oceanic nutrient fractionation and glacial/interglacial CO_2 cycles. *Nature*, **331**, 55–56.

CALVERT, S. E. & PRICE, N. B. 1983. Geochemistry of Namibian shelf sediments. *In*: SUESS, E. & THIEDE, J. (eds), *Coastal Upwelling, Part A*, Plenum, New York, 337–375.

CLEMENS, S. C. & PRELL, W. L. 1990. Late Pleistocene variability of Arabian Sea summer monsoon winds and continental aridity: Eolian records from the lithogenic component of deep-sea sediments. *Paleoceanography*, **5**, 109–145.

COCHRAN, J. K. & OSMOND, J. K. 1976. Sedimentation patterns and accumulation rates in the Tasman Basin. *Deep-Sea Research*, **23**, 193–210.

CODISPOTI, L. A. 1981. Temporal nutrient variability in three different upwelling regions. *In*: RICHARDS, F. A. (ed.) *Coastal Upwelling, Coastal Estuarine Science Series*, **1**, American Geophysical Union, Washington, DC., 209–220.

COLLEY, S., THOMSON, J. & TOOLE, J. 1989. Uranium relocations and derivation of the quasi-isochrons for a turbidite/pelagic sequence in the Northeast Atlantic. *Geochimica et Cosmochimica Acta*, **53**, 1223–1234.

DEHAIRS, F., CHESSELET, R. & JEDWAB, J. 1980. Discrete suspended particles of barite and the barium cycle in the open ocean. *Earth and Planetary Science Letters*, **49**, 528–550.

DONNELLY, T. W. 1982. Worldwide continental denudation and climatic deterioration during the late Tertiary: Evidence from deep-sea sediments. *Geology*, **10**, 451–454.

DUPONT, L. M., BEUG, H.-J., STALLING, H. & TIEDEMANN, R. 1989. First palynological results from Site 658 at 21°N off Northwest Africa: Pollen as climate indicators. *In*: RUDDIMAN, W., SARNTHEIN, M. *et al.*, *Proceedings of the Ocean Drilling Program, Scientific Results*, **108**, College Station, Texas, 93–111.

DYMOND, J. 1981. Geochemistry of Nazca plate surface sediments: An evaluation of hydrothermal, biogenic, detrital, and hydrogenous sources. *Geological Society of America Memoir*, **154**, 133–173.

EMERSON, S. 1985. Organic carbon preservation in marine sediments. *In*: SUNQUIST, E. T. & BROECKER, W. S. (eds) *The Carbon Cycle and Atmospheric CO_2: Natural Variations Archean to Present*. American Geophysical Union,

Washington, D.C., Geophysical Monograph, **32**, 78–87.

EPPLEY, R. & PETERSON, B. J. 1979. Particulate organic matter flux of planktonic new production in the deep ocean. *Nature*, **282**, 677–680.

FLOHN, H. 1982. Oceanic upwelling as a key for abrupt climatic change. *Journal of the Meteorological Society of Japan*, **60**, 268–273.

FRANCOIS, R., BACON, M. P. & SUMAN, D. O. 1990. Thorium-230 profiling in deep-sea sediments: High resolution records of flux and dissolution of carbonate in the equatorial Atlantic during the last 24 000 years. *Paleoceanography*, **5**, 761–788.

KALLEL, N., LABEYRIE, L., JUILLET-LECLERC, A. & DUPLESSY, J.-C. 1988. A deep hydrological front between intermediate and deep-water masses in the glacial Indian Ocean. *Nature*, **333**, 651–655.

KHAN, A. A. 1989. *Geochemistry and Palaeoclimate Changes in Sediments: Northern Arabian Sea.* PhD Thesis, University of Edinburgh.

KOBLENTZ-MISCHKE, O. J., VOLKOVINSKY, V. V. & KABANOVA, J. G. 1970. Plankton primary production of the world ocean. *In:* WOOSTER, W. S. (ed.), *Scientific Exploration of the South Pacific*, National Academy of Sciences, Washington DC., 183–193.

KUTZBACH, J. E. 1981. Monsoon climate of the early Holocene: climatic experiment using the earth's orbital parameters for 9000 years ago. *Science*, **214**, 59–61.

LEA, D. W. & BOYLE, E. A. 1989. Barium content of benthic foraminifera controlled by bottom water composition. *Nature*, **338**, 751–753.

——, SHEN, G. T. & BOYLE, E. A. 1989. Coralline barium records temporal variability in equatorial Pacific upwelling. *Nature*, **340**, 373–376.

LYLE, M., HEATH, G. R., MURRAY, D. W., FINNEY, B. P., DYMOND, J., ROBBINS, J. M. & BROOKSFORCE, K. 1988. The record of late Pleistocene sedimentation in the eastern equatorial Pacific Ocean. *Paleoceanography*, **3**, 39–59.

MANGINI, A. & DIESTER-HAASS, L. 1983. Excess Th-230 in sediments off NW Africa traces upwelling in the past. *In:* SUESS, E. & THIEDE, J. *Coastal Upwelling: Its Sediment Record.* Plenum, New York, 455–471.

MIX, A. C. 1989. Pleistocene productivity: evidence from organic carbon and foraminiferal species. *In:* BERGER, W. H., SMETACEK, V. S. & WEFER, G. (eds) *Productivity of the Ocean: Present and Past*, Wiley, New York.

MORRIS, R. J., MCCARTNEY, M. J. & WEAVER, P. P. E. 1984. Sapropelic deposits in a sediment core from the Guinea Basin, South Atlantic. *Nature*, **309**, 611–614.

MÜLLER, P. J. & SUESS, E. 1979. Productivity, sedimentation rate, and sedimentary organic matter in the oceans — I. Organic carbon preservation. *Deep-Sea Research*, **26**, 1347–1362.

——, ERLENKEUSER, H. & VON GRAFENSTEIN, R. 1983. Glacial-interglacial cycles in oceanic productivity inferred from organic carbon contents in eastern North Atlantics sediment cores. *In:*

SUESS, E. & THIEDE, J. (ed), *Coastal Upwelling: Its Sediment Record.* Plenum, New York, 365–398.

MURRAY, D. & PRELL, W. L. 1991. Pliocene to Pleistocene variations in calcium carbonate, organic carbon and opal on the Owen Ridge, northern Arabian Sea. *In:* PRELL, W. L. & NIITSUMA, N. *et al. Proceedings of the Ocean Drilling Program, Science Results*, **117**, College Station, Texas, 343–364.

NAIR, R. R., ITTEKOT, V., MANGANINI, S. J., RAMASWAMY, V., HAAKE, B., DEGENS, E. T., DESAI, B. N. & HONJO, S. 1989. Increased particle flux to the deep ocean related to monsoons. *Nature*, **338**, 749–750.

NEWELL, R. E. & HSUING, J. 1984. Sea surface temperature, atmospheric CO_2 and the global energy budget: Some comparisons between the past and present. *In:* MÖRNER, N.-A. & KARLEN, W. (eds) *Climatic Changes on a Yearly to Millenial Basis*, Reidel, Dordrecht, 533–561.

PEDERSEN, T. F. 1983. Increased productivity in the eastern equatorial Pacific during the last glacial maximumn (19 000 to 14 000 yr B.P.). *Geology*, **11**, 16–19.

——, PICKERING, M., VOGEL, J. S., SOUTHON, J. N. & NELSON, D. E. 1988. The response of benthic foraminifera to productivity cycles in the eastern equatorial Pacific: Faunal and geochemical constraints on glacial bottom water oxygen levels. *Paleoceanography*, **3**, 157–168.

PRELL, W. L. 1984. Monsoon climate of the Arabian Sea during the late Quaternary; A response to changing solar radiation. *In:* BERGER, A., IMBRIE, J., HAYS, J., KUKLA, G. & SALTZMAN, B. (eds), *Milankovitch and Climate*, Reidel, Hingham, Mass., 349–366.

—— & CURRY, W. B. 1981. Faunal and isotopic indices of monsoonal upwelling: Western Arabian Sea. *Oceanologica Acta*, **4**, 91–98.

—— & KUTZBACH, J. E. 1987. Monsoon variability over the past 150 000 years. *Journal of Geophysical Research*, **92**, 8411–8425.

—— & STREETER, H. F. 1982. Temporal and spatial patterns of monsoonal upwelling along Arabia: A modern analogue for the interpretation of Quaternary SST anomalies. *Journal of Marine Research*, **40**, 143–155.

—— & VAN CAMPO, E. 1986. Coherent response of the arabian Sea upwelling and pollen transport to late Quaternary monsoonal winds. *Nature*, **323**, 526–528.

REVELLE, R., BRAMLETTE, M., ARRHENIUS, G. & GOLDBERG, E. D. 1955. Pelagic sediments of the Pacific. *Geological Society of America Special Paper*, **62**, 221–235.

RUDDIMAN, W. F. & KUTZBACH, J. E. 1989. Forcing of late Cenozoic Northern Hemisphere climate by plateau uplift in Southern Asia and the American West. *Journal of Geophysical Research*, **94**, 18409–18427.

——, SARNTHEIN, M., BACKMAN, J., BALDAUF, J. G., CURRY, W., DUPONT, L. M., JANECEK, T., POKRAS, E. M., RAYMO, M. E., STABELL, B.,

STEIN, R. & TIEDEMANN, R. 1989. Late Miocene to Pleistocene evolution of climate in Africa and the low-latitude Atlantic: Overview of Leg 108 results. *In*: RUDDIMAN, W., SARNTHEIN, M. *et al.* *Proceedings of the Ocean Drilling Program, Scientific Results*, **108**, College Station, Texas, 463–484.

SARNTHEIN, M. & TIEDEMANN, R. 1989. Toward a high-resolution stable isotope stratigraphy of the last 3.4 million years: Sites 658 and 659 off north-west Africa. *In*: RUDDIMAN, W., SARNTHEIN, M. *et al.*, *Proceedings of the Ocean Drilling Program, Scientific Results*, **108**, College Station, Texas, 167–185.

—— & WINN, K. 1990. Reconstruction of low and middle latitude export productivity, 30 000 years BP to Present: Implications for global carbon reservoirs. *In*: SCHLESINGER, M. E. (ed.) *Climate–Ocean Interaction*, Kluwer, Amsterdam, 319–342.

——, ——, & ZAHN, R. 1987. Paleoproductivity of oceanic upwelling and the effect on atmospheric CO_2 and climatic change during deglaciation times. *In*: BERGER, W. H. & LABEYRIE, L. (eds), *Abrupt Climatic Change*, Reidel, Dordrecht, 311–337.

——, ——, DUPLESSY, J.-C. & FONTUGNE, M. R. 1988. Global variations of surface ocean productivity in low and mid latitudes: Influence of CO_2 reservoirs of the deep ocean and atmosphere during the last 21 000 years. *Paleoceanography*, **3**, 361–399.

SCHMITZ, B. 1987*a*. The TiO_2/Al_2O_3 ratio in the Cenozoic Bengal abyssal fan sediments and its use as a palaeostream energy indicator. *Marine Geology*, **76**, 195–206.

—— 1987*b*. Barium, high productivity, and northward wandering of the Indian continent. *Paleoceanography*, **2**, 63–77.

SHIMMIELD, G. B. 1985. *The geochemistry and mineralogy of Pacific sediments, Baja California, Mexico.* PhD thesis, University of Edinburgh.

—— & MOWBRAY, S. R. 1991*a*. The inorganic geochemical record of the northwest Arabian Sea: A history of productivity variation over the last 400 ka from Sites 722 and 724. *In*: PRELL, W. L. & NIITSUMA, N. *et al.*, *Proceedings of the Ocean Drilling Program, Science Results*, **117**, College Station, Texas, 409–429.

—— & —— 1991*b*. U-series disequilibrium, particle scavenging and sediment accumulation during the late Pleistocene on the Owen Ridge, Site 722. *In*: PRELL, W. L. & NIITSUMA, N. *et al.*, *Proceedings of the Ocean Drilling Program, Science Results*, **117**, College Station, Texas, 465–472.

—— & PEDERSEN, T. F. 1990. The geochemistry of reactive trace metals and halogens in hemipelagic continental margin sediments. *Critical Reviews in Aquatic Sciences*, **3**, 255–279.

——, PRICE, N. B. & PEDERSEN, T. F. 1990. The influence of hydrography, bathymetry and productivity on sediment type and composition of the Oman Margin and in the Northwest Arabian Sea. *In*: ROBERTSON, A. H. F., SEARLE, M. P. & RIES, A. C. (eds), *The Geology and Tectonics of the Oman Region*, Geological Society, London, Special Publication, **49**, 761–771.

——, MOWBRAY, S. R. & WEEDON, G. P. 1990. A 350 k.y. history of the Indian Southwest Monsoon — evidence from deep-sea cores, northwest Arabian Sea. *Transactions of the Royal Society of Edinburgh, Earth Sciences*, **81**, 289–299.

SIROCKO, F. & SARNTHEIN, M. 1989. Wind-borne deposits in the Northwestern Indian Ocean: record of Holocene sediments versus modern satellite data. *In*: LEINEN, M. & SARNTHEIN, M. (eds), *Paleoclimatology and Paleometeorology: Modern and Past Patterns of Global Atmospheric Transport*. NATO Advanced Workshop, Norwalk, MA., Kluwer, Dordrecht, 401–433.

STABELL, B. 1989. Initial diatom record of Sites 657 and 658: On the history of upwelling and continental aridity. *In*: RUDDIMAN, W., SARNTHEIN, M. *et al.* (eds), *Proceedings of the Ocean Drilling Program, Science Results*, **108**, College Station, Texas, 149–156.

STEENS, T. N. F., KROON, D., TEN KATE, W. G. & SPRENGER, A. 1991. Late Pleistocene periodicities of oxygen isotope ratios, calcium carbonate contents and magnetic susceptibilities of western Arabian Sea margin Hole 728A (ODP Leg 117). *In*: PRELL, W. L. & NIITSUMA, N. *et al.*, *Proceedings of the Ocean Drilling Program, Science Results*, **117**, College Station, Texas, 309–320.

STEIN, R., TEN HAVEN, H. L., LITTKE, R., RULLKÖTTER, J. & WELTE, D. H. 1989. Accumulation of marine and terrigenous organic carbon at upwelling Site 658 and nonupwelling Sites 657 and 659: Implications for the reconstruction of paleoenvironments in the eastern subtropical Atlantic through late Cenozoic times. *In*: RUDDIMAN, W. SARNTHEIN, M. *et al.* (eds), *Proceedings of the Ocean Drilling Program, Science Results*, **108**, College Station, Texas, 361–385.

STREET, A. F. & GROVE, A. T. 1979. Global maps of lake-level fluctuations since 30 000 yr BP. *Quaternary Research*, **12**, 83–118.

THOMPSON, R. & CLARK, R. M. 1989. Sequence slotting for stratigraphic correlation between cores: theory and practice. *Journal of Paleolimnology*, **2**, 173–184.

TIEDEMANN, R., SARNTHEIN, M. & STEIN, R. 1989. Climatic changes in the western Sahara: Aeolomarine sediment record of the last 8 million years (Sites 657–661). *In*: RUDDIMAN, W. SARNTHEIN, M. *et al.* (eds), *Proceedings of the Ocean Drilling Program, Science Results*, **108**, College Station, Texas, 241–277.

VAN CAMPO, E., DUPLESSY, J. C. & ROSSIGNOL-STRICK, M. 1982. Climatic conditions deduced from a 150-kyr oxygen isotope-pollen record from the Arabian Sea. *Nature*, **296**, 56–59.

VEEH, H. H. 1967. Deposition of uranium from the ocean. *Earth and Planetary Science Letters*, **3**, 145–150.

VON BREYMANN, M. T., EMEIS, K.-C. & CAMERLENGHI, A. 1990. Geochemistry of sediments from the Peru upwelling area: Results from Sites 680, 682, 685 and 688. *In*: SUESS, E., VON HUENE, R. *et al. Proceedings of the Ocean Drilling Program, Science Results*, **112**, College Station, Texas, 491–504.

WEEDON, G. P. & SHIMMIELD, G. B. 1991. Late Pleistocene upwelling and productivity variations in the Northwest Indian Ocean deduced from spectral analyses of geochemical data from ODP Sites 722 and 724. *In*: PRELL, W. L. & NIITSUMA, N. *et al. Proceedings of the Ocean Drilling Program, Science Results*, **117**, College Station, Texas, 431–443.

YANG, Y.-L., ELDERFIELD, H. & IVANOVITCH, M. 1990. Glacial to Holocene changes in carbonate and clay sedimentation in the equatorial Pacific ocean estimated from Thorium 230 profiles. *Paleoceanography*, **5**, 789–810.

ZAHN, R. PEDERSEN, T. F. 1991. Late Pleistocene evolution of surface and mid-depth hydrography at the Oman margin: Planktonic and benthic isotope records at ODP Site 724. *In*: PRELL, W. L. & NIITSUMA, N. *et al. Proceedings of the Ocean Drilling Program, Science Results*, **117**, College Station, Texas, 291–308.

——, WINN, K. & SARNTHEIN, M. 1986. Benthic foraminiferal $\delta^{13}C$ and accumulation rates of organic carbon: *Uvigerina peregrina* group and *Cibicidoides wuellerstorfi. Paleoceanography*, **1**, 27–42.

Faunal and floral indicators of ocean coastal upwelling (NW African and Peruvian Continental Margins)

J. THIEDE & B. JÜNGER

GEOMAR Research Center for Marine Geosciences, Wischhofstr. 1–3, Bldg. no. 4, D-2300 Kiel 14, Germany

Abstract: Sediments under coastal upwelling regimes contain pelagic fossil assemblages that differ from those of non-upwelling coastal areas and of the open ocean. In this paper we describe the composition and biogeographical distribution of skeletal material of living planktic and benthic organisms in two of the most important coastal upwelling regions. Particular attention is paid to planktic foraminifers and pelagic gastropods off NW Africa and off NW South America. In both regions, near-surface water masses covering coastal waters of the upwelling region *per se*, of the coastal regions to the North and South of the upwelling centres as well as of the adjacent open ocean, were sampled during 1971 and 1977. The upwelled water masses were characterized by very high concentrations of radiolarians, planktic foraminifers, pteropods and small fish bones (the latter off NW South America only).

The biogeographical distribution of planktic foraminifers and pelagic gastropods can be related particularly well to upwelling. Off NW South America, *Globigerinoides ruber*, *Globigerina bulloides* and *Globoquadrina dutertrei* are found in high abundances near the coast. A region of high concentrations of these species extends from the areas of maximum occurrence towards the west and south into the open Pacific Ocean. Analogous biogeographical patterns can be observed off NW Africa. Concentrations of pelagic gastropods also are high in both coastal upwelling regions. Typical upwelling species are *Limacina inflata*, *L. trochiformis* and *Creseis acicula a.*. The biogeography of pelagic fossil groups is therefore particularly well suited to delimit the spatial extent of coastal upwelling regions.

Upwelling regions, especially coastal upwelling regions, are areas of very strong hydrographic gradients because of the generation of a particular water mass with temperatures and often salinities different from the surrounding ocean surface and because of their enhanced nutrient load. Often these waters are derived from depths of a few tens to hundreds of metres, where levels of dissolved oxygen are greatly reduced due to the decomposition of the organic materials produced in the photic zone. Upwelled water bodies can be identified relatively easily (Richards 1981). Upwelling occurs in isolated cells kilometres to tens of kilometres in diameter, is discontinuous, and can be found in isolated bodies at considerable distances from the shelf edge: such bodies have lost most of their temperature signal, but can still be identified by means of their nutrient levels and their biota.

Upwelling often occurs predominantly in the same location (Jones *et al.* 1983) because of special physiographic features of the shelf and coast or because of semi-permanent elements of the winds which drive the upwelling. Therefore it can occur in the pelagic realm as a result of divergences between different currents or along continental margins (coastal upwelling, Smith 1983). Under the influence of the wind and of the Coriolis Force the upwelled water masses move out into the open ocean where they are slowly mixed into the normal pelagic surface waters. Pelagic biota of upwelling regions reflect these gradients. Because of its special characteristics the upwelling process leaves an identifiable geochemical (Brongersma-Sanders 1983; Calvert & Price 1983) and paleontological (Diester-Haass 1978, 1983; Schrader & Sorknes 1991) signal in the geological record. The process of upwelling affects most intensively parts of the oceanic surface water masses generating very specific ecological conditions for the pelagic biota, whereas the living conditions on the sea floor deteriorate because of the deficiency, or complete lack, of dissolved oxygen in the bottom waters under many upwelling areas. The special hydrographic properties of the upwelling centre result in a high primary productivity as well as the occurrence of species which are adapted either to subsurface waters or waters cooler than usual in such areas (the latter is only found in tropical to temperate upwelling areas).

The upwelling biota experience characteristic changes in composition and productivity as the waters 'age' on their way to the open ocean (as

From Summerhayes, C. P., Prell, W. L. & Emeis, K. C. (eds), 1992, *Upwelling Systems: Evolution Since the Early Miocene.* Geological Society Special Publication No 64, pp 47–76.

47

described schematically by Jones *et al.* 1983). Standing stocks of plankton and nekton can be very high as compared to the adjacent open ocean because they are sustained by the continuous replenishment of the nutrients. Shutting off the nutrient supply, as in El Niño events, usually has catastrophic consequences for the upwelling biota including the end members of the marine food web such as fish and birds.

In addition, coastal elements, such as meroplanktic larvae of benthic organisms, benthic foraminifers suspended in the water column or growing on algae, and large amounts of materials from marine plants, are observed offshore in upwelling regions. Since the wind regimes over coastal upwelling regions often carry high dust loads (Prospero & Carlson 1972), upwelling waters and depositional environments under coastal upwelling areas are often characterized by high terrigenous detrital fluxes (Sarnthein *et al.* 1982). Upwelling regions are also characterized by the development of anaerobic or oxygen deficient depositional environments as a result of oxygen consumption by the decay of organic materials (Stein 1990) and by their regional restriction caused by the physiography of the sea floor intersecting with the different water masses of the upwelling regimes (Suess & Thiede 1983).

In this paper we will draw on modern distributions of shell- and skeleton-producing plankton and nekton in an attempt to define palaeontological characteristics of general importance for identifying fossil upwelling, in particular coastal upwelling areas.

Figure 1a shows the major coastal upwelling regions of the modern ocean. They are all well defined areas of high organic productivity even though this may be subject to large seasonal fluctuations. The best known coastal upwelling regions are those which are under the influence of the trade wind systems and are found in the Indian, Pacific and Atlantic oceans.

For the purpose of this study we have chosen the coastal upwelling regimes off NW Africa in the Atlantic in the northern hemisphere and off NW South America in the Pacific in the southern hemisphere (Fig. 1b). Both are typical coastal upwelling regimes, have been studied in great detail recently by the Ocean Drilling Program (Ruddiman, Sarnthein *et al.* 1989; Suess, von Huene *et al.* 1990) and are known to leave an identifiable signal in the pelagic sediment cover (Diester-Haass 1978).

Beside identifying the biogeographical distributions of most major geologically important plankton groups, our study also allows us to make a quantitative assessment of the standing stocks of organisms such as diatoms, radiolarians, planktic foraminifers, pelagic gastropods, larval stages of usually benthic-living molluscs and other organisms. By choosing Atlantic and Pacific coastal upwelling regions we explore the variability and possibly identify compositional end members of the plankton and nekton communities occupying the upwelled water masses. The sampling strategy we have adopted prevents an assessment of the entire food web with its seasonal and other biological cycles (Berger *et al.* 1989*b*; Peinert *et al.* 1989), but still allows us to recognize some of the typical trademarks of upwelling biota which are preserved in the geological record.

Scientific approach and comparison of NW African and NW South American coastal upwelling regimes

The basis of this study are data sets obtained from sampling plankton in surface water masses of the coastal upwelling areas off NW Africa and off NW South America. Both data sets have already partly been used for other studies, namely for a detailed description of most major plankton components in the upwelling region off NW Africa (Thiede 1974, 1975*a*), in particular of the planktic foraminifers (Thiede 1975*b*) and for a preliminary comparative study of distribution patterns of some of the typical, apparently 'upwelling controlled', plankton components (Thiede 1983).

New data have since been generated for most of the individual plankton components of these two sample sets, allowing new insight into the relation of biogeographical patterns to coastal upwelling. The data set on the distributions of pelagic gastropods is new and discussed here in detail for the first time. The extensive data bases collected from both upwelling regions will be published in a separate report (Thiede & Jünger, in prep.).

The coastal upwelling regions off NW Africa and NW South America display many differences. The shapes, widths and water depths of the shelves, which have a controlling influence on the location of upwelling cells and fronts, are well known for their widely different character, as is the orography of the hinterland. The two boundary currents — the Canary Current off NW Africa, the Humboldt Current off NW South America — are similar in their character as eastern boundary currents, but quite different in strength and nutrient content. The differences in productivity and sediment input result in

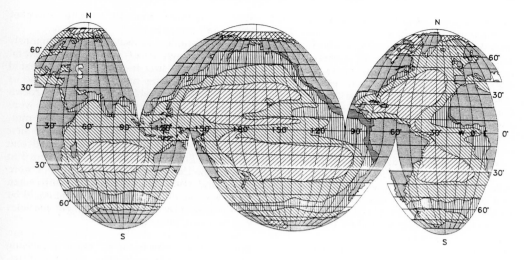

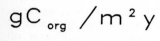

$$gC_{org} /m^2 y$$

▨ 25–40   ▥ 90–180
▧ 40–90   ▬ 180–500

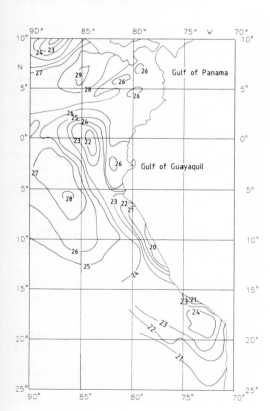

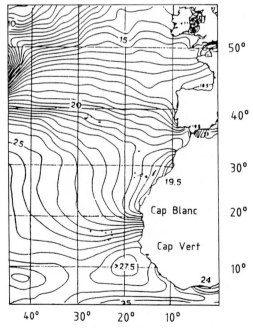

Fig. 1. (a) Global distribution of ocean productivity (calculated primary production of the worlds ocean after Berger *et al*. 1987). (b) Surface ocean temperature (°C) off NW South America (i) (EASTROPAC ATLAS 1967) and off NW Africa (ii) (Sarnthein *et al*. 1982).

oxygen deficient laminated diatomaceous muds on the outer shelf and upper continental slope off NW South America, whereas off NW Africa pelagic calcareous oozes are the typical sediment facies. Recent ODP drilling has shown that these depositional environments existed for a relatively long time during the Neogene and Quaternary (Suess, von Huene et al. 1990; Ruddiman, Sarnthein et al. 1989), confirming the long-term existence and activity of these coastal upwelling regimes.

The coastal upwelling region off NW South America lies between 6° and 15°S (Fig. 1b), as indicated by the low surface water temperatures and high temperature gradient in this area (EASTROPAC Atlas 1967). The area affected by coastal upwelling extends over 15° of latitude off NW South America. Seaward the belt of elevated concentrations of biogenic components can be traced to about 650 km offshore. All areas of high concentrations show nearly the same distribution as the total primary productivity measured by Zuta & Guillen (1970), Forsbergh (1969), Love (1970) and EASTROPAC (1967–1968).

The coastal upwelling region off NW Africa is located between 14° and 24°N (Fig. 1b), as indicated by low temperatures and high particulate organic carbon concentrations (Bishop 1989). The area affected is much smaller than the region off NW South America, extending over only 10° of latitude. Seaward the belt of high concentrations of planktic foraminifers can be traced to only 250 km offshore, showing small amounts of westward transport of the surface water masses. To the north and south of the main upwelling area the concentration of planktic foraminifers decreases very quickly. A narrow belt of enrichment in biogenic components can be followed between 16° and 24°N all along the continental margin.

The Canary and Cape Verde Islands sometimes generate upwelling in the area between 26° and 30°N. Nutrient-rich water with high primary productivity reaches the surface, just as observed around the Galapagos Islands (Moore et al. 1973). However, the concentration of the skeletal plankton is not as high as in the main coastal upwelling region.

Sampling operations and methods

The plankton samples discussed in this paper were collected during cruise no 25 of the METEOR (Seibold 1972) in November– December 1971 off the coast of NW Africa and during the cruise WECOMA 77, Leg 6 of the Wecoma in May–June 1977 off the coast of NW South America.

In both studies, seawater was continuously pumped through a set of filters for several hours. Several size fractions were collected while a water meter measured the volume of water used to filter each sample. Off NW Africa the mesh sizes of the screens used were >1.0 mm, 1.0–0.25 mm and 0.25–0.12 mm, while off NW South America one sieve first separated >0.15 mm and then a second one >1.0 mm. The filtered seawater came from 3 to 4 m below the sea surface. The samples were taken under way and on stations. Only when there was the chance that the sample could be contaminated by suspended sediment particles was pumping interrupted.

Selected parts of the available data are presented as biogeographic maps displaying quantitative and qualitative regional distributions of all major shell- and skeleton-producing plankton and nekton components within size fractions larger than 0.12 mm off NW Africa, and larger than 0.15 mm off NW South America. The focus on the coarse plankton components came from coarse-sediment fraction studies of similar size classes. However, one has to be aware that many important plankton groups such as diatoms and coccolithophorids are not evaluated by this method or are under-represented.

The speed of the ship exceeded that of the surface currents, so it was assumed that the data collected by this method reflect a 'quasi-synoptic' distributional pattern of plankton and nekton. We are aware of the limitations of this assumption, but as major parts of both regions have been visited several times without producing contradictory results, the assumption seems to be justified. The problem of small-scale plankton patchiness (Boltovskoy 1971) was minimized either by pumping over extended distances (2–3 hours while en route) or times (3–5 hours while on station). The largest size fraction of these samples (>1.0 mm) usually did not contain enough particles to yield statistically meaningful results.

On board, the samples were preserved in buffered formalin. During the cruise off NW Africa the quality of samples and of the living plankton and nekton were controlled by means of a plankton microscope (Thiede 1975a). A total of 177 samples were collected during this cruise and have been described and documented in detail by Thiede (1975a).

The samples from the cruise off NW South America were preserved with formaldehyde buffered with sodium borate to prevent calcite and aragonite dissolution after return. A total of 220 samples were collected (Thiede 1975a).

All samples were counted under a binocular microscope and reflected light (Tables 1–3). Planktic foraminifers and pteropods were identified to species level. To draw maps, the data were first processed by a computer program (SURFER, version 4.0, Golden Software Inc.). The interpolation method used an inverse distance gridding. Data points which are used in the inverse distance option are weighted such that the influence of one data point on another declines with distance from the point being estimated.

$$z = \sum_{i=1}^{n} z_i/(d_i)^2 \left(\sum_{i=1}^{n} 1/(d_i)^2 \right)^{-1}.$$

where z_i is the neighbouring point, d is distance and n is the number of z elements.

For each interpolated grid value, a neighbourhood (search area) is defined. The interpolation algorithm will select only a certain number of points from each neighbourhood. The number of points from each neighbourhood is determined by distance (search radius) and a maximum quantity of points (number of nearest data points). The quadrant search method specifies that original data points used to estimate a grid element be found by dividing the area around a grid element into four quadrants. A quadrant search then finds the nearest points in each quadrant around the element estimated, where n is limited by search radius in x data units (9.8995) and number of nearest points (10). To modify the contour lines, cubic spline interpolation is used to smooth the data.

Results

Benthic components

Some of the most unexpected components of the plankton samples consisted of elements of obviously benthic origin which were found in low concentrations in samples taken at the greatest distance from land. They comprised benthic foraminifers and meroplanktic larvae of otherwise benthic living organisms such as benthic molluscs (both gastropods and bivalves), echinoderms and a number of other unidentified particles which occurred sporadically. As their distributions have already been discussed in some detail by Thiede (1983), only some of their important distributional trends will be described here.

Benthic foraminifers have been found in samples of both coastal upwelling areas. Since none of the specimens have been determined to the species level except *Rosalina globularis*, which is known to live attached to drifting sea weed (Spindler 1980), not much can be said about their origin. However, even though they have been found in quite different quantities off NW Africa and NW South America, their distributional patterns are regionally consistent with the coastal upwelling cells which seem to have existed during the time of sampling, namely close to Cape Blanc and off the mouth of the Gulf of Guayaquil.

Larval stages of benthic gastropods have been observed in samples from both coastal upwelling regions. Their distributional patterns are shown in Figs 2 and 3 with important concentrations between Cape Blanc and Cape Vert off NW

Table 1. Major components of shell- and skeleton-producing plankton and nekton observed in the coastal upwelling regions off NW South America and off NW Africa.

	NW South America (>0.15 mm)		NW Africa (0.25–0.12 mm)	
	No/m³ max.	% max.	No/m³ max.	% max.
Diatoms	61	56	4698	97
Radiolarians	236	73	124	88
Planktic foraminifers	59	65	375	100
Pteropods	137	100	1972	77
Heteropods	72	77		
Fish (bones)	271	36		
Gastropods			1920	75
Bivalves	218	13	122	95
Larvae benthic gastropods	29	59		
Benthic foraminifers	20	9		
Echinoderm larvae	3	5		
Ostracods			8	6
Other biogenic components	5	2	4	50

Table 2. Planktic foraminifers: Species occurring off NW Africa and NW South America.

	NW South America (>0.15 mm)		NW Africa (0.25−0.12 mm)	
	No/m³ max.	% max.	No/m³ max.	% max.
Hastigerina pelagica	0.3	0.1	1.2	0.7
Orbulina universa	0.1	3.5	0.3	25.0
Globigerinoides conglobatus	1.2	1.9	0.2	2.7
G. ruber	54.3	64.2	55.9	100.0
G. sacculifer	73.5	49.1	95.7	72.1
G. tenellus	2.1	2.2	6.5	7.6
Globigerina bulloides	120.3	94.5	102.3	100.0
G. calida	7.4	20.0	22.0	100.0
G. digitata	0.4	0.9		
G. falconensis	7.4	10.2	18.2	31.8
G. humilis	0.2	1.2	10.0	37.5
G. quinqueloba	0.5	1.1	39.2	80.0
G. rubescens	1.1	28.6	2.3	30.6
Globigerinella aequilateralis	2.1	17.7	2.8	10.0
Globigerinita glutinata	43.9	63.5	44.9	75.0
G. uvula	0.3	1.4		
Neogloboquadrina pachyderma	1.4	1.0	39.6	66.7
Globoquadrina conglomerata	29.4	25.0	1.4	4.4
G. dutertrei	176.8	65.9	79.4	37.5
G. hexagona	3.1	5.8	4.2	6.2
Pulleniatina obliquiloculata	3.7	5.8	1.0	8.6
Globorotalia crassaformis			1.8	3.9
G. hirsuta			0.1	0.8
G. inflata	0.2	0.6	16.7	80.0
G. menardii	72.7	66.4	16.5	18.9
G. tumida	11.6	55.4		
G. scitula	0.4	0.5	6.1	11.9
G. truncatulinoides	2.2	3.2	0.8	16.8
Candeina nitida	0.1	0.5		

Africa. Because of their difficult taxonomies no attempt has been made to assess species distributions as has, for example, been carried out by Scheltema (1971, 1988).

Meroplanktic bivalve larvae are frequent and ubiquitous components in the samples from both coastal upwelling regions. Their concentrations are highest close to the coast in both areas and they are higher close to the shallow island shelf areas of the Canary and Cape Verde Islands than in the adjacent East Atlantic. In low concentrations, they extend far out into the open Atlantic and Pacific oceans, drifting for many months (Scheltema 1971) and covering areas of entire ocean basins. Precisely how they are able to endure the obviously long distances of their trans-ocean travel remains to be seen; are they following stream lines of the current systems or are they able to cross over from one eddy to the next? Even though much research on modes of their production and biogeographical distribution remains to be done, they are obviously typical elements of the shell- and skeleton-producing plankton and nekton assemblages of coastal upwelling areas which can be preserved in the geological record.

Siliceous plankton

The methods employed for these studies are not suited to a quantitative assessment of distributional patterns of most siliceous plankton components, mainly because the mesh sizes selected for filtering were too large to sample diatom frustules adequately. However, since high concentrations of siliceous plankton are believed to be typical indicators of fertile surface water masses of upwelling systems (Heath 1974; Schrader & Baumgartner 1983), an attempt has been made to quantify at least the coarse grain sized siliceous elements of the diatoms, silicoflagellates and radiolarians in these samples. The bulk of radiolarians would be expected to be within the size range of the plankton filtered

Table 3. Pelagic gastropods (thecasomatos pteropods): Species occurring off NW Africa and NW South America.

	NW South America (>0.15 mm)		NW Africa (0.25−0.12 mm)	
	No/m^3 max.	% max.	No/m^3 max.	% max.
Limacina helicina	1.8	4.9		
L. helicoides			0.3	7.1
L. retroversa r.	3.5	15.7		
L. inflata	55.5	79.6	663.3	100.0
L. lesueurii	5.7	30.2	41.7	91.7
L. bulimoides	98.8	96.9	1.1	33.3
L. trochiformis	7.7	66.7	1202.4	73.7
Creseis acicula a.	13.1	86.7	131.0	87.3
C. acicula clava	1.0	50.0		
C. virgula v.	53.1	87.5	151.3	100.0
C. virgula conica	0.7	55.6		
Styliola subula	0.3	5.0	0.1	0.7
Hyalocylis striata	0.5	1.5		
Clio pyramidata p.	0.1	1.8	18.8	49.6
C. polita	1.5	13.5		
Cuvierina columnella a.	0.5	25.0		
Cavolina inflexa i.	1.6	33.3		
C. inflexa imitans			0.7	100.0
Paedoclione doliiformis			957.8	89.4
Cymbulia peroni			5.0	44.4
Peraclis bispinosa	0.1	1.5		

from the sea water for this study, whereas the two former groups are mostly too small to be caught by the mesh sizes applied. In many of the samples near the coast, however, large concentrations of large diatoms have been observed. Their locations and regional distributions will be reported elsewhere (Thiede & Jünger, in prep.).

For the purpose of this study we present only the distributions of radiolarians in the surface waters of both upwelling regions (Figs 4 & 5). They had been collected and counted in the belief that radiolarians can comprise relatively deep living elements of the pelagic plankton. Quantitative and relative distributions are quite different in both regions. Off NW South America they are 2−3 times more abundant than off NW Africa and appear to be concentrated in upwelled waters, only a limited record of their high abundances being preserved in the underlying sediments (Molina-Cruz 1977). Off NW Africa, however, their highest relative abundances are observed in waters at a certain distance from the continental margins, while they are relatively common in the waters over the Cape Verde Island shelves. The radiolarian record in NW African upwelling sediments (Diester-Haass 1978) is as modest as it is off NW South America.

Calcareous plankton and nekton:
(a) planktic foraminifers

Calcareous shells and skeletons within the size range studied in this paper are produced by a wide variety of organisms adapted to a pelagic mode of life. Coccoliths have not been sampled by our filtering device because of their much smaller grain sizes. Planktic foraminifers are protozoans secreting a calcitic shell. They are one of the most important contributors of calcareous shell material in deep-sea sediments, are known to be adapted to ecological conditions ranging from upwelling regions to restricted basins (Auras-Schudnagies *et al.* 1989; Hemleben *et al.* 1988) and are therefore an important component of the samples under investigation.

NW South America. High concentrations of planktic foraminifers (Fig. 6) are found between 2° and 10°S (>30% and >60 specimens/m^3). North of 2°S concentrations are decreasing (<20% and <35 specimens/m^3), while south of 10°S there are two maxima of higher abundances (>30% and >35 specimens/m^3) indicating less upwelling than in the high concentration area further north.

The most abundant species of planktic

J. THIEDE & B. JUNGER

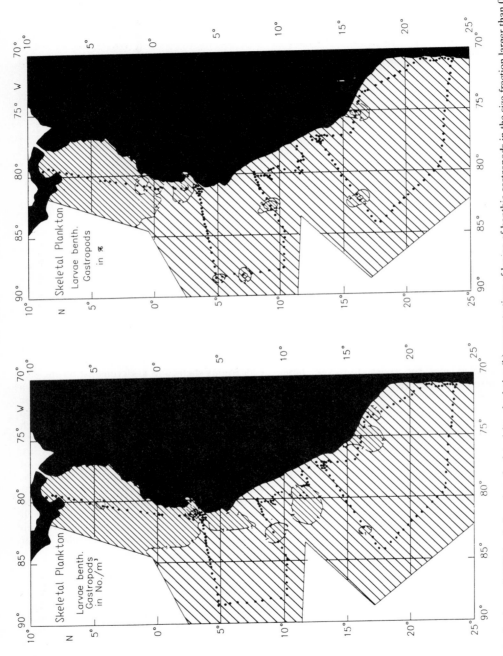

Fig. 2. Skeletal nekton off NW South America: absolute (a) and relative (b) concentrations of larvae of benthic gastropods in the size fraction larger than 0.15 mm. High concentrations of gastropods are located in the Gulf of Guayaquil. In the upwelling region gastropods occur only in low abundances.

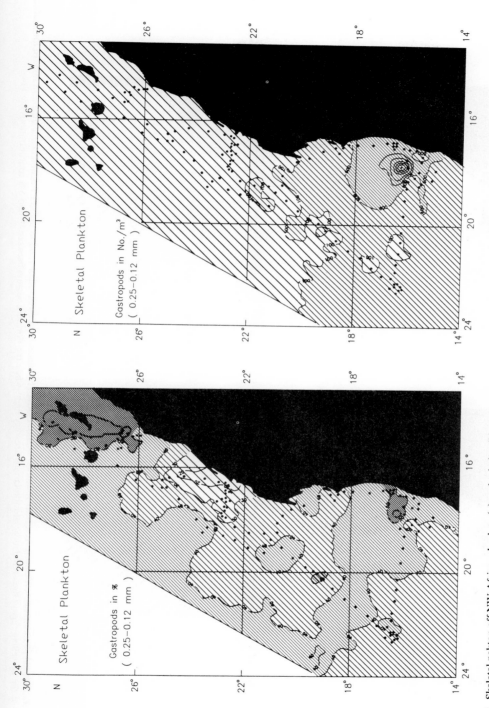

Fig. 3. Skeletal nekton off NW Africa: absolute (a) and relative (b) concentrations of gastropods in the size fraction 0.25–0.12 mm. High abundances occur between 14° and 18°N and 26° and 30°N in an area which is only little influenced by upwelling water masses. At 18°N the concentration gradient indicates a westward transport of upwelled water masses into the open ocean.

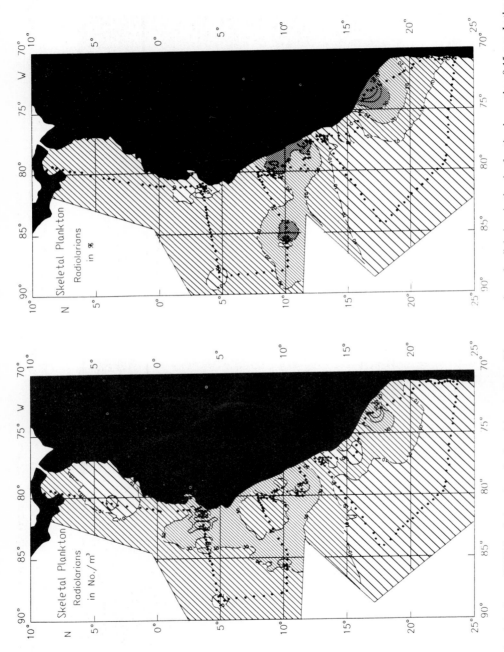

Fig. 4. Skeletal plankton off NW South America: absolute (a) and relative (b) concentrations of radiolarians in the size fraction larger than 0.15 mm. In the southern part of the upwelling region the abundances of radiolarians are very high, while the northern section between 0° and 5°S concentrations are low.

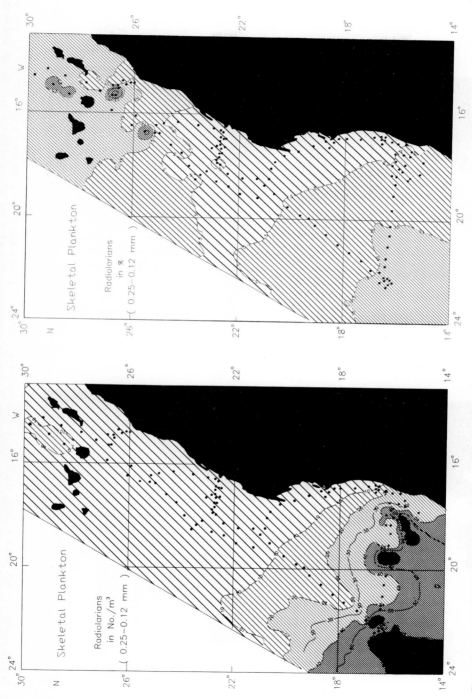

Fig. 5. Skeletal plankton off NW Africa: absolute (a) and relative (b) concentrations of radiolarians in the size fraction 0.25–0.12 mm. High concentrations occur in the main upwelling area south 18°N. The region between 26° and 18°N is characterized by very low concentrations.

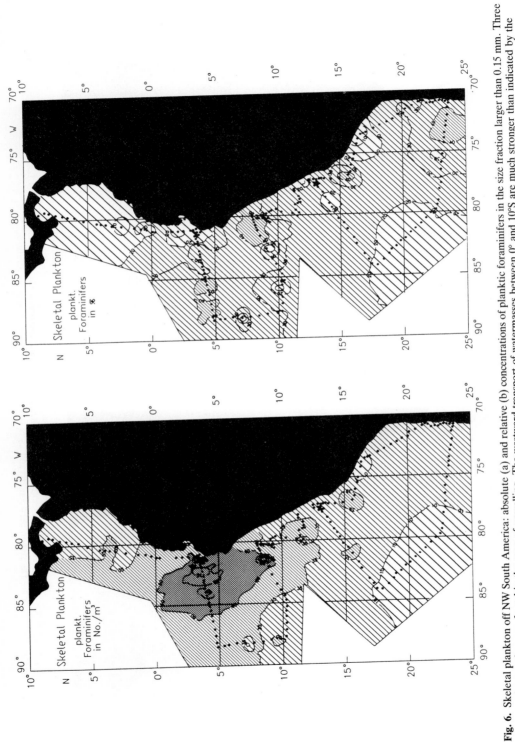

Fig. 6. Skeletal plankton off NW South America: absolute (a) and relative (b) concentrations of planktic foraminifers in the size fraction larger than 0.15 mm. Three concentration maxima are found in the area of upwelling. The westward transport of watermasses between 0° and 10°S are much stronger than indicated by the radiolarians. The area of high abundances between 20° and 25°S is situated in a region only slightly influenced by upwelling.

foraminifers in the upwelling system are *Globigerina bulloides*, *Globigerinoides ruber*, *G. sacculifer*, *Globigerinita glutinata* and *Globoquadrina dutertrei*, while *Globigerina falconensis*, *Globoquadrina conglomerata* and *G. hexagona* play a less important role. *Neogloboquadrina pachyderma* and *Pulleniatina obliquiloculata* are nearly absent in the study area, *Globorotalia menardii* and *G. tumida* are warm water species and therefore appear in areas where no coastal upwelling occurs.

Globigerina bulloides (Fig. 8a) is closely associated with the coastal upwelling region off Peru. It is a species which mainly appears in temperate subpolar water masses. Because *G. bulloides* is typical for upwelled waters, it is found in high concentrations off NW South America. The relative abundance exceeds 40% of the total planktic foraminiferal fauna and is restricted to the region where upwelling occurs (5°−20°S).

A good correlation is found between the maxima of *G. bulloides* and the highest concentrations of organic material in the surface waters. The areas of high abundances are between 5° and 10°S (>40% and >30 specimens/m³) and 12° and 16°S (>50% and >30 specimens/m³) and can be traced up to 450 km offshore indicating a seaward transport of the upwelled waters.

Globigerinoides ruber (Fig. 9a) is highly abundant in the study area. This species belongs to warm water surface dwelling faunas, is characteristic of subtropical regions and is therefore very sensitive to the influence of coastal upwelling. It is most abundant between 17° and 20°S, reaching over 50% and 5 specimens/m³ in the Peruvian offshore area. While further north the relative abundance decreases (10−20% and 5 specimens/m³), concentration increases again in the main upwelling region between 9° and 13°S (30−40% and 5−15 specimens/m³). Between 7° and 16°S the relative abundance can be traced westward up to 400 km offshore, indicating the transport of the Peruvian waters in this direction. North of 7°S *G. ruber* is very rare, as shown in the warm waters of the Gulf of Guayaquil.

Globigerinoides sacculifer occurs in low concentration in restricted areas in the main coastal upwelling region. The areas with high abundances (>15% and >10 specimens/m³) are found at 10°S near the coast and in a westward reaching plume between 2° and 8°S. North and south of this area *G. sacculifer* is nearly absent, sometimes only reaching up to 5%.

Globigerinita glutinata shows higher relative abundances in areas close to the main coastal upwelling region between 5° and 12°S (>15%). Westward high concentrations of >10% and >6 specimens/m³ can be traced up to 400 km offshore into the open Pacific Ocean. South of 17°S and north of 0° *G. glutinata* appears only in very low concentrations.

Globoquadrina dutertrei is another species of planktic foraminifers closely related to upwelling regions (Thiede 1983). The areas where *G. dutertrei* reaches high concentrations are in the main upwelling region (>20% and >10 specimens/m³), but the distribution of the plume is oriented more to the southwest. Smaller areas of lower relative abundance occur north in the Gulf of Guayaquil and south of the upwelling area.

Globorotalia menardii is a tropical species and therefore marks the areas where warm waters occur. Areas of high concentrations (>30% and >6 specimens/m³) are found in regions where no upwelling occurs. One of these regions occurs south of 15°S and has a strong concentration gradient with maxima of more than 50% and 11 specimens/m³ south of 22°S. A smaller area between 0° and 8°S 100 km offshore is only influenced in some regions by the upwelling system.

Globorotalia tumida has the same appearance as *Globorotalia menardii*. High abundances (>10% and 1 specimen/m³) of this species are found in an area south of 15°S with concentration maxima of more than 20% and 3 specimens/m³ south of 21°S. The region of high abundance is therefore a certain distance from the upwelling system. Near the coastal upwelling current *G. tumida* occurs only in low concentrations.

NW Africa. The distribution of planktic foraminifers off NW Africa (Fig. 7) shows high occurrences (>30% and >50 specimens/m³) between 22° and 26°N in an area where the main upwelling appears. North and south of that region the abundance is low (<20% and >10 specimens/m³). South of 17°S the standing stock increases again to more than 70 specimens/m³. Along the coast between 15° and 25°N high abundances can be traced 100 km into the ocean. Seaward, this belt is limited by

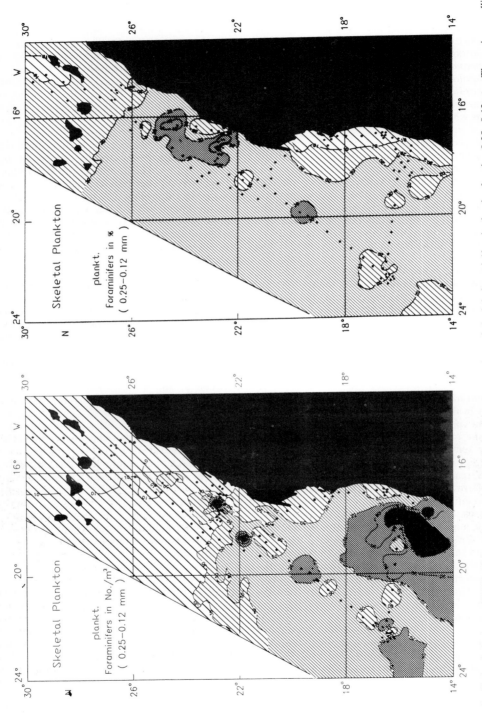

Fig. 7. Skeletal plankton off NW Africa: absolute (a) and relative (b) concentrations of planktic foraminifers in the size fraction 0.25–0.12 mm. The main upwelling region between 22° and 25°N reveals high abundances of planktic foraminifers. South of 18°N there is another area of high concentrations.

water masses with low amounts of planktic foraminifers.

The most important species of NW Africa which respond to upwelling waters are *Globigerina bulloides*, *Globigerinoides sacculifer*, *G. ruber*, *Globigerinita glutinata* and *Globoquadrina dutertrei*. Most other species are only of minor importance because of their low concentrations in the upwelling region.

The distribution of high concentrations of *Globigerina bulloides* indicates the main coastal upwelling region (Fig. 8b). Areas with high abundance are found between 22° and 26°N reaching more than 30% and 10 specimens/m³). The region of relative abundances covers an area reaching up to 200 km offshore. North of 26°N concentrations decrease, while south of 22°N *G. bulloides* is nearly absent.

Globigerinoides ruber is a warm water species and has peak relative abundances in the Canary Current (Fig. 9b) indicating the coastal upwelling region off NW Africa. In a broad area between 14° and 22°N high standing stock of *G. ruber* appear. Concentration maxima reach up to 30% and 30 specimens/m³ between 14° and 17°N. *G. ruber* persists between 18° and 22°N but with decreasing abundances.

Globigerinoides sacculifer is found in very high abundances along the coast of NW Africa. North of 23°N concentrations are less than 20% and 10 specimens/m³. To the south, the abundance, which can be traced up to 50 km offshore, increases, with maximum occurrences (>30% and >30 specimens/m³) between 14° and 18°N. The area south of 18°N is influenced only by minor upwelling.

Globigerinita glutinata is relatively abundant in areas close to the coastal upwelling system. One region is found north of 26°N (>20%) indicating upwelling caused by the Canary Islands. South of 18°N concentrations reach more than 10% and 10 specimens/m³, again in an area only slightly influenced by upwelling. In the main coastal upwelling region between 18° and 24°N *G. glutinata* is rare.

Globoquadrina dutertrei is closely associated with the upwelling region. It is abundant from 15° to 24°N (>20%) in a narrow belt along the coast. Elsewhere concentrations of *G. dutertrei* are low, indicating warm water masses.

Globorotalia menardii has a peculiar distributional pattern between Cape Vert and Cape Blanc in the upwelled water off NW Africa.

The occurrence of this species is usually confined to tropical−subtropical subsurface waters, and is related to a subsurface counter-current (Thiede 1975b) which brings this species north and presumably feeds the upwelled waters.

Calcareous plankton and nekton:
(b) pelagic gastropods

Pelagic gastropods comprise two important groups, namely heteropods and pteropods. Only the latter were studied in any detail (Figs 10 & 11), not so much because they leave an important geological record in the sediments, but rather because they are active swimmers and carnivorous predators and as such may play an important role in the pelagic food web of upwelling regions. Pteropods are able to respond to movements of water masses and to the drift of the organisms they are feeding upon. Since they build aragonitic shells, they have little chance of being preserved in the geological record, but are so ubiquitous that they must play an important part in the processes of carbonate fixation and recycling in the oceanic water column. Previous studies (van der Spoel 1967) have shown that their distribution is also restricted to specific water masses, making them suitable indicators of upwelling (Auras-Schudnagies et al. 1989).

NW South America. High standing stocks of pteropods extend all along the coast, with four areas of maximum concentrations (over 25 specimens/m³) within the continental margin. One is off Peru in the main upwelling region between 13° and 16°S and can be traced 450 km offshore. The second is off Peru between 22° and 25°S. Concentrations decrease to the west, which indicates a seaward transport and dilution of the current into the Pacific Ocean. Two other areas of pteropod occurrences are a small belt along the coast off Peru, beginning in the Gulf of Guayaquil and ending in the Panama Basin (5°S−5°N). The second is in the Gulf of Panama characterized by high primary productivity. A tongue of high standing stock (over 10 specimens/m³) extends from these areas of maximum occurrence west and south into the Pacific, suggesting considerable seaward transport of surface water masses in the northernmost part of the Peruvian upwelling region. This westerly transport can also be seen in the distribution of the primary productivity, temperature and low oxygen concentration (EASTROPAC Atlas 1967). Isolated water masses with high concentration of standing stock can obviously become

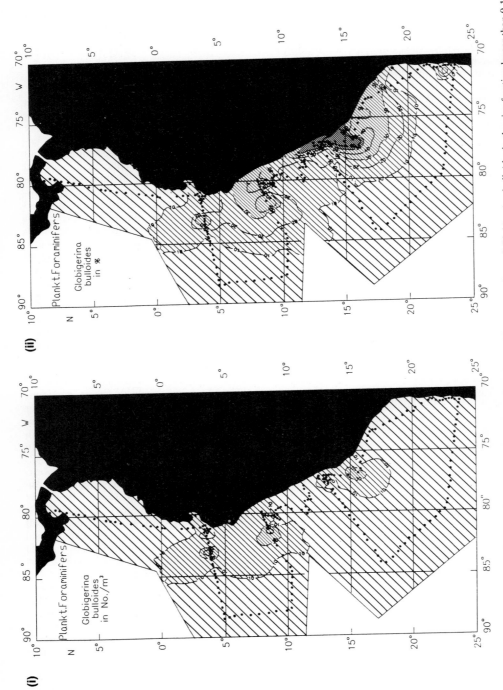

Fig. 8(a). Planktic foraminifers off NW South America: absolute (i) and relative (ii) concentrations of *Globigerina bulloides* in the size fraction larger than 0.15 mm. *G. bulloides* is typical for upwelling water masses. Off South America two main centres of upwelling occur between 0° and 20°S. The concentration gradient to the ocean decreases abruptly, showing a small westward transport of surface waters between 0° and 10°S.

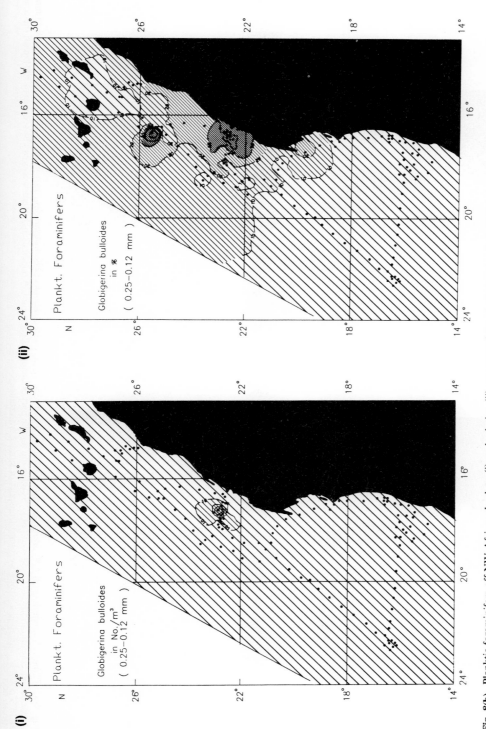

Fig. 8(b). Planktic foraminifers off NW Africa: absolute (i) and relative (ii) concentrations of *Globigerina bulloides* in the size fraction 0.25–0.12 mm. The main region of upwelling is characterized by high concentrations between 20° and 26°N, while areas of low abundance indicate only minor influence of upwelling.

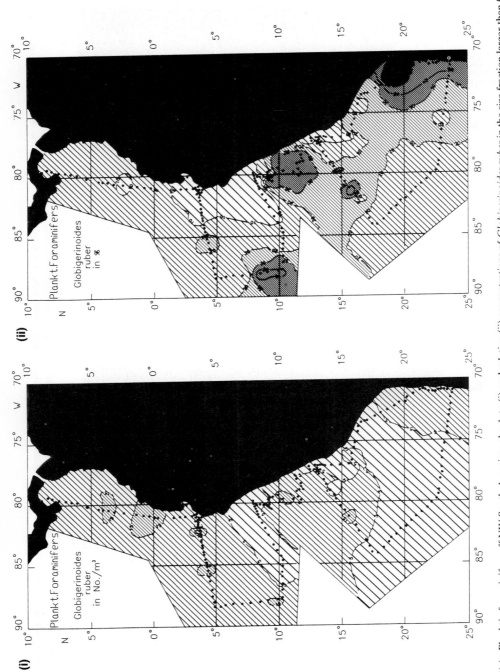

Fig. 9(a). Planktic foraminifers off NW South America: absolute (i) and relative (ii) concentrations of *Globigerinoides ruber* in the size fraction larger than 0.15 mm. Areas of high concentrations are found south of 17°S and in the middle part of the upwelling region. A region of high abundances can be seen up to 500 km off the coast at 10°S possibly indicating a strong westward transport of surface watermasses.

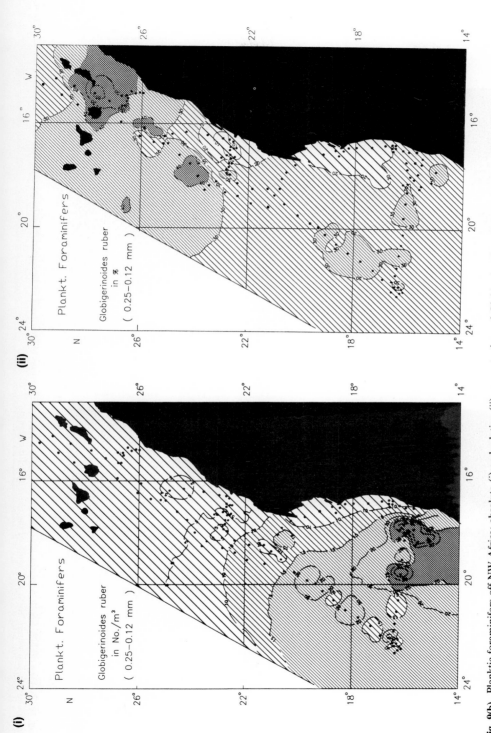

Fig. 9(b). Planktic foraminifers off NW Africa: absolute (i) and relative (ii) concentrations of *Globigerinoides ruber* in the size fraction 0.25–0.12 mm. South and north of the main upwelling region, areas of high abundances occur, while in the center of the upwelling concentrations are low because *G. ruber* is a warm water surface dwelling species.

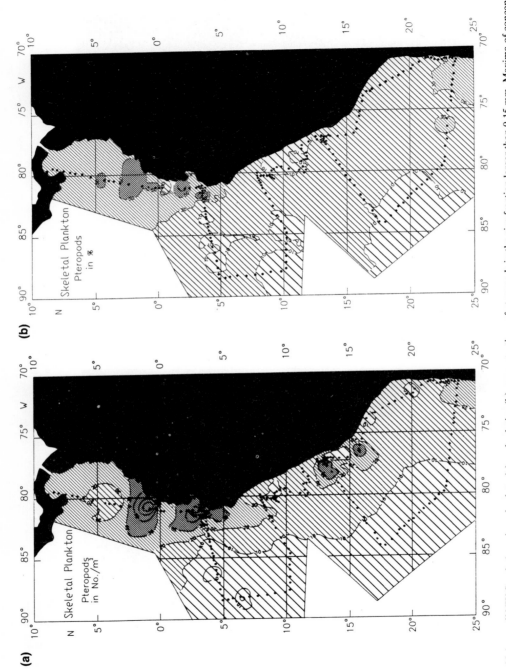

Fig. 10. Nekton off NW South America: absolute (a) and relative (b) concentrations of pteropods in the size fraction larger than 0.15 mm. Maxima of concentrations are found in warm waters north and south of the main upwelling region.

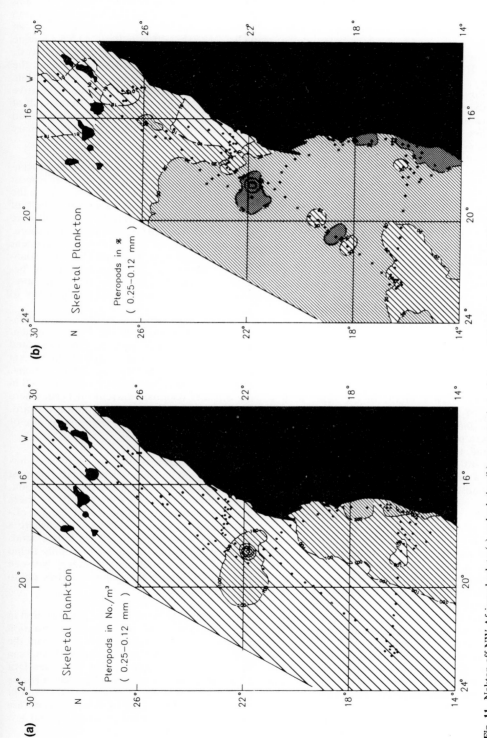

Fig. 11. Nekton off NW Africa: absolute (a) and relative (b) concentrations of pteropods in the size fraction 0.25–0.12 mm. A broad region between 14° and 24°N show high occurrences of pteropods, whereas the abundances are low in the main upwelling area.

detached from the continental margins and drift seawards. This mostly happens at 5°S, where the northernmost part of the Peruvian upwelling region is transported to the west and southwest.

The most abundant species in the upwelling region off Peru is *Limacina bulimoides*. *Creseis virgula v.* and *Limacina inflata* are not as abundant. *Limacina trochiformis* and *Creseis acicula a.* are even less abundant. *Clio polita*, *Limacina lesueurii* and *Limacina retroversa* are found in very low concentrations. *Limacina helicina*, *Creseis acicula clava*, *Creseis virgula conica*, *Cuvierina columnella altas* and *Cavolinia inflexa* occur only rarely.

Limacina bulimoides is the species which has the highest abundance in this region. Maximum concentrations of over 80% and over 30 specimens/m³ occur in the upwelling region between 12° and 16°S and can be traced 270 km offshore. Around this core of maximum concentration is an area of lower abundance which extends over 1000 km offshore. Another area of high abundance is between 20° and 25°S in the coastal upwelling region; it extends 800 km offshore, indicating northwest and westward transport of the current.

Abundances of 20 to 40% and 5 to 30 specimens/m³ occur in the Gulf of Panama, where there is high primary productivity. Between 5° and 10°S a plume of high relative abundance (40 to 80%) reaches south. In the same area a plume of 5 to 30 specimens/m³ extends west, which indicates seaward transport of the northern part of the upwelling regime.

In the area of high primary productivity between 10° and 15°S in the coastal upwelling region of NW South America *L. bulimoides* is nearly absent.

Limacina inflata is found over a wide region of the northern part of the upwelling region (Fig. 12a). It is very interesting that the highest concentrations (>40% or 10−60 specimens/m³) are found in the Gulf of Panama and the Gulf of Guayaquil with their high primary productivity and warm water masses. *L. inflata* is very rare or absent south of 10°S, where concentrations are lower than 10% or 2 specimens/m³. There is only one small zone of higher abundances along the coast off Peru reaching to 15°S. A tongue of high abundances extends from the area of maximum concentration towards the west and southwest into the open Pacific Ocean indicating a seaward transport of the northern part of the upwelling region.

Most of *Limacina trochiformis* are found in the northern part of the upwelling region (Fig.

13a). The maximum concentration (>10% and 2 specimens/m³) is in the upwelling region between 8° and 16°S with two plumes which can be traced 360 km offshore Peru. At 5°S a tongue of high abundance extends towards the west. Here again it indicates the influence of the northernmost Peruvian upwelling region, while in the mouth of the Gulf of Guayaquil, relative abundances are lower than 10%. In the Gulf of Panama there is again a high concentration in the warm water zone of high primary productivity.

Limacina retroversa occurs in very low concentrations and only in restricted areas. It is most abundant (>5%) between 10° and 16°S, in the coastal upwelling region. Seaward a belt of concentration can be traced 200 km offshore Peru with a small eddy about 650 km offshore. The distribution of the number of specimens per m³ is different from the relative abundances. Maximum concentrations occur between 10° and 12°S, reaching 200 km offshore, and between 14° and 16°S, reaching up to 720 km offshore.

Several other regions where the concentrations are more than 5% and over 1 specimen/m³ display the same pattern. One is located between 2°N and 0° and reaches about 100 km offshore Peru, another is in the Gulf of Panama. There is a further area between 21° and 23°S in the offshore boundary current off Peru, where *Limacina retroversa* is not transported seaward. Outside these few areas *L. retroversa* is rare or absent.

Limacina lesueurii is also found in very low concentrations and in restricted areas. It is most abundant (>5%) in the main upwelling region, for example (1) between 8° and 10°S, where high concentrations can be traced 360 km offshore, and (2) between 11° and 20°S, where a plume 390 km wide and 720 km long extends seaward. Elsewhere *L. lesueurii* is only found along the continental margin, except between 2°N and 0° where the plume reaches up to 200 km offshore.

Creseis acicula a. occurs in low concentration in the study area. The maximum concentration (>10% and >1 specimen/m³) occurs in the upwelling region between 7° and 15°S and can be traced over 900 km offshore Peru. South of 15°S and north 7°S off Peru this species is rare or absent, except for small areas in the Gulf of Guayaquil and the Gulf of Panama. Both are areas with high primary productivity and low oxygen saturation.

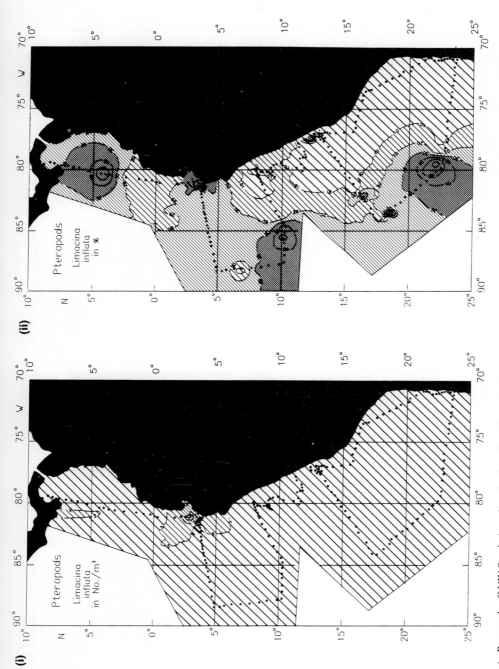

Fig. 12(a). Pteropods off NW South America: absolute (i) and relative (ii) concentrations of *Limacina inflata* in the size fraction larger than 0.15 mm. Areas of high concentrations occur far off the coast, while along the coast in the central upwelling region abundances are low. *L. inflata* therefore appears mostly in warm waters outside the upwelling regime.

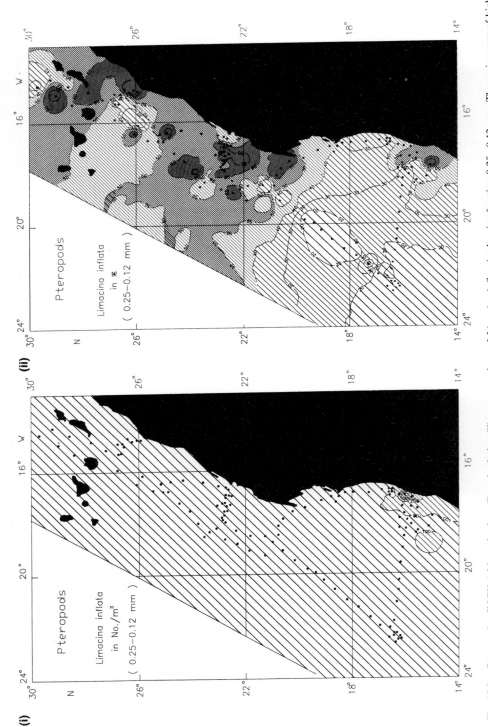

Fig. 12(b). Pteropods off NW Africa: absolute (i) and relative (ii) concentrations of *Limacina inflata* in the size fraction 0.25–0.12 mm. The main areas of high abundance are concentrated in a broad region in the north of the upwelling region.

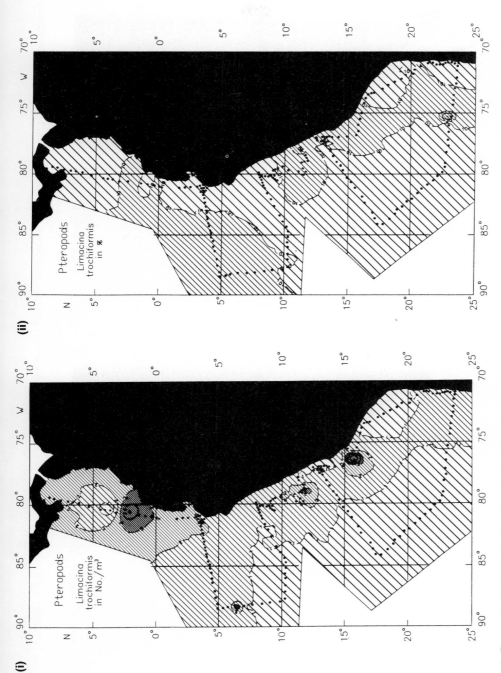

Fig. 13(a). Pteropods off NW South America: absolute (i) and relative (ii) concentrations of *Limacina trochiformis* in the size fraction larger than 0.15 mm. In the southern part of the upwelling area concentrations are high. Another region of high abundances appears in the warmer waters of the Gulf of Guayaquil. At 5°S concentrations indicate a westward transport into the open ocean.

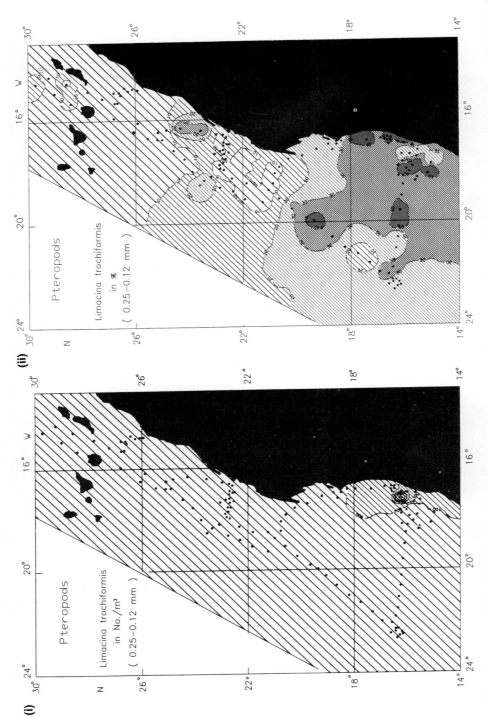

Fig. 13(b). Pteropods off NW Africa: absolute (i) and relative (ii) concentrations of *Limacina trochiformis* in the size fraction 0.25–0.12 mm. *L. trochiformis* reaches high abundance between 20° and 14°N in the coastal upwelling region.

Creseis virgula v. is very abundant but is only found in restricted areas. The maximum concentration (>10% and >1 specimen/m^3) occurs between 5° and 10°S, with a centre of over 60% (8° to 9°S), and can be traced about 400 km offshore Peru. Two smaller areas of enrichment occur in the high primary productivity regions of the Gulf of Guayaquil and the Gulf of Panama. Outside these areas of high concentrations *C. virgula v.* is absent or rare.

Clio polita occurs in very low concentration (1–14%) in only one restricted area, elsewhere it is absent or rare. It is most abundant in the upwelling region between 11° and 15°S, extending 900 km southwest of the coast off Peru. A small isolated area of enrichment occurs 600 km away from the shore between 7° and 10°S. Most probably it is an eddy which left the coast and is now drifting with the surface water masses from the northern part of the upwelling region to the west or southwest.

NW Africa. The coastal upwelling regime off NW Africa where the sediments contain pteropod concentrations (Diester-Haass & van der Spoel 1978) shows two maxima of concentration in pteropods. One extends from 14° to 18°N and is attached to the coast, the other lies several kilometres offshore between 20° and 24°N. In these areas the standing stock of pteropods can rise to over 300 specimens/m^3 (Fig. 11).

The main pteropod species in the coastal upwelling areas off NW Africa are *Limacina inflata*, *Limacina trochiformis* and *Creseis acicula a.*

Limacina inflata is the most abundant species (Fig. 12b). It occurs nearly all along the coast with a broad region in the north. This species occurs in the upwelling waters generated by the Canary and Cape Verde Islands. Besides the high concentrations of >60% in this area, the standing stock is lower than in the other regions.

Further south its abundance increases again to over 60% (<100 specimens/m^3). At 20°N there is a strong concentration gradient, where the relative abundance of *L. inflata* decreases southward to less than 20%. Only in a small area between 14° and 16°N does the concentration reach >60% again. This area is attached to the coast of NW Africa and the standing stock exceeds 200 specimens/m^3.

Limacina trochiformis is also highly abundant in the study area (Fig. 13b), but compared to

L. inflata the broad region of high relative abundance occurs in the south where the water masses are subtropical.

Maximum concentrations (>40%, >100 specimens/m^3) are found in the upwelling region between 14° and 16°N; there are two eddies several kilometres offshore which show some westward transport. Further north concentrations decrease and only exceed >30% in a small area at 24°N.

Creseis acicula a. occurs nearly in the same places as *Limacina trochiformis* but in much lower concentrations. Areas of maximum concentration (>30% and >20 specimens/m^3) occur between 17° and 19°N close to the coast. Two other high abundance areas occur several kilometres offshore at 16° and 18°N indicating a westward transport of the surface water.

Major biotic characteristics of coastal upwelling areas

1. The distributions of planktic foraminifers and pelagic gastropods off NW Africa and NW South America are closely associated with major water masses. Therefore they allow mapping of the areas where upwelling water occurs and influences the surrounding water masses.

2. As far as is shown by our data, the two coastal upwelling regions off NW Africa and NW South America are different in their extension, to the north and south and seaward. The coastal upwelling off NW Africa occurs in a narrow belt all along the coast and shows small offshore westward transport, while the upwelling water masses off NW South America show extreme seaward transport into the Pacific Ocean.

3. Benthic components are found in low concentrations in the upwelling regions off NW Africa and NW South America. They comprise benthic foraminifers which live attached to seaweeds, larval stages of benthic gastropods and meroplanktic bivalve larvae. Their abundance is highest in the coastal upwelling region.

4. The most abundant planktic foraminifer in both upwelling regions is *Globigerina bulloides*, reaching over 30 specimens/m^3 and over 40% of the total foraminiferal fauna. This species is a very good indicator of water masses influenced by upwelling. Looking at the distribution of pteropods, *Limacina bulimoides* indicates upwelling water masses off NW Africa and NW South America. Its concentration reaches over 30 specimens/m^3 and over 80% of the total pteropod fauna in both areas.

What might fossil upwelling signals look like?

The two data sets from the coastal upwelling areas off NW Africa and NW South America which are used as examples in this study, represent synoptic distributions of modern plankton and nekton assemblages. The components, illustrated in some detail, nearly all produce shells and/or skeletons which can be preserved in the geological record. How can such data be made useful to scientists interested in identifying fossil upwelling systems?

The coastal upwelling systems off South America (Suess, Kulm & Killingley 1987; Suess, von Huene et al. 1990) and off NW Africa (Sarnthein et al. 1982) seem to have existed for most of the Neogene and Quaternary, even though the intensity of the upwelling must have changed considerably with time in response to climatic changes. It seems worthwhile to think about the validity of this restriction because it basically only addresses a world ocean with a deep water renewal controlled by cold polar regions (Kennett 1982). During the Palaeogene and Mesozoic more equable climates ruled on earth, possibly giving room to upwelling systems completely different from those occurring in a stratified ocean.

In this study we have attempted to define additional palaeontological criteria based on the characteristics of modern upwelling biota. Together with modern isotopic and organic geochemical techniques and palaeoceanographic interpretations these criteria should help us to identify the location, intensity and nature of fossil upwelling regimes.

The main palaeontological criteria derived from these two sets of samples can be summarized as follows.

1. Coastal upwelling areas and their extent, as well as the 'oceanographic' age of upwelled water masses, can be mapped by means of the distributions of shell- and skeleton producing plankton and nekton.

2. A considerable proportion of the pelagic biota is made up of benthic organisms. They can comprise true benthos or the mero-planktic larval stages; their distribution allows the offshore surface water movements of the upwelling system to be mapped.

3. Siliceous microplankton communities of upwelling systems are dominated by diatoms. The ratio of diatoms to radiolarians can be used to map the area of most intense upwelling as

previously suggested by Diester-Haass (1983) and Thiede (1975a).

4. Planktic foraminifers can be used to identify upwelling regions because they are composed of species adapted to colder waters than found in the surrounding ocean. In certain instances they can be used to trace the source of upwelled waters, which usually is the subsurface counter current observed in all modern coastal upwelling systems.

5. Certain species of planktic foraminifers (*Globigerina bulloides*, *Globigerinoides ruber*, *G. sacculifer*, *Globigerinita glutinata* and *Globoquadrina dutertrei*) and pelagic gastropods (*Limacina bulimoides*, *L. inflata*, *L. trochiformis* and *Creseis virgula*) seem to be especially well adapted to upwelling water masses.

6. Pelagic biota in upwelling regimes are characterized by unusually high standing stocks of virtually all components, and probably high turnover rates.

Since most modern coastal upwelling regimes are located in subtropical and tropical zones, species compositions of many of their biota are similar. In the past, one can easily envisage situations when coastal upwelling regimes may have been spread over a wide range of climatic zones, thus allowing quite different plankton communities to adapt to upwelling systems which then could have properties much different from those we observe today.

These samples could not have been collected without the kind co-operation of the chief scientists of RV METEOR cruise no 25 (E. Seibold, formerly Kiel, now Freiburg) and WELOC 77, Leg 6 of RV WECOMA (E. Suess, formerly Corvallis, now Kiel) and the help of members of the scientific parties of these two cruises. Collection of the samples was supported by the German Research Foundation (DFG-Bonn) and by the Office of Naval Research (ONR-Arlington/VA.).

References

Auras-Schudnagies, A., Kroon, D., Ganssen, G., Hemleben, C. & Van Hinte, J. E. 1989. Distributional pattern of planktonic foraminifers and pteropods in surface waters and top core sediments of the Red Sea, and adjacent areas controlled be the monsoonal regime and other ecological factors. *Deep-Sea Research*, **36**, 1515–1533.

Berger, W. H., Fisher, K., Lai, C. & Wu, O. 1987.

Ocean carbon flux: global maps of primary production and export production. *In*: AGEGIAN, C. (ed.), *Biogeochemical Cycling and Fluxes between the Deep Euphotic Zone and Other Oceanic Realms. NOAA Symp. Ser. for Undersea Research, NOAA Undersea Research Program,* 3(2), Preprint in SIO ref 87–30.

——, SMETACEK, V. S. & WEFER, G. 1989a. *Productivity in the Ocean: Past and Present. Rep. Dahlem-Conf.* (Berlin, Apr. 1988), Wiley, New York.

——, —— & —— 1989b. Ocean productivity and paleoproductivity — an overview. *In*: BERGER, W. H., SMETACEK, V. S. & WEFER, G. (eds), *Productivity in the Ocean: Past and Present. Rep. Dahlem-Conf.* (Berlin, Apr. 1988), Wiley-Interscience, New York, 1–34.

BISHOP, J. K. B. 1989. Regional extremes in particulate matter composition and flux: Effects on the chemistry of the ocean interior. *In*: BERGER, W. H., SMETACEK, V. S. & WEFER, G. (eds), *Productivity in the Ocean: Past and Present. Rep. Dahlem-Conf.* (Berlin, Apr. 1988), Wiley, New York, 117–138.

BOLTOVSKOY, E. 1971. Patchiness in the distribution of planktonic foraminifera. *In*: FARINACCI, A. (ed.) *Proc. 2nd Plankt. Conf. Roma,* 1, 107–115.

BRONGERSMA-SANDERS, M. 1983. Unconsolidated phosphorites, high barium and diatom abundances in some Namibian shelf sediments. *In*: SUESS, E. & THIEDE, J. (eds), *Coastal Upwelling — Its Sediment Record.* Part A: Responses of the Sedimentary Regime to Present Coastal Upwelling. Plenum, New York, 421–437.

CALVERT, S. & PRICE, N. B. 1983. Geochemistry of Namibian shelf sediments. *In*: SUESS, E. & THIEDE, J. (eds) *Coastal Upwelling — Its Sediment Record.* Part A: Responses of the Sedimentary Regime to Present Coastal Upwelling. Plenum, New York, 337–375.

DIESTER-HAASS, L. 1977. Radiolarian/planktonic foraminiferal ratios in a coastal upwelling region. *Journal of Foraminiferal Research,* 7(1), 26–33.

—— 1978. Sediments as an indicator of upwelling. *In*: BOJE, R. & TOMCZAM, M. (eds) *Upwelling Ecosystems.* Springer, Berlin, 261–281.

—— 1983. Differentiation of high organic fertility in marine sediments caused by coastal upwelling and/or river discharge off northwest Africa during the Late Quaternary. *In*: THIEDE, J. & SUESS, E. (eds) *Coastal Upwelling — Its Sediment Record.* Part B: Sedimentary Records of Ancient Coastal Upwelling. Plenum, New York, 399–419.

—— & VAN DER SPOEL, S. 1978. Late Pleistocene pteropod-rich sediment layer in the northeast Atlantic and protoconch variation of *clio pyramidata* Linné 1767. *Palaeogeography, Palaeoclimatology, Palaeoecology,* 24, 85–109.

EASTROPAC Atlas 1967. WOOSTER, W. S. & LONGHURST, A. R. (Coordinators), U.S. Government Printing Office, Washington, vols 1–11.

FORSBERGH, E. D. 1969. The climatology. *Bull. Inter. Amer. — Tropical Tuna Comm. Bull.,* 14, 49–385.

HEATH, G. R. 1974. *Dissolved Silica in Deep-sea Sediments.* Society of Economic Paleontologists and Mineralogists Special Publication 20, 77–93.

HEMLEBEN, C., SPINDLER, M. & ANDERSON, O. R. 1988. *Modern Planktonic Foraminifera.* Springer, New York.

JONES, B. H., BRINK, K. H., DUGDALE, R. C., STUART, D. W., VAN LEER, J. C., BLASCO, D. & KELLEY, J. C. 1983. Observations of a persistent upwelling center off Point Perception. California. *In*: SUESS, E. & THIEDE, J. (eds) *Coastal Upwelling — Its Sediment Record.* Part A: Responses of the Sedimentary Regime to Present Coastal Upwelling, Plenum, New York, 37–60.

KENNETT, J. 1982. *Marine Geology.* Prentice Hall, Englewood Cliffs.

LOVE, C. M. 1970. EASTROPAC Atlas, WOOSTER, W. S. & LONGHURST, A. L. (Coordinators), U.S. Government Printing Office, Washington. Vol. 4.

MOLINA-CRUZ, A. 1977. Radiolarian assemblages and their relationship to the oceanography of the subtropical southeastern Pacific. *Marine Micropalaeontology,* 2, 315–352.

MOORE, T. C., HEATH, G. R. & KOWSMANN, R. O. 1973. Biogenic sediments of the Panama Basin. *Journal of Geology,* 81, 458–472.

PEINERT, R., VON BODUNGEN, B. & SMETACEK, V. S. 1989. Food web structure and loss rate. *In*: BERGER, W. H., SMETACEK, V. S. & WEFER, G. (eds), *Productivity in the Ocean: Past and Present. Rep. Dahlem-Conf.* (Berlin, Apr. 1988), Wiley-Interscience, New York, 35–48.

PROSPERO, J. M. & CARLSON, T. N. 1972. Vertical and aerial distribution of Saharan dust over the Western Equatorial North Atlantic Ocean. *Journal of Geophysical Research,* 77, 5255–65.

RICHARDS, F. A. (ed.) 1981. *Coastal Upwelling.* Coastal and Estuarine Science, vol. 1, American Geophysical Union.

RUDDIMAN, W. W., SARNTHEIN, M. *et al.* 1989. Late Miocene to Pleistocene evolution of climate in Africa and the low-latitude atlantic: overview of leg 108 results. *Proceedings of the Ocean Drilling Program Scientific Results.* Ocean Drilling Program, College Station, TX, 108.

SARNTHEIN, M., THIEDE, J., PFLAUMANN, U., ERLENKEUSER, H., FÜTTERER, D., KOOPMANN, B., LANGE, H. & SEIBOLD, E. 1982. Atmospheric and oceanic circulation patterns off Northwest Africa during the past 25 million years. *In*: VON RAD, U., HINZ, K., SARNTHEIN, M. & SEIBOLD, E. (eds) *Geology of the Northwest African Continental Margin.* Springer, Berlin, 545–604.

SCHELTEMA, R. S. 1971. The dispersal of larvae of shoal-water benthic invertebrate species over long distances by ocean currents. *In*: CRISP, D. J. (ed.) *Proceedings of the 4th European Marine Biology Symposium,* 7–28.

—— 1988. Initial evidence for the transport of tele-

planktic larvae of benthic invertebrates across
the East Pacific barrier. *Biological Bulletin*, **174**,
145−152.

SCHRADER, H.-J. & BAUMGARTNER, T. 1983. Decadal
variation of upwelling in the central Gulf of
California. *In*: THIEDE, J. & SUESS, E. (eds)
Coastal Upwelling − Its Sediment Record. Part
B: Sedimentary Records of Ancient Coastal
Upwelling. Plenum, New York, 247−276.

——— & SORKNES, R. 1991. Peruvian coastal upwelling:
Late Quaternary productivity changes revealed
by diatoms. *Marine Geology*, **97**, 233−249.

SEIBOLD, E. 1972. Cruise 25/1971 of R. V. 'Meteor':
Continental margin of West Africa − General
report and preliminary results. *'Meteor' Forsch.
Ergebn.*, **C10**, 17−28.

SMITH, R. L. 1983. Circulation patterns in upwelling
regimes. *In*: SUESS, E. & THIEDE, J. (eds)
Coastal Upwelling − Its Sediment Record. Part
A: Responses of the Sedimentary Regime to
Present Coastal Upwelling, Plenum, New York,
13−35.

SPINDLER, M. 1980. The pelagic gulfweed *Sargassum
natans* as a habitat for the benthic foraminifera
Planorbulina acervalis and *Rosalina globularis*.
*Neues Jahrbuch für Geologie und Palaeontology.
Monatshefte*, **9**, 569−580.

STEIN, R. 1990. *Accumulation of Organic Carbon in
Marine Sediments*. Lecture Notes in Earth
Sciences, **34**, Springer, New York.

SUESS, E., KULM, L. D. & KILLINGLEY, J. S. 1987.
Coastal upwelling and a history of organic-rich
mudstone deposition off Peru. *In*: BROOKS, J. &
FLEET, A. J. (eds) *Marine Petroleum Source
Rocks*. Geological Society, London, Special
Publication, **26**, 181−197.

——— & THIEDE, J. 1983. *Coastal Upwelling − Its
Sediment Record*. Part A: Responses of the
Sedimentary Regime to Present Coastal Up-
welling, Plenum, New York.

SUESS, E., VON HUENE, R. *et al.* 1990. Peruvian
continental margin. *Proceedings of the Ocean
Drilling Program, Scientific Results*. Ocean
Drilling Program, College Station, TX, **112**.

THIEDE, J. 1974. Marine bivalves: Distribution of
mero-planktonic shell-bearing larvae in eastern
North Atlantic surface waters. *Palaeogeography,
Palaeoclimatology, Palaeoecology*, **15**, 267−290.

——— 1975a. Shell- and skeleton-producing plankton
and nekton in the eastern North Atlantic Ocean.
'Meteor' Forsch. Ergebn., **C20**, 33−79.

——— 1975b. Distribution of foraminifera in surface
waters of a coastal upwelling area. *Nature*, **253**,
712−714.

——— 1983. Skeletal plankton and nekton in upwelling
water masses off northwestern South America
and northwest Africa. *In*: SUESS, E. & THIEDE, J.
(eds) *Coastal Upwelling − Its Sediment Record*.
Part A: Responses of the Sedimentary Regime to
Present Coastal Upwelling, Plenum, New York,
183−207.

——— & JÜNGER, B. in prep. Quantitative distributions
of skeletal plankton in two coastal upwelling
regimes.

——— & SUESS, S. 1983. *Coastal Upwelling − Its
Sediment Record*. Part B: Sedimentary Records
of Ancient Coastal Upwelling, Plenum,
New York.

VAN DER SPOEL, S. 1967. *Euthecosomata*. Noorduyn
& Zn, Gorinchem.

ZUTA, S. & GUILLEN, O. 1970. Oceanografia de las
aguas costeras del Peru. *Bol. Inst. Mar Peru*, **2**,
157−324.

Planktonic foraminiferal faunal and stable isotopic indices of upwelling: a sediment trap study in the San Pedro Basin, Southern California Bight

ROBERT THUNELL[1] & LESLIE REYNOLDS SAUTTER[2]

[1] *Department of Geological Sciences, University of South Carolina, Columbia, South Carolina 29208, USA*

[2] *Lamont-Doherty Geological Observatory, Palisades, New York 10964, USA*

Abstract: A planktonic foraminiferal faunal and stable isotopic study has been carried out on sediment trap samples collected in 1988 from the San Pedro Basin (Southern California Bight) in order to examine the response of this group of plankton to coastal upwelling. Hydrographic monitoring indicates that a period of upwelling occurred in the basin from late April to early June, with a brief spring bloom of planktonic foraminifera occurring prior to upwelling. The onset of upwelling resulted in a significant increase in total foraminiferal shell flux; the upwelling assemblage was initially dominated by *Globigerina quinqueloba*, with *Globigerina bulloides* dominating the latter half of upwelling. Following upwelling, the upper water column became thermally stratified and *Neogloboquadrina dutertrei* dominated the fauna. The observed pattern of faunal succession may be partly related to changes in food availability.

Stable isotope analyses ($\delta^{18}O$ and $\delta^{13}C$) of *Neogloboquadrina pachyderma*, *N. dutertrei* and *G. bulloides* indicate that all three species adjust their depth habitats in response to upwelling. *Globigerina bulloides* migrates from below the thermocline to the surface at the onset of upwelling. Both *N. pachyderma* and *N. dutertrei* appear to adjust their depth habitats in order to remain within specific temperature ranges.

Upwelling and its attendant high primary productivity play an important role in the biogeochemical cycling of the oceans. Upwelling regions serve as both sources and sinks for many biologically active elements, and it may be that these marginal areas exert a strong influence on processes occurring in the open ocean. In particular, the continental margins beneath coastal upwelling zones are major sites for the sequestering of carbon. It stands to reason that past changes in the intensity and/or areal extent of upwelling may have caused considerable perturbations in the oceanic carbon budget and, perhaps more importantly, atmospheric CO_2 levels. As such, it is important to be able to identify and understand the history of upwelling as it is recorded in deep sea sediments. In recent years a number of syntheses have been published on physical and biological processes in upwelling regions (Richards 1981), the sedimentary response to modern upwelling regimes (Suess & Thiede 1983) and the imprint of upwelling in the geological record (Thiede & Suess 1983).

One way of transferring an upwelling signal into the sedimentary record is through the accumulation of various plankton assemblages that are diagnostic of upwelling conditions. Several studies have previously documented the sedimentary assemblages of planktonic foraminifera (Prell & Curry 1981; Thiede 1983; Ganssen & Sarnthein 1983; Wefer *et al.* 1983; Prell 1984), diatoms (Schuette & Schrader 1979, 1981; Juillet-Leclerc & Schrader 1987) and silicoflagellates (Murray & Schrader 1983; Schrader & Baumgartner 1983) found in modern upwelling regions. Such studies suffer from the fact that sedimentary assemblages represent composite mixtures of different seasons over many years, making it difficult to identify specific plankton species which are diagnostic of seasonally occurring upwelling conditions. Plankton net towing and sediment trapping provide alternative approaches to studying the response of plankton to upwelling. For example, seasonal variability in the faunal and stable isotopic composition of planktonic foraminifera has been monitored using sediment traps in two Pacific upwelling regions, the Panama Basin (Curry *et al.* 1983; Thunell *et al.* 1983; Thunell & Reynolds 1984) and the northeast Pacific (Reynolds & Thunell 1985; Sautter & Thunell 1989). Studies such as these provide a better understanding of the plankton response to temporal changes in surface water hydrography and allow for the identification of species which are true upwelling indicators.

The present study is an extension of our

From SUMMERHAYES, C. P., PRELL, W. L. & EMEIS K. C. (eds), 1992, *Upwelling Systems: Evolution Since the Early Miocene.* Geological Society Special Publication No 64, pp 77–91.

previous work in the Panama Basin (Thunell &
Reynolds 1984) and subpolar North Pacific
(Reynolds & Thunell 1985; Sautter & Thunell
1989). In 1988 a high-resolution time-series
sediment trapping and hydrographic monitoring
program was carried out off the coast of Los
Angeles, California, in the San Pedro Basin.
This basin is part of the Southern California
Bight and experiences strong episodes of upwelling, particularly during late spring and early
summer. The objective of this study is to examine temporal changes in the flux and stable
isotopic (oxygen and carbon) composition of
planktonic foraminifera prior to, during and
immediately following upwelling.

California Current and upwelling

The California Current, which flows equatorward along the west coast of North America,
is the eastern limb of the North Pacific gyre
(Fig. 1). Upwelling is a characteristic feature of
the California Current, with the timing and

intensity of upwelling being related to the position and strength of the North Pacific high-
pressure system. South of approximately 40°N,
wind stress is primarily equatorward throughout
the year (Hickey 1979), although it does vary in
strength on a seasonal basis. The general north–
south trend of the coastline combined with the
prevailing northerly winds results in offshore
Ekman transport and coastal upwelling. Along
most of the California coast, this coastal upwelling is strongest during spring. In-depth
reviews of the California Current System and
associated coastal upwelling can be found in
Hickey (1979) and Huyer (1983).

The Southern California Bight, which extends
from Point Conception (34°N) to Cape Colnett
(31°N), has a somewhat more complicated hydrographic setting. The Bight consists of a series
of basins and ridges, and a coastline that trends
northwest–southeast (Fig. 2). As a result of
this coastline orientation, the California Current
lies farther offshore in the Bight than it does
along northern California or Baja. The Southern

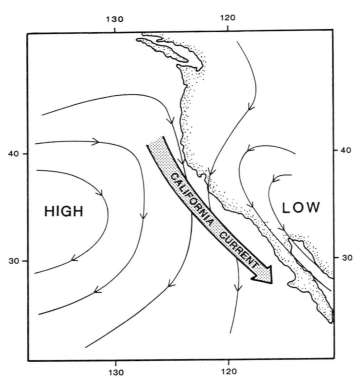

Fig. 1. Map of the eastern North Pacific showing the general positions of the North Pacific high and continental
low pressure systems, and the equatorward flowing California Current. Due to the prevailing northerly winds
and north–south orientation of the coastline, offshore Ekman transport occurs along the west coast of North
America.

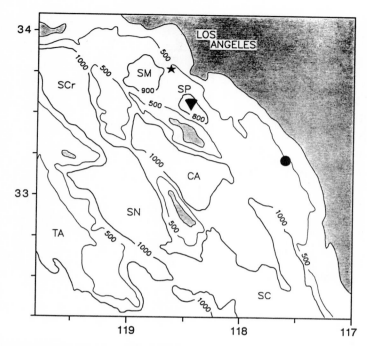

Fig. 2. Map of the Southern California Bight showing the locations of the various Borderland basins (CA, Catalina; SC, San Clemente; SCr, Santa Cruz; SM, Santa Monica; SN, San Nicolas; SP, San Pedro). The sediment trap study was carried out in the San Pedro Basin (cone). Also shown are the locations of CalCOFI station 87.35 (star) and the coastal station at Balboa (circle).

California Countercurrent (SCC) flows northward along the coast of the Bight and is composed of eddies spun off by the California Current and water from south of the Bight. At Point Conception, most of the SCC water rejoins the southward flowing California Current. The interaction of the Southern California Countercurrent and the California Current result in a cyclonic flow pattern around the Bight. A more detailed description of the physical oceanography of the Southern California Bight is provided in Eppley (1986).

Offshore Ekman transport is lower in the Bight than along the regions immediately to the north and south (Fig. 3a) due to the offshore position of the California Current and the unfavourable orientation of the coastline relative to the prevailing winds. However, significant upwelling does occur in the Bight due to local wind stress curl. Between 30° and 40°N there is a positive wind stress curl that induces upwelling and this in turn reinforces the coastal upwelling (Nelson 1977). In the California Bight, this curl-induced upwelling is greatest during the spring (Fig. 3b).

Experimental design and methods

A Mark VI automated time-series sediment trap (Honjo & Doherty 1988) was deployed in the San Pedro Basin (33°33′N, 118°30′W) in January 1988. The water depth at this location is approximately 880 m and the trap was positioned approximately 400 m off the bottom. Twenty-eight consecutive week-long samples were collected between January 7 and July 26, 1988. Temperature and salinity variations in the upper 200 m of the water column were monitored through CTD casts taken on a biweekly basis for all of 1988. In conjunction with the CTD casts, water samples were collected at depths of 0, 30, 60 and 90 m. Daily sea surface temperature (SST) measurements were obtained for the study period from a coastal station at Balboa, just to the south of Los Angeles by the Scripps Institution of Oceanography (1989).

A one-quarter split of each trap sample was used for planktonic foraminiferal faunal and stable isotopic analyses. Individual specimens were removed from the wet sample using a pipette and dried. The planktonic foraminiferal

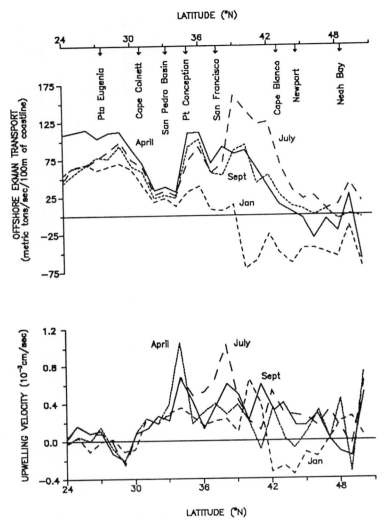

Fig. 3. A. Offshore Ekman transport based on Nelson's (1977) mean wind stress data for January, April, July and September (from Huyer 1983). B. Vertical upwelling velocity based on the curl in the wind stress (from Huyer 1983). Note that during April, maximum upwelling velocities occur in the San Pedro Basin region.

tests were then measured with an ocular micro-meter and weighed on a microbalance. Individuals greater than 125 μm were identified at the species level and the raw counts were converted to shell fluxes ($\#m^{-2}\,d^{-1}$).

Stable isotopic analyses (oxygen and carbon) of different planktonic foraminiferal species were carried out on distinct size fractions and morphotypes. The species analyzed and the size fractions used include *Neogloboquadrina dutertrei* (400−500 μm), dextrally-coiled *Neogloboquadrina pachyderma* (180−212 μm) and

Globigerina bulloides (300−350 μm). These three species were most abundant prior to, during and after the late spring upwelling period. Likewise, the size fraction chosen represents the most common size in the largest number of samples. The number of individuals used for each analysis varied because of inter-species differences in size. For *N. dutertrei* two or three individuals were sufficient for an analysis, whereas from five to twenty specimens were required for the *G. bulloides* and *N. pachyderma* analyses. Multiple analyses for each species were run for each sample and mean values were then calculated.

Estimates of the $\delta^{13}C$ and $\delta^{18}O$ of equilibrium calcite were made for the study period for water depths of 0, 30, 60 and 90 m in order to determine whether the foraminiferal calcite was secreted in equilibrium. The $\delta^{13}C$ of total dissolved inorganic carbon ($\Sigma\, CO_2$) was measured on water samples collected at 0, 30 and 60 m. Equilibrium calcite $\delta^{13}C$ was then calculated using the equation of Grossman (1982), modified from Epstein et al. (1953), where

$$\text{Equilibrium calcite } \delta^{13}C = (\delta^{13}C \text{ of } \Sigma CO_2) + \left[10.51 - \left(\frac{2980}{T_w + 273} \right) \right]$$

and T_w = the temperature of ambient water (°C). The temperatures used in these calculations were from the biweekly CTD casts. The $\delta^{18}O$ of equilibrium calcite was estimated for the same water depths using the CTD temperature and salinity data and the palaeotemperature equation of Epstein et al. (1953):

$$t_w = 16.4 - 4.2(\delta_s - \delta_w) + 0.13(\delta + \delta_w)^2$$

where δ_s and δ_w are the oxygen isotopic compositions of the calcite sample and the seawater sample, respectively. The latter term, δ_w, was estimated using the relationship determined by Epstein & Mayeda (1953) where

$$\delta_w = (0.59 \text{ salinity}) - 20.68.$$

Although this equation was derived using δ_w and salinity data from the Atlantic, published salinity and δ_w values for the California Current (Epstein & Mayeda 1953) indicate that the same relationship holds for this region.

Results and discussion

An in-depth discussion of the ecology, seasonal succession and stable isotopic changes in planktonic foraminifera from the San Pedro Basin can be found in Sautter and Thunell (1991a, b). In this paper we focus only on upwelling. First, we will briefly describe the hydrographic conditions associated with upwelling in San Pedro Basin, followed by a discussion of the faunal and stable isotopic response of planktonic foraminifera to the upwelling conditions. The discussion of the planktonic foraminiferal results will concentrate on the period from March to July 1988. This will allow us to compare faunal and isotopic signatures associated with pre-upwelling (March−early April), upwelling (late April−early June) and post-upwelling (late June−July) conditions.

Hydrography

Sea surface temperature (SST) data and thermal profiles derived from the CTD measurements indicate that a number of distinct upwelling events occurred in San Pedro Basin during 1988 (Fig. 4). The most well defined periods of upwelling occurred in early May, early June, and mid-November. Early August SST data indicate a rapid decrease in surface temperatures not recorded by the CTD profiling. During each of these periods, cold deep waters were introduced into the photic zone causing sudden decreases in SST. The four upwelling events mentioned above are marked by SST decreases of 4−7°C (Fig. 4).

The late April to early June period is typically the time of most intense upwelling along the California coast (Nelson 1977) and in the vicinity of the San Pedro Basin (Fig. 3b). In early April, just prior to the onset of upwelling, the upper part of the water column is fairly well stratified with the thermocline located between 25 and 35 m (Fig. 5a). With the initiation of upwelling in late April, the thickness of the surface mixed layer is reduced. This is clearly illustrated by the shoaling of the thermocline to a depth of approximately 15 m during the early June upwelling event (Fig. 5a). During the post-upwelling period, surface waters warm rapidly and the upper water column again becomes well stratified.

Nutrient data collected as part of the California Cooperative Fisheries Investigations (CalCOFI 1989) clearly indicate that significant differences exist between upwelling and non-upwelling periods in the concentrations of silicate, nitrate and chlorophyll-a in the upper water column (Figs 5b−d). Nitrate and silicate concentrations in the upper 40 m were considerably higher during upwelling (May) than during the two non-upwelling periods that were sampled. Significantly higher chlorophyll-a concentrations were also observed during upwelling due to increased primary productivity, with a pronounced chlorophyll maximum centred at approximately 30 m (Fig. 5d).

Faunal response to upwelling

Sautter & Thunell (1991a) have demonstrated that planktonic foraminifera respond rapidly to sudden changes in surface water hydrography. One of the most obvious responses of planktonic foraminifera to spring upwelling in the San Pedro Basin is the tremendous increase in total shell flux (Fig. 6). As can be seen in Fig. 4, there is a broad upwelling interval from late

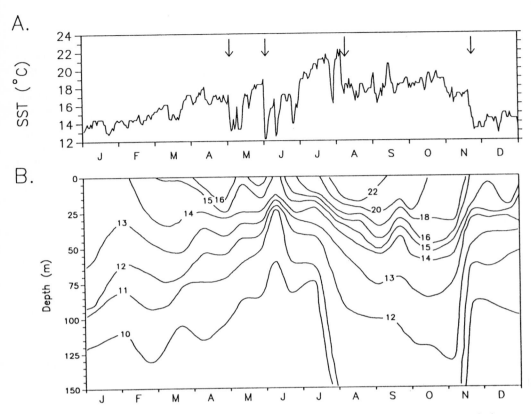

Fig. 4. A. Daily sea surface temperature (SST) data collected from a coastal station at Balboa by Scripps Institute of Oceanography. Periods of upwelling are indicated by arrows. B. Temperature cross section for the San Pedro Basin for 1988 based on biweekly CTD casts.

April to early June. The SST data indicate that upwelling was not continuous throughout this six-week period, but rather there were multiple brief upwelling events separated by surface water warming. Associated with each of these upwelling events is a significant increase in total foraminiferal shell flux (Fig. 6). The only other significant increase in shell flux occurred just prior to upwelling (early–mid April) in conjunction with an increase in phytoplankton species typical of spring blooms (Sancetta, unpublished data). Prior to the spring bloom of planktonic foraminifera (early April) and after upwelling (late June–July) the average total flux is approximately 500 shells/m²/day, increasing to nearly 2000 and 4000 shells/m² day during the spring bloom and each upwelling episode, respectively. If this trend is typical of the entire year, then the annual shell flux to the seafloor should be dominated by individuals produced during these relatively brief events. For

example, the total foraminiferal flux for the five month period being considered (March to July) is approximately 1.6×10^5 shells/m², with over 50% of these being produced during the six-week upwelling period. Based on this observation, in well preserved sediments, the accumulation of foraminiferal shells should be an excellent monitor of long-term changes in upwelling intensity. This also has important implications for interpreting the stable isotopic composition of sedimentary assemblages since, in terms of isotopic mass balance, most of the calcite is being produced during a relatively brief interval of the year.

The flux records for the six planktonic foraminiferal species most abundant from March through July are illustrated in Fig. 6. The shell flux records have not been adjusted to account for either foraminifer life span or settling time through the water column, as was done in previous studies by Reynolds & Thunell (1985) and

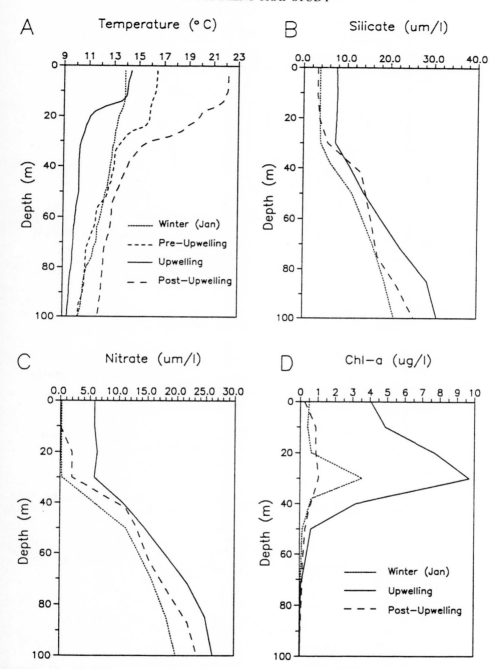

Fig. 5. A. Temperature profiles for January, pre-upwelling (early April), upwelling (June) and post-upwelling (July). Profiles of (B) nitrate, (C) silicate and (D) chlorophyll-a concentrations for the upper 100 m of the water column at the Santa Monica CalCOFI station (33°49′N, 118°38′W) (CalCOFI, 1989) for January, upwelling and post-upwelling conditions.

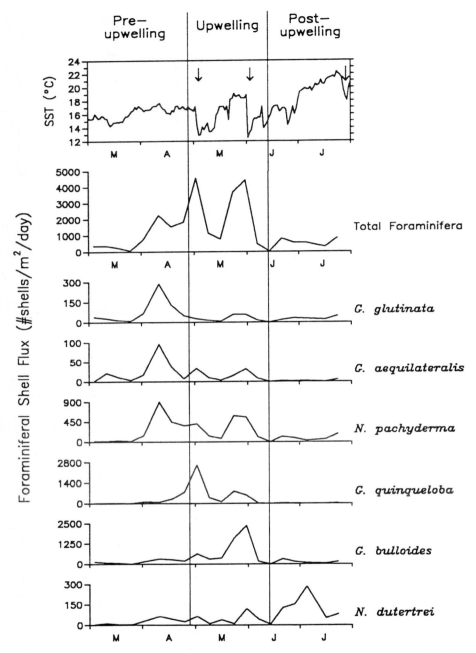

Fig. 6. Seasonal flux records of total planktonic foraminifera and individual species (#shells m^{-2} d^{-1}) from the San Pedro Basin sediment trap. The daily sea surface temperature (SST) record is also shown.

Sautter & Thunell (1989). The non-adjusted records allow for the simplest and most direct comparison between the species flux data and the hydrographic data. The individual species flux records clearly show that planktonic foraminifera respond rapidly at the species level to sudden hydrographic changes and that individual species have a preference for either pre-upwelling, upwelling or post-upwelling conditions. The flux records for each species have several features in common. First, all of the records contain a distinct period of increased flux that lasts for three to five weeks. *Neogloboquadrina pachyderma* is the only species with a true bimodal distribution (two episodes of comparably high flux).

The second feature that is characteristic of the individual species flux records is that the maximum flux is a short-lived event, not lasting more than one week (Fig. 6). In all cases there is a significant decrease in flux (50—90%) during the week immediately following the time of peak flux. These rapid increases and decreases, on timescales of a week or less, in foraminiferal production and flux are a further indication of how rapidly planktonic foraminifera respond to changes in surface water conditions, particularly in a hydrographically dynamic region such as the Southern California Bight.

The planktonic foraminiferal flux during the pre-upwelling period (March to mid-April) is dominated by *Globigerinita glutinata*, *Globigerinella aequilateralis* and *N. pachyderma* (Fig. 6). All three of these species have maximum fluxes prior to the onset of upwelling. During this time, the upper water column was fairly well stratified and surface water temperatures were 16—18°C. The relatively high total shell flux which occurred just prior to upwelling in mid-April (Fig. 6) is comprised mostly of *N. pachyderma* and is temporally associated with an increase in the flux of large diatoms often produced during spring bloom conditions (Sancetta, unpublished data). In terms of relative abundance, *N. pachyderma* makes up ~60% of the pre-upwelling fauna.

As discussed earlier, upwelling began in late April and manifested itself as two sudden drops in SST at the beginning of May and the beginning of June (Fig. 4). The total foraminiferal flux during the upwelling period is dominated by *G. quinqueloba* and *G. bulloides*, with *N. pachyderma* being of secondary importance (Fig. 6). *Globigerina bulloides* and *G. quinqueloba* account for approximately 70% of the total flux during the upwelling events. *Globigerina quinqueloba* makes up 70% of the flux peak associated with the first upwelling event,

while *G. bulloides* accounts for 60% of the second peak in total foraminiferal shell flux. The observation that the flux of *G. bulloides* increases during upwelling confirms previous sediment-based studies (Prell & Curry 1981; Thiede 1983; Prell 1984; Kroon & Ganssen 1989) that this species is a good indicator of upwelling conditions. Our results are also fairly consistent with a earlier plankton tow study (Lidz 1966) of an upwelling area off of the Newport Beach, California, just to the southeast of our sediment trap location. Lidz (1966) found that *G. bulloides* and *G. quinqueloba* comprise nearly 90% of the upwelling assemblage, with *N. pachyderma* accounting for most of the remainder of the fauna. During the mid-to-late stages of upwelling there is an increase in the flux of *N. dutertrei*, although the maximum flux for this species does not occur until after upwelling (Fig. 6).

The post-upwelling period (late June—July) was a time of low total shell flux (Fig. 6). The most notable faunal change during this interval is the increase in flux of *N. dutertrei*, with maximum values being attained several weeks after the termination of upwelling. During this time, *N. dutertrei* accounts for as much as 60% of the total fauna. The increase in flux of *N. dutertrei* is associated with a warming of surface waters and the re-establishment of a well stratified upper water column.

Neogloboquadrina dutertrei is often quite abundant in sedimentary assemblages found beneath modern upwelling zones (Bradshaw 1959; Thiede 1975; Cifelli & Bernier 1976; Wefer *et al.* 1983). In addition, Fairbanks *et al.* (1982) have shown that this species congregates at the chlorophyll maximum. Based on our results, it would seem that *N. dutertrei* is not a true upwelling indicator in that its flux does not increase significantly during upwelling. Rather, *N. dutertrei* may be showing a delayed response to conditions established during upwelling. In particular, at the end of the upwelling period phytoplankton concentrations in the San Pedro Basin were very high (Sancetta, unpublished data) and this may have provided the necessary food source to increase *N. dutertrei* production. If this is true, *N. dutertrei* may serve as an indirect indicator of upwelling.

The observed sequence of faunal changes associated with the development of upwelling in the San Pedro Basin differs somewhat from the model recently proposed by Kroon & Ganssen (1988) for upwelling in the northern Indian Ocean. Based on carbon isotopic differences between coexisting specimens of *G. bulloides* and *N. dutertrei* collected from surface water pumping, Kroon & Ganssen predicted that *N. dutertrei* should be most abundant at the beginning of upwelling when phytoplankton production is highest and then be replaced by *G. bulloides* in the latter stages of upwelling. However, Kroon & Ganssen (1988) had no data regarding temporal variability in the abundance of planktonic foraminifera in the northern Indian Ocean and thus could not validate their model. In contrast, our results show that *G. quinqueloba* dominates the fauna during the first half of the upwelling period, with *G. bulloides* being most abundant during the latter stage of upwelling (Fig. 6). *Neoglobo-quadrina dutertrei* does not become important in San Pedro Basin until after upwelling. This succession of species may reflect a series of changes in food availability and upper water column stratification which may differ from conditions occurring in the northern Indian Ocean. In general, phytoplankton production increases at the beginning of either an upwelling period or a spring bloom and this in turn leads to an increase in zooplankton production. *Globigerina quinqueloba* is a spinose, symbiont-bearing species (Hemleben *et al.* 1989), and like most other species with symbionts, *G. quinqueloba* is probably herbivorous. The high flux of this species at the beginning of upwelling may be related to high production rates of phytoplankton. In contrast to *G. quinqueloba*, *G. bulloides* is a symbiont-free species (Hemleben *et al.* 1989) that is probably carnivorous. The high flux of this species probably reflects the overall increase in zooplankton production during the latter half of upwelling. Finally, the dominance of *N. dutertrei* during the post-upwelling period may reflect its preference for a thermally stratified water column, with a pronounced chlorophyll maximum.

Stable isotopic signature of upwelling

The advection of cold, nutrient-rich waters into the upper water column during upwelling should leave its imprint in the stable isotopic composition of planktonic foraminifera. Specifically, the decrease in temperature during upwelling should result in higher $\delta^{18}O$ values, while the simultaneous increase in nutrient content of the upper water column should cause a decrease in the $\delta^{13}C$ of foraminiferal calcite. In the following section we examine the $\delta^{18}O$ and $\delta^{13}C$ records of *N. pachyderma*, *G. bulloides* and *N. dutertrei* (Fig. 7) in order to determine how well the stable isotopic composition of these species reflects the hydrographic changes prior to, during and after upwelling. In addition, by

plotting the temporal changes in foraminiferal $\delta^{18}O$ and $\delta^{13}C$ relative to the appropriate depths for equilibrium calcite it is possible to estimate relative changes in the depth habitats of these three species during the period from March to July (Fig. 8). In making these depth habitat calculations, we are not assuming that the planktonic foraminifera analyzed secrete their shells in oxygen or carbon isotopic equilibrium. To the contrary, previous studies have shown that the tests of most species of planktonic foraminifera are in disequilibrium with ambient seawater for oxygen and/or carbon (Shackleton *et al.* 1973; Williams *et al.* 1977; Berger *et al.* 1978; Kahn & Williams 1981; Bouvier-Soumagnac & Duplessy 1985; among others). However, by comparing depth–habitat changes calculated from both oxygen and carbon isotopes, we hope to determine which isotope is providing the most realistic picture of an individual species responses to the changing hydrographic conditions associated with upwelling.

Neogloboquadrina pachyderma, which has peaks in shell flux just prior to upwelling and during the latter half of upwelling in late May (Fig. 6), shows no systematic difference in either $\delta^{18}O$ or $\delta^{13}C$ between upwelling and non-upwelling conditions (Fig. 7). With the exception of two samples (one in late March and one in early May) which have 'anomalously' low values, very little variability (less than 0.5 per mil) exists in the $\delta^{18}O$ and $\delta^{13}C$ of *N. pachyderma* during the pre-upwelling and upwelling periods.

The predicted depth distributions based on the $\delta^{18}O$ and $\delta^{13}C$ of *N. pachyderma* are similar in overall trend but differ in terms of absolute depths (Fig. 8). Both records suggest that *N. pachyderma* occupied a deeper habitat prior to and after upwelling when the upper water column was thermally stratified, then it migrated to shallower depths during upwelling. The $\delta^{18}O$ record indicates that *N. pachyderma* migrates from 50–70 m water depth (below the thermocline) prior to upwelling up to 20 m during upwelling in order to maintain a preferred temperature habitat of approximately 11–14°C (Fig. 8). In contrast, the $\delta^{13}C$ record suggests that *N. pachyderma* occupies depths greater than 100 m (~10°C) prior to upwelling and then migrates to approximately 40 m (11–12°C) during upwelling. These results indicate that there is a slight but constant deviation from oxygen and/or carbon equilibrium for this species, but that both δ^{18} and $\delta^{13}C$ provide reliable records of relative changes in depth habitat. Lidz (1966) found that *N. pachyderma* was most abundant in plankton tows taken

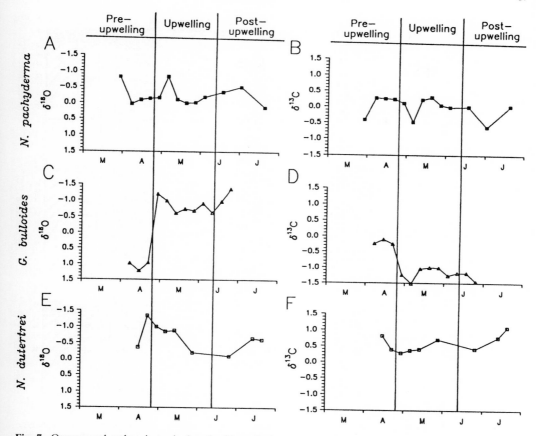

Fig. 7. Oxygen and carbon isotopic data for *N. pachyderma*, *G. bulloides* and *N. dutertrei*.

deeper than 100 m in this general area, and therefore the predicted depth distributions based on carbon equilibrium may be more accurate for this species.

Globigerina bulloides, the species whose flux increases most dramatically during upwelling (Fig. 6), records a significant change in both $\delta^{18}O$ and $\delta^{13}C$ at the onset of the upwelling period (Fig. 7). At the end of April, 2.0 and 1.0‰ decreases occurred in the $\delta^{18}O$ and $\delta^{13}C$, respectively, of this species. The change in $\delta^{18}O$ is the opposite of what would be expected if this species was recording the upwelling of colder water. In contrast, the $\delta^{13}C$ change is consistent with the upwelling of nutrient-rich water. This upwelling-induced change in the $\delta^{13}C$ of *G. bulloides* from the San Pedro Basin differs from that recently reported by Kroon & Ganssen (1989) for the northern Indian Ocean. According to these authors, upwelling in this region results in an enrichment in ^{13}C in *G. bulloides*.

Both the $\delta^{18}O$ and $\delta^{13}C$ data indicate that *G. bulloides* was living at a depth of approximately 100 m (10°C) during April prior to upwelling (Fig. 8). However, for May and June the $\delta^{18}O$ and $\delta^{13}C$ predicted habitat depths differ significantly for this species. The depth distribution based on the $\delta^{18}O$ of equilibrium calcite would indicate that *G. bulloides* ascended from 100 m water depth to the surface at the end of April, and remained close to the surface (upper 20 m) throughout the upwelling period of May and June (Fig. 8). Such a migration would also represent a considerable change in habitat temperature, from ~10°C during April to 14−18°C during May and June. In contrast, the predicted depth habitat for *G. bulloides* based on the $\delta^{13}C$ results suggests that this species migrated from approximately 100 m prior to upwelling up to 75 m during late May−early June (Fig. 8). This would mean that *G. bulloides* consistently resided below the thermocline. The carbon

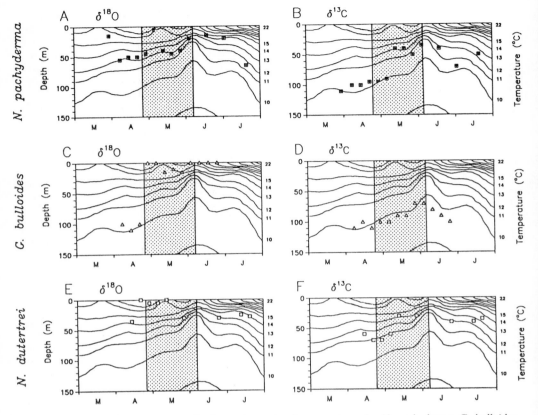

Fig. 8. Predicted seasonal depth distribution and associated temperatures for *N. pachyderma*, *G. bulloides*, and *N. dutertrei*. For each species, depths were estimated based on both the $\delta^{18}O$ and $\delta^{13}C$ of equilibrium calcite. The upwelling period is indicated by the stippled pattern.

isotopes also suggests that *G. bulloides* maintained a fairly uniform habitat temperature (~10°C) from April to June.

It is difficult to determine which of the two predicted depth distributions for *G. bulloides* is more accurate. Previous stable isotope studies seem to indicate that this species calcifies fairly close to oxygen isotopic equilibrium (Curry & Matthews 1981; Dunbar 1983; Ganssen & Sarnthein 1983) but is in strong disequilibrium with respect to carbon (Williams *et al.* 1977; Kahn & Williams 1981; Dunbar 1983). In addition, plankton tow and water pumping studies indicate that *G. bulloides* is very abundant in surficial waters of upwelling regions off Peru and northwest Africa (Thiede 1983) and in the northern Indian Ocean (Kroon 1988). Based on these stable isotopic and distributional observations, we tentatively conclude that the depth habitats predicted from the $\delta^{18}O$ data are more reliable and that during upwelling *G. bulloides*

ascends to very shallow depths.

The stable isotopic composition of *N. dutertrei*, the species which dominates the post-upwelling period flux, shows more differences in $\delta^{18}O$ and $\delta^{13}C$ between upwelling and non-upwelling conditions (Fig. 7). $\delta^{18}O$ values are generally 0.5–1.0‰ lower during upwelling relative to pre- and post-upwelling values. On average, the $\delta^{13}C$ values for *N. dutertrei* specimens collected during upwelling are slightly lower, possibly reflecting enhanced nutrient concentrations in the upper water column.

Equilibrium-derived depth distributions for *N. dutertrei* reveal significant differences between that predicted for oxygen and carbon (Fig. 8). The $\delta^{18}O$ depth estimates suggest that *N. dutertrei* lived at approximately 40 m in early April, migrated to the surface in late April–early May, descended back to 40 m in late May, residing at that depth through July. The $\delta^{13}C$ predicted depths show *N. dutertrei* calcifying at

60–70 m during April to early May followed by a migration up to 30–40 m from mid-May through July. The $\delta^{18}O$ and $\delta^{13}C$ depth distributions are thus similar for late May–July, which corresponds to the time of highest N. dutertrei flux (Fig. 6). A depth habitat of 30–40 m during and just after upwelling seems reasonable for this species, since this is the depth of the chlorophyll maximum (CalCOFI, 1989) and it has been shown that this species is commonly associated with both the thermocline and the chlorophyll maximum (Fairbanks et al. 1982). Based on the above associations, it seems unrealistic that N. dutertrei would have migrated to the surface during mid-April to early May, leading us to conclude that the $\delta^{18}O$ predicted depths for this period are erroneous. Overall, the $\delta^{13}C$-based depth distribution appears to be more consistent with that of a species known to have a preference for residing within the thermocline. It would appear that N. dutertrei migrates vertically in order to maintain a thermal habitat of approximately 11–13°C (Fig. 8).

Conclusions

A six-week long upwelling period occurred in the San Pedro Basin from late April to early June 1988. Based on a sediment trapping study conducted to monitor the faunal and stable isotopic response of planktonic foraminifera to upwelling, the following conclusions can be drawn.

(1) Total foraminiferal shell flux increases significantly with the onset of upwelling in San Pedro Basin. The only other period of relatively high shell flux during the five-month study period (March to July) occurred in mid-April in association with a spring plankton bloom.

(2) Globigerina quinqueloba dominates the early part of the upwelling period, with G. bulloides becoming dominant during the latter half of upwelling. This change in dominance may reflect a change in food source; G. quinqueloba being most abundant when phytoplankton concentrations are high and G. bulloides preferring conditions when zooplankton dominate. These results confirm previous sediment-based studies that concluded that G. bulloides is a good indicator of upwelling.

(3) Neogloboquadrina dutertrei increases in abundance immediately following upwelling. This may be in response to both the presence of a phytoplankton food source generated during upwelling and the re-establishment of a thermally stratified upper water column following upwelling.

(4) Oxygen and carbon isotopic results indicate that G. bulloides, N. pachyderma and N. dutertrei migrate upwards during upwelling. This is most pronounced for G. bulloides which migrates from below the thermocline (~100 m) prior to upwelling to the surface during upwelling. It appears that N. pachyderma and N. dutertrei adjust their respective depth habitats in order to remain within fairly uniform temperatures.

We thank Eric Tappa for technical assistance throughout the course of this study and D. Williams for use of the stable isotope facilities at the University of South Carolina. We also acknowledge the efforts of the staff at the University of Southern California Marine Support Facility. This research was supported by NSF Grants OCE-8710459 and OCE-9102151.

References

BERGER, W. H., KILLINGLEY, J. S. & VINCENT, E. 1978. Stable isotopes in deep sea carbonates: boxcore ERDC-92, west equatorial Pacific. Oceanologica Acta, 1, 203–216.

BIJMA, J., EREZ, J. & HEMLEBEN, C. 1990. Lunar and semi-lunar reproductive cycles in some spinose planktonic foraminifers. Journal of Foraminiferal Research, 20, 117–127.

BOUVIER-SOUMAGNAC, Y. & DUPLESSY, J. C. 1985. Carbon and oxygen isotopic composition of planktonic foraminifera from laboratory culture, plankton tows and Recent sediments: Implications for the reconstruction of paleoclimatic conditions and the global carbon cycle. Journal of Foraminiferal Research, 15, 302–320.

BRADSHAW, J. S. 1959. Ecology of living planktonic foraminifera in the north and equatorial Pacific Ocean. Contributions of the Cushman Foundation for Foraminiferal Research, 10, 25–64.

CalCOFI 1989. Data Report: physical, chemical and biological data, California Cooperative Fisheries Investigations, Scripps Institute of Oceanography References 88–23 and 89–2.

CIFELLI, R. & BERNIER, C. S. 1976. Planktonic foraminifera from near the west African coast and a consideration of faunal parceling in the North Atlantic. Journal of Foraminiferal Research, 6, 258–273.

CRAIG, H. & GORDON, L. I. 1965. Deuterium and oxygen-18 variations in the ocean and the marine atmosphere, In: Stable Isotopes in Oceanographic Studies and Paleotemperatures, TONGIORGI E. Cons. Naz. Ric., Lab. Geol. Nucl., Pisa, 9–130.

CURRY, W. B. & MATTHEWS, R. K. Equilibrium ^{18}O fractionation in small size fraction planktonic foraminifera: evidence from Recent Indian Ocean sediments, Marine Micropaleontology, 6, 327–337.

——, THUNELL, R. C. & HONJO, S. 1983. Seasonal

changes in the isotopic composition of planktonic foraminifera collected in Panama Basin sediment traps, *Earth and Planetary Science Letters*, **64**, 33–43.

DUNBAR, R. B. 1983. Stable isotope record of upwelling and climate from Santa Barbara Basin, California. *In*: SUESS, E. & THIEDE, J. (eds) *Coastal Upwelling: Its Sedimentary Record*, Part B, Plenum, New York, 217–246.

EPSTEIN, S., BUCHSBAUM, R., LOWENSTAM, H. A. & UREY, H. C. 1953. Revised carbonate-water isotopic temperature scale. *Bulletin of the Geological Society of America*, **64**, 1315–1326.

EPSTEIN, R. & MAYEDA, T. 1953. Variation of ^{18}O content of waters from natural sources. *Geochimica et Cosmochimica Acta*, **27**, 213–224.

FAIRBANKS, R. G., SVERDLOVE, M., FREE, R., WIEBE, P. H. & BE, A. W. H. 1982. Vertical distribution and isotopic fractionation of living planktonic foraminifera from the Panama Basin. *Nature*, **298**, 841–844.

HICKEY, B. M. 1979. The California Current System — hypotheses and facts. *Progress in Oceanography*, **8**, 191–279.

HUYER, A. 1983. Coastal upwelling in the California Current System. *Progress in Oceanography*, **12**, 259–284.

GANSSEN, G. & SARNTHEIN, M. 1983. Stable-isotope composition of foraminifers: the surface and bottom water record of coastal upwelling, *In*: *Coastal Upwelling: Its Sedimentary Record*, Part A, THIEDE, J. & SUESS, E. (eds) Plenum, New York, 99–121.

GROSSMAN, E. L. 1982. Stable isotopes in live benthic foraminifera from the Southern California Borderland. Thesis, University of Southern California, Los Angeles.

HEMLEBEN, C., SPINDLER, M. & ANDERSON, O. R. 1989. *Modern Planktonic Foraminifera*, Springer, New York.

HONJO, S. & DOHERTY, K. W. 1988. Large aperture time-series oceanic sediment traps; design objectives, construction and application, *Deep-Sea Research*, **35**, 133–149.

JUILLET-LECLERC, A. & SCHRADER, A. 1987. Variations of upwelling intensity recorded in varved sediment from the Gulf of California during the past 3,000 years. *Nature*, **329**, 146–149.

KAHN, M. & WILLIAMS, D. F. 1981. Oxygen and carbon isotopic composition of living planktonic foraminifera from the Northeast Pacific Ocean. *Palaeogeography, Palaeoclimatology, Palaeoecology*, **33**, 47–69.

KROON, D. 1989. Distribution of extant planktonic foraminiferal assemblages in Red Sea and northern Indian Ocean surface waters. *Deep-Sea Research*, **36**, 1219–1236.

—— & GANSSEN, G. 1988. Northern Indian Ocean upwelling cells and the stable isotope composition of living planktic foraminifers. *In*: *Planktonic Foraminifers as Tracers of Ocean-Climate History*, KROON, D. & BRUMMER, G.-J. (eds), Free University Press, Amsterdam, 299–317.

LIDZ, L. 1988. Planktonic foraminifera in the water column of the mainland shelf off Newport Beach, California. *Limnology and Oceanography*, **11**, 257–267.

MURRAY, D. & SCHRADER, H. 1983. Distribution of silico-flagellates in plankton and core top samples from the Gulf of California. *Marine Micropaleontology*, **7**, 517–539.

NELSON, C. S. 1977. *Wind Stress and Wind Stress Curl over the California Current*, NOAA Technical Report, NMFS SSRF-714, U.S. Dept. of Commerce.

PRELL, W. L. 1984. Variation of monsoonal upwelling: a response to changing solar radiation, *In*: *American Geophysical Union, Geophysical Monograph*, HANSEN, J. E. & TAKAHASHI, T. **29**, 48–57.

—— & CURRY, W. B. 1981. Faunal and isotopic indices of monsoonal upwelling: Western Arabian Sea. *Oceanologica Acta*, **4**, 91–98.

REYNOLDS, L. & THUNELL, R. C. 1985. Seasonal succession of planktonic foraminifera in the subpolar North Pacific, *Journal of Foraminiferal Research*, **15**, 282–301.

RICHARDS, F. A. 1981. *Coastal Upwelling*. American Geophysical Union, Washington.

SAUTTER, L. R. & THUNELL, R. C. 1989. Seasonal succession of planktonic foraminifera: results from a four-year time-series sediment trap experiment in the northeast Pacific, *Journal of Foraminiferal Research*, **19**, 253–267.

—— & ——. 1991a. Planktonic foraminiferal response to upwelling and seasonally variable hydrographic conditions: sediment trap results from the San Pedro Basin, Southern California Bight, *Journal of Foraminiferal Research*, **21**, 347–363.

—— & ——. 1991b. Seasonal variability in the oxygen and carbon isotopic composition of planktonic foraminifera from an upwelling environment: sediment trap results from the San Pedro Basin, Southern California Bight. *Paleoceanography*, **6**, 307–334.

SCHRADER, H. & BAUMGARTEN, J. 1983. Decadal variation of upwelling in the Central Gulf of California. *In*: THIEDE, J. & SUESS, E. (eds), *Coastal Upwelling*, Part B, Plenum, New York, 247–276.

SCHUETTE, G. & SCHRADER, H. 1979. Diatom taphocoenoses in the coastal upwelling areas off western South America, *Nova Hedwigia*, **64**, 359–378.

—— & ——. 1981. Diatom taphocoenoses in the coastal upwelling area off southwest Africa. *Marine Micropaleontology*, **6**, 131–155.

Scripps Institute of Oceanography 1989. Surface water temperatures, salinities and densities at shore stations, United States West Coast, *SIO Reference*, 89–9.

SHACKLETON, N. J., WISEMAN, J. D. H. & BUCKLEY, H. A. 1973. Non-equilibrium isotopic fractionation between seawater and planktonic foraminiferal tests, *Nature*, **242**, 177–179.

SPINDLER, M., HEMLEBEN, C., BAYER, U., BE, A. W. H. & ANDERSON, O. 1979. Lunar periodicity of reproduction in the planktonic foraminifera

Hastigerina pelagica, Marine Ecology Progress Series, **1**, 61−64.

SUESS, E. & THIEDE, J. 1983. *Coastal Upwelling, Its Sedimentary Record, Part A: Responses of the Sedimentary Regime to Present Coastal Upwelling*. Plenum Press, New York.

THIEDE, J. 1975. Distribution of foraminifera in surface waters of a coastal upwelling area, *Nature*, **253**, 712−714.

—— 1983. Skeletal plankton and nekton in upwelling water masses off northwestern South America and northwestern Africa, *In*: THIEDE, J. & SUESS, E. (eds) *Coastal Upwelling: Its Sedimentary Record*, Part A, Plenum, New York, 183−208.

—— & SUESS, E. 1983. *Coastal Upwelling, Its Sedimentary Record, Part B: Sedimentary Record of Ancient Coastal Upwelling*, Plenum, New York.

THUNELL, R. C., CURRY, W. B. & HONJO, S. 1983. Seasonal variation in the flux of planktonic foraminifera: time series sediment trap results from the Panama Basin, *Earth and Planetary Science Letters*, **64**, 44−55.

—— & REYNOLDS, L. 1984. Sedimentation of planktonic foraminifera: seasonal changes in species flux in the Panama Basin. *Micropaleontology*, **30**, 241−260, 1984.

WEFER, G., DUNBAR, R. B. & SUESS, E. 1983. Stable isotopes of foraminifers off Peru recording high fertility and changes in upwelling history, *In*: *Coastal Upwelling: Its Sedimentary Record*, Part B, SUESS, E. & THIEDE, J. Plenum, New York, 295−308, 1983.

WILLIAMS, D. F., SOMMER, M. A. & BENDER, M. L. 1977. Carbon isotopic composition of Recent planktonic foraminifera of the Indian Ocean, *Earth and Planetary Science Letters*, **36**, 391−403.

——, BE, A. W. H. & FAIRBANKS, R. G. 1981. Seasonal oxygen isotopic variations in living planktonic foraminifera off Bermuda, *Palaeogeography, Palaeoclimatology, Palaeoecology* **33**, 71−102.

Foraminiferal production and monsoonal upwelling in the Arabian Sea: evidence from sediment traps

W. B. CURRY[1], D. R. OSTERMANN[1], M. V. S. GUPTHA[2] & V. ITTEKKOT[3]

[1] Woods Hole Oceanographic Institution, Woods Hole, MA 02543, USA
[2] National Institute of Oceanography Goa, India
[3] University of Hamburg, Hamburg, Germany

Abstract: Planktonic foraminifera collected in sediment traps in the Arabian Sea during 1986 and 1987 responded to the southern Asian monsoon with changes in productivity, relative abundance of species and isotopic shell chemistry. Most species of foraminifera increased in flux shortly after the advent of the southwest monsoon. G. bulloides increased its production rate by three orders of magnitude. The isotopic chemistry of G. ruber recorded the increase in monsoon upwelling by increasing its $\delta^{18}O$ values by about 1‰, accurately reflecting the average 4°C sea surface temperature decrease associated with the upwelling. The mean value of $\delta^{18}O$ for G. ruber was greater in the western Arabian Sea than in the central or eastern basins because upwelling in that region cools surface water. The carbon isotopic composition of G. ruber does not have a clear temporal or geographical relationship to upwelling. While its $\delta^{13}C$ values decreased in the western Arabian Sea during the upwelling event, the mean $\delta^{13}C$ values remained higher in the western than in the eastern and central Arabian Sea. This longitudinal gradient is opposite to that expected from the geographical gradient of upwelling: the region with the most intense upwelling should have lower $\delta^{13}C$ values in surface waters because of the upwelling of low-$\delta^{13}C$ water to the surface.

For many years, palaeoceanographers have been trying to identify sediment-based indices of upwelling, often with contradictory results. Research efforts on marine fossils have focussed on both the variations in relative abundance (e.g. Gardner & Hays 1976; Thiede 1975, 1977; Prell & Curry 1981; Prell 1984) and isotopic shell chemistry of foraminifera (e.g. Berger et al. 1978; Prell & Curry 1981; Kroon & Ganssen 1989). In general, the variations observed in fossil species abundances have displayed consistent patterns in upwelling systems, while variations in isotopic shell chemistry have often been contradictory. For instance, in the Arabian Sea the relationship between foraminiferal abundance and monsoon upwelling was observed as an increase in the relative proportion of G. bulloides in core-top sediments near the coasts of Somalia and Oman (Prell & Curry 1981). The gradients in G. bulloides abundance closely paralleled the gradients in sea surface temperature that were caused by the southwest monsoon. But while the faunal abundances relationships with upwelling were clear, foraminiferal carbon isotopic composition displayed no systematic variation related to upwelling.

Several previous investigations have reported variations in foraminiferal carbon isotopic composition related to upwelling. Observations by Berger et al. (1978) documented that $\delta^{13}C$ of planktonic foraminifera was lower during previous episodes of upwelling in a core from the continental margin off northwest Africa. Their conclusions were based on the covariation of foraminiferal $\delta^{13}C$ and sedimentological indices that suggested past increases in upwelling intensity. More recently Kroon & Ganssen (1989) proposed a relationship between foraminifera $\delta^{13}C$ and upwelling based on measurements of the isotopic composition of several planktonic foraminiferal species in planktonic tows from the northern Indian Ocean. They observed changes in both oxygen and carbon isotopic composition as a function of surface temperature (assumed by them to vary from upwelling). Kroon & Ganssen (1989) present evidence that different species of foraminifera may respond to upwelling with opposite $\delta^{13}C$ changes: G. bulloides increasing its carbon isotopic composition in the same tows that N. dutertrei decreases its carbon isotopic composition. They attributed the differences to temporal differences in the production of the two species. They proposed that N. dutertrei increased its production early in response to upwelling and therefore it was affected by low-$\delta^{13}C$ waters upwelled into the euphotic zone. G. bulloides, on the other hand, increased production late in the upwelling event and did not sense the same upwelled water. Since the samples that Kroon & Ganssen measured were plankton tows, the

From SUMMERHAYES, C. P., PRELL, W. L. & EMEIS, K. C. (eds), 1992, *Upwelling Systems: Evolution Since the Early Miocene*. Geological Society Special Publication No 64, pp 93–106.

N. dutertrei and *G. bulloides* could not have been too different in age. Consequently their explanation for the opposite patterns of $\delta^{13}C$ is not convincing. Nonetheless, the opposite patterns of carbon isotopic variability are clear, may be related to upwelling, and need to be explained.

In this paper we present isotopic and abundance data for foraminifera collected in sediment traps in the Arabian Sea in an effort to determine the effects of upwelling on foraminiferal abundance and chemistry. Because seasonal variations in the heating of the southern Asian continent produce a seasonal reversal in the wind direction in the Arabian Sea, it contains one of the largest and most dramatic seasonal changes in upwelling intensity observed in the oceans. We have sampled the effect of the upwelling on the faunal assemblage and isotopic composition of the planktonic foraminifera using sediments traps deployed at ~1000 m below the sea surface and ~1000 m above the sea floor in three locations in the Arabian Sea (Fig. 1). We have determined the abundance variations of the 20 species of planktonic foraminifera which were present in the trap samples and measured the oxygen and carbon isotopic composition in the planktonic foraminifer *Globigerinoides ruber*.

Our results document distinctive and consistent changes in the species composition of the planktonic foraminifera between upwelling and non-upwelling intervals. The most prominent change is the marked increase in the flux of *Globigerina bulloides* during the southwest monsoon upwelling; it increases in abundance by three orders of magnitude reaching maximum fluxes of >9000/m²/d in the western Arabian

Sea. Other species exhibit large increases during the southwest monsoon as well (*Globigerina glutinata*, *Neogloboquadrina dutertrei*, *Globorotalia menardii* & *G. ruber*), but none increase nearly to the extent of *G. bulloides*. Oxygen isotopic compositions of *G. ruber* increase as a result of the decrease in surface water temperature induced by monsoon upwelling in the western Arabian Sea. The magnitude of the increase is about 1.0‰, the equivalent of about 4°C cooler calcification temperature during the southwest monsoon. Its $\delta^{18}O$ also increases during the northeast monsoon by about 1‰ because of seasonal surface water cooling.

But like the previous studies before, carbon isotopic variations as a function of upwelling are contradictory. While there appears to be a decrease in $\delta^{13}C$ as upwelling begins each summer, the mean $\delta^{13}C$ value in the western Arabian Sea is higher than in the central and eastern Arabian Sea, a geographical trend opposite that predicted from the upwelling of nutrient enriched, low $\delta^{13}C$ water in the western Arabian Sea. These patterns of $\delta^{13}C$ change will complicate the interpretation of carbon isotopic variation as an upwelling indicator.

Study area

The Arabian Sea is affected by seasonal upwelling caused by the monsoon of southern Asia. In the northern hemisphere summer, unequal heating of the continents and the near-by ocean cause a cell of rising air over the southern Asian continent. This rising air is replaced by southwesterly surface winds that parallel the Somali and Omani coastline. Ekman drift results in coastal upwelling as surface waters are reflected away from the coastline. In the winter, the continents cool faster and to a greater extent than the near-by ocean, a descending cell of air is located over the southern Asian continent, and northeasterly surface winds occur. Ekman drift in this case deflects surface waters toward the Somali and Omani coasts and upwelling is suppressed.

The seasonal variations in upwelling and the seasonal cycle of insolation combine to produce two maxima and minima in the annual record of sea surface temperature (SST) in the western Arabian Sea (Fig. 2). Lowest SSTs of ~25°C occur during January–February and June–July–August of each year while maxima reach >29°C during spring and fall (Wyrtki 1971; Rao *et al.* 1989). According to Rao *et al.* (1989) the amplitude of the semi-annual harmonic of sea surface temperature decreases to the south and east from a maximum along the coast of Somalia

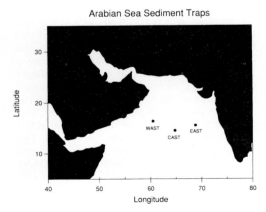

Fig. 1. Location of Arabian Sea sediment traps. (WAST = Western Arabian Sea; CAST = Central Arabian Sea; EAST = Eastern Arabian Sea).

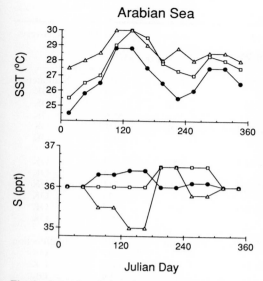

Arabian Sea

Julian Day

Fig. 2. Annual variations in sea surface temperature (SST) and salinity (S) for the three sediment trap locations (closed circle = WAST; open square = CAST; open triangle = EAST). The surface water properties are from Wyrtki (1971).

and Oman. Thus the annual cycle of sea surface temperatures in the central and eastern Arabian Sea exhibit only a single maximum and minimum each year. In the central Arabian Sea SSTs of 25°C are attained during northern hemisphere winter and maximum SSTs of near 30°C are attained during summer prior to the onset of the southwest monsoon. The smallest annual range in SST (27–30°C) occurs in the eastern Arabian Sea.

Seasonal variations in salinity and $\delta^{18}O_w$ are small in the Arabian Sea. During the 1963 Indian Ocean expedition (Wyrtki 1971), seasonal salinity variations in the western and central Arabian Sea near our trap locations were <0.5‰ (Fig. 2). In the eastern Arabian Sea during 1963, salinity varied by about 1‰ because of the seasonal incursion of low-salinity, Bay of Bengal surface waters into this region. Since $\delta^{18}O_w$ varies by about 0.5‰ per 1‰ in salinity, most of the annual oxygen isotopic variability in foraminifera from the western and central Arabian Sea trap locations will be caused by changes in SST. A significant salinity effect may be observed in the eastern Arabian Sea.

Nutrients in the surface waters of the Arabian Sea must vary as a function of upwelling intensity. Unfortunately there are few data to document the seasonality of nutrient concentration in the surface of the Arabian Sea. The Wyrtki

(1971) data demonstrate that PO_4 concentrations in the zone of coastal upwelling during the southwest monsoon increase to about 1 μgm-atom/l from <0.4 μgm-atom/l during the non-upwelling interval. Farther from the coast, at all three trap locations, the contrast between seasons is closer to 0.3 μgm-atom/l. Since the gradient of $\delta^{13}C/PO_4$ is about 0.9‰ per μmole/kg, the maximum seasonal variation in $\delta^{13}C$ of surface water should be limited to about 0.9‰ in the zone of coastal upwelling. (For this estimate, we assume that equilibration with atmospheric CO_2 is slow and that mixing between surface and subsurface waters dominates the $\delta^{13}C$ variability.) Offshore, nearer to our trap locations the annual range of nutrient variability is much lower, so the seasonal range in $\delta^{13}C$ should be more like 0.2 to 0.3‰. Unfortunately we do not know of any measurements of the annual variation in $\delta^{13}C$ of surface water ΣCO_2 in the Arabian Sea.

Methods

Sediment trap logistics

Three moorings were deployed in the Arabian Sea in May of 1986 (Nair *et al.* 1989). These sediment trap moorings were part of a cooperative research program mounted by the University of Hamburg (FRG), the National Institute of Oceanography (Goa, India) and the Woods Hole Oceanographic Institution (USA). Each mooring consisted of two sediment traps, one at about 1000 m below the surface and another at 1000 m above the sea floor (Table 1). The sediment traps were PARFLUX Mark VI time series traps (Honjo & Dougherty 1988) which were programmed to recover 13 consecutive samples of 12 to 13 day duration for six month periods. The moorings were recovered and redeployed twice during this phase of the field program, producing a total observational period of 18 months. Thus the sediment traps sampled the southwest monsoon in two consecutive years (1986 and 1987).

Sample analysis

Splits of the sediment trap samples were soaked in Calgon solution and H_2O_2 to clean the foraminifera and to remove organic carbon. The sample was then filtered through a 63 μm sieve and onto 0.47 μm Nuclepore filters. The fraction >63 μm was dry sieved into five size fractions for foraminiferal identification (63–125 μm, 125–150 μm, 150–250 μm, 250–500 μm, >500 μm). In this paper we present the for-

Table 1. Arabian Sea sediment trap logistics.

Location	Deployment	Latitude	Longitude	Water	Trap	Recovery
				Depth (m)		
Western	01	16°19′N	60°28′E	4020	1032	Malfunction
(WAST)					3024	OK
	02	16°19′N	60°28′E	4018	1034	OK
					3026	OK
	03	16°20′N	60°28′E	4010	1022	OK
					3014	OK
Central	01	14°28′N	64°46′E	3900	732	OK
(CAST)					2914	OK
	02	14°28′N	64°46′E	3912	744	OK
					2926	OK
	03	14°28′N	64°46′E	3890	722	OK
					2904	OK
Eastern	01	15°30′N	68°45′E	3770	1395	Malfunction
(EAST)					2787	OK
	02	15°28′N	68°45′E	3782	1407	OK
					2799	OK
	03	15°26′N	68°43′E	3770	1395	OK
					2787	OK

aminiferal fluxes and abundances for only the four largest size fractions. Foraminiferal fluxes were calculated from the counts, the splits, the known aperture of the sediment trap and the duration of each sample; they are presented as a number per square metre per day. PARFLUX Mark VI sediment traps are microprocessor controlled and record the date and time of each sample cup change. Thus we know with great confidence the duration of each sample. From these data we also identify trap failures: the shallow traps during the first deployment for both the western and eastern moorings. Foraminiferal flux data for the shallow and deep sediment traps from the western, central and eastern deployments have been deposited as Supplementary Publication no SUP 18077 (25 pp) with the British Library Document Supply Centre, Boston Spa, Wetherby, W. Yorkshire, UK, and with the Geological Society Library, Burlington House, London, UK. In the figures we present the flux variations for the combined fraction >150 μm; this is the size fraction commonly used for palaeotemperature reconstructions (e.g. CLIMAP 1976).

For several samples in the Supplementary Publication tables, we have estimated the foraminiferal fluxes to be near zero although no foraminiferal sample split was counted. This situation occurred when the total flux of all sedimentary components was so small that individual splits could not be obtained for foraminiferal analysis. Since the microprocessor indicated that the sediment trap functioned normally and since the total mass flux for the sample was close to zero, we know that the flux of foraminifera must also have been close to zero. We assigned values of zero to foraminiferal fluxes when the sample's total mass flux suggested that the sample contained less than 10 foraminifera (>125 μm) of all species. We have identified these samples in the tables with ND and plotted the species abundances in the figures as zero.

G. ruber were picked from the 250–500 μm size fraction for isotopic analysis. We followed standard procedures for this analysis (Curry & Lohmann 1982): sample roasting in a vacuum for one hour, reaction in H_3PO_4 at 50°C, distillation of the evolved CO_2 and H_2O, and analysis in a VG Micromass 602E mass spectrometer at Woods Hole Oceanographic Institution. Replicate analyses of the NBS-20 standard for this data set produce a standard deviation of ±0.05‰ for $\delta^{18}O$ and ±0.02‰ for $\delta^{13}C$. All of the isotopic data are referred to the PDB standard using the 'δ' notation. The stable isotopic data are presented in Table 2 for the deep sediment traps.

Data

Foraminiferal fluxes: Western Arabian Sea

The total fluxes (>150 μm) of six of the abundant foraminifera in the western Arabian Sea

Table 2. Isotopic data for Deep Arabian Sea Sediment Traps. Isotopic data are presented with respect to the PDB standard without correction for isotopic disequilibrium. *G. ruber* in the 250–500 μm size fraction were analyzed in each sample.

Julian Day	$\delta^{18}O$ PDB	$\delta^{13}C$ PDB
West Arabian Sea Trap (WAST)		
149	−2.65	0.57
162	−2.67	0.26
188	−2.28	0.64
188	−2.37	0.47
188	−2.25	0.29
201	−2.11	0.48
201	−2.10	0.38
201	−2.33	−0.57
214	−2.54	0.54
214	−1.84	−0.58
214	−2.15	0.00
227	−1.71	0.47
227	−1.59	−0.64
240	−1.68	0.16
311	−2.22	0.11
331	−2.54	0.56
331	−2.49	0.31
343	−2.41	0.87
343	−2.44	0.65
343	−2.40	0.86
356	−2.54	0.18
356	−2.12	0.47
382	−2.04	0.22
382	−1.90	0.38
382	−1.38	0.59
395	−2.03	−0.61
395	−1.15	1.54
541	−2.56	0.81
541	−2.56	0.04
554	−2.22	0.91
566	−1.77	1.11
566	−2.56	0.08
579	−2.49	0.15
579	−2.46	0.52
591	−2.41	0.26
591	−2.38	0.03
604	−2.01	0.41
616	−1.80	0.88
616	−2.04	0.07
629	−1.96	0.88
641	−1.94	1.10
East Arabian Sea Trap (EAST)		
189	−3.01	−0.08
202	−2.14	0.30
215	−2.71	−0.42
241	−2.54	−0.20
254	−2.91	−0.91
293	−3.12	−0.76
541	−2.85	0.15
541	−2.64	0.05
554	−2.58	−0.11
579	−2.43	−0.42
591	−2.77	−0.22
604	−2.66	0.27

Julian Day	$\delta^{18}O$ PDB	$\delta^{13}C$ PDB
Central Arabian Sea Trap (CAST)		
176	−2.65	0.87
189	−2.29	0.37
202	−2.75	−1.66
215	−2.52	0.31
228	−2.74	−0.74
267	−2.57	−0.67
329	−2.20	0.87
368	−2.26	0.04
381	−2.24	0.22
394	−2.11	0.11
529	−2.94	−0.69
541	−2.65	0.38
566	−2.72	−0.03
591	−2.74	0.37

deployment are presented in Fig. 3 and the Supplementary Publication. All of the species present in these sediment traps exhibit prominent increases in production during the monsoon seasons and reach highest production rates at that time. During non-monsoon intervals foraminiferal productivity is very low. The foraminiferal assemblage is dominated by *G. bulloides* and *G. glutinata*, each of which exhibits large increases in flux to the sediment trap during the southwest monsoon, but much reduced fluxes at all other times. *G. ruber*, *Globigerinoides tenellus* and *G. menardii* exhibit an increase in production during the southwest monsoon and also during the northeast monsoon in the winter of 1986–87.

During the southwest monsoon of 1986 (day 210 on Fig. 3), the *G. bulloides* flux increased abruptly and remained high in five consecutive sediment trap samples (total duration of around 2 months). In contrast during 1987, this species increased in abundance to greater levels and was present in the sediment trap for 10 consecutive samples (~4 months). This same pattern occurred to some extent for other species as well: the high productivity of foraminifera during the southwest monsoon of 1987 lasted about twice as long as it did during the same event in 1986.

Foraminiferal fluxes: Central Arabian Sea

Foraminiferal fluxes in the central Arabian Sea exhibit many of the same seasonal patterns as the western Arabian, but overall the rate of productivity is about one half as large (Fig. 4 and Supplementary Publication). Here the most abundant species are *G. bulloides* and *G. ruber*.

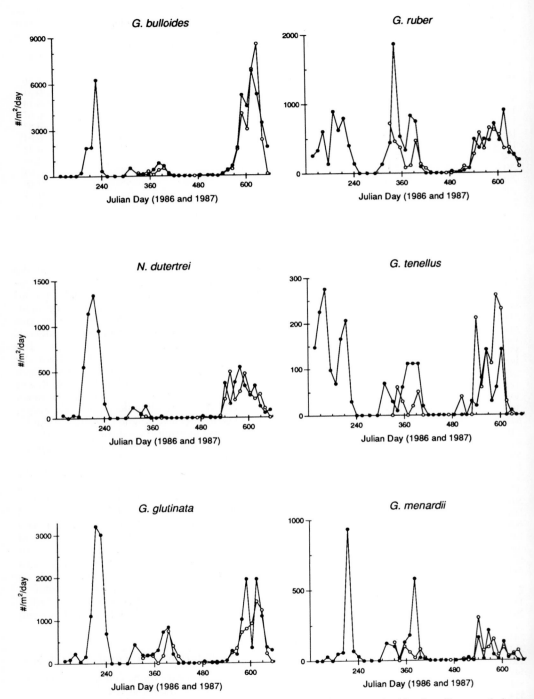

Fig. 3. Foraminiferal fluxes (>150 μm) for six abundant species in the western Arabian Sea. Open symbols are from the shallow trap and closed symbols are from the deep trap. See Table 1 for sediment trap logistics and the Supplementary Publication for foraminiferal abundance data.

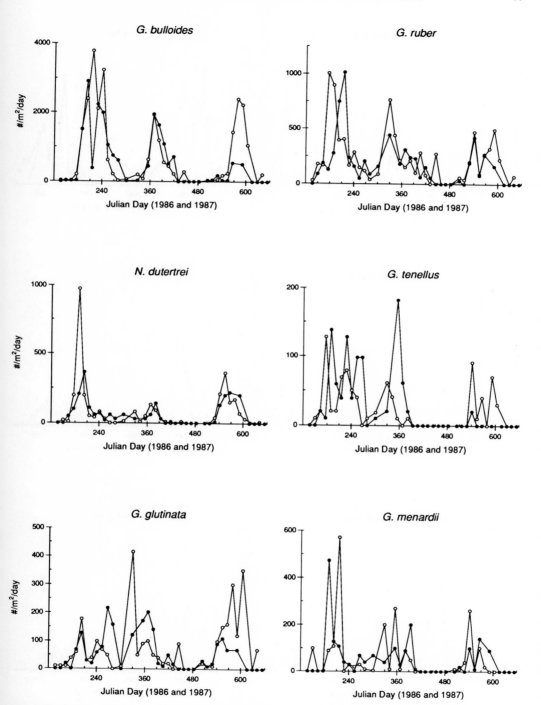

Fig. 4. Foraminiferal fluxes (>150 μm) for six abundant species in the central Arabian Sea. Open symbols are from the shallow trap and closed symbols are from the deep trap. See Table 1 for sediment trap logistics and the Supplementary Publication for foraminiferal abundance data.

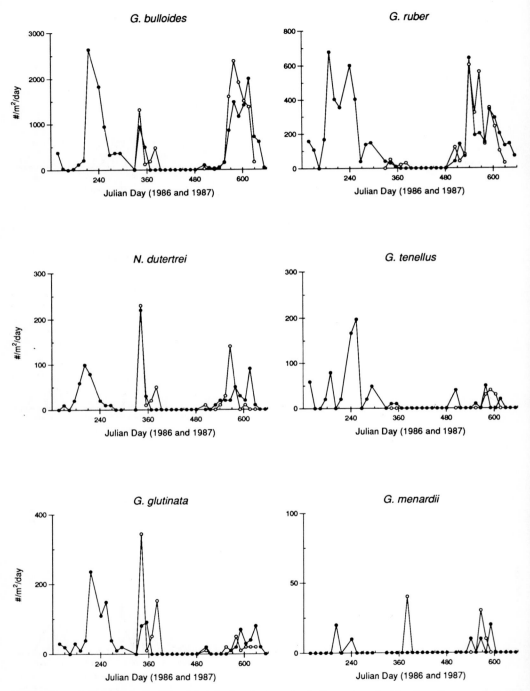

Fig. 5. Foraminiferal fluxes (>150μm) for six abundant species in the eastern Arabian Sea. Open symbols are from the shallow trap and closed symbols are from the deep trap. See Table 1 for sediment trap logistics and the Supplementary Publication for foraminiferal abundance data.

In the central trap, highest abundances for several species (*Globigerinoides sacculifer*, *Globorotalia ungulata*, *Globigerina aequilateralis* and *Pulleniatina obliquiloculata*) occur during the northeast monsoon rather than the southwest monsoon (Supplementary Publication). The increase in foraminiferal production at this time is more prominent than at the eastern or western trap locations.

Foraminiferal fluxes: Eastern Arabian Sea

Lowest foraminiferal productivities are observed in the sediment traps in the eastern Arabian (Fig. 5 and Supplementary Publication), overall about one third of the flux observed in the western Arabian Sea. As in the central Arabian Sea, *G. bulloides* and *G. ruber* dominate the assemblage. Highest production rates for these species occur during the southwest monsoon. However this location differs from the other locations in one respect: *G. ruber*, which exhibited prominent increases in production during the northeast monsoon at the western and central trap locations, shows no increase in production here, while *G. bulloides* exhibits only a modest increase.

G. ruber $\delta^{18}O$, $\delta^{13}C$

The oxygen isotopic composition of *G. ruber* varies as a function of surface water temperature, which in this region is controlled by variations in the intensity of upwelling and the seasonal heating of the surface water. At the western Arabian Sea trap location, we have enough isotopic measurements to produce a continuous time series of *G. ruber* $\delta^{18}O$ for 1986 and 1987 (Fig. 6). There the $\delta^{18}O$ values for *G. ruber* exhibit a semiannual cycle with a 1‰ amplitude. This temporal pattern of $\delta^{18}O$ is similar in magnitude and timing to that expected for equilibrium isotopic fractionation following a seasonal temperature cycle like that in Fig. 2. The isotopic temperatures for the *G. ruber* $\delta^{18}O$ are about 2°C higher than equilibrium calcite precipitation would predict using the O'Neil (1969) palaeotemperature equation and an estimated isotopic composition for surface water (Curry & Matthews 1981). This comparison assumes that the annual cycle of SST during 1986 and 1987 was the same as during 1963 and that foraminiferal life spans and settling velocities do not introduce phase biases in the comparison.

The $\delta^{18}O$ values for *G. ruber* in the central and eastern Arabian Sea are generally lower than contemporary $\delta^{18}O$ values in the western

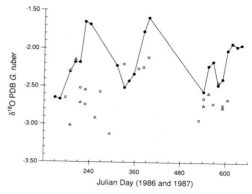

Fig. 6. $\delta^{18}O$ for *G. ruber* (250–500 μm) in the Arabian Sea. (Closed circles = WAST deep trap; open squares = CAST deep trap; open triangles = EAST deep trap). The isotopic data are presented in Table 2. Note that the $\delta^{18}O$ values in the western region are uniformly greater than those in the eastern or central regions.

trap (Fig. 6). Again this geographic pattern of $\delta^{18}O$ in *G. ruber* is consistent with the known temperature gradients across the Arabian Sea, which are usually about 2 to 3°C, but may exceed 4°C (Fig. 2). The difference in $\delta^{18}O$ between traps may be as large as 1‰, but usually falls in the range of 0.3 to 0.7‰.

The carbon isotopic composition decreases by about 0.5‰ in the western Arabian Sea during the southwest monsoons of both 1986 and 1987 (Fig. 7). During 1987 the average $\delta^{13}C$

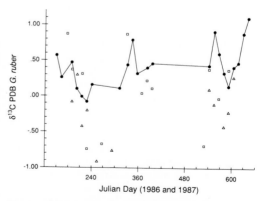

Fig. 7. $\delta^{13}C$ for *G. ruber* (250–500 μm) in the Arabian Sea. (Closed circles = WAST deep trap; open squares = CAST deep trap; open triangles = EAST deep trap). The isotopic data are presented in Table 2. $\delta^{13}C$ values decrease during the southwest monsoon of both 1986 and 1987. The average $\delta^{13}C$ values during the 1987 monsoon is greater than during 1986.

value for *G. ruber* is about 0.3‰ greater than during 1986. Thus the interannual variability (because of changes in upwelling intensity?) is nearly the same magnitude as the temporal variability caused by the upwelling. *G. ruber* $\delta^{13}C$ in the western Arabian Sea appears to be greater than contemporary $\delta^{13}C$ values in the central and eastern regions, often by as much as 0.5‰. This gradient is opposite to what would be expected if upwelling in the western Arabian Sea introduced sub-surface sea water with low $\delta^{13}C$ into the euphotic zone.

Dicussion

Interannual variability in foraminiferal flux and upwelling intensity

Year-to-year differences in the intensity of the Indian Ocean monsoon and upwelling in the Arabian Sea are exhibited in the fluxes of planktonic foraminifera. During 1986, the cumulative production of *G. bulloides* during the southwest monsoon was two-thirds lower than during 1987. In 1986, high production rates of *G. bulloides* occurred in five consecutive sediment trap samples (62 day duration) beginning in early July (JD = 188 in Table 3). Cumulatively, the production rate of *G. bulloides* was about 137 000/m^2 for that interval. In contrast, for the equivalent period in 1987, the cumulative production rate was about 156 000/m^2, about 14% greater. But during 1987, the increase in production continued for another four consecutive sediment trap samples (total duration = 112 days). Thus the cumulative production of *G. bulloides* during the southwest monsoon of 1987 was about 372 000/m^2, nearly three times the total produced during 1986.

Although we have few real-time oceanographic measurements for this deployment, satellite observations for the western Arabian Sea suggest that the upwelling associated with the southwest monsoon began about two to three weeks later in 1987 than in 1986. Using unprocessed AVHRR (Advanced Very High Resolution Radiometer) Nimbus series satellite images, the sea-surface image change indicating surface water cooling occurred about the third week in July during 1986, but not until the second week of August in 1987, about three weeks later. As yet we do not know if the intensity of surface cooling was greater during 1987 than 1986, nor do we know if the duration of surface water cooling was longer in 1987. We do know that the interannual difference in the timing of the monsoon is observed in the foraminiferal fluxes and isotopic composition.

The initiation of upwelling in the western

Arabian Sea and the subsequent increase in *G. bulloides* flux indicates that the foraminiferal population responded within a few weeks to changes in near-surface hydrography. In the deep sediment trap for the western location, the increase in *G. bulloides* flux during 1986 was first recorded in the sample cup for the first two weeks of July; during 1987, the rapid increase in *G. bulloides* flux occurred in the cup for July 26 to August 7. Each year the earliest increase in *G. bulloides* flux predated the surface water expression of upwelling (reflected in the satellite images) by about one week. Since settling velocities for these foraminifera are usually greater than 400 m/day for these size fractions (Takahashi & Be 1984; Curry, unpublished data), the individuals probably reached the deep traps about seven days after leaving the zone of living foraminifera. This is within the temporal resolution of the sediment trap samples.

Like the *G. bulloides* fluxes, the $\delta^{18}O$ values for *G. ruber* indicate that subsurface cooling may have affected their isotopic composition before the surface water cooled because of an early increase in $\delta^{18}O$. In Fig. 6, the increase in $\delta^{18}O$ for *G. ruber* began sometime during the period July 2 to July 15, about two weeks before the observation of surface water cooling in the western Arabian Sea. This early increase in *G. ruber* $\delta^{18}O$ correlates with the early increase in *G. bulloides* flux. Similar phase relationships occurred during 1987. Thus the effects of upwelling probably began cooling the water in the near-surface zone where *G. ruber* calcifies (the upper 50 m) about two weeks before reaching the surface.

While year-to-year differences in $\delta^{18}O$ are small for *G. ruber*, its $\delta^{13}C$ show considerable interannual differences that suggest the carbon isotopic composition of foraminifera is not simply related to upwelling intensity. During the southwest monsoons of both 1986 and 1987, $\delta^{13}C$ of *G. ruber* decreases as the upwelling event proceeds and intensifies. After the upwelling event, $\delta^{13}C$ returns to the values observed prior to the event. Thus these changes in *G. ruber* $\delta^{13}C$ follow a simple pattern of lower carbon isotopic compositions caused by upwelling. But the average $\delta^{13}C$ values observed during 1987 are greater than during 1986 by about 0.3‰, despite the observation from *G. bulloides* fluxes that the 1987 upwelling event may have been stronger than the 1986 event. Thus the foraminiferal $\delta^{13}C$ values change within an event in a manner that would be expected given that upwelling injects water with lower $\delta^{13}C$ into the zone where foraminifera live and calcify. But if upwelling was more intense during 1987, then the *G. ruber* $\delta^{13}C$ values should have been lower at that time, if this simple model is correct. Thus we must conclude that either (1) the production rate of *G. bulloides* does not accurately reflect the intensity of upwelling or (2) the carbon isotopic composition of *G. ruber* is not simply related to upwelling.

Besides injecting low-δ^{13}C sea water into the euphotic zone, there are several ways to vary the δ^{13}C of surface water ΣCO_2. Two possibilities include interannual variations in the Redfield ratio of organic detritus and interannual variations in δ^{13}C of the organic carbon produced by photosynthesis. If the Redfield ratio of organic detritus varies year to year in the Arabian Sea, it would be possible to produce surface water with greater δ^{13}C during 1987, even if upwelling were more intense at that time. If the ratio of carbon to nutrients in settling organic debris was higher in 1987 than in 1986, then carbon (with a δ^{13}C value of $-20‰$) would have been more efficiently removed from the surface water by photosynthesis. Because of mass balance, the remaining pool of ΣCO_2 in the surface water would have an increased δ^{13}C value even though upwelling may have been more intense. The magnitude of the effect is such that a 10% increase in Redfield ratio would increase surface water δ^{13}C by about 0.2‰. Interannual variations in C/N in these sediment traps, although large enough to produce this magnitude of δ^{13}C difference, are in the opposite sense (Ittekkot, unpublished data). During 1986, the C:N ratio in the organic debris of the sediment traps during the southwest monsoon was about 10.1; during 1987 it was about 9.3. Thus during 1986 more efficient removal of carbon from the surface water potentially enriched the surface water ΣCO_2. This mechanism cannot explain why δ^{13}C in *G. ruber* is greater on average during 1987.

Another mechanism for enriching surface water during 1987 relative to 1986 may be found in the carbon isotopic composition of the organic debris. If the δ^{13}C values were more negative during 1987, then the surface water ΣCO_2 reservoir would have been increased in δ^{13}C. Again a 10% change in δ^{13}C (from $-20‰$ to $-22‰$ for instance) would enrich the surface water ΣCO_2 by about 0.2‰. Unfortunately at this time there are no data on interannual variations in the carbon isotopic composition of the organic debris in the Arabian Sea.

Geographical variability of foraminiferal production and shell chemistry

Throughout the entire sediment trap deployment, foraminiferal production was higher in the western Arabian Sea than in the eastern and central regions. During periods of intense upwelling the gradient across the basin was very large for *G. bulloides*. The rate of *G. bulloides* production varied by a factor of three between the western and eastern traps during the peak of the southwest monsoon in both 1986 and 1987 (Fig. 8). Similarly large gradients can be observed for *G. ruber*, *G. glutinata* and *N. dutertrei*. High productivity associated with the monsoonal upwelling is generally restricted to the western Arabian Sea and can be observed in the overall higher fluxes of biogenic opal, carbonate and organic carbon in the western traps during the southwest monsoon (Nair *et al.* 1989). Total fluxes of the biogenic components are often two to three times greater in the western Arabian Sea at that time than in other regions. Thus the enhanced foraminiferal production appears to be a response to the higher productivity and higher food availability. At the same time that productivity is higher in the western Arabian Sea, the δ^{18}O values for *G. ruber* were up to 1‰ greater in the western traps than in the central or eastern traps, which reflects the local cooling of surface waters by upwelling of colder water into the euphotic zone. The magnitude of the increase in δ^{18}O is equivalent to a decrease in calcification temperature for *G. ruber* of about 4°C, equal in magnitude to the average decrease in SST observed in the western Arabian Sea during the southwest monsoon.

In contrast, the regional gradient in *G. ruber* δ^{13}C is not what would be expected for a simple upwelling system, where nutrient-rich, ^{13}C-depleted subsurface waters, brought to the surface by upwelling, mix with nutrient-depleted and ^{13}C-rich surface water. The resulting δ^{13}C of the surface water should be lower than for nutrient-depleted water until the phytoplankton utilize the nutrients for photosynthesis (Curry *et al.* 1983). Thus the foraminifera which calcify in this lower δ^{13}C surface water should have lower δ^{13}C values. If photosynthesis is rapid enough to constantly strip the surface water of nutrients at a rate which exceeds the input rate of upwelled water, then the surface water and foraminiferal δ^{13}C should be constant before, during and after an upwelling event. Regionally, the carbon isotopic composition of surface water in the upwelling region, where nutrients are greater than zero, should have surface water δ^{13}C values which are lower than in oligotrophic, non-upwelling regions, where surface water nutrients are always near zero. Thus the regional gradient in δ^{13}C during an upwelling event should be toward more negative δ^{13}C values closer to the centre of the upwelling cell. But the δ^{13}C of *G. ruber* collected in these

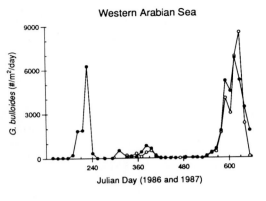

Western Arabian Sea

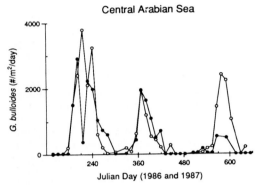

Central Arabian Sea

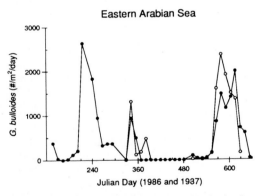

Eastern Arabian Sea

Fig. 8. The foraminiferal flux of *G. bulloides* in the western, central and eastern Arabian Sea. The production rate of this species exhibits a two- to threefold increase toward the western region during the upwelling period. This strong regional gradient parallels the overall higher productivity observed in the western traps during the monsoon (Nair *et al.* 1989).

varied significantly across the Arabian Sea, this simple model for upwelling and surface water $\delta^{13}C$ would be invalid. In order to have greater $\delta^{13}C$ values in the upwelling cell than in the non-upwelling, oligotrophic regions of the Arabian Sea, C/N must have been significantly greater in the upwelling region. Unfortunately the C/N values in the western trap are not greater (Nair *et al.* 1989). Rather during 1986, the ratio was the same in both the western and central trap locations and slightly higher in the eastern location. Thus we must conclude that the $\delta^{13}C$ values of *G. ruber* are not simply related to upwelling and, until we can sort out their relationship to $\delta^{13}C$ of ΣCO_2, carbon isotopic composition of *G. ruber* is probably not a useful indicator of past upwelling intensity.

Past upwelling indicators

The geographical gradients and temporal changes in foraminiferal flux and isotopic composition suggest that past upwelling intensity is recorded in both the assemblage composition and the chemistry of fossil foraminifera in the Arabian Sea. Two approaches appear to be promising: reconstructions based on the past flux of foraminiferal species and reconstructions based on the synoptic $\delta^{18}O$ gradients across the Arabian Sea.

On the basis of the patterns observed in the Arabian Sea sediment traps, past upwelling intensity is probably best recorded in the past production rate and flux of *G. bulloides*. The relationship between upwelling and *G. bulloides* abundance has been used extensively as a proxy for upwelling intensity. Prell & Curry (1981) observed that the geographical distribution of *G. bulloides* abundance in core-top sediments paralleled the hydrography induced by the southwest monsoon and that highest abundances of this species were observed near the centre of the upwelling cell. Prell (1984) used this observation to postulate that history of monsoon intensity would be recorded in the down-core percentage of *G. bulloides*. From our observations it is clear that *G. bulloides* is not the only species to increase in abundance as a result of upwelling, although *G. bulloides* production increases to such an extent that its relative abundance also increases in the foraminiferal assemblage. Our results suggest that a clearer record of monsoonal upwelling intensity may be recorded in the down-core abundance variation of *G. bulloides* expressed as a number per square metre per day or per square centimetre per 10^3 years. The geographical variability of *G. bulloides* flux in the sediment

sediment traps display the opposite geographical trend: more ^{13}C enriched values occur in the western Arabian Sea than in the eastern or central regions. Again, if the Redfield ratio

traps demonstrates that abundance calculated in this manner reflects the geographical gradients of upwelling intensity. Unfortunately, the relative abundance of *G. bulloides* in these sediment traps is less clearly related to this geographical gradient. For instance, during the southwest monsoon in 1986, *G. bulloides* percentages increase to about 60% in the western trap, to about 50% in the central trap and up to 70% in the eastern trap. At the same time *G. bulloides* productivity was two to three times greater in the western trap. Anderson & Prell (in press) and Anderson (1990) have made the first attempts at reconstructing the history of the Arabian Sea upwelling system using past calculated values of *G. bulloides* productivity. This methodology has the advantages that the past flux of *G. bulloides* is not affected by changes in production of other species (as is percent abundance) and that the flux of *G. bulloides* and the intensity of the monsoonal upwelling may be related in such a way that past intensities may be quantified. Like other sediment-based indices, however, application of this method assumes that reliable past fluxes can be calculated from sediment samples that may have been altered by post-depositional processes like dissolution or sediment transport.

The $\delta^{18}O$ of *G. ruber* also appears to record the decreasing sea surface temperatures that are associated with intense upwelling. Thus geographical gradients of past $\delta^{18}O$ for surface dwelling foraminifera may be key indicators of upwelling intensity. The $\delta^{18}O$ increase toward the upwelling cell in the western Arabian Sea was observed in core-top sediment samples by Prell & Curry (1981) for *G. ruber*, *G. bulloides* and *G. sacculifer*. Our observation that western Arabian Sea *G. ruber* are always enriched in ^{18}O relative to coeval eastern and central Arabian Sea *G. ruber* confirms this observation. Thus the $\delta^{18}O$ gradient between non-upwelling and upwelling locations should record the temperature gradient between these locations. Inasmuch as the temperature gradient is directly related to the intensity of upwelling, this isotopic gradient should be proportional to the intensity of the upwelling event.

Unfortunately, the regional gradients of $\delta^{13}C$ are not as easily interpreted. Although past research has suggested that lower planktonic foraminiferal $\delta^{13}C$ values may reflect upwelling processes (e.g. Berger *et al.* 1978; Kroon & Ganssen 1989), the geographical gradients observed in these sediment trap samples contradict simple models of upwelling effects on foraminiferal $\delta^{13}C$. Until we can identify the causes of the $\delta^{13}C$ variability in the sediment trap

samples, we hesitate to label $\delta^{13}C$ of *G. ruber* as an upwelling proxy. Much clearer indications of upwelling occurrence and intensity are recorded in the faunal assemblage and in the $\delta^{18}O$ values of the planktonic foraminifera.

Summary

Planktonic foraminifera respond to seasonal changes in monsoonal upwelling with large changes in species composition and isotopic chemistry. On the basis of our observations of foraminiferal production and chemistry in the Arabian Sea, we make the following conclusions.

(1) Foraminiferal productivity is about two to three times greater in the western region during the SW monsoon, near to the upwelling cell, than in the central or eastern regions of the Arabian Sea. During the peak intensity of the southwest monsoon, the production rate of most species of foraminifera increases. For *G. bulloides* the increase in production is at least three orders of magnitude, reaching maximum rates of $9000/m^2/day$. Although most species of foraminifera increase in abundance at the same time, the large increase in *G. bulloides* caused its relative abundance to increase during the southwest monsoon to about 60% of the foraminiferal population in 1986 and to 80% of the population in 1987. The relative intensity of monsoonal upwelling, which increases toward the western trap, is not reflected in the relative abundance of *G. bulloides*, but in the production rate increase toward the upwelling cell. Thus reconstructions of past *G. bulloides* productivity may provide an index of the past intensity of the upwelling associated with monsoon system.

(2) In the western Arabian Sea, the oxygen isotopic composition of *G. ruber* records the expected change in surface temperature (~4°C) during the southwest monsoon; there is a similar $\delta^{18}O$ increase during the northeast monsoon. Thus the seasonal record of $\delta^{18}O$ in the western Arabian Sea exhibits two maxima and minima each year. The regional gradients in *G. ruber* $\delta^{18}O$ show that their $\delta^{18}O$ is usually greater in the western Arabian Sea than in coeval samples from the central or eastern Arabian Sea, reflecting the SST gradient across the Arabian Sea that is caused by the southwest monsoon.

(3) The $\delta^{13}C$ values for *G. ruber* exhibit a complicated relationship with upwelling. Western Arabian Sea time series show that the $\delta^{13}C$ values for *G. ruber* decrease during the southwest monsoon in both 1986 and 1987. This is the type of change to be expected if the upwelling mixed nutrient-rich, low-$\delta^{13}C$ water

into surface water, lowering the $\delta^{13}C$ values of ΣCO_2. But the $\delta^{13}C$ of coeval *G. ruber* are greater in the western Arabian Sea than in the eastern and central regions, opposite to the trend expected from upwelling. The available C/N data for organic carbon in each region do not differ enough to produce such regional differences in surface water $\delta^{13}C$. Thus biological effects may play an important role in producing these observed gradients.

This research was supported by grants from Germany, India and the United States. The field program was sponsored by grants from the Federal German Ministry for Research and Technology and the German Research Council to V. Ittekkot of the University of Hamburg and from the Council of Scientific and Industrial Research and the Department of Ocean Development to R. Nair of the National Institute of Oceanography in India. This laboratory research was sponsored by National Science Foundation grant OCE87–10782 to W. Curry. We thank S. Manganini and S. Honjo for their continued support of foraminiferal research using PARFLUX sediment trap samples. This manuscript benefited from discussions with R. Thunell and W. Prell, and from the comments of two anonymous reviewers. This is Woods Hole Oceanographic Institution number 7975.

References

ANDERSON, D. M. 1990. *Foraminifer Evidence of Monsoon Upwelling off Oman during the Late Pleistocene*, PhD Thesis, Brown University.

—— & PRELL, W. L. (in press). Foraminifer abundance in the Arabian Sea upwelling region during the late Pleistocene, *In*: PRELL, W. L. *et al. Proceedings of the Ocean Drilling Program, Scientific Results, Leg 117*: College Station, TX (Ocean Drilling Program).

BERGER, W. H., DIESTER-HAASS, L. & KILLINGLEY, J. S. 1978. Upwelling off Northwest Africa: the Holocene decrease as seen in carbon isotopes and sedimentological indicators, *Oceanologica Acta*, **1**, 1–7.

CLIMAP Project Members 1976. The surface of the Ice-Age Earth, *Science*, **191**, 1131–1137.

CURRY, W. B. & LOHMANN, G. P. 1982. Carbon isotopic changes in benthic foraminifera from the western South Atlantic: Reconstruction of glacial abyssal circulation patterns, *Quaternary Research*, **18**, 218–235.

—— & MATTHEWS, R. K. 1981. Paleo-oceanographic utility of oxygen isotopic measurements on planktonic foraminifera: Indian Ocean core-top evidence, *Paleogeography, Paleoclimatology, Paleoecology*, **31**, 173–191.

——, THUNELL, R. C. & HONJO, S. 1983. Seasonal changes in the isotopic composition of planktonic foraminifera collected in Panama Basin sediment traps, *Earth and Planetary Science Letters*, **64**, 33–43.

GARDNER, J. V. & HAYS, J. D. 1976. Response of sea-surface temperature and circulation to global climate change during the past 200 000 years in the eastern equatorial Atlantic Ocean. *In*: R. M. CLINE & HAYS, J. D. (eds) *Investigation of Late Quaternary Paleoceanography and Paleoclimatology*. Geological Society of America Memoir, **145**, 221–246.

HONJO, S. & DOHERTY, K. W. 1988. Large aperture time-series sediment traps: design objectives, construction and application, *Deep-Sea Research*, **35**(1), 133–149.

KROON, D. & GANSSEN, G. 1989. Northern Indian Ocean upwelling cells and the stable isotope composition of living planktonic foraminifers, *Deep-Sea Research*, **36** (8), 1219–1236.

NAIR, R. R., ITTEKKOT, V., MANGANINI, S. J., RAMASWAMY, V., HAAKE, B., DEGENS, E. T., DESAI, B. N. & HONJO, S. 1989. Increased particle flux to the deep ocean related to monsoons, *Nature*, **338**, 749–751.

O'NEIL, J. R., CLAYTON, R. N. & MAYEDA, T. K. 1969. Oxygen isotope fractionation in divalent metal carbonates. *Journal of Chemical Physics*, **51**, 5547–5558.

PRELL, W. 1984. Variation of monsoonal upwelling: a response to changing solar radiation. *In*: HANSEN, J. E. & TAKAHASHI, T. (eds) *Climate Processes and Climate Sensitivity*, American Geophysical Union Geophysics Monograph, **29**, 48–57.

—— & CURRY, W. B. 1981. Faunal and isotopic indices of monsoonal upwelling: western Arabian Sea. *Oceanologica Acta*, **4**, 91–98.

RAO, R. R., MOLINARI, R. L. & FESTA, J. F. 1989. Evolution of the climatological near-surface thermal structure of the tropical Indian Ocean, 1. Description of mean monthly mixed layer depth, and sea surface temperature, surface current, and surface meteorological fields. *Journal of Geophysical Research*, **94** (8), 10 801–10 815.

TAKAHASHI, K., BE, A. W. H. 1984. Planktonic foraminifera: factors controlling sinking speeds, *Deep-Sea Research*, **31**, 1477–1500.

THIEDE, J. 1975. Distribution of foraminifera in surface waters of a coastal upwelling area, *Nature*, **253**, 712–714.

—— 1977. Aspects of the variability of the glacial and interglacial North Atlantic eastern boundary current (last 150 000 years), *Meteor Forschungsergb.*, *Reihe C*, **28**, 1–36.

WYRTKI, K. 1971. *Oceanographic Atlas of the International Indian Ocean Expedition*, National Science Foundation, Washington, D.C.

Oxygen and carbon isotopes in planktonic foraminifera as indicators of upwelling intensity and upwelling-induced high productivity in sediments from the northwestern Arabian Sea

TINEKE N. F. STEENS[1], GERALD GANSSEN[1] & DICK KROON[2]

[1] Geomarine Center, Institute of Earth Sciences, Free University, De Boelelaan 1085, 1081 HV Amsterdam, The Netherlands

[2] University of Edinburgh, Grant Institute of Geology, West Mains Road, Edinburgh EH9 3JW, UK

Abstract: Oxygen and carbon isotopes in the tests of *Globigerina bulloides* and *Neogloboquadrina dutertrei* from the Indian Ocean provide indicators for the intensity of upwelling and upwelling-related high productivity. The difference in $\delta^{18}O$ between the surface dwelling *G. bulloides* and the thermocline dwelling *N. dutertrei* reflects the mixing of the water column during upwelling situations, and hence the intensity of upwelling. The difference in $\delta^{13}C$ isotope distribution between the two species is smallest within upwelling areas, indicating that upwelling induced the high productivity. The two parameters are applied to Hole 728A (ODP 117), in the Arabian Sea on the continental margin of Oman. Both upwelling indicators show that from isotopic stage 2 till stage 11 upwelling was stronger during interglacial periods, and that upwelling intensified down core for the same period. In older sediments, stages 12 and 13, the signal from the upwelling indicators is reversed, showing stronger upwelling during glacials.

Background

Oxygen isotopes

Much work has been done on the stable isotope ratios of foraminifera to reconstruct the history of upwelling in various regions: off California (Dunbar 1983), Peru (Wefer *et al.* 1983), Northwest Africa (Oberhänsli 1991; Sarnthein & Thiedemann 1989; Zahn-Knoll 1986) and Arabia (Prell & Curry 1981; Van Campo *et al.* 1982; Steens *et al.* 1991).

For oxygen isotopes there has been much debate as to whether or not planktonic foraminifera build their tests in equilibrium with the ambient seawater (e.g. Kahn 1979; Erez & Luz 1983; Ganssen 1983). Most authors find a small deviation from the isotopic equilibrium with a constant offset, suggesting that the oxygen isotope ratios in the tests should reflect the $\delta^{18}O$ values of the seawater and its temperature. Since under non-upwelling conditions *Globigerina bulloides* (d'Orbigny) lives in the surface waters and *Neogloboquadrina dutertrei* (d'Orbigny) is a thermocline dweller (Kroon 1988) their oxygen isotope signals should reflect the differences in temperature between the depth where they build their tests. As a consequence, the difference between the $\delta^{18}O$ values of these two species should be relatively large. Under upwelling conditions, however, the

thermocline disappears and both species will grow within nearly the same temperature range. Consequently the difference in their isotopic signal decreases, and can become zero under maximum upwelling conditions.

Carbon isotopes

The complexity of the carbon isotopic signal of foraminiferal tests is as yet poorly understood, as it is governed by unknown vital effects, and depends on the ontogenetic stage of the specimens and their depth habitat.

Kroon & Ganssen (1989) proposed an empirical model which explains the observed $\delta^{13}C$ variations of seven species from the northern Indian Ocean (Fig. 1) as representing different phases of a pulsating upwelling system, rather than as 'vital effects', the processes of high productivity influencing the $\delta^{13}C$ of the total dissolved inorganic carbon (ΣCO_2). *N. dutertrei* and *G. bulloides* represent the most extreme conditions with respect to the $\delta^{13}C$ signal of upwelling, *N. dutertrei* showing the most negative values of the initial phase of upwelling, while *G. bulloides* is most enriched in ^{13}C during the final stage of the upwelling cycle (Kroon & Ganssen 1989). Thus under upwelling conditions the difference between $\delta^{13}C$ values of *G. bulloides* and *N. dutertrei* becomes smaller than under non-upwelling conditions.

From SUMMERHAYES, C. P., PRELL, W. L. & EMEIS, K. C. (eds), 1992, *Upwelling Systems: Evolution Since the Early Miocene*. Geological Society Special Publication No 64, pp 107–119.

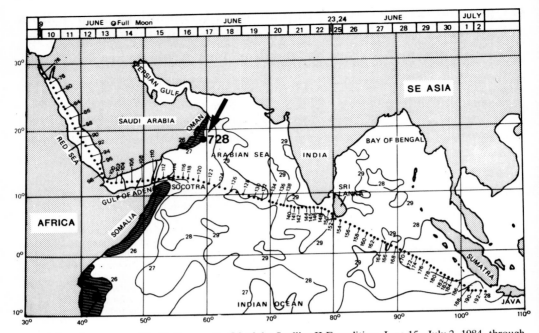

Fig. 1. Sample transect of R. V. *Tyro* cruise G0 of the Snellius II Expedition, June 15–July 2, 1984, through the northern Indian Ocean, with surface temperature isolines and location of ODP Hole 728A at 17°40.790′N, 57°49.553′E (after Kroon & Ganssen 1989).

Palaeoceanographic setting

This study attempts to further document the two upwelling indicators on the modern data set from the Indian Ocean (Fig. 1) and apply them to Site 728 (ODP 117) for the last 524 ka. Site 728 is situated on the continental margin of Oman (Fig. 1) where, at present, upwelling is related to the southwest monsoonal summer winds (e.g. Bruce 1974; Prell 1984). In response to the SW monsoon, strong upwelling occurs off the coasts of Oman and Somalia during the summer months, due to wind induced offshore Ekman transport. During the winter months prevailing NE monsoon winds result in Ekman transport of surface waters toward shore, which ends all upwelling activity along the continental margin of the northwestern Indian Ocean.

Various authors have shown that, for the Late Pleistocene, upwelling was stronger during interglacial periods (e.g. Van Campo *et al.* 1982; Prell 1984; Fontugne & Duplessy 1986; Prell & Kutzbach 1987; Anderson & Prell 1991; Niitsuma *et al.* 1991; Steens *et al.* 1991).

The results presented here provide constraints which can be taken into consideration in the evaluation of the monsoonal climatic history of the Arabian Sea.

Material and methods

Plankton samples were collected from June 15 to July 2, 1984, during the outward voyage of the Dutch R. V. *Tyro* on its Indonesian Dutch Snellius II Expedition (Fig. 1). A continuous set of samples was obtained by a pump method, filtering 40–60 m³ of seawater every 2–4 h through a 75 μm sieve, from 4 m water depth. The samples were preserved in alcohol.

A Low Temperature Asher (LTA) was used to obtain a concentrate of shelled plankton. Duplessy *et al.* (1981) showed that roasting by means of a LTA has no profound effect on the stable isotope ratios. From 25 samples, specimens of *G. bulloides* and *N. dutertrei* were analysed from different size fractions (125–250 μm and 250–400 μm).

The analyses were performed on a MAT 251 mass-spectrometer equipped with a fully automated carbonate preparation device. Analytical procedures have been described by Zahn-Knoll (1986). The analytical precision during the measurements from working standards was 0.04‰ for δ^{13}C and 0.08‰ for δ^{18}O. The isotope values are referred to PDB by the standard notation (Craig 1957) and are calibrated to the NBS 19 standard. The data have been published in Kroon & Ganssen (1989).

Table 1a. Stable isotope values for first measured, and remeasured samples of *Neogloboquadrina dutertrei* from ODP Hole 728A. Those values marked with an asterisk are rejected because fractionation in the first measured values is obvious. First measured samples: *N. dutertrei* from the >250 μm fraction. Remeasured samples: *N. dutertrei* from the 355–425 μm fraction.

A	B	C	D	E	F	G
1–1–65/67	0.92	0.70	0.22	1.05	0.72	0.33
1–2–115/117	0.62*	0.18	0.78*	0.78*	0.45	0.36*
1–2–140/142	−0.06	−0.06	0.00	0.90	0.49	0.41
1–3–40/42	0.80	0.52	0.28	0.69	0.43	0.26
1–3–115/117	−0.11	−0.14	0.03	0.79	0.88	−0.09
1–3–140/140	0.17	−0.01	0.18	0.87	0.58	0.29
1–4–15/17	−0.12	−0.39	0.27	0.98	0.51	0.47
1–4–40/42	−0.05*	−0.49	0.93*	0.93*	0.56	0.37*
1–4–65/67	−0.71	−0.94	0.23	0.68	0.51	0.17
1–4–90/92	−0.04*	−0.58	0.54*	0.51*	0.13	0.48*
1–4–115/117	0.58	0.24	0.34	0.29	0.10	0.19
1–5–15/17	0.60	0.42	0.18	0.63	0.52	0.11
1–5–40/42	0.50	0.41	0.09	0.44	0.31	0.13
1–5–65/67	0.72	0.55	0.17	0.51	0.49	0.02
1–7–40/42	0.22	0.04	0.18	0.33	0.19	0.14
2–1–15/17	0.73*	0.01	0.72*	1.37*	0.70	0.67*
2–3–15/17	−0.05	0.15	−0.20	0.10	0.31	−0.21
2–4–90/92	0.52	0.30	0.22	0.02	−0.14	0.16
2–4–140/142	0.51	0.48	0.03	−0.02	0.04	−0.06
2–6–15/17	−0.33	0.23	−0.10	0.74	0.42	0.32
2–6–65/67	0.08	0.20	−0.12	0.10	0.20	−0.10
3–1–65/6	0.37	0.41	−0.04	0.37	0.39	−0.20
			(mean: 0.16)			(mean: 0.22)

A = Sample
B = $\delta^{18}O$ (>250 μm)
C = $\delta^{18}O$ (355–425 μm)
D = $\Delta\delta^{18}O$ (>250 μm) − (355–425 μm)

E = $\delta^{13}C$ (>250 μm)
F = $\delta^{13}C$ (355–425 μm)
G = $\Delta\delta^{13}C$ (>250 μm) − (355–425 μm)

Table 1b. Stable isotope values for first measured, and remeasured samples of *Globigerina bulloides* from ODP Hole 728A. Those values marked with an asterisk are rejected because fractionation in the first measured values is obvious. First measured samples: *G. bulloides* from the 125–250 μm fraction. Remeasured samples: *G. bulloides* from the 212–250 μm fraction.

A	B	C	D	E	F	G
1–2–115/117	−0.37*	−0.89	0.52*	−1.31*	−2.45	1.14*
1–2–140/142	−0.93	−0.84	−0.09	−1.90	−2.29	0.37
1–3–40/42	−0.22	−0.48	0.26	−1.93	−2.28	0.35
1–3–115/117	−0.82	−0.85	0.03	−1.60	−1.66	0.06
1–3–140/142	−0.77	−0.96	0.19	−1.60	−1.88	0.28
1–4–15/17	−0.89	−1.11	0.22	−1.89	−1.69	−0.20
1–4–40/42	−1.09	−1.09	0.00	−1.45	−1.61	0.16
1–4–65/67	−1.37	−1.54	0.17	−1.43	−1.90	0.47
1–4–90/92	−0.79	−0.98	0.19	−1.79	−1.98	0.19
1–4–115/117	−0.14*	−0.62	0.48*	−2.20*	−2.46	0.26*
1–4–140/142	−0.12	−0.17	0.05	−2.12	−2.48	0.36
1–5–15/17	−0.27	−0.33	0.06	−2.39	−2.59	0.20
1–5–40/42	0.08*	−0.46	0.38*	−1.94*	−2.50	0.56*
1–5–65/67	0.03	0.10	−0.07	−2.00	−2.39	0.39
2–6–15/17	−0.60	−0.74	0.14	−1.08	−1.36	0.28
3–1–65/67	0.15	−0.08	0.23	−1.38	−1.74	0.36
			(mean: 0.13)			(mean: 0.28)

A = Sample
B = $\delta^{18}O$ (125–250 μm)
C = $\delta^{18}O$ (212–250 μm)
D = $\Delta\delta^{18}O$ (125–250 μm) − (212–250 μm)

E = $\delta^{13}C$ (125–250 μm)
F = $\delta^{13}C$ (212–250 μm)
G = $\Delta\delta^{13}C$ (125–250 μm) − (212–250 μm)

From Hole 728A (ODP 117) stable isotope measurements on the tests of planktonic foraminifera were made on 88 samples. At first, fifty specimens per sample of *N. dutertrei* from the >250 μm fraction and 120 specimens of *G. bulloides* from the 125−250 μm fraction were picked for stable isotope analyses. The tests were ultrasonically cleaned for two minutes in analytical grade methanol. The carbonate of the fossil foraminiferal tests was dissolved in 100% phosphoric acid in vacuum at 50°C. Isotopic analyses were performed off line on a MAT 251 mass-spectrometer. Analytical precision of our working standard (Merck 100% CaCO$_3$) was 0.04‰ for δ^{13}C and 0.05‰ for δ^{18}O during the measuring period.

In order to check the isotopic variations within our relatively large size ranges (125−250 μm and >250 μm) we made duplicate analyses of 22 samples for *G. dutertrei* and 16 samples for *G. bulloides*, within those size ranges where specimen of *G. bulloides* and *N. dutertrei* are most frequent in the samples, i.e. 212−250 μm for *G. bulloides* and 355−425 μm for *N. dutertrei* (Tables 1a, 1b, Figs 2a−d). Duplicate analyses were also made on 'suspicious' measurements. Obviously fractionated values were rejected and replaced by the new results (Tables 1a, 1b). The mean reproducibility of the samples is within 0.14‰ for δO and 0.25‰ for δ^{13}C. Data from ODP Hole 728A are listed in Table 2. They were linearly transformed from depth to time (Table 3), and smoothed with a five points running average to reduce noise.

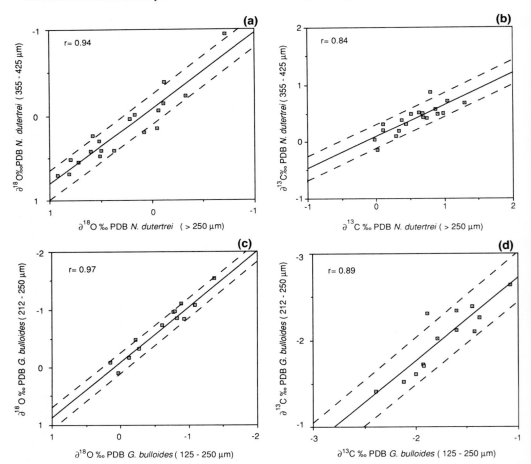

Fig. 2. Diagrams showing the correlation of the first measured (fractions: 125−250 μm for *G. bulloides* and > 250 μm for *N. dutertrei*), and remeasured (fractions 212−250 μm for *G. bulloides*; 13 samples, and 355−425 μm for *N. dutertrei*; 19 samples) samples for ODP Site 728 (a) Oxygen isotope ratios in *N. dutertrei*. (b) Carbon isotope ratios in *N. dutertrei*. (c) Oxygen isotope ratios in *G. bulloides*. (d) Carbon isotope ratios in *G. bulloides*. The dashed lines indicate the mean reproducibility of all samples.

Table 2. Stable isotope data for *N. dutertrei* and *G. bulloides*. For remeasured samples (Table 1), we used the mean of the first measured and the re-measured values, except for the rejected values.

A	B	C	D	E	F
1−1−15−17	0.16	0.33	0.93	−0.58	−1.73
1−1−40−42	0.41	0.75	1.00	−0.22	−1.86
1−1−65−67	0.66	0.81	0.88	−0.17	−1.91
1−1−90−92	0.91	0.69	0.96	−0.44	−1.71
1−1−115−117	1.16	0.61	0.89	−0.71	−1.95
1−1−140−142	1.41	1.22	1.03	−0.27	−1.76
1−2−15−17	1.66	0.43	0.75	−0.79	−1.83
1−2−40−42	1.91	0.40	0.50	−0.52	−1.65
1−2−65−67	2.16	0.26	0.59	−0.52	−1.60
1−2−90−92	2.41	0.29	0.40	−0.65	−1.71
1−2−115−117	2.66	0.18	0.45	−0.89	−2.27
1−2−140−142	2.91	−0.06	0.70	−0.89	−2.11
1−3−15−17	3.16	0.40	0.67	−0.45	−2.06
1−3−40−42	3.41	0.66	0.56	−0.30	−2.11
1−3−65−67	3.66	0.49	0.92	−0.38	−1.59
1−3−90−92	3.91	0.00	0.96	−0.68	−1.50
1−3−115−117	4.16	−0.13	0.84	−0.84	−1.63
1−3−140−142	4.41	0.08	0.73	−0.87	−1.74
1−4−15−17	4.66	−0.26	0.75	−1.00	−1.79
1−4−40−42	4.91	−0.49	0.56	−1.09	−1.53
1−4−65−67	5.16	−0.83	0.60	−1.45	−1.77
1−4−90−92	5.41	−0.58	0.13	−0.89	−1.89
1−4−115−117	5.66	0.41	0.20	−0.62	−2.46
1−4−140−142	5.91	0.64	0.37	−0.15	−2.30
1−5−15−17	6.16	0.51	0.58	−0.30	−2.49
1−5−40−42	6.41	0.46	0.38	−0.46	−2.50
1−5−65−67	6.66	0.64	0.50	0.07	−2.20
1−5−90−92	6.91	0.79	0.80	−0.19	−2.16
1−5−115−117	7.16	1.05	0.92	0.07	−1.60
1−5−140−142	7.41	0.97	0.46	−0.03	−2.14
1−6−15−17	7.66	0.96	0.54	0.27	−1.96
1−6−40−42	7.91	0.74	0.68	−0.28	−2.27
1−6−65−67	8.16	0.55	0.84	−0.35	−2.07
1−6−90−92	8.41	0.58	0.87	−0.02	−1.80
1−6−115−117	8.66	0.28	0.75	−0.37	−1.84
1−6−140−142	8.91	0.30	0.69	−0.23	−1.87
1−7−15−17	9.16	0.36	0.48	−0.60	−1.79
1−7−40−42	9.41	0.13	0.26	−0.49	−2.01
2−1−15−17	9.76	0.01	0.70	−0.46	−1.91
2−1−40−42	10.01	−0.08	0.96	−0.45	−1.75
2−1−65−67	10.26	−0.32	0.76	−0.74	−1.50
2−1−90−92	10.51	−0.44	0.85	−0.84	−1.61
2−1−115−117	10.76	0.07	0.48	−0.45	−1.65
2−1−140−142	11.01	0.47	0.52	0.11	−1.44
2−2−15−17	11.26	0.32	0.61	−0.53	−1.86
2−2−40−42	11.51	−0.21	0.51	−1.07	−1.79
2−2−65−67	11.76	0.27	0.28	−0.13	−2.02
2−2−90−92	12.01	0.18	0.46	−0.60	−1.91
2−2−115−117	12.26	0.31	0.34	−0.43	−2.42
2−2−140−142	12.51	0.72	0.71	−0.04	−1.95
2−3−15−17	12.76	0.05	0.21	−0.18	−2.00
2−3−40−42	13.01	0.19	0.63	−0.32	−2.29
2−3−65−67	13.26	0.49	0.64	0.00	−2.03
2−3−90−92	13.51	0.42	0.70	0.12	−1.89
2−3−115−117	13.76	0.09	0.62	−0.05	−1.90
2−3−140−142	14.01	−0.09	1.04	−0.62	−1.39
2−4−15−17	14.26	−0.09	0.48	−0.31	−1.56
2−4−40−42	14.51	−0.37	0.62	−0.83	−1.79

A	B	C	D	E	F
2–4–65–67	14.76	−0.23	0.26	−0.43	−1.72
2–4–90–92	15.01	0.41	0.06	−0.28	−1.77
2–4–115–117	15.26	0.92	0.16	0.16	−2.02
2–4–140–142	15.51	0.50	0.01	−0.09	−1.87
2–5–15–17	15.76	0.50	0.48	−0.11	−1.82
2–5–40–42	16.01	0.48	0.59	−0.10	−1.73
2–5–65–67	16.26	0.66	0.60	−0.32	−2.09
2–5–90–92	16.51	0.68	0.87	−0.01	−1.15
2–5–115–117	16.76	0.35	0.65	−0.23	−1.58
2–5–140–142	17.01	0.45	0.85	0.50	−1.35
2–6–15–17	17.26	−0.28	0.58	−0.67	−1.22
2–6–40–42	17.51	−0.47	0.78	−1.17	−1.98
2–6–65–67	17.76	0.14	0.15	−0.64	−1.84
2–6–90–92	18.01	0.75	0.37	1.14	−1.30
2–6–115–117	18.26	0.68	0.43	1.26	−1.08
2–6–140–142	18.51	1.07	0.61	0.81	−1.57
2–7–15–17	18.76	1.34	0.79	1.17	−1.32
2–7–40–42	19.01	0.89	0.59	0.65	−1.51
3–1–15–17	19.26	0.39	0.10	0.19	−1.29
3–1–40–42	19.51	0.61	0.49	0.40	−1.07
3–1–65–67	19.76	0.39	0.38	0.04	−1.56
3–1–90–92	20.01	0.35	0.53	−0.43	−1.88
3–1–115–117	20.26	0.45	0.69	−0.42	−1.89
3–1–140–142	20.51	0.48	0.77	−0.01	−1.81
3–2–15–17	20.76	−0.22	0.80	−0.69	−1.73
3–2–40–42	21.01	0.10	0.70	−0.63	−1.70
3–2–65–67	21.26	−0.09	0.35	−0.74	−1.92
3–2–90–92	21.51	0.22	0.38	−0.56	−1.81
3–2–115–117	21.76	0.33	0.54	−0.57	−1.79
3–2–140–142	22.01	0.03	0.54	−0.49	−1.35

A = Sample
B = depth (mbsf)
C = $\delta^{18}O$ *N. dutertrei* ‰ PDB

D = $\delta^{13}C$ *N. dutertrei* ‰ PDB
E = $\delta^{18}O$ *G. bulloides* ‰ PDB
F = $\delta^{13}C$ *G. bulloides* ‰ PDB

Upwelling indicators in a modern setting

In 1984, plankton tow samples and surface water temperature measurements were taken on the outgoing voyage of the Dutch R. V. *Tyro* (Fig. 1). Drops in temperature along the sample transect in the Arabian Sea and south of India indicate upwelling areas (Fig. 3). The correlation of temperature and the $\delta^{18}O$ values for *G. bulloides* and *N. dutertrei* (Fig. 4a and b) is quite good, as is to be expected. In upwelling areas, with lower water temperatures, the oxygen isotope values are most positive: this is observed for both species.

Since *G. bulloides* lives in the surface waters and *N. dutertrei* is a thermocline dweller, we consider the difference in oxygen isotope values ($\Delta\delta^{18}O$ *G. bulloides*−*N. dutertrei*; or $\Delta\delta^{18}O$) to be a measure of the intensity of upwelling. When strong upwelling drives *N. dutertrei* to the surface, the two species will build their tests in the same waters and the $\Delta\delta^{18}O$ will become smaller, whereas in non-upwelling areas the species have different depth habitats in a stratified water column and the $\Delta\delta^{18}O$ will be larger. More negative oxygen isotope values in the tests of *G. bulloides*, compared to *N. dutertrei*, are expected. Thus upwelling areas roughly correspond to intervals along the sample transect with $\Delta\delta^{18}O$ values close to zero, which tend to coincide with temperature minima. The $\Delta\delta^{18}O$ is only weakly correlated with the temperature fluctuations ($r = 0.51$; Fig. 4c), presumably caused by summing the errors in both $\delta^{18}O$ signals.

Empirically we found that the difference in carbon isotope values for the same two species also reflects upwelling, as Kroon & Ganssen (1989) suggest in their paper. The difference in $\delta^{13}C$ values between *G. bulloides* and *N. dutertrei* ($\Delta\delta^{13}C$) is smallest in upwelling areas (Fig. 5a). The high correlation between

Table 3. List of data to construct the depth-time relationships, using the SPECMAP stacked curve (Imbrie *et al.* 1984).

Depth (mbsf)	Age (ka)	Event
0.35	12	2.0
1.49	24	3.0
3.23	59	4.0
3.41	64	4.2
3.89	71	5.0
4.07	80	5.1
4.66	100	5.3
5.21	122	5.5
5.33	128	6.0
9.96	186	7.0
10.53	216	7.3
11.55	238	7.5
11.63	245	8.0
11.71	250	8.2
12.76	286	8.5
13.89	303	9.0
14.09	310	9.1
14.71	330	9.3
14.95	339	10.0
16.30	362	11.0
16.76	368	11.1
17.55	405	11.3
17.75	423	12.0
20.35	478	13.0
21.70	524	14.0

temperature and the difference in carbon isotopes between the two species ($r = -0.83$; Fig. 5b), proves that $\Delta\delta^{13}C$ is a valuable indicator for upwelling induced high productivity.

The upwelling history off Oman for the last 525 ka

Since the two upwelling indicators seem to work well in the modern environment, we decided to apply them to the sediments from Site 728 (ODP 117), underlying an upwelling area with known fluctuations in the intensity of upwelling through time (see Prell & Kutzbach 1987).

We used the $\delta^{18}O$ depth profile of *N. dutertrei* to identify the isotopic stages (Steens *et al.* 1991). The calculated, smoothed, values for $\Delta\delta^{18}O$ together with the smoothed $\delta^{18}O$ time profile for *N. dutertrei* are plotted in Fig. 6. The smallest values in the $\Delta\delta^{18}O$ curve indicate periods of intense mixing of the water column and thus strong upwelling. A long-term trend towards smaller values deeper in the core can be observed, which implies more or less continuously decreasing upwelling strength for the last 374 ka. Down to about 374 ka the strongest upwelling occurred during the interglacial stages 3, 5, 7 and 9. Between 374 ka and 524 ka, in stages 11, 12, and 13, the situation is reversed. We calculated the correlation between the two curves in Fig. 6, and, as expected, because of the shift in the lower part of the section the correlation is very poor (Fig. 7a). We then split the section in two parts, 0–374 ka and 374–525 ka, and correlated them separately. For the upper part of the curves we find a moderately good negative correlation ($r = -0.57$, Fig. 7b), and for the lower part a good positive relationship ($r = 0.76$, Fig. 7c), which confirms the idea of a shift at 17.15 m, 374 ka.

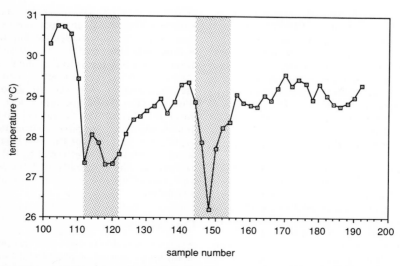

Fig. 3. Temperature variations along the north Indian Ocean sample transect. Upwelling areas are stippled.

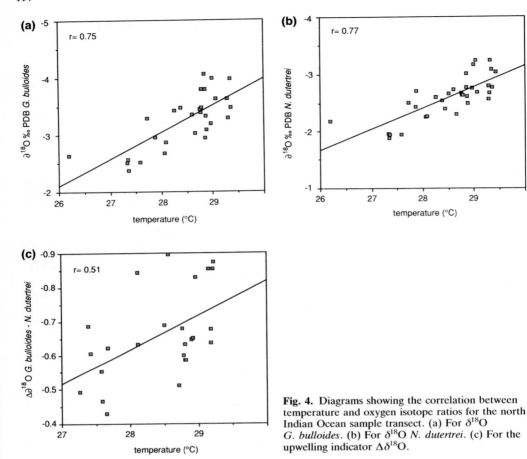

Fig. 4. Diagrams showing the correlation between temperature and oxygen isotope ratios for the north Indian Ocean sample transect. (a) For $\delta^{18}O$ *G. bulloides*. (b) For $\delta^{18}O$ *N. dutertrei*. (c) For the upwelling indicator $\Delta\delta^{18}O$.

Figure 8a shows the smoothed time profile of both upwelling indicators ($\Delta\delta^{18}O$, mixing; $\Delta\delta^{13}C$ productivity). Just like the $\Delta\delta^{18}O$, the $\Delta\delta^{13}C$ also shows the trend towards stronger upwelling in the past, and the shift at 374 ka. This results in a good correlation between the two upwelling indicators ($r = 0.71$; Fig. 8b), and confirms our interpretation of the upwelling history off Oman, as the two upwelling indicators, caused by different processes (changes in temperature and productivity), show the same trends.

Off Oman, dissolution in the oxygen minimum zone (OMZ) causes fragmentation of foraminiferal tests. During interglacial periods fragmentation, and thus dissolution, is strongest (Steens *et al.* 1991; Fig. 9a). Dissolution might affect the isotopic signal (Bonneau *et al.* 1980; Wu & Berger 1989). To check the possibility that our upwelling indicators are influenced by dissolution, we plotted our dissolution index:

$(W/(W + F))*100$ (W = whole foraminiferal tests; F = fragments), in which low values indicate strong dissolution, against one of the upwelling indicators ($\Delta\delta^{13}C$; Fig. 9a). If dissolution influenced the isotopic signal we would expect a high correlation between the two for the whole section. However, this is not the case (Fig. 9b). The dissolution index does not show the shift at 374 ka. For the upper part we find a moderately good negative correlation ($r = -0.62$; Fig. 9c), and for the lower part a good positive correlation ($r = 0.89$; Fig. 9d). Thus we can exclude the possibility that the stable isotope upwelling indicators are an artifact of dissolution.

Conclusions

Analyses of stable oxygen and carbon isotopes of different species of planktonic foraminifera from the northern Indian Ocean surface waters

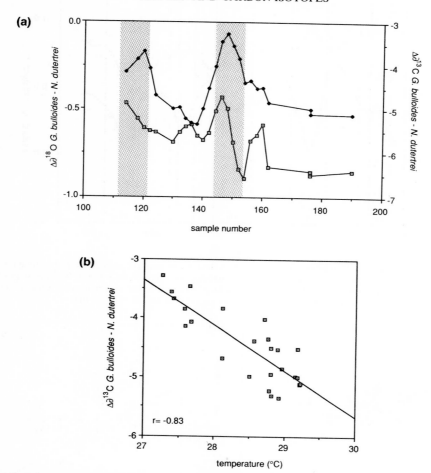

Fig. 5. (a) Fluctuations in upwelling indicators ($\Delta\delta^{18}O$; open squares and $\Delta\delta^{13}C$; dots) along the north Indian Ocean sample transect. Note low values for both indicators in upwelling areas (stippled). (b) Correlation between temperature and the indicator for upwelling related high productivity ($\Delta\delta^{13}C$).

provide us with a tool to detect upwelling intensity and upwelling induced high productivity.

Applying this tool to the sedimentary record of Site 728 off Oman, leads us to the interpretation that the last 374 ka are characterized by strong upwelling during the interglacials. We can demonstrate that the signal is not influenced by dissolution.

The observed long-term trend in both parameters points to decreased upwelling intensity from 374 ka to the present day.

Some problems remain. It does not seem possible to quantify the intensity of upwelling and productivity by this method. Although the oxygen isotope signal seems to be fairly well understood, the carbon isotopic composition of the foraminifera is governed by more complex

factors, such as vital effects, depending on the ontogenetic stage of the specimens and their depth habitat.

Although the upwelling indicators work very well in the upper part of Hole 728A their shift in isotopic stage 11 (17.15 m; 374 ka), which seems to point to stronger upwelling during the glacials, remains difficult to interpret. It might be explained by a complete change in the upwelling regime. However this would imply a change of the monsoonal system with more intense southwestern winds during glacial periods, which does not seem feasible. Further research on other parameters and, if possible, downcore stable isotope measurements of *G. bulloides* and *N. dutertrei*, is needed to clarify this ambiguous signal.

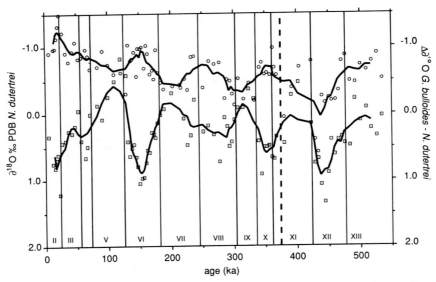

Fig. 6. Time series for $\delta^{18}O$ *N. dutertrei*, used to create a time frame, and the indicator for upwelling intensity ($\Delta\delta^{18}O$). Both curves are smoothed with a five points running average to reduce noise. Isotopic stages are marked with roman numbers. The wide dotted line marks 374 ka, where the correlation between the curves shifts. Open circles: calculated $\Delta\delta^{18}C$ values. Open squares: $\delta^{18}O$ values of *N. dutertrei*.

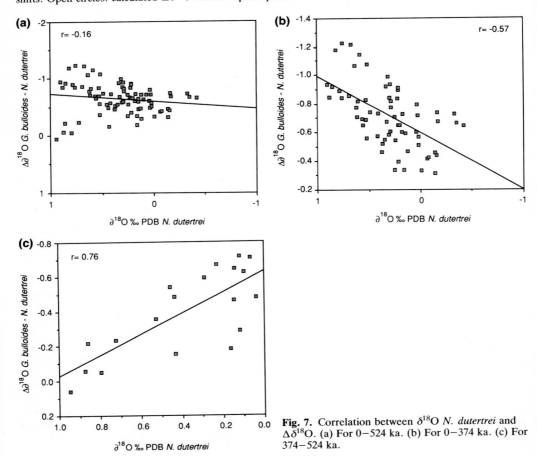

Fig. 7. Correlation between $\delta^{18}O$ *N. dutertrei* and $\Delta\delta^{18}O$. (a) For 0−524 ka. (b) For 0−374 ka. (c) For 374−524 ka.

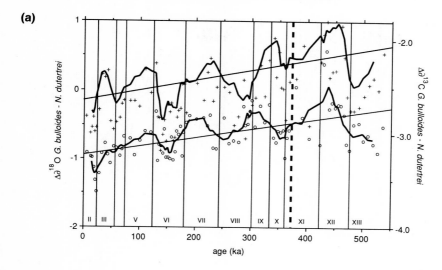

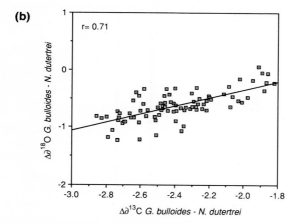

Fig. 8. (a) Time series for the upwelling indicators $\Delta\delta^{18}O$ and $\Delta\delta^{13}C$. Both curves are smoothed with a five points running average to avoid noise. Isotopic stages are marked with roman numbers. The wide dotted line marks 374 ka. +, calculated $\Delta\delta^{13}C$ values; ○, calculated $\Delta\delta^{18}O$ values. (b) Correlation between the two upwelling indicators for 0–524 ka.

We would like to thank Jan van Hinte, who initiated this project, and also William Curry, Warren Prell and an anonymous reviewer for their critical reviews and their many useful suggestions which greatly improved this manuscript. We also thank Sandra Nederbragt, Janneke Ottens, Geert-Jan Brummer and Kay Beets for their numerous remarks, from which the manuscript benefitted. This study was supported by the "Nederlandse Organisatie voor Wetenschappelijk Onderzoek" (NWO; first and third author, grant 751–356–018) and the "Stichting Onderzoek der Zee" (SOZ). This is a publication of the Geomarine Center Amsterdam.

References

ANDERSON, D. M. & PRELL, W. L. 1991. Coastal upwelling gradient during the late Pleistocene. *In*: PRELL, W. L. & NIITSUMA, N. (eds) *Proceedings of the Ocean Drilling Program Scientific Results*. Ocean Drilling Program, College Station, TX, **117**, 265–276.

BONNEAU, M.-C., VERGNAUD-GRAZZINI, C. & BERGER, W. H. 1980. Stable isotope fractionation and differential dissolution in Recent planktonic foraminifera from Pacific box-cores. *Oceanologica Acta*, **3**, 377–382.

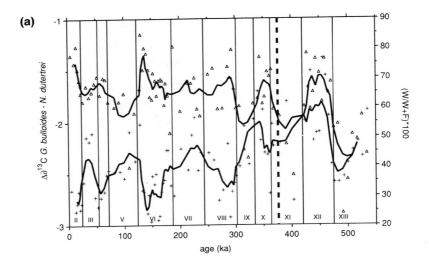

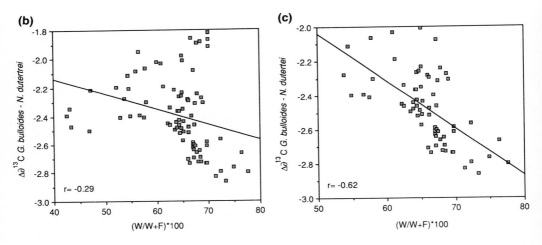

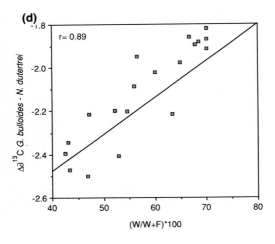

Fig. 9. (a) Time series for $\Delta\delta^{13}C$ and the dissolution index $(W/(W + F)) \times 100$ (W = whole planktonic foraminifera, F = fragments). Both curves are smoothed with a five points running average to avoid noise. Isotopic stages are marked with roman numbers. The wide dotted line marks 374 ka, where correlation between the curves shifts. Open triangles: calculated $(W/(W + F)) \times 100$ values. +: calculated $\Delta\delta^{13}C$ values. (b) Correlation between the dissolution index and $\Delta\delta^{13}C$ for 0–525 ka. (c) For 0–374 ka. (d) For 374–524 ka.

BRUCE, J. G. 1974. Some details of upwelling off the Somali and Arabian coasts. *Journal of Marine Research*, **32**, 419–423.

CRAIG, H. 1957. Isotopic standards for carbon and oxygen and correction factors for mass spectromatic analysis of CO_2. *Geochimica et Cosmochimica Acta*, **12**, 133–149.

DUNBAR, R. B. 1983. Stable isotope record of upwelling and climate from Santa Barbara basin, California. *In*: THIEDE, J. & SUESS, E. (eds) *Coastal Upwelling: Its Sediment Record, Part B*, Plenum, New York, 217–246.

DUPLESSY, J. C., BÉ, A. H. W. & BLANC, P. L. 1981. Oxygen and carbon isotopic composition and the biogeographic distribution of planktonic foraminifera in the Indian Ocean. *Palaeogeography, Palaeoclimatology, Palaeoecology*, **33**, 9–33.

EREZ, J. & LUZ, B. 1983. Experimental paleotemperature equation for planktonic foraminifera. *Geochimica et Cosmochimica Acta*, **4**, 1025–1031.

FONTUGNE, M. R. & DUPLESSY, J. C. 1986. Variations of the monsoon regime during the upper Quaternary: evidence from carbon isotopic record of organic matter in north Indian Ocean sediment cores. *Palaeogeography, Palaeoclimatology, Palaeoecology*, **56**, 69–88.

GANSSEN, G. 1983. Dokumentation von Küstennahem Aftrieb anhand stabiler Isotope in rezenten Foraminiferen vor Nordwest-Africa. *'Meteor' Forschungsergebnisse*, **37**, 1–46.

IMBRIE, J., HAYS, J. D., MARTINSON, D. G., McINTYRE, A., MIX, A. C., MORLEY, J. J., PISIAS, N., PRELL, W. L. & SHACKLETON, N. J., 1984. The orbital theory of Pleistocene climate: support from a revised chronology of the marine $\delta^{18}O$ record. *In*: BERGER, A., IMBRIE, J., HAYS, J., KUKLA, G., and SALZMAN, B. (eds), *Milankovitch and Climate* (Pt. 1). Reidel, Dordrecht, 269–305.

KAHN, M. I. 1979. Non equilibrium oxygen and carbon isotopic fractionation in tests of living planktonic foraminifera. *Oceanologica Acta*, **2**, 195–200.

KROON, D. 1988. Distribution of extant planktic foraminiferal assemblages in the Red Sea and northern Indian Ocean surface waters. *In*: BRUMMER, G. J. A. & KROON, D. *Planktonic foraminifers as tracers of ocean-climate history*. VU Boekhandel/Uitgeverij, Amsterdam, 229–267.

—— & GANSSEN, G. 1989. Northern Indian Ocean upwelling cells and the stable isotope composition of living planktonic foraminifers. *Deep-Sea Research*, **36**, 1219–1236.

NIITSUMA, N., OBA, T. & OKADA, M., 1991. Oxygen and carbon isotope stratigraphy at site 723, Oman Margin. *In*: PRELL, W. L. & NIITSUMA, N. (eds) *Proceedings of the Ocean Drilling Program Scientific Results*. Ocean Drilling Program, College Station, TX, **117**, 321–341.

OBERHÄNSLI, H. 1991. Upwelling signals at the western Walvis Ridge during the past 500 000 years. *Paleoceanography*, **6**, 53–71.

PRELL, W. L. 1984. Variations of monsoonal upwelling: a response to changing solar radiation. *In*: HANSEN, J. E. & TAKAHASI, T. (eds) *Climatic processes and climate sensitivity* Washington (American Geophysical Union) Geophysical Monograph, 29, Maurice Ewing Series **5**, 48–57.

—— & CURRY, W. B. 1981. Faunal and isotopic indices of monsoonal upwelling: Western Arabian Sea. *Oceanologica Acta*, **4**, 91–98.

—— & KUTZBACH, J. E. 1987. Monsoon variability over the past 150 000 years. *Journal of Geophysical Research*, **92**, 8411–8425.

SARNTHEIN, M. & THIEDEMANN, R. 1989. Toward a high-resolution stable isotope stratigraphy of the last 3.4 million years: sites 658 and 659 off Northwest Africa. *In*: RUDDIMAN, W., & SARNTHEIN, M. (eds) *Proceedings of the Ocean Drilling Program, Scientific Results*. Ocean Drilling Program, College Station, TX, **108**, 167–185.

STEENS, T. N. F., KROON, D., TEN KATE, W. G. & SPRENGER, A. 1991. Late Pleistocene periodicities of oxygen isotope ratios, calcium carbonate contents and magnetic susceptibilities of western Arabian Sea margin hole 728A. In: PRELL, W. L. & NIITSUMA, N. (eds) *Proceedings of the Ocean Drilling Program Scientific Results*. Ocean Drilling Program, College Station, TX, **117**, 309–320.

VAN CAMPO, E., DUPLESSY, J. C. & ROSSIGNOL-STRICK, M. 1982. Climatic conditions deduced from a 150-kyr oxygen isotope-pollen record from the Arabian Sea. *Nature*, **296**, 56–59.

WEFER, G., DUNBAR, R. B. & SUESS, E. 1983. Stable isotopes of foraminifers off Peru recording high fertility and changes in upwelling history. *In*: THIEDE, J. & SUESS, E. (eds) *Coastal Upwelling: Its Sediment Record, Part B*. Plenum, New York, 295–308.

WU, G. & BERGER, W. H. 1989. Planktonic foraminifera: differential dissolution and the Quaternary stable isotope record in the west equatorial Pacific. *Paleoceanography*, **4**, 181–198.

ZAHN-KNOLL, R. 1986. *Spätquartäre Entwicklung von Küstenauftrieb und Tiefwasserzirkulation im Nordost-Atlantik. Rekonstruktion anhand stabiler Isotope kalkschaliger Foraminiferen*. Thesis, University Kiel, 1–111.

Physical upwelling processes, upper ocean environment and the sediment record of the southwest monsoon

DAVID M. ANDERSON[1],*, JOHN C. BROCK[2] & WARREN L. PRELL[1]

[1] *Department of Geological Sciences, Brown University, Providence, RI 02912, USA*
[2] *Code 971, Oceans and Ice Branch, NASA/GSFC, Greenbelt, MD 20771, USA*

Abstract: We used a one-dimensional model of upwelling driven by the surface windfield to examine the relationship between wind-driven physical upwelling processes, changes in the plankton environment and modern (coretop) sediments in the northwest Arabian Sea. The model resolves the vertical upwelling velocity into a coastal component related to transport away from a solid boundary and a second component related to the curl in the wind stress. The coastal component is an order of magnitude larger than the curl component but restricted to <100 km offshore. In offshore waters (>100 km), upwelling is directly related to the curl in the wind stress. Model-derived upwelling is in reasonable agreement with estimates of the vertical velocity off Oman, and correlated with the cool waters and thin mixed layer found along the coast of Oman. The response of the biota to these environmental changes is observed in remotely sensed images of phytoplankton biomass during the Southwest Monsoon, and in distinct foraminifer species distributions in modern (coretop) sediments.

The marine geological record of upwelling provides a history of atmospheric circulation because upwelling is driven by the surface windfield. In upwelling regions, the transfer of momentum from the atmosphere to the surface layer of the ocean brings cool, nutrient-rich subsurface waters into the photic zone. Marine plankton leave a fossil record of these changes in the form of increased biogenic sedimentation and distinct species assemblages. To understand how upwelling is related to the physical forcing (wind stress), we examined the relationship between wind speed and upwelling velocity using a simple one-dimensional upwelling model forced by the climatological winds along a nearshore−offshore transect in the northwest Arabian Sea. We compare model-derived upwelling with changes in the physical environment and in phytoplankton biomass and relate these observations to the modern (coretop) sediment record.

Coastal upwelling off Oman is driven by the Southwest Monsoon winds. Upwelling is entirely seasonal here because the winter winds (the northeast trades) do not produce offshore transport. During the summer months, the atmospheric pressure gradient created by the heating of the Tibetan plateau relative to the central Indian Ocean causes a reversal in the NE low-level winds so that the monsoon winds blow from the southwest during June, July and August. The winds are focused in a narrow SW−NE trending jet that crosses the submarine Owen Ridge at approximately 15°N 60°E (Luther & O'Brien 1985), producing a region of positive curl in the wind stress between the coast and the axis of the jet (Fig. 1). The component of the southwest winds parallel to the coast produces Ekman transport away from the solid boundary (the coast), and the positive curl produces divergence of the surface waters between the coast and the axis of the Findlater jet (Swallow 1984). A phytoplankton bloom occurs each summer and extends several hundred kilometres offshore, observed in remotely sensed images of ocean colour (Fig. 2; Brock *et al.* 1990). Near the coast of Oman, the surface mixed layer thins to less than 20 m and sea surface temperatures cool by 4°C relative to the waters offshore (Brock *et al.* in press). Off Oman, the combined effect of offshore transport and positive curl produces some of the largest onshore−offshore environmental gradients in sea surface temperature (SST) and phytoplankton biomass found in the world oceans (Brock *et al.* in press; Bruce 1974).

Modelling the response to the southwest winds

A hierarchy of models has been used to examine the relationship between wind stress and upwelling in the western Arabian Sea. Prell & Streeter (1982) used a one-dimensional model to calculate the Ekman transport along the coast related to wind speed. Smith & Bottero (1977)

---

* Present address: Department of Geological Sciences, University of South Carolina, Columbia, SC 29208, USA.

From SUMMERHAYES, C. P., PRELL, W. L. & EMEIS, K. C. (eds), 1992, *Upwelling Systems: Evolution Since the Early Miocene.* Geological Society Special Publication No 64, pp 121−129.

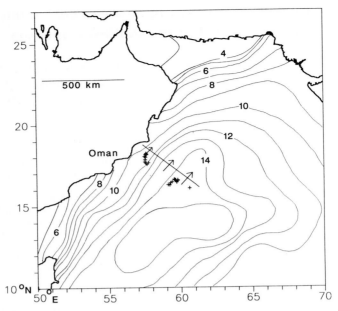

Fig. 1. July resultant wind speed (m/s) in the Arabian Sea (figure modified from Hastenrath & Lamb 1979). The wind direction off Oman is indicated by arrows. The jet structure of the surface wind produces a region of positive curl extending from the coast of Oman offshore to the axis of the jet. The closely spaced isopleths along the coast indicate the region of maximum positive curl. Upwelling is calculated between the coast and 500 km offshore along the transect shown and compared with coretop sediment samples (+).

adapted a different one-dimensional model from Yoshida (1955) that integrates the Ekman transport over a finite distance offshore and includes a term related to the positive curl in the windfield. Three-dimensional models have also been constructed that include horizontal advection and diffusion (Luther & O'Brien 1985; McCreary & Kush 1989). The 3D simulations are forced by the annual cycle of climatological winds to simulate the circulation and thickness of the upper layer, and the Luther & O'Brien model has been used with windfields produced by general circulation model simulations of past climate to simulate upwelling fields at different times in the past (Luther *et al.* 1990; Prell *et al.* 1990).

We used the Yoshida model that was originally formulated to explain upwelling off the California coast (Yoshida 1955; Smith & Bottero 1977). We selected this 1D model for several reasons. The model is applicable to all coastal regions and is the simplest model that considers the effect of both the coastal boundary and the curl in the wind stress. A 1D model is also appropriate to the inverse problem that confronts the marine geologist: the time-series of the physical forcing (wind stress) must be determined from the response that is known or inferred from the geological record at discrete

geographical points. The model neglects two important processes. The effect of wind mixing is not included. Wind stirring deepens the surface mixed layer and introduces cool, nutrient-rich subsurface waters into the photic zone. The model also ignores horizontal diffusion and exchange on all scales that can smooth and reduce gradients in the surface layer.

The model

We calculated the vertical upwelling velocity along a transect between the coast and 500 km offshore using the July climatological wind speeds from Hastenrath & Lamb (1979). The model has two terms: a coastal component that integrates the Ekman transport away from a physical boundary (the coast) over a finite distance offshore, and a second term incorporating the positive curl in the wind field that produces a divergence in the surface layer of the ocean:

$$w = \frac{k}{\rho f} \tau_\mathrm{p} \, e^{-kx} + \frac{1}{\rho f} \frac{\mathrm{d}\tau}{\mathrm{d}x} \qquad (1)$$

where

$$k = f \left(g \, h \, \frac{\mathrm{d}\rho}{\rho} \right)^{-0.5}.$$

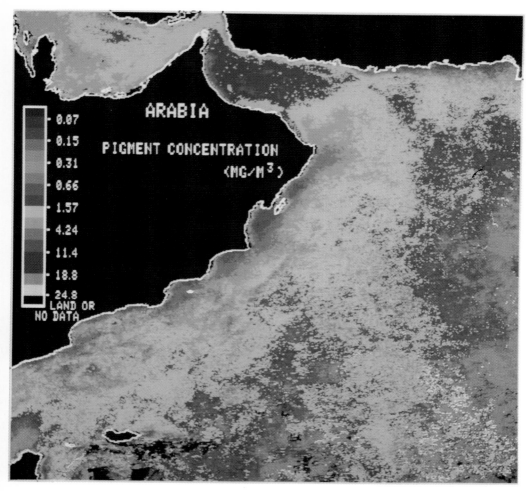

Fig. 2. Four-year composite image of August–September near-surface phytoplankton pigment concentration determined from Coastal Zone Color Scanner images.

Wind stress was calculated using the relationship

$$\tau = \rho_a C_d U^2. \qquad (2)$$

The symbols and constants are defined in Table 1. The constants for the drag coefficient (C_d) and air density (ρ_a) were chosen to be compatible with Prell & Streeter (1982) and Smith & Bottero (1977). The offshore extent of the coastal upwelling component depends on the value of k. We used a constant value of $k = 0.503 \times 10^{-6}$ cm^{-2} based on density sections for June–July (Brock et al. in press). This value is 30% lower than typical values described for coastal waters off California (Yoshida 1955), and the result is that the coastal upwelling component that we calculate off Oman extends farther offshore. A larger density contrast in the surface layer, or a thicker surface mixed layer, would cause the coastal component to decrease even more rapidly with distance offshore.

The July mean windfield of Hastenrath & Lamb (1979) shows winds parallel to the coast, and thus we assume $\tau_p = \tau$ in the first term. The transect was oriented normal to the wind direction, so the gradient $d\tau/dx$ could be calculated in 20 km increments along the transect as the change in the resultant stress between increments divided by the displacement along the transect. Although this model simplifies actual geometry and processes operating off Oman, it is useful because it allows one to scale the relative importance of coastal and offshore processes, and to relate changes in the windfield to upwelling intensity.

Upwelling calculated from July climatological winds

Wind stress along the transect (Fig. 3a) was calculated from the July climatological wind speed (Hastenrath & Lamb 1979) using equation (2). The jet structure of the surface windfield produces a region of increasing wind speed between the coast (0 km) and the axis of the jet located just beyond the end of the transect (approximately 600 km offshore). The wind stress increases offshore from 1.6 dynes/cm^2 to 3.6 dynes/cm^2 at the end of the transect (500 km), and the curl of the wind stress is positive everywhere. The gradient in wind stress is largest between 100 and 200 km offshore, producing a maximum in the curl of the wind stress within this region.

The non-linear relationship between wind speed and wind stress has important consequences. Because the stress is related to the square of the wind speed, a doubling the wind speed increases the wind stress (and upwelling) by a factor of four. The ocean response (upwelling) to changes in wind speed is amplified when the momentum is transferred to the ocean surface layer. With respect to the geological record, this means that upwelling variations are a sensitive but non-linear recorder of wind speed.

The vertical upwelling velocity (w) was calculated along the transect in 20 km steps (Fig. 3b), and expressed as a coastal component (first term in equation (1)), a component related to the curl (second term in equation (1)), and a sum. At the coast (0 km), the upward velocity related to movement away from the solid boundary (first term in equation (1)) is an order of magnitude larger than the velocity produced by the divergence in the ocean surface layer which results from the positive curl (second term in equation (1)). The coastal component decreases exponentially offshore and becomes less than the curl component at distances greater than 60 km offshore. The curl component is maximal in the region 100–200 km offshore where the gradient in the wind stress is large. Between 300–500 km the velocity is constant, approximately 0.0005 cm/sec. The combination of processes produces vertical velocities 5–10 times

Table 1. Symbols and constants used in the model.

w	= vertical velocity in the ocean surface layer (cm/s)
x	= distance offshore normal to wind direction (cm)
τ_p	= component of wind stress parallel to the coast (dynes/cm^2)
f	= coriolis parameter (s^{-1}), 4.26×10^{-5}
ρ	= density of the upper layer (g/cm^3), 1.026
d_ρ	= density difference in upper layer (g/cm^3)
	= $1.025_{0m} - 1.026_{75m} = 0.001$
h	= upper layer thickness (cm), 7500
$d\tau/dx$	= gradient in wind stress (x normal to the wind direction)
ρ_a	= air density (0.00122 g/cm^3)
C_d	= drag coefficient (0.0013)
U	= resultant wind speed U (cm/s)

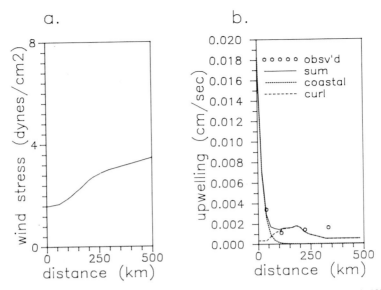

Fig. 3. (a) Wind stress calculated from July climatological wind speed (Hastenrath & Lamb 1979) along the transect shown in Fig. 1 (b) Coastal component, curl component, and the sum of the vertical upwelling velocity (cm/sec) calculated from the July wind stress (Fig. 3a) and estimates of vertical velocity (○) derived from hydrographic measurements made during the 1963 monsoon (Smith & Bottero 1977).

higher near the coast relative to the region 100−500 km offshore. Smith & Bottero (1977) compared the vertical velocity predicted using equation (1) with estimates of w (○, Fig. 3b) based on hydrographic measurements of dynamic topography made during June−July 1963 near our transect (line 3 in Smith & Bottero 1977). They observe that the vertical velocities calculated from equation (1) using winds measured during the 1963 cruise agree reasonably well with the hydrographic observations in the nearshore region. Although the model results shown in Fig. 3b are based on climatological winds, they also agree reasonably well with the estimates based on hydrographic observations made during the 1963 monsoon between 0 and 250 km. Offshore (340 km) the velocity based on the 1963 measurements (○) is larger by a factor of two. These observations support the hypothesis explicit in equation (1) that the coastal component dominates the nearshore region (0−50 km), while offshore (>100 km) upwelling is related to the curl in the windfield.

Comparison with the upper ocean environment

We compared the model vertical upwelling velocities with two climatological SST fields (Fig. 4a) selected to represent conditions that exist during the monsoon season. The two profiles were constructed differently. One SST pro-

file (H&L) was constructed from July atlas values (Hastenrath & Lamb 1979). The atlas was constructed by averaging observations from 60 years at 1 × 1° resolution, the same resolution as the wind data. The second profile was derived from 11 different June−July hydrocasts collected by the National Oceanographic Data Center (NODC) from the interval 1960−1987 (Brock *et al.*, submitted). Some of the differences between these profiles can be attributed to the way they were constructed. The atlas represents a multi-year average with 1 degree resolution (approximately 100 km), whereas the NODC profile is constructed from discrete observations collected during different years.

The atlas SST (Hastenrath & Lamb 1979) increases by 3°C from less than 23°C at the coast to >26°C offshore (Fig. 4a). The increase is most rapid near the coast and more gradual offshore. The NODC climatological June−July SSTs (Fig. 4a, dashed line) indicate a larger (7°C) gradient with more structure between the coast and 500 km. NODC SST increases rapidly near the coast, from 19 to >24°C between 0−75 km, and decreases below 24°C 150 km offshore. The NODC observations indicate cool water in the region 50−200 km offshore that corresponds to the region of maximum positive wind stress curl. Farther offshore, SSTs increase rapidly to over 27°C. At the eastern end of the transect, (300−500 km) SSTs decrease slightly. In general, both profiles indicate that the coolest

a.

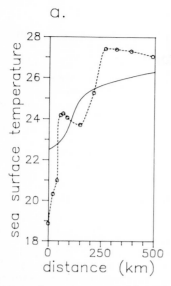

b.

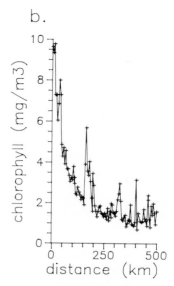

Fig. 4. (a) July sea surface temperatures (°C, SST) from Hastenrath & Lamb (1979) atlas data (solid line) and NODC June–July SST observations (---) from a multi-year composite section adjacent this transect 100 km north (from Brock *et al.* submitted). (b) August–September near-surface phytoplankton pigment concentrations determined from the four-year composite image (Fig. 2).

waters are found at the coast, with warmer water offshore. However, the discrete observations indicate a larger range of variation relative to the atlas values.

The changes in SST along the transect are related to changes in the upper layer of the ocean. Upwelling displaces the isotherms upward in the upper 500 m causing cooler waters to reach the surface, evident in the NODC June–July temperature section (Fig. 5; from Brock *et al.* submitted). The displacement is greatest near the coast, causing the greatest change in SST. The 20°C isotherm that lies at 100–150 m depth over most of the transect outcrops at the surface 25 km offshore. Farther offshore between 100–200 km, the isotherms are also displaced upwards, although the effect is not as great as the nearshore displacement. The two regions of upward displacement observed in the NODC section are coincident with the two regions of maximal upward velocity calculated from the windfield, one at the coast related to coastal upwelling and the other offshore within the region of maximum positive curl.

Phytoplankton pigment concentrations

The spatial scales and temporal variability of upwelling systems can be examined at the lowest trophic level using satellite remote sensing of ocean colour. Coastal zone colour scanner

(CZCS) measurements of ocean colour can yield quantitative estimates of near-surface phytoplankton pigment concentrations (Figs 2, 4b), and provide an index of phytoplankton biomass (McClain *et al.* 1990; Esais 1980; Yentsch 1983). To examine the Arabian Sea phytoplankton response to upwelling, a four-year composite image of August–September ocean colour was produced from 105 separate scenes acquired during August–September of 1979 through 1982 (Figs 2, 4b). Few scenes are available from July when extensive clouds cover the region. The CZCS scenes were individually processed to depict pigment concentration at 4 km spatial resolution for the northwest Arabian Sea region within 12–25° north latitude and 52–65°E longitude. The branching, two-channel bio-optical algorithm of Gordon *et al.* (1983) was used to retrieve phytoplankton pigment concentration. The surface pigment concentration images were transformed to a uniform equidistant-rectangular projection, registered to a standard coastline contour, and averaged to create a four-year summer phytoplankton bloom climatology (Brock *et al.* in press).

The highest chlorophyll concentrations (10 mg/m^3) are found along the coast where the surface waters are coldest (Fig. 4b). Chlorophyll content decreases rapidly offshore to approximately 2 mg/m^3 at 100 km. A small peak in chlorophyll concentration occurs between 150–200 km. Farther offshore, chlorophyll con-

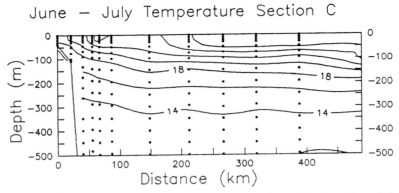

Fig. 5. June−July temperature (°C) section from the NODC composite section located parallel this transect 100 km north (from Brock *et al.* submitted).

tent decreases to 1.5 mg/m³ at 500 km. However, at 500 km the pigment concentrations remain 5−10 times higher than other oligotrophic regions in the Arabian Sea (Brock *et al.* 1990). High pigment concentrations covary with the upwelling velocity predicted from the July windfield, and with the cool SSTs observed in July.

We found one important difference between the model-predicted upwelling and the upwelling effects observed in SST and pigment. In contrast to the calculated upwelling velocity, the coastal upwelling effects (cool SST and high pigment concentrations) extend farther offshore, with a smoother, more gradual slope. The distinction is difficult to evaluate because the scales of the observations are different. One possible explanation is that we overestimated k, the coefficient that describes the density structure of the upper ocean. An alternate explanation is that the effects of coastal upwelling are distributed offshore by advective or turbulent motion, processes that are ignored in our model. Diffusive processes in particular would act to decrease the steep coastal gradient, and distribute cool, chlorophyll-rich water farther offshore, in better agreement with the observed patterns.

The sediment record of upwelling

Previous studies have related the distribution of planktonic foraminifer shells in coretop sediments to upwelling in the Arabian Sea (Prell & Curry 1981; Prell 1984, Cullen & Prell 1984; Anderson & Prell 1991; Prell *et al.* 1990). We examined these patterns with respect to the wind forcing. The time and space scales of the observations are coarse compared to the environmental observations. Only a few sediment

samples are available and are widely spaced along the transect. No samples are available within 50 km of the coast, so the nearshore maximum in upwelling is poorly resolved. The sediments represent accumulation of several hundreds of years, and thus integrate seasonal and inter-annual variation. We assume that the sediment record is dominated by foraminifers produced during the summer upwelling bloom and thus reflects the SW Monsoon hydrographic conditions over the past few hundred years. This assumption is supported by sediment trap observations that show that most of the foraminifer shells are produced during the SW monsoon interval (Curry *et al.*, this volume).

To express the changes in foraminifer species abundance that occur along the transect, we constructed profiles (Fig. 6a) from maps of species abundance in coretop samples. The maps and sample distribution are described in Cullen & Prell (1984). Onshore-offshore gradients have also been examined by Prell *et al.* (1990) and Anderson & Prell (1991). In the northwest Arabian Sea three species are most abundant, together comprising more than 60% of the shells in the >150 μm fraction. *Globigerina bulloides* is most abundant in the nearshore environment and decreases offshore from >35% to less than 20%. *Globigerinita glutinata* increases offshore to maximum values at approximately 250 km. Thus, these two species form a nearshore−offshore gradient in fauna. Together they dominate the upwelling region between 0−500 km offshore. Everywhere along the transect, tropical species such as *Globigerinoides ruber*, *Globigerinoides sacculifer* and other species with warm-water affinities are low in abundance (less than 10%; Cullen & Prell 1984). Farther offshore (more than 500 km), *G. ruber* and other tropical

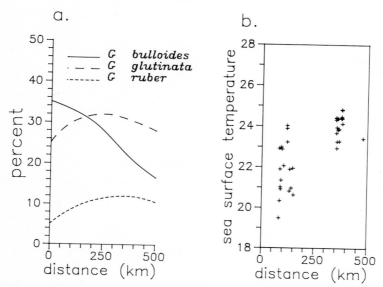

Fig. 6. (a) Foraminifer abundance in coretop sediments (based on maps of foraminifer abundance from Cullen & Prell 1984) along the transect shown in Fig. 1. (b) Sea surface temperature estimates calculated from 18 nearshore and 17 offshore coretop samples using the transfer function FI-2.

species dominate the species assemblage (Cullen & Prell 1984). Hutson & Prell (1980) observe that the *G. glutinata* distribution is typical of an ecotone species. *G. glutinata* is most abundant between the cool eutrophic water dominated by *G. bulloides* and the warmer oligotrophic water dominated by tropical species such as *G. ruber* and *G. sacculifer*.

The response of the foraminifer fauna can also be expressed using a transfer function to relate faunal patterns to environmental parameters. Transfer functions that relate the multivariate (species) response of the plankton to a univariate environmental gradient contain some uncertainty because several environmental variables often covary and are correlated in the modern environment (Imbrie & Kipp 1971). In our application of a transfer function, SST is considered to be a proxy for an ensemble of conditions that includes cool SST, a thin mixed layer, and enhanced pigment concentrations. The advantage of the transfer function is that the degree of environmental change produced by upwelling can be estimated as a common unit (°C) from the multivariate species composition observed in the sediments.

We calculated SST estimates using the warm-season transfer equation FI-2 (Hutson & Prell 1980) developed for the Indian Ocean (Fig. 6b). To examine the variability in SST along the transect, we selected a set of 27 coretop samples collected during cruise RC2704 (Anderson &

Prell 1991). The distribution consists of essentially two groups of samples: one in the nearshore and the other in the offshore region (Fig. 1). Eighteen samples are located on the continental margin in 400–1400 m water depth and the others are situated approximately 380–400 km offshore in 1800–4000 m water depth. The nearshore estimates are variable and range between 19 and 24°C, (mean SST = 21.9°C; 1σ = 1.2). The offshore estimates are warmer and less variable (mean SST = 24.0°C; 1σ = 0.5). The estimates are generally colder than the observed SSTs, however the difference between the nearshore and offshore sites (2°C) is similar to the observed difference. A more uniform sample distribution would improve the resolution of variation along the transect, particularly in the region near the coast. These two groups of samples resolve only the large-scale differences between the nearshore and offshore region.

The patterns of foraminifer abundance (expressed as species percentages or SST estimates) observed in maps and at single sites can be related to the effects of wind-driven upwelling. The nearshore sites examined here lie at the outer edge of coastal upwelling effects observed in SST and phytoplankton biomass. Within this region, the upper ocean environment is dominated by the coastal upwelling process, and upwelling is proportional to the magnitude of the wind speed parallel to the coast. Ideally, sites used to monitor the effect of coastal up-welling should be located within 100 km of the coast. Farther offshore, the upper ocean en-vironment is influenced only by curl-driven upwelling, and the upwelling effects are thus proportional to the gradient in wind stress. In the modern environment, the combination of coastal upwelling together with curl-driven pro-cesses produces an upwelling gradient between the nearshore and the offshore sites that is reflected in the physical environment and also in the zooplankton abundance patterns in core-top sediments. With reference to the marine geological record of upwelling, we attribute the faunal differences between the nearshore and offshore sites to the combined effect of coastal upwelling and curl-driven upwelling that are both strongest at the nearshore sites.

Summary

A simple one-dimensional model of upwelling related to wind stress forced by the July clima-tological windfield gives reasonable agreement with estimates of the vertical upwelling velocity off Oman. The model defines the spatial scales of nearshore upwelling related to the wind stress and offshore upwelling processes related to the curl in the wind stress.

The non-linear relationship between wind speed and wind stress related to transfer of momentum from the atmosphere to the surface ocean amplifies the response to changes in wind speed. Changes in wind speed (or the gradient in the wind speed) result in squared changes in wind stress and in the upwelling velocity. This relationship makes sediment indicators of up-welling a sensitive but non-linear index of the wind speed.

The wind-driven physical processes of coastal upwelling and offshore upward Ekman pumping are observed to create distinct surface layer environments that are defined by temperature, thermal structure, and phytoplankton biomass. Cool, phytoplankton-rich surface waters fringe the coast. A secondary, moderate bloom and SST depression is centred approximately 100–250 km offshore associated with the maxi-mum curl in the windfield. Farther offshore (200–500 km) the effects of Ekman pumping remain evident in the form of enriched phyto-plankton biomass. These differing coastal and offshore environments are associated with dis-tinct patterns of foraminifer abundance in the underlying sediments.

The ideas in this paper benefitted from discussions with S. C. Clemens, C. McClain, D. Murray, R. Oglesby, and R. C. Smith, and from the comments from two anonymous reviewers. J. C. Brock acknowl-edges funding from the NASA graduate Assistantship Program and the assistance of C. R. McClain and J. Firestone in processing the satellite and hydro-graphic data. Funding for W. Prell and D. Anderson was provided by grants from the National Science Foundation (OCE-8511571) and from the Department of Energy (DEFG02-85ER60304) to W. Prell at Brown University.

References

ANDERSON, D. M. & PRELL, W. L. 1991. The Coastal upwelling gradient during the Late Pleistocene. *In*: PRELL, W. L., NIITSUMA, N. *et al. Proceedings of the Ocean Drilling Program, Scientific Results*, Ocean Drilling Program, College Station, TX, **117**, 265–276.

BROCK, J. C., McCLAIN, C. R. & HAY, W. W. 1990. Southwest monsoon biological variability in the northwest Arabian Sea, *EOS*, **71**, 532.

——, —— & —— (submitted). A Southwest monsoon hydrographic climatology for northwestern Arabian Sea. *Journal of Geophysical Research*.

——, ——, LUTHER, M. E. & HAY, W. W. (in press). The phytoplankton bloom in the northwest Arabian Sea during the southwest monsoon of 1979. *Journal of Geophysical Research*, **96**, 20 623–20 642.

BRUCE, J. G. 1974. Some details of upwelling off the Somali and Arabian coasts. *Journal of Marine Research*, **32**, 419–422.

CULLEN, J. L. & PRELL, W. L. 1984. Planktonic foraminifera of the northern Indian Ocean: distri-bution and preservation in surface sediments, *Marine Micropaleontology*, **9**, 1–52.

ESAIS, W. E. 1980. Remote Sensing of oceanic phyto-plankton: present capabilities and future goals. *In*: FALOWSKI, P. G. (ed.) *Primary Productivity in the Sea*, Plenum, New York, 321–337.

HASTENRATH, S. & LAMB, P. 1971. *Climatic Atlas of the Indian Ocean. Part I: Surface Circulation and Climate*, University of Wisconsin Press.

HUTSON, W. H. & PRELL, W. L. 1980. A paleo-ecological transfer function, FI-2, for Indian Ocean planktonic foraminifera, *Paleontology*, **54** (2), 381–399.

IMBRIE, J. & KIPP, N. J. 1971. A new micropaleonto-logical method for paleoclimatology: application to a late Pleistocene Caribbean core. *In*: TUREKIAN, K. K. (ed.) *The Late Cenozoic Glacial Ages*, Yale University Press, New Haven, 1–81.

GORDON, H. R., CLARK, D. K., BROWN, J. W., BROWN, O. B., EVANS, R. H. & BROENKOW, W. W. 1983. Phytoplankton pigment concen-trations in the mid-Atlantic Bight: Comparison of ship determinations and CZCS estimates. *Applied Optics*, **22** (1), 20–36.

LUTHER, M. E. & O'BRIEN, J. J. 1985. A model of the seasonal circulation in the Arabian Sea forced by observed winds. *Progress in Oceanography*, **14**, 353–385.

——, —— & PRELL, W. L. 1990. Variability in up-welling fields in the northwestern Indian Ocean, 1, Model experiments for the Past 18000 Years. *Paleoceanography*, **5**, 433–446.

MCCLAIN, C. R., ESAIAS, W. E., FELDMAN, G. C., ELROD, J., EUDRES, D., FIRESTONE, J., DARZI, M., EVANS, R. & BROWN, J. 1990. Physical and biological processes in the North Atlantic during the EGGE year. *Journal of Geophysical Research*, **95**, 18027–18048.

MCCREARY, J. P. & KUNDU, P. 1989. A numerical investigation of sea surface temperature varia-bility in the Arabian Sea. *Journal of Geophysical Research*, **94** (C11), 16097–16114.

PRELL, W. L. 1984. Variation of monsoonal upwelling: a response to changing solar radiation. *In*: HANSEN, J. E. & TAKAHASHI, T., (eds) *Climate Processes and Climate Sensitivity*. American Geo-physical Union Geophysical Monograph, **29**, 48–57.

—— & CURRY, W. B. 1981. Faunal and isotopic indices of monsoon upwelling: Western Arabian Sea. *Oceanologica Acta*, **4** (1), 91–98.

——, MARVIL, R. E. & LUTHER, M. E. 1990. Varia-bility in upwelling fields in the northwestern Indian Ocean 2, data-model comparison at 9000 years B. P., *Paleoceanography*, **5**, 447–457.

—— & STREETER, H. F. 1982. Temporal patterns of monsoonal upwelling along Arabia: a modern analogue for the interpretation of Quaternary SST anomalies. *Journal of Marine Research*, **40**, 143–155.

SMITH, R. L. & BOTTERO, J. S. 1977. On upwelling in the Arabian Sea. *In*: ANGEL, M. (ed.) *A Voyage of Discovery*, Permagon, New York.

SWALLOW, J. C. 1984. Some aspects of the physical oceanography of the Indian Ocean. *Deep-Sea Research*, **31**, 639–650.

YENTSCH, C. S. 1983. Remote sensing of biological substances. *In*: CRACKNELL, A. P. (ed.) *Remote Sensing Applications in Science and Technology*, Reidel, New York, 267–297.

YOSHIDA, K., 1955. Coastal upwelling off the California Coast. *Records of Oceanographic Works in Japan*, **2**, 8–20.

A lamina-scale geochemical and sedimentological study of sediments from the Peru Margin (Site 680, ODP Leg 112)

A. C. APLIN[1,2], A. N. BISHOP[3,2], C. J. CLAYTON[1], A. T. KEARSLEY[3], J.-R. MOSSMANN[4,5], R. L. PATIENCE[1,6], A. W. G. REES[7] & S. J. ROWLAND[7]

[1] *BP Research, Chertsey Road, Sunbury-on-Thames, Middlesex, TW16 7LN, UK*
[2] *Present address: Newcastle Research Group (NRG) in Fossil Fuels and Environmental Geochemistry, Drummond Building, The University, Newcastle upon Tyne, NE1 7RU, UK*
[3] *Department of Geology, Oxford Polytechnic, Gypsy Lane, Oxford, OX3 0BP, UK*
[4] *Department of Geology, University of Sheffield, Sheffield, S3 7HF, UK*
[5] *Present address: B.R.G.M. Service Geochimie, Fluides et Roches, Avenue de Concyr, B.P. 6009 45 060 Orleans Cedex 2, France*
[6] *Present address: Statoil, Postboks 300, N-4001 Stavanger, Norway*
[7] *Department of Environmental Sciences, Polytechnic South West, Drake Circus,*

Abstract: Individual laminae (mm−cm) were isolated from late Pliocene−Holocene sediments cored at Site 680 during ODP Leg 112 (Peru upwelling region). At all depths, individual laminae alternate between (1) pale, high porosity, clay-poor, diatom 'framework' oozes containing a high proportion of complete, well preserved diatom frustules and (2) dark, low porosity diatomaceous muds containing abundant diatom debris and foraminifer tests. In some instances, detrital-rich laminae with low amounts of diatom debris were also observed.

Hydrogen-rich organic matter is finely disseminated throughout the sediments, perhaps occurring as coatings on detrital and biogenic grains. Both carbon isotopic and pyrolysis-GCMS analyses suggest that the organic matter is derived mainly from a marine algal and/or bacterial input. Py-GCMS further shows that, even in the sediments from 4.91 mbsf, the organic matter is significantly altered from the composition of living organisms. Only in two organic-lean Pliocene samples was there any sign of a significant input of terrestrial organic matter. Relative to laminae deposited during the Pleistocene−Holocene, late Pliocene laminae are depleted in TOC. This may reflect variations in primary productivity. TOC contents also vary between adjacent diatomaceous mud laminae in Pleistocene−Holocene sediments. In these laminae, TOC is inversely proportional to diatom abundance (which is believed to be related to productivity) but correlates positively with detrital content. Variations in the TOC content of closely spaced laminae is apparently not controlled by variations in productivity or preservation, but probably by variations in the TOC content of particulate matter reaching the sediment−water interface.

Some parameters (organic S/C; δ^{34} S) vary on a lamina scale − no larger scale trends are apparent. These variations are presumably the result of short-term, local changes in diagenetic conditions and are hard to quantify. In these H_2S-rich sediments, differential uptake of sulphur into organic matter may be caused by variations in the availability of specific, reactive inorganic sulphur species, perhaps polysulphides.

This study shows that conventional geochemical analysis of bulk, or of widely spaced samples can hide significant variations in sediment composition and inferred palaeoceanographical conditions. Although bulk samples may be used to determine the gross characteristics of a sedimentary sequence, fine-scale sampling is needed to define the processes which determined those characteristics.

Geochemical analyses of sediments are conventionally carried out on samples which cover a depth interval of centimetres to metres and which often contain different lithologies, organic carbon contents etc. This is partly because of the difficulty of sampling on a smaller scale and also so that an overall geochemical picture can be drawn for a large ($10-10^2$ metre) depth interval. However, geological events are often recorded on a millimetre to centimetre scale, most obviously in laminated sediments. It is by no means certain that analysis of bulk

From SUMMERHAYES, C. P., PRELL, W. L. & EMEIS, K. C. (eds), 1992, *Upwelling Systems: Evolution Since the Early Miocene.* Geological Society Special Publication No 64, pp 131−149.

samples will give much insight into the sedimentological and oceanographical processes which
control the physical and chemical nature of
the sediment record. Bulk samples average
chemical information from sediments which
accumulated over at least 10^3 years, whereas
oceanographical processes (e.g. vertical flux of
solid phases) vary on much shorter timescales
(e.g. Honjo 1982). Therefore, it seems likely
that in order to understand the processes which
control the chemical characteristics of the sediment record, sampling may be needed on a
finer scale than is generally performed.

In the present study, individual laminae
(mm−cm) were isolated from sediments cored
at Site 680 during ODP Leg 112, covering the
depth interval 4.91−88.00 metres below seafloor
(mbsf). The sedimentology of individual
laminae was determined by scanning electron
microscopy (SEM) and a wide range of geochemical measurements were made. These data
have been combined to investigate (1) controls
on the amount, nature, distribution of and
preservation of organic matter, (2) the nature
of and variations in the inorganic species present
and (3) the incorporation of inorganic sulphur
into organic matter.

Site location and general lithostratigraphy

Site 680 of ODP Leg 112 was drilled in 250 m of
water on an E−W transect of three sites (679,
680 and 681) in the Salaverry Basin off Peru
(Suess, von Huene *et al.* 1988). The site was
chosen for the present study because it contains
an expanded record of late Pliocene to Holocene
coastal upwelling. Three generalized lithostratigraphic units have been identified (Suess, von
Huene *et al.* 1988). Unit 1 (0−48 mbsf) is a
thinly laminated, dark olive green foraminifer−
diatomaceous mud rich in organic matter (up to
12% total organic carbon (TOC)), which was
deposited during the late Pleistocene and
Holocene. Unit 2 (48−56.4 mbsf) consists of
thinly laminated, diatomaceous silty mud with
authigenic dolomites and phosphates concentrated in diatom-rich laminae or sandy layers.
TOC contents in Unit 2 are somewhat lower
than in Unit 1. Average sedimentation rates in
Units 1 and 2 were 20−50 m/Ma. Units 2 and 3
are separated by a hiatus at 56.4 mbsf. Average
sedimentation rates in Unit 3 were around
100 m/Ma and TOC contents are generally lower
than in Units 1 and 2. All lithological units
appear to be broken repeatedly by hiatuses.
More detailed information on the lithology and
stratigraphy of sites drilled during ODP Leg 112
has been reported by Suess, von Huene *et al.*

(1988), Kemp (1990), Oberhaensli *et al.* (1990)
and Wefer *et al.* (1990). Further information on
the general organic geochemistry can be found
in Patience *et al.* (1990), on pore-water chemistry in Kastner *et al.* (1990) and Mossman *et al.*
(1990), and on $\delta^{18}O$ stratigraphy in Wefer *et al.*
(1990).

There are considerable lithological variations
within each lithostratigraphic unit (Kemp 1990)
and the broad units are too diverse for a detailed
palaeoclimatic/oceanographic overview. This
diversity also renders geochemical analyses of
bulk samples (i.e. those covering depth intervals
of tens of centimetres) useful only as an average
representation of a wide range of sediment
compositions. From studies of bulk samples, it
is difficult to understand the relationship
between measured geochemical properties and
the palaeoceanographical and sedimentological
processes which control them. Site 680 was an
excellent source of lamina-scale samples with
which to study these relationships.

Experimental

SEM

The method used has been described in detail in
Patience *et al.* (1990). Briefly, for each sample,
a slab approximately 5 mm thick was cut from
the vertical surface of wet, cold but unfrozen
core. In some cases this was then stained with
osmium tetroxide (OsO_4), which reacts with
organic matter in the sample. Samples were
placed in moulds and vacuum dried. Epoxy
resin was then released upon the dry slab,
which caused impregnation of the pore space
when the sample was returned to atmospheric
pressure.

Polished thin sections were carbon coated
and analysed in a JSM 840 electron microscope.
Backscattered electron imagery (BEI) was
employed to produce compositional contrast
images of fine textures. Organic matter was
located using osmium element mapping by
energy dispersive X-ray (EDS) microanalysis.
Low-magnification BEI mosaics were compiled
for each sample to provide basic information
about different lamina types and for the physical
isolation of individual laminae for further study.

Sampling

Laminae identified in thin section were cross-
referenced back to the bulk sample. Individual
laminae were then cut from the bulk sample
using a scalpel, homogenized and subdivided
for the various analyses described below.

Elemental analysis

Total carbon (TC) was determined on a Carlo Erba 1106 Elemental Analyser as described by Patience *et al.* (1990). TOC was calculated as the difference between TC and carbonate carbon, which was determined by reaction with 6M HCl followed by detection of evolved CO_2 using infrared spectroscopy.

Total sulphur (TS) was determined using a LECO C–S analyser. Pyrite and iron monosulphide were removed from the sediment using the chromium (II) reduction technique (Canfield *et al.* 1986). Chromium (II) reduction converts reduced inorganic sulphur to H_2S, which was reprecipitated as Ag_2S, cleaned with ammonia solution and distilled water, and weighed. The weight was used to calculate the pyrite content of the samples. S/C ratios of organic matter were determined by simultaneous LECO analysis of sulphur and carbon in samples from which pyrite had been chemically removed (Canfield *et al.* 1986).

Si, Al and Fe were determined by ICPAES following fusion of samples with a lithium metaborate flux.

Py-GCMS

The pyrolysis system used was a CDS pyroprobe with a platinum coil inserted directly into the heated (200°C) injection port of the GC. Pyrolysis occurred for 20 seconds at a maximum temperature of 610°C. GCMS was performed on a Carlo Erba Mega gas chromatograph coupled to a Kratos MS-25 mass spectrometer. The chromatograph was fitted with a DB5 fused silica column (30 m × 0.32 mm internal diameter). The column temperature was held initially at 40°C for 5 minutes and then increased to 300°C at 5°C per minute. Electron impact mass spectra (mass range m/z 50 to 500) were acquired at an ionization voltage of 38 eV and an emission current of 400 μA.

Isotopic analyses

Silver sulphide (Ag_2S) resulting from the chromium (II) reduction procedure was used to determine the isotopic composition of pyritic sulphur ($\delta^{34}S$). Sulphides were converted to SO_2 using the method of Robinson & Kusakabe (1975) and analysed on an automated VG903 mass spectrometer. Results are reported relative to the CDT standard and have a reproducibility of 0.3‰.

The carbon isotopic composition of kerogen was determined, after removal of carbonate

with HCl, on a SIRA 10 isotope ratio mass spectrometer following combustion in a Carlo Erba NA1500 nitrogen analyser and cryoscopic separation of CO_2 and H_2O. After correction for isotopic interference effects (Deines 1970), the results were adjusted to the PDB scale using NBS-22 (-29.8‰ PDB) as a secondary standard.

Results and discussion

Laminae were analysed from lithostratigraphic units 1, 2 and 3 at Sites 680A and 680B (mostly the latter), covering the depth interval 4.91 to 88.00 mbsf (Table 1). In most cases, series of adjacent laminae were analysed and these are given sample letters A, B, C, D or E after the leg, core and section in Table 1. Examples of these are shown in Figs 1–3, which are BEI micrographs, along with sketches, of three of these series. In a few cases, individual laminae (rather than series) were analysed and these are coded G in Table 1.

Sedimentology

At all depths, individual laminae mostly alternate between: (1) dark, low porosity, clay (and scattered silt)-rich diatomaceous muds containing abundant diatom debris and foraminifer tests; and (2) pale, high porosity, clay-poor diatom 'framework' oozes containing a high proportion of complete, well preserved diatom frustules (see Table 1 for a brief lithological description of each lamina). In some instances, detrital-rich laminae with low amounts of diatom debris were observed. The smaller pellets referred to in Table 1 are probably from copepods, whilst the larger are from anchoveta. Mottling could be due to either disrupted copepod faeces or minor bioturbation.

Samples from Units 1 and 2 (<56.4 mbsf) are generally organic-rich and have moderate carbonate contents (Table 2). Laminae from Unit 3 have moderate to low TOC contents, low carbonate contents but more abundant diagenetic iron sulphide.

Each individual lamina has been classified as the most appropriate of the types described by Kemp (1990). The codes (a,b,c,d,e,f) are assigned in Table 1 and the types of lamina which they represent are summarized briefly here.

a. Simple ooze laminae representing fallout from an individual bloom event, mainly consisting of intact diatoms (0.3–1 mm).

b. Composite ooze laminae representing fallout from sequential bloom events without

Table 1. Sample locations, depths and lithologies.

Leg, core, section, sample	Depth (m) Top	Bottom	Lamina type*	Lithological unit	Description
112–680B-1H-4-G	4.91	4.93	a	1	Dark brown homogeneous diatom mud, strongly mottled, probably pelleted (100–300 μm)
112–680A-2H-1-A	9.31		b	1	Dark brown homogeneous diatom mud, slightly mottled
112–680A-2H-1-B			b	1	Pale buff laminated diatom framework, slightly mottled, strongly pelleted (100–200 μm)
112–680A-2H-1-C			b	1	Mid-brown laminated diatom framework, slightly mottled
112–680A-2H-1-D		9.33	b	1	Dark brown poorly laminated mud, slightly mottled
112–680B-2H-4-G	10.86	10.88	e	1	Pale grey coarse silt, rare mottles, burrows?
112–680B-2H-5-G	12.37	12.39	d	1	Dark olive green laminated diatom mud, slightly mottled, some pellets throughout
112–680B-2H-6-G	14.12	14.14	a	1	Dark brown homogeneous diatom mud, slightly mottled, some pellets throughout
112–680B-2H-6-A	14.14		b	1	Pale olive green diatom framework, slightly mottled
112–680B-2H-6-B			b	1	Mid-olive green diatom mud, slightly mottled, anchovetta pellets (2 mm)
112–680B-2H-6-C			b	1	Dark olive green diatom mud, slightly mottled, pellets
112–680B-2H-6-D			b	1	Pale to mid-olive green diatom mud, slightly mottled
112–680B-2H-6-E		14.16	b	1	Dark olive green diatom mud, slightly mottled
112–680B-6H-7-A	52.61		a/b	2	Dark brown mud, texture broken by dewatering veins, pelleted
112–680B-6H-7-B		52.63	a/b	2	Mid-brown laminated diatom mud, texture broken by dewatering veins, pelleted
112–680B-7H-3-A	56.16		b	2	Pale buff laminated diatom mud, texture broken by dewatering veins, pelleted
112–680B-7H-3-B		56.18	b	2	Dark grey-green vein, texture broken by dewatering veins, pelleted
112–680B-7H-6-G	69.35	69.37	e	3	Mid-brown homogeneous feldspathic fine silt, no mottling, gypsum abundant

112–680B-9H-6-A	80.26	a	3	Dark grey-green vein, texture broken by dewatering veins, pelleted
112-680B-9H-6-B	80.28	a	3	Mid-grey-green homogeneous diatom mud, texture broken by dewatering veins, pelleted
112–680B-10H-5-A	87.98	b	3	Dark olive green diatom framework, mottled
112–680B-10H-5-B		b	3	Mid-olive green diatom mud, mottled
112–680B-10H-5-C		b	3	Pale to dark olive green diatom framework, mottled, pelleted
112–680B-10H-5-D		b	3	Banded mid and pale olive green diatom framework, mottled
112–680B-10H-5-E	88.00	b	3	Dark olive green diatom framework, mottled, strongly pelleted

* Classification after Kemp (1990), described in text

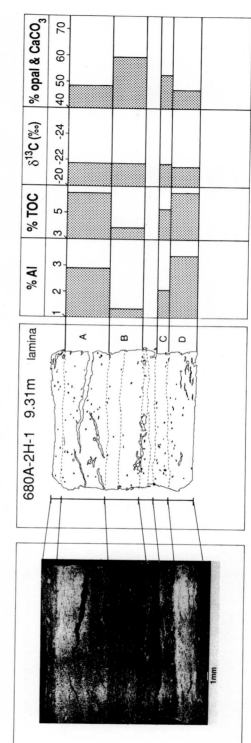

Fig. 1. Backscattered electron image micrograph and sketch of lamina set 680A-2H-1-A to D (9.31–9.33 mbsf), with variations in key geochemical parameters.

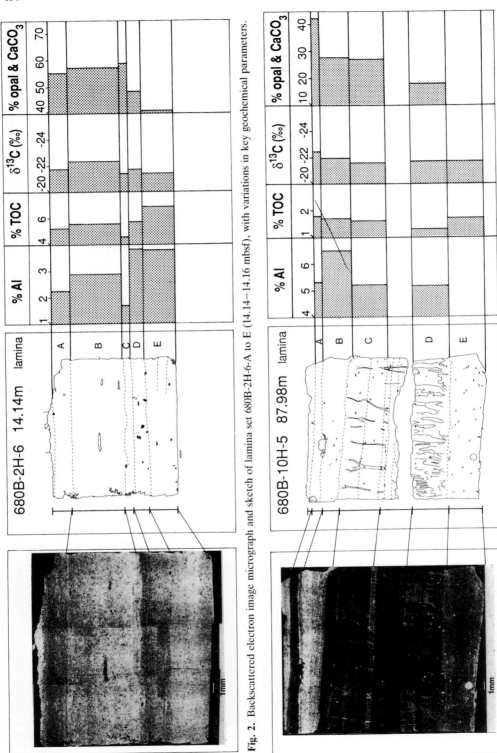

Fig. 2. Backscattered electron image micrograph and sketch of lamina set 680B-2H-6-A to E (14.14−14.16 mbsf), with variations in key geochemical parameters.

Fig. 3. Backscattered electron image micrograph and sketch of lamina set 680B-10H-5-A to E (87.98−88.00 mbsf), with variations in key geochemical parameters.

Table 2. Elemental and isotopic analyses on individual laminae.

Sample	Depth (m) Top	Bottom	TC (1)	TOC (2)	TS (3)	$\delta^{13}C$ (4)	$\delta^{34}S$ (5)	Fe	Si	Al
B-1H-4-G	4.91	4.93	6.7	5.6	2.1	−21.5	−26.3	2.3	22.0	4.5
A-2H-1-A	9.31		8.4	6.4	1.7	−21.4	−18.5	1.3	21.2	2.8
A-2H-1-B			6.5	3.7	1.1	−21.4	n.d.	0.6	22.0	1.2
A-2H-1-C			7.1	5.4	1.4	−21.4	−12.8	1.1	23.5	2.1
A-2H-1-D		9.33	8.3	6.7	1.8	−21.2	−18.2	1.6	22.2	3.2
B-2H-4-G	10.86	10.88	1.4	1.2	0.9	−21.8	−32.4	2.0	30.5	5.7
B-2H-5-G	12.37	12.39	4.8	4.8	1.8	−21.7	−26.8	3.2	24.7	8.1
B-2H-6-G	14.12	14.14	6.3	4.7	2.4	−21.5	−23.3	1.9	18.6	4.2
B-2H-6-A	14.14		7.3	5.1	1.5	−21.5	−18.9	1.1	22.6	2.2
B-2H-6-B			7.7	5.4	1.7	−22.1	−22.0	1.5	24.5	2.8
B-2H-6-C			6.6	4.6	1.3	−21.4	n.d.	1.2	23.9	1.7
B-2H-6-D			8.1	6.1	1.8	−21.5	−19.5	1.3	21.4	3.9
B-2H-6-E		14.16	9.1	7.3	2.2	−21.5	−4.9	2.3	21.4	3.9
B-6H-7-A	52.61		5.8	5.6	1.8	−20.7	−9.3	1.0	28.6	1.8
B-6H-7-B		52.63	5.6	5.4	1.9	−20.6	−7.6	2.4	30.9	2.4
B-7H-3-A	56.16		4.1	4.0	1.6	−21.5	−12.8	1.7	29.0	2.8
B-7H-3-B		56.18	5.0	5.0	2.0	−20.8	−15.6	2.0	28.9	3.7
B-7H-6-G	69.35	69.37	0.8	0.5	2.9	−23.9	−24.3	4.2	22.6	9.4
B-9H-6-A	80.26		1.1	1.1	3.0	−22.0	−18.9	4.1	24.3	7.0
B-9H-6-B		80.28	0.5	0.5	3.0	−23.7	−16.2	4.1	25.1	7.6
B-10H-5-A	87.98		1.8	1.7	2.1	−22.3	−14.0	3.2	31.5	5.3
B-10H-5-B			1.7	1.6	2.7	−22.0	−13.2	3.3	27.4	6.5
B-10H-5-C			1.6	1.5	2.5	−21.3	−11.3	3.0	24.5	5.2
B-10H-5-D			1.4	1.3	2.3	−21.8	−10.3	2.7	21.8	5.3
B-10H-5-E		88.00	1.8	1.7	2.7	−21.8	−12.5	n.d.	n.d.	n.d.

All elemental abundances are weight per cent.
(1) TC = total carbon
(2) TOC = total organic carbon
(3) TS = total sulphur
(4) isotopic value for organic carbon
(5) isotopic value for inorganic sulphur (i.e. in pyrite)
n.d. = not determined

intervening terrigenous sediment deposition, consisting of distinct layers of different diatom species (up to 10 mm).

c. Coccolith ooze (up to 1 mm).

d. Mixed diatom ooze/terrigenous sediment representing deposition from turbidity and/or bottom currents containing resuspended sediment. These consist of layers of diatoms alternating with thinner microlayers of terrigenous sediment (0.5 to tens of millimetres).

e. Terrigenous sediment consisting of silt/sand with subordinate clay (0.05 mm to decimetre beds).

f. Chemical or diagenetic origin, consisting of dolomite or phosphate (0.5 to tens of millimetres).

In many cases, it proved difficult to distinguish clearly between types a and b, whilst many laminae should really be classified between type b and d 'end members'.

Three main sets of laminae were analysed and classified by SEM in this study. These are: 680A-2H-1-A to D, 680B-2H-6-A to E and 680B-10H-5-A to E (Table 1). All fourteen of these laminae were classified as mainly type b. Of these three sets, 680A-2H-1-A to D contain least seasonal terrigenous input, and are not reworked (i.e. 'pure' b). 680B-2H-6-A to E have some terrigenous input and signs of current reworking, and thus start to approach type d. 680B-10H-5-A to E have thin silts and may be current reworked and also approach type d. It should be noted that the qualitative assessment of terrigenous input here is based on SEM analysis. A more detailed microscopic analysis and the quantitative elemental analyses in Tables 2 and 3 would suggest that even the purest type b laminae contain at least 10% by weight detrital minerals. Hence the laminae in these three series fall at different points on a scale between types b (least detrital input) and d (most detrital input). Nevertheless, the sedimentology of these three sets is sufficiently similar that the geochemical data can be meaningfully compared.

Each lamina is about 4−5 mm thick; because these are composite laminae (i.e. they consist of

Table 3. Inorganic constituents derived from elemental analysis of individual laminae.

Sample	CaCO₃ (1)	Detrital (2)	Opal (3)	Biogenic (4)	Inorganic (5)	Total (6)
			Weight percent			
B-1H-4-G	9.3	47.9	23.9	33.2	81.1	88.6
A-2H-1-A	16.3	29.8	31.0	47.3	77.1	85.6
A-2H-1-B	23.0	12.8	41.0	64.0	76.8	81.7
A-2H-1-C	14.5	22.3	39.5	54.0	76.3	83.5
A-2H-1-D	13.7	34.0	31.0	44.7	78.7	87.6
B-2H-4-G	1.6	60.6	35.9	37.5	98.1	99.7
B-2H-5-G	0.1	86.1	11.2	11.3	97.4	104.0
B-2H-6-G	13.7	44.6	18.2	31.9	76.5	82.8
B-2H-6-A	17.7	23.4	37.0	54.7	78.1	84.9
B-2H-6-B	19.0	29.8	38.0	57.0	86.8	94.0
B-2H-6-C	17.0	18.1	42.4	59.4	77.5	83.6
B-2H-6-D	17.0	29.8	33.3	50.3	80.1	88.2
B-2H-6-E	15.2	41.5	25.7	40.9	82.4	94.1
B-6H-7-A	2.0	19.1	51.9	53.9	73.0	80.5
B-6H-7-B	1.7	25.5	53.8	55.5	81.0	88.2
B-7H-3-A	0.6	29.8	47.7	48.3	78.1	83.4
B-7H-3-B	0.1	39.4	42.8	42.9	82.3	89.0
B-7H-6-G	2.7	100.0	0.0	2.7	102.7	103.4
B-9H-6-A	0.0	74.4	16.0	16.0	90.4	91.9
B-9H-6-B	0.0	80.9	14.6	14.6	95.5	96.2
B-10H-5-A	0.9	56.4	40.2	41.1	97.5	99.6
B-10H-5-B	0.6	69.1	25.2	25.8	94.9	97.0
B-10H-5-C	0.3	55.3	25.7	26.0	81.3	83.0
B-10H-5-D	0.4	56.4	19.4	19.8	76.2	78.5
B-10H-5-E	0.4	n.d.	n.d.	n.d.	n.d.	n.d.

(1) Assumes all inorganic carbon is CaCO₃
(2) Based on Al concentration
(3) Excess silica by difference based on 'non detrital' Si content
(4) Opal + CaCO₃
(5) Biogenic + Detrital
(6) Biogenic + Detrital + Total Organic Matter (assumes latter = TOC/0.75)
n.d. = not determined
See text for detailed explanations of calculations

more than one seasonal bloom), it is not possible to determine the timespan represented by a single lamina. Average sedimentation rates of 20–50 m/Ma in Units 1 and 2 and 100 m/Ma in Unit 3 have been reported (Suess, von Huene *et al.* 1988). A more detailed study has been recently reported for Unit 1 (Wefer *et al.* 1990). In this, the average sedimentation rate for the depth interval of the laminae in Unit 1 studied here (4.91–14.16 m) was 50–75 m/Ma. By assuming an average sedimentation rate for each unit, one can calculate that each centimetre of laminae in Unit 1 corresponds to roughly 130–200 years, in Unit 2 to 200–500 years, and in Unit 3 to 3–100 years. However, these figures should be treated with caution since there is good evidence that sedimentation was episodic at Site 680.

The so-called 'general' laminae (i.e. those with the G sample identifier) are somewhat thicker samples (up to 2 cm) and have more diverse origins; types a, d and e are all represented. There are also three adjacent pairs of laminae (Table 1) with type a laminae representing undisturbed sediment and type b representing dewatering veins. Not one of the laminae studied is from classes c (coccolith ooze) or f (dolomite or phosphate).

A detailed oxygen isotope stratigraphy has been carried for Unit 1 (Wefer *et al.* 1990) and related to glacial or interglacial periods of sedimentation. In general, sediments deposited during glacial periods have lower organic carbon contents than sediments deposited during interglacials. Most of the laminae from Unit 1 (i.e. all those from less than 14.16 mbsf) are believed to be interglacial. Only 680B-2H-4-G and 680B-2H-5-G are likely to have been deposited during glacial periods. Laminae in Unit 1 are part of the interval considered to be the least disturbed section and most representative of material sedimented from a coastal upwelling zone.

Major inorganic sedimentary components

Elemental analyses are reported in Table 2 and were used to estimate the relative proportions of major sedimentary components: carbonate, detrital minerals, biogenic silica and organic matter (Table 3). Carbonate was calculated from the inorganic carbon data, assuming that the cation was calcium (i.e. $CaCO_3$). The abundance of detrital minerals was estimated from the Al content, by assuming that the sample with most Al (680B-7H-6-G; Table 2) is composed of 100% detrital minerals. Microscopic analysis suggests that this assumption is reasonable, as does the Al content of the sample, which is close to that of 'average shale'. Thus:

% detrital content = $(Al_{sample}/Al_{7H-6}) \times 100$

The amount of biogenic silica (or 'opal' in Table 3) was determined by partitioning silicon between detrital and biogenic phases thus:

excess Si = $Si_{sample} - ([Si/Al]_{7H-6} * Al_{sample})$

and

excess SiO_2 = opal = excess Si * 60/28

The sum of calcium carbonate + detrital + opal + total organic matter (approximately = TOC/ 0.75) should be 100% if there are no other significant inputs to the sediments and the assumptions above are correct. In fact, most totals are somewhat less than 100 (Table 3). It is close to 100% for the three samples with the most terrestrial input (680B-2H-4-G, 2H-5-G and 7H-6-G (the last by definition)). Most of the more biogenic laminae have totals between 80 and 95%. The main reasons for the discrepancy are that: (1) the clay mineralogy of sediments in Unit 3 is slightly different to that of Units 1 and 2, with a higher percentage of Si-rich expandable clay in Unit 3 (Clayton & Kemp 1990); (2) there is considerable hydration water, particularly in the opal-rich samples.

The uncertainties described above do not hide several clear trends in the elemental data and calculated sedimentary components. Sediments in Unit 3 generally have higher contents of detrital minerals than those in Units 1 and 2 (Table 3, Fig. 4). A plot of Fe vs Al gives a strong correlation which passes through the origin (Fig. 5). This suggests that a relatively constant type of detrital material has been supplied to the sediments, with no major transfer of Fe between laminae. This is reasonable in these highly sulphidic sediments, where reduced Fe is quickly precipitated as sulphide (see below).

Conversely, calcium carbonate is generally enriched in sediments from Unit 1 compared to Units 2 and 3. The abundance of opal shows no systematic difference between Units 1 and 3, whilst it is somewhat higher in Unit 2 (Table 3; Fig. 4).

Compositional differences *within* each group of laminae reflect variations in the relative amounts of opal and detrital material. There is also a positive correlation between opal and carbonate for the type a and b laminae from Unit 1 (Table 3; Fig. 1). Microscopic evidence suggests that the carbonate is predominantly primary and mainly comprises benthic foraminifera. Whilst foraminifera were once abundant in laminae from Unit 3, they now appear as ghosts, which would explain the low carbonate contents in these samples. Diagenetic carbonate was observed by SEM as small rhombs, often of dolomite, but it was not quantified. If the carbonate is predominantly primary, then this suggests that the production of benthic foraminifera is related to that of siliceous organisms in the photic zone. More quantitative information is needed to interpret these data further.

Type and abundance of organic matter

Palynological work has shown that >95% of the organic matter in these sediments is 'amorphous' (Powell *et al.* 1990). This means that it lacks biological structure on the scale observable by light microscopy. Furthermore, osmium staining work demonstrated that the organic matter is, in all laminae, extremely finely disseminated, possibly 'coating' the surfaces of the inorganic particles. There are few discrete particles of amorphous organic matter, even in the faecal pellets.

In the absence of biological structure, py-GCMS was carried out on selected laminae in order to look for variations in the material which might contribute to the amorphous organic matter. Samples were pyrolysed from Units 1 (11 samples) and 3 (5 samples) only.

The results (see Fig. 6 for examples) indicate that there are no obvious differences in the type of organic matter entering the sediments in Unit 1. The sediments contain organic matter derived from a marine algal/bacterial source. As for the bulk samples (Rees *et al.* in press), the pyrolysis products are typical of those from pyrolysis of organisms such as algae or bacteria. However, the distribution of pyrolysis products are very different to those of algae and bacteria,

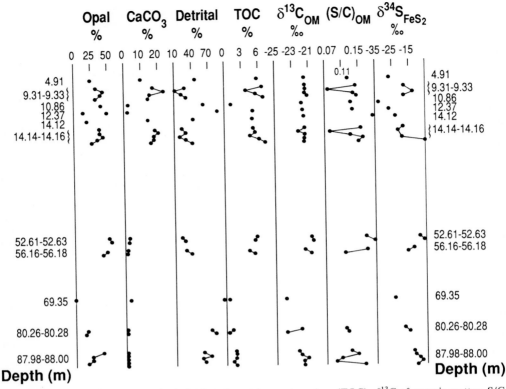

Fig. 4. Opal, calcium carbonate, detrital minerals, total organic carbon (TOC), $\delta^{13}C$ of organic matter, S/C weight ratio of organic matter and $\partial^{34}S$ of pyrite in individual laminae.

indicating substantial alteration of the precursor organic material. The samples from Unit 3 contain lower relative amounts of aliphatic components but are otherwise similar to samples from Units 1 and 2 (Fig. 6).

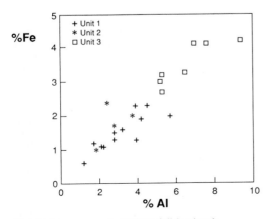

Fig. 5. Iron versus aluminium (all laminae).

Carbon isotope values ($\delta^{13}C$) are tightly clustered between -20.7 and -22.3‰ for all but two laminae (Table 2). These values are typical of Recent, marine-derived organic carbon. The latter two samples are from Unit 3 and are approximately 2‰ lighter than the 'average' of the remaining samples (Fig. 4). Combined with the py-GCMS work, these data suggest that most laminae contain essentially the same type of organic matter: marine algal/bacterial, which has been substantially modified compared to that of living organisms such as diatoms. Only in two of the deeper samples, with the lowest TOC contents, is there an indication of some terrestrial organic matter.

TOC contents are generally higher in Units 1 and 2 than in Unit 3 (Table 2). Wefer *et al.* (1990) have noted that in Unit 1, sediments deposited during glacial periods have lower organic carbon contents than those deposited during interglacials. They also observed that there is a clear relationship between lithology and $\delta^{18}O$, with laminated diatomaceous mud preferentially preserved during warm intervals

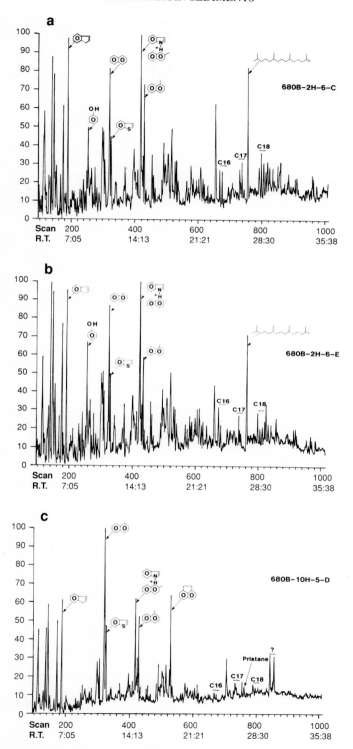

Fig. 6. Chromatograms resulting from pyrolysis-GCMS analysis of individual laminae.

(light $\delta^{18}O$ values), and burrowed sands and silty muds deposited during cold times (heavy $\delta^{18}O$ values). The Unit 1 laminae studied here are part of the interval considered to be representative of material sedimented from a coastal upwelling zone during interglacials.

If the laminae from all units are included, there is a general inverse relationship between Al (i.e. detrital minerals) and TOC (Fig. 7). This arises from the fact that samples from Units 1 and 2 are enriched in TOC and depleted in detrital minerals compared to samples from Unit 3. However, within Unit 1, organic matter is concentrated in Al-rich laminae (Figs 7 & 8). This trend is demonstrated by the two series of laminae in Unit 1, which show strong *negative* correlations between TOC and biogenic opal plus carbonate, and strong *positive* correlations between TOC and Al (Figs 1 & 8). Very similar correlations have been observed previously by Donegan & Schrader (1982) in sediments from the Gulf of California, and by Isaacs (1987) in the Monterey Formation on the California coast. In both cases, the sediments are lithologically similar to those examined in this study.

Controls on TOC contents

As described above, variations in TOC occur on two scales in these sediments. Firstly, laminae from Unit 3 are generally depleted in TOC relative to lithologically similar laminae from Units 2 and 3. Secondly, within sets of laminae from Unit 1, organic matter is enriched in laminae with a higher proportion of detrital minerals. This implies that the conditions controlling the relative rates of deposition of detrital minerals and organic matter were differ-

ent depending on the timescale involved (10^6 years for variations between units; $10-10^3$ years for lamina-scale variations). We will consider each timescale in turn, placing particular emphasis on comparison of type b laminae in each unit.

Unit-scale variations

The main factors influencing the TOC contents of sediments are: (1) primary productivity (i.e. rate of generation of organic matter in surface waters); (2) the rate at which organic carbon is delivered to the sediment surface (i.e. remineralization of organic matter in the water column); (3) the proportion of organic matter which survives remineralization in surface sediments ('burial efficiency') and (4) sedimentation rate (Muller & Suess 1979; Suess 1980; Ibach 1982; Henrichs & Reeburgh 1987; Canfield 1989; Pedersen & Calvert 1990). Generalizing from these and other studies, the accumulation of organic-rich sediments is expected where

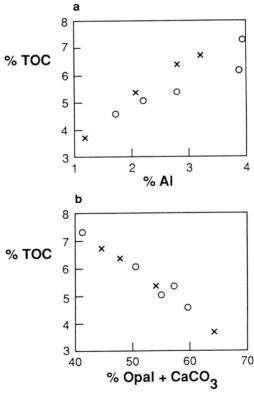

Fig. 8. Total organic carbon versus (a) aluminium and (b) opal plus calcium carbonate for lamina sets 680A-2H-1-A to D ($\times$) and 680B-2H-6-A to E ($\circ$).

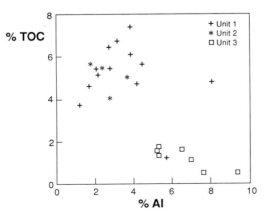

Fig. 7. Total organic carbon versus aluminium (all laminae).

(1) primary productivity is high; (2) water depth is low, but greater than storm wavebase; (3) bottom waters are oxygen-depleted and (4) bulk sediment accumulation rates are high. Comparing Units 1/2 with Unit 3, we note that sediments from both units accumulated under similar depths of water (most during inter-glacials), that the bottom waters were probably oxygen-depleted in all cases (laminated sediments) and that the type of organic matter was similar in both units (all marine algal/bacterial) and thus equally susceptible to early diagenetic degradation. One difference between units 1/2 and 3 is their respective sedimentation rates. However, contrary to expectation, the organic-lean sediments in Unit 3 accumulated more rapidly than those in Units 1/2 (Suess, Von Huene et al. 1988). One is thus tempted to infer that sediments in Units 1/2 are enriched in TOC mainly because primary productivity was higher during the deposition of Units 1 and 2.

Two other factors should be considered. Firstly, sediments from Unit 3 may be partly reworked. Secondly, relatively small changes in carbon burial efficiency can lead to dramatic changes in the TOC content of the buried sediment (Canfield 1989). Using MANOP Site M as an example (water depth = 3100 m), Canfield showed that reducing the rate of carbon remineralization by 20% resulted in a change in TOC in the buried sediment from 1% to 7%, as great as the differences between sediments at Site 680. Such subtle variations in burial efficiency are impossible to recognize in buried sediments but could easily have influenced the carbon contents of the units studied here.

Lamina-scale variations

Within Unit 1, organic matter is enriched in the more Al-rich, opal-depleted laminae (Table 2). This observation is contrary to expectations, since it was anticipated that higher TOC contents would be associated with biogenic, siliceous sediments, which have been assumed to be the result of high productivity diatom 'blooms' (e.g. Oberhaensli et al. 1990; Schrader & Sorknes 1990).

Although diatom-rich laminae represent periods when organic matter was most rapidly produced in surface waters, this does not necessarily mean that the concentration of organic matter in the suspended particulate matter is highest during periods of highest productivity. Changes in the surface water ecosystem during periods of higher and lower productivity are well documented (e.g. Berger 1976) and may result in variations in the concentration of organic matter in the particulate matter delivered to the sediment surface. Bogdanov et al. (1980) have shown that the ratio of $TOC:SiO_2$ in particulates suspended in Pacific surface waters decreases as productivity increases. Silica can thus act as a diluant of organic matter, a fact recorded not only in these sediments, but in lithologically similar sediments from the Gulf of California and the Monterey Formation in California (Donegan & Schrader 1982; Isaacs 1987).

We believe that variations in the TOC content of suspended, and presumably sinking particulates offer an attractive explanation for the observation that TOC is depleted in those silica-rich laminae which record high productivity events. Other factors, such as water depth and sedimentation rate, are inapplicable on a lamina-scale. Nor need one invoke variations in productivity or preservation to explain the variations in the concentration of organic matter in adjacent laminae. We accept, however, that the rate of accumulation of silica-rich laminae may be greater than that of clay-rich laminae, and hence that the rate of accumulation of organic matter may be greater in the silica-rich laminae (see Isaacs 1987).

Factors which might confuse this simple picture include variations in (1) the state in which organic matter is packaged in the water column and (2) burial efficiency at different parts of the productivity cycle. Both these factors are difficult to quantify but we have no reason to believe that either varied through time. Most of the organic matter in all types of lamina is finely dispersed and there is no evidence that organic matter was preferentially packaged into (for example) rapidly sinking faecal pellets during periods of low primary productivity. In addition, the rate of carbon remineralization in laminated sediments is related to the extent to which oxidants such as oxygen and sulphate can diffuse into surface sediments. This is controlled, for both porous diatomacous laminae and less porous clay laminae, by the rate at which diffusion occurs through the least permeable laminae.

Sulphur diagenesis

From the measured values for total and pyrite Fe, the degree of pyritization (DOP_T), i.e. the fraction of total iron present as pyrite, was calculated (Table 4). DOP_T ranges between 0.3 and 0.8, with most samples falling between 0.5 and 0.7. Pyrite formation can be limited by the availability of one of three reactants: organic matter, iron minerals or sulphate/sulphide

Table 4. The iron budget.

Sample	Fe (1)	Fe (P) (2)	DOP$_T$ (3)
B-1H-4-G	2.3	1.5	0.6
A-2H-1-A	1.3	0.7	0.5
A-2H-1-B	0.6	0.7	1.3
A-2H-1-C	1.1	0.6	0.5
A-2H-1-D	1.6	0.7	0.5
B-2H-4-G	2.0	0.6	0.3
B-2H-5-G	3.2	1.2	0.4
B-2H-6-G	1.9	1.2	0.7
B-2H-6-A	1.1	0.6	0.6
B-2H-6-B	1.5	1.1	0.8
B-2H-6-C	1.2	0.7	0.5
B-2H-6-D	1.3	0.7	0.5
B-2H-6-E	2.3	1.0	0.4
B-6H-7-A	1.0	1.0	1.0
B-6H-7-B	2.4	1.1	0.4
B-7H-3-A	1.7	1.0	0.6
B-7H-3-B	2.0	1.3	0.7
B-7H-6-G	4.2	2.5	0.6
B-9H-6-A	4.1	2.5	0.6
B-9H-6-B	4.1	2.6	0.6
B-10H-5-A	3.2	1.6	0.5
B-10H-5-B	3.3	2.2	0.7
B-10H-5-C	3.0	2.0	0.7
B-10H-5-D	2.7	1.9	0.7
B-10H-5-E	n.d.	2.1	n.d.

(1) Weight percent total Fe (measured).
(2) Fe in pyrite.
(3) DOP$_T$ = degree of pyritization = pyrite Fe/total Fe (Berner 1970)
n.d. = not determined.

(Berner 1970). Since the sediments studied here are organic-rich, and their pore-water is sulphide-rich and never sulphate-depleted, the availability of reactive iron almost certainly limits the formation of pyrite (Emeis & Morse 1990; Mossmann *et al.* 1990). Evidence for this also comes from the absence of any upward or downward trend for DOP$_T$ between deeper detrital-rich and shallower detrital-poor laminae, implying that all the reactive iron is converted to pyrite, regardless of its initial concentration. In summary, all the evidence suggests that sulphide was always present in concentrations in excess of that required to convert reactive iron to pyrite.

The fact that the average DOP$_T$ is about 0.6 suggests that around 40% of iron minerals cannot be converted to pyrite. This unreactive iron is probably bound in aluminosilicates and is not likely to be converted to sulphide under any typical, sulphidic early diagenetic conditions.

The $\delta^{34}S$ values are for sulphur in pyrite and vary widely within units, with a total range of −32.4 to −4.9‰ (Table 2). Furthermore, there is no significant difference in the data from different units (Fig. 4). The range of $\partial^{34}S$ values covers a large part of the total variation seen in marine sediments of all types (−40 to +20‰, e.g. Gautier 1987). Within a given set of laminae, the variation is generally 4‰, but can be as much as 18‰. Because small variations in the nature of the early diagenetic sulphur cycle can lead to large variations in $\delta^{34}S$, interpretation of sulphur isotope ratios in terms of specific diagenetic conditions is difficult (Chanton *et al.* 1987; Mossmann *et al.* 1991). However, most of the data are between −10 and −25‰ and are consistent with the idea that pyrite formed close to the sediment-water interface, where sulphate was diffusing down from overlying seawater (Mossmann *et al.* 1991).

The measured organic S/C weight ratios also show considerable variation, ranging from 0.069 to 0.193 (Table 5). The variation within each unit is also large and there is no significant difference in the range of values observed for each unit (Fig. 4). All of the values are, however, high compared to the values typically found in algae (about 0.01; Francois 1987). These results demonstrate that abundant sulphur has been incorporated diagenetically into the organic matter, even in the shallowest of the Site 680 sediments. Where laminae were sampled near to a bulk sample analysed previously (Mossmann *et al.* 1990), the average value from the laminae analyses is similar to the value obtained previously for the bulk. These bulk values were shown by Mossmann *et al.* (1990) to increase with increasing burial depth, and this was attributed to a systematic sulphurisation of the organic matter taking place through the top 20 m of burial. However, very large variations can occur between adjacent laminae (Table 5; Fig. 4). The fact that very shallow laminae can have very high S/C ratios (e.g. 0.141 for 680A-2H-1-A) is also evidence against gradual sulphurisation over 20 m burial, and in favour of rapid sulphurization during very early burial. This revised interpretation, based on these data and a re-examination of earlier data, has been given in greater detail by Mossmann *et al.* (1991).

Kerogens with high sulphur contents (up to 15% by weight) are generally associated with marine carbonate or biogenic siliceous sediments, such as the Monterey Formation (Orr 1986). Petroleums from such sources are statistically richer in sulphur than petroleums from clastic (or 'terrigenous') sources (Aksenov & Kamyanov 1981). Variations in organic S/C ratios in sediments are thus considered to be inversely related to the proportions of detrital

Table 5. Organic sulphur parameters from elemental and py-GCMS analyses.

Sample	S/C (1)	BZTHIO / NAPTH (2)	C2THIO / C2BZ (3)
B-1H-4-G	0.121	0.38	0.34
A-2H-1-A	0.141	0.62	0.47
A-2H-1-B	0.079	0.61	0.40
A-2H-1-C	0.132	0.44	0.30
A-2H-1-D	0.141	0.52	0.38
B-2H-4-G	0.129	0.56	0.23
B-2H-5-G	0.133	n.d.	n.d.
B-2H-6-G	0.180	n.d.	n.d.
B-2H-6-A	0.151	0.49	0.15
B-2H-6-B	0.079	0.46	0.42
B-2H-6-C	0.128	0.49	0.38
B-2H-6-D	0.157	0.40	0.26
B-2H-6-E	0.145	0.51	0.66
B-6H-7-A	0.172	n.d.	n.d.
B-6H-7-B	0.193	n.d.	n.d.
B-7H-3-A	0.165	n.d.	n.d.
B-7H-3-B	0.114	n.d.	n.d.
B-7H-6-G	0.069	n.d.	n.d.
B-9H-6-A	0.114	n.d.	n.d.
B-9H-6-B	0.118	n.d.	n.d.
B-10H-5-A	0.131	0.60	0.51
B-10H-5-B	0.147	0.48	0.55
B-10H-5-C	0.109	0.41	0.41
B-10H-5-D	0.095	0.40	0.33
B-10H-5-E	0.160	0.55	0.41

(1) S/C = measured organic sulphur/carbon weight ratio determined directly from elemental analyser
(2) BZTHIO/NAPTH = benzothiophene/naphthalene ratio from py-GCMS
(3) C2THIO/C2BZ = ethylthiophene/xylene ratio from py-GCMS
n.d. = not determined

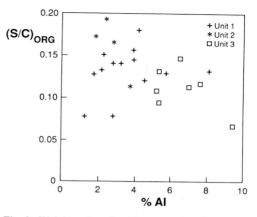

Fig. 9. Weight ratios of sulphur to carbon in organic matter, versus aluminium (all laminae).

minerals in a sediment. It is commonly claimed that this is because detrital iron minerals react with inorganic sulphide species to form pyrite (e.g. Gransch & Posthuma 1973; Orr 1986), leaving less sulphide to react with the organic matter. In the Site 680 samples, the S/C ratio in the laminae might therefore be expected to be proportional to their Al content (which represents the detrital mineral content and is well correlated with the Fe content, Fig. 5). This is not the case, as is shown in Fig. 9. In fact, there is no correlation between Al and S/C at any level; for the sample set as a whole, within units, or for series of laminae.

Pore-water data show that inorganic sulphides are present throughout Site 680 sediments in concentrations in excess of those required to react with all the reactive iron. Variable sulphide availability cannot therefore be the control on

differential uptake of sulphur into organic matter. Possible explanations for the variable S/C ratios are that (1) the S/C ratios are in error; (2) the ratio is controlled by variations in organic matter type; (3) there are differences in the nature of the sulphate reduction zone where organic sulphur (and pyrite) form; (4) the ratio is controlled by variations in the availability of specific inorganic sulphur reactants (as opposed to total sulphide). Let us examine each in turn:

(1) The S/C ratios are in error. We have no reason to believe this, but ideally an independent measure of S/C is needed to test this hypothesis. Pyrolysis data for sulphur- and carbon-containing compounds might provide one such measure. The idea here is that pyrolysis of macromolecular organic matter containing carbon and sulphur will produce smaller C-containing and S-containing fragments (for example, benzene and thiophene) and that the relative abundances of S and C might be preserved in the ratio of pyrolysis products (e.g. thiophene/benzene). Indeed, just such a relationship has been found to hold for the S/C ratio of kerogen and the ratio of thiophenes: (aromatic + aliphatic hydro-carbons) released from composite samples from Site 680 (Rees et al. in press). Furthermore, Eglinton et al. (1990) found a similar correlation between the S/C ratio of crude oil asphaltenes and the ratio of thiophenes: (aromatic + aliphatic hydro-carbons) in the products of flash pyrolysis at 610°C for 10 seconds (cf this study, 610°C for 20 seconds). Based on this idea, two pyrolysis ratios were measured for the present samples: the benzothiophene/benzene ratio and the C_2-thiophene/C_2-benzenes ratio (Fig. 10, Table 5).

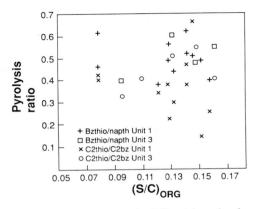

Fig. 10. Relation between the S/C weight ratio of organic matter and the pyrolysis ratios of (1) benzothiophene:napthalene and (2) ethylthiophene:xylene.

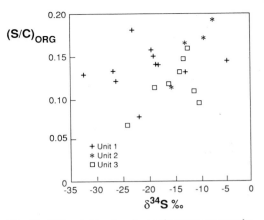

Fig. 11. S/C weight ratio of organic matter versus the sulphur isotopic composition of coexisting pyrite (all laminae).

These ratios were chosen in place of the simple thiophene/benzene ratio because the latter compounds are too volatile to be recovered reproducibly by our methods. The ratios do not correlate with the bulk S/C ratios in these samples. This might lead us to the conclusion that the S/C ratios are indeed in error. However, it is clear that neither do the ratios correlate closely to one another! It would be premature to rely on these ratios until we are more certain of the way in which the pyrolysis products relate to the S/C ratios of bulk organic matter.

(2) The ratio is controlled by variations in organic matter type. Isotopic evidence ($\delta^{13}C$) and the py-GCMS results discussed above suggest that the organic matter type in most of the laminae is very similar. Exceptions to this are two organic-lean laminae from Unit 3 (see above and Fig. 4). Whilst one of these does have a low S/C ratio, the other does not. Hence gross variations in organic matter type cannot explain differences in S/C, even where a more terrestrial input can be justified. It is possible, however, that variations in the *molecular* composition of the organic matter might influence the uptake of sulphur into the organic structure (Sinninghe Damsté *et al.* 1989). Our data give no insight into this possibility.

(3) The nature of the sulphate reduction zone varies. The isotopic composition of pyrite is variable (see above and Table 2) but there is no correlation between $\delta^{34}S$ and S/C (Fig. 11).

(4) The ratio is controlled by variations in the availability of reactive inorganic sulphide (as opposed to total sulphide). The precise chemical identity of the inorganic reactant is not known.

Many authors have proposed that dissolved H_2S reacts with sedimentary organic matter (Nissenbaum and Kaplan 1972; Casagrande *et al.* 1979; Mango 1983; Vairavamurthy & Mopper 1987) during early diagenesis (Casagrande 1987). Bestougeff & Combaz (1974) demonstrated that H_2S can react with biological debris, recent and ancient sediments resulting in enhanced organic sulphur contents. Others have implicated polysulphides (HS_x^-) as the reactant in early diagenesis (Aizenshtat *et al.* 1983; LaLonde *et al.* 1987) or elemental sulphur (Kaplan *et al.* 1963; Casagrande & Ng 1979). Alternatively, some workers have been less confident and proposed both H_2S and/or polysulphides (Boulegue *et al.* 1982; Francois 1987; Moers *et al.* 1988). There is perhaps one piece of evidence, from molecular sulphur geochemistry, that polysulphides do play some role in the incorporation of sulphur into sedimentary organic matter. Kohnen *et al.* (1989) identified sulphur-containing lipids in some offshore Peru sediments with two, and perhaps three, sulphur atoms linked together in the same molecule. This would imply that the reacting species was HS_x^-, where x might equal 2 or 3. It is not clear that one can extrapolate from a single compound (a phytanyl skeleton with two and perhaps three sulphur atoms incorporated) to an entire process. However, Mossmann *et al.* (1991), on the basis of isotopic data, argued for polysulphides as significant sulphurizing species in sediments from Sites 680 and 686.

The lack of agreement on the precise mechanism by which sulphur is incorporated into organic matter arises from the fact that it is very difficult to establish which species are involved, and that the key species may vary with the depositional environment. The geochemistry of sulphur in early diagenetic environments is complex and not entirely understood (see Boulegue & Michard 1979). However, we suggest that a likely explanation for the variation in organic S/C ratios in these laminae is the variation in the availability of specific reactant sulphide species, possibly polysulphides. Local variations in polysulphide concentrations may result from variations in the oxidizing species required to generate them from sulphide. For example, enhanced oxicity of the bottom waters, or the presence of sulphur-oxidizing bacteria such as *Beggiatoa*, could result in local increases in the concentration of polysulphides.

Summary

Millimetre- to centimetre-scale laminations in sediments deposited at ODP Site 680 on the Peru Margin are defined by variations in the relative amounts of their two main components: diatoms and detrital minerals. Diatom-rich laminae are presumed to represent periods of relatively high primary productivity in the surface ocean.

Detailed sedimentological and geochemical studies of individual laminae have shown that the organic matter they contain is hydrogen-rich and is finely disseminated throughout the sediments. Most of the organic matter has a marine algal/bacterial source but is substantially modified during early diagenesis. Laminae deposited in the late Pliocene are depleted in TOC compared to lithologically similar laminae deposited in the Pleistocene and Holocene. This may reflect generally lower primary productivity in the Pliocene. However, subtle variations in carbon burial efficiency cannot be recognized in buried sediments but can lead to large changes in the TOC content of buried sediments (Canfield 1989). Caution should therefore be exercised in linking TOC contents to variations in either palaeoproductivity or preservation.

The TOC contents of laminae deposited during the Pleistocene and Holocene are inversely proportional to diatom abundance but correlate positively with detrital mineral contents. This implies an inverse relation between primary productivity and the organic richness of buried sediment. Similar relationships have been observed in sediments from the Gulf of California and the Monterey Formation in California (Donegan & Schrader 1982; Isaacs 1987). An attractive explanation for this is that organic matter is diluted by skeletal opaline silica at times of higher primary productivity

(Bogdanov *et al.* 1980). In this case, variations in the TOC contents of buried sediments cannot be easily related to variations in primary productivity or preservation. Rather, they result from variations in the TOC content of material reaching the sediment surface.

Although the sulphur content of organic matter is high throughout the sequence, it can vary significantly in adjacent laminae. Because all the sediments at Site 680 are highly sulphidic, differential uptake of sulphur into organic matter may be caused by variations in the availability of specific, reactive sulphur species, perhaps polysulphides.

Lamina-scale studies like that reported here reveal sedimentological and geochemical diversity which is missed by conventional geochemical analyses of bulk or widely-spaced samples. The advantage of fine-scale studies is that each sample represents a period of time which can be more readily related to processes occurring in the modern ocean. Although bulk samples may adequately define the general characteristics of a sedimentary sequence, fine-scale sampling gives one a better chance of determining the oceanographical processes which created those characteristics.

We are particularly grateful to NERC for enabling this collaborative project through the provision of several grants within an ODP Special Topic. Samples were kindly provided by the UK Shipboard Scientists, Geoff Eglinton and Alan Kemp. Thanks also to the reviewers, and to Richard Tyson for his encyclopaedic knowledge of organic matter. BP is thanked for granting permission for the work to be published.

References

AIZENSHTAT, Z., STOLER, A., COHEN, Y. & NIELSEN, H. 1983. The geochemical sulphur enrichment of recent organic matter by polysulphides in the Solar Lake. *In*: BJOROY, M. (ed.) *Advances in Organic Geochemistry 1981*, Wiley, Chichester, 279–288.

AKSENOV, V. S. & KAMYANOV, V. F. 1981. Regularities in composition and structures of native sulphur compounds from petroleum. *In*: FREIDLINA, R. Kh. & SKOROVA, A. E. (eds), *Organic Sulphur Chemistry*, Pergamon, Oxford, 1–12.

BERGER, W. H. 1976. Biogenous deep sea sediments: production, preservation and interpretation. *In*: RILEY, J. P. & CHESTER, R. (eds), *Chemical Oceanography, Volume 5*, Academic, New York, 265–388.

BERNER, R. A. 1970. Sedimentary pyrite formation. *American Journal of Science*, **268**, 1–23.

BESTOUGEFF, M. & COMBAZ, A. 1974. Action d'H_2S et de S sur quelques substances organiques et fossiles. *In*: TISSOT, B. & BIENER, F. (eds),

Advances in Organic Geochemistry 1973, Editions Technip, Paris, 747−759.

BOGDANOV, Y. A., GURVICH, Y. G. & LISITSYN, A. P. 1980. Model for the accumulation of calcium carbonate in bottom sediments of the Pacific Ocean. *Geochemistry International,* **17** (2), 125−131.

BOULEGUE, J., LORD, C. J. & CHURCH, T. M. 1982. Sulphur speciation and associated trace metals (Fe, Cu) in the pore waters of Great Marsh, Delaware. *Geochimica et Cosmochimica Acta,* **46**, 453−464.

—— & MICHARD, G. 1979. Sulphur speciations and redox processes in reducing environments. *American Chemical Society Symposium Series,* **93**, 25−49.

CANFIELD, D. E. 1989. Sulphate reduction and oxic respiration in marine sediments: implications for organic carbon preservation in euxinic environments. *Deep-Sea Research,* **36**, 121−138.

——, RAISWELL, R., WESTRICH, J. T., REAVES, C. M. & BERNER, R. A. 1986. The use of chromium reduction in the analysis of reduced inorganic sulphur in sediments and shales. *Chemical Geology,* **54**, 149−155.

CASAGRANDE, D. J. 1987. Sulphur in peat and coal. *In:* SCOTT, A. C. (ed.) *Coal and Coal-Bearing Strata: Recent Advances.* Geological Society, London, Special Publication, **32**, 87−105.

—— & NG, L. 1979. Incorporation of elemental sulphur in coal as organic sulphur. *Nature,* **282**, 598−599.

——, IDOWU, G., FRIEDMAN, A., RICKERT, P., SIEFERT, K. & SCHLENZ, D. 1979. H₂S incorporation in coal precursors: origins of organic sulphur in coal. *Nature,* **282**, 599−600.

CHANTON, J. P., MARTENS, C. S. & GOLDHABER, M. B. 1987. Biogeochemical cycling in an organic-rich coastal marine basin. 8. A sulphur isotopic budget balanced by differential diffusion across the sediment-water interface. *Geochimica et Cosmochimica Acta,* **51**, 1201−1208.

CLAYTON, T. & KEMP, A. E. S. 1990. Clay mineralogy of Cenozoic sediments from the Peruvian continental margin. *Proceedings of the Ocean Drilling Program, Scientific Results.* Ocean Drilling Program, College Station, TX, **112B**, 59−68.

DEINES, P. 1970. Mass spectrometer correction factors for the determination of small isotopic composition variations of carbon and oxygen. *International Journal of Mass Spectrometry and Ion Physics,* **4**, 283−295.

DONEGAN, D. & SCHRADER, H. 1982. Biogenic and abiogenic components of laminated hemipelagic sediments in the central Gulf of California. *Marine Geology,* **48**, 215−237.

EGLINTON, T. I., SINNINGHE DAMSTÉ, J. S., KOHNEN, M. E. L. & DE LEEUW, J. W. 1990. Estimation of the sulphur content of kerogens and related materials by pyrolysis-gas chromatography. *Fuel,* **69**, 1394−1404.

EMEIS, K.-C. & MORSE, J. W. 1990. Organic carbon, reduced sulphur and iron relationships in sediments of the Peru margin, ODP Sites 680 and 688. *In: Proceedings of the Ocean Drilling Program, Scientific Results.* Ocean Drilling Program, College Station, TX, **112B**, 441−453.

FRANCOIS, R. 1987. A study of sulphur enrichment in the humic fraction of marine sediments during early diagenesis. *Geochimica et Cosmochimica Acta,* **51**, 17−27.

GAUTIER, D. L., 1987. Isotopic composition of pyrite: relationship to organic matter type and pyrite availability in some North American shales. *Chemical Geology,* **65**, 293−303.

GRANSCH, J. A. & POSTHUMA, J. 1973. On the origin of sulphur in crudes. *In:* TISSOT, B. & BIENNER, F. (eds) *Advances in Organic Geochemistry,* 1973, Editions Technip, Paris, 727−739.

HENRICHS, S. M. & REEBURGH, W. S. 1987. Anaerobic mineralization of marine sediment organic matter: rates and the role of anaerobic processes in the oceanic carbon economy. *Geomicrobiology Journal,* **5**, 191−237.

HONJO, S. 1982. Seasonality and interaction of biogenic and lithogenic particulate flux in the Panama Basin. *Science,* **218**, 883−884.

IBACH, L. E. J. 1982. Relationship between sedimentation rate and total organic carbon content in ancient marine sediments. *AAPG Bulletin,* **66**, 170−188.

ISAACS, C. M. 1987. Sources and deposition of organic matter in the Monterey Formation, south-central coastal basins of California. *In:* MEYER, R. F. (ed.) *Exploration for Heavy Crude Oil and Natural Bitumen. American Association of Petroleum Geologists Studies in Geology,* **25**, 193−205.

KAPLAN, I. R., EMERY, K. O. & RITTENBURG, S. C. 1963. The distribution and isotopic abundance of sulphur in recent marine sediments off southern California. *Geochimica et Cosmochimica Acta,* **27**, 297−331.

KASTNER, M., ELDERFIELD, H., MARTIN, J. B., SUESS, E., KVENVOLDEN, K. A. & GARRISON, R. E. 1990. Diagenesis and interstitial-water chemistry at the Peruvian continental margin — major constituents and strontium isotopes. *Proceedings of the Ocean Drilling Program, Scientific Results.* Ocean Drilling Program, College Station, TX, **112B**, 413−440.

KEMP, A. E. S. 1990. Sedimentary fabrics and variation in lamination style in Peru continental margin upwelling sediments. *In: Proceedings of the Ocean Drilling Program, Scientific Results.* Ocean Drilling Program, College Station, TX, **112B**, 43−58.

KOHNEN, M. E. L., SINNINGHE DAMSTÉ, J. S., TEN HAVEN, H. L. & DE LEEUW, J. W. 1989. Early incorporation of polysulphides in sedimentary organic matter. *Nature,* **341**, 640−641.

LALONDE, R. T., FERRARA, L. M. & HAYES, M. P. 1987. Low temperature, polysulphide reactions of conjugated ene carbonyls: a reaction model for the geologic origin of S-heterocycles. *Organic Geochemistry,* **11**, 563−571.

MANGO, F. D. 1983. The diagenesis of carbohydrates by hydrogen sulphide. *Geochimica et*

Cosmochimica Acta, **47**, 1433–1441.

MOERS, M. E. C., DE LEEUW, J. W., COX, H. C. & SCHENCK, P. A. 1988. Interaction of glucose and cellulose with hydrogen sulphide and polysulphides. *Organic Geochemistry*, **13**, 1079–1091.

MOSSMANN, J. R., APLIN, A. C., CURTIS, C. D. & COLEMAN, M. L. 1990. Sulphur geochemistry at Sites 680 and 686 on the Peru Margin. *Proceedings of the Ocean Drilling Program, Scientific Results*. Ocean Drilling Program, College Station, TX, **112B**, 455–464.

——, ——, —— & —— 1991. Geochemistry of inorganic and organic sulphur in organic-rich sediments from the Peru-Chile margin. *Geochimica et Cosmochimica Acta*, **55**, 3581–3595.

MULLER, P. S. & SUESS, E. 1979. Productivity, sedimentation rate and sedimentary organic carbon content in the oceans. *Deep-Sea Research*, **26**, 1347–1362.

NISSENBAUM, A. & KAPLAN, I. R. 1972. Chemical and isotopic evidence for the in situ origin of marine humic substances. *Limnology and Oceanography*, **17**, 570–572.

OBERHAENSLI, H., HEINZE, P., DIESTER-HAASS, L. & WEFER, G. 1990. Upwelling off Peru during the last 430 000 years and its relationship to the bottom water environment, as deduced from coarse grain size distributions and analyses of benthic foraminifers at holes 679D, 680B and 681B, ODP Leg 112. *In: Proceedings of the Ocean Drilling Program, Scientific Results*. Ocean Drilling Program, College Station, TX, **112B**, 369–390.

ORR, W. L. 1986. Kerogen/asphaltene/sulfur relationships in sulfur-rich Monterey oils. *Organic Geochemistry*, **10**, 499–516.

PATIENCE, R. L., CLAYTON, C. J., KEARSLEY, A. T., ROWLAND, S. J., BISHOP, A. N., REES, A. W. G., BIBBY, K. G. & HOPPER, A. C. 1990. An integrated biochemical, geochemical and sedimentological study of organic diagenesis in sediments from ODP Leg 112. *Proceedings of the Ocean Drilling Program, Scientific Results*. Ocean Drilling Program, College Station, TX, **112B**, 135–153.

PEDERSEN, T. F. & CALVERT, S. E. 1990. Anoxia vs. productivity: What controls the formation of organic-carbon-rich sediments and sedimentary rocks? *AAPG Bulletin*, **74**, 454–466.

POWELL, A. J., DODGE, J. D. & LEWIS, J. 1990. Late Neogene to Pleistocene palynofacies and microplankton biofacies of the Peruvian continental margin upwelling, ODP Leg 112. *Proceedings of the Ocean Drilling Program, Scientific Results*. Ocean Drilling Program, College Station, TX, **112B**, 297–321.

REES, A. W. G., PATIENCE, R. L., CLAYTON, C. J. & ROWLAND, S. J. in press. An organic geochemical and biochemical study of the diagenesis of organic matter in a core of Quaternary sediments from the Peru upwelling area. *Geochimica et Cosmochimica Acta*.

ROBINSON, B. W. & KUSAKABE, M. 1975. Quantitative preparation of sulphur dioxide, for $^{34}S/^{32}S$ analysis, from sulphides by combustion with cuprous oxide. *Analytic Chemistry*, **47**, 1179–1181.

SCHRADER, H. & SORKNES, R. 1990. Spatial and temporal variation of Peruvian coastal upwelling during the late Quaternary. *In: Proceedings of the ODP Scientific Results*. Ocean Drilling Program, College Station, TX, **112B**, 391–406.

SINNINGHE DAMSTÉ, J. S., RIJPSTRA, W. I. C., KOCK-VAN DALEN, A. C., DE LEEUW, J. W. & SCHENCK, P. A. 1989. Quenching of functionalised lipids by inorganic sulphur species: Evidence for the formation of sedimentary organic sulphur compounds at the early stages of diagenesis. *Geochimica et Cosmochimica Acta*, **53**, 1343–1355.

SUESS, E. 1980. Particulate organic carbon in the oceans — surface productivity and oxygen utilization. *Nature*, **288**, 260–263.

——, VON HUENE, R. et al. 1988. *Proceedings of Ocean Drilling Program, Leg 112 Initial Reports, Part A*. College Station, Texas A&M University.

VAIRAVAMURTHY, A. & MOPPER, K. 1987. Geochemical formation of organosulphur compounds (thiols) by addition of H_2S to sedimentary organic matter. *Nature*, **329**, 623–625.

WEFER, G., HEINZE, P. & SUESS, E. 1990. Stratigraphy and sedimentation rates from oxygen isotope composition, organic carbon content, and grain size distribution at the Peru upwelling region: holes 680B and 686B. *Proceedings of the Ocean Drilling Program, Scientific Results*. Ocean Drilling Program, College Station, TX, **112B**, 355–367.

Variations in the benthic foraminiferal fauna of the Arabian Sea: a response to changes in upwelling intensity?

J. O. R. HERMELIN

Deep Sea Geology Division, University of Stockholm, S-106 91 Stockholm, Sweden

Abstract: Results from ODP Leg 117 show that abundance and species composition of the benthic foraminiferal fauna in the northwestern Arabian Sea vary extensively through time. Studies of the Recent faunas from the region show that the distribution of benthic foraminifers is strongly correlated with the depositional environments present, of which some are associated with the OMZ (oxygen minimum zone). The OMZ is a result of strong seasonal upwelling caused by monsoonal winds and the Recent benthic foraminifers that thrive in this specific environment form a characteristic assemblage. Assuming that this relation between this benthic foraminiferal assemblage and OMZ/upwelling conditions were present in the geological past the relative abundance of the species forming that assemblage can be used to reconstruct past changes in the intensity of the monsoonal upwelling and changes in the water circulation pattern in this area.

A deepening of the lower boundary of the OMZ occurred between 6.5 and 3.0 Ma with a maximum at 5.0 Ma (= more intense upwelling ?). After 5.0 Ma, mixing of more oxygenated outflow water originating in the Red Sea weakened the severity of the OMZ in the interval 200 to 500 m in this part of the Arabian Sea. This mixing became more intense with time, as reflected in the benthic foraminiferal fauna, and today there is a pronounced intercalation of oxygenated water at this water depth and a low percentage of the assemblage associated with the OMZ.

The upwelling system off Arabia lies within a western boundary current (i.e. off the eastern coast of Africa) and has a strong seasonal variability. This is in contrast to other prominent upwelling systems, which often are located in eastern boundary currents (i.e. on western boundaries of continents) and are caused by large-scale and persistent atmospheric and oceanographic circulation.

The seasonal nature of the upwelling system in the Arabian Sea is driven by the large-scale atmospheric phenomenon of the Southwest Monsoon which reaches an acme during the summer months (Wyrtki 1971; Krey & Babenerd 1976; Prell & Streeter 1982). Summer heating and ascending air masses create an intense low-pressure cell centred on 30°N over the Tibetan Plateau. The pressure gradient between the low-pressure zone over Asia and a high-pressure zone over the southern Indian Ocean drives winds of considerable force in a generally southwest to northeast direction. Resulting divergence and Ekman transport of surface waters in a southeasterly direction allows relatively cold, nutrient-rich water to well up into the nutrient-depleted euphotic zone along a broad stretch from the coast to Owen Ridge (Prell & Streeter 1982).

The semi-enclosed character of the Arabian Sea, between the Arabian Peninsula and Indian (Fig. 1) and the stability of intermediate waters together with high rates of productivity cause extremely low oxygen concentrations of less than 0.5 ml/l and form an oxygen minimum zone that extends from less than 200 m to about 1500 m (Wyrtki 1971, 1973; Slater & Kroopnick 1984). The most severe depletion of oxygen occurs in the northern part of the Owen Basin (Price & Shimmield 1987; Hermelin & Shimmield 1990).

Upwelling and benthic foraminifers

The Recent benthic foraminiferal fauna in this area has been studied by Hermelin & Shimmield (1990). They found that the benthic foraminiferal fauna was strongly related to the geochemistry of the sediment and the depositional environment. In short, their results revealed six different foraminiferal assemblages, each with a specific regional distribution pattern (Fig. 2). The benthic foraminifers making up these assemblages and their preferred depositional environment in the northwestern Arabian Sea can be summarized as follows.

Assemblage 1. The species *Bolivina pygmaea*, *Bulimina* sp. 1, and *Lenticulina iota* are good indicators for organic-rich sediment deposited on the shelf in the upper bathyal zone within the upper part of the OMZ.

Assemblage 2. The benthic foraminiferal fauna in the lower part of the OMZ (middle bathyal zone) where the carbonate content is high, is dominated by the species *Ehrenbergina*

From SUMMERHAYES, C. P., PRELL, W. L. & EMEIS, K. C. (eds), 1992, *Upwelling Systems: Evolution Since the Early Miocene.* Geological Society Special Publication No 64, pp 151–166.

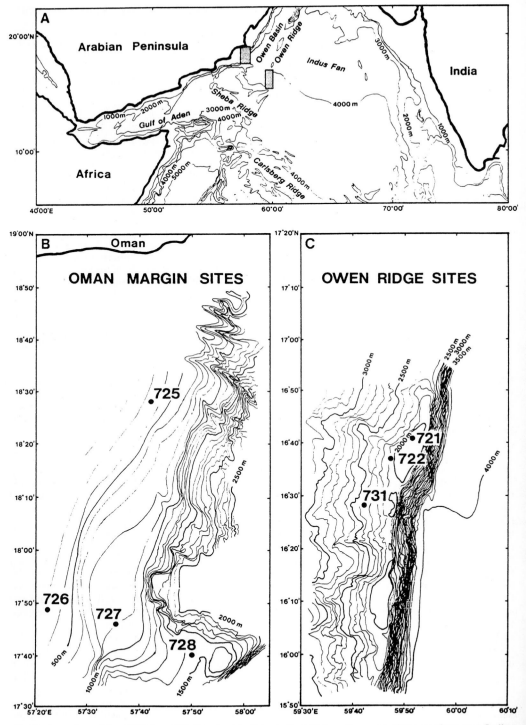

Fig. 1. Location of the ODP Leg 117 sites used in this study. (A) Location map of the northwestern Indian Ocean. (B) Location of Sites 725, 726, 727, and 728 on the Oman margin. (C) Location of Sites 721, 722, and 731 in the Owen Ridge. Bathymetry from Mountain & Prell (1989).

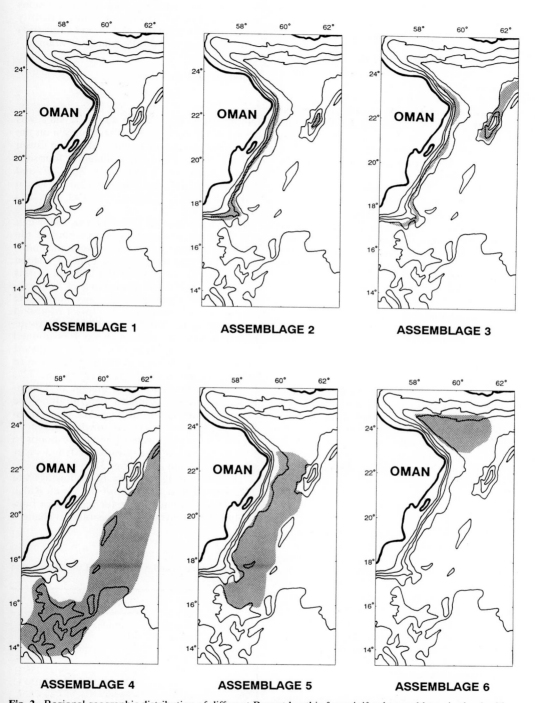

Fig. 2. Regional geographic distribution of different Recent benthic foraminiferal assemblages in the Arabian Sea. For definition of the different assemblages, see text.

trigona, *Hyalinea balthica*, *Tritaxia* sp. 1 and *Uvigerina peregrina*. The sediment is often coarse grained, with lag deposits at top of the slope.

Assemblage 3. Just below the OMZ, in the lower bathyal zone is the sediment often more fine grained and the fauna is dominated by *Bulimina aculeata* and *Uvigerina hispida*.

Assemblage 4. The area furthest from the continent on the ridges and on the outer Indus fan (abyssal zone) is dominated by *Bulimina aculeata*, *Oridorsalis umbonatus*, and *Uvigerina spinicostata*. The deposition is characterized by clay accumulation.

Assemblage 5. The sediment deposited closer to the continent at the base of the continental slope and in the Owen Basin is characterized by a high content of hydrogenous metals in the fine-grained clay and the benthic foraminiferal fauna is dominated by the agglutinated species *Reophax bilocularis* and *Reophax dentaliniformis*.

Assemblage 6. The Gulf of Oman, characterized by a largely terrigenous sediment type with (presumably) high sediment accumulation rate, exhibits a different faunal composition with the agglutinated form *Cribrostomoides wiesneri* as the dominant species. The species *Reophax bilocularis* is also important in this depositional environment.

Other studies of Recent and late Neogene benthic foraminifers of this area are scarce, although some have been carried out in other parts of the Indian Ocean: Ninetyeast Ridge (McGowran 1974; Boltovskoy 1977, 1978; Peterson 1984); southeast Indian Ocean (Corliss 1978, 1979*a*, *b*); southwest Indian Ocean (Corliss 1983).

This study

The climatic history of Asia and Africa during the Neogene depended to a large extent on the strength and variations of monsoonal upwelling, and these changes are potentially encoded in the sedimentary records. ODP Leg 117 was dedicated to studying the continental margin off the coast of Oman and the crest of the Owen Ridge (Fig. 1). One of the problems ODP Leg 117 was designed to address was to understand the origin and variability of organic carbon-rich sediments that result from the combined effects of monsoon-induced upwelling and the related OMZ.

The main objectives of this study are to investigate the Neogene benthic foraminiferal fauna and analyse whether or not changes in the faunal assemblages are related to variations in

oceanographic conditions such as (1) variations in the monsoonal and/or upwelling intensity and (2) variations in the outflow and circulation of the Red Sea and the Persian Gulf waters.

Material and methods

Locations

During ODP Leg 117, a series of sites was drilled in the northwestern Arabian Sea on the continental margin of Oman and on the Owen Ridge (Table 1, Fig. 1A). In this study four sites on the Oman margin (Sites 725, 726, 727, and 728) (see Fig. 1B) and three sites on the Owen Ridge (Sites 721, 722, and 731) (see Fig. 1C) are discussed.

The Oman margin sites are the following: Site 725 is located near the upper limit of the OMZ, in a transitional zone between the continental shelf and the landward edge of a slope basin (Fig. 3). Because of the location of this site at the shelf edge, winnowing of fine sediment can be expected, especially during the summer months when the Southwest Monsoon reaches its acme. Site 726, located on the continental shelf off the shore of Oman, is positioned near the shelf-edge transition on the landward flank of a slope basin and like Site 725 close to the upper limit of the OMZ (Fig. 3). Site 727, located on the continental margin of Oman, is located in the southern part of the slope basin, near the centre of the OMZ (Fig. 3). In Site 728, located on the continental margin of Oman, the present water depth corresponds to the lower part of the pronounced mid-water oxygen minimum zone (Fig. 3).

The Owen Ridge sites are the following: Site 721, located near the crest of the Owen Ridge (Fig. 3) is positioned above the regional carbonate lysocline to avoid major dissolution changes

Table 1. Location and water depth of the sites used in this study.

ODP Site	Water depth (m)	Location	
		Latitude	Longitude
721	1945	16°40.636′N	59°51.879′E
722	2028	16°37.312′N	59°47.755′E
725	311	18°29.200′N	57°42.030′E
726	331	17°48.965′N	57°22.290′E
727	914	17°46.096′N	57°35.216′E
728	1428	17°40.790′N	57°49.553′E
731	2366	16°28.229′N	59°42.149′E

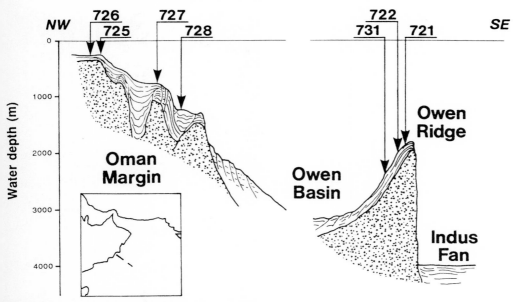

Fig. 3. Schematic profile showing the structure of the Oman margin and the Owen Ridge with the studied ODP sites indicated. Approximate location of the idealized depth transect is indicated on inserted location map.

in the calcareous deposits. Site 722 is located near the crest of the Owen Ridge (Fig. 3) and Site 731 located just below the crest (Fig. 3).

Age models

The age models for the sites used in this study are based on biostratigraphic and palaeomagnetic information from the *Initial Reports* of ODP Leg 117 (Prell *et al.* 1989). The 'absolute' ages for nannofossil, radiolarian, planktonic for-aminiferal datum levels, magnetostratigraphic boundaries, and zonal boundaries are derived from various sources. The datum markers used, their location in the different sites, and their age assignments with references are presented in Table 2. In the *Initial Reports* of ODP Leg 117 (Prell *et al.* 1989) additional biostratigraphic datum levels were recognized but these were excluded here due to their unreliability as 'ab-solute' age markers. Therefore, the age models used here and presented in Figs 4 & 5 are slightly different from those initially presented (Prell *et al.* 1989).

Benthic foraminifers

Approximately 10 cm^3 of sediment were washed through a 63 μm sieve. The larger fraction was thereafter dry-sieved through a 125 μm sieve,

and the benthic foraminifers were picked from the larger fraction. The counting procedure consisted of splitting the >125 μm fraction into an aliquot containing 300–400 specimens. The specimens were then identified to species level, counted and statistically analyzed. Sub-sequently the cumulative relative percentages of the species that comprises the typical upwelling assemblage were calculated. The resulting curves representing the relative abundance of upwelling species were then smoothed by a moving average ($N = 3$). This smoothing does not alter the interpretation of the result; it makes a possible trend in the data more distinct by decreasing the noise level of the curve.

Distribution of the oxygen minimum zone

Hydrographic data collected during cruise 17 of the R.R.V. *Charles Darwin* show the distri-bution of dissolved oxygen in the water column in various parts of the northwestern Indian Ocean. The most severe depletion of oxygen occurs in the Owen Basin with the relative depth of the OMZ (defined by oxygen contents <0.5 ml/l) of 200 to 1200–1500 m (Fig. 6). Wyrtki (1971) defined the OMZ in the Indian Ocean as comprising both a shallow and a deep oxygen minimum. In the northern part of the Arabian Sea the intervening oxygen maximum is

Table 2. Stratigraphic list of faunal events and palaeomagnetic reversals for ODP Holes used in this study. Depths are from Prell et al. (1989), whereas the ages are derived from various sources.

	Event	AGE (Ma)	Hole 721A[a]	Hole 721B	Hole 722A	Hole 722B	Hole 731A	Hole 725C	Hole 726A	Hole 727A	Hole 728A
FAD	Emiliania huxleyi	0.27[1,2]	8.40–9.90		5.65–7.15		5.62–7.15	25.78–28.50	11.08–14.08	23.08–26.08	10.78–13.78
LAD	Pseudoemiliania lacunosa	0.46[1,2]	18.20–19.70		16.95–18.45		18.45–19.30	50.18–51.68	25.08–26.98	41.98–44.98	19.10–20.28
T	Brunhes/Matuyama	0.73[3]									
T	Jaramillo	0.91[3]								81.75–83.25	
B	Jaramillo	0.98[3]	41.30–42.80		37.65–38.40		45.45–46.25		38.75–39.45	95.87–96.41	40.70–42.20
LAD	Calcidiscus macintyrei	1.45[4,5]	50.30–51.25		52.35–53.85		64.45–65.95		61.28–63.60	104.14–106.01	51.68–54.68
LAD	Globigerinoides extremus*	1.80[6,7]			57.50–59.65					134.96–138.06	57.00–66.50
LAD	Discoaster brouweri	1.89[4]	61.70–63.20		63.14–69.65					153.30–163.00	64.25–66.50
T	Matuyama/Gauss	2.47[8]	82.51–82.90	85.05–86.35	82.45–83.95		83.85–86.40		63.60–64.71	179.90–182.40	72.20–73.70
T	Kaena	2.92[3]									78.80–80.30
B	Mammoth	3.18[3]		116.65–117.45	103.35–110.05						84.80–86.90
	Gauss/Gilbert	3.40[8]									92.90–94.40
LAD	Sphenolithus abies	3.47[9,10]		114.80–115.95	103.35–104.85		96.00–97.15		73.20–74.38		95.30–96.48
LAD	Reticulofenestra pseudoumbilica	3.56[7]		114.80–115.95	105.90–107.06		97.15–98.66		77.12–77.85		96.48–99.48
FAD	Spongaster tetras tetras	3.83–3.85[11]	124.40–129.75	124.40–129.75	115.60–120.95		105.70–111.05				114.40–120.95
T	Cochiti	3.88[3]									121.70–125.35
B	Cochiti	3.97[3]									131.40–132.89
T	Nunivak	4.10[3]									142.60–144.70
B	Nunivak	4.24[3]									
T	Sidufjall	4.40[3]		156.15–159.15	142.03–142.85						152.08–155.80
B	Sidufjall	4.47[3]									167.08–168.41
T	Thvera	4.57[3]		167.35–171.85	151.00–151.83						176.75–178.22
B	Thvera	4.77[3]									184.67–186.32
LAD	Discoaster quinqueramus	4.98[12]		177.05–178.55	163.90–165.05		112.85–114.35				230.50–231.68
FAD	Globorotalia tumida tumida	5.20[7,13]		204.15–211.70	166.05–168.18				97.55–102.10		240.10–249.80

Datum	Taxon	Age (Ma)				
LAD	Stichocorys johnsoni[†] Gilbert/Chronozone 5[5]	5.35[3]	207.65–208.35	180.73–182.25		278.80–284.15
	Chronozone 5/Chronozone 6	5.70–5.80[14]	211.70–215.55	193.00–202.70		
	Chronozone 6	5.89[3]		211.33–221.05		
LAD	Stichocorys delmontensis[14] / S. peregrina	6.10–6.70[14]	230.50–235.85	212.40–217.75	115.40–125.00	298.10–307.80
LAD	Calocycletta caepa	6.20–6.60[14]		227.35–231.70	120.70–125.00	303.45–307.80
LAD	Diartus hughesi	7.10–7.20[14]	279.20–289.00	241.70–251.00	140.95–144.40	
FAD	Discoaster quinqueramus	7.46[15]	260.65–262.17	270.40–271.54	163.70–165.05	322.85–327.20
LAD	Botryostrobus miralestensis	8.10–8.20[14]		270.40–272.75	169.05–173.40	342.15–346.40
LAD	Discoaster hamatus	8.67[15]	283.37–289.00	304.70–305.85	202.50–203.79	
FAD	Discoaster hamatus	9.50–10.50[16]	309.55–311.05	324.00–333.70	238.75–240.25	
FAD	Catinaster coalitus	11.10[15]			241.30–245.47	
LAD	Sphenolithus heteromorphus	13.60[15]	311.05–318.00		299.20–300.35	
LAD	Sphenolithus belemnos	18.80[15]	366.30–375.90	382.41–384.02		

[a] Depths in Hole 721 A reflect an addition of 2.75 m at the top of the hole to account for loss due to coring (see Site 721; Prell et al. 1989)

FAD First Appearance Datum
LAD Last Appearance Datum
T Top
B Bottom
→ Evolutionary transition
* G. obliquus extremus in Berggren et al. (1985)
† E. cf. diaphanes in Johnson & Nigrini (1985)
1 Thierstein et al. (1977)
2 Berggren et al. (1980)
3 Berggren et al. (1985)
4 Backman & Shackleton (1983)
5 Backman et al. (1983)

6 Thompson & Sciarrillo (1978)
7 Keigwin (1982)
8 Mankinen & Dalrymple (1979)
9 Monechi & others (1985)
10 Rio (1982)
11 Johnson et al. (1989)
12 Backman (pers. comm. March 1989)
13 Saito et al. (1975)
14 Johnson & Nigrini (1985)
15 Backman et al. (1990)
16 Backman (pers. comm. September 1990)

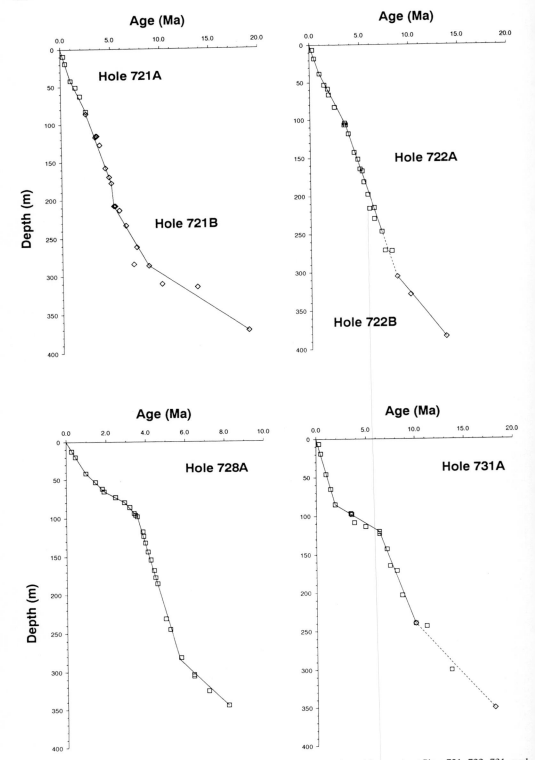

Fig. 4. Age/depth relationships for biostratigraphic and magnetostratigraphic events at Sites 721, 722, 731, and 728. Note the different scales along the age-axis. For a detailed listing of events, see Table 2.

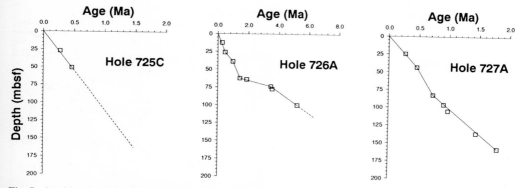

Fig. 5. Age/depth relationships for biostratigraphic and magnetostratigraphic events at Sites 725, 726, and 727. Note the different scales along the age-axis. For a detailed listing of events, see Table 2.

ill-defined and the oxygen minimum is more or less homogenous (see Fig. 5, stations CD1730 and CD1733). Thus, in the southern part sinking saline water from the Red Sea is carrying more oxygenated water into the Indian Ocean. This tongue of more saline outflow water is pronounced in the study area and can be recognized as peaks in dissolved oxygen at around 300 m in the southern oxygen profiles (see Fig. 6, stations CD1712, CD1713, and CD1715).

Results

The composition of the Recent benthic foraminiferal fauna of the northwestern Arabian Sea is strongly related to the geochemistry of the sediment and the depositional environment according to Hermelin & Shimmield (1990). From their results it is possible to extract a number of species which together are characteristic for the bathymetric interval comprising the OMZ. This assemblage is not necessarily a product of the OMZ itself, or of the upwelling; it may also be a response to the sedimentary conditions caused by the upwelling and the OMZ. In any case, a specific assemblage, here called *Assemblage A*, is found in the bathymetric interval that comprises the OMZ. The species belonging to Assemblage A are *Bolivina ordinaria*, *Bolivina pygmaea*, *Bolivina seminuda*, *Bulimina* sp. 1, *Chilostomella ovoidea*, *Ehrenbergina trigona*, *Hyalinea balthica*, *Lenticulina iota*, *Textularia bermudezi*, *Tritaxia* sp. 1, *Uvigerina peregrina* and *Virgulinella pertusa*. For actual relative percentages of the different species see Hermelin & Shimmield (1990). Together these species represent between 75% and 90% of the total benthic foraminiferal fauna in the upper part of the OMZ and gradually decrease with greater depth (Fig. 7). At 1500 m,

in the lowermost part of the OMZ, the percentage of species belonging to Assemblage A is between 0 and 10, and below 1500 m they are more or less absent.

These Recent species characteristic of upwelling conditions (Assemblage A) can also be found in late Miocene to Pleistocene material collected during ODP Leg 117 in the northwestern Arabian Sea. The relative abundance of species belonging to Assemblage A shows significant concordance through time at the Owen Ridge sites (721, 722, and 731) (Fig. 8). Species belonging to Assemblage A are present in very low frequencies during the time interval 8–10 Ma at all three sites. The two shallowest sites (721 and 722) exhibit an increase to about 5% between 8 and 5.5 Ma, whereas the deeper site (731) shows lowered (about 1%) relative abundances during that time interval. Subsequently, the two shallowest sites exhibit a peak in the relative abundance of species belonging to Assemblage A at about 5.0 Ma whereas the peak at the deeper site appears at about 4.5 Ma. This is followed by a decrease with a minimum at about 3 Ma at all three sites. The peaks are significant and the relative abundances reaches 15 to 20%, whereas they decreases to about 2% during the subsequent minimum. After this minimum the relative abundances increase and are today between 5 and 10%.

Site 728 is located in the lowermost part of the OMZ and covers only the time back to 8 Ma. The species belonging to Assemblage A constitute about 5% of the benthic foraminiferal fauna during most of this time interval (Fig. 9), although peaks in the relative abundance of Assemblage A, amounting to about 20% do occur at approximately at 6.5 Ma, 4.0 Ma and 1.0 Ma.

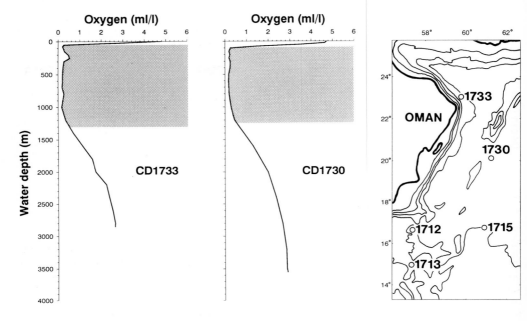

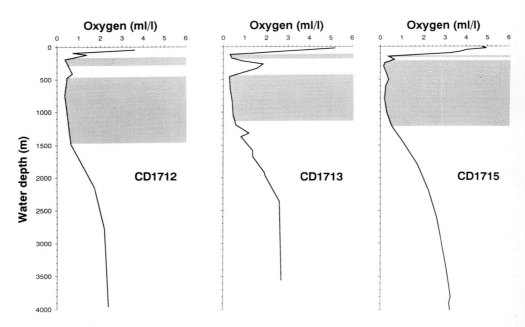

Fig. 6. Dissolved oxygen data (ml/l) for five selected stations in the northwestern Arabian Sea. Location of stations is indicated on the inserted location map. The data were obtained during cruise 17 with R.R.S. *Charles Darwin* (Price & Shimmield 1987).

Assemblage A (%)

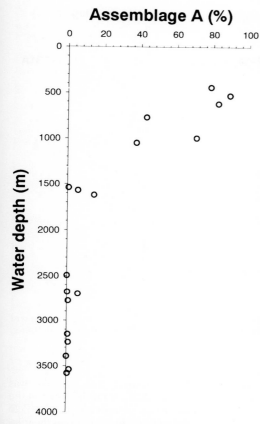

Fig. 7. Relative abundance of Assemblage A in Recent surface sediment samples obtained during cruise 17 with R.R.S. *Charles Darwin* in the northwestern Arabian Sea. For original data see Hermelin & Shimmield (1990).

Three sites are clearly located within the OMZ (725, 726 and 727), Sites 725 and 726 in the uppermost part and Site 727 in middle part. Site 726 has the longest record of these three and covers the interval 0 to 6.5 Ma, whereas sites 725 and 726 only cover the Pleistocene (0–1.7 Ma). The relative abundance of species belonging to Assemblage A within the OMZ is generally decreasing over the last 6.5 Ma from above 75% between 6.5 Ma and 3.0 Ma to between 20 and 40% during the Holocene (Fig. 10).

Discussion

A gradual decrease in the relative abundance of species belonging to Assemblage A with measured depth can be recognized in the Recent material from this area and this decrease occurs within the bathymetric interval that comprises the OMZ (see Fig. 7). To some extent the relative abundance of species belonging to Assemblage A is inversely correlated to oxygen concentration in the water column (see Fig. 6). In well oxygenated water the same species are present only in very low relative abundances or are totally absent. The correlation is not perfect but from Fig. 7 one can easily see that where the relative abundance of species belonging to Assemblage A exceeds 75%, i.e. in this area generally above 1000 m, we find the bathymetric interval in which the oxygen depletion is most severe (around 0.2 ml/l). At depths of 1000 to 1600–1800 m, the percentage of species belonging to Assemblage A decreases to below 50%, whereas the amount of dissolved oxygen increases to between 0.5 and 1.5 ml/l. In deeper water, where the percentage of species belonging to Assemblage A has decreased to less than 10%, the oxygen values reach well above 2.0 ml/l. If we assume that this relationship between the relative abundance of species belonging to Assemblage A and the severity of the OMZ also existed in the geological past, the relative abundance of this assemblage in sedimentary cores could be a tool to reconstruct possible changes in the OMZ. Using Assemblage A as an indicator of the severity of the OMZ does not imply that the presence of species belonging to Assemblage A is directly linked to low oxygen content. Several other factors are probably involved in a complex way and some may be more important than the oxygen content *per se*. The relative abundance of Assemblage A may be controlled by the sedimentary environment, the food supply, and/or the quality of the food (Caralp 1989; Corliss 1985; Corliss & Chen 1988; Corliss & Emerson 1990). Nevertheless the relative abundance of Assemblage A may be regarded as a function of the intensity of the monsoonal upwelling.

The Owen Ridge sites (721, 722, and 731) have been subjected to an uplift which is attributed to compression along the Owen Fracture Zone caused by changes in the spreading direction associated with the continued collision of India and Asia and the opening of the Gulf of Aden (Whitmarsh 1979). The rate of uplift was probably relatively rapid during the late Miocene and decreased significantly in the Pliocene (Hermelin 1990). The relative abundances of Assemblage A at these sites are generally less than 5%, as expected, at sites located close to and below 2000 m; however, a significant increase to values of 15–20% occurred from 3.5–5.5 Ma. Values of this magnitude are today normally found at water depths above 1500 m.

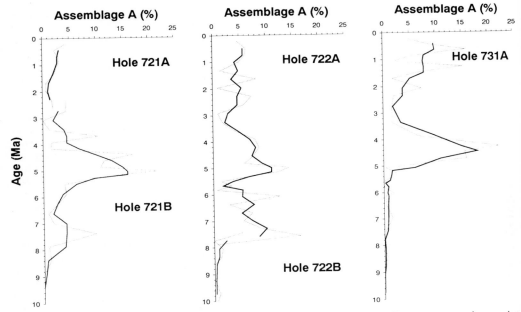

Fig. 8. Relative abundance of Assemblage A at the Owen Ridge sites. The solid line represent a three-point moving average. (A) Site 721 (water depth 1945 m). (B) Site 722 (water depth 2028 m). (C) Site 731 (water depth 2366 m).

The present-day knowledge of the evolution of the Owen Ridge shows no evidence or indication of a further uplift of the ridge followed by a subsidence to its present location with the crest of the ridge at about 2000 m. The enhanced abundance of Assemblage A may therefore be attributed to a deepening of the OMZ, which in turn could have been caused by stronger monsoonal winds/more intense upwelling. The time lag of about 0.5 Ma between the peaks at the shallower sites (721 and 722) and the deeper site (731) may be explained by their differences in water depth. A deepening of the OMZ would by definition affect first the sites immediately below the OMZ and deeper sites later on. This possible deepening of the OMZ, indicated by higher abundance of species belonging to Assemblage A, is followed by very low abundances around 3 Ma indicating that these sites were below the influence of the OMZ at that time. After 3 Ma the relative abundances of Assemblage A show a slight increase.

The two shallowest sites (725 and 726, in 311 and 331 m of water, respectively) are located in the bathymetric interval where mixing with sinking saline water from the Red Sea makes the depletion of oxygen less severe. During the time interval 6.5–1.5 Ma the relative abundance of species belonging to Assemblage A is above

60% (Site 726) indicating that this site was located within the OMZ. After this interval the relative abundance of Assemblage A at Site 726 decreases and significant fluctuations in the relative abundance occur, both at Site 725 and Site 726. The general trend at both sites is one of decreasing abundance, down to a present-day value of 20–30%, indicating less severe oxygen depletion. This decrease in the relative abundance of Assemblage A can be explained either by a general weakening of the OMZ, vertical fluctuations of the upper boundary of the OMZ or an increasing dilution and mixing with Red Sea outflow water.

A general weakening of the OMZ starting at 1.5 Ma is not supported at the deeper sites and no other evidence is present to indicate a major decrease in upwelling intensity during the Pleistocene.

Most upwelling areas, regardless of the strength of the upwelling, exhibit severe depletion in oxygen already at a water depth of 50–75 m (see Wyrtki 1971; Ingle *et al.* 1980). Therefore vertical variations in the upper boundary of the OMZ seem less likely.

Differences in the marine fauna between the Red Sea and the Arabian Sea suggest the opening of a connection with the Indian Ocean in the Pliocene (Read & Watson 1975). Structural

Assemblage A (%)

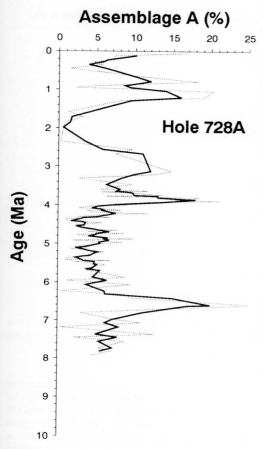

Fig. 9. Relative abundance of Assemblage A at Site 728 (water depth 1428 m) on the Oman margin. The solid line represent a three-point moving average.

analysis of the Red Sea region shows that the spreading was initiated at about 5.0 Ma (Crane & Bonatti 1987). Continued spreading and widening of the Red Sea makes an increased outflow of water from the Red Sea plausible and input of oxygenated water into the Arabian Sea at this water depth would take place and possibly increase with time. Unfortunately, the Recent abundance of benthic foraminiferal species belonging to Assemblage A at shallower water depths are not known since the *Charles Darwin* cruise only covers water deeper than 440 m. Today a tongue of oxygenated water centred around 300 m is present in the southern Arabian Sea (see Fig. 6). This increase in oxygen content would probably promote an interval with relatively low relative abundance of species belonging to Assemblage A as seen at Sites 725

and 726. This scenario with an increased outflow of oxygenated water from the Red Sea fits well to the changes seen in the relative abundance of species belonging to Assemblage A at these shallow sites.

Site 727, located in the middle of the OMZ (915 m of water), covers only the Pleistocene. The relative abundance of species belonging to Assemblage A during this time interval is around 50%, with some fluctuations (Fig. 10C). These figures can be expected from the present-day situation where the relative abundance of species belonging to Assemblage A varies between 40 and 65% at a water depth of 1000 m (Fig. 7). The fluctuations in the relative abundance seen at Site 727 are probably due to variations in the strength of the monsoonal upwelling.

The relative abundance-signal of Assemblage A of Site 728 is complicated, although it is generally between 5 and 10%, indicating a location below the influence of the OMZ (Fig. 9). Today, Site 728 is located at the lower boundary of the OMZ, but its history is marked by a possible uplift event in the latest Miocene and a rapid subsidence event in the early Pliocene. Based on the composition of the benthic foraminiferal fauna, Site 728 is calculated to have been located in 500 to 1000 m of water during the late Miocene and raised to a location in the neritic zone (100–300 m) by an uplift event in the latest Miocene (Hermelin 1991*a, b*). During the late Pliocene a rapid subsidence to its present location at the lower boundary of the OMZ occurred. The uplift and the subsidence events when the site moved through the OMZ are recorded in the relative abundance pattern of Assemblage A as peaks (Fig. 9). Comparing this with the result from the Owen Ridge sites shows that the period of intensified upwelling or stronger monsoonal winds at Site 728 is masked by the uplift event. According to this scenario Site 728 was located in 500 to 1000 m of water during late Miocene. This depth interval clearly is within the OMZ of today. The increase in species belonging to Assemblage A at about 7.0 Ma may therefore represent the strengthening of upwelling in this area provided that the scenario presented above is correct. Another explanation for the presence of a neritic benthic foraminiferal assemblage in the time interval 6.4–4.0 Ma is extensive down-slope transport of sediment, but no evidence for this is seen. Turbiditic sediments, or at least a change in the sedimentary sequence, would be expected if down-slope transport had occurred; likewise, down-slope transport would have caused remixing of stratigraphically important microfossils.

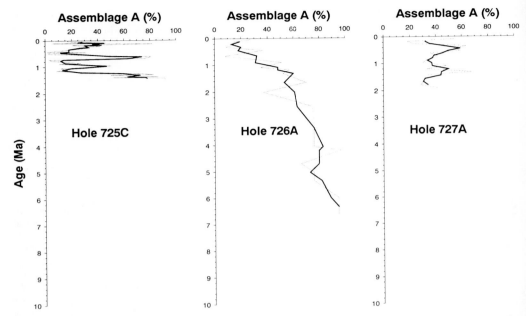

Fig. 10. Relative abundance of Assemblage A at the Oman margin sites. The solid line represent a three-point moving average. (A) Site 725 (water depth 311 m). (B) Site 726 (water depth 331 m). (C) Site 727 (water depth 914 m).

That is not recognized in the sequence studied (see Site 728 in Prell *et al.* 1989).

Conclusions

The Recent benthic foraminiferal fauna and the Recent distribution and nature of the OMZ in the northwestern Arabian Sea have been studied, and their inter-relationship has been used to decipher the late Neogene upwelling history in this area. This study only takes into account broad-scale changes in the monsoonal upwelling; systematic variations with period-icities in the Milankovitch frequency band are therefore probably not detectable. Specific events can clearly be recognized from variations in the relative abundance of species character-istic for this OMZ/upwelling area, but the exact causes are difficult to clarify.

Data from the Owen Ridge suggest that deep-ening of the lower boundary of the OMZ oc-curred between 6.5 and 3.0, with a maximum at 5.0 to 4.5 Ma. This deepening was probably caused by more intense upwelling or stronger monsoonal winds resulting in an expansion of the OMZ.

Data the shallower Oman margin sites suggest that after 4.5 Ma mixing of more oxygenated outflow water originating in the Red Sea started to form a tongue of more oxygenated water in the southwestern part of the Arabian Sea at water depths of 200 to 400 m. This intercalation of more oxygenated water became more pro-nounced with time to the extent that today it forms a barrier between a shallow and a deep OMZ in this part of the Arabian Sea. A more intense outflow of water from the Red Sea with time was probably caused by increased mixing. A connection with the Indian Ocean was formed at approximately 5.0 Ma and subsequent sea-floor spreading has widened the Red Sea.

I thank all scientists from the shipboard party of ODP Leg 117 and the technical staff and the crew on D.V. *Joides Resolution* for their contribution to this suc-cessful cruise. I also thank G. B. Shimmield for giving me access to data and samples from R.R.S. *Charles Darwin* cruise 17, without which this study would not have been possible. Financial support from the Swedish Natural Science Research Council (NFR) is acknowledged.

References

BACKMAN, J. & SHACKLETON, N. J. 1983. Quantitative biochronology of Pliocene and early Pleistocene calcareous nannofossils from the Atlantic, Indian and Pacific oceans. *Marine Micropaleontology*, **8**, 141–170.

——, —— & TAUXE, L. 1983. Quantitative nanno-fossil correlation to open ocean deep-sea sections from Plio-Pleistocene boundary at Vrica, Italy. *Nature*, **304**, 156–158.

——, SCHNEIDER, D. A., RIO, D. & OKADA, H. 1990. Neogene low-latitude magnetostratigraphy from Site 710 and revised age estimates of Miocene nannofossil datum events. *In*: DUNCAN, R. A. *et al. Proceedings of the Ocean Drilling Program, Scientific Results*, Ocean Drilling Program, College Station, TX, **115**, 271–276.

BERGGREN, W. A., BURCKLE, L. H., CITA, M. B., COOKE, H. B. S., FUNNELL, B. M., GARTNER, S., HAYS, J. D., KENNETT, J. P., OPDYKE, N. D., PASTOURET, L., SHACKLETON, N. J. & TAKAYA-NAGI, Y. 1980. Towards a Quaternary time scale. *Quaternary Research*, **13**, 277–302.

——, KENT, D. V. & VAN COUVERING, J. A. 1985. The Neogene: Part 2. Neogene geochronology and chronostratigraphy. *In*: SNELLING, N. J. (ed.) *The Chronology of the Geological Record*. Geological Society, London, Memoir, **10**, 211–260.

BOLTOVSKOY, E. 1977. Neogene deep water benthonic foraminifera if the Indian Ocean. *In*: ZEITSCHEL, B. & GERLACH, S. A. (eds) *The Biology of the Indian Ocean, Ecological Studies*, vol. 3, Springer, Berlin, 599–616.

—— 1978. Late Cenozoic benthonic foraminifera of the Ninetyeast Ridge (Indian Ocean). *Marine Geology*, **26**, 139–175.

CARALP, M. H. 1989. Abundance of *Bulimina exilis* and *Melonis barleeanum*: relationship to the quality of marine organic matter. *Geo-Marine Letters*, **9**, 37–43.

CORLISS, B. H. 1978. Studies of deep-sea benthonic Foraminifera in the southeast Indian Ocean. *Antarctic Journal*, **13**, 116–117.

—— 1979a. Recent deep-sea benthonic foraminiferal distributions in the southeast Indian Ocean: inferred bottom-water routes and ecological implications. *Marine Geology*, **31**, 115–138.

—— 1979b. Taxonomy of Recent deep-sea benthonic foraminifera from the southeast Indian Ocean. *Micropaleontology*, **25**, 1–19.

—— 1983. Distribution of Holocene deep-sea benthonic foraminifera in the southwest Indian Ocean. *Deep-Sea Research*, **30**, 95–117.

—— 1985. Microhabitats of benthic foraminifera within deep-sea sediments. *Nature*, **314**, 435–438.

—— & CHEN, C. 1988. Morphotype patterns of Norwegian Sea deep-sea benthic foraminifera and ecological implications. *Geology*, **16**, 716–719.

—— & EMERSON, S. 1990. Distribution of Rose Bengal stained deep-sea benthic foraminifera from the Nova Scotian continental margin and Gulf of Maine. *Deep-Sea Research*, **37**, 381–400.

CRANE, K. & BONATTI, E. 1987. The role of fracture zones during early Red Sea rifting: structural analysis using Space Shuttle radar and LAND-SAT imagery. *Journal of the Geological Society, London*, **144**, 407–420.

CULVER, S. J. & BUZAS, M. A. 1980. Distribution of Recent benthic foraminifera off the North American Atlantic coast. *Smithsonian Contributions to Marine Science*, **6**, 1–512.

—— & —— 1981. Distribution of Recent benthic foraminifera in the Gulf of Mexico: Volume II. *Smithsonian Contribution to Marine Science*, **8**, 413–898.

—— & —— 1982. Distribution of Recent benthic foraminifera in the Caribbean Region. *Smithsonian Contribution to Marine Science*, **14**, 1–382.

CURRIE, R. I., FISHER, A. E. & HARGREAVES, P. M. 1973. Arabian Sea upwelling. *In*: ZEITSCHEL, B. & GERLACH, S. A. (eds) *The Biology of the Indian Ocean, Ecological Studies*, vol. 3, Springer, Berlin, 37–52.

DEUSER, W. G., ROSS, E. H. & MLODZINSKA, Z. J. 1978. Evidence for and rate of denitrification in the Arabian Sea. *Deep-Sea Research*, **25**, 431–445.

HERMELIN, J. O. R. 1990. Benthic foraminifera and the evolution of the Owen Ridge (northwestern Indian Ocean). *In*: *Geology of the Oceans*, E.S.F. Consortium for Ocean Drilling, Milano, 49.

—— 1991a. The benthic foraminiferal faunas of ODP Sites 725, 726, and 728 (Oman margin, northwestern Arabian Sea). *In*: PRELL, W. L. *et al. Proceedings of the Ocean Drilling Program, Scientific Results*, Ocean Drilling Program, College Station, TX, **117**, 55–87.

—— 1991b. *Hyalinea balthica* (Schroeter) in lower Pliocene sediments of the northwest Arabian Sea. *Journal of Foraminiferal Research*, **21**, 299–251.

—— & SHIMMIELD, G. B. 1990. The importance of the oxygen minimum zone and sediment geochemistry on the distribution of Recent benthic foraminifera from the NW Indian Ocean. *Marine Geology*, **91**, 1–29.

INGLE, J. C. JR., KELLER, G. & KOLPACK, R. L. 1980. Benthic foraminiferal biofacies, sediments and water masses of the southern Peru-Chile Trench area, southeastern Pacific Ocean. *Micropaleontology*, **26**, 113–150.

JOHNSON, D. A. & NIGRINI, C. A. 1985. Synchronous and time-transgressive radiolarian datum levels in the equatorial Indian and Pacific Oceans. *Marine Micropaleontology*, **9**, 489–523.

——, SCHNEIDER, D. A., NIGRINI, C. A. & CAULET, J. P. 1989. Pliocene-Pleistocene radiolarian events and magnetostratigraphic calibrations for the tropical Indian Ocean. *Marine Micropaleontology*, **14**, 33–66.

KEIGWIN, L. D. JR. 1982. Neogene planktonic foraminifera from Deep Sea Drilling Project Sites 502 and 503. *In*: PRELL, W. L. *et al. Initial Reports of the Deep Sea Drilling Project*, United States Printing Office, Washington, D.C., **68**, 269–288.

KREY, J. & BABENERD, B. 1976. Phytoplankton Production: Atlas of the International Indian Ocean Expedition. *Intergovernmental Oceanographic Commission, UNESCO*.

KUZ'MENKO, L. O. 1974. Primary productivity of the northern Arabian Sea. *Oceanology*, **20**, 164–167.

MANKINEN, E. A. & DALRYMPLE, G. B. 1979. Revised geomagnetic polarity time scale for the interval 0–5 m.y.B.P. *Journal of Geophysical Research*, **84**, 615–626.

McGOWRAN, B. 1974. Foraminifera. *In*: VON DER BORCH, C. C. *et al. Initial Reports of the Deep Sea Drilling Project*, United States Printing Office, Washington, D.C., **22**, 609–627.

MONECHI, S., BLEIL, U. & BACKMAN, J. 1985. Magnetobiochronology of late Cretaceous– Paleogene and late Cenozoic pelagic sedimentary sequences from the northwest Pacific (DSDP Leg 86, Site 577). *In*: HEATH, G. R. *et al. Initial Reports of the Deep Sea Drilling Project*, United States Printing Office, Washington, D.C., **86**, 787–797.

MOUNTAIN, G. S. & PRELL, W. L. 1989. Geophysical reconnaissance for ODP Leg 117 in the northwest Indian Ocean. *In*: PRELL, W. L. *et al. Proceedings of the Ocean Drilling Program, Initial Reports*, Ocean Drilling Program, College Station, TX, **117**, 51–64.

NAQVI, S. W. A., NORONHA, R. J. & GANGADHARA REDDY, C. V. 1982. Denitrification in the Arabian Sea. *Deep-Sea Research*, **29**, 459–469.

PETERSON, L. C. 1984. Recent abyssal benthic foraminiferal biofacies of the eastern equatorial Indian Ocean. *Marine Micropaleontology*, **8**, 479–519.

PFLUM, C. E. & FRERICHS, W. 1976. Gulf of Mexico deep-water foraminifers. *Cushman Foundation for Foraminiferal Research, Special Publication*, **14**, 1–122.

PRELL, W. L. & CURRY, W. B. 1981. Faunal and isotopic indices of monsoonal upwelling: western Arabian Sea. *Oceanologica Acta*, **4**, 91–98.

—— & STREETER, H. F. 1982. Temporal and spatial patterns of monsoonal upwelling along Arabia: A modern analogue for the interpretation of Quaternary SST anomalies. *Journal of Marine Research*, **40**, 143–155.

——, NIITSUMA, N. *et al.* 1989. *Proceedings of the Ocean Drilling Program, Initial Reports*, Ocean Drilling Program, College Station, TX, **117**.

PRICE, N. B. & SHIMMIELD, G. B. 1987. *Cruise report for R/V Charles Darwin, Leg 17, NW Indian Ocean*. Unpublished report, University of Edinburgh.

QUASIM, S. Z. 1982. Oceanography of the northern Arabian Sea. *Deep-Sea Research*, **29**, 1041–1068.

READ, H. H. & WATSON, J. 1975. *Introduction to Geology, Volume 2: Earth History, Part II: Later Stages of Earth History*. Macmillan, London.

RIO, D. 1982. The fossil distribution of coccolithophore genus *Gephyrocapsa* KAMPTNER and related Plio-Pleistocene chronostratigraphic problem. *In*: PRELL, W. L. *et al. Initial Reports of the Deep Sea Drilling Project*, United States Printing Office, Washington, D.C., **68**, 325–343.

SAITO, T., BURCKLE, L. H. & HAYS, J. D. 1975. Late Miocene to Pleistocene biostratigraphy of equatorial Pacific sediments. *In*: SAITO, T. & BURCKLE, L. H. (eds) *Late Neogene epoch boundaries*. Micropaleontology, Special Paper, **1**, 226–244.

SLATER, R. D. & KROOPNICK, P. 1984. Controls on dissolved oxygen distribution and organic carbon deposition in the Arabian Sea. *In*: HAQ, B. U. & MILLIMAN, J. D. (eds) *Marine Geology and Oceanography of Arabian Sea and Costal Pakistan*. Van Nostrand Reinhold, New York, 305–313.

STEIN, C. A. & COCHRAN, J. R. 1985. The transition between the Sheba Ridge and Owen Basin: rifting of old oceanic lithosphere. *Geophysical Journal of the Royal Astronomical Society*, **81**, 47–74.

THIERSTEIN, H. R., GEITZENAUER, K. R., MOLFINO, B. & SHACKLETON, N. J. 1977. Global synchroneity of late Quaternary coccolith datum levels: validation by oxygen isotopes. *Geology*, **5**, 400–404.

THOMPSON, P. R. & SCIARRILLO, J. R. 1978. Planktonic foraminiferal biostratigraphy in the Equatorial Pacific. *Nature*, **276**, 29–33.

WHITMARSH, R. B. 1979. The Owen Basin off the south-east margin of Arabia and the evolution of the Owen Fracture Zone. *Geophysical Journal of the Royal Astronomical Society*, **58**, 441–470.

WYRTKI, K. 1971. *Oceanographic Atlas of the International Indian Ocean Expedition*. National Science Foundation, Washington.

—— 1973. Physical oceanography of the Indian Ocean. *In*: ZEITSCHEL, B. & GERLACH, S. A. (eds) *The Biology of the Indian Ocean, Ecological Studies, vol. 3*, Springer, Berlin, 18–36.

Organic carbon removal in the sea: the continental connection

V. ITTEKKOT[1], B. HAAKE[1], M. BARTSCH[1], R. R. NAIR[2] & V. RAMASWAMY[2]

[1] *Institute of Biogeochemistry and Marine Chemistry, University of Hamburg, Bundesstraße 55, D-2000 Hamburg 13, Germany*

[2] *National Institute of Oceanography, Dona Paula, 403 004 Goa, India*

Abstract: Time series sediment traps have been deployed since May 1986 in the Arabian Sea and since October 1987 in the Bay of Bengal. The results of one and a half years from the western, central, and eastern Arabian Sea and of one year from the northern Bay of Bengal show that particle flux patterns are related to the strong monsoon winds and heavy rains. Particle flux maxima in the Arabian Sea are mainly related to wind-induced deeper mixing and nutrient enrichment of surface waters during the SW and NE monsoons. Extremely high particle fluxes with high biogenic opal contents during the SW monsoon at the western location show that it is reached by nutrient-rich water from the near-shore upwelling centres. In the northern Bay of Bengal, particle flux maxima coincide with the period of maximum discharge of the Ganges and Brahmaputra rivers during which river plumes enriched in nutrients are advected into offshore areas. Additionally, the winds and river plumes supply enormous amounts of mineral matter during the periods of high productivity and high particle fluxes. The interaction between marine−biogenic material with eolian and fluviatile mineral particles plays a key role in sedimentation. The incorporation of mineral matter into biologically formed aggregates ensures their rapid sedimentation and thus enhances the removal of biologically fixed atmospheric carbon dioxide to the deep sea.

In order to predict the impact of anthropogenic changes on the oceanic carbon cycle and to interpret the signals preserved in the sedimentary record it is necessary to understand the processes that control (i) fixation of organic carbon in the surface waters and (ii) its transport to the deep ocean. Collection of settling particles in various oceanic regions (Wakeham *et al.* 1980; Honjo 1982; Deuser *et al.* 1981) has greatly improved our knowledge of sedimentation processes in the water column. The degree of biogenic matter degradation seems to depend on its residence time in the water column (Honjo 1986) which is reflected in a decrease of organic carbon fluxes with depth (Suess 1980). The bulk of sedimentation occurs in rare large aggregates of biogenic origin (e.g. McCave 1975; Alldredge & Silver 1988; Fowler & Knauer 1986) into which lithogenic material from various different sources can be incorporated (Honjo *et al.* 1982; Deuser *et al.* 1983a, b, Monaco *et al.* 1987). The downward flux of biogenic and abiogenic particles may, therefore, be in phase with surface biological productivity (e.g. Hargrave 1985; Deuser *et al.* 1990). Thus the seasonality of lithogenic sedimentation in the deep sea does not neccessarily coincide with the seasonality of its input to the surface ocean but may be controlled by productivity (Deuser *et al.* 1983a).

Here we will present results of sediment trap investigations from three stations in the Arabian Sea and from one station in the Bay of Bengal.

It turns out that enhanced carbon fixation in the surface waters is a response to the same meteorological phenomena that provide peak supply of terrigenous mineral matter which accelerates the downward flux of aggregates.

Study area

Climate and hydrography of the Northern Indian Ocean are mainly determined by the monsoon circulation. Strong SW winds blow across the area from June to September and lead to heavy rainfall over Asia. Between December and February, NE winds blow across the region and bring rains to the east coast of India. The surface circulation is in a clockwise direction during the SW monsoon, leading to coastal upwelling along the western margins of both basins (Brown *et al.* 1980; Currie *et al.* 1973) and also along the west coast of India (Sharma 1976). During the NE monsoon, the surface circulation is in an anticlockwise direction and coastal upwelling disappears (e.g. Slater & Kroopnick 1984). The high runoff and monsoon-related winds supply enormous amounts of terrigenous material from rivers (Ittekkot & Arain 1986; Ittekkot *et al.* 1985) and the atmosphere, respectively (Chester 1986; Sirocko & Sarnthein 1989). The Northern Indian Ocean, i.e. the Arabian Sea and the Bay of Bengal is thus one of the oceanic areas severely influenced by the adjacent continents.

From SUMMERHAYES, C. P., PRELL, W. L. & EMEIS, K. C. (eds), 1992, *Upwelling Systems: Evolution Since the Early Miocene.* Geological Society Special Publication No 64, pp 167−176.

Materials and methods

Time series sediment traps (Honjo & Doherty 1988) have been deployed in the Arabian Sea and the Bay of Bengal since May 1986 and November 1987, respectively. The results presented here cover the first one and a half years of deployment in the western, central, and eastern Arabian Sea and the first year in the northern Bay of Bengal (Fig. 1). At each stations, two sediment traps were deployed in intermediate and deep water (Table 1). 26 samples are collected per year, each individual samples representing intervals of 9.5 to 14.5 days. The sampling cups were poisoned with mercuric chloride, which has been shown to be among the better preservatives (Knauer *et al.* 1984). The samples were sieved at 1 mm to remove the major swimmers such as pteropods. After copepods were picked from the <1 mm fraction, four aliquots were filtered through nuclepore filters and then analyzed for carbonate, biogenic silica, lithogenic matter, organic carbon and total nitrogen according to methods described elsewhere (Honjo *et al.* 1982; Nair *et al.* 1989).

Results

Arabian Sea

Total particle fluxes show a bimodal pattern in the western and central Arabian Sea, with maxima during the SW and the NE monsoons (Fig. 2). In the eastern Arabian Sea, only one maximum occurred between August and October. These patterns are coherent with the available seasonal productivity and pigment data (Banse 1987; Banse & McClain 1986; Qasim 1982). Highest particle fluxes were encountered during July/August 1986 and during September 1987 in the western Arabian Sea. During these high flux periods, biogenic opal contents have their maxima with up to 40% of total fluxes during both years (Nair *et al.* 1989 and unpublished results). This, together with the foraminiferal assemblage (Curry *et al.*, this volume), shows that the location in the western Arabian Sea is affected by the upwelling. Although the location is away from the centres of active upwelling (e.g. Luther *et al.* 1990; Prell *et al.* 1990) it is evidently regularly reached by patches of nutrient-rich upwelled water

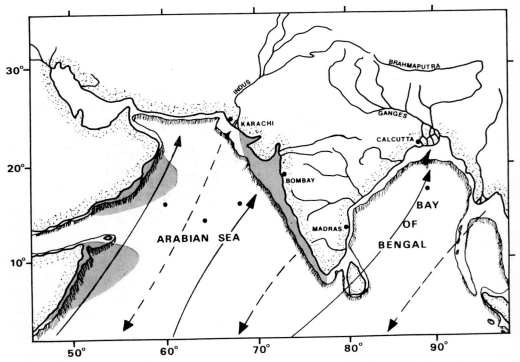

Fig. 1. Sediment trap locations in the western, central, and eastern Arabian Sea and in the northern Bay of Bengal (•). Areas of monsoonal upwelling are marked and arrows show the wind directions during the SW (——) and NE (– –) monsoons.

Table 1. Sediment trap locations, deployment periods, sampling intervals and depths in the Arabian Sea and the Bay of Bengal.

Station	No.	Lat. N	Long. E	Deployment period	Interval (days)	Trap depths shallow (m)	Trap depths deep (m)
Arabian Sea							
Eastern	1	15°32'	68°45'	May 10-Oct 26 86	13	1395	2787
	2	15°28'	68°45'	Nov 20 86-May 2 87	12.6	1205	2764
	3	15°26'	68°43'	May 12-Oct 21 87	12.5	1705	2773
Central	1	14°32'	64°44'	May 12-Oct 21 87	13	732	2914
	2	14°29'	64°46'	May 10-Oct 26 86	12.6	834	2894
	3	14°28'	64°46'	Nov 20 86-May 2 87	12.5	1375	2913
Western	1	16°23'	60°32'	May 12-Oct 21 87	13	1023	3024
	2	16°18'	60°28'	May 10-Oct 26 86	12.6	1051	3021
	3	16°19'	60°28'	Nov 20 86-May 2 87 May 12-Oct 21 87	12.5	1085	3033
Bay of Bengal							
Northern	1	17°26'	89°35'	Oct 28 87-Feb 28 88	9.5	809	1767
	2	17°26'	89°36'	Apr 1-Oct 6 88	14.5	764	2029

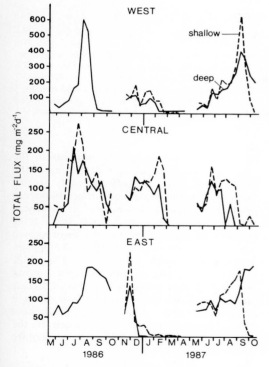

Fig. 2. Total particulate fluxes to the shallow (−−) and deep (——) sediment traps (g m^{-2} d^{-1}) in the western, central and eastern Arabian Sea from May 1986 to October 1987. Due to malfunctioning, seasonal data of the shallow western and eastern traps are not available for the first deployment period. Sampling gaps are due to recovery and deployment of sediment trap moorings.

transported far into the open Arabian Sea (Swallow 1984).

The flux maxima at the other locations, as well as the secondary maximum during the NE monsoon at the western location, can be attributed to a different process (Nair *et al.* 1989). During both monsoons, a cooling of surface waters occurs (Wyrtki 1971) which is due to the wind-induced deepening of the surface mixed layer from about 30 m in the tranquil premonsoon periods to more than 100 m during the monsoons (Rao 1984; Sastry & Ramesh Babu 1984) (Fig. 3). This, together with enhanced turbulent nutrient entrainment at the base of the thermocline (Klein & Coste 1984), leads to nutrient enrichment and high primary productivity during both monsoon seasons in large parts of the Arabian Sea (Banse & McClain 1986; Banse 1987; Qasim 1982). Increased particle fluxes to the deep sea occur within two weeks of the beginning of the monsoons.

In the eastern Arabian Sea, weaker winds (Ramage 1969; Indian Daily Weather Report, Pune, 1986/87) and inflow of nutrient-poor low salinity water from the central Indian Ocean and the Bay of Bengal lead to low productivity, especially during the NE monsoon. The particle flux maximum in August /September 1986 coincided with upwelling along the coast at the same latitude (Madhupratap *et al.* 1990). Moreover, the deep trap received material laterally advected from the continental shelf or slope (Ramaswamy *et al.* 1991).

The supply of mineral particles to the surface waters has its maximum also during the SW monsoon (Fig. 4a, b). The bulk of the lithogenic

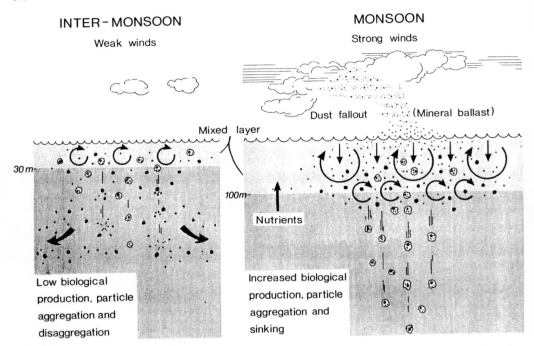

Fig. 3. Wind and marine sedimentation: (a) During the tranquil intermonsoon periods the water column in well stratified, the mixed layer depth is about 30 m and productivity in the nutrient depleted surface waters is low. The material sinking out of the surface layer has low sinking speeds and is remineralized in the water column. (b) During the monsoons strong winds lead to mixed layer deepening to about 100 m and thus to nutrient enrichment in the surface waters and plankton blooms. The dust supplied by the winds is incorporated into the organic aggregates and leads as ballasting material to a fast downward transport of fresh organic matter.

material consists of dust transported from the desert areas on the Arabian Peninsula and Somalia between June and August (Sirocko & Sarnthein 1989). In addition, the maximum input of riverine lithogenic matter from the Indus occurs during August/September (Ittekkot & Arain 1986). Eolian input from India and Pakistan has not been quantified so far, but could be an important source during the NE monsoon (Chester *et al.* 1984). During the last 40 years a reduction of the Indus discharge has occurred due to the building of dams and barrages (Ittekkot & Arain 1986; Milliman *et al.* 1984). The suspended load was reduced from more than 400×10^6 t to only 50×10^6 t annually. Moreover, about 95% of the riverine suspension is at present trapped on the wide shelves (e.g. Ramaswamy *et al.* 1991). The remaining 5% is mainly confined to the eastern Arabian Sea due to the prevailing clockwise surface circulation (Ramaswamy *et al.* 1991).

The role of the winds in sedimentation in the Arabian Sea is thus twofold: they are responsible for triggering plankton blooms at the sea surface by making available nutrients in the euphotic zone by inducing a deepening of the mixed layer (Fig. 3). Left by itself, organic matter originating from high surface biological production should decompose in relatively shallow layers. However, winds carry large amounts of dust which may be incorporated into biogenic particle aggregates, thereby increasing the particle settling rates (Krank & Milligan 1988). This ensures the rapid removal not only of dust particles but also of freshly photosynthesized organic matter and stores it away in the deep ocean (Haake & Ittekkot 1990). Thus wind and dust jointly accelerate the removal of organic carbon from the sea surface to the ocean's interior.

Bay of Bengal

In the northern Bay of Bengal, moderate particle fluxes prevail between October and May (between 44 and 144 mg m^{-2} d^{-1}) and maxima of up to 374 mg m^{-2} d^{-1} occur from June to September (Fig. 5). The flux maxima in the

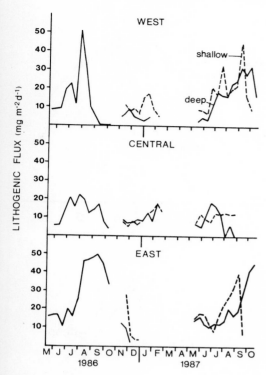

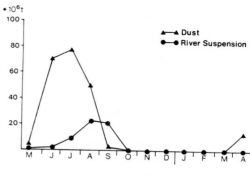

Fig. 4. (a) Fluxes of lithogenic matter to the shallow $(--)$ and deep $(——)$ sediment traps (mg m^{-2} d^{-1}) in the western, central, and eastern Arabian Sea. For the shallow traps data are given from November 1986 to October 1987 and for the deep traps from May 1986 to October 1987. (b) Seasonality of dust transport from the Arabian peninsula and Somalia (Sirocko & Sarnthein 1989) and of suspended matter discharge from the Indus (Ittekkot & Arain 1986) to the Arabian Sea.

northern Bay of Bengal coincide with the discharge maxima of the Ganges and Brahmaputra Rivers. The enormous amounts of freshwater runoff lead to a reduction of salinity in the surface waters by 7‰ in the northernmost Bay of Bengal (La Violette 1967). The river plumes are enriched in nutrients which are derived from the soils because of anthropogenic deforestation and agricultural land utilization (Ittekkot & Zhang 1989). This riverine nutrient supply leads to increased primary productivity not only in near-shore regions but also, due to the enormous river discharge, in the open Bay of Bengal. Moreover, the rivers discharge annually about 2×10^6 t suspended load (Millimann & Meade 1983), of which a large amount by-passes the shelf and is directly transported into the open ocean. Part of the material reaches the Bengal Fan as near-bottom flow and part of it is laterally advected in river plumes and can thus reach areas far away from the coast.

Whereas particulate matter in the Arabian Sea is clearly carbonate dominated with carbonate/opal ratios between 4 and 7 and organic/inorganic carbon ratios of less than 1, particles in the northern Bay of Bengal are dominated by lithogenic material which contributes 54% to the total annual flux (Table 2). Such high amounts of lithogenic matter are normally encountered only in near-shore regions and in areas affected by ice-rafting such as the Fram Strait and the Greenland Basin (Honjo 1986). The annual total biogenic fluxes in the northern Bay of Bengal are about the same as in the central Arabian Sea, but biogenic opal and organic carbon contents are higher. Lowest carbonate/opal ratios (1) occur during the SW monsoon in the northern Bay of Bengal (Table 2) suggesting higher productivity with a shift from calcareous to siliceous primary producers (Dymond & Lyle 1985). Sediment traps deployed in areas south of the present station, i.e. the central and southern Bay of Bengal showed that the opal, lithogenic and organic carbon fluxes decrease and carbonate fluxes increase towards the south as the riverine influence becomes weaker (Ittekkot et al. 1991). Nevertheless, organic to inorganic carbon ratios and organic carbon fluxes to the deep Bay of Bengal are consistently higher than those to the deep Arabian Sea at all sediment trap sites.

Discussion

Previous studies using sediment traps have shown that planktonic organisms and their metabolic waste products play an important

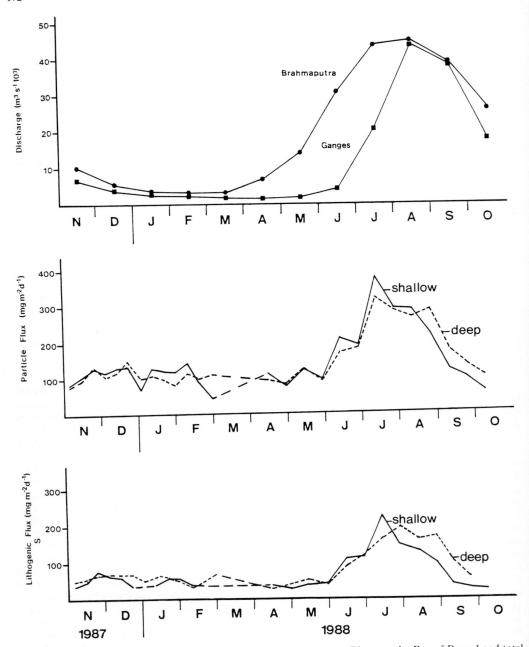

Fig. 5. Seasonality of water discharge of the Ganges and Brahmaputra Rivers to the Bay of Bengal and total particulate fluxes and lithogenic fluxes in the shallow (——) and deep (— —) northern Bay of Bengal (mg m^{-2} d^{-1}).

role in the downward flux of particles (Alldredge & Hartwig 1986). This biological mediation leads to the formation of large particle aggregates which, though rare, account for most of the vertical flux out of the ocean's surface layers (e.g. McCave 1975; Alldredge & Silver 1988; Fowler & Knauer 1986). Filter-feeding zooplankton ingest particles from seawater and

Table 2. Fluxes of components (carbonate, biogenic opal, lithogenic material, organic carbon, total nitrogen) and total material to the deep central Arabian Sea and to the deep northern Bay of Bengal for the NE and SW monsoons and for one year. Ratios of weight percentages organic carbon/total nitrogen (C/N), of organic carbon/carbonate carbon (C_{org}/C_{carb}) and of carbonate/opal.

	NE (g m^{-2})	SW (g m^{-2})	annual (g m^{-2})
Central Arabian Sea			
Carbonate	5.55	9.31	17.50
Opal	1.16	1.51	3.08
Lithogenic	0.79	1.84	3.05
C_{org}	0.53	0.74	1.53
N	0.07	0.09	0.19
Total Flux	8.36	14.02	26.45
C/N	7.57	8.22	8.05
C_{org}/C_{carb}	0.79	0.66	0.73
Carbonate/Opal	4.78	6.17	5.68
Northern Bay of Bengal			
Carbonate	2.54	4.50	10.70
Opal	1.40	4.17	8.06
Lithogenic	4.94	15.40	27.74
C_{org}	0.53	1.30	2.65
Lithogenic	0.06	0.15	0.30
C_{org}	9.85	26.68	51.59
N	8.83	8.67	8.83
Total Flux	1.74	2.41	2.07
C/N	1.81	1.08	1.33
C_{org}/C_{carb}			
Carbonate/Opal			

eject them incorporated in fecal pellets, which settle much faster than individual algal cells. Yet another way of large aggregate formation involves algal excretion products. For example, under conditions of nutrient depletion, extracellular production of carbohydrates is high (Degens & Ittekkot 1983). The sticky nature of this newly excreted material facilitates the aggregation of fine particles into large aggregates, which subsequently settle rapidly to the seafloor. The observations further show that this biological control embraces not only particles generated in situ but also abiogenic particles which are introduced to the sea surface from external sources. Thus, there is evidence for biologically mediated removal of atmospherically derived natural particles and of those having an industrial origin (Deuser et al. 1983a, b).

The observed biological removal is an ecologically significant mechanism by which the biologically active surface layers of the sea are cleansed of the detrimental effects of higher particle concentrations, which interfere with the availability of light and nutrients (Gliwicz 1986). Furthermore, it implies that bottom-dwelling biological communities are assured of a supply of edible material which is associated with rapidly sinking large particle aggregates in phase with high surface primary productivity (Tyler 1988). It is remarkable that even clay-sized particles, which otherwise would have remained suspended in the water column for years, thus reach the deep sea within a matter of days (Degens & Ittekkot 1984; Ittekkot & Haake 1989). Our results show that this intimate biotic–abiotic association also has an impact on the removal of freshly produced organic matter at the sea surface to the seafloor.

Particle fluxes in the deep ocean are correlated with high wind speeds in the Arabian Sea. Upwelling along the coasts of Somalia and Arabia during the southwest monsoon has so far been held responsible for high primary productivity. However, the correlation between high wind speeds and high particle fluxes has been found to exist also in regions away from the upwelling areas, and it also appears to be characteristic for the northeast monsoon (Nair et al. 1989).

Like the wind, any geological agent which introduces nutrients and fine particles to the euphotic zone should, in principle, enhance the removal of CO_2 from the atmosphere to the deep ocean. In the northern Bay of Bengal a major role is played by rivers and their plumes (Fig. 6). High nutrient loads in rivers influenced by human impact has been suggested to increase carbon fixation in the coastal seas (Walsh et al. 1981). The sedimentation of this carbon out of the system can be accelerated by mineral particles carried by the same rivers. This apparently also happens in offshore areas within river plumes. For example, plumes from the Orinoco and the Amazon Rivers have been detected in offshore areas of the tropical Atlantic, and primary productivity within these plumes has been implicated in the observed variability of particle fluxes there (Deuser et al. 1988). Another factor which can increase the efficiency of the oceanic 'biological pump' is cross-shelf transport of organic matter-rich sediments to offshore areas. It releases nutrients trapped in sediment pore waters which increase productivity when advected into the euphotic zone. The resuspended fine particles can accelerate the downward transport of particles both from the surface waters and through scavenging by sinking aggregates in intermediate waters.

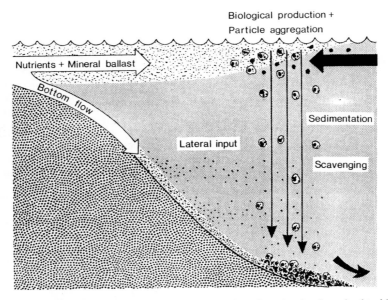

Fig. 6. River plumes and marine sedimentation. The supply of nutrients by the rivers lead to high primary productivity in river plumes advected far into the open ocean. The biogenic particles incorporate suspended lithogenic particles which are also supplied by the river and can thus be transported fast into the deep sea where they scavenge fine lithogenic particles advected from the continental slope.

Conclusion

Windborne dust and river- and shelf-derived particles are significant in the rapid transfer of newly fixed organic carbon from the sea surface to the sea bottom. Consequently, they increase the efficiency of the oceanic biological CO_2 pump. Wind-blown dust blankets vast areas of the ocean floor, especially in the Pacific and Indian Oceans. Sporadic dust storms over the oceans should leave their imprint by stimulating high primary productivity in the surface layers via wind-induced mixing leading to nutrient injection into the euphotic zone, but also ensure the rapid removal of this newly fixed carbon to the ocean's abyss. Continuous monitoring of the ocean surface by remote sensing techniques, and of particle fluxes by moored sediment traps, could be used to monitor these accelerations of the 'biological pump', and may help answer some of the unsolved questions relating to marine carbon cycling.

We thank the Federal Ministry of Science and Technology (BMFT, Bonn), the Council of Scientific and Industrial Research (CSIR, New Delhi), and the Department of Ocean Development (DOD, New Delhi) for financial support. Help from the officers and crew of the research vessels R/V SONNE and ORV SAGAR KANYA in deployment and recovery of the mooring systems, and from the mechanical and electronical engineers of the University of Hamburg and the National Institute of Oceanography (Goa) are gratefully acknowledged.

References

ALLDREDGE, A. L. & HARTWIG, E. O. (eds) 1986. *Aggregate Dynamics in the Sea*. American Institute of Biological Sciences, Workshop Report, Office of Naval Research.

—— & SILVER, M. W. 1988. Characteristics, dynamics, and significance of marine snow. *Progress in Oceanography*, **20**, 41–80.

BANSE, K. 1987. Seasonality of phytoplankton chlorophyll in the central and northern Arabian Sea, *Deep-Sea Research*, **34**, 713–723.

—— & MCCLAIN, C. R. 1986. Winter blooms of phytoplankton in the Arabian Sea as observed by the Coastal Zone Color Scanner. *Marine Ecology Progress Series*, **34**, 201–211.

BROWN, O. B., BRUCE, J. G. and EVANS, R. H. 1980. Evolution of sea surface temperature in the Somali basin during the southwest monsoon of 1979. *Science*, **209**, 595–597.

CHESTER, R. 1986. The marine mineral aerosol. *In*: BUAT-MENARD, P. (ed.) *The Role of Air-Sea Exchange in Geochemical Cycling*, 443–476.

——, SHARPLES, E. J. & SANDERS, G. S. 1984. The concentrations of particulate aluminium and clay minerals in aerosols from the northern Arabian Sea. *Journal of Sedimentary Petrology*, **55**, 37–41.

CURRIE, R. I., FISHER, A. E. & HARGRAVES, P. M. 1973. Arabian Sea upwelling. *In*: ZEITZSCHEL, B. (ed.), *The Biology of the Indian Ocean.* Springer, Berlin, 37–52.

DEGENS, E. T. & ITTEKKOT, V. 1983. Dissolved organic carbon — an overview. *Mitt. Geol.-Paläont. Inst. Univ. Hamburg*, SCOPE/UNEP Sonderbd., **55**, 21–38.

—— & —— 1984. A new look at clay-organic interactions. *Mitt. Geol.-Paläont. Inst. Univ. Hamburg*, **56**, 229–248.

DEUSER, W. G., BREWER, P. G., JICKELS, T. D. & COMMEAU, R. F. 1983*a*. Biological control of the removal of abiogenic particles from the surface ocean. *Science*, **214**, 388–391.

——, EMEIS, K.-C., ITTEKKOT, V. & DEGENS, E. T. 1983*b*. Fly-ash particles intercepted in the deep Sargasso Sea. *Nature*, **305**, 216–218.

——, MÜLLER-KARGER, F. E., EVANS, R. H., BROWN, O. B., ESAIAS, W. E. & FELDMAN, G. C. 1990. Surface-ocean color and deep-ocean carbon flux: how close a connection. *Deep-Sea Research*, **37**, 1331–1343.

——, —— & HEMLEBEN, C. 1988. Temporal variations of particle fluxes in the deep subtropical and tropical North Atlantic: Eulerian versus Lagrangian effects. *Journal of Geophysical Research*, **93** (C6), 6857–6862.

——, ROSS, E. H. & ANDERSON, R. F. 1981. Seasonality in the supply of sediment to the deep Sargasso Sea and implications for the rapid transfer of matter to the deep ocean, *Deep-Sea Research*, **28**, 495–505.

DYMOND, J. & LYLE, M. 1985. Flux comparison between sediments and sediment traps in the eastern tropical Pacific: Implications for atmospheric CO$_2$ variations during the Pleistocene, *Limnology and Oceanography*, **30**, 699–712.

FOWLER, S. W. & KNAUER, G. A. 1986. Role of large particles in the transport of elements and organic compounds through the oceanic water column, *Progress in Oceanography*, **16**, 147–194.

GLIWICZ, M. Z. 1986. Suspended clay concentration controlled by filter-feeding zooplankton in a tropical reservoire, *Nature*, **323**, 330–332.

HAAKE, B. & ITTEKKOT, V. 1990. Die wind-getriebene biologische Pumpe und der Kohlenstoffentzug im Ozean, *Naturwissenschaften*, **77**, 75–79.

HARGRAVE, B. T. 1985. Particle sedimentation in the ocean, *Ecological Modelling*, **30**, 229–246.

HONJO, S. 1982. Seasonality and interaction of biogenic and lithogenic particulate flux at the Panama Basin, *Science*, **218**, 883–884.

—— 1986. Oceanic particles and pelagic sedimentation in the western North Atlantic Ocean. *In*: *The Geology of North America*, Vol. M, The Western North Atlantic Region, The Geological Society of America, 469–478.

—— & DOHERTY, K. W. 1988. Large apperture time series oceanic sediment traps; design objectives, construction, and application, *Deep-Sea Research*, **35**, 133–149.

——, MANGANINI, S. J. & COLE, J. J. 1982. Sedimentation of biogenic matter in the deep ocean, *Deep-Sea Research*, **29**, 609–625.

ITTEKKOT, V. & ARAIN, R. 1986. Nature of particulate organic matter in the river Indus, Pakistan, *Geochimica et Cosmochimica Acta*, **50**, 1643–1653.

ITTEKKOT, V. & HAAKE, B. 1990: The terrestrial link in the removal of organic carbon in the Sea. *In*: ITTEKKOT, V., KEMPE, S., MICHAELIS, W. & SPITZY, A. (eds) *Facets of Modern Biogeochemistry*, Springer, Berlin, 318–325.

——, NAIR, R. R., HONJO, S., RAMASWAMY, V., BARTSCH, M., MANGANINI, S. J. & DESAI, B. N. 1991. Enhanced particle fluxes to the deep ocean induced by freshwater inputs, *Nature*, **351**, 385–387.

——, SAFIULLAH, S., MYCKE, B. & SEIFERT, R. 1985. Seasonal variability and geochemical significance of organic matter in the river Ganges, Bangladesh, *Nature*, **317**, 800–802.

—— & ZHANG, S. 1989. Pattern of particulate nitrogen transport in world rivers, *Global Biogeochemical Cycles*, **3**, 383–391.

KLEIN, P. & COSTE, B. 1984. Effects of wind-stress variability on nutrient transport into the mixed layer, *Deep-Sea Research*, **31**, 21–37.

KNAUER, G. A., KARL, D. A., MARTIN, J. H. & HUNTER, C. N. 1984. In situ effects of selected preservatives on total carbon, nitrogen and metals collected in sediment traps, *Journal of Marine Research*, **42**, 445–462.

KRANK, K. & MILLIGAN, T. C. 1988. Macroflocs of diatoms, in-situ photography of particles in Bedford Basin, Nova Scotia. *Marine Ecology Progress Series*, **44**, 183–189.

LA VIOLETTE, P. E. 1967. Temperature, salinity and density of the world's seas: Bay of Bengal and Andaman Sea, Informal Report Physical Properties Section, Oceanographic Analysis Division, Marine Science Department, Naval Oceanographic Office, Washington D.C.

McCAVE, I. N. 1975. Vertical flux of particulates in the ocean, *Deep-Sea Research*, **22**, 491–502.

MADHUPRATAP, M., NAIR, S. R. S., HARIDAS, P. & PADMAVATI, G. 1990. Response of zooplankton to physical changes in the environment: coastal upwelling along the central west coast of India, *Journ. Coastal Research*, **6**, 413–426.

MILLIMAN, J. D. & MEADE, R. H. 1983. World-wide delivery of river sediments to the oceans, *Journal of Geology*, **91**, 1–21.

——, QURAISHEE, G. S. & BEG, M. A. A. 1984. Sediment discharge from the Indus river to the ocean: past, present and future. *In*: HAQ, B. U. & MILLIMAN, J. D. (eds) *Geology and Oceanography of the Arabian Sea and Coastal Pakistan*, Van Nostrand Reinhold, New York, 66–70.

MONACO, A., HEUSSNER, S., COURP, T., BUSCAIL, R., FOWLER, S. W., MILLIOT, C. & NYFELDER, F. 1987. Particle supply by nepheloid layers on the northwestern mediterranean margin, *In*: DEGENS, E. T., IZDAR, E. & HONJO, S. (eds), *Particle Flux in the Ocean.* Mitt. Geol.-Paläont. Inst. Univ. Hamburg, SCOPE/UNEP Sonderbd., **62**, 127–147.

NAIR, R. R., ITTEKKOT, V., MANGANINI, S. J., RAMASWAMY, V., HAAKE, B., DEGENS, E. T., DESAI, B. N. & HONJO, S. 1989. Increased particle flux to the deep ocean related to monsoons. *Nature*, **338**, 749−751.

PRELL, W. L., MARVIL, R. E. & LUTHER, M. E. 1990. Variability in upwelling fields in the northwestern Indian Ocean, 2, Data-Model comparison at 9000 years b.p. *Paleoceanography*, **5**, 447−457.

QASIM, S. Z. 1982. Oceanography of the northern Arabian Sea, *Deep-Sea Research*, **29**, 1041−1068.

RAMAGE, C. S., MILLER, F. R. & JEFFERIES, C., 1969. International Indian Ocean Expedition Atlas 1: the surface climate of 1963 and 1964, East West Center, Honolulu.

RAMASWAMY, V., NAIR, R. R., MANGANINI, S. J., HAAKE, B. & ITTEKKOT, V. 1991. Lithogenic fluxes to the deep Arabian Sea, *Deep-Sea Research*, **38**, 169−184.

RAO, R. R. 1984. A case study on the influence of summer monsoonal vortex on the thermal structure of upper central Arabian Sea during the onset phase of MONEX-79, *Deep-Sea Research*, **31**, 1511−1521.

SASTRY, J. S. & RAMESH, BABU, V. 1984. Summer cooling of the Arabian Sea-a review, *Proceedings of the Indian Academy of Science* (Earth and Planetary Science), **94**, 117−128.

SHARMA, G. S. 1978. Upwelling off the southwest coast of India. *Indian Journal of Marine Science*, **7**, 209−218.

SIROCKO, F. & SARNTHEIN, M. 1989. Holocene distribution patterns and mass balance of the eolian sediment load in the Northwest Indian Ocean, *In*: LEINEN, M. & SARNTHEIN, M. (eds), *Paleoclimatology and Paleometeorology: Modern and Past Patterns of Global Atmospheric Transport*, Proceedings NATO ARW Oracle, Arizona, 401−433.

SLATER, R. D. & KROOPNICK, P. 1984. Controls of dissolved oxygen distribution and organic carbon deposition in the Arabian Sea, *In*: HAQ, B. U. & MILLIMAN, J. D. (eds) *Geology and Oceanography of the Arabian Sea and Coastal Pakistan*, Van Nostrand Reinhold, 305−313.

SUESS, E. 1980. Particulate organic carbon flux in the oceans-surface productivity and oxygen utilization, *Nature*, **288**, 260−262.

SWALLOW, J. C. 1984. Some aspects of the physical oceanography of the Indian Ocean, *Deep-Sea Research*, **31**, 639−650.

TYLER, P. A. 1988. Seasonality in the deep sea, *Oceanography Marine Biology Annual Review*, **26**, 227−258.

WAKEHAM, S. G., FARRINGTON, J. W., GAGOSIAN, R. B., LEE, C., DEBAAR, H., NIGRELLI, G. E., TRIPP, B. W., SMITH, S. O. & FREW, N. M. 1980. Organic matter fluxes from sediment traps in equatorial Atlantic Ocean. *Nature*, **286**: 798−800.

WALSH, J. J., ROWE, G. T., IVERSON, R. L. & McROY, P. C. 1981. Biological export of shelf carbon is a sink of the global CO_2 cycle, *Nature*, **291**, 196−201.

WYRTKI, K. 1971. *Oceanographic Atlas of the International Indian Ocean Expedition*. National Science Foundation, Washington D.C.

Radiolarian microfauna in the northern California Current System: indicators of multiple processes controlling productivity

LEIGH A. WELLING, NICKLAS G. PISIAS & ADRIENNE K. ROELOFS

College of Oceanography, Oceanography Admin. Bldg. 104, Oregon State University, Corvallis, Oregon 97331−5503, USA

Abstract: Radiolaria, as other plankton, appear to be highly tuned to specific oceanographic environments. Thus, in a transitional region such as the eastern North Pacific, where many different water masses are mixed, radiolaria provide very sensitive tracers of these water masses and the currents that carry them. We present the first two years of radiolarian results from the Multitracers sediment trap study across the northern California Current System. Three moorings, positioned along a transect at approximately 130, 280 and 650 km from the coast, sample a wide variety of oceanographic conditions both spatially and temporally. Selected species or species groups are presented along with hydrographic data from the region in order to demonstrate the basic trends in the radiolarian data and illustrate their relationships to fluctuations in their physical environment. Multiple linear regression is used to explore the relationship between radiolarian composition and the export of carbon from this system.

The most important physical process controlling variability in the radiolarian composition along this transect is attributed to variability in the intensity of the southward-flowing California Current. The seasonality of the California Current is clearly reflected by changes in the composition of the radiolarian trap assemblages; very different species dominate this region in summer as compared to winter. In addition to seasonal trends, evidence in both the offshore and onshore environments suggests significant differences between years. This region appears to have been more strongly influenced by cold, subarctic water during the winter of 1988/1989 than during the previous year.

The relationship between radiolarian species abundances and the flux of organic carbon strongly indicates that a number of different oceanographic processes contribute to enhanced productivity at these sites. This has important implications when making inferences from the geological record about past changes in the intensity of upwelling in this eastern boundary current system.

An important feature of eastern boundary currents is enhanced biological productivity associated with various oceanographic processes found in these complex regions. How the intensity of these processes have changed in the geological past is of major interest to palaeoceanographers. To unravel the history of these regions, it is critical that we understand how modern oceanographic processes, which affect productivity in the eastern boundary current regime, are recorded in marine sediments.

To better quantify how changes in eastern boundary current systems affect material which is ultimately buried in the deep sea sediment record, we have examined a series of sediment trap samples collected along an east−west transect across the California Current System of the North Pacific at approximately 42°N. This study area was selected because hydrographic and biological properties vary strongly here on both regional and seasonal scales. Thus, with a small number of long-term sediment trap moorings it is possible to sample a wide range of oceanographic conditions. This experiment, the

Multitracers Experiment, is an interdisciplinary project designed to relate seasonal and annual flux variations of microfossils, organic carbon, and geochemical tracers to contemporaneous oceanographic conditions in order to identify those processes most important in the production of carbon and its transfer from the surface to deep waters. This strategy of ground-truthing an array of sediment components allows us to establish the special utility as well as the limitations of each tracer. The ultimate goal is a set of highly tuned independent proxies that we can use to describe the palaeoceanography of this area using the sediment record.

One of the important palaeoceanographic proxies found in the moored sediment trap sample array are the Polycystine Radiolaria. It has been known for some time that the distribution patterns of these siliceous microfauna, as with other plankton (Johnson & Brinton, 1963), reflect the geographical extent of specific currents and water masses (e.g. Casey 1971; Moore 1973; Renz 1976; Kling 1979). Certain species have frequently been used in palae-

From SUMMERHAYES, C. P., PRELL, W. L. & EMEIS, K. C. (eds), 1992, *Upwelling Systems: Evolution Since the Early Miocene.* Geological Society Special Publication No 64, pp 177−195.

177

oceanography as indicators of water mass and temperature (Moore 1978; Morley & Hays 1983; Romine 1985; Schramm 1985; Pisias *et al.* 1986; Hays *et al.* 1989). Radiolaria are particularly well suited for this purpose. They have relatively long life spans, are very diverse, and are distributed in all major oceans (Anderson 1983). The environmental specificity of these organisms is further illustrated by the distinct depth preferences exhibited by many radiolarian species, some living as deep as 1000 m (Kling 1979; Dworetzky & Morley 1987). While there is indication that some radiolarians may respond to increased productivity (Pisias *et al.* 1986), this relationship has not been unequivocally established.

In this paper we analyse radiolarian compositional changes in sediment traps and examine their relationship to oceanographic processes of the California Current System. Our focus is twofold: (1) to examine Radiolaria as oceanographic indicators of temperature, water masses, and currents and (2) to determine their relationship to export productivity. Our aim is to improve our understanding of the processes which lead to changes in export production and associated radiolarian populations and thus to be better able to interpret past oceanographic conditions from microfossil assemblage data.

Background and general oceanographic setting

Water masses and current regime

The Multitracers study area is located in a transition zone in the eastern North Pacific (Fig. 1). This is a region of high oceanic variability, both spatially and temporally, defined by the mixing of several North Pacific water masses (Sverdrup *et al.* 1942; Roden 1970; Hickey 1979; Lynn & Simpson 1987). Located at 42°N the Multitracers transect lies just south of where the eastward-flowing North Pacific Current diverges into northward-flowing and southward-flowing branches, the latter defining the origin of the California Current. Interannual variations in the location of the divergence are reported to be as large as seasonal variations (Hickey 1979), but generally it occurs at about 45°N during the winter and about 50°N in summer (Pickard & Emery 1982). Variations in the location of divergence as well as other seasonal and non-seasonal fluctuations of this eastern boundary current regime are responsible for the high variability of the Multitracers study area which is influenced by Subarctic, Transitional, Subtropical, coastally upwelled and Columbia River waters.

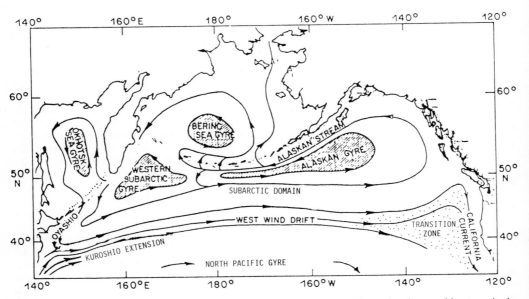

Fig. 1. North Pacific surface circulation patterns and upper ocean domains illustrating the transition zone in the east where the West Drift and North Pacific Current diverge at the coast, thus defining the origin of the California Current (adapted from Hickey 1989).

The southward-flowing California Current delivers Subarctic water, identified by low salinity, relatively low temperature (Tibby 1941; Bernal & McGowen 1981) and high oxygen and phosphate from high latitudes. This current, best developed in summer and fall (Hickey 1987, 1989) (Figs 2c, d), represents the eastern arm of the North Pacific Gyre and has a pre-dominant influence on the oceanographic en-vironment in this region. The classical view of the California Current as a broad, slow eastern boundary current (Wooster & Reid 1963) has evolved in recent years (Smith, this volume). Satellite data have revealed a complex Coastal Transition Zone (CTZ) along the North American coast during the summer that was previously unresolved from shipboard obser-vations. The conceptual model which has emerged from recent surveys of the CTZ is that of a meandering coastal jet which rapidly trans-ports higher latitude water southward and defines a distinct and dynamic transition from

rich, coastally upwelled waters to an offshore, oceanic environment (Hood et al. 1990; Huyer et al. 1991; Kosro et al. 1991; Strub et al. 1991).

Equatorial water enters the California Current System at depth via the poleward-flowing California Undercurrent (Hickey 1979; Lynn & Simpson 1987). At its origin this water is relatively warm, salty (Tibby 1941), high in nutrient concentration, but low in dissolved oxygen (Pickard & Emery 1982). However, the distinguishing characteristics of this water mass are diluted as it makes its way north so that off northern California and southern Oregon the influence of low latitude water is detected primarily by higher relative salinities (Huyer et al. 1989, 1991). The location of the core of the California Undercurrent appears to vary with latitude and season but it is generally said to exist below the main pycnocline at depths of 200–300 m and seaward of the continental shelf (e.g. Hickey 1979; Chelton 1984; Huyer et al. 1989). The time of maximum flow in the Under-

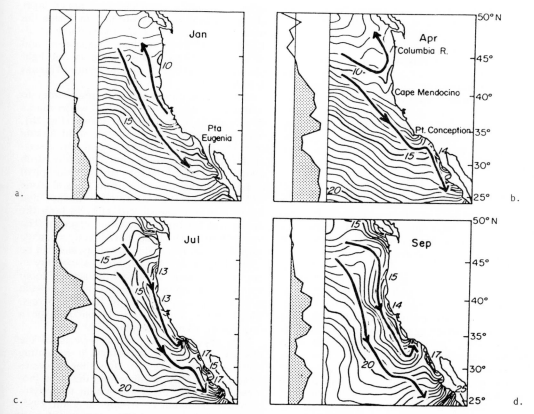

Fig. 2. Seasonal sea surface temperature, surface currents and offshore Ekman transport (shaded) in the California Current (adapted from Huyer 1983 and Hickey 1979).

current is thought to coincide with maximum surface flow in the California Current (Hickey 1989; Huyer *et al*. 1989). North of Point Conception the Undercurrent either disappears or shoals during fall and winter and a poleward-flowing, surface current, traditionally known as the Davidson Current, develops near the coast (Hickey 1979; Chelton 1984; Huyer *et al*. 1989) (Fig. 2a).

North Pacific Central water lies to the southwest of the transect. While this surface water mass is the least saline of the central water masses of the oceans, it has relatively high temperature and salinity but low oxygen and nutrient content as it mixes into the California Current System from the west (Lynn & Simpson 1987; Pickard & Emery 1982). North Pacific Central water represents an oligotrophic, oceanic influence in the Multitracers study region.

Upwelled water, found along the coast, is a mixture of Equatorial and Subarctic water masses (Bernal & McGowen 1981). It is cold and nutrient rich, but has lower oxygen than Subarctic water and higher salinity than Central or Subarctic water masses (Lynn & Simpson 1987; Huyer *et al*. 1991).

Finally, the Columbia River significantly modifies the composition and density structure of near surface water masses in the northeast Pacific (Landry *et al*. 1989). During winter the effluent flows poleward and is primarily confined to the Washington shelf but can extend several hundred miles off the coast of Oregon during the summer when the coastal current is southward and Ekman transport is directed offshore (Hickey 1989).

Processes affecting productivity

While planktonic populations in the California Current exhibit a high degree of spatial and temporal variability (Hayward & McGowen 1979), the coastal environment in the northeast Pacific can be generally characterized as highly productive. Primary production is enhanced during the summer with the development of persistent north-northwesterly winds which drive the coastal current southward and regulate mixing and upwelling processes that enrich surface waters (e.g. Huyer 1983; Thomas & Strub 1989). In general, highest biomass occurs in the upwelling zone to the inside of the coastal jet across which exists a strong gradient in both physical and biological properties (Chavez *et al*. 1991; Hood *et al*. 1990; Strub *et al*. 1991). The development of eddies, filaments, and meanders in the coastal jet can concentrate nutrients and

biomass and transport them hundreds of kilometres offshore and downstream (e.g. Hood *et al*. 1990; Strub *et al*. 1991). The activity of the coastal jet has important ramifications for the Multitracers study since our nearshore mooring site is frequently within the range of influence of a prominent and recurring filament that develops off Cape Blanco during summer and fall (Ikeda & Emery 1984).

In contrast, low pressure and southerly winds during the winter are associated with the northward-flowing Davidson current and downwelling along the coast (Fig. 2a) (Hickey 1979; Huyer *et al*. 1979; Strub *et al*. 1987). However, short-term upwelling events are known to occur off Oregon during the winter even when the mean wind stress is not favourable, and can cause a change in the oceanographic regime which persists for several months (Huyer 1983). Biological measurements in the northeast Pacific during the winter are few but there is some evidence of wintertime increases in production (Roesler & Chelton 1987; Collier *et al*. 1989). While it is often generally assumed that low light levels and a relatively deep mixed layer effectively limit primary production during the winter (e.g. Landry *et al*. 1989; Perry *et al*. 1989), calculations of light availability and *in situ* data suggest this region is not light limited even in the mid- to late winter (Thomas & Strub 1989).

In spring, a rapid transition from winter to summer oceanographic regimes, which marks the beginning of the upwelling season (Fig. 2b), occurs in response to large-scale wind forcing (e.g. Huyer *et al*. 1979) and is generally associated with a large-scale bloom. Thomas & Strub (1989) investigated the sea−surface chlorophyll response to this transition from Coastal Zone Color Scanner (CZCS) satellite images and found high interannual variability in both the timing and location of increased pigment. The bloom apparently need not directly coincide with the onset of coastal upwelling and can be centred up to 300 km offshore. Variability in the intensity and location of the spring bloom seems to be related primarily to basin-wide wind forcing and the curl of the wind stress, which implies the offshore bloom may be a response to Ekman pumping.

It is apparent that several aspects of the physical system are important in regulating productivity in this region. Upwelling processes clearly affect an immediate and dramatic biological response, especially within the phytoplankton community (Abbott & Zion 1985, 1987). On the other hand, interannual variability in the intensity of southward advection has been shown to exert a major effect on zooplankton populations in the California Current (Bernal 1981; Bernal & McGowen 1981; Chelton *et al*. 1982; Roesler & Chelton 1987). The complexities of modern systems are important to keep in mind when reconstructing palaeoproductivity from sediment records since, as noted by Berger *et al*. (1989), export of biogenic material from the surface ocean reflects the physical and biological dynamics of the whole ecosystem rather than just the activity of the primary producers. Thus, in order to unravel the long-term interactions between physical and biological processes in this eastern boundary current system, it is necessary to consider both regional and large-scale forcing mechanisms. To this end, the Multitracers project was designed to provide the field data necessary to critically evaluate the information which is transferred to and preserved in the geological record.

Mooring design and sampling procedure

The Multitracers transect consists of three sediment trap moorings across the California Current System at approximately 42°N (Fig. 3). These three sites, referred to as Nearshore, Midway and Gyre, are approximately 130, 280, and 650 km respectively from the coast. Each mooring has four six-sample-cup traps and a fifth trap with fifteen cups that was recently designed and developed at OSU for high-resolution sampling. Traps are located at depths ranging from 500 m below the surface to 500 m above the bottom. Samples were collected at 2 week to 2 month intervals from 9/87–9/91. The exact sampling interval depends on year,

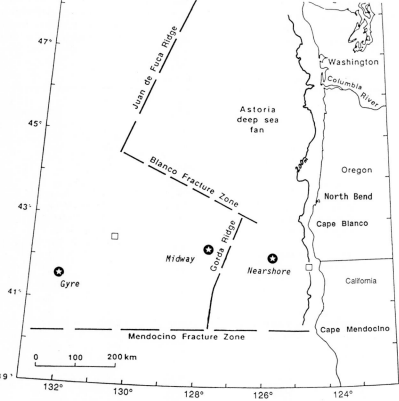

Fig. 3. Multitracers transect in the eastern North Pacific. Circled stars locate sediment trap moorings, boxes locate National Data Buoy Center buoys which provide surface hydrographic information for this region.

location and water depth. Results presented here are from the first two years of data collection, 9/87—9/89. For the period 9/87—10/88 we have six samples from each site collected at 1000 m depth, each representing approximately two-month intervals. For the period 10/88—9/89 we have thirteen samples from the Midway and Gyre sites and twelve from Nearshore, collected at 1500 m, each representing approximately one-month intervals.

Sediment trap samples were preserved with sodium azide. Each sample was wet-split into fourths; three-fourths of which was dried and analysed for organic carbon, calcium carbonate, opal and various trace metals. The remaining fourth was further split for microplankton analysis. Approximately one sixteenth of a sediment trap sample is used for radiolarian analysis. Preparation and determination of the >63 μm fraction followed the technique outlined in Roelofs & Pisias (1986).

Seventy-six species were identified in both trap and sediment samples following the taxonomies referenced in Table 1. In all cases we have made every effort to adhere strictly to the classification guidelines outlined by the authors cited and all references include photographic plates. For this reason we have not included

detailed descriptions or photographs in this paper. The species identified account for between 50% and 75% of the total number of individuals counted in a given sample and the fraction of any particular species rarely exceeds 10%. This minimizes the inherent problem that a closed system presents on the interpretation of fluctuations in relative abundance, since no one species ever dominates the entire sample.

In this paper we focus on radiolarian composition rather than fluxes. While fluxes are probably the best measure for evaluating the functional response of the organism, relative abundances are probably the best indication of the differential influence of water masses and currents, since these are both proportional measures. Ideally we would choose to examine both composition and flux from the traps. However, determination of absolute values is more subject to error than percentage calculations and is, therefore, a less robust measure. Work in progress will address and quantify the potential sources of error involved in calculating radiolarian fluxes for the complete four-year Multitracers data set. This will include a comparison of values between different trap depths. This is an important consideration for this data set since it is necessary to link together data

Table 1. Referenced list of radiolarian species identified in this study.

Species Code	Species Name	Reference
S1	*Spongurus* sp.	[3]p.333, pl.1, fig. 2
S1A	*Spongurus elliptica*	[1]p.S63, pl.8, fig. 2
S3	*Actinomma medianum*	[1]p.S31, pl.3, figs. 5,6
S4	*Actinomma leptodermum*	[1]p.S35, pl.3, fig. 7
S7	*Echinomma* cf. *leptodermum*	[5]p.258, pl.3, fig. 6
S8	*Prunopyle antarctica*	[1]p.S127, pl.16, fig. 4
S9	*Amphiropalum ypsilon*	[1]p.S75, pl.10, fig. 1
S10	*Echinomma delicatum*	[3]p.333, pl.1, fig. 5
S13	*Acrosphaera spinosa*	[1]p.S19, pl.2, fig. 5
S14	*Heliodiscus astericus*	[1]p.S73, pl.9, figs. 1,2
S17	*Hexacontium enthacanthum*	[1]p.S45, pl.5, figs. 1A,B
S18	*Hymeniastrium euclidis*	[1]p.S91, pl.12, fig. 3
S19	*Larcospira quadrangula*	[1]p.S133, pl.17, fig. 2
S23	*Didymocyrtis tetrathalamus*	[1]p.S49, pl.6, fig. 1
S24	*Lithelius minor*	[1]p.S135, pl.17, figs. 3,4
S29	*Larcopyle butschlii*	[1]p.S131, pl.17, fig. 1
S30	*Stylochlamydium asteriscus*	[1]p.S113, pl.14, fig. 5
S34	*Acrosphaera murrayana*	[1]p.S17, pl.2, fig. 4
S36	*Dictyocoryne truncatum*	[1]p.S89, pl.12, fig. 2A
S36C	*Euchitonia triangulum*	[4]p.10, pl.6, fig. 8
S41	*Spongurus pylomaticus*	[5]p.261, pl.4, figs. 8,9
S42	*Spongocore puella*	[1]p.S69, pl.8, fig. 5
S43	*Spongopyle osculosa*	[3]p.334, pl.V, fig. 18
S44	*Spongotrochus glacialis*	[1]p.S117, pl.15, fig. 2
S47	*Stylodictya validispina*	[1]p.S103, pl.13, fig. 5

Species Code	Species Name	Reference
S48	*Porodiscus* (?) sp. B	[1]p.S109, pl.14, figs. 3,4
S51	*Stylatractus* spp.	[1]p.S55, pl.7, fig. 1
S52	*Styptosphaera spumacea*	[1]p.S71, pl.8, fig. 6
S53	*Hexapyle* spp.	[1]p.S121, pl.16, fig. 1
S54	*Tetrapyle octacantha* &	[1]p.S123−S125, pl.16, figs. 2,3
	Octopyle stenozona	
N1	*Liriospyris reticulata*	[1]p.N13, pl.19, fig. 4
N1C	*Zygocircus* sp.	[2]pl.20, figs. 2,8,9
N3	*Anthocyrtidium zanguebaricum*	[1]p.N69, pl.25, fig. 2
N4	*Carpocanistrum* spp.	[1]p.N23, pl.21, fig. 1
N5	*Lamprocyrtis nigriniae*	[1]p.N81, pl.24, fig. 7
N7	*Pterocorys minythorax*	[1]p.N87, pl.25, fig. 10
N8	*Carpocanistrum papillosum*	[1]p.N27, pl.21, fig. 3
N10	*Eucyrtidium acuminatum*	[5]p.275, pl.9, fig. 5
N11	*Eucyrtidium hexagonatum*	[P]p.N63, pl.24, fig. 4
N14	*Tholospyris scaphipes*	[1]p.N19, pl.20, fig. 2
N15	*Lamprocytris* (?) *hannai*	[1]p.N83, pl.25, fig. 8
N18	*Botryostrobus auritus/australis* group	[1]p.N101, pl.27, fig. 2
N23	*Peripyramis circumtexta* &	[1]p.N29−N31, pl.21, figs. 4,5
	Plectopyramis dodecomma	
N24	*Pterocanium* sp.	[1]p.N49, pl.23, fig. 6
N25	*Pterocanium praetextum eucolpum*	[1]p.N43, pl.23, fig. 3
N26	*Pterocanium korotnevi*	[1]p.N39, pl.23, fig. 1
N28	*Pterocanium trilobum*	[1]p.N45, pl.23, fig. 4
N29	*Dictyophimus crisiae* & *D. hirundo* group	[1]p.N33−35, pl.22, figs. 1−4
N32	*Phormostichoartus corbula*	[1]p.N103, pl.27, fig.3
N33	*Botryostrobus aquilonaris*	[1]p.N99, pl.27, fig. 1
N34	*Stichopilium bicorne*	[1]p.N91, pl.26, fig. 1
N35	*Cycladophora davisiana davisiana*	[7]pl.1, figs. 1−5
N35A	*Cycladophora davisiana cornutoides*	[7]pl.1, figs. 6−10
N36	*Theocalyptra bicornis* var.	[4]pl.15, figs. 4,5
N38	*Theocalyptra bicornis*	[4]pl.15, fig. 6
N40	*Pterocorys clausus*	[6]pl.1, figs. 6,7,10
N42	*Theocorythium trachelium trachelium*	[1]p.N93−N95, pl.26, figs. 2,3
N44	*Dictyophimus clevei*	[8]p.70−72, fig. 40, I−VIII
N45	*Helotholus histricosa*	[2]p.459, pl.30, fig. 11; pl.31, fig. 1
GN1	*Dictyophimus infabricatus*	[1]p.N37, pl.22, fig. 5
GN2	*Dictyophimus gracilipes*	[8]p.69−70, figs. 38,I−VIII; 39,I−III
GN3	*Lithomelissa hystrix*	[2]p.363, pl.24, figs. 6−9
GN4	*Lithomelissa thoracites*	[2]p.366, pl.24, figs. 10−13
GN5	*Lithomelissa* cf. *galeata*	[2]p.371, pl.24, figs. 16−18
GN8	*Ceratospyris polygona*	[1]p.N15, pl.19, fig.5
GN9	*Litharachnium tentorium*	[2]p.427, pl.29, figs. 5,6
GN14	*Desmospyris anthocyrtoides*	[2]p.332, pl.23, figs. 6−8
GN15	*Lophocorys polyacantha*	[2]p.494, pl.34, figs. 1−3
GN16	*Eucecryphalus* sp.	[2]p.450, pl.30, figs. 6,7
GN18	*Peridium longispinum*	[9]p.135, pl.XV, figs. 75−79; XVI:80
GN19	*Lithostrobus* cf. *hexagonalis*	[2]p.508, pl.35, figs. 1,2
GN21	*Lampromitra* cf. *coronata*	[2]p.455, pl.30, figs. 8−10
GN22	*Plectacantha oikiskos*	[9]p.131−132, pl.XIII, figs. 50−57
GN27	*Dictyoceras acanthicum*	[2]p.417, pl.28, figs. 8−10
GN28	*Dictyphimus columba*	[2]p.414, pl.28, fig. 7
GN29	*Amphiplecta* cf. *acrostoma*	[2]p.464, pl.32, figs. 1,2

[1] Nigrini and Moore (1979)
[2] Benson (1966)
[3] Molina-Cruz (1977)
[4] Moore (1974)
[5] Robertson (1975)
[6] Caulet and Nigrini (1988)
[7] Morley (1980)
[8] Petrushevskaya (1967)
[9] Jorgensen (1905)

from different depths in order to attain a continuous collection record. Accurate quantification of radiolarian composition requires only that the number of radiolarians counted adequately represent the proportion of the original sample. This can be accomplished by counting a minimum of 800 individuals. For this paper we utilize radiolarian compositional changes as the most robust measure, which best reflects the overall variability in the spatial and temporal patterns of the region.

Results

Hydrographic conditions along the Multitracers Transect

Of the 76 species examined in the sediment trap data set we present the distribution patterns of six which, based on a more complete multivariate analysis (Welling 1990), illustrate the most important aspects of the data set. In addition, the selected species all have distinct surface sediment distributions which reflect their oceanographic ranges. Sediment distributions together with the spatial and temporal variability provided by the sediment trap time series allow us to make inferences as to the oceanographic settings preferred by each species.

The radiolarian sediment trap records are a direct reflection of biological change associated with time varying hydrographic conditions. Two National Data Buoy Center buoys, located at 41.8°N, 124.4°W and 42.5°N, 130.4°W, monitor these conditions in our study area (Fig. 3). Sea surface temperature records from these buoys, along with a record of wind vectors from the

North Bend airport at the Oregon coast, provide a high-resolution description of the onshore and offshore physical environment which we use to clarify the radiolarian abundance patterns observed in the traps (Fig. 4).

One buoy is located over the continental shelf (Fig. 4b) and the other is approximately 500 km offshore (Fig. 4a). These records, covering our trapping period of August 87 to October 89, are consistent with the general seasonality of this region depicted in Fig. 2. The average temperature difference between the two buoys allows a rough comparison of the horizontal gradient across the core of the California Current. The offshore temperatures typify the mid-latitude annual cycle of summer heating and winter cooling. The temperatures over the shelf are similar to that in the offshore region during the winter. In summer, temperatures over the shelf are punctuated by rapid fluctuations associated with mixing and/or upwelling events at the coast and maintain an average value near that during the winter. The spring transition from winter to summer physical regimes at the coast can be seen both in the onset of the first major cold temperature spike and in the change in magnitude and direction of the wind vectors at the North Bend airport. Figures 4b and 4c show this to occur in late March of 1988 and early May of 1989. While the coldest temperatures at the coast occur in spring and summer in association with maximum upwelling, the strongest gradient occurs in late summer/early fall when the offshore temperatures are highest. This strong gradient coincides with maximum southward transport in the California Current and the development of

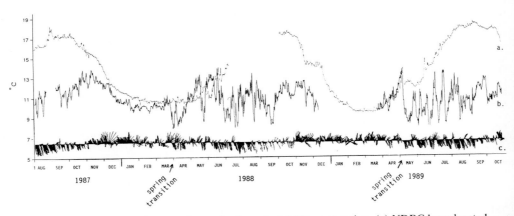

Fig. 4. Temperature and wind vector time series from the Multitracers region. (a) NDBC buoy located approximately 500 km offshore, (b) NDBC buoy located over continental shelf, (c) wind vectors from North Bend airport, Oregon coast; North = up, South = down (provided courtesy of A. Huyer).

meanders and filaments in the coastal jet which appear to strongly influence both our Nearshore and Midway sites at this time.

Seasonal changes in radiolarian species

The general seasonality of this region, apparent in the wind and temperature patterns described above, are reflected in the abundance patterns of the three species shown in Figs 5a–5c. *Spongurus* sp. (S1) appears to have an affinity for the coastal environment during late summer/fall (Fig. 5a). While it never accounts for more than 10% of the total radiolarians present in the trap samples, its temporal and spatial patterns are distinctive. This species is most prominent at Nearshore, secondarily at Midway and never accounts for more than 2% at Gyre. The highest relative abundance of *Spongurus* sp. coincides with a maximum thermal gradient across the California Current when southward advection and offshore Ekman transport are highest (Figs 4a, 4b, 2c and 2d). This is the time when meanders in the coastal jet are well developed and our Nearshore and Midway sites are influenced by coastal processes as well as high latitude waters. Analysis of radiolarian sediment assemblages off the coast of Peru have found *Spongurus* sp. to be strongly associated with coastal upwelling and the Peru Current (Molina-

Cruz 1977). The sediment distribution of this species in the North Pacific further supports its association with Subarctic water and the eastern boundary current (Fig. 6a).

With the onset of wintertime conditions *Spongurus* sp. (S1) declines (Fig. 5a) and *Porodiscus* (?) sp. B (S48) begins to increase in relative abundance (Fig. 5b). This latter species reaches its highest trap abundance at Midway during January and February for both sample years. However, *Porodiscus* (?) sp. B shows even less of an affinity for the extreme offshore environment than *Spongurus* sp., as evidenced by its very low abundance at Gyre. Temporally, *Porodiscus* (?) sp. B is most abundant when surface temperatures across the California Current are similarly cold in both coastal and oceanic regions (Figs 2a, 4a and 4b). Lack of a strong gradient during this season suggests equatorward flow is at a minimum and is concentrated farther offshore than during the summer since poleward flow exists at the surface near the coast. The surface sediment distribution of *Porodiscus* (?) sp. B in the North Pacific suggests its source to be very cold, northern water (Fig. 6b). Molina-Cruz (1975) also found this species in sediments of the southeast Pacific. However, Q-mode factor analysis did not reveal any noteworthy pattern in its surface distribution. This may be because all of the stations

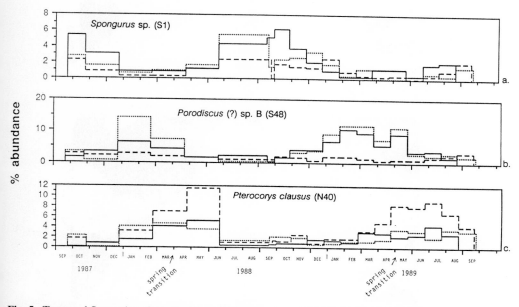

Fig. 5. Temporal fluctuations from the traps of three species exhibiting seasonal variability. (a) *Spongurus* sp. (S1), (b) *Porodiscus* (?) sp. B (S48) and (c) *P. clausus* (N40). Nearshore = solid; Midway = dotted; Gyre = dashed.

Spongurus sp. (S1)

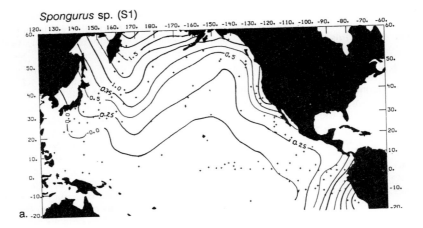

a.

Porodiscus (?) sp. B (S48)

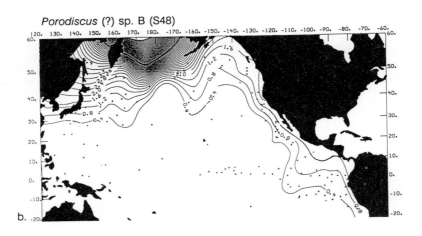

b.

Pterocorys clausus (N40)

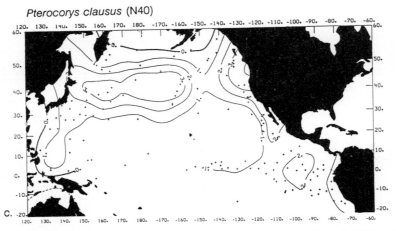

c.

Fig. 6. Surface sediment distribution of: (a) *Spongurus* sp. (S1), (b) *Porodiscus* (?) sp. B (S48) and (c) *P. clausus* (N40). Contours are in relative abundance. (data from Pisias, in prep).

were located north of 35°S. We suggest this species is a cold water, northern species whose range is extended south via the California Current during the winter.

Surface sediment distributions of *Spongurus* sp. (S1) and *Porodiscus* (?) sp. B (S48) in the North Pacific are quite similar (Figs 6a and 6b). Both appear to be related to cold northern water brought south along the coast. However, their records in the sediment traps make it clear they do not coexist in this region but rather they represent very different oceanographic conditions in the California Current, summer and winter respectively (Figs 5a and 5b).

The transition from winter to summer regimes in the spring is represented by yet another radiolarian trap assemblage than exists during the other two seasons. *Pterocorys clausus* (N40) illustrates this trend in the radiolarian data which is most conspicuous in the Gyre samples (Fig. 5c). The percentage of this species begins to increase in late winter and reaches a maximum during late spring or early summer for both sample years. The high surface sediment abundances of *P. clausus* beneath the transition zone in the North Pacific-further support the association of this species with a transitional environment (Fig. 6c). Previous studies of North Pacific sediments have found

similar geographical distributions for this species (Sachs 1973; Robertson 1975). The fluctuations in abundance of *P. clausus* in the trap samples indicate a strong influence of transitional waters along this transect in the spring, especially at Gyre, as the West Wind Drift intensifies and the region of divergence shifts southward.

Non-seasonal variations

In addition to seasonal trends illustrated above, significant differences between years are apparent in the fluctuations of some radiolarian species. For example, two important offshore species counted as a single group, *Tetrapyle octacantha* & *Octopyle stenozona* (S54), show high abundances at the Gyre site during the 1987/88 fall and winter, but are much less prominent the following year (Fig. 7a). *O. stenozona* has been interpreted as a tropical, oceanic species which is rare to non-existent at temperate and high latitudes (Benson 1966). In the North Pacific *T. octacantha* has been found to be most important south of 45°N in sediments beneath the Subtropical Gyre (Sachs 1973; Robertson 1975). These two species have previously been grouped together as indicative of a warm, subtropical environment (e.g. Molina-Cruz 1977; Pisias 1986). Surface sedi-

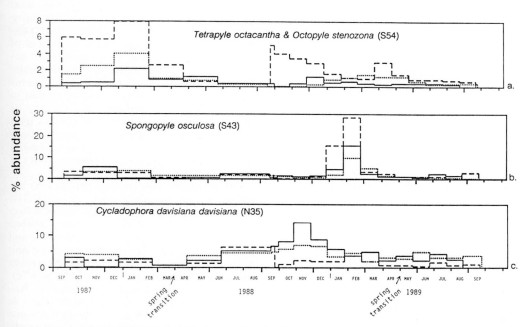

Fig. 7. Temporal fluctuations from the sediment traps showing nonseasonal variability in both the onshore and offshore regions. (a) *T. octacantha* & *O. stenozona* (S54), (b) *S. osculosa* (S43) and (c) *C. davisiana davisiana* (N35). Nearshore = solid; Midway = dotted; Gyre = dashed.

ment distribution of this group supports this interpretation (Fig. 8b). In the Multitracers study region this group of species is our best indicator of an offshore, oligotrophic environment representing the influence of the Central Gyre water mass. This water mass most strongly affects the offshore region during fall and early winter and apparently had a much more pronounced influence along the Multitracers transect during 1987/88 than during 1988/89.

Samples from the winter of 1988/89 were dominated by the occurrence one species, *Spongopyle osculosa* (S43). The predominance of this species can be seen at all three of our mooring sites but is most marked at Gyre where it reaches nearly 30% abundance (Fig. 7b). *S. osculosa* has previously been interpreted as a gyre margin species from sediments of the South Atlantic (Morley 1977). We infer a similar environmental preference for this species in the North Pacific where it has highest surface sediment abundances along the North American coast and beneath the Alaskan Gyre (Fig. 8b). The pronounced occurrence of this species suggests a greater influence of cold, Subarctic gyre water along the Multitracers transect during the 1988/89 winter than in 1987/88.

Further evidence for this difference between years exists in species which prefer the nearshore environment. *Cycladophora davisiana davisiana* (N35), a species very abundant in the sediments in this region, is much more prevalent during the late fall/early winter of 1988 than in 1987 (Fig. 7c). This species, which has previously been linked to very cold, deep water (Morley & Hays 1983), exhibits highest abundances in sediments beneath the Sea of Okhotsk as well as in sediments beneath the California Current (Fig. 8c). The indication that this region may have been more strongly influenced by cold, northern water during our second sample year is supported by the offshore NDBC buoy temperature records; the 1987/88 wintertime surface temperature was about 1.5°C warmer than that during the winter of 1988/89 (Fig. 4a).

Carbon flux and radiolarian species

An important goal of the Multitracers project is to identify processes important in the transfer of carbon from the surface to the deep ocean. By comparing the radiolarian data to the flux of organic carbon in the traps we can get some insight into what processes enhance the export of carbon from surface waters in this region.

In general, average values for organic carbon flux decrease by about a factor of four from Nearshore to Gyre (Lyle *et al.* 1989). Temporal

variations in organic carbon flux range from a factor of three at Nearshore to more than a factor of 15 at Gyre (Figs 9a–c). While Midway and Gyre demonstrate roughly similar seasonal patterns for both years, fluctuations at Nearshore show distinctive differences from year one to year two. In 1987/88 the highest flux at Nearshore begins in the winter and extends into the spring. High fluxes are also observed at Midway during the 1987/88 winter, though to a lesser extent. Organic carbon fluxes for the 1988/89 year have more than one maxima at all three sites; high fluxes occur in the fall/early winter, spring and again in late summer.

The relationship between radiolarian compositional changes and organic carbon flux is examined using multiple linear regression. Organic carbon variations are used as the dependent variable in this analysis. Species which exhibit a maximum value of 2.0% or more at some time during the first two years of trap data have been included as the 'independent' variables. Using an equal-tails test with 54 degrees of freedom and $\alpha = 5.0\%$ significance level, a correlation coefficient >0.3 indicates a significant correlation between an individual species and organic carbon. Based on this test, seven species exhibit a significant correlation to organic carbon flux (Table 2).

Of the seven species in Table 2 which have a significant relationship to organic carbon flux, five have a positive and two have a negative correlation. *Dictyophimus gracilipes* (GN2) has the strongest positive correlation coefficient of 0.61. This species, though apparently rare, has been found in high abundances in diatomite facies in the Gulf of California sediments (Benson 1966) suggesting it may be related to high-productivity environments there. Its occurrence in the sediment trap samples indicates a preference for the Nearshore environment in the California Current System where it is most abundant during the fall/early winter of 1988 (Fig. 10a).

Other species with positive correlations are *C. davisiana davisiana* (N35, $r = 0.31$), *Spongurus* sp. (S1, $r = 0.32$), *Lithomelissa hystrix* (GN3, $r = 0.33$), and *Botryostrobus aquilonaris* (N33, $r = 0.37$). *C. d. davisiana* and *Spongurus* sp. were previously introduced and both are primarily important at the Nearshore site primarily during the fall (Figs 5a and 7c). *L. hystrix* (GN3), though more common than *D. gracilipes* (GN2), has also been found in diatomite facies in Gulf of California sediments (Benson 1966). Its temporal pattern in the sediment traps is somewhat similar to that of *Porodiscus* (?) sp. B (S48) as it is most important

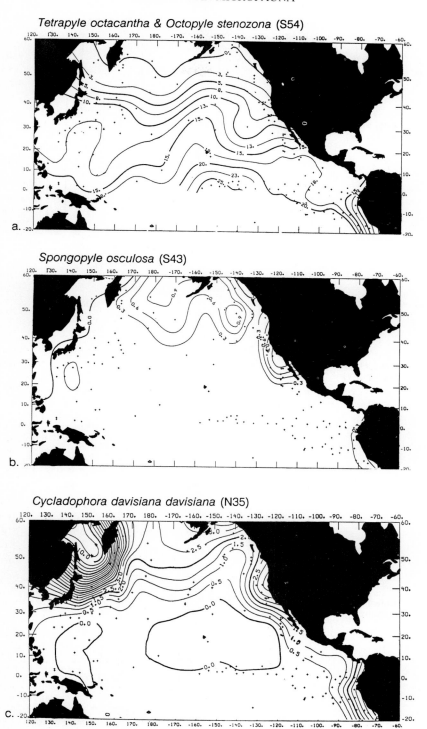

Fig. 8. Surface sediment distributions of: (a) *T. octacantha* & *O. stenozona* (S54), (b) *S. osculosa* (S43) and (c) *C. davisiana davisiana* (N35). Contours are in relative abundance. (data from Pisias, in prep).

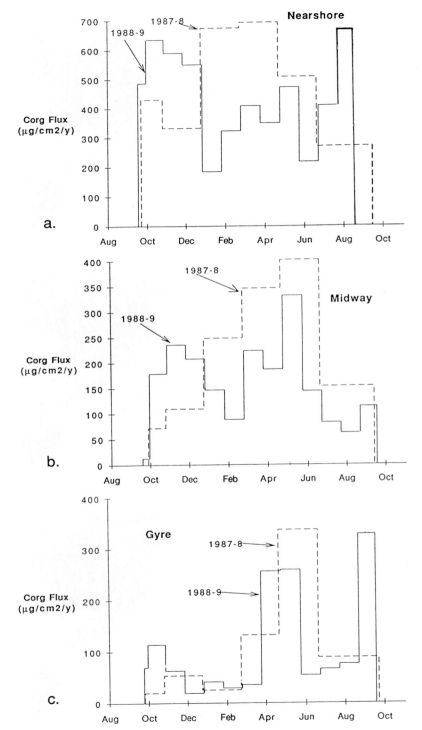

Fig. 9. Organic carbon flux from the first two years of sediment trap samples. (data supplied courtesy of Jack Dymond).

Table 2. Correlation coefficients for 35 radiolarian species to organic carbon flux. See Table 1 for species codes. Underlined values are significant (54 degrees of freedom; $\alpha = 0.05$)

S1 = 0.32	S43 = −0.21	N10 = −0.11	<u>N35 = 0.31</u>	GN4 = 0.25
S8 = −0.18	S44 = 0.12	N11 = −0.11	N38 = 0.01	GN5 = 0.18
S13 = −0.28	S47 = 0.14	N14 = 0.16	N40 = −0.03	GN9 = −0.10
S17 = −0.05	S48 = 0.19	N15 = 0.15	N44 = −0.10	GN18 = −0.06
S24 = −0.03	<u>S54 = −0.35</u>	N18 = −0.08	N45 = 0.03	GN21 = 0.10
S29 = −0.19	N4 = −0.28	<u>N24 = −0.35</u>	<u>GN2 = 0.61</u>	GN22 = −0.10
S30 = −0.24	N5 = −0.06	<u>N33 = 0.37</u>	<u>GN3 = 0.33</u>	GN27 = −0.23

during the winter and early spring at Nearshore and Midway (Fig. 10b). *B. aquilonaris* (N33) is reported to be a transitional or cosmopolitan species (Benson 1966; Sachs 1973; Robertson, 1975). It generally accounts for around 2% of a sediment trap sample with highest abundances in spring of 1988 at Midway and again in the fall of 1988 at Nearshore (Fig. 10c).

Pterocanium sp. (N24) and *T. octacantha* & *O. stenozona* (S54) show significant negative correlations to organic carbon both have an $r = −0.35$. *Pterocanium* sp. is reportedly rare but cosmopolitan in the North Pacific (Nigrini and Moore 1979). It is also rare in the sediment trap samples and displays no distinctive pattern other than seeming to be somewhat relatively more abundant offshore. *T. octacantha* &

O. stenozona have been previously mentioned as indicative of an offshore, oligotrophic environment.

The following regression equation based on the 35 species from Table 2 has $r = 0.75$:

$$Corg = 51(GN2) + 34(GN3) + 57(N33) \quad (1)$$
$$- 76(N24) + 77(GN27) + 26$$

with a standard error of estimate $= +/−130$ $\mu g/cm^2/yr$. Clearly there exists a statistical relationship between radiolarian abundances and flux of organic carbon for these two sample years. We should point out that while *Dictyoceras acanthicum* (GN27) shows a negative (though not significant) correlation to organic carbon (Table 2), it enters into the regression equation (1) in a positive manner.

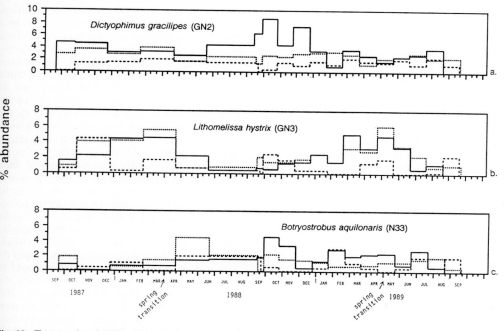

Fig. 10. Temporal variability of the first three species in equation (1). (a) *D. clevei* (GN2), (b) *L. hystrix* (GN3) and (c) *B. aquilonaris* (N33). Nearshore = solid; Midway = dotted; Gyre = dashed.

This species has not been widely studied in sediments outside the Gulf of California where it appears to be rare but ubiquitous (Benson 1966). This species is also rare in the trap samples and does not display a pattern linking it to any specific environment or process.

The form of equation (1) represents the additive effects of several individual species, which seem to be important at distinctively different locations or times of the year. Examination of equation (1) together with Table 2 suggests that species which display the strongest or most consistent relationships to organic carbon flux seem to be those with coastal affinities and are most abundant in the late summer and fall. Also important are species with high abundances during winter and early spring at the Nearshore and Midway sites. Finally, offshore species important during the fall and winter show a negative relationship with organic carbon. This suggests that the relationship between radiolarian composition and organic carbon flux is not necessarily causal and that both are primarily controlled by physical changes in the oceanic environment. While it is apparent that the coastal environment is more productive than the more offshore regions, the evidence suggests that more than one time of year, thus, more than one process is important to export flux in the California Current System.

Discussion and conclusions

Our results suggest a strong relationship exists between changes in radiolarian abundance patterns and fluctuations in the physical oceanography in the eastern North Pacific. Temporal fluctuations of individual radiolarian species in the sediment traps show both seasonal and non-seasonal variability. This is understandable since circulation in the California Current System exhibits both strong seasonal and interannual variability. The species presented were selected as representatives of the predominant trends which emerged from a multivariate analysis of the entire radiolarian data set (Welling 1990). These examples demonstrate the value of process-oriented studies in unravelling the various inputs to the sediment record.

The most important process controlling radiolarian variability in this region appears to be related to fluctuations in the intensity of equatorward flow in the California Current. Very different assemblages dominate this region in the summer and fall, when southward flow is strong and meanders in the coastal jet are well developed, as compared to wintertime, when southward flow is weak. Based on sediment distributions alone, this seasonality could not be discriminated. Sediment distributions of *Spongurus* sp. (S1), a species showing high abundances in summer (Fig. 5a), and *Porodiscus* (?) sp. B (S48), a species important in the winter (Fig. 5b) are very similar, both being associated with northern water and the eastern boundary of the North Pacific (Figs 6a, b). Only by examining the temporal differences provided by the sediment traps can we discern that they represent very different oceanographic and, therefore, environmental conditions.

In addition to the strong seasonality of this current system, differences between years are also apparent. Radiolarian evidence from both onshore and offshore environments suggest the influence of cold, Subarctic water was stronger during the winter of 1988/89 than it was during the previous winter. This interpretation is supported by sea surface temperature data from the offshore meteorological buoy in the Multitracers study region. Such differences between years may be due to variability in the strength of the geostrophic current, in the magnitude and direction of basin-wide winds, or variations in the latitude of divergence of the West Wind Drift.

The results from the regression analysis yield a statistical relationship between radiolarian composition and organic carbon flux of $r = 0.75$ (1). However, we do not consider this relationship, based on two years of trap data, to be a strong predictive tool for two reasons. (1) Four of the five species in the equation, *D. gracilipes* (GN2), *L. hystrix* (GN3), *D. acanthicum* (GN27) and *Pterocanium* sp. (N24) are either rare, or have not been well studied on an oceanwide basis. In the case of *D. clevei*, *L. hystrix* and *D. acanthicum*, this may be because they do not preserve well as there is some indication that they are not as well represented in the sediments in this region as they are in the traps (Welling 1990). Interpretation of their records in the sediments must be done cautiously at this point and will probably only be useful when more is known about their modern ecology and distributions. (2) The error of estimate for equation (1) is almost 20% of the observed range of values for carbon flux. While this would allow us to resolve the overall onshore trend for carbon flux, the temporal variability would be difficult to predict with confidence with this equation (Fig. 9). Thus, while we may be able to tell generally when the California Current System becomes either more or less productive, we could still only offer conjecture about exactly what aspect of the system is changing.

One might logically assume that a regression of radiolarian fluxes against organic carbon flux might yield a more robust relationship. We hope to achieve this once we have the entire four-year data set. However, use of such a relationship for palaeoprediction is difficult except in regions of extremely high accumulation rates.

We conclude from this study that extracting signals of past upwelling intensity from palaeo-productivity estimates is not a straightforward process. The radiolarian data and the rather complicated patterns for carbon flux suggest more than one process is important in controlling export production in this region. Based on these two years of data, one cannot invoke one or two of the most prominent processes, for example coastal upwelling and the spring bloom, to account for times of maximum flux. Other times of the year, and thus other processes such as southward advection, wintertime production and a fall transition are aspects of this system which may also play very important roles in productivity variability. Clearly investigations which consider only one or two processes as being of primary importance to carbon cycling in this region may overlook a significant component of the signal.

This leads to an interesting and important question. How representative of the long-term average are the carbon fluxes for these two years? While high material fluxes during the winter may be more frequent than has been previously thought, it is possible, and even likely, that the importance of wintertime fluxes is over-represented in this data set. We are optimistic that the additional two years of sediment trap data from the Multitracers study in conjunction with reliable estimates for radiolarian fluxes will yield a statistical relationship between radiolarians and organic carbon flux which better reflects all the processes controlling carbon flux and thus will provide more insights into the relative importance of the multiple processes leading to enhanced oceanic productivity in the Northern California Current.

Thanks to Jack Dymond for providing us with the carbon data and for thoughtfully reviewing the formative stages of this work. Bob Collier and Ted Strub helped us access the NDBC data. Jane Huyer provided the coastal wind vector time series and together with Bob Smith has offered valuable insight into the physical dynamics of this region. We also thank Catherine Nigrini and Ted Moore for their pertinent comments and constructive reviews of the manuscript. This research was funded by NSF grant OCE86–09366.

References

ABBOTT M. R. & ZION, P. M. 1985. Satellite observations of phytoplankton variability during and upwelling event. *Continental Shelf Research*, **4**, 661–680.

—— & —— 1987. Spatial and temporal variability of phytoplankton pigment off northern California during Coastal Ocean Dynamics Experiment 1. *Journal of Geophysical Research*, **92**, 1745–1755.

ANDERSON, O. R. 1983. *Radiolaria*. Springer, New York.

BENSON, R. N. 1966. *Recent Radiolaria from the Gulf of California*. PhD Thesis, University of Minnesota.

BERGER, W. H., SMETACEK, S. S. & WEFER, G. 1989. Ocean productivity and paleoproductivity — an overview. *In*: BERGER, W. H., SMETACEK, V. & WEFER, V. (eds) *Productivity of the Ocean: Past and Present*, Life Sciences Research Report **44**, Wiley, New York.

BERNAL, P. A. 1981. A review of the low-frequency response of the pelagic ecosystem in the California Current. *CalCOFI Report*, Volume XXII.

—— & McGOWEN, J. A. 1981. Advection and upwelling in the California Current. *In*: RICHARDS, F. A. (ed.) *Coastal Upwelling*, AGU, Washington, D.C., 381–399.

CASEY, R. E., 1971. Distribution of Polycistine radiolaria in the oceans in relation to physical and chemical conditions. *In*: FUNNELL, B. M. & RIEDEL, W. R. (eds) *The Micropaleontology of the Oceans*, Cambridge University Press, 151–159.

CAULET, J. P. & NIGRINI, C. 1988. The genus *Pterocorys* (Radiolaria) from the tropical late Neogene of the Indian and Pacific Oceans. *Micropaleontology*, **34**, 217–235.

CHAVEZ, F. P., BARBER, R. T., HUYER, A., KOSRO, P. M., RAMP, S. & STANTON, T. 1991. Transport of nutrients by the jets of the Coastal Transition Zone, *Journal of Geophysical Research*, **96**(c8), 14833–14859.

CHELTON, D. B. 1984. Seasonal variability of alongshore geostrophic velocity off central California. *Journal of Geophysical Research*, **89**, 3473–3486.

——, BERNAL, P. A. & McGOWEN, J. A. 1982. Large-scale interannual physical and biological interaction in the California Current. *Journal of Marine Research*, **40**, 1095–1125.

COLLIER, R. W., DYMOND, J. & PISIAS, N. 1989. Effects of seasonal oceanographic cycles on the paleoceanographic record: initial results from the Multitracers experiment. *EOS*, Trans. AGU 70:365, [abstract].

DWORETZKY, B. A. & MORLEY, J. J. 1987. Vertical distribution of radiolaria in the eastern equatorial Atlantic: Analysis of a multiple series of closely-spaced plankton tows. *Marine Micropaleontology*, **12**, 1–9.

HAYS, P. E., PISIAS, N. G. & ROELOFS, A. K. 1989. Palaeoceanography of the Eastern Equatorial Pacific during the Pliocene: A high-resolution radiolarian study. *Paleoceanography*, **4**, 57–73.

HAYWARD, T. L. & McGOWEN, J. A. 1979. Pattern and structure in an oceanic zooplankton community. *American Zoology*, **19**, 1045–1055.

HICKEY, B. M. 1979. The California Current system — hypothesis and facts. *Progress in Oceanography*, **8**, 191–279.

—— 1989. Patterns and processes of circulation over the Washington continental shelf and slope. *In*: LANDRY, M. R. & HICKEY, B. M. (eds) *Coastal Oceanography of Washington and Oregon*, Elsevier Oceanography Series, 41–115.

HOOD, R. R., ABBOTT, M. R., HUYER, A. & KOSRO, P. M. 1990. Physical and biological structure along and upwelling front off northern California: Surface patterns in temperature, flow, phytoplankton biomass and species composition. *Journal of Geophysical Research*, **95**, 18081–18094.

HUYER, A. 1983. Coastal upwelling in the California Current system. *Progress in Oceanography*, **12**, 259–284.

——, KOSRO, P. M., FLEISCHBEIN, J., RAMP, S. R., STANTON, T., WASHBURN, L., CHAVEZ, F. P. & COWLES, T. J. 1991. Currents and water masses of the Coastal Transition Zone off northern California, June to August 1988. *Journal of Geophysical Research*, **96**(c8), 14809–14832.

——, ——, LENTZ, S. J. & BEARDSLEY, R. C. 1989. Poleward flow in the California Current system. *In*: NESHYBA, S., MOOERS, S. N. K., SMITH, R. L. & BARBER, R. T. (eds) *Poleward Flows Along Eastern Ocean Boundaries*, Springer, New York, Coastal and Estuarine Lecture Note Series, 142–156.

——, SOBEY, E. J. C. & SMITH, R. L. 1979. The spring transition in currents over the Oregon continental shelf. *Journal of Geophysical Research*, **84**, 6995.

IKEDA, M. & EMERY, W. J. 1984. Satellite observations and modeling of meanders in the California Current system off Oregon and northern California. *Journal of Physical Oceanography*, **14**, 1434–1450.

JOHNSON, M. W. & BRINTON, E. 1963. Biological species, water-masses and currents. *In*: HILL, M. N. (ed.) *The Sea*, vol. 2, Wiley, New York, 381–414.

JORGENSEN, E. 1905. The protist plankton and the diatoms in bottom samples. *Bergens Mus. Skr.*, 49–51, 195–225.

KLING, S. A. 1979. Vertical distribution of Polycistine radiolarians in the central North Pacific. *Marine Micropaleontology*, **4**, 295–318.

KOSRO, P. M., HUYER, A., RAMP, S. R., SMITH, R. L., CHAVEZ, F. P., COWLES, T. J., ABBOTT, M. R., STRUB, P. T., BARBER, R. T., JESSEN, P. and SMALL, L. F. 1991. The structure of the transition zone between coastal waters and the open ocean off northern California, winter and spring 1987. *Journal of Geophysical Research*, **96**(c8) 14707–14730.

LANDRY, M. R., POSTEL, J. R., PETERSON, W. K. & NEWMAN, J. 1989. Broad-scale distributional patterns of hydrographic variables on the Washington/Oregon shelf. *In*: LANDRY, M. R. & HICKEY, B. M. (eds.) *Coastal Oceanography of Washington and Oregon*, Elsevier Oceanography Series, **47**, 1–40.

LYLE, M. W., COLLIER, R., DYMOND, J. & PISIAS, N. 1989. The Multitracers calibration of paleoceanographic variations in the California Current since the last glacial maximum. *EOS*, Transactions of the AGU, **70**, 364.

LYNN, R. J. & SIMPSON, J. J. 1987. The California Current system: The seasonal variability of its physical characteristics. *Journal of Geophysical Research*, **92**, 12947–12966.

MOLINA-CRUZ, A. 1975. *Paleo-oceanography of the Subtropical south-eastern Pacific during late Quaternary: A study of Radiolaria, opal and quartz contents of deep-sea sediments*. MS Thesis. Oregon State Univ., Corvalis, OR.

—— 1977. Radiolarian assemblages and their relationship to the oceanography of the subtropical southeastern Pacific. *Marine Micropaleontology*, **2**, 315–352.

MOORE, T. C. Jr. 1973. Late Pleistocene-Holocene Oceanographic Changes in the Northeastern Pacific. *Quaternary Research*, **3**, 99–109.

—— 1974. Taxonomy of Holocene-Late Pleistocene Radiolaria. CLIMAP Project (unpublished).

—— 1978. The distribution of radiolarian assemblages in the modern and ice-age Pacific. *Marine Micropaleontology*, **3**, 229–266.

MORLEY, J. J. 1977. *Upper Pleistocene Climatic Variations in the South Atlantic derived from a quantitative radiolarian analysis: accent on the last 18000 years*. PhD Thesis, Columbia Univ., New York, NY.

MORLEY, J. J. 1980. Analysis of the abundance variations of the subspecies of *Cycladophora davisiana*. *Marine Micropaleontology*, **5**, 205–214.

—— & HAYS, J. D. 1983. Oceanographic conditions associated with high abundances of the radiolarian *Cycladophora davisiana*. *Earth and Planetary Science Letters*, **66**, 63–72.

NIGRINI, C. & MOORE, T. C. 1979. *A guide to Modern Radiolaria*. Spec. Publ. Cushman Found. Foraminiferal Res. 16.

PERRY, M. J., BOLGER, J. P. & ENGLISH, D. C. 1989. Primary production in Washington coastal waters. *In*: LANDRY, M. R. & HICKEY, B. M. (eds) *Coastal Oceanography of Washington and Oregon*, Elsevier Oceanography Series, 117–138.

PETRUSHEVSKAYA, M. G. 1967. Radiolarii otriador spumellaria y Nasselaria antarkticheskoi oblasti. *In*: *Issled. Fauni Morei*, **6**(12), *Rez. biol. issled. Sov. Antartc. Exped.*, 1955–1958, no 3, 5–186.

PICKARD, G. L. & EMERY, W. J. 1982. *Descriptive Physical Oceanography*. 4th edn, Pergamon, New York.

PISIAS, N. G. 1986. Vertical water mass circulation and the distribution of radiolaria in surface sediments of the Gulf of California. *Marine Micropaleontology*, **10**, 189–205.

——. Spatial variability of the eastern Equatorial

Pacific during the last 150 000 years: radiolarian evidence (to be submitted to *Paleoceanography*).

——, MURRAY, D. W. & ROELOFS, A. K. 1986. Radiolarian and silicoflagellate response to oceanographic changes associated with the 1983 El Nino. *Nature*, **320**, 259–252.

RENZ, G. W. 1976. The distribution and ecology of radiolaria in the central Pacific plankton and surface sediments. *Scripps Institute of Oceanography, Bulletin*, **22**, 1–267.

ROBERTSON, J. H. 1975. *Glacial to interglacial Oceanographic Changes in the Northwest Pacific, including a Continuous Record of the last 400 000 years*. PhD Thesis, Columbia University, New York, NY.

RODEN, G. I. 1970. Aspects of the mid-Pacific transition zone. *Journal of Geophysical Research*, **75**, 1097–1109.

ROELOFS, A. K. & PISIAS, N. G. 1986. Revised technique for preparing quantitative radiolarian slides from deep-sea sediments. *Micropaleontology*, **24**, 182–185.

ROESLER, C. S. & CHELTON, D. B. 1987. Zooplankton variability in the California Current, 1951–1982. *CalCOFI Report*, Vol. XXVIII.

ROMINE, K. 1985. Radiolarian biogeography and paleoceanography of the North Pacific and 8 Ma, *Memoir of the Geological Society of America*, **163**, 237–272.

SACHS, H. M. 1973. *Quantitative radiolarian-based paleo-oceanography in Late Pleistocene subarctic Pacific sediments*. PhD Thesis, Brown University, Providence, R.I.

SCHRAMM, C. T. 1985. Implications of radiolarian assemblages for late Quaternary paleoceanography of the eastern equatorial Pacific. *Quaternary Research N.Y.*, **24**, 204–218.

STRUB, P. T., ALLEN, J. S., HUYER, A., SMITH, R. L. & BEARDSLEY, R. C. 1987. Seasonal cycles of currents, temperatures, winds, and sea level over the northeast Pacific continental shelf: 35N to 48N. *Journal of Geophysical Research*, **92**, 1507–1526.

——, et al. 1991. The nature of the cold filaments in the California Current System. *Journal of Geophysical Research*, **96** (c8), 14 763–14 768.

SVERDRUP, H. U., JOHNSON, M. W. & FLEMING, R. H. 1942. *The Oceans*, Prentice-Hall, Englewood Cliffs, N.J.

THOMAS, A. C. & STRUB, P. T. 1989. Interannual variability in phytoplankton pigment distribution during the spring transition along the west coast of North America. *Journal of Geophysical Research*, **94**, 18 095–18 117.

TIBBY, R. B. 1941. The water masses off the west coast of North America. *Journal of Marine Research*, **4**, 112–121.

WELLING, L. A. 1990. *Radiolarian Microfauna in the Northern California Current System: Spatial and Temporal Variability and Implications for Paleoceanographic Reconstructions*. MS Thesis. Oregon State Univ., Corvallis, OR.

WOOSTER, W. S. & REID, J. L. Jr. 1963. Eastern boundary currents. *In*: HILL, M. N. (ed.) *The Sea* vol. 2, Wiley, New York, 253–280.

The spatial distribution and seasonal succession of planktonic foraminifera in the California Current off Oregon, September 1987 — September 1988

JOSEPH D. ORTIZ & ALAN C. MIX

College of Oceanography, Oregon State University, Corvallis, OR 97331–5503, USA

Abstract: Preliminary results are presented from the September 1987 to September 1988 deployment of the Multitracers Project, a moored sediment trap experiment in the California Current. Three sediment trap moorings were deployed on a transect off Cape Blanco at 130, 280, and 650 km offshore. The seasonal distribution of foraminifers in the California Current at 42°N reflect variations in the temperatures and water masses present at each site. The winter assemblage of foraminifers at the sites 130 and 280 km offshore comprise mainly the subarctic/transitional species: *N. pachyderma* (right), *N. dutertrei, G. bulloides, G. quinqueloba* and *G. glutinata*. From late June to September 1988 at the site 130 km offshore, *G. bulloides, G. falconensis, N. pachyderma* (left) and the P-D intergrade category record high fluxes, apparently in response to upwelling conditions. The subtropical species *O. universa, G. ruber* and *T. humilis* are most important at the site 650 km offshore. The foraminiferal communities present from September 1987 to September 1988 off Cape Blanco seem to be more diverse but less productive than assemblages from the Alaskan Gyre at Station P (45°N, 150°W) as described in the literature.

The planktonic foraminifera exhibit broad changes in abundance and diversity in northeast Pacific sediments from the Miocene to present (Ingle 1973). These changes in the structure of the planktonic foraminiferal community are generally interpreted as a response to variations in regional oceanographic and climatic regimes though the exact nature of these climatic changes is not well understood. It is not known whether the observed faunal variations reflect changes in coastal upwelling driven by local winds or are linked to large-scale variability in the California Current System. Study of the temporal and spatial variability in the modern system provides an analogue to the long-term fluctuations seen in the sediments, and will aid in developing more accurate reconstructions of the region's climatic history.

The Multitracers experiment compares various geochemical and micropalaeontological methods that are used to estimate paleoproductivity. One of the goals of the project is to determine the conditions under which these methods are reliable. The data available for this analysis include sediment trap samples, hydrographic data and gravity and piston cores. In this paper we analyse foraminiferal flux time series from the first year of the study: September 1987 to September 1988. The study sites are located on an east–west transect off Cape Blanco at 130, 280 and 650 km from the coast

(Fig. 1). We refer to the three sediment trap moorings as 'Nearshore' (42.086°N, 125.771°W), 'Midway' (42.192°N, 127.578°W) and 'Gyre' (41.542°N, 132.016°W). Particulate flux at 1000 m depth is collected by sediment trap sample cups that are set to rotate at approximately two month intervals, yielding six samples per year at each of the three sites. The dates and durations of sampling times are listed in Table 1. The entire flux series will eventually span the four-year period from September 1987 to September 1991.

Recent work addresses separately the temporal (Deuser 1987; Deuser *et al.* 1981; Reynolds & Thunell 1985, 1986; Thunell & Honjo 1987; Sautter & Thunell 1989) or spatial (Fairbanks & Wiebe 1980; Kroon & Ganssen 1989) distribution of foraminifers in the modern ocean. The goal of these previous studies is to relate foraminiferal distributions to changing hydrographic conditions (e.g. Thunell & Honjo 1987; Bé *et al.* 1985; Kroon and Ganssen 1989). A key element of our study is to assess both the spatial and temporal variability from three sediment traps deployed in the California Current off Oregon. We compare the foraminiferal flux records to changes in local hydrographic conditions and bulk organic carbon flux, a measure of export productivity (Eppley & Peterson 1979; Eppley 1989). General descriptions of the hydrographic conditions in upwelling regions,

From SUMMERHAYES, C. P., PRELL, W. L. & EMEIS, K. C. (eds), 1992, *Upwelling Systems: Evolution Since the Early Miocene.* Geological Society Special Publication No 64, pp 197–213.

Table 1. Multitracers foraminiferal species fluxes: September 1987 to September 1988 in units of Shells/m²/day.

(a) >150 µm size fraction

	Nearshore samples							Midway samples							Gyre samples						
	1	2	3	4	5	6	Annual average	7	8	9	10	11	12	Annual average	13	14	15	16	17	18	Annual average
Date opened:	22 Sept	25 Oct	24 Dec	22 Feb	22 Apr	21 June		28 Sept	25 Oct	24 Dec	22 Feb	22 Apr	21 June		25 Sept	25 Oct	24 Dec	22 Feb	22 Apr	21 June	
Date closed:	25 Oct	24 Dec	22 Feb	22 Apr	21 June	16 Sept		25 Oct	24 Dec	22 Feb	22 Apr	21 June	14 Sept		25 Oct	24 Dec	22 Feb	22 Apr	21 June	23 Sept	
Days per sample:	33	60	60	60	60	87		27	60	60	60	60	85		30	60	60	60	60	94	
O. universa	4	9	11	0	4	6	6	38	17	9	0	0	11	13	64	81	5	17	1	27	33
G. ruber	0	4	4	0	0	27	6	10	13	6	0	0	0	5	7	60	1	0	0	1	12
G. calida	0	2	4	0	16	0	4	0	0	0	2	2	5	0	4	7	2	6	1	13	6
G. bulloides	8	30	13	0	5	260	53	0	4	86	41	2	5	23	0	2	8	51	0	5	11
G. falconensis	4	0	2	0	2	655	111	0	11	15	11	2	6	8	0	0	1	28	0	3	5
G. digata	0	0	0	0	0	0	0	0	0	0	0	0	0	0	0	0	0	0	0	0	0
T. humilis	0	0	0	0	0	0	0	0	0	0	0	0	0	0	0	0	0	11	0	3	2
G. quinqueloba	8	0	24	0	25	0	10	14	11	9	6	2	14	9	0	0	0	6	1	11	9
N. pachyderma (L)	43	53	135	0	72	566	145	5	2	21	21	4	17	11	2	2	4	0	0	2	1
N. pachyderma (R)	47	197	188	6	14	27	80	5	47	77	56	2	12	33	0	4	1	21	0	7	6
N. duertrei	16	47	15	0	1	3	14	0	6	36	6	2	9	10	2	1	0	4	0	10	3
G. hexagona	0	0	0	0	0	0	0	0	0	0	0	0	0	0	0	0	0	0	0	0	0
G. inflata	0	0	0	0	0	0	0	0	0	2	2	0	0	1	0	0	1	0	0	0	0
G. crassaformis	0	0	2	0	0	0	0	0	6	17	17	0	0	0	0	0	0	2	0	2	1
P–D Intergrade	16	0	41	0	3	239	50	10	0	0	47	0	11	7	0	0	0	11	2	1	2
G. scitula	35	0	2	2	6	8	8	0	0	19	26	0	0	11	2	4	0	28	0	4	6
G. glutinata	4	11	19	2	6	0	6	0	0	0	0	0	0	9	2	0	0	0	0	3	1
G. iota	0	0	0	0	0	0	0	0	0	0	0	0	0	0	0	0	0	0	0	1	0
G. bradyi	0	0	0	0	0	0	0	0	0	0	0	0	0	0	0	0	0	0	0	0	0
Total	185	353	460	10	154	1783	491	77	26	297	235	12	85	139	79	162	24	185	5	93	91

(b) 125–150 µm size fraction

	Nearshore samples							Midway samples							Gyre samples						
	1	2	3	4	5	6	Annual average	7	8	9	10	11	12	Annual average	13	14	15	16	17	18	Annual average
O. universa	0	0	0	0	1	0	0	0	0	0	0	0	0	0	0	0	0	9	0	0	2
G. ruber	0	2	13	0	0	0	3	0	0	0	0	0	0	0	1	4	0	0	0	0	1
G. calida	0	0	75	0	50	0	21	0	0	15	38	0	3	11	0	0	0	9	0	0	2
G. bulloides	0	9	58	0	5	21	20	0	0	90	11	2	3	18	0	0	0	2	1	0	0
G. falconensis	27	6	21	0	0	19	8	0	0	11	26	2	0	6	0	0	0	2	0	0	0
G. rubescens	0	0	0	0	3	0	3	0	0	2	0	0	0	1	9	2	6	26	9	18	12
T. humilis	0	0	2	2	3	0	3	62	71	165	11	2	0	53	2	2	0	4	3	20	6
G. quinqueloba	19	11	419	2	53	1	84	9	41	34	2	11	8	15	2	2	0	4	3	0	1
N. pachyderma (L)	35	38	216	2	25	99	69	6	77	30	4	2	5	20	2	2	4	4	1	0	2
N. pachyderma (R)	19	38	88	2	18	3	19	66	41	4	5	20	20	20	1	2	2	1	0	3	1
N. duertrei	47	15	88	2	5	0	26	0	0	0	0	0	0	0	0	0	0	0	0	0	0
G. hexagona	0	0	0	0	0	0	0	0	0	0	17	0	3	4	0	0	0	0	0	3	4
P–D Intergrade	12	6	43	0	5	12	13	0	4	41	41	2	2	10	2	2	0	2	2	18	2
G. scitula	16	4	11	0	4	0	6	0	49	28	2	2	2	18	2	5	2	28	3	18	10
G. glutinata	4	11	75	4	6	17	17	6	51	00	0	0	0	5	0	0	0	0	0	0	0
G. iota	0	0	0	0	9	0	2	0	0	0	0	0	0	0	0	0	0	0	0	0	0
G. bradyi	0	0	0	0	14	0	2	0	0	0	0	0	0	0	0	0	0	0	0	0	0
Total	179	140	1059	10	198	155	290	25	92	428	482	25	34	177	19	17	11	94	22	66	38

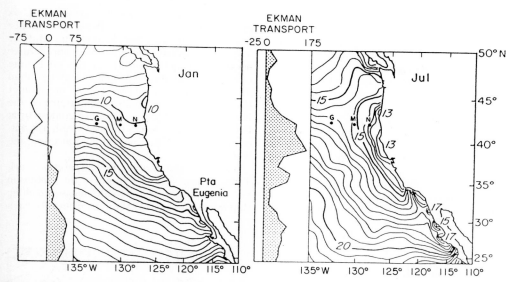

Fig. 1. Monthly mean sea surface temperature in °C for the California Current region (Robinson 1976). Side panels indicate Ekman transport in units of metric tons/sec/1000 m of coastline. Positive Ekman transports are shaded to indicate offshore flow and associated upwelling (after Huyer 1983).

and specifically off the coast of Oregon and California, can be found in Smith (this volume) and in the section to follow.

Environmental setting

Circulation and water masses

Our study area lies in a transition zone between relatively cool, fresh Pacific Subarctic water to the north, and warm, salty North Pacific Central water to the south (Hickey 1979). A second transition, the Coastal Transition Zone (CTZ) occurs between 100 and 250 km from the coast near our study sites (Lynn & Simpson 1987; Kosro *et al.* 1990; Strub *et al.* 1990). West of the CTZ lies North Pacific Central water, while east of the CTZ is water produced by coastal upwelling. This water is a mixture of Pacific Subarctic water and Equatorial Pacific water brought into the region by the poleward flowing California Undercurrent. Equatorial Pacific water is high in temperature, salinity and nutrients (Lynn & Simpson 1987). Water of upwelling origin is characterized by relatively low temperature, high salinity and high nutrients.

Our three sediment trap moorings sample a variety of environments. The 'Nearshore' mooring, at 130 km from the coast is near the CTZ boundary. The 'Midway' mooring at 280 km from the coast is within the southward

flowing California Current, which lies between 250 and 350 km from the coast (Lynn & Simpson 1987; Hickey 1979). The 'Gyre' site, 650 km from the coast, samples both the North Pacific Central and Pacific Subarctic water masses. The east–west nature of our transect provides us with a strong productivity gradient between sites.

This transitional region is characterized by strong interannual variability in physical factors such as current strength (Chelton 1981), sea level pressure (Davis 1976) and phytoplankton biomass. Based on satellite measurements, high phytoplankton pigment concentrations associated with the spring transition are sometimes observed as far offshore as 300 km, while in ENSO years, the spring transition is far less dramatic (Thomas & Strub 1989). Roesler & Chelton (1987) find that biomass of large zooplankton in the CalCOFI region off southern California is largely dependent on interannual variability in current strength. Years of strong southward flow bring subarctic species farther south, while the situation is reversed in ENSO years. The distribution of planktonic organisms in the California Current is strongly affected by their physical environment.

The Coastal Transition Zone

The CTZ is delineated by a southward flowing geostrophic jet located some 50–100 km from the coast (Kosro *et al.* 1991; Strub *et al.* 1991). Much of the spring and summer flow in the California Current appears to be associated with this 30–50 km wide jet which transports between 2 and 3 Sv (Kosro *et al.* 1991). Inshore of the jet, chlorophyll 'a' concentration is patchy, but generally high (Hood *et al.* 1990, 1991; Abbott & Zion 1985, 1987; Peláez & McGowan 1986). To the west of the jet, waters are more oligotrophic, as demonstrated by warmer surface temperatures, and lower chlorophyll 'a' concentrations (Strub *et al.* 1991; Hood *et al.* 1990, 1991).

Seasonal variability within the coastal region is strongly linked to fluctuations in wind forcing (Huyer 1977). Northerly winds drive coastal upwelling and produce offshore Ekman transport that is greatest in July (Fig. 1). Vertical velocities in the surface layer reach a maximum during September in response to variations in wind stress curl (Huyer 1983). Summer temperature gradients are generally east–west in response to coastal upwelling, while those in winter are predominantly north–south (Fig. 1). Coastal upwelling causes shoreward shoaling of isolines of salinity, temperature, density and nutrients, while winter downwelling in response to southerly winds reverses this pattern (Landry *et al.* 1989; Huyer 1977). Seasonal changes in wind forcing are also related to the wintertime presence of the poleward Davison Current, which flows along the continental shelf (Hickey 1979).

Active coastal upwelling is limited by the Rossby radius of deformation to a band 10–20 km from the coast. Yet waters influenced by coastal upwelling can be observed more than 100 km from the coast, after being carried offshore by advection and eddy diffusion (Fig. 1) (Huyer 1983). Our Nearshore site, while not within the zone of the active coastal upwelling, is located within the range of a prominent, recurring filament off Cape Blanco and thus is influenced by coastal upwelling processes (Ikeda & Emery 1984).

Temperatures at the study sites

Figure 2 illustrates the average seasonal temperature cycle as a function of depth based on monthly means from the *Atlas of the North Pacific Ocean* (Robinson 1976). Data is binned at 1° latitude and longitude and at five depths: 0, 30, 61, 91 and 122 m to produce monthly temperature charts. The Nearshore site is the coolest of the three locations. Monthly mean surface temperatures at Nearshore (130 km from the coast) are slightly greater than 16°C in

September and cool water less than 9°C is present above 91 m in response to summer upwelling (Fig. 2a). In contrast, the Midway and Gyre sites have mean surface temperatures up to two degrees warmer at the same time (Fig. 2b,c). At the Gyre site, water less than 9°C is not present above 122 m in summer (Fig. 2c). Monthly mean temperatures at the Nearshore and Midway sites are coldest from February to April when the 10°C isotherm outcrops. The 10°C does not outcrop at Gyre, the warmest site.

To assess the short-term temperature variability at our sites, we compare the Robinson (1976) monthly averages to SST measured along ship tracks and at CTD stations, from two-week

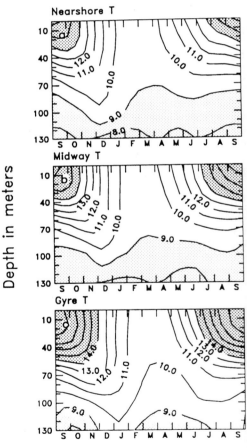

Fig. 2. Monthly mean temperature in °C at (a) Nearshore, (b) Midway and (c) Gyre, the Multitracers locations. The light shading indicates temperatures less than 9°C, while dark shading indicates temperatures greater than 14°C (data from Robinson 1976).

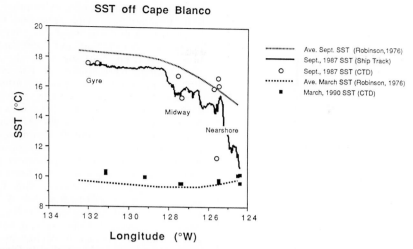

Fig. 3. Comparison of monthly mean SST (Robinson 1976) in September and March off Cape Blanco to SST from CTD stations and SST measured along a ship track during two Multitracers cruises (Collier, unpublished data). The cruise dates are 22 September, 1987 to 2 October, 1987 and 9 March, 1990 to 17 March, 1990.

Multitracers cruises in September 1987 and March 1990 (Collier, unpublished data) (Fig. 3). The Robinson (1976) averages and CTD data from March are in good agreement, indicating low cross-shelf SST variability in winter. In contrast, the September 1987 SST data indicate strong cross-shelf variability during the upwelling season. The SST values measured along the ship track are consistently cooler than the Robinson averages (Fig. 3), and the CTD station data indicate increasing SST variability toward the coast. At the Nearshore site, CTD temperatures range from approximately 11.5°C to 17°C over this two-week period in September 1987. The changes in surface temperature are related to either cold filaments meandering east–west off Cape Blanco, or the advection of eddies through the study site. The Robinson (1976) average SST values decrease toward the coast, but sampling bias and spatial and temporal averaging smooth out much of the meso-scale variability associated with coastal upwelling conditions.

Organic carbon flux

Figure 4 displays the organic carbon flux data in units of $\mu g/cm^2/year$ from the first year of the Multitracers project (Lyle et al. 1991; Collier et al. 1989). These data are useful for comparison to the foraminiferal flux data because they provide a concurrent measure of export flux to 1000 m at each location. Given the large inter-annual variability at our sites, the temporal

patterns observed in this first year of organic carbon flux data are not necessarily representative of the average organic carbon flux at our locations (Lyle et al. 1991; Welling et al. this volume).

A prominent feature in both the first and second year of data is the offshore decrease in organic carbon flux. During the first year of the Multitracers project the organic carbon flux maxima shifts later in the year from Nearshore to the offshore sites. Organic carbon fluxes at Nearshore reach values of almost 700 $\mu g/cm^2/$ year from January to April. At Midway, high fluxes occur from February through June, with peak fluxes of 400 $\mu g/cm^2/year$ occurring during May and June. At the Gyre site, the period of maximal flux also occurs from May to June, with peak values of approximately 300 $\mu g/cm^2/$ year. All three sites show dramatic decreases in flux values from late June to July during the first year of the project.

Methods

Sample processing

Six samples at approximately two-month intervals were analysed from three sediment traps deployed during the first year of the Multitracers experiment (September 1987–September 1988). Splits from the same samples were processed for organic carbon content (Collier et al. 1989) and planktonic foraminifer counts. For foraminiferal faunal analysis, sample splits of

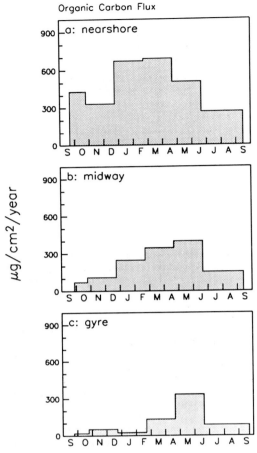

Fig. 4. Organic Carbon Flux at 1000 m for (a) Nearshore, (b) Midway and (c) Gyre from September 1987–September 1988 (data from Lyle *et al.* 1991).

generally 1/16 or 1/64 size are first cleaned of organic matter using a solution of H_2O_2, buffered at pH 7.0–7.5 by the addition of NH_4OH and NH_4Cl. The samples are then wet sieved into >63 and <63 μm size fractions. The >63 μm size fraction is further wet sieved using ethanol or pH 7.0–7.5 water into 63–125 μm, 125–150 μm and >150 μm size fractions.

Taxonomy

Foraminifers in the 125–150 μm ('small') and >150 μm ('large') size fractions are identified to species level using the taxonomies of Parker (1962) and Bé (1977). The number of foraminifers present in each sample split varies from tens of individuals to several hundred individuals. Foraminiferal data presented here are given in shell flux (shells/m^2/day). We use size fractions of 125–150 μm and >150 μm to facilitate comparisons with work in the Gulf of Alaska done by Reynolds & Thunell (1985, 1986) and Sautter & Thunell (1989) who measure foraminifers >125 μm, and sediment studies such as CLIMAP (1976), who measure foraminifers >150 μm. Slight differences between our taxonomy and the taxonomy used by other workers must be taken into consideration when comparing results from various projects. We recognize a *Pachyderma–Dutertrei* Intergrade category, in keeping with CLIMAP taxonomy (Kipp 1976). Reynolds & Thunell (1985, 1986) and Sautter & Thunell (1989) did not use this category. One goal of our analysis is to evaluate the ecological validity, as opposed to the taxonomic utility, of the *P–D* Intergrade category.

Results

Total foraminiferal flux

We identify 20 species of planktonic foraminifers at the three Multitracers localities (Table 1). Thirteen of these species account for over 98% of the total flux (Fig. 5). Of the three sites, Nearshore has the highest total foraminiferal shell flux (Figs 5 & 6). The annual average flux at this site is 780 shells/m^2/day and reaches peaks of 1500 shells/m^2/day between January and February and 2000 shells/m^2/day between late June and September (Fig. 6a). The foraminiferal community at Nearshore is composed primarily of seven species: *Neogloboquadrina pachyderma* (left), *Globigerina falconensis*, *N. pachyderma* (right), *Globigerina quinqueloba*, *Globigerina bulloides*, *P–D* Intergrade and *Neogloboquadrina dutertrei*. These species exhibit decreases in their annual average shell flux from the Nearshore site at 130 km to the Gyre site 650 km from the coast (Fig. 5).

The species composition at Midway is similar to that at the Nearshore site (Fig. 5). Annual average fluxes at the Midway site reach 318 shells/m^2/day, with maximal values of approximately 1000 shells/m^2/day from January through April (Fig. 6b). Fluxes throughout much of the remainder of the year at this site are roughly a factor of four less than those observed during the flux maximum. Species with large contributions to the total shell flux at this site include *G. quinqueloba*, *N. pachyderma* (right), *G. bulloides*, *N. dutertrei*, *Globigerinita glutinata* and *Globorotalia scitula* (Fig. 5).

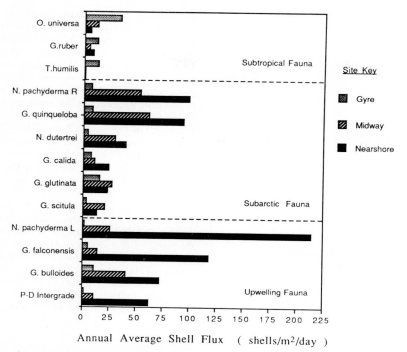

Fig. 5. Annual average shell fluxes at 1000 m for the >125 μm size fraction at the Multitracers locations from September 1987–September 1988. Species groupings are defined in the results and discussion sections.

The total flux at the Gyre site is lower than at the more coastal sites (Figs 5 & 6). Total fluxes at Gyre do not exceed 500 shells/m²/day in any of the two month samples, resulting in an annual average flux of 130 shells/m²/day. Maximal flux at Gyre (450 shells/m²/day) occurs in March and April (Fig. 6c). The foraminifers with highest fluxes at this site include *Orbulina universa*, *Turborotalita humilis* and *Globigerinoides ruber*. Although their fluxes are greater at Nearshore and Midway *G. glutinata*, *N. pachyderma* (right), *G. quinqueloba* and *G. bulloides* also contributed significantly to the total flux at Gyre.

The two size fractions show differing flux patterns at the three sites (Fig. 6). The small size fraction accounts for approximately 60% of the annual flux at Nearshore, compared to approximately 40% at Midway and 30% at Gyre. Larger shells are most common at the Nearshore site from July to September whereas flux of the smaller size fraction peaks in January and February. At the Midway site, foraminifers in both size fractions reach their maximum fluxes from January through April. Fluxes at the Gyre site are comprised mostly of large foraminifers.

Species distributions

'Upwelling' fauna. *G. bulloides* and *N. pachyderma* (left) exhibit flux patterns with a small peak in the winter or spring depending on site, and a larger peak (in the >150 μm size fraction), which occurs only at the Nearshore site, from late June to September (Fig. 7). *G. falconensis* and the *P–D* Intergrade categories have similar seasonal flux patterns (Table 1). *G. bulloides* was present at the Nearshore site from September to February 1988 and had fluxes that reached 100 shells/m²/day from January to February (Fig. 7a). At Midway, from January to February, fluxes of *G. bulloides* are 200 shells/m²/day, but the summer flux period that was present at Nearshore is absent (Fig. 7b). Fluxes of *G. bulloides* from late February to April at the Gyre site are comparable to the Nearshore winter flux period.

The foraminiferal flux from late June to September at the Nearshore site is coincident with the timing of maximum coastal upwelling off Cape Blanco (Fig. 1). SST data from the September 1987 Multitracers cruise demonstrate the presence of cold (presumably up-

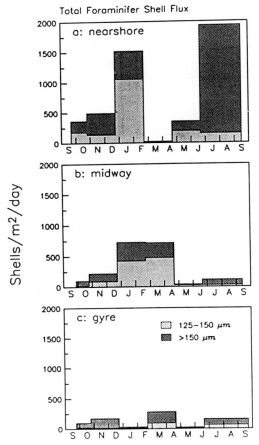

Fig. 6. Cumulative bar charts of total foraminifer shell flux at 1000 m for (a) Nearshore, (b) Midway and (c) Gyre from September 1987–September 1988. Flux is separated by size fraction: light shading (125–150 μm), dark shading (>150 μm). The high of the bar marks total flux (>125 μm).

welled) water at our Nearshore location for at least part of that time (Fig. 3). From June to September 1988, fluxes of *G. bulloides* reached 300 shells/m²/day at Nearshore. Specimens of *G. bulloides* also exhibit interesting morphological differences between the winter and summer peaks. Individuals collected during the winter, and especially those at the Gyre site, tend to be thinly calcified and sometimes have spines retained. Individuals collected in the summer are more thickly calcified and lack spines.

Like *G. bulloides*, *N. pachyderma* (left) exhibits high fluxes at the Nearshore site, and has

diminishing fluxes at the offshore sites. *N. pachyderma* (left) exhibits two periods of maximal flux at Nearshore. A brief flux maximum of over 300 shells/m²/day (Fig. 7d) occurs in January and February. This winter flux event is comprised of small individuals. The second flux peak occurs from late June to September. Flux at this time approaches 700 shells/m²/day and is composed mainly of large individuals. The presence of *N. pachyderma* (left) is greatly attenuated at the Midway site, reaching only 75 shells/m²/day from January through April (Fig. 7e), and is essentially absent at the Gyre site (Fig. 7f).

Subarctic transitional fauna. *N. pachyderma* (right) and *N. dutertrei*, reach flux maxima during the fall and winter at Nearshore and decrease in flux offshore (Fig. 8). The species *G. quinqueloba*, *G. glutinata*, and *Globorotalia scitula* (Table 1) also exhibit flux maxima that occur in the fall or winter at the Nearshore site and later in the year at Midway and Gyre, showing some similarity to the flux patterns of *N. pachyderma* (right) and *N. dutertrei*.

Flux of *N. pachyderma* (right) is highest at Nearshore, around 250 shells/m²/day, from November through February (Fig. 8a). At the Midway site, the occurrence of *N. pachyderma* (right) is shifted later in the year and extends from November to late April (Fig. 8b). Peak flux at Midway is approximately 150 shells/m²/day and occurs from January to February. At the Gyre site, fluxes of *N. pachyderma* (right) decrease to less than 30 shells/m²/day. Maximum flux occurs later in the year at Gyre occurs (March to April) than at Nearshore or Midway (Fig. 8c). *N. dutertrei* exhibits a broad flux peak at Nearshore from September to February, with maximum values near 100 shells/m²/day from January to February (Fig. 8d). The majority of the flux of this species at this site is of small individuals. The flux of *N. dutertrei* at Midway is similar in magnitude to that at Nearshore, but is shifted later in the year occurring from late December through April (Fig. 8e). At the Gyre site the flux of *N. dutertrei* is greatly diminished (Fig. 8f).

Subtropical fauna. The spatial and temporal patterns apparent at Gyre are markedly different from those at Nearshore and Midway. Species such as *N. pachyderma* (right), *G. quinqueloba*, *G. glutinata*, and *G. bulloides* exhibit later timing and diminished fluxes at Gyre relative to Nearshore and Midway. In addition to these differences, *O. universa*, *G. ruber* and *T. humilis* reach their highest fluxes

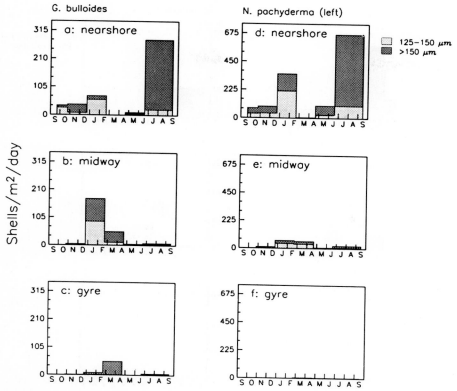

Fig. 7. Cumulative bar charts for foraminifer shell flux of *G. bulloides* and *N. pachyderma* (left) at 1000 m for (a),(d) Nearshore, (b),(e) Midway and (c),(f) Gyre during September 1987–September 1988. Shading as in Fig. 6. Note change in axis between species.

at Gyre (Fig. 9). *O. universa*, is most common here from October to December, reaching fluxes of approximately 80 shells/m²/day. *G. ruber* shows a distributional pattern similar to that of *O. universa* (Table 1). During the latter part of the year at the Gyre site, from March through September, the species *T. humilis* reaches its highest flux values (Fig. 9f). The flux values of *T. humilis* drop considerably at the Midway (Fig. 9e) and Nearshore sites (Fig. 9d).

Discussion

Relations between foraminifers and hydrography

From September 1987 to September 1988 the foraminifers present at the Multitracers sites are primarily from the Subarctic, Transitional and Subtropical foraminiferal provinces of Bradshaw (1959), Parker (1962) and Bé (1977). These species can be further grouped based on

the processes related to their spatial and temporal patterns at the three Multitracers locations.

The foraminiferal flux peak which occurs from late June 1988 to September 1988 at the Nearshore site is coincident with the timing of maximum coastal upwelling off Cape Blanco (Fig. 1). This fauna is composed primarily of the cold water species *G. bulloides*, *G. falconensis*, the *Pachyderma-Dutertrei* Intergrade category, and the Arctic morphotype *N. pachyderma* (left). Sea surface temperatures obtained along the ship track during the September, 1988 Multitracers cruise demonstrate the presence of cold surface water at our Nearshore location for at least part of that time (Fig. 3). Cold surface temperatures are most likely related to east−west meandering cold filaments, which carry coastal waters offshore. These features are prominent in other years in Coastal Zone Colour Scanner (CZCS) and Advanced Very High Resolution Radiometry (AVHRR) satellite

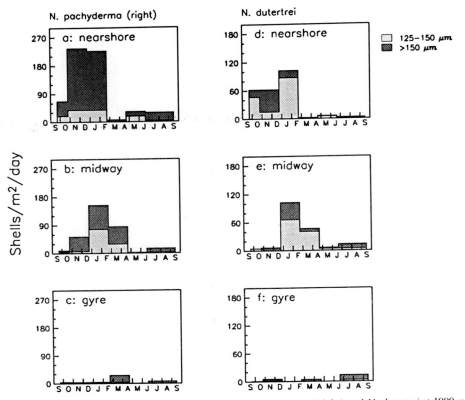

Fig. 8. Cumulative bar charts for foraminifer shell flux of *N. pachyderma* (right) and *N. dutertrei* at 1000 m for (a),(d) Nearshore, (b),(e) Midway and (c),(f) Gyre during September 1987–September 1988. See Fig. 7. Note change in axis between species.

images from this region (Ikeda & Emery 1984; Abbott & Zion 1985, 1987; Peláez & McGowan 1986). We infer the presence of cold water species at Nearshore during summer to reflect the offshore advection of cold, upwelled water. We refer to these cold water species as the 'Upwelling' fauna. They are also present during the winter at the Nearshore and Midway sites, although their wintertime presence at Nearshore and Midway appears to be related to Subarctic, rather than upwelling conditions.

The distributional pattern of *G. bulloides* at Nearshore is particularly striking with regard to this point. While this species is utilized extensively as an upwelling indicator (e.g. Cullen & Prell 1984; Anderson & Prell; Curry *et al*. Ganssen & Kroon, Thiede & Jünger; Thunell & Sautter, all this volume) it is also well known that its global distribution is predominantly subarctic in the open ocean (Bradshaw 1959; Bé 1977; Vincent & Berger 1981). The bimodal flux pattern exhibited by *G. bulloides* at Near-

shore (Fig. 7a), and the phenotypic variability we observed, which has also been reported by Reynolds & Thunell (1986), suggests there may in fact be two populations of this species present at our Nearshore site. The Nearshore location is far enough north (42°N) and close enough to the coast (130 km) to sample both a subarctic population of *G. bulloides* in winter, and an upwelling related population of *G. bulloides* in summer (Fig. 7a).

The observation of a seasonally bimodal distribution for *G. bulloides* and other species of the 'Upwelling' fauna implies the need for great caution when using them as upwelling indicators in sediment studies at high latitudes. Because information regarding the seasonal production of these species is lost in the sedimentary record, the annual average fluxes or percentage abundance of these species in the sediments do not reflect upwelling conditions alone, but rather a combination of upwelling and Subarctic conditions at high-latitude sites. Because the pos-

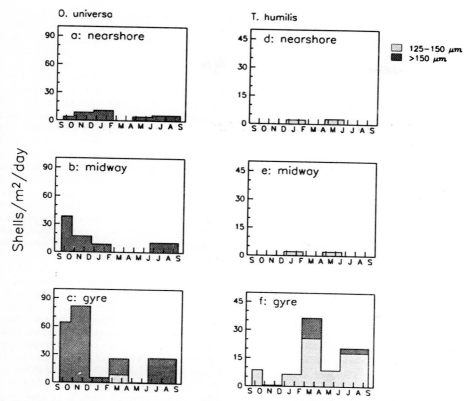

Fig. 9. Cumulative bar charts for Foraminifer shell flux of *O. universa* and *T. humilis* at 1000 m for (a),(d) Nearshore (b),(e) Midway and (c),(f) Gyre during September 1987–September 1988. See Fig. 7. Note change in axis between species.

itions of current systems and water masses vary interannually and on geological timescales, limiting studies to locations closer to the coast may not be sufficient to resolve this dilemma.

In addition to cold water species, the summer sample at Nearshore includes specimens of the subtropical species *O. universa* and *G. ruber* (Fig. 9a, Table 1), indicating that near surface waters were warm and stratified for at least part of the 80-day sampling period. There are two possible physical regimes that could produce the foraminiferal pattern recorded at Nearshore from late June to September 1988: (1) mesoscale variability in the flow field, related to meandering filaments or the advection of eddies; (2) continuous thermal stratification. The combination of warm and cold fauna recorded in the Nearshore summer sample would reflect patchy distributions if the first explanation applies or species-specific depth habitat stratification if the second explanation applies. Given the variability in the September 1987 SST

measurements (Fig. 3) and knowledge that July to September is the time of maximum offshore Ekman transport at this latitude (Huyer 1983), we favour the mesoscale variability explanation.

The influence of subpolar water at the Nearshore and Midway sites during the winter is clearly evident in the community composition of these sites from October to February. This community is composed of species from both the 'Upwelling' fauna (see above) and the subarctic/transitional fauna. Subarctic/Transitional species with distributions at our sites related to cold winter conditions, but unrelated to upwelling conditions include *N. pachyderma* (right), *G. quinqueloba*, *N. dutertrei*, *G. calida*, *G. glutinata* and *G. scitula* (Figs 5 & 8, Table 1).

Subtropical conditions

In contrast to the more coastal sites, the Gyre fauna are indicative of warmer waters. The

Subtropical species *O. universa* (Fig. 9) and *G. ruber* (Table 1) were common during the warmest months at this site, in response to the northward shift in the divergence of the North Pacific Current and the presence of North Pacific Central water. As the divergence of the North Pacific Current moves southward and the influence of the Pacific subarctic water mass increases, significant fluxes of subarctic species such as *G. bulloides*, (Fig. 7c), *N. pachyderma* (right) (Fig. 8c) and *G. quinqueloba* (Table 1) occur at the Gyre site. While these species are not as common numerically at the Gyre site as they were at the Nearshore and Midway sites, they compose a significant fraction of the relatively small, total foraminiferal community at Gyre (Fig. 5) during the cooler times of the year.

The subtropical species *T. humilis* (Fig. 9) is present at the Gyre site throughout much of the year but accounts for 20% of the total flux at this site from January to March and 40% from May to July (Fig. 9). This species is seldom discussed in the literature, apparently because it is rare in comparison to other species and because most studies focus on size fractions greater than 150 μm. Vincent & Berger (1981) identify this species as subtropical, with the most common occurrence in sediment samples from the South Pacific between 25°S and 45°S. The summer, offshore maximum of this species fits well with its description as subtropical in nature.

Relations between the foraminifers and organic carbon flux

The offshore decrease in organic carbon flux (Fig. 4) at our sites is paralleled by an offshore decrease in the total foraminiferal shell flux (Fig. 6). Many of the individual species present during this first year of the project demonstrate this general pattern of decreasing offshore flux (Table 1). Although correspondence between the two types of data is not perfect, increases in foraminiferal flux seem to lead those in organic carbon flux. This feature can be seen in contour plots of the data sets as a function of offshore distance and time (Fig. 10).

The apparent lead of the foraminiferal flux over organic carbon flux could be related at least in part to the higher setting velocities of the foraminiferal shells. Foraminiferal shells greater than 125 μm in size should reach our 1000 m traps in seven days or less, based on a settling velocity of 150 m/day or greater (Fok-Pun & Komar 1983). While a quantitative settling time for the organic particles or aggregates in our traps is difficult to estimate due to

lack of information regarding their size and density, organic matter generally settles at slower rates than dense particles such as foraminiferal shells (Siegel *et al.* 1990). A second possible cause for the lead-lag relationship may be related to differences between the recycling of organic matter and calcite by the planktonic community (Legendre & Le Fèvre 1989; Williams *et al.* 1989). Regeneration of organic matter occurs at shallower depth and higher rates than the regeneration of calcite (Walsh *et al.* 1988). Knauer *et al.* (1990) observe an inverse correlation between maximal primary production and carbon and nitrogen based estimates of new production in the VERTEX sediment trap time series. These relationships could result in a lag time between the production of organic matter in surface waters and its eventual export from the system which would not occur for exported calcite.

While there seems to be a general correspondence between primary production rates, organic carbon flux and foraminiferal shell flux which all decreases offshore, it is unclear how the timing of primary productivity is related to the timing of exported organic carbon and foraminiferal shells at our sites. Determining if this hypothesized lead-lag relationship is a recurring feature in this region will require further analysis. The three additional years of Multitracers data, with improved sample resolution (one month to two weeks for some deployments) will allow us to resolve this issue.

Comparison to Alaskan Gyre: Station P

Fluxes and diversity. Annual average shell fluxes at station P (45°N 150°W) from October 1982 to August 1986 range from 1471 to 4918 shells/m^2/day (Sautter & Thunell 1989). In contrast, the annual average shell fluxes we observe at the Multitracers sites from September 1987 to September 1988 are 780, 318 and 130 shells/m^2/day for Nearshore, Midway and Gyre respectively. This pattern is consistent with bulk carbonate flux, which is higher at station P (Reynolds & Thunell 1985) than at the Multitracers sites (Dymond, pers. comm.). These differences could result from interannual variability, or reflect a difference in the relative productivities of the foraminiferal communities at these localities. Analysis of the next three years of the Multitracers time series will provide an estimate of the foraminiferal flux variability at the Multitracers sites and help to resolve this question.

The assemblages of foraminifers at the Multitracers sites during 1987–1988 are much more

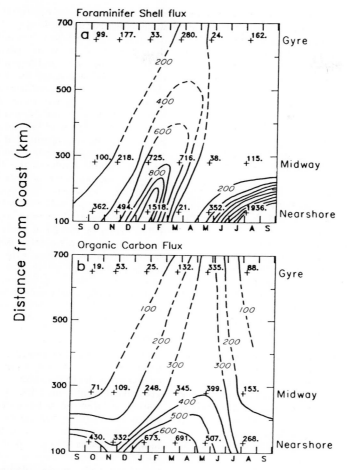

Fig. 10.(a) Foraminifer shell Flux >125 μm, contours of 200 shells/m²/day and (b) organic carbon flux, contours of 100 μg/cm²/year at the Multitracers sites from September 1987 to September 1988. Contours are hand drawn. Dashed lines mark interpolations between the Midway and Gyre sites.

diverse than those recorded at station P from 1982 to 1986. We observe some twenty different species at the three Multitracers sites, although 13 subarctic, subtropical and transitional species account for over 98% of the annual average flux (Table 1 and Fig. 5). Seven minor species that are present include three transitional to subarctic forms: *Globorotalia inflata*, *Globigerinita iota* and *Globigerina bradyi*, and four Tropical forms: *Globorotalia crassaformis*, *Globigerina rubescens*, *Globigerina digitata* and *Globigerina hexagona*. Individuals of these species may represent expatriated populations that do not reproduce under the conditions at our sites. In contrast, only seven species are reported in the assemblage of foraminifers at Station P: *G. quinqueloba*, *N. pachyderma* (left), *N. pachy-*

derma (right), *G. bulloides*, *G. glutinata*, *G. scitula* and *O. universa* (Reynolds & Thunell 1985; Sautter & Thunell 1989). No one species at the Multitracers sites ever accounted for more than 27% of the annual average shell flux. In contrast, at Station P the species *G. quinqueloba* always accounts for more than 45% of the annual average shell flux (Sautter & Thunell 1989). Thus, the annual assemblages of foraminifers at the Multitracers sites are not dominated by a single species during this first year of the Multitracers study, while the annual assemblages at Station P are always dominated by a single species.

While we stress that our results are preliminary, this comparison between the Alaskan Gyre and the Multitracers sites is consistent with Bradshaw's (1959) study of over 700 plankton tows from the North Pacific. Bradshaw (1959) notes that, while foraminiferal standing stock is greatest in the subarctic region which includes the location of Station P, diversity is greatest in the Transitional region which includes the Multitracers locations. Recent sediment trap studies, such as the Multitracers project, are improving our understanding of the fossil record by demonstrating possible seasonal bias in the sediments and exploring the linkages between changes in foraminiferal flux, diversity and environmental variability.

N. pachyderma (left and right) and the P−D intergrade category. The temporal distributions of *N. pachyderma* (left) and *N. pachyderma* (right) in the Alaskan Gyre are distinct due to the differential temperature tolerances of the two morphotypes (Reynolds & Thunell 1986, Sautter & Thunell 1989). *N. pachyderma* (left) is prevalent when surface temperatures are less than 8°C, while *N. pachyderma* (right) is more common when surface temperatures exceed 8°C (Reynolds & Thunell 1986). Surface temperatures at the Multitracers sites are in general warmer than at station P, with the possible exception of the Nearshore site during the coastal upwelling season (Fig. 3). The distributions of *N. pachyderma* (left) (Fig. 7d−f) and *N. pachyderma* (right) (Fig. 8d−f) are distinct at the Nearshore site, but overlap at the Midway location where temperatures are warmer. At Gyre, the warmest of the three sites, *N. pachyderma* (left) is virtually absent, while flux of *N. pachyderma* (right) still occurs. The left and right coiling populations of *N. pachyderma* sampled across the California Current thus exhibit overlapping spatial and temporal patterns similar to the well studied latitudinal coiling gradients seen in the sediments and in living populations (e.g. Ericson, 1959; Bé, 1969; Bé & Tolderlund 1971; Echols & Kennett 1973).

Comparison of our work with that of Reynolds & Thunell (1985, 1986) and Sautter & Thunell (1989) must be made with some caution due to the difference between our taxonomies regarding the *P−D* Intergrade category. The overlapping seasonal and spatial distributions of *N. pachyderma* (left) (Fig. 7d−f), *N. pachyderma* (right) (Fig. 8a−c) and *N. dutertrei* (Fig. 8d−f) demonstrate that gradational forms between these species are possible, but by no means necessary. It is interesting to note that when *N. pachyderma* (left) was most common, left coiling *P−D* individuals were most common, and that when *N. pachyderma* (right) was

most common, right coiling *P−D* individuals were most common. If the *P−D* Intergrade category is an artificial taxonomic construct, then incorporation of its individuals into the *N. pachyderma* (left) and *N. pachyderma* (right) taxons would emphasize the separation in the distributions of *N. pachyderma* (left) and *N. pachyderma* (right) at our sites. This effect would be greatest at Nearshore where the highest fluxes of the *P−D* intergrade category occur, and the distributions of *N. pachyderma* (left) and *N. pachyderma* (right) are already distinct. Alternatively, if the *P−D* intergrade category does indeed represent a morphological gradation between *N. pachyderma* and *N. dutertrei*, one would expect its distribution in time and space to present a distinct pattern which could be linked to environmental variability, rather than random variability resulting from taxonomic noise. Our data seem to indicate that the *P−D* intergrade category may simply be a taxonomic convenience, without strong environmental meaning at these localities.

Conclusions

The seasonal distributions of foraminifers in the California Current off Cape Blanco reflect variations in the temperatures and water masses present at each site. The thirteen common species of foraminifers from the subarctic, transitional and subtropical foraminiferal provinces can be grouped in terms of their spatial and temporal distributions, which are related to specific processes acting at each site (see A, B, C below) such as the offshore advection of upwelled water or changes in the location of associated water masses.

(A) The species *G. bulloides*, *N. pachyderma* (left), *G. falconensis* and the *P−D* intergrade category exhibit maximal fluxes at Nearshore from late June to September, presumably in response to coastal upwelling. However, fluxes of these cold water species are relatively high during the winter when Subarctic water is present at our sites and upwelling is minimal. The annual average fluxes and percent abundance of these species in the sediments thus reflect a combination of subarctic and upwelling conditions. Sedimentary studies at high latitudes that attempt to use these cold water species as upwelling indicators will overestimate the influence of upwelling recorded in the sediments if information regarding the seasonal production of the indicator species is unknown.

(B) Subarctic/transitional species with maximal fluxes at Nearshore during the late fall and winter that decrease offshore include *N. pachy-derma* (right), *N. dutertrei*, *G. quinqueloba*, *G. glutinata* and *G. scitula*. The distributions of these Subarctic and Transitional species is consistent with the occurrence of moderate to cold temperatures and is related to Subpolar/Transitional conditions at these sites during the fall and winter.

(C) Species of Subtropical origin exhibit flux maxima at Gyre and decrease in flux toward the coast. These species include *O. universa*, *G. ruber* and *T. humilis*.

The foraminiferal shell fluxes at the Multitracers sites from September 1987 to September 1988 were lower than those in the Alaskan Gyre recorded from October 1982 to August 1986 (Sautter & Thunell 1989). These differences could have resulted from interannual variability, or reflect a difference in the relative productivity of the foraminiferal communities at these localities. Annual average assemblages of foraminifers at the Multitracers sites are more diverse and less dominated by one species than any of the annual assemblages from station P.

The offshore decrease in organic carbon flux at our sites is paralleled by an offshore decrease in the total foraminiferal shell flux during this first year of the project. Although correspondence between the data is not perfect, increases in foraminiferal flux seem to lead those in organic carbon flux. The apparent lead of the foraminiferal flux over organic carbon flux could be related to the higher settling velocities of the foraminiferal shells or to differences between the recycling of organic matter and calcite by the planktonic community. Additional years of data will be necessary to determine if this lead–lag relationship is a recurring feature at these localities.

The authors wish to thank the Multitracers sediment trap group: J. Dymond, B. Collier, N. Pisias, M. Lyle, E. Suess, a host of technicians, the crews of the *R/V's Wecoma* and *New Horizon* and our colleagues at OSU who have taken an interest in this work: P. Wheeler, F. Prahl, J. Huyer and B. Smith. The first author would like to thank L. Welling for the many interesting and fruitful discussions we have had regarding this project and for her careful reading of the manuscript. An anonymous reviewer's thorough job also helped to make this a more complete paper. Research for the Multitracers project was funded by National Science Foundation grant # OCE-860936. Core Lab curation at OSU was funded by NSF grant OCE88-00458.

References

ABBOTT, M. R. & ZION, P. M. 1985. Satellite observations of phytoplankton variability during an upwelling event. *Continental Shelf Research*, **4**, 661–680.

—— & —— 1987. Spatial and temporal variability of phytoplankton pigment off northern California during the Costal Ocean Dynamics Experiment I. *Journal of Geophysical Research*, **92**, 1745–1755.

BÉ, A. W. H. 1969. Planktonic foraminifera. *In*: Distribution of selected groups of marine invertebrates in waters south of 35°S latitude. *Antarctic Map Folio Series 11*. American Geographical Society, New York.

—— 1977. An ecological, zoogeographic, and taxonomic review of recent planktonic Foraminifera. *In*: RAMSEY, A. T. S. (ed.) *Oceanic Micropaleontology*. vol. 1. Academic, London.

——, BISHOP, J., SVERDLOVE, M. & GARDNER, W. 1985. Standing stock, vertical distribution and flux of planktonic Foraminifera in the Panama basin. *Marine Micropaleontology*, **9**, 307–333.

—— & TOLDERLUND, D. S. 1971. Distribution and ecology of living planktonic Foraminifera in surface waters of the Atlantic and Indian Oceans. *In*: *The Micropaleontology of Oceans*. Cambridge University Press.

BRADSHAW, J. 1959. Ecology of living planktonic Foraminifera in the north and equatorial Pacific oceans. *Contributions of the Cushman Foundation for Foraminiferal Research*, **10**, 25–64.

CHELTON, D. 1981. Interannual variability of the California Current — physical factors. California Cooperative Fisheries Investigations, Report Vol. XXII, 34–48.

CLIMAP Project Members. 1976. The surface of the ice age earth. *Science*, **191**, 1131–1137.

COLLIER, R. W., DYMOND, J., PISIAS, N. & LYLE, M. 1989. Effects of seasonal oceanographic cycles on the paleoceanographic record: Initial results of the Multitracers experiment. *Eos*, **70**, 365.

CULLEN, J. L. & PRELL, W. L. 1984. Planktonic Foraminifera of the northern Indian Ocean: distribution and preservation in surface sediments. *Marine Micropaleontology*, **9**, 1–52.

DAVIS, R. 1976. Predictability of sea surface temperature and sea level pressure anomalies over the North Pacific Ocean. *Journal of Physical Oceanography*, **6**, 249–266.

DEUSER, W. G. 1987. Seasonal variation in isotopic composition and deep-water fluxes of the tests of perennially abundant planktonic Foraminifera of the Sargasso Sea: Results from sediment-trap collections and their paleoceanographic significance. *Journal of Foraminiferal Research*, **17**, 14–27.

——, ROSS, E. H., HEMLEBEN, C. & SPINDLER, M. 1981. Seasonal changes in species composition, mass, size, and isotopic composition of planktonic Foraminifera settling into the deep Sargasso Sea. *Paleogeography, Paleoclimatology and Paleoecology*, **33**, 103–127.

ECHOLS, R. J. & KENNETT, J. P. 1973. Distribution of Foraminifera in the surface sediments. *In*: BUSHNELL, V. (ed.) *Marine Sediments of Southern Oceans Antarctic Map Folio Series 17*.

American Geographical Society, New York.

EPPLEY, R. 1989. New production: History, methods, problems. *In*: BERGER, W. H., SMETACEK, V. S. & WEFER, G. (eds) *Productivity of the Oceans: Past and Present*. Wiley, Chichester.

—— & PETERSON, B. 1979. Particulate organic matter flux and planktonic new production in the deep ocean. *Nature*, **282**, 677–680.

ERICSON, D. B. 1959. Coiling direction of *Globigerina pachyderma* as a climatic index. *Science*, **130**, 219–220.

FAIRBANKS, R. & WIEBE, P. 1980. Foraminiferan and chlorophyll maximum: Vertical distribution, seasonal succession, and paleoceanographic significance. *Science*, **209**, 1524–1526.

FOK-PUN, L. & KOMAR, P. D. 1983. Settling velocities of planktonic Foraminifera: Density variations and shape effects. *Journal of Foraminiferal Research*, **13**, 60–68.

HICKEY, B. 1989. Patterns and processes of circulation over the Washington continental shelf and slope. *In*: LANDRY, M. & HICKEY, B. (eds) *Coastal Oceanography of Washington and Oregon*. Elsevier, Amsterdam.

HOOD, R. R., ABBOTT, M. R., HUYER, A. & CTZ collaborators. 1991. Phytoplankton and photosynthetic light response in the Coastal Transition Zone in June, 1987. *Journal of Geophysical Research*, **96**, 14 769–14 780.

——, ——, —— & KOSRO, P. M. 1990. Surface patterns in Temperature, flow, phytoplankton biomass, and species composition in the Costal Transition Zone off northern California. *Journal of Geophysical Research*, **95**, 18,081–18,094.

HUYER, A. 1977. Seasonal variation in temperature, salinity, and density over the continental shelf off Oregon. *Limnology and Oceanography*, **22**, 442–453.

—— 1983. Coastal upwelling in the California Current System. *Progress in Oceanography*, **12**, 259–284.

IKEDA, M. & EMERY, W. J. 1984. Satellite observations and modeling of meanders in the California Current System off Oregon and northern California. *Journal of Physical Oceanography*, **14**, 1434–1450.

INGLE, J. C. 1973. Summary comments on Neogene biostratigraphy, physical stratigraphy, and paleoceanography in the marginal northeastern Pacific Ocean. *In*: KULM, L.C., VON HUENE, R. *et al.* (eds) *Initial Reports of the Deep Sea Drilling Project*, vol. 18, U.S. Govt. Printing Office, Washington, D.C.

KIPP, N. G. 1976. New transfer function for estimating past sea-surface conditions from sea-bed distributions of planktonic foraminiferal assemblages in the north atlantic. *In*: TUREKIAN, K. K. (ed.) *Investigations of Late Quaternary Paleoceanography and Paleontology*. Geological Society of America, Memoir 145.

KNAUER, G. A., REDALIE, D. G., HARRISON, W. G. & KARL, D. M. 1990. New production at the VERTEX time-series site. *Deep Sea Research*, **37**, 1121–1134.

KOSRO, P. M., HUYER, A., RAMP, A. R., SMITH, R. L., CHAVEZ, F. P., COWLES, T. J., ABBOTT, M. R., STRUB, P. T., BARBER, R. T., JENSEN, P. & SMALL, L. F. 1991. The structure of the transition zone between coastal waters and the open ocean off northern California, winter and spring 1987. *Journal of Geophysical Research*, **96**, 14 707–14 730.

KROON, D. & GANSSEN, G. 1989. Northern Indian Ocean upwelling cells and the stable isotope composition of living planktonic Foraminifera. *Deep Sea Research*, **36**, 1219–1236.

LANDRY, M., PETERSON, W. & NEWMAN, J. 1989. Chapter 1: Broadscale patterns in the distribution of the hydrographic variables. *In*: LANDRY, M. & HICKEY, B. (eds) *Coastal Oceanography of Washington and Oregon*. Elsevier, Amsterdam.

LEGENDRE, L. & LE FÈVRE, J. 1989. Hydrodynamical singularities as controls of recycled versus export production in the ocean. *In*: BERGER, W. H., SMETACEK, V. & WEFER, G. (eds) *Productivity of the Ocean: Past and Present*. Wiley, Chichester.

LYLE, M., ZAHN, R., PRAHL, F., DYMOND, J., COLLIER, R., PISIAS, N. & SUESS, E. 1992. Paleoproductivity and carbon burial across the California Current: the Multitracers transect, 42°N. *Paleoceanography*.

LYNN, R. J. & SIMPSON, J. J. 1987. The California Current System: The seasonal variability of its physical characteristics. *Journal of Geophysical Research*, **92**, 12,947–12,966.

PARKER, F. 1962. Planktonic Foraminiferal species in Pacific sediments. *Micropaleontology*, **8**, 219–254.

PELÁEZ, J. & McGOWAN, J. 1986. Phytoplankton pigment patterns in the California Current as determined by satellite. *Limnology and Oceanography*, **31**, 927–950.

REYNOLDS, L. & THUNELL R. 1985. Seasonal succession of planktonic Foraminifera in the subpolar North Pacific. *Journal of Foraminiferal Research*, **15**, 282–301.

—— & —— 1986. Seasonal production and morphologic variation of *Neogloboquadrina pachyderma* (Ehrenberg) in the northeast Pacific. *Micropaleontology*, **32**, 1–18.

ROBINSON, M. M. 1976. *Atlas of the North Pacific Ocean: monthly mean temperature and mean salinities of the surface layer*. Reference Publication 2, Naval Oceanographic Office, Washington, D.C.

ROESLER, C. S. & CHELTON, D. B. 1987. *Zooplankton Variability in the California Current, 1951–1982*. California Cooperative Fisheries Report Vol. XXVIII, 59–96.

SAUTTER, L. & THUNELL, R. 1989. Seasonal succession of the planktonic Foraminifera: Results from a four year time-series sediment trap experiment in the northern Pacific. *Journal of Foraminiferal Research*, **19**, 253–267.

SIEGEL, D. A., GRANATA, T. C., MICHAELS, A. F. &

DICKEY, T. D. 1990. Mesoscale eddy diffusion, particle sinking, and the interpretation of sediment trap data. *Journal of Geophysical Research*, **95**, 5305–5311.

STRUB, P. T., KOSRO, P. M. & HUYER, A. 1991. The nature of the cold filaments in the California Current System. *Journal of Geophysical Research*, **96**, 14743–14768.

THOMAS, A. & STRUB, P. T. 1989. Interannual variability in phytoplankton pigment distribution during the spring transition along the west coast of North America. *Journal of Geophysical Research*, **94**, 18095–18117.

THUNELL, R. & HONJO, S. 1987. Seasonal and Interannual changes in planktonic Foraminiferal production in the North Pacific. *Nature*, **328**, 335–337.

VINCENT, E. & BERGER, W. H. 1981. Planktonic Foraminifera and their use in paleoceanography. *In*: EMILIANI, C. (ed.) *The Oceanic Lithosphere*. vol. 7. Wiley, New York.

WALSH, I., DYMOND, J. & COLLIER, R. 1988. Rates of recycling of biogenic components of settling particles in the ocean derived from sediment trap experiments. *Deep Sea Research*, **35**, 43–58.

WILLIAMS, P. L. Leb., VON BODUNGEN, B., BATHMAN, U., LEGENDRE, L., BERGER, W. H., MINSTER, J. -F., EPPLEY, R. W., REYNOLDS, C. S., FELDMAN, G. C., SMETACEK, V. S., FISHER, G. & TOGGWEILER, J. R. 1989. Group report Export productivity from the photic zone. *In*: BERGER, W. H., SMETACEK, V. & WEFER, G. *Productivity of the Ocean: Past and Present*, Wiley, Chichester.

WOOSTER, W. S. & REID, J. L. Jr. 1963. Eastern boundary Currents. *In*: HILL, M. N. (ed.) *The Sea*, vol. 2. Wiley, New York.

The palynological expressions of post-Palaeogene upwelling: a review

A. JAMES POWELL[1], JANE LEWIS[2] & JOHN D. DODGE[3]

[1] Millennia Ltd, Unit 3, Weyside Park, Newman Lane, Alton, Hampshire GU34 2PJ, UK

[2] School of Biological and Health Sciences, The Polytechnic of Central London, 115 New Cavendish Street, London W1M 8JS, UK

[3] Department of Biology, Royal Holloway and Bedford New College, University of London, Egham, Surrey TW20 0EX, UK

Abstract: This paper reviews the known palynological expressions of post-Palaeogene upwelling, and changes in upwelling. In Plio-Pleistocene upwelling regimes, levels of amorphogen tend to swamp other palynoclasts present; the application of transmission electron microscopy has great potential for elucidating the origins of amorphogen. The recovery of foraminiferal test linings may be controlled by their progressive microbial destruction; the more juvenile stages in the ontogenetic record stand the greatest chance of preservation. The study of dinoflagellate cyst biofacies offers the greatest potential for palynological characterization and interpretation of post-Palaeogene upwelling systems. Cysts of heterotrophic peridiniacean dinoflagellates (P-cysts) tend to dominate cysts of autotrophic gonyaulacacean forms (G-cysts). The ratio of P-cysts to G-cysts (P/G ratio) is therefore considered to be a useful indicator of variable upwelling strength in these settings, reflecting the degree of water column turbulence. It is uncertain to what degree palynological patterns recognizable in one system are representative of other contemporaneous upwelling regimes. Nevertheless, palynological studies of upwelling systems should be used to interpret geochemical data and thereby provide a tangible link between cause (palaeobiological) and effect (geochemical).

Despite the generally high recovery of organic material from sediments deposited under conditions of upwelling since Palaeogene times, relatively little palynological research has been undertaken. This paper sets out to review what is currently known about Neogene and Quaternary upwelling systems from a palynological perspective.

The major autochthonous contributors to post-Palaeogene palynofacies in upwelling regimes are amorphogen, foraminiferal test linings and dinoflagellate cysts. Each component is reviewed in terms of its recovery and significance within upwelling systems, and recommendations for future research are suggested. Allochthonous components (e.g. terrestrial plant debris and miospores) are not treated in full within the review. It is hoped that by highlighting the potential contribution that palynological studies can make in the interpretation of other geological (particularly geochemical) data, future integrated research projects will be initiated.

Amorphogen in post-Palaeogene upwelling systems

Review

Often the most significant contributor to the palynofacies of post-Palaeogene upwelling regimes is amorphogen (otherwise known as amorphous organic matter or 'AOM', e.g. Tyson 1987). According to Bujak et al. (1977, p 199) 'Amorphogen comprises unorganized structureless organic material which may be finely disseminated or coagulated into fluffy masses'. As the definition implies, amorphogen has no distinct shape or outline, and apparently no identifiable structure. Furthermore, it is moderately transparent and shades in colour from yellow to brown, to dark grey, to black. The character of the amorphogen in a palynological preparation depends upon the interaction of a number of factors. The nature and amount of the source material, the conditions at the site of deposition (particularly in terms of Eh) and the degree of thermal alterations are the most critical factors.

Little published research has been carried out on amorphogen in post-Palaeogene upwelling systems. The most detailed is that by Powell et al. (1990). Working on ODP Leg 112 material from offshore Peru (Fig. 1), Powell et al. (1990) found that amorphogen dominates the palynological assemblages consistently and overwhelmingly (Fig. 2). The presence of rich dinoflagellate cyst assemblages, and the absence of accompanying terrestrial palynoclasts (including palynomorphs), indicates an almost exclusive marine origin to the amorphogen in this setting. Deposition of such massive amounts

From SUMMERHAYES, C. P., PRELL, W. L. & EMEIS, K. C. (eds), 1992, *Upwelling Systems: Evolution Since the Early Miocene*. Geological Society Special Publication No 64, pp 215–226.

215

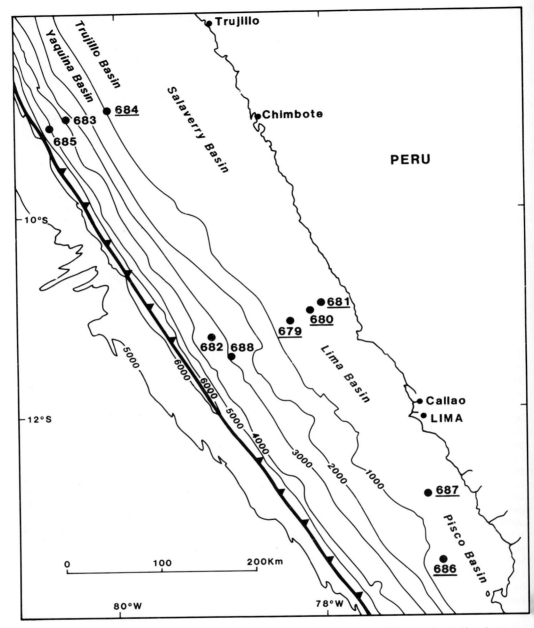

Fig. 1. Location of ODP Leg 112 sites offshore Peru. Sites underlined were drilled on the shelf and upper slope, and were studied by Powell *et al.* (1990).

of amorphogen suggests high palaeoproductivity. However, because samples derived from laminated sediments (i.e. deposited under conditions of strong upwelling) are indistinguishable from those from bioturbated units (i.e. deposited under conditions of weak upwelling),

in terms of amorphogen levels, no meaningful interpretations are possible.

According to ten Haven *et al.* (1990), the unusually small particle size of the organic matter in Plio-Pleistocene sediments offshore Peru indicates that faecal pellets, as well as

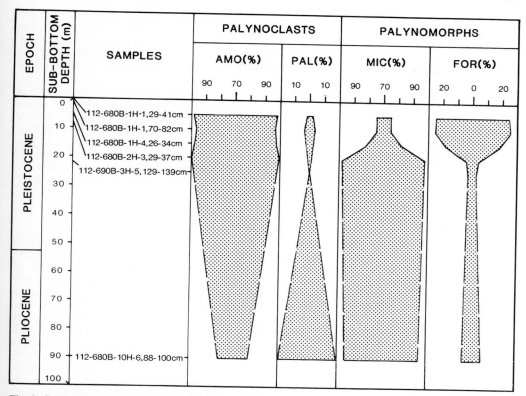

Fig. 2. Palynofacies and palynomorph biofacies analysis of ODP Hole 680B, offshore Peru. AMO, amorphogen; PAL, palynomorphs; MIC, microplankton (predominantly dinoflagellate cysts); FOR, foraminiferal test linings. From Powell *et al.* (1990, fig. 7).

anaerobic bacterial reworking and bacterial bioproductivity in the surface sediments, were the major influences on the organic facies (and hence palynofacies). Molecular organic geochemical data confirm that marine planktonic organisms are the main contributors to the sedimentary organic matter.

Recommendations

Using conventional light microscopy alone, the origins of amorphogen recovered from post-Palaeogene upwelling systems can only be assessed by considering the nature of the accompanying palynomorph biofacies.

The application of transmission electron microscopy (Raynaud *et al.* 1989) has great potential for revealing relict structures within amorphogen, which may provide evidence for its origins. Such studies should not be undertaken in isolation from the geochemical organic facies.

Assessment of the source potential of amorphogen found in sediments deposited under conditions of upwelling should not be carried out using light microscopy alone (Powell *et al.* 1982). The use of fluorescence techniques on palynological preparations offers the best hope of distinguishing hydrogen-rich from hydrogen-poor amorphogen (Powell *et al.* 1982; Kinghorn & Rahman 1983). However, integration with geochemical data would be a prerequisite.

Foraminiferal test linings in post-Palaeogene upwelling systems

Review

Foraminiferal test linings represent the thick, structurally tough, acid-resistant, 'chitinous' inner organic layer ('IOL' of Hemleben *et al.* 1977) of benthic and planktonic individuals. They have a lipid or polysaccharide composition (Banner *et al.* 1973; Hemleben *et al.* 1977). The recovery of foraminiferal test linings in palynological preparations may reflect the number of individuals that have attained sufficient maturity for their pre-adult chambers to be thick enough to survive both microbial destruction and acid treatment during routine preparation procedures.

Although foraminiferal test linings have been recognized in palynological preparations for a long time, they have never been considered in detail; few records from modern or ancient upwelling regimes exist. However, a number of palynologists have attempted to apply these microfossils to palaeoecological studies.

The initial work in this respect was conducted by Muller (1959), who studied the palynology of Holocene sediments from the Orinoco delta and shelf sediments centred around the island of Trinidad. Muller (1959) found that foraminiferal test linings were widely distributed, except in deltaic and prodeltaic littoral zones. He related their relative abundance in marine, as opposed to littoral and estuarine, environments to a salinity control in offshore areas.

Cross *et al.* (1966) recorded foraminiferal test linings (which they assumed to be of benthic species) in the bottom sediments from the southern Gulf of California. The concentration of tests at two particular localities coincides with upwelling of nutrient-rich waters. However, Cross *et al.* (1966) also recorded concentrations elsewhere in the region and related these to greater salinity and shallower marine conditions, where there is high foraminiferal productivity. They did not rule out the possible influence of upwelling.

Melia (1984) examined palynomorphs from aeolian dust and bottom sediments off the coast of northwestern Africa. Although mentioning foraminiferal test linings as an aside, Melia (1984) showed that considerable potential exists for future oceanographic research in this sphere. Melia found that foraminiferal test linings were concentrated in bottom sediments from the areas of upwelling. Melia (1984) concluded that a decrease in the level of foraminiferal test linings can be correlated with increasing water depth.

The most detailed study of foraminiferal test linings from post-Palaeogene upwelling regimes has been carried out by Powell *et al.* (1990) on material from ODP Leg 112, offshore Peru (Fig. 1). Powell *et al.* (1990) observed that foraminiferal test linings tend to be particularly abundant (relative to dinoflagellate cysts) within the uppermost 10 metres (Fig. 2). Samples with peaks in foraminiferal test lining abundance tend to be from laminated sedimentary units (deposited under the influence of upwelling with anoxic bottom conditions).

Powell *et al.* (1990) suggested that the strength of upwelling (as measured by relatively low surface water palaeo-temperatures) was the most significant factor controlling the levels of foraminiferal test linings recorded. However, the decreasing abundance of their recovery with depth may also be due to their progressive degradation in sulphate-reducing environments below the sediment–water interface. After the calcareous layers are dissolved, the linings (particularly those of the younger, thinner chambers) are exposed to microbial attack. The level of recovery of foraminiferal test linings from any one sample may thus also reflect the number of adults in the population to have reached adult development.

Recommendations

The recovery of foraminiferal test linings in relatively high numbers within post-Palaeogene upwelling regimes renders them worthy of further investigation, in tandem with conventional foraminiferal studies (e.g. Malmgren & Funnell 1991). It is suggested that foraminiferal test linings in palynological preparations may represent those individuals with chambers which are thick enough to withstand the rigours of microbial attack and preparation. Thus, according to this hypothesis, only the more juvenile stages in the ontogenetic record (Brummer *et al.* 1986) are preserved. Testing of the hypothesis may allow greater confidence in allocating morpho-groups to particular taxa. Obviously, these studies cannot be carried out in isolation of evidence from complete specimens prior to palynological preparation.

Once the true affinities of foraminiferal test linings have been established, interpretation of their palaeoenvironmental significance may be possible. Analysis of the accompanying geochemical record (levels of sugars and amino acids as a proportion of the total organic carbon) should also be of assistance in this respect.

Dinoflagellate cysts in post-Palaeogene upwelling systems

Review

Dinoflagellate cysts are planktonic organisms which are predominantly marine in nature, certainly in upwelling regimes. The distribution and productivity of dinoflagellate thecae in biocoenoses depends upon factors such as water temperature, salinity, nutrient levels, sunlight and the nature of water mass movements and currents. Benthic dinoflagellate resting cysts contribute to thanatocoenses and stand a chance of fossilization, depending upon the nature of the cyst wall. Not all dinoflagellates produce fossilizable cysts.

In post-Palaeogene sediments, most known dinoflagellate cysts are 'P-cysts' or the 'G-cysts' of Evitt (1985). P-cysts are the cysts of peridiniacean dinoflagellates; most Plio-Pleistocene P-cysts are representatives of the heterotrophic thecate genus *Protoperidinium*. G-cysts are the cysts of gonyaulacacean dinoflagellates; most Plio-Pleistocene G-cysts are derived from the motile, photosynthetic thecae of the genus *Gonyaulax*. Other dinoflagellates which may be common in post-Palaeogene upwelling sediments include gymnodiniacean forms.

Davey (1971) conducted the first detailed palynological study of dinoflagellate cyst assemblages within a modern upwelling system, examining their distribution off the southwestern tip of southern Africa. He observed that, in sediments below the cold Benguela Current, *Spiniferites ramosus* (G-cyst) was dominant, while beneath the warm Agulhas Current, *Operculodinium centrocarpum* (G-cyst) predominated. Working in the same geographical area, Davey & Rogers (1975) confirmed that *S. ramosus* is associated with relatively cool, upwelled waters along the shelf-slope break and nearshore, and *O. centrocarpum* with relatively warm waters.

These studies were extended substantially by Wall *et al.* (1977) who made a semi-quantitative study of the ecology of dinoflagellate cysts in modern sediments. They studied the inshore zone off western South Africa, including the Benguelan upwelling system, and the offshore zone near Pisco on the continental margin of Peru. They did not consider the stratigraphical record of the upwelling system and the response of the dinoflagellate cyst populations to it.

Contrary to the findings of Davey (1971) and Davey & Rogers (1975), Wall *et al.* (1977) found that G-cysts, specifically *Operculodinium centrocarpum*, dominated the Benguelan upwelling assemblages. Subordinate numbers of *Spiniferites ramosus* and *Nematosphaeropsis labyrinthea*, *Impagidinium* spp. (all G-cysts) and *Protoperidinium* spp. (P-cysts) were found to be present. By contrast, the assemblages associated with the Peruvian upwelling system (characterized by cooler surface water temperatures) are dominated by P-cysts (Fig. 3), with *Nematosphaeropsis* and *Impagidinium* spp. present in low numbers. *Operculodinium centrocarpum* was found to be present in lesser abundances than in other slope-rise zones examined by Wall *et al.* (1977).

The differences between the South African and Peruvian dinoflagellate cyst assemblages may be explained by the different amounts of terrestrial material entering the marine realm. Offshore southern Africa, Davey (1971) and Davey & Rogers (1975) observed varying quantities of terrestrial plant material and miospores, both of which are largely absent from the Peruvian continental margin.

The effect of upwelling on dinoflagellate cyst assemblage composition offshore Peru is to cause enrichment of P-cysts. These conditions seem to prevent the development of typical oceanic assemblages (characterized by *Impagidinium* spp. and other G-cysts) like those recognized by Wiseman (1976) at DSDP Site 321 offshore Peru, and by Jarvis & Tocher (1986) at DSDP Site 572 from the central Pacific Ocean. Lewis *et al.* (1990) have reviewed the limited published information concerning living dinoflagellate populations off Peru.

The first paper to associate the dominance of fossil P-cysts to palaeo-upwelling conditions was that by Bujak (1984). Working on the Cenozoic dinoflagellate cyst biostratigraphy of the Bering Sea and northern Pacific Ocean, he observed Upper Miocene to Holocene assemblages dominated by P-cysts. Although he found G-cysts forming only a minor contribution to the assemblages overall, he did observe that they were common locally. The development of assemblages with dominant P-cysts coincides with an increase in the upwelling of nutrient-rich waters (and high diatom productivity) in the area from late Miocene times onward.

Melia (1984) noticed a north–south linear trend in the distribution of dinoflagellates (cysts per gram of bottom sediment) along the northwest coast of Africa. This observed trend is generally coincident with the area of upwelling. Melia did not observe the nature of the dinoflagellate cyst assemblages recorded.

Dinoflagellate cyst assemblages from Middle Miocene through to Lower Pliocene sediments at DSDP Site 362 (Walvis Ridge, eastern Atlantic Ocean) were reported briefly by Duffield & Stein (1985). Although both gonyaulacacean and peridiniacean forms were recorded, Duffield & Stein believed that the abundance of P-cysts in the Upper Miocene to Pliocene succession is related to the upwelling conditions that were prevalent at that time.

Working on Recent material from the eastern Banda Sea (Indonesia), Van Waveren (in press) has recognized a relationship between P-cyst dominance and associated seasonal upwelling. The area is characterized by high levels of both diatoms in the phytoplankton and influx of terrestrial material from the rivers of Irian Jaya.

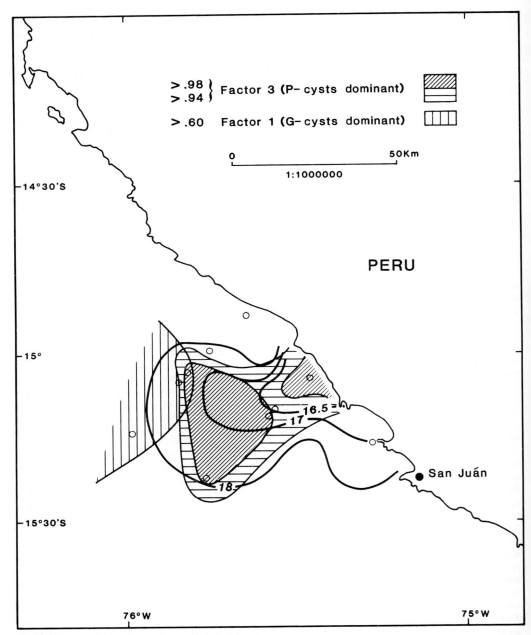

Fig. 3. Horizontal variation of dinoflagellate cyst dominance in surface sediments in relation to upwelling. High factor-loading values for Factor 3 (P-cysts dominant) correspond with upwelling water as indicated by surface water temperature (°C). After Wall *et al.* (1977, fig. 21).

Van Waveren suggests that the seasonal variations in the rainfall (and the resultant variability of terrestrial influx) is the most dominant factor in controlling the nature of the dinoflagellate cyst assemblages.

Powell *et al.* (1990) explored the relationship between dinoflagellate cyst biofacies and upwelling strength in the Pliocene-Pleistocene succession offshore Peru (Figs 1 & 4). They found that P-cysts (81.5% mean) dominate G-cysts (17.0% mean). In detail, G-cysts tend to be most common, though not necessarily dominant, in bioturbated strata. In these assemblages, *Spiniferites* spp. are generally present in higher numbers than *Operculodinium centrocarpum*.

The relationship between bioturbation and depressed levels of P-cysts is not always clear, which suggests the interaction of other factors. P-cysts are known to be particularly abundant in relatively cool waters (e.g. Dale 1985). A combination of factors, including glacial/interglacial cyclicity, as well as upwelling strength, may have been responsible for their recovery. They are most abundant in laminated, unbioturbated units deposited under the influence of strong upwelling.

Powell *et al.* (1990) concluded that the greatest chance of palynological characterization of the Peruvian upwelling system is provided by the dinoflagellate cyst record. The ratio between P-cysts and G-cysts (Fig. 5) appears to indicate the strength of palaeoupwelling.

The findings of Powell *et al.* (1990) were based upon the analysis of a few samples spaced at irregular intervals. In order to rectify this situation, and to investigate the upwelling system in greater detail, Site 686B was selected for intense study. The results were published by Lewis *et al.* (1990).

The plot of the ratio between P-cysts and G-cysts (P/G ratio) over the Quaternary interval in Hole 686B (Lewis *et al.* 1990, fig. 2) shows some interesting trends. Three periods of high values (P-cysts dominant) are separated by periods of lower values (G-cysts dominant). When compared with the U_{37}^k profile over the same section (Farrimond *et al.*, 1990, fig. 1), a clear inverse relationship is apparent (Fig. 5). The U_{37}^k curve is interpreted as a measure of palaeo-temperature of surface waters (Brassell *et al.*, 1986). Intervals of relatively cool surface water (about 18°C) are associated with P-cyst dominance, and may be taken to represent times of strong upwelling. Sections with inferred warmer waters (about 27°C) show depressed levels of P-cysts, which may be interpreted as a sign of weak upwelling. Thus Lewis *et al.* (1990) confirmed that the P/G ratio is a useful independent indicator of variable upwelling strength, at least offshore Peru during the Quaternary.

Upwelling areas are acknowledged regions of high diatom productivity. Margalef (1978) considered water column turbulence to be the dominant controlling factor of the life-forms observed in the phytoplankton. His paper describes a model of diatoms dominating in turbulent conditions with good nutrient supply moving through a successional sequence to dominance by dinoflagellates in non-turbulent conditions with poor nutrient supply. The heterotrophic life style of *Protoperidinium* species has been known for some time but only recently have they been shown to feed actively on diatoms (Gaines & Taylor 1984; Jacobson & Anderson 1986). Thus, it would be expected that *Protoperidinium* species would be more prevalent in an area of enhanced diatom production (see Bujak 1984). Applying this information to Margalef's model, *Protoperidinium* species would be expected to be more common in turbulent areas.

Margalef's model contains a further refinement in that red tide-forming dinoflagellates (notably some gonyaulacacean species) dominate in regions of low turbulence but high nutrients. Other dinoflagellates generally dominate in stratified conditions. Predominance of G-cysts may therefore be expected in regions of lower turbulence.

Apart from upwelling areas, other regions of high turbulence and high diatom productivity are polar seas, not necessarily associated with upwelling. Dominance of P-cyst has been noted in these areas; Balech & El-Sayed (1965) found this relationship in material from the Weddell Sea of Antarctica.

The occurrence of relatively abundant P-cysts in sediments related to cold, arctic waters is well documented (e.g. Scott *et al.* 1984; Mudie & Aksu 1984; Dale 1985; de Vernal *et al.* 1987). In these higher latitude Arctic settings, the dominance of P-cysts reflects the independence of peridiniacean dinoflagellate thecae to unstable lights conditions in colder ice-dominated marine environments (where autotrophs are at a disadvantage).

Recommendations

The study of dinoflagellate cysts offers the greatest potential for the palynological characterization and interpretation of post-Palaeogene upwelling systems.

It is becoming increasingly apparent that the cysts of heterotrophic peridiniacean dinoflagellates (P-cysts) tend to be associated with strong upwelling. Conversely, the cysts of autotrophic gonyaulacacean forms (G-cysts) attain high relative abundance levels during periods of weak or absent upwelling associated with stratified water columns. The ratio of P-cysts to G-cysts (P/G ratio) may be a useful measure of variable upwelling strength.

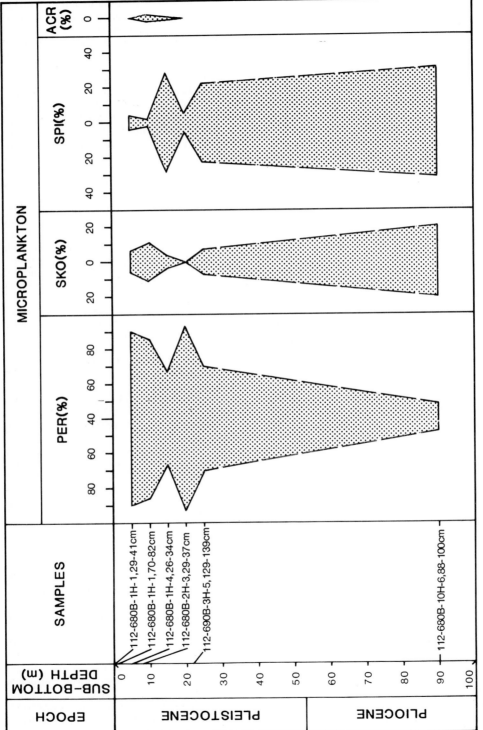

Fig. 4. Microplankton biofacies analysis of ODP Hole 680B, offshore Peru. PER, peridiniacean dinoflagellate cysts (P-cysts); SKO, skolochorate gonyaulacacean dinoflagellate cysts (G-cysts); SPI, spiniferate gonyaulacacean dinoflagellate cysts (G-cysts); ACR, acritarchs.

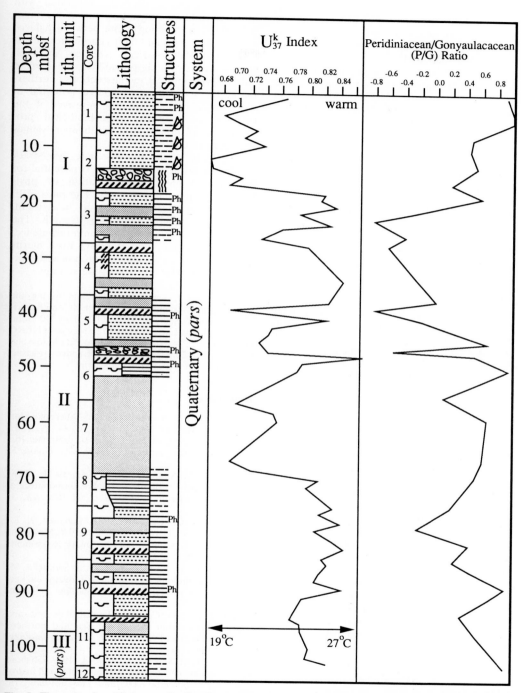

Fig. 5. The ratio of peridiniacean dinoflagellate cysts to gonyaulacacean dinoflagellates cysts (P/G ratio) compared to the U_{37}^k index over the same interval in ODP Hole 686B, offshore Peru. Modified after Suess, von Huene *et al.* (1988, fig. 4), Lewis *et al.* (1990, fig. 2) and Farrimond *et al.* (1990, fig. 1).

The inverse relationship between the P/G ratio and the geochemically derived plot of palaeotemperatures for surface waters (U_{37}^k ratio) indicates that cool upwelling conditions show dominance of P-cysts, and the warmer waters (with G-cysts dominant) are correlated with weaker upwelling conditions. These associations have only been shown to apply in one Quaternary section (ODP Hole 686B), and exciting possibilities for research exist for testing the relationship with other sections both off Peru and elsewhere.

The Peruvian regime is distinctive in that there is little or no evidence for the influx of terrestrial material (either in the form of woody debris or miospores). Off western South Africa, including the Benguelan upwelling system, where there is a significant terrestrial influx to the marine realm, the balance between P-cysts and G-cysts is apparently disturbed. The severity of this disruption and its variability has yet to be established. It would be instructive to ascertain how varying levels of terrestrial influx affect the P/G ratio, the recovery of foraminiferal test linings and the nature of amorphogen recovered. Furthermore, it would be worthwhile to establish a relationship between any trends observed and the pertinent geochemical parameters (see Van Waveren in press).

It is as yet unknown if particular dinoflagellate cyst species are characteristic of individual upwelling regimes, both in modern settings and at specific contemporaneous levels in the post-Palaeogene succession. However, it may be the species composition of the dinoflagellate cyst assemblages which is of greatest significance. Extrapolation of modern trends through the Quaternary and Neogene should be undertaken with extreme caution, particularly in view of the fact that not all dinoflagellates produce fossilizable cysts. Thus although peridiniacean dinoflagellates may prey on diatoms today, those that form fossilizable cysts are not fully representative of the biological activity taking place.

The relationship between water column turbulence and the P/G ratio merits further testing as a palaeoenvironmental indicator. Application of Margalef's (1978) model may also lead to a better appreciation of the relationship between P-cyst dominance and diatom-rich water masses in pre-Neogene settings.

Conclusions

The analysis of the palynological record has much to contribute in interpretation of the sequence of geological events in post-Palaeogene upwelling regimes. Properly integrated with other disciplines, palynology has a very real potential for providing a link between palaeobiological controls and their geochemical manifestations. Palynological research in such settings offers exciting possibilities for detailed palaeoenvironmental reconstructions. Furthermore, the assessment of source potential in older rocks may be greatly improved if the relationships between palaeobiological productivity and the resultant geochemical signals are appreciated.

The study of the dinoflagellate cyst stratigraphic record offers the greatest potential for the palynological characterization of post-Palaeogene upwelling systems. The ratio of P-cysts to G-cysts (P/G ratio) may be a useful measure of variable upwelling strength. The relationship between water column turbulence, diatom dominance and the P/G ratio merits further testing as a palaeoenvironmental indicator particularly in pre-Neogene settings.

Much of this review was undertaken during the authors' involvement with the NERC multidisciplinary shore-based project on ODP Leg 112. John Dodge and Jane Lewis acknowledge receipt of NERC grant GST/02/246. Thanks are due to Peta Mudie and Kay-Christian Emeis for their constructive criticisms of an earlier version of the manuscript.

References

BALECH, E. & EL-SAYED, S. Z. 1965. Microplankton of the Weddell Sea. *In*: LLANO, G. A. (ed.) *Biology of the Antarctic Seas II.* Antarctic Research Series, American Geophysical Union, **5**, 107–124.

BANNER, F. T., SHEEHAN, R. & WILLIAMS, E. 1973. The organic skeletons of rotaline foraminifera: a review. *Journal of Foraminiferal Research*, **3**, 30–42.

BRASSELL, S. C., EGLINTON, G., MARLOWE, I. T., PFLAUMANN, U. & SARNTHEIN, M. 1986. Molecular stratigraphy: a new tool for climatic assessment. *Nature*, **320**, 129–133.

BRUMMER, G.-J. A., HEMLEBEN, C. & SPINDLER, M. 1986. Planktonic foraminiferal ontogeny and new perspectives for micropalaeontology. *Nature*, **319**, 50–52.

BUJAK, J. P. 1984. Cenozoic dinoflagellate cysts and acritarchs from the Bering Sea and northern North Pacific, DSDP Leg 19. *Micropaleontology*, **30**, 180–212.

——, BARSS, M. S. & WILLIAMS, G. L. 1977. Offshore East Canada's organic type and color and hydrocarbon potential. *Oil and Gas Journal*, **75**, 198–202.

CROSS, A. T., THOMPSON, G. G. & ZAITZEFF, J. B. 1966. Source and distribution of palynomorphs in bottom sediments, southern part of Gulf of

California. *Marine Geology*, **4**, 467–524.

DALE, B. 1985. Dinoflagellate cyst analysis of Upper Quaternary sediments in core GIK 15530–4 from the Skagerrak. *Norsk Geologisk Tidsskrift*, **65**, 97–102.

DAVEY, R. J. 1971. Palynology and palaeo-environmental studies with special reference to the continental shelf sediments of South Africa. *In*: FARINACCI, A. (ed.) *Proceedings of the Second Planktonic Conference, Roma, 1970*. Tecnoscienza, Rome, **1**, 331–347.

—— & ROGERS, J. 1975. Palynomorph distribution in Recent offshore sediments along two traverses off South West Africa. *Marine Geology*, **18**, 213–225.

DE VERNAL, A., HILLAIRE-MARCEL, C., AKSU, A. E. & MUDIE, P. J. 1987. Palynostratigraphy and chronostratigraphy of Baffin Bay deep sea cores: Climatostratigraphic implications. *Palaeogeography, Palaeoclimatology, Palaeoecology*, **61**, 97–105.

DUFFIELD, S. L. & STEIN, J. A. 1985. Biostratigraphy and taxonomy of Neogene dinoflagellate cysts in sediments from Walvis Ridge, eastern Atlantic Ocean (Deep Sea Drilling Project Leg 40). *Palynology*, **10**, 245–246 (Abstract).

EVITT, W. R. 1985. *Sporopollenin Dinoflagellate Cysts — Their Morphology and Interpretation*. American Association of Stratigraphic Palynologists Foundation.

FARRIMOND, P., POYNTER, J. G. & EGLINTON, G. 1990. A molecular stratigraphic study of Peru Margin sediments, Hole 686B, Leg 112. *In*: SUESS, E., VON HUENE, R. *et al.*, 1990. *Proceedings of the Ocean Drilling Program, Scientific Results*. College Station, TX (Ocean Drilling Program), **112**, 547–553.

GAINES, G. & TAYLOR, F. J. R. 1984. Extracellular digestion in marine dinoflagellates. *Journal of Plankton Research*, **6**, 1057–1061.

HEMLEBEN, C., BE, A. W. H., ANDERSON, O. R. & TUNTIVATE, S. 1977. Test morphology, organic layers and chamber formation of the planktonic foraminifer Globorotalia menardii (d'Orbigny). *Journal of Foraminiferal Research*, **7**, 1–15.

JACOBSON, D. M. & ANDERSON, D. M. 1986. Thecate heterotrophic dinoflagellates: feeding behaviour and mechanisms. *Journal of Phycology*, **22**, 249–258.

JARVIS, I. & TOCHER, B. 1985. Neogene and Quaternary dinoflagellate biostratigraphy of the eastern Equatorial Pacific: Deep Sea Drilling Project Leg 85. *In*: MAYER, L., THEYER, F. *et al.* 1985. *Initial Reports of the Deep Sea Drilling Project*. U.S. Government Printing Office, Washington, **85**, 407–412.

KINGHORN, R. R. F. & RAHMAN, M. 1983. Specific gravity as a kerogen type and maturation indicator with special reference to amorphous kerogens. *Journal of Petroleum Geology*, **6**, 179–194.

LEWIS, J., DODGE, J. D. & POWELL, A. J. 1990. Quaternary dinoflagellate cysts from the upwelling system offshore Peru, Hole 686B, ODP

leg 112. *In*: SUESS, E., VON HUENE, R. *et al.* 1990. *Proceedings of the Ocean Drilling Program, Scientific Results*. College Station, TX (Ocean Drilling Program), **112**, 323–328.

MALMGREN, K. A. & FUNNELL, B. M. 1991. Benthic foraminifera from Middle to Late Pleistocene coastal upwelling sediments of ODP Hole 686B, Pacific Ocean, off Peru. *Journal of Micropalaeontology*, **9**, 153–158.

MARGALEF, R. 1978. Life-forms of phytoplankton as survival alternatives in an unstable environment. *Oceanologica Acta*, **1**, 493–509.

MELIA, M. B. 1984. The distribution and relationship between palynomorphs in aerosols and deep-sea sediments off the coast of northwest Africa. *Marine Geology*, **58**, 345–371.

MUDIE, P. J. & AKSU, A. E. 1984. Palaeoclimate of Baffin Bay from 300,000-year record of foraminifera, dinoflagellates and pollen. *Nature*, **312**, 630–634.

MULLER, J. 1959. Palynology of Recent Orinoco delta and shelf sediments: Reports of the Orinoco Shelf Expedition; Volume 5. *Micropaleontology*, **5**, 1–32.

POWELL, A. J., DODGE, J. D. & LEWIS, J. 1990. Late Neogene to Pleistocene palynological facies of the Peruvian continental margin upwelling, Leg 112. *In*: SUESS, E., VON HUENE, R. *et al.* 1990. *Proceedings of the Ocean Drilling Program, Scientific Results*. College Station, TX (Ocean Drilling Program), **112**, 297–321.

POWELL, T. G., CREANEY, S. & SNOWDON, L. R. 1982. Limitations of use of organic petrographic techniques for identification of petroleum source rocks. *AAPG Bulletin*, **66**, 430–435.

RAYNAUD, J.-F., LUGARDON, B. & LACRAMPE-COULOUME, G. 1989. Structures lamellaires et bactéries, composants essentiels de la matière organique amorphe des roches mères. *Bulletin des Centres de Recherches Exploration-Production Elf-Aquitaine*, **13**, 1–21.

SCOTT, D. B., MUDIE, P. J., VILKS, G. & YOUNGER, D. C. 1984. Latest Pleistocene-Holocene palaeoceanographic trends on the continental margin of eastern Canada: foraminiferal, dinoflagellate and pollen evidence. *Marine Micropaleontology*, **9**, 181–218.

SUESS, E., VON HUENE, R. *et al.* 1988. Site 686. *Proceedings of the Ocean Drilling Program, Initial Reports*. College Station. TX (Ocean Drilling Program), **112**, 705–802.

TEN HAVEN, H. L., LITTKE, R., RULLKOTTER, J., STEIN, R. & WELTE, D. H. 1990. Accumulation rates and composition of organic matter in Late Cenozoic sediments underlying the active upwelling area off Peru. *In*: SUESS, E., VON HUENE, R. *et al.* 1990. *Proceedings of the Ocean Drilling Program, Scientific Results*. College Station, TX (Ocean Drilling Program), **112**, 591–606.

TYSON, R. V. 1987. The genesis and palynofacies characteristics of marine petroleum source rocks. *In*: BROOKS, J. & FLEET, A. J. (eds) *Marine Petroleum Source Rocks*. Geological Society, London, Special Publication, **26**, 46–67.

van Waveren, I. (in press). Protoperidinioid cysts in sediments from the eastern Banda Sea (Indonesia). *American Association of Stratigraphic Palynologists, Contributions Series*.

Wall, D., Dale, B., Lohmann, G. P. & Smith, W. K. 1977. The environmental and climatic distribution of dinoflagellate cysts in modern sediments from regions in the North and South Atlantic oceans and adjacent sea. *Marine Micropaleontology*, **2**, 121–200.

Wiseman, J. F. 1976. Palynological investigation of samples from holes 319, 320, 320A and Site 321 of DSDP Leg 34. *In*: Yeats, R. S., Hart, S. R. *et al.*, 1976. *Initial Reports of the Deep Sea Drilling Project*. U.S. Government Printing Office, Washington, **34**, 741–742.

Diagenetic conditions

Variations in the content and composition of organic matter in sediments underlying active upwelling regimes: a study from ODP Legs 108, 112, and 117

H. L. TEN HAVEN[1], G. EGLINTON[2], P. FARRIMOND[3], M. E. L. KOHNEN[4],
J. G. POYNTER[4], J. RULLKÖTTER[5] & D. H. WELTE[5]

[1] *Institut Français du Pétrole, BP 311, Rueil Malmaison Cedex, France. (Present address: TOTAL, Route de Versailles, 78470 St Rémy les Chevreuse, France)*
[2] *Organic Geochemistry Unit, University of Bristol, Bristol BS8 1TS, UK*
[3] *Department of Geology, University of Newcastle, Newcastle upon Tyne, NE1 7RU, UK*
[4] *Organic Geochemistry Unit, Delft University of Technology, de Vries van*
[5] *Institut für Erdöl und Organische Geochemie, KFA Jülich, Postfach 1913, 5170 Jülich, Germany*

Abstract: An overview is presented of organic geochemical studies on sediments underlying the active upwelling cells off Northwest Africa (ODP Leg 108; Site 658), off Peru (Leg 112; Sites 679, 681, 684, 686) and off Oman (Leg 117; Sites 723, 725, 728). The investigated sediments are all characterized by high organic carbon contents (0.5−9% C_{org}), being the sedimentary expression of an increased primary bioproductivity induced by upwelling currents of deep nutrient-rich waters. The organic matter is predominantly of marine origin with variable admixtures of a terrigenous component; the highest relative contribution is found at Site 658. The extractable lipids are composed of a wide variety of compounds, of which the most characteristic and abundant compounds were quantified. Long-chain unsaturated ketones usually dominate. Steroids, alkanediols and their corresponding keto-ols are also present in high concentrations, although strong variations in their abundances were noted. In addition, organic sulphur compounds are omnipresent and reveal strong variations in their distribution, but do not make a major contribution to the total amount of extractable lipids.

Organic-matter-rich deep-sea sediments (frequently referred to as 'black shales') have been the subject of numerous studies since the mid-1970s (e.g. Schlanger & Jenkyns 1976; Thiede & van Andel 1977; Fisher & Arthur 1977). Their worldwide occurrence in Cretaceous sediment sequences has been ascribed to 'global anoxic events' (Schlanger & Jenkyns 1976). For many deep-sea black shales this has more recently been restricted on the geological timescale to a 'Cenomanian−Turonian boundary event' (e.g. Herbin et al. 1986). Different models have been suggested to explain the widespread accumulation of organic-matter-rich sediments, particularly during Cretaceous times, the most important ones being the stagnant basin model and the productivity model (Schlanger & Jenkyns 1976; Thiede & van Andel 1977; Arthur et al. 1984; de Graciansky et al. 1984; Stein et al. 1986). These two advocated models are, in principle, derived

from extrapolations to the past of observations made in modern-day analogues, the Black Sea serving as a prototype for the stagnation model and coastal upwelling areas, such as off Peru and off Namibia, for the productivity model. However, the principal causes for the formation of organic matter-rich-sediments still remain a matter of controversial discussion (e.g. Pedersen & Calvert 1990; Demaison 1991; Pedersen & Calvert 1991).

Variations in the quality and quantity of organic matter as well as in the distribution of black shales in time and space (e.g. Dean & Gardner 1982; Rullkötter et al. 1982; de Graciansky et al. 1984; Stein et al. 1989a) indicate that there will be no simple answer to the controversy about their formation. Methods to resolve this controversy, besides geological models, include the inference of surface-water palaeoproductivity from sediment data (Stein 1986a), the consideration of organic carbon/

From SUMMERHAYES, C. P., PRELL, W. L. & EMEIS, K. C. (eds), 1992, *Upwelling Systems: Evolution Since the Early Miocene*. Geological Society Special Publication No 64, pp 229−246.

229

sedimentation rate relationships (Stein 1986*b*), and the study of biological marker distributions in extractable lipid fractions which may be representative of a particular depositional environment (e.g. Powell 1986; Brassell *et al.* 1987; Mello *et al.* 1988). Interest in the elucidation of the black shale problem has also been influenced by the fact that organic-carbon-rich sediments are considered potential petroleum source rocks (e.g. Demaison & Moore 1980; Parrish 1982).

Our aims for studying sediments deposited in coastal upwelling areas were to define the source(s) of the organic matter, to monitor diagenetic changes within the organic phase, and to look for specific organic molecules which could serve as indicators for upwelling environments. All this was intended with a view to understand the processes which, at present, favour the deposition of organic-matter-rich sediments, and with the intention to apply this information for a reconstruction of the palaeo-environmental conditions prevailing during deposition of older organic-matter-rich sediments ('black shales').

In the course of coastal upwelling, deep waters are brought to the surface by upwelling currents, which themselves are driven by winds associated with the earth's major atmospheric circulation. The replenishment of surface waters by nutrient-rich waters results in a high fertility of the surface-water masses and a concomitant high primary productivity. This productivity causes an increase in the flux of organic matter settling through the water column and therefore sediments deposited underneath coastal upwelling areas typically contain elevated organic carbon contents primarily of marine origin. In addition, mineralization of the sinking organic matter at depth causes a depletion of dissolved oxygen which, locally, in combination with sluggish water circulation and stable intermediate waters results in an intense oxygen minimum zone which also may enhance preservation of organic matter.

Since the start of the Ocean Drilling Program (ODP) in 1985, several legs were devoted to investigate some of the world's important coastal upwelling areas. One of the major objectives of ODP Legs 108, 112 and 117 (Fig. 1) was to study the evolution of the upwelling system currently active along the coasts off west Africa, Peru, and Oman respectively. To this end numerous studies, applying different approaches and techniques, were carried out, the results of which have been published in the *Proceedings of the Ocean Drilling Program* (Ruddiman, Sarnthein *et al.* 1989; Suess, von

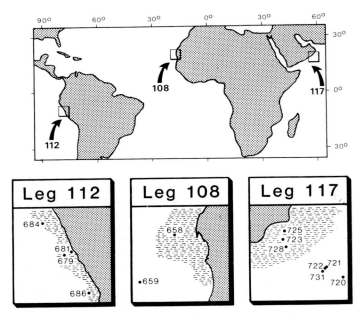

Fig. 1. Map showing drilling locations of ODP Legs 108, 112, and 117. Drill sites discussed in the text and the areal extent of upwelling-induced high productivity zones are indicated. Note that the high productivity zone in the Arabian Sea (ODP Leg 117) only occurs during a limited period of the year in response to the southwestern monsoon.

Huene *et al.* 1990; Prell, Niitsuma *et al.* 1990). Here we present an overview of our organic geochemical studies including previously unpublished results.

Materials and methods

A large number of sediment samples from different sites, located in presently active upwelling areas, were investigated (Fig. 1). For comparative purposes we also studied some samples from reference sites outside the upwelling area.

The experimental techniques comprise determination of bulk parameters (elemental analysis, Rock-Eval pyrolysis), optical characterization of the organic matter, lipid extraction, chromatographic separation, gas chromatographic analyses and gas chromatographic–mass spectrometric analyses. More details of the techniques employed can be found elsewhere (e.g. Poynter *et al.* 1989; ten Haven *et al.* 1990*a*). Quantitative analysis of individual compounds was performed relative to known amounts of added internal standards.

Results and discussion

Bulk parameters

The organic carbon values of the sediments underlying the coastal upwelling areas are consistently high with a maximum of about 9%. In Peru margin sediments organic carbon values exceeding 10% have been reported (e.g. Suess, von Huene *et al.* 1990; McCaffrey *et al.* 1990). In contrast, sediments from Site 659 outside the present upwelling area off Northwest Africa (Fig. 1) contain low amounts of organic carbon (0.1–0.3%), typical of modern deep-ocean sediments (Degens & Mopper 1976). As an example detailed organic carbon profiles for Site 658 (Leg 108; Stein *et al.* 1989*b*), Site 679 (Leg 112; ten Haven *et al.* 1990*a*) and Site 723 (Leg 117; Shipboard Scientific Party 1989) are shown in Fig. 2. It can be seen that on average the organic carbon content at Site 658 is lower than at the other two sites (notably in Pleistocene sediments), and that high-amplitude variations occur at all sites. There is also a sharp increase in TOC at the beginning of the Pleistocene at Site 679. Changes in the sedimentary content of organic carbon can result from changes in both the flux of both organic carbon and inorganic components. Therefore, organic carbon data are better discussed after conversion to mass accumulation rates, by the equation

$$\text{MARTOC} = \text{TOC}/100 \times \text{SR} \times (\text{WBD} - 1.025 \; \text{PO}/100)$$

(cf. van Andel *et al.* 1975), where MARTOC = mass accumulation rate of total organic carbon

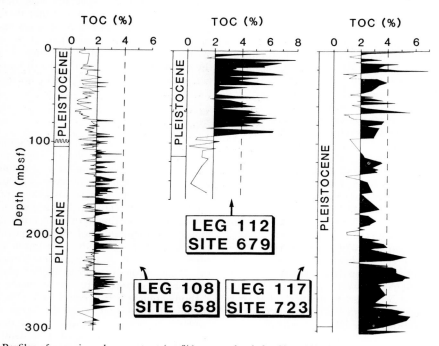

Fig. 2. Profiles of organic carbon content (wt %) versus depth for Sites 658, 679, and 723.

$(g/cm^2/ka)$, TOC = total organic carbon (%), SR = mean sedimentation rate (cm/ka), WBD = wet bulk density (g/cm^3), and PO = porosity (%). This approach requires a good knowledge of sedimentation rates which are, however, not always available in the desirable resolution and accuracy. In the case of the three ODP sites considered here the following ranges of organic carbon accumulation rates were calculated: $0.05-0.5$ $gC/cm^2/ka$ (Site 658; Stein *et al.* 1989b), $0.04-0.5$ $gC/cm^2/ka$ (Site 679; ten Haven *et al.* 1990a), and $0.3-0.9$ $gC/cm^2/ka$ (Site 723; Shipboard Scientific Party 1989). At Site 658 the highest values of organic carbon accumulation rates were found for the depth interval between 240 and 280 mbsf. At Site 679 the highest accumulation rates occur in the uppermost part of the recovered sediment sequence, whereas the contrary was found for Site 723. At the latter site there is a more or less continuous decrease in the accumulation rates towards the top. All these values are at least an order of magnitude higher than the organic carbon accumulation rates determined for non-upwelling sites, such as Site 659 (0.003 and 0.04 $gC/cm^2/ka$; Stein *et al.* 1989b). The strong variations in both mass accumulation rates as well as organic carbon (wt %) are thought to reflect fluctuations in the magnitude of productivity, most likely resulting from changes in the upwelling intensity and/or location of upwelling centres. The accumulation rate values for upwelling Site 679 off Peru are low, however, in comparison to those calculated by Reimers & Suess (1983) for the Peru upper slope. These authors reported TOC accumulation rates of 0.5 to 6.3 $gC/cm^2/ka$ based on accurately determined sedimentation rates derived from ^{210}Pb activity profiles. The availability of more accurate sedimentation rates for the sites we have studied may eventually lead to a revision of our preliminary estimates.

The hydrogen index values from Rock–Eval pyrolysis vary between 200 and 450 mg hydrocarbons/g C_{org} with a few values falling outside this range. Samples from Site 658 off Northwest Africa have somewhat lower average values (HI: $200-350$ mg HC/g C_{org} than those from Site 723 off Oman (HI: $250-450$ mg HC/g C_{org} and those from Site 679 off Peru (HI: $300-450$ mg HC/g C_{org}). This is consistent with the results of elemental analysis of isolated kerogens: for Site 658 the average atomic H/C ratio was 1.38 ($n = 26$), whereas at Site 679 kerogens have an average value of 1.54 ($n = 48$). Commonly, variations in the HI-values are attributed to changes in the sources of organic matter, i.e. terrigenous versus marine, although the vari-

ations can also be induced by differences in the degree of preservation of hydrogen-rich labile organic matter. Thus, the HI-values may indicate either a higher contribution of terrigenous organic matter at Site 658, or a better preservation at Sites 679 and 723.

Organic petrography

The principal macerals found in sediments from the different upwelling areas are alginite and liptodetrinite (liptinites which are too small to be classified into a specific liptinite group) of marine origin, and inertinite and vitrinite of terrigenous origin (Stein *et al.* 1989b; ten Haven *et al.* 1990a; ten Haven & Rullkötter 1991). Sporinite, also of terrigenous origin, occurs rarely. In the Peru sediment samples common brightly fluorescing organic matter, sometimes occurring in foraminifera, was described as unstructured lipitinite. Based on the sum of identifiable macerals of marine origin (alginite, liptodetrinite, unstructured liptinite) an estimate of that part of the organic matter which is of marine origin gives a range of $29-81\%$ (av. = 54%; $n = 18$) for Site 658 off Northwest Africa and of $26-100\%$ (av. = 58%; $n = 27$) for Sites 679, 681 and 684 off Peru. In the latter sediments as well as in sediments from offshore Oman it was noted, however, that the particle size of the macerals (especially those of marine origin) is extremely small and that there is an abundance of dark brown fluorescing material. In these cases only a minor part of the organic matter is microscopically visible and, therefore, the estimates of the contribution of marine organisms to the total organic matter are definitely too low.

Extractable lipids

Until recently, most organic geochemists restricted their interest on the investigation of the aliphatic hydrocarbon fractions of sedimentary lipid extracts mainly because of technical limitations in the analysis of other fractions. Although the aliphatic hydrocarbon fraction is an important constituent of many crude oils and mature sediments, it is of minor importance in extracts of immature sediments and in addition often is heavily biased towards the contribution of alkanes from terrestrial higher plants. In extracts considered here, the aliphatic hydrocarbons comprise between 1 and 13%. Functionalized lipids (e.g. alcohols, ketones, fatty acids) have been the focus of many studies in the past as well, but most of these dealt with a single isolated compound class and not the full spectrum of analysable lipids. Due to rapid instrumental advancements in the seventies, especially in the field of gas chromatography—mass spectrometry, and an increased knowledge of the natural product precursor/geochemical marker product relationships on the molecular level during the last two decades the analyses of more polar fractions are now routinely carried out. In our ODP studies (ten Haven et al. 1989; 1990a; ten Haven & Rullkötter 1991; ten Haven & Kroon 1991; Poynter et al. 1989; Farrimond et al. 1990a, b) we analysed the total solvent extracts of sediments directly by GC and GC-MS after converting acid and alcohol functionalities into methyl esters and trimethylsilyl ethers, respectively. For more detailed compound identifications some extracts were chromatographically separated, and the subfractions thus obtained analysed by GC and GC-MS (after appropriate derivatization). The obvious advantages of this 'total lipid' approach are: a less time-consuming procedure, minimal loss of compounds during work-up procedures and an immediate assessment of the relative importance of various organic constituents. The major disadvantage is that coelution problems may hamper structural identification as well as accurate quantitative determinations. Some examples of gas chromatograms of total lipid extracts from deep-sea sediments from different sites are shown in Figs 3 to 6.

Partial gas chromatograms of the total lipid fractions in sediments from upwelling Site 658 and non-upwelling Site 659 are shown in Fig. 3. A series of long-chain alkenones and a wide variety of sterols are most abundant at Site 658, pointing to a major contribution of marine organic matter. In addition, a homologous series of n-alkanes maximizing at C_{17} and C_{31} is present. At Site 659 this series is dominant. The odd-over-even carbon number predominance of long-chain n-alkanes ($C_{25}-C_{33}$) reflects terrigenous organic matter (e.g. Eglinton & Hamilton 1963; Simoneit 1978), whereas short-chain n-alkanes, C_{15} and C_{17}, are primarily ascribed to a marine origin (e.g. Simoneit 1978). Based on an investigation only of the aliphatic hydrocarbon fraction in these samples, one would conclude that the organic matter at both sites is of terrigenous origin to a considerable extent, and that at Site 659 the marine portion (n-$C_{17} > n$-C_{31}) is even higher than at Site 658 (n-$C_{17} < n$-C_{31}). Clearly, this is in conflict with the results emerging from the total lipid analysis, as well as with elemental analysis data and microscopical kerogen observations. Such a bias stems from the fact that alkanes of land-plant origin are introduced to the sediments as such,

whereas most marine lipids must undergo a series of diagenetic reactions before they are converted to saturated hydrocarbons. Although this note of caution may seem to be superfluous in the eyes of many organic geochemists, there are still organic geochemical papers published in 1991 with palaeoenvironmental reconstructions solely based on the study of the aliphatic hydrocarbon fractions of recent sediments. This problem is addressed by Poynter & Eglinton (1991). Moreover, certain hydrocarbons may be selectively quenched by inorganic sulphur species (see Sinninghe Damsté & de Leeuw, 1990, for an overview), thereby causing additional problems in the interpretation of hydrocarbon profiles.

On the other hand it is even questionable if extractable lipids are representative of all the organic matter, because in most cases they account only for a small part ($<10\%$) thereof. For example, in a study of Messel oil shale, Robinson et al. (1989) came to the conclusion that, based on extractable lipids, the main part of the organic matter was probably of dinoflagellate origin, whereas Goth et al. (1988), applying scanning electron microscopy and pyrolysis techniques, invoked an origin from Tetraedron algae. Hence, if possible, interpretations of biological marker data should be backed up by complementary techniques, such as petrography. Most of the samples investigated during our involvement in the ODP programme have also been investigated by organic petrography and the results thus obtained were, generally, in good agreement with extractable lipid data. This is illustrated by an example from ODP Leg 117 (ten Haven & Rullkötter 1991), where at Site 720, located in the Indus Fan, microscopy and Rock-Eval data indicate an overwhelming presence of terrigenous organic matter. In the total lipid fraction this found its expression in an abundance of highly specific angiosperm biological markers, such as β- and α-amyrin, and friedelin. These compounds were below the limit of detection at the upwelling sites offshore Oman. Therefore, for comparative purposes we feel confident in applying extractable lipid distributions as indicators for palaeoenvironmental changes.

In the following sections we will focus our discussion on selected organic compounds, chosen because of their abundance and/or their specificity. Absolute concentrations of selected compounds are given in Table 1.

Long-chain alkenones. The C_{37}-C_{39} di- and tri-unsaturated alkenones are biological markers of Prymnesiophyte algae (Volkman et al. 1980;

Table 1. Quantitative results of selected compounds (μg/g sed.).

Samples	depth (mbsf)	Corg (%)	Selected compounds* 1	2	3	4	5	6	7	8	9	10	11
Site 658													
average (n = 27)[†]			0.5				0.4	1.8				2.8	3.0
Site 679													
1H-1, 30–37	0.35	7.90	0.6	1.1	0.6	2.3	3.1	6.6	7.7	2.2	6.2	14.6	10.4
1H-6, 133–140	8.85	2.09	0.1	0.5	0.2	0.4	0.3	1.1	1.5	0.4	0.9	5.5	4.3
2H-4, 30–37	13.85	3.72	0.2	—	—	1.1	—	1.9	1.2	0.5	0.8	10.1	9.2
3H-4, 30–37	23.85	8.95	0.3	—	—	4.7	1.8	7.2	4.4	2.6	2.7	33.7	27.3
4H-4, 30–37	32.85	3.21	<0.1	—	1.5	1.3	—	1.1	0.6	—	—	12.4	12.1
5H-4, 30–37	42.85	3.05	0.2	1.5	0.3	1.0	0.4	2.3	1.2	0.8	1.0	5.4	4.6
6H-4, 30–37	51.85	2.57	0.1	—	—	0.7	1.1	1.7	0.5	1.2	2.3	6.6	8.0
7H-4, 30–37	61.85	2.68	—	1.4	—	0.8	0.9	1.5	—	0.7	1.6	8.5	10.4
8H-2, 30–37	67.85	7.52	—	3.0	1.4	1.8	1.2	3.1	1.1	1.7	4.2	19.1	19.1
8H-6, 30–37	73.85	5.31	0.3	3.2	1.3	1.8	1.7	3.8	1.3	2.3	3.8	18.0	14.1
average			0.2	1.8	0.9	1.6	1.3	3.0	2.2	1.4	2.6	19.3	12.0
Site 681													
1H-1, 30–37	0.35	4.65	0.7	1.2	0.7	2.2	3.8	5.3	3.7	3.0	4.3	7.7	5.1
2H-1, 30–37	6.25	4.47	0.7	0.6	0.9	1.4	2.0	4.4	4.0	1.0	2.0	13.5	10.6
2H-6, 5–12	13.50	1.32	0.1	0.4	0.1	0.2	0.3	1.2	1.4	0.6	1.4	4.0	3.3
3H-4, 30–36	20.25	3.13	0.4	0.7	0.5	1.2	1.3	2.7	1.5	0.9	1.7	9.0	7.9
4H-4, 30–36	29.75	6.51	0.6	1.7	1.1	2.4	2.4	7.5	5.0	2.3	6.1	16.7	13.9
5H-4, 32–38	39.25	2.71	0.3	0.8	0.6	1.0	0.9	1.6	1.6	0.5	1.3	14.9	12.1
7H-4, 30–37	58.25	0.20	<0.1	<0.1	<0.1	0.2	<0.1	<0.1	<0.1	<0.1	<0.1	<0.1	<0.1
8H-4, 30–37	67.75	1.16	0.2	0.2	—	0.2	0.3	0.3	0.3	0.1	0.3	1.5	1.3
9H-4, 30–37	77.25	0.53	<0.1	<0.1	<0.1	<0.1	<0.1	—	0.1	—	—	0.6	0.6
10H-4, 30–37	86.75	3.09	0.3	0.6	—	0.7	0.7	2.0	1.0	0.4	0.8	10.1	7.5
average			0.4	0.8	0.7	1.1	1.5	3.1	2.1	1.1	2.2	8.7	6.9
Site 684													
1H-1, 30–37	0.35	3.56	0.4	<1.5	0.4	1.0	1.3	2.3	2.4	0.9	1.7	7.8	9.8
1H-4, 30–37	4.85	2.57	0.3	—	0.3	0.5	0.5	2.1	2.6	0.9	1.7	4.3	3.4
2H-4, 30–37	12.65	0.86	<0.1	0.2	<0.1	0.2	0.1	0.3	0.3	<0.1	0.2	1.2	0.9
3H-1, 30–37	17.65	6.21	0.8	1.2	0.9	1.4	1.6	7.1	4.6	1.7	4.6	23.2	16.6
3H-6, 30–37	25.15	5.89	0.7	0.7	0.4	0.9	0.8	4.9	1.9	1.9	2.2	37.1	26.1
4H-3, 30–37	30.15	7.46	0.9	2.1	2.0	3.4	2.8	4.8	1.8	2.3	3.0	31.6	19.3
4H-7, 30–37	36.15	4.09	0.9	1.4	2.0	3.2	3.0	3.6	1.0	1.6	1.5	16.4	13.1
average			0.7	1.2	1.0	1.5	1.4	3.6	2.1	1.6	2.1	17.4	12.7
Site 686													
average (n = 82)[‡]			0.4				1.2	3.5				14.6	
Site 722													
4H-2, 80–86	31.30	1.41	0.4	<0.1	—	<0.1	0.1	1.6	—	0.5	—	2.1	1.5
19X-2, 74–80	175.84	2.57	—	—	—	—	—	—	—	—	—	3.1	1.8
32X-5, 16–18	301.16	3.09	0.6	0.3	—	0.1	0.4	1.2	—	0.6	—	10.1	7.4
Site 723													
17X-1, 69–75	149.59	2.75	0.3	2.5	—	2.2	2.5	1.3	—	0.3	—	4.9	4.2
25X-2, 49–52	228.19	4.36	0.3	3.3	—	3.7	3.2	1.0	—	0.3	—	12.7	10.8
33X-2, 70–76	315.20	4.49	—	4.5	—	6.9	8.4	1.3	—	0.4	—	13.6	14.4
40X-3, 97–103	375.27	3.91	0.5	3.2	—	4.2	6.5	2.1	—	0.5	—	5.6	6.8
41X-2, 50–53	383.00	8.24	6.6	3.2	—	3.0	5.8	27.8	—	6.5	—	48.6	35.2
Site 728													
5H-7, 53–58	39.13	2.21	0.6	0.1	—	0.1	0.3	2.2	—	0.6	—	2.9	2.1
10X-4, 74–80	82.54	5.23	2.3	1.1	—	1.0	2.0	9.6	—	2.1	—	14.2	10.1
15X-1, 75–80	126.25	3.17	1.5	0.4	—	0.6	1.3	1.2	—	0.4	—	7.0	4.7
20X-3, 80–86	177.60	2.48	0.4	0.3	—	0.4	1.0	1.6	—	0.4	—	5.6	4.6
25X-2, 125–130	224.95	2.43	0.7	0.5	—	0.3	1.3	2.4	—	0.5	—	5.9	4.8
30X-3, 72–78	280.20	1.67	0.4	0.9	—	0.7	1.2	1.0	—	0.3	—	5.8	4.7
35X-4, 80–86	328.50	2.22	0.4	1.1	—	0.8	1.2	1.2	—	0.5	—	6.1	5.3

* 1, Hexacosanol; 2, Cholest-5-en-3β-ol; 3, 24-Ethylcholesta-5,22-dien-3β-ol; 4, 24-Ethylcholest-5-en-3β-ol; 5, Dinosterol; 6, Triacontanediols; 7, Triacontaneketo-ols; 8, Dotriacontanediols; 9, Dotriacontaneketo-ols; 10, C37-Alkenones; 11, C38-Alkenones.

[†] See Poynter *et al.* (1989).

[‡] See Farrimond *et al.* (1990*b*)

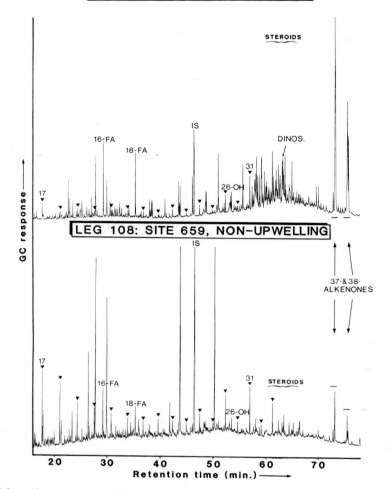

Fig. 3. Partial gas chromatograms of the total lipid extract from Sample 108-658A-33X-3, 130–137 cm (276 meters below sea floor), and Sample 108-659B-3H-4, 130–137 (40 mbsf) offshore Northwest Africa. Triangles indicate homologous series of *n*-alkanes. FA indicates straight-chain fatty acids, OH straight-chain alcohols, DINOS. stands for dinosterol, and IS is the internal standard. Major unlabelled peaks in the lower GC-trace are contaminants (plasticisers).

Marlowe 1984; Marlowe *et al.* 1984; Brassell *et al.* 1986*a*), and the C_{37} and C_{38} members are very often the most quantitatively important GC-amenable lipid compounds in the total extracts (Table 1; Fig. 3). Besides being source indicators, these alkenones contain information about past sea-surface water temperatures (Brassell *et al.* 1986*a*). The rationale for this is that in order to maintain membrane fluidity aquatic organisms react to changing temperatures by changing the molecular composition

of their lipid bilayer. In the case of *Prymnesiophytes*, it is suggested that this may result in an inverse relationship between the overall degree of unsaturation and the surface-water temperature. To illustrate this, two partial gas chromatograms of total lipid extracts from Site 658 sediments are shown in Fig. 4. In the interglacial sediment the diunsaturated alkenone ($C_{37:2}$) is twice as abundant as the triunsaturated alkenone ($C_{37:3}$: first eluting black peak), whereas in the glacial sediment the relative importance

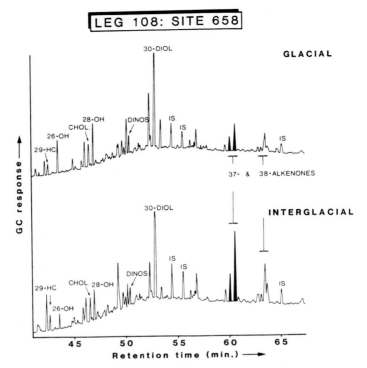

Fig. 4. Partial gas chromatograms of the total lipid extract of a sediment from Site 658 (offshore Northwest Africa) deposited during a glacial (top) and an interglacial period (bottom). HC stands for straight-chain hydrocarbon, CHOL. for cholest-5-en-3β-ol, and DIOL. for alkanediols. For further explanation see caption of Fig. 3.

of the ($C_{37:2}$ compound is enhanced. Brassell *et al.* (1986*a*) defined an alkenone unsaturation index U^k_{37} as $C_{37:2}/(C_{37:2}+ C_{37:3})$ to illustrate these changes in sediment extract data. Subsequently, Prahl & Wakeham (1987) and Prahl *et al.* (1988) calibrated this ratio to actualistic sea surface-water temperatures (SST) by field samples and laboratory culture experiments with *Emiliania huxleyi* (cf. Marlowe 1984), and provided further legitimation for its application in studies of marine environments. The validity of the U^k_{37} method has been further strengthened recently by Sikes *et al.* (1991). However, values for SST calculations in this way can only be regarded as a first approximation, as other factors, such as the evolution of the prymnesiophyte species over geological time and their biosynthesis of alkenones, remain unknown.

We measured the U^k_{37} ratio in numerous samples from Site 658 (Poynter *et al.* 1989), Site 686 (Farrimond *et al.* 1990*b*), and Sites 721, 723, 728, 731 (ten Haven & Kroon 1991) in the three upwelling areas, and calculated the SST

using the equation of Prahl *et al.* (1988): $U^k_{37} = 0.034T + 0.039$. Off Northwest Africa (Site 658) the U^k_{37} ranges between 0.60 and 0.82, corresponding to a SST range of 16.5° to 23.0°C. A very close similarity was found between the U^k_{37} profile and a stacked oxygen isotope record (Poynter *et al.* 1989), indicating that mainly glacial/interglacial cycles are documented. In the upper 70 m of the sedimentary record at Site 686 off Peru the U^k_{37} record displays rapid fluctuations from a minimum of 0.66 (18.2°C) to a maximum of 0.88 (24.7°C) (Farrimond *et al.* 1990*b*). Below this depth the record indicates warmer SST with a smaller variability (0.78–0.92; 21.8°–25.9°C). This changing pattern was attributed to reflect the palaeoceanographic conditions, i.e. before the onset of subsidence of the Peru continental margin Site 686 was located inshore of the region influenced by upwelling with the result that relatively high SST with superimpositions of glacial/interglacial cycles are recorded by the U^k_{37} signal; during subsidence and concomitant increasing water depth, the upwelling centre progressively moved shorewards and lower SST with high-amplitude variations related to changes in the upwelling intensity occurred. Indeed, a high-resolution U_{37}^k profile of a box core from this area enabled McCaffrey et al. (1990) to tentatively identify the 1982–1983 El Niño southern oscillation event, a period during which warm waters disturbed the normal Peruvian upwelling conditions.

At the sites located in the Arabian Sea, the U_{37}^k values vary from 0.65 to 0.97, corresponding to a temperature range from 18.0° to 27.4°C, in accordance with the present-day SST range (ten Haven & Kroon 1991). Such a wide range of present-day temperatures results from the periodically changing wind pattern of the monsoon, whereby the southwestern monsoon causes upwelling along the coast of Somalia and Oman during the northern hemisphere summer. An inconsistency was noted with model calculations of these summer monsoonal winds by Prell & Kutzbach (1987), who estimated the strongest winds (and likewise upwelling) to occur during interglacials, especially during isotopic stage 5. However, the U_{37}^k record indicated relatively high SST during this period as well as other interglacials. As there were indications (e.g. biota assemblages) that upwelling was indeed stronger during interglacials, it was suggested that the northwestern monsoon (which does not induce upwelling) was very cool during glacial periods and cooled the surface waters of the Arabian Sea. This temperature effect, thus, was even stronger than the temperature effect induced by intensified upwelling in interglacials.

The laboratory culture experiments of Prahl et al. (1988) with Emiliana huxleyi (presumably the prime algae responsible for biosynthesizing these compounds during the late Pleistocene) also revealed a consistency in the total ketone concentration per cell (independent of growth temperature), suggesting that down-core concentration profiles might provide a clue to palaeoproductivity of prymnesiophytes. Although it was shown that these compounds pass almost quantitatively through the pelagic food chain (Corner et al. 1986), a strong degradation (85%) in sediments under aerobic conditions was observed (Prahl et al. 1989). Recently, McCaffrey et al. (1990) noted a 30% loss in the surface 1 cm of a dysaerobic sediment from the Peruvian upwelling area. Both these studies have shown that the internal ratio (U_{37}^k) is hardly affected, and hence the application as SST indicators is still valid. Under the assumption that the degradation in surface sediments is relatively constant under anaerobic conditions

(cf. McCaffrey et al. 1990), and that the most intense degradation takes place near the sediment–water interface (Westrich & Berner 1984; Middelburg 1989), we may still be able to retrieve qualitative information on past productivity changes and to make comparisons between the different upwelling areas.

Strong variations in the absolute concentration of the ketones are observed (Table 1), with a maximum of around 50 $\mu g/g$ sed. found in a late Quaternary sample from Site 686 (Farrimond et al. 1990b) and a Pliocene sample from Site 723. Sediments at Site 658 on average contain the lowest amounts of ketones indicating a lower productivity of prymnesiophytes along the coast of West Africa. A rough estimate of their contribution to the sedimentary organic matter can be made assuming that the total ketone concentration (C_{37}, C_{38}, C_{39}) represents $\approx 10\%$ of the total organic carbon of prymnesiophytes (Prahl et al. 1988; Prahl & Muelhausen 1989) and that the degradation rate of the ketones is similar to that of the total organic matter. For example, Sample 41X-2, 50–52 cm from Site 723 with a C_{org} content of 8.24% contains ≈ 90 μg ketones/g sed., corresponding to 900 μg prymnesiophyte contribution for 82 400 μg C_{org}, thus representing $\approx 1.1\%$. For all sediments, this contribution varies between 0.3 and 1.1%. These values are presumably minimum values as ketones are likely to be more stable than, for example, proteins and carbohydrates. Admittedly, such values should be viewed with extreme caution, because of the many uncertainties involved in the estimation.

Alkanediols and keto-ols. The C_{28}–C_{32} alkanediols are considered as biological markers of planktonic cyanobacteria (Morris & Brassell 1988) and planktonic microalgae of the class Eustigmatophycae (Volkman, cited in McCaffrey et al. 1991). The corresponding series of keto-ols have not yet been found, but the close structural relationship to the alkanediols points to a similar origin, the structural difference being due to partial oxidation. Although sometimes dominant (Fig. 4) these compounds occur normally second in quantitative abundance, with the C_{30} member being prominent in most cases (Fig. 5; Table 1). Very high concentration of C_{30}-alkanediols was found in a sample from Site 723 (27.8 $\mu g/g$ sed.; Table 1; Fig. 6). With the exception of this one sample, average values of the Peru sediments are somewhat higher than sediments from the upwelling areas offshore West Africa and Oman. In Oman sediments the strongest relative concentration

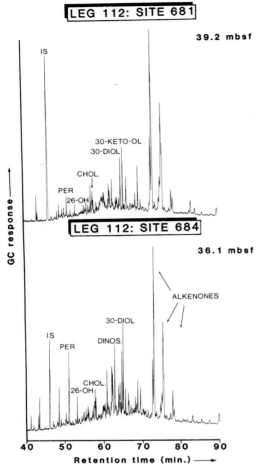

Fig. 5. Partial gas chromatograms of the total lipid extract of Sample 112-681C-5H-4, 32−38 cm (top), and Sample 112-684C-4H-7, 30−37 cm (bottom), offshore Peru. PER. stands for perylene. For further explanation see captions of Figs 3 & 4.

differences were noted, and in some samples the C_{28} compounds (mainly 1,14- and 1,12-diols) are even more abundant than the C_{30} homologs (Fig. 6; ten Haven & Rullkötter 1991). The GC peak corresponding to an alkanediol usually consists of a number of coeluting isomers, each displaying characteristic fragment ions upon GC-MS analysis (de Leeuw *et al.* 1981). An example of a mass spectrum of a mixture of C_{30} alkanediols, eluting as one peak, from the total lipid extract of a Site 684 sample (offshore Peru) is shown in Fig. 7 (top), together with a schematic representation of the most characteristic fragmentation. In order of abundance this mixture consists of the 1,15-diol

(m/z 313, 387), the 1,13-diol (m/z 341, 359) and the 1,14-diol (m/z 327, 373). This is in accordance with previous observations from a variety of marine sediments (e.g. de Leeuw *et al.* 1981; Morris & Brassell 1988). However, in some samples from the Arabian Sea the cluster of C_{30} alkanediols is dominated by the 1,14-diol (Fig. 7, bottom). The abundance of the structurally related 15-keto-1-ols relative to the alkanediols shows a strong variability; sometimes they are present in higher concentrations, and at other times in lower concentrations (Fig. 5; Table 1). As the biochemical/physiological role of these compounds is still unknown, we can only speculate that this changing occurrence reflects in some way the palaeoenvironmental conditions.

Sterols. A wide variety of sterols was found with various degrees of unsaturation and with and without alkylation at C-4. Of these, the 4-methylsterols, and in particular $4\alpha,23,$ 24-trimethyl-5α(H)-cholest-22-en-3β-ol ('dinosterol'), are regarded to be specific for a contribution of dinoflagellates (Boon *et al.* 1979), whereas multiple sources can be assigned to the others (Volkman 1986). Dinosterol is often one of the most important sterols, reaching a maximum of ≈ 8 μg/g sed. at Site 723 (Table 1) and Site 686 (Farrimond *et al.* 1990*b*). Other important sterols include: cholest-5-en-3β-ol, 5α(H)-cholestan-3β-ol, and their 24-ethyl counterparts (Figs 5 and 6; Table 1). A larger part of the former two can most likely be ascribed to faeces and carcasses of zooplankton and fish (Gagosian *et al.* 1983*a*; 1983*b*), whereas the origin of the latter two is less clear (Volkman, 1986; Volkman *et al.* 1987). This ambiguity is due to the occurrence of 24-ethylcholest-5-en-3β-ol in vascular plants. However, we are tempted to invoke primarily a marine origin for this sterol, based on the low abundance of other terrigenous biological markers (see hereafter). Exceptions to this are the samples from Site 720 in the Indus Fan, where abundant terrigenous biological markers co-occur with this sterol, and at this particular site a terrigenous origin is more plausible.

A particular class of steroidal compounds for which the sedimentary distributions have not been studied in detail before are steryl esters. This may partly be due to the fact that earlier reports (de Leeuw *et al.* 1977; Cranwell & Volkman 1981) suggested that these compounds are susceptible to hydrolysis, and hence would not survive early diagenesis. We have previously studied the distribution of the steroidal moieties of steryl esters in a near-surface sediment sample

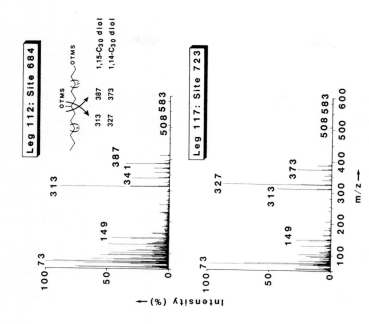

Fig. 7. Mass spectra of triacontanediols, analysed as trimethylsilyl derivatives, in a total lipid extract from Site 684 (top), offshore Peru, and Site 723 (bottom), Oman margin. The spectra were recorded with a VG 7070E mass spectrometer operating at 70 eV.

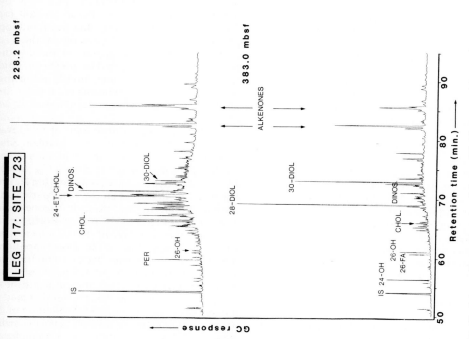

Fig. 6. Partial gas chromotograms of the total lipid extract of Sample 117-723B-25X-2, 49–52 cm (top) and 117-723b-41X-2, 50–53 cm (bottom), Oman margin.

(0.35 mbsf) by saponification of the chromatographically separated ketone + ester fraction and subsequent isolation of the alcohols (ten Haven *et al*. 1990*a*). In this way we primarily found a variety of 4-desmethylsterols. This has prompted us to perform a similar procedure with other extracts from more deeply buried sediments from Sites 676 and 684 (offshore Peru). Again, we found numerous sterols dominated either by cholest-5-en-3β-ol, 24-ethylcholest-5-en-3β-ol, and their 5α(H)-counterparts or by 24-methylcholesta-5,22-dien-3β-ol and 24-methyl-5α(H)-cholest-22-en-3β-ol. Even in the oldest sample (112-684C-4H-7, 30−37 cm; 36.15 mbsf; Pliocene) sterols were abundant, indicating that in the Peruvian environment steryl esters do survive early diagenesis and are potential biological markers provided that the source organisms are known.

Compounds of terrigenous origin. As discussed before, long straight-chain alkanes with a strong odd-over-even carbon number predominance ($C_{25}-C_{33}$) reflect a contribution of terrigenous organic matter (Eglinton & Hamilton 1963). Similarly, long straight-chain alcohols and fatty acids both with an even-over-odd carbon number predominance derive from the same source (Simoneit 1978). These compounds are brought to the marine environment either by aeolian or fluvial transport. Terrigenous triterpenoid biological markers were only observed in identifiable quantities at Site 720 in the Indus Fan, located far away from the areal extension of upwelling. However, it should be noted that such compounds were also found in Peruvian upwelling sediments at 15°S by Volkman *et al*. (1987).

Concentrations of *n*-alkanes have only been calculated for three sites, with an average for the *n*-C_{29} of 0.3 µg/g sed. found for Site 658 ($n = 27$), 0.5 µg/g sed. for Site 680 ($n = 20$), and 0.6 µg/g sed. for Site 686 ($n = 82$). Similar concentrations were found for the *n*-C_{26} alkanol, with the exception of a value of 6.6 µg/g sed. for a sample of Site 723 (Table 1). As the total organic carbon values of Site 658 samples on average are lower than at the other sites (e.g. Fig. 2), the relative contribution of the terrigenous organic compounds is thus higher at this site, which is in accord with bulk parameters and optical characterization.

Organic sulphur compounds. Although the existence of organically bound sulphur has been known for many years, it was only recently that molecular evidence for early incorporation of inorganic sulphur species into organic matter

was established (see Sinninghe Damsté & de Leeuw 1990 for an overview). For the Peruvian sediments this incorporation was shown to take place in the upper 15 metres and that up to 45% of the total sedimentary sulphur can be organically bound (Mossman *et al*. 1990). The basic carbon skeleton of many of the organic sulphur compounds (OSC) so far identified shows an unambiguous link to natural product precursors and thus OSC can also be used for the assessment of the palaeoenvironment of deposition. For the sediments of this study, the aromatic hydrocarbon fraction, which contains OSC, comprised between 1% and 6% of the total lipid extract and thus is quantitatively not very important. A partial gas chromatogram of such a fraction from Site 684 (offshore Peru) is shown in Fig. 8. The aromatic hydrocarbon perylene is the dominating compound (corresponding to the perylene peak indicated in Fig. 5), but OSC are present in abundance as well. The two C_{20} isoprenoid thiophenes were found in almost all sediments, which is in accordance with the observations made earlier in a study dealing with other deep-sea sediments (ten Haven *et al*. 1990*b*). The C_{20} isoprenoid disulphides and trisulphide have only been found in the Peruvian sediments and their formation most likely involves a reaction with polysulphides (Kohnen *et al*. 1989). Analogous to the quenching model of labile functionalized lipids proposed by Sinninghe Damsté *et al*. (1989) to account for OSC in the geosphere, a sulphur incorporation scheme explaining the formation of the C_{20} isoprenoid sulphur compounds in these sediments is given in Fig. 9. The precursor lipid originates either from ubiquitously occurring phytol derived from chlorophyll or from archaebacterial phytenyl moieties (Brassell *et al*. 1986*b*).

A totally different distribution of OSC was found in sediments from the Arabian Sea. Although the two C_{20} isoprenoid thiophenes are also present, in many samples a C_{25} and/or a C_{27} 2-alkylthiophene are dominant (ten Haven & Rullkötter 1991). As an example, partial gas chromatograms of the aromatic hydrocarbon fraction from two Site 722 (Owen Ridge) sediments are shown in Fig. 10. In the upper trace 2-tricosanyl-thiophene is the most important compound in the aromatic hydrocarbon fraction of a sample from a depth of 175 mbsf, while in the lower trace (301 mbsf sediment depth) it is 2-henicosanylthiophene. We previously noted a similar patchy occurrence and distribution of 2-tricosanyl-thiophene in several Cenozoic sediment samples from different geographical locations (off California, Gulf of California, off

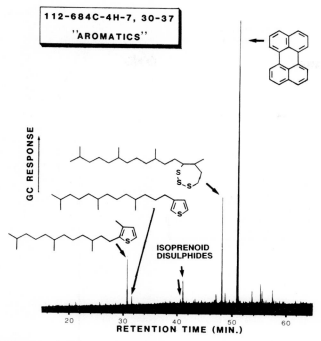

Fig. 8. Partial gas chromatogram of the 'aromatic hydrocarbon' fraction of a sample from Site 684 (36 mbsf), offshore Peru. The structures of the most important compounds are given.

Namibia, Blake Outer Ridge), but never in older samples (ten Haven *et al.* 1990*b*). Based on this observation we suggest that these compounds reflect an evolutionary diversification of biota, although at present it is not possible to assign them to a certain origin due to lack of suitable known precursors in the biosphere.

Two samples from Site 684 (off Peru) and one from Site 723 (Oman Margin) were analysed by high-temperature gas chromatography (up to 450°C) in order to detect high-boiling OSC. These OSC comprise a series of 3,4-dialkyl-thiophenes (Kohnen *et al.* 1990), and their distribution in the Site 723 sample is illustrated by a

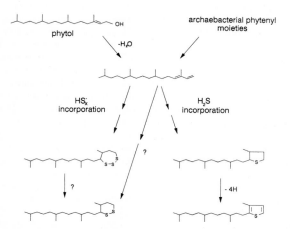

Fig. 9. Scheme for the incorporation of inorganic sulphur species into a phytadiene precursor, explaining the occurrence of the observed C_{20} isoprenoid OSC in Peruvian sediments.

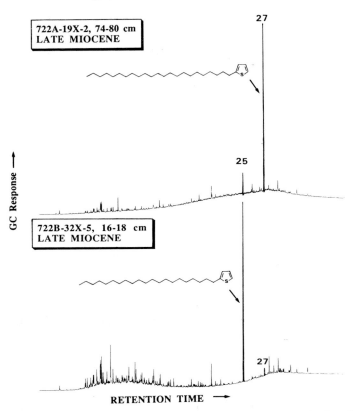

Fig. 10. Partial gas chromatograms of the 'aromatic hydrocarbon' fraction of two samples from Site 722, Owen Ridge. The structures of the C_{25} and C_{27} 2-alkylthiophenes are presented.

partial gas chromatogram in Fig. 11. In the Peruvian sediments only the C_{44} and C_{46} members are present. Again no natural precursors are known and the origin remains unclear at the moment. In the same sample shown in Fig. 11 a thienylhopanoid is indicated. This compound is found in most sediments and is ascribed to sulphur incorporation into bacteriohopanetetrol (Valisolalao *et al.* 1984).

Conclusions

The sediments recovered from areas underlying present-day active upwelling cells all have elevated organic-carbon contents, indicating that such environments are favourable for the accumulation and preservation of organic matter and that such sediments can be modern analogues of black shales. From bulk parameters, optical characterization and molecular organic geochemical data on extractable lipids we infer a predominantly marine origin (including bacterial) for the organic matter with variable admixtures of a terrigenous component. At Site

658, offshore Northwest Africa, the highest relative contribution of terrigenous organic matter was found.

The extractable and GC-amenable lipids are composed of a wide variety of organic compounds but, as noted in previous studies (Brassell & Eglinton 1983), none of these can be regarded as specific upwelling indicators. This is not surprising considering that it is not the diversity of organisms that is increased during upwelling-induced productivity, but merely the abundances of the standing crop of primary producers. However, this puts constraints on our initial intention of utilizing biological markers to discern whether the productivity model or the stagnation model is the cause for the formation of organic-carbon-rich marine sediments. To this end, the log-log plot of C_{org} versus sedimentation rate, as proposed by Stein (1986*a*, *b*) seems to be better applicable.

Quantitative analyses of selected specific biological markers reveals strong variations in their concentration, which are not parallelled to a

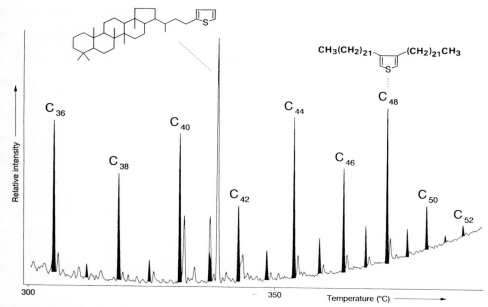

Fig. 11. Partial high-temperature gas chromatogram of Sample 117-723B-41X-2, 50–53 cm (Oman margin, 383 mbsf) showing the distribution of 3,4-dialkylthiophenes (shaded black) and the relative abundance of a thienylhopanoid. The structures of the latter compound and of the C_{48} member of the 3,4-dialkylthiophenes are indicated.

similar extent by variations in the organic carbon content. Provided that accurate sedimentation rates are known and that the amount of organic matter of marine origin can be estimated, variations in the organic carbon content can be interpreted and related to changes in the primary productivity. Similarly, variations in the absolute concentration of specific organic compounds may be used to indicate changes in the productivity of certain primary producers, if they possess a source specific biological marker (e.g. dinoflagellate blooms *vs.* prymnesiophyte blooms). With the reservation that we have not carried out a high resolution sampling like McCaffrey *et al.* (1990), and that, hence, our samples contain the sedimentary expression of upwelling averaged over a minimum of fifty years up to a thousand years per sample (depending on the sedimentation rate), in the case of prymnesiophyte algae we can still identify periods of increased abundance. Clearly quantitative analyses of biological markers bear important connotations for palaeoceanographic studies, but a full interpretation is still hampered by our scant knowledge of the possible lipid composition of appropriate organisms and basic questions such as: how much of the organic matter of dinoflagellates is represented by dinosterol, and what is the degradation rate of

individual organic compounds? An additional problem in the application of free extractable lipids as palaeoenvironmental indicators is that the efficiency of quenching on labile lipids by inorganic sulphur species (a process definitely occurring in the environments discussed herein) and the extent of this process, are not yet fully quantitated. Recently, Kohnen *et al.* (1991) have shown that, for a recent Peruvian sediment, certain hydrocarbon biological markers are quenched to such an extent that they occur almost totally in a sulphur-bound mode. The efficiency of this natural sulphurization process towards other classes of lipid compounds is, however, still unknown. The importance for understanding this is clear, because the strongest variations between the different upwelling areas are found, next to the differences in distribution of alkanediols, in the free occurring organic sulphur compounds.

Samples were obtained through the assistance of the international Ocean Drilling Program. P. F., G. E., and H. L. t. H. thank the Ocean Drilling Program for inviting them to participate onboard the *JOIDES Resolution* on Legs 108, 112, and 117, respectively. The help of Dr. R. Stein in the collection of some of the data is gratefully acknowledged. This research was financially supported by the Deutsche Forschungsgemeinschaft (grant We 346/27), the

Natural Environment Research Council (grants GR3/
2951, GR3/3758, GR3/5957, GR3/02/247) and by the
Netherlands Organization for Scientific Research. We
gratefully acknowledge the support by numerous
persons from the technical staff at Jülich, Bristol and
Delft.

References

VAN ANDEL, T. H., HEATH, J. R. & MOORE, T. C.
1975. *Cenozoic history and paleoceanography of
the central equatorial Pacific.* Geological Society
of America, Memoir **140**.

ARTHUR, M. A., DEAN, W. E. & STOW, D. A. V.
1984. Models for the deposition of Mesozoic-
Cenozoic fine-grained organic-carbon-rich sedi-
ments in the deep sea. *In*: STOW, D. A. V. &
PIPER, D. J. W. (eds) *Fine-Grained Sediments:
Deep-Water Processes and Facies.* Geological
Society, London, Special Publication, **15**
527–560.

BOON, J. J., RIJPSTRA, W. I. C., DE LANGE, F., DE
LEEUW, J. W., YOSHIOKA, M. & SHIMUZU, Y.
1979. Black Sea sterol — a molecular fossil for
dinoflagellate blooms. *Nature*, **277**, 125–127.

BRASSELL, S. C. & EGLINTON, G. 1983. The potential
of organic geochemical compounds as sedimentary indicators of upwelling. *In*: SUESS, E. &
THIEDE, J. (eds) *Coastal Upwelling: Its Sedimentary Record, Part A*, Plenum, New York,
545–571.

——, —— & HOWELL, V. J. 1987. Palaeoenviron-
mental assessment of marine organic-rich sedi-
ments using molecular organic geochemistry. *In*:
BROOKS, J. & FLEET, A. J. (eds) *Marine Petroleum
Source Rocks.* Geological Society, London,
Special Publication, **26**, 79–98.

——, ——, MARLOWE, I. T., PLAUMANN, U. &
SARNTHEIN, M. 1986*a*. Molecular stratigraphy: a
new tool for climatic assessment. *Nature*, **320**,
129–133.

——, LEWIS, C. A., DE LEEUW, J. W., DE LANGE, F.
& SINNINGHE DAMSTÉ, J. S. 1986*b*. Isoprenoid
thiophenes: novel products of sediment diagenesis? *Nature*, **320**, 160–162.

CORNER, E. D. S., O'HARA, S. C. M., NEAL, A. C. &
EGLINTON, G. 1986. Copepod faecal pellets and
the vertical flux of biolipids. *In*: CORNER,
E. D. S. & O'HARA, S. C. M. (eds) *The Bio-
logical Chemistry of Marine Copepods*, Science
Publications, Oxford, 260–321.

CRANWELL, P. A. & VOLKMAN, J. K. 1981. Alkyl and
steryl esters in a recent lacustrine sediment.
Chemical Geology, **32**, 29–43.

DEAN, W. E. & GARDNER, J. V. 1982. Origin and
geochemistry of redox cycles of Jurassic to
Eocene age, Cape Verde Basin (DSDP Site 367),
continental margin off Northwest Africa. *In*:
SCHLANGER, S. O. & CITA, M. B. (eds) *Nature
and Origin of Cretaceous Carbon-Rich Facies.*
Academic, London, 55–78.

DEGENS, E. T. & MOPPER, K. 1976. Factors controlling
the distribution and early diagenesis of organic
material in marine sediments. *In*: RILEY, J. P. &

CHESTER, R. (eds) *Chemical Oceanography*, **6**,
59–113. Academic, New York.

DEMAISON, G. J. 1991. Anoxia vs. productivity: what
controls the formation of organic-carbon-rich
sediments and sedimentary rocks: Discussion.
AAPG Bulletin, **75**, 498–499.

—— & MOORE, G. T. 1980. Anoxic environments
and oil source bed genesis. *Organic Geochemistry*, **2**, 9–31.

EGLINTON, G. & HAMILTON, R. J. 1963. The distribution of alkanes. *In*: SWAIN, T. (ed.) *Chemical
Plant Taxonomy*, 187–208. Academic, London.

FARRIMOND, P., POYNTER, J. G. & EGLINTON, G.
1990*a*. Molecular composition of sedimentary
lipids off the Peru margin, Leg 112. *In*: SUESS,
E., VON HUENE, R. *et al.* (eds) *Proceedings of
Ocean Drilling Program, Scientific Results*, Ocean
Drilling Program, College Station, TX, **112**,
539–546.

——, —— & —— 1990*b*. A molecular stratigraphic
study of Peru margin sediments, Hole 686B, Leg
112. *In*: SUESS, E., VON HUENE, R. *et al.* (eds)
*Proceedings of Ocean Drilling Program, Scientific
Results*, Ocean Drilling Program, College
Station, TX, **112**, 547–553.

FISHER, A. G. & ARTHUR, M. A. 1977. Secular variations in the pelagic realm. *In*: COOK, H. E. &
ENOS, P. (eds) *Deep Water Carbonate Environments.* Society of Economic Paleontologists and
Mineralogists, Special Publication, **25**, 19–50.

GAGOSIAN, R. B., VOLKMAN, J. K. & NIGRELLI, G. E.
1983*a*. The use of sediment traps to determine
sterols sources in coastal sediments off Peru. *In*:
BJORØY *et al.* (eds) *Advances in Organic Geochemistry 1981*, Wiley, Chichester, 369–379.

——, NIGRELLI, G. E. & VOLKMAN, J. K. 1983*b*.
Vertical transport and transformation of biogenic
compounds from a sediment trap experiment off
the coast of Peru. *In*: SUESS, E. & THIEDE, J.
(eds) *Coastal Upwelling. Its Sedimentary Record,
Part A*, Plenum, New York. pp 241–272.

GOTH, K., DE LEEUW, J. W., PÜTTMANN, W. &
TEGELAAR, E. W. 1988. Origin of Messel oil shale
kerogen. *Nature*, **336**, 759–761.

DE GRACIANSKY, P. C., DEROO, G., HERBIN,
J. P., MONTADERT, L., MÜLLER, C., SCHAAF, A.
& SIGAL, J. 1984. Ocean-wide stagnation episode
in the late Cretaceous. *Nature*, **308**, 346–349.

TEN HAVEN, H. L. & KROON, D. 1991. Late Pleistocene
surface water temperature variations off Oman
as revealed by the distribution of long-chain alkenones. *In*: PRELL, W. L., NIITSUMA, N. *et al.*
(eds) *Proceedings of Ocean Drilling Program,
Scientific Results.* Ocean Drilling Program, College Station, TX, **117**, 445–452.

——, LITTKE, R., RULLKÖTTER, J., STEIN, R. & WELTE,
D. H. 1990*a*. Accumulation rates and compo-
sition of organic matter in late Cenozoic sedi-
ments underlying the active upwelling area off
Peru. *In*: SUESS, E., VON HUENE, R. *et al.* (eds)
*Proceedings of Ocean Drilling Program, Scientific
Results*, Ocean Drilling Program, College
Station, TX, **112**, 591–606.

—— & RULLKÖTTER, J. 1991. Preliminary lipid analyses of sediments recovered during Leg 117. *In*:

PRELL, W. L., NIITSUMA, N. *et al*. (eds) *Proceedings of Ocean Drilling Program, Scientific Results*, Ocean Drilling Program, College Station, TX, **117**, 561–569.

——, —— & STEIN, R. 1989. Preliminary analysis of extractable lipids in sediments from the eastern North Atlantic (Leg 108): Comparison of a coastal upwelling area (Site 658) with a nonupwelling area (Site 659). *In*: RUDDIMAN, W., SARNTHEIN, M. *et al*. (eds) *Proceedings of Ocean Drilling Program, Scientific Results*, Ocean Drilling Program, College Station, TX, **108**, 351–360.

——, ——, SINNINGHE DAMSTÉ, J. S. & DE LEEUW, J. W. 1990b. Distribution of organic sulfur compounds in Mesozoic and Cenozoic sediments from the Atlantic and Pacific Ocean and the Gulf of California. *In*: ORR, W. L. & WHITE, C. M. (eds) *Geochemistry of Sulfur in Fossil Fuels*. ACS Symposium Series, **429**, 613–632.

HERBIN, J. P., MONTADERT, L., MÜLLER, C., GOMET, R., THUROW, J. & WIEDMANN, F. 1986. Organic-rich sedimentation at the Cenomanian-Turonian boundary in oceanic and coastal basins in the North Atlantic and Tethys. *In*: SUMMERHAYES, C. P. & SHACKLETON, N. J. (eds) *North Atlantic Palaeoceanography*. Geological Society, London, Special Publication, **22**, 377–387.

KOHNEN, M. E. L., SINNINGHE DAMSTÉ, J. S., TEN HAVEN, H. L. & DE LEEUW, J. W. 1989. Early incorporation of polysulphides in sedimentary organic matter. *Nature*, **341**, 640–641.

——, —— & DE LEEUW, J. W. 1991. Biases from natural sulphurization in palaeoenvironmental reconstruction based on hydrocarbon biomarker distributions. *Nature*, **349**, 775–778.

——, PEAKMAN, T. M., SINNINGHE DAMSTÉ, J. S. & DE LEEUW, J. W. 1990. Identification and occurrence of novel C_{36}-C_{54} 3,4-dialkylthiophenes with an unusual carbon skeleton in immature sediments. *In*: DURAND, B. & BEHAR, F. (eds) *Advances in Organic Geochemistry 1989. Organic Geochemistry*, **16**, 1103–1113.

DE LEEUW, J. W., RIJPSTRA, W. I. C., BOON, J. J., DE LANGE, F. & SCHENCK, P. A. 1977. The relationship between lipids from *Fontinalis antipyretica*, its detritus and the underlying sediment.: the fate of wax esters and sterol esters. *In*: GOLTERMAN, H. L. (ed.) *Interactions between Sediments and Fresh Water*, Junk B. V., Den Haag, 141–147.

——, —— & SCHENCK, P. A. 1981. The occurrence and identification of C_{30}, C_{31} and C_{32} alkan-1,15-diols and alkan-15-one-1-ols in Unit I and Unit II Black Sea sediments. *Geochimica et Cosmochimica Acta*, **45**, 2281–2285.

MARLOWE, I. T. 1984. *Lipids as Palaeoclimatic Indicators*. PhD Thesis, University of Bristol.

——, BRASSELL, S. C., EGLINTON, G. & GREEN, J. C. 1984. Long-chain unsaturated ketones and esters in living algae and marine sediments. *In*: SCHENCK, P. A., DE LEEUW, J. W. & LIJMBACH, G. W. M. (eds) *Advances in Organic Geochemistry 1983. Organic Geochemistry*, **6**, 135–141.

MCCAFFREY, M. A., FARRINGTON, J. W. & REPETA, D. J. 1990. The organic geochemistry of Peru margin surface sediments: I. A comparison of the C_{37} alkenone and historical El Nino records. *Geochimica et Cosmochimica Acta*, **54**, 1671–1682.

——, —— & —— 1991. The organic geochemistry of Peru margin surface sediments: II. Paleoenvironmental implications of hydrocarbon and alcohol profiles. *Geochimica et Cosmochimica Acta*, **55**, 483–498.

MELLO, M. R., GAGLIANONE, P. C., BRASSELL, S. C. & MAXWELL, J. R. 1988. Geochemical and biological marker assessment of depositional environments using Brazilian offshore oils. *Marine and Petroleum Geology*, **5**, 205–223.

MIDDELBURG, J. J. 1989. A simple rate model for organic matter decomposition in marine sediments. *Geochimica et Cosmochimica Acta*, **53**, 1577–1581.

MORRIS, R. J. & BRASSELL, S. C. 1988. Long-chain alkanediols: biological markers for cyanobacterial contributions to sediments. *Lipids*, **23**, 256–258.

MOSSMAN, J. R., APLIN, A. C., CURTIS, C. D. & COLEMAN, M. L. 1990. Sulfur geochemistry at Sites 680 and 686 on the Peru margin. *In*: SUESS, E., VON HUENE, R. *et al*. (eds) *Proceedings of Ocean Drilling Program, Scientific Results*. Ocean Drilling Program, College Station, TX, **112**, 455–464.

PARRISH, J. T. 1982. Upwelling and petroleum source beds with reference to Paleozoic. *AAPG Bulletin*, **66**, 750–774.

PEDERSEN, T. F. & CALVERT, S. E. 1990. Anoxia vs. productivity: what controls the formation of organic-carbon-rich sediments and sedimentary rocks. *AAPG Bulletin*, **74**, 454–466.

PEDERSEN, T. F. & CALVERT, S. E. 1991. Anoxia vs. productivity: what controls the formation of organic-carbon-rich sediments and sedimentary rocks: Reply. *AAPG Bulletin*, **75**, 500–501.

POWELL, T. G. 1986. Petroleum geochemistry and depositional settings of lacustrine source rocks. *Marine and Petroleum Geology*, **3**, 200–219.

POYNTER, J. G. & EGLINTON, G. 1991. The biomarker concept. Strengths and weaknesses. *Fresenius Journal of Analytical Chemistry*, **339**, 725–7.

——, FARRIMOND, P., BRASSELL, S. C. & EGLINTON G. 1989. Molecular stratigraphic study of sediments from Holes 658A and 660A, Leg 108. *In*: RUDDIMAN, W., SARNTHEIN, M. *et al*. (eds) *Proceedings of Ocean Drilling Program, Scientific Results*. Ocean Drilling Program, College Station, TX, **108**, 387–394.

PRAHL, F. G. & MUELHAUSEN, L. A. 1989. Lipid biomarkers as geochemical tools for paleo oceanographic study. *In*: BERGER, W. H., SMETACEH, V. & WEFER, D. (eds) *Productivity of the Ocean. Present and Past*, Wiley, New York, 271–284.

——, —— & ZAHNLE, D. L. 1988. Further evaluation of long-chain alkenones as indicators of paleoceanographic conditions. *Geochimica et Cosmochimica Acta*, **52**, 2303–2310.

——, DE LANGE, G. J., LYLE, M. & SPARROW, M. A. 1989. Postdepositional stability of long-chain alkenones under contrasting redox conditions. *Nature*, **341**, 434–437.

—— & WAKEHAM, S. G. 1987. Calibration of unsaturation patterns in long-chain ketone compositions for palaeotemperature assessment. *Nature*, **330**, 367–369.

PRELL, W. L. & KUTZBACH, J. E. 1987. Monsoon variability over the past 150 000 years. *Journal of Geophysical Research*, **92**, 8411–8425.

——, NIITSUMA, N. *et al.* 1990. *Proceedings of Ocean Drilling Program, Scientific Results*. Ocean Drilling Program, College Station, TX, **117**.

REIMERS, C. E. & SUESS, E. 1983. Spatial and temporal patterns of organic matter accumulation on the Peru continental margin. *In*: THIEDE, J. & SUESS, E. (eds) *Coastal Upwelling. Its Sediment Record, Part B*, Plenum Press, New York, 311–345.

ROBINSON, N., EGLINTON, G., CRANWELL, P. A. & ZENG, Y. B. 1989. Messel oil shale (western Germany): assessment of depositional palaeoenvironment from the content of biological marker compounds. *Chemical Geology*, **76**, 153–173.

RUDDIMAN, W., SARNTHEIN, M. *et al.* 1989. *Proceedings of Ocean Drilling Program, Scientific Results*. Ocean Drilling Program, College Station, TX, **108**.

RULLKÖTTER, J., CORNFORD, C. & WELTE, D. H. 1982. Geochemistry and petrography of organic matter in Northwest African continental margin sediments: Quantity, provenance, depositional environment and temperature history. *In*: VON RAD, U. *et al.* (eds) *Geology of the Northwest African Continental Margin*. Springer, Heidelberg, 686–703.

SCHLANGER, S. O. & JENKYNS, H. C. 1976. Cretaceous anoxic events: causes and consequences. *Geologie en Mijnbouw*, **55**, 179–184.

SIKES, E. L., FARRINGTON, J. W. & KEIGWIN, L. D. 1991. Use of the alkenone ratio U^k_{37} to determine past sea surface temperatures: core top SST calibrations and methodology considerations. *Earth and Planetary Science Letters*, **104**, 36–47.

SIMONEIT, B. R. T. 1978. The organic geochemistry of marine sediments. *In*: RILEY, J. P. & CHESTER, R. (eds) *Chemical Oceanography*, Academic, London, **7**, 233–311.

SINNINGHE DAMSTÉ, J. S. & DE LEEUW, J. W. 1990. Analysis, structure and geochemical significance of organically-bound sulphur in the geosphere: state of the art and future research. *In*: DURAND, B. & BEHAR, F. (eds) *Advances in Organic Geochemistry 1989. Organic Geochemistry*, **16**, 1077–1101.

——, RIJPSTRA, W. I. C., KOCK-VAN DALEN, A. C., DE LEEUW, J. W. & SCHENCK, P. A. 1989. Quenching of labile functionalised lipids by inorganic sulphur species: Evidence for the formation of sedimentary organic sulphur compounds at the early stages of diagenesis. *Geochimica et Cosmochimica Acta*, **53**, 1343–1355.

STEIN, R. 1986*a*. Surface-water paleoproductivity as inferred from sediments of the Mesozoic Atlantic

Ocean. *In*: DEGENS, E. T., BRASSELL, S. C. & MEYERS, P. (eds) *The Biogeochemistry of Black shales. Mitteilungen Geologisches und Palaeontologisches Institute Universität Hamburg*, **60**, 55–70.

—— 1986*b*. Organic carbon and sedimentation rate — Further evidence for anoxic deep-water conditions in the Cenomanian/Turonian Atlantic Ocean. *Marine Geology*, **72**, 199–209.

——, RULLKÖTTER, J. & WELTE, D. H. 1986. Accumulation of organic-carbon-rich sediments in the late Jurassic and Cretaceous Atlantic Ocean — A synthesis. *Chemical Geology*, **56**, 1–32.

——, —— & —— 1989*a*. Changes in palaeoenvironments in the Atlantic Ocean during Cretaceous times: Results from black shale studies. *Geologische Rundschau*, **78**, 883–901.

——, TEN HAVEN, H. L., LITTKE, R., RULLKÖTTER, J. & WELTE, D. H. 1989*b*. Accumulation of marine and terrigenous organic carbon at upwelling Site 658 and nonupwelling Sites 657 and 659: Implications for the reconstruction of paleoenvironments in the eastern subtropical Atlantic through late Cenozoic times. *In*: RUDDIMAN, W., SARNTHEIN, M. *et al.* (eds) *Proceedings of Ocean Drilling Program, Scientific Results*. Ocean Drilling Program, College Station, TX, **108**, 361–385.

Shipboard Scientific Party, 1989. Site 723. *In*: PRELL, W. L., NIITSUMA, N. *et al.* (eds) *Proceedings of Ocean Drilling Program, Initial Reports*, Ocean Drilling Program, College Station, TX, **117**, 319–384.

SUESS, E., VON HUENE, R. *et al.* 1991. *Proceedings of Ocean Drilling Program, Scientific Results*. Ocean Drilling Program, College Station, TX, **112**.

THIEDE, J. & VAN ANDEL, T. H. 1977. The paleoenvironment of anaerobic sediments in the late Mesozoic South Atlantic Ocean. *Earth and Planetary Science Letters*, **33**, 301–309.

VALISOLALAO, J., PERAKIS, N., CHAPPE, B. & ALBRECHT, P. 1984. A novel sulphur containing C_{35} hopanoid in sediments. *Tetrahedron Letters*, **25**, 1183–1186.

VOLKMAN, J. K. 1986. A review of sterol markers for marine and terrigenous organic matter. *Organic Geochemistry*, **9**, 83–99.

——, EGLINTON, G., CORNER, E. D. S. & SARGENT, J. R. 1980. Novel unsaturated straight chain C_{37}–C_{39} methyl and ethylketones in marine sediments and a coccolithophore *Emiliania huxleyi*. *In*: DOUGLAS, A. G. & MAXWELL, J. R. (eds) *Advances in Organic Geochemistry 1979*, Pergamon, Oxford, 219–228.

——, FARRINGTON, J. W. & GAGOSIAN, R. B. 1987. Marine and terrigenous lipids in coastal sediments from the Peru upwelling region at 15°S: Sterols and triterpene alcohols. *Organic Geochemistry*, **11**, 463–477.

WESTRICH, G. T. & BERNER, R. A. 1984. The role of sedimentary organic matter in bacterial sulfate reduction: the G model tested. *Limnology and Oceanography*, **29**, 236–249.

Carbon/sulphur/iron relationships in upwelling sediments

JOHN W. MORSE[1] & KAY C. EMEIS[2]

[1] *Department of Oceanography, Texas A&M University, College Station, Texas 77843, USA*

[2] *Geologisch-Paläontologisches Institut, Universität Kiel, Olshausenstrasse 40, 2300 Kiel, Germany*

Abstract: Carbon/sulphur/iron relationships in sediments from beneath three upwelling areas (Benguela, Peru and Oman) were investigated using DSDP and ODP cores. The three areas displayed markedly different C/S/Fe characteristics. Metabolizable organic matter appears to limit production of reduced sulphur in the Benguela upwelling area sediments, as evidenced by incomplete reduction of dissolved sulphate. On the Peru shelf infusion of a sulphate-containing brine at depth has a major influence on diagenesis.

Weight ratios of organic carbon to reduced inorganic sulphur are generally higher in sediments from upwelling areas than in normal marine sediments. C/S ratios generally increase with increasing organic carbon concentration in upwelling sediments. This does not appear to be the result of limited availability of reactive iron. Both carbon and reduced sulphur accumulation rates are well correlated with sediment accumulation rates, but are higher than in non-upwelling sediments having similar accumulation rates.

C/S/Fe relationships in sediments have gained increasing use as paleoenvironmental indicators (e.g. Berner 1982; Davis *et al.* 1988). One of the most important applications has been to use these relationships to distinguish between depositional environments overlain by oxic and euxinic waters. In 'normal' marine (i.e. clastic sediments overlain by oxic waters with a typical ocean salinity) coastal sediments, positive correlations are found between TRS and organic carbon concentrations (e.g. Berner 1982; Berner & Raiswell 1983) and the C/S ratio is typically about 2.8 ± 0.8 (e.g. Berner 1984). The availability of metabolizable organic matter is generally the limiting factor for production of reduced sulphur in these sediments where it is dominantly retained as pyrite (e.g. Berner 1970, 1984). In euxinic environments, such as the Black Sea, where sulphide is present in bottom waters, pyrite can form in the water column and H_2S can be supplied to these sediments from overlying waters. This often results in lower than normal C/S ratios in such sediments (e.g. Raiswell & Berner 1985) and the availability of 'reactive' iron may limit pyrite formation (e.g. Raiswell 1982; Raiswell & Berner 1985; Raiswell *et al.* 1988).

Hemipelagic sediments in areas of oceanic upwelling typically have significantly higher organic carbon concentrations than most marine sediments. Consequently, it is possible that the abundance of metabolizable organic carbon may not be depleted when the limit of sulphide mineral formation is reached in these sediments and other factors, such as the availability of reactive iron, may control C/S ratios. C/S ratios in sediments from beneath upwelling areas may, therefore, deviate from the ratio that is characteristic of most other marine sediments. To test this hypothesis, we have selected sediments from three widely separated areas where upwelling and associated high oceanic productivity result in deposition of organic-rich sediments.

Study sites

Only a brief summary will be presented of the most pertinent characteristics of the sediments used for this study because extensive information is available in the associated DSDP (Hay, Sibuet *et al.* 1984) and ODP (Suess, von Huene *et al.* 1988; Prell, Niitsuma *et al.* 1989) Initial Report volumes.

The sediments studied from beneath the Benguela upwelling area were obtained at Site 532 of DSDP Leg 75 (19°33.61'S, 10°31.13'E). This site is located on the eastern part of the Walvis Ridge on the Southwest African continental margin at a water depth of 1331 m. The dominant lithology is hemipelagic calcareous and siliceous biogenic ooze that accumulated at rates between 25 and 50 m/Ma and exhibits pronounced dark–light cyclicity on a scale of metres. The opal-rich upper Pliocene sediment is characterized by a peak in TOC concentrations of up to 8.65 wt%. The increase in

From Summerhayes, C. P., Prell, W. L. & Emeis, K. C. (eds), 1992, *Upwelling Systems: Evolution Since the Early Miocene*. Geological Society Special Publication No 64, pp 247–255.

247

diatoms and TOC in the upper Pliocene reflects an increase in primary productivity and a strengthening of the Benguela upwelling system (Meyers et al. 1983, 1984). The sediments are thoroughly bioturbated indicating oxic conditions in the overlying water. Samples were selected to cover light—dark cycles in all age units.

Oman margin sediments were collected at Site 723 of ODP Leg 117 (18°03.079′N, 57°36.561′E) that was drilled in water 808 m deep in the Arabian Sea upwelling area. Uppermost Pliocene to Holocene sediments are composed of foraminifer-bearing nannofossil oozes to calcareous clayey silts. The sedimentation rate is high throughout the section (130 to 240 m/Ma) and reflects variability in eolian and biogenic input due to changes in the strength of the monsoon (Prell, Niitsuma et al. 1989). Abundance of TOC and the occurrence of laminations in intervals of latest Pliocene to early Pleistocene age suggest that bottom-water oxygen contents were low and precluded bioturbation. Because our primary interest is in marine sediments overlain by oxic waters, only bioturbated Pleistocene sediments deposited under oxic conditions are considered in this paper.

The sediments investigated on the Peru margin are from sites 680 and 688 of ODP Leg 112. Site 680 (11°03.90′S, 78°04.67′W) is located on the upper Peruvian slope at a depth of 263 m. The sediments studied were from the Quaternary lithologic Unit I that is dominantly composed of foraminifer-diatom mud with occasional shell-rich beds and graded sand and silt layers. A striking feature at this site is the occurrence of a hypersaline subsurface brine. This brine has a major influence on diagenesis that considerably complicates interpretation of C/S/Fe relationships, as will be subsequently discussed.

Site 688 (11°32.26′S, 78°56.57′W) is located on the lower continental slope at a water depth of 3820 m. The presence of turbidites indicates that at least some of the material was resuspended on the shelf and upper slope and has been redeposited. Organic-carbon-rich diatomaceous oozes and muds accumulated throughout the Pleistocene and Holocene. Calcium carbonate content in these sediments is typically less than 10 wt% and biogenic silica is generally less than ~5 wt%, but reaches close to 24 wt% in some sections. Older sediments (Eocene to Pliocene) are less organic-carbon-rich, contain more clastic components, and are coarser-grained. Because our interest is in organic-rich sediments, we have confined our

study to lithologic Unit I which is of Holocene to Pleistocene age. It is composed of bioturbated diatomaceous mud indicating that the sediments were deposited under oxic conditions.

Methods and data

Details of the analytical methods and tables containing analytical results are given in Emeis & Morse (1990) and Emeis et al. (1991). Here we will present only particularly salient points and definitions of terms.

The method for determining abundances of total inorganic reduced sulphur (TRS) follows Zhabina et al. (1978), as modified by Canfield et al. (1986). This method is specific for inorganic sulphur and does not include organic sulphur, which is generally a minor fraction of the total reduced sulphur. We interpret TRS and pyrite-S as being equivalent.

The 'reactive' iron fraction is the fraction of total iron available for participation in chemical reactions under diagenetic conditions. It is used in conjunction with pyrite concentrations to obtain the degree of pyritization (DOP). This is useful in assessing the fraction of the reactive iron which has been converted to pyrite (Berner 1970) and is given as

$$DOP = \frac{Pyrite_{Fe}}{Pyrite_{Fe} + Reactive_{Fe}}$$

where $Pyrite_{Fe}$ is generally well approximated as 0.5 TRS (in molar units), based on the molar ratio of iron and sulphur in pyrite.

We have chosen 1N HCl leachable iron (80 to 1 solution to solid ratio extracted for 12 h) to represent a reasonable and conservative approximation of the 'reactive' iron fraction. Recent work by Levanthal & Taylor (1990) indicates that this is probably the best method for determination of reactive iron in non-Recent sediments.

Sediment burial rates, where not given in the respective ODP and DSDP volumes, were calculated according to palaeontological age models, average porosities and wet bulk densities for each interval, a density of seawater of 1.025, and average TOC and TRS for each interval.

Results

TOC concentrations are highly variable at each site (Fig. 1) and range from less than 0.5 to over 12 wt%. Sediments from the Benguela upwelling area and the deep (3820 m) Peru Site (688) had similar average TOC concentrations of 4.0

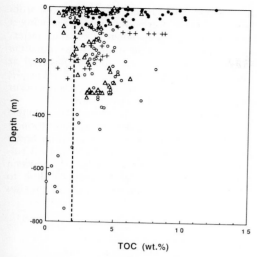

Fig. 1. TOC at the Benguela (+), Oman (△), Peru 680 Site (●) and Peru 688 Site (○). Dashed line is 2 wt% TOC.

and 3.7 wt%, respectively. TOC in sediments from the Oman Margin averaged slightly lower (2.9 wt%) and the shallow (250 m) Peru Site (680) had the highest average TOC concentration of 4.9 wt%.

Profiles of TRS (Fig. 2) scatter widely but exhibit no consistent trends with depth at any site. This is consistent with the assumption that pyrite forms mainly in near-surface sediments

(e.g. Goldhaber *et al.* 1977), even though sulphate reduction and pyrite formation continue deeper. Average TRS concentrations are 0.87, 0.41, 0.97 and 0.87 wt%, respectively, at the Benguela, Oman, and Peru 680 and 688 sites.

C/S weight ratios in the sediments also exhibit a wide scatter, with particularly high values occurring in the upper 100 mbsf (metres below sea floor) of the samples from the Oman Margin. The average C/S ratios (average C concentration to average S concentration) for sediments below the zone of apparent active sulphate reduction are 3.3 (±1.6 SD), 6.2 (±2.8) and 4.6 (±1.9) for the Benguela, Oman, and Peru 688 sites, respectively. As will be discussed later, sulphate reduction appears to be active throughout the Peru 680 sediments, and a similar comparison is consequently not possible. The overall average C/S ratio there is 5.1. The average C/S ratios for the Benguela upwelling and Peru (Site 688) Margin sites are about 1.2 and 1.6 times, respectively, that of normal marine sediments (2.8 ± 0.8, Berner & Raiswell 1983), whereas the average C/S ratio at the Oman Margin site is about 2.2 times higher. However, the large standard deviations in the data sets result in a significant statistical overlap.

We were not able to determine DOP on all samples due to limits of sample size. However, DOP was determined throughout most depth intervals (Fig. 3). DOP values generally range between 0.2 and 0.6, never exceeding 0.73 at all sites except for Peru Site 680. DOP values of

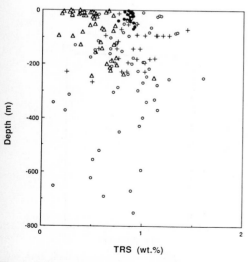

Fig. 2. TRS at the Benguela (+), Oman (△), Peru 680 Site (●) and Peru 688 Site (○).

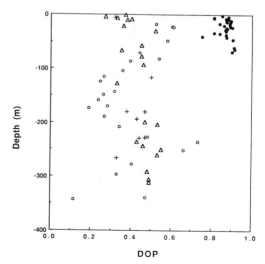

Fig. 3. DOP at the Benguela (+), Oman (△), Peru 680 Site (●) and Peru 688 Site (○).

0.5 or less are typical of most fine-grained clastic sediments in which reactive iron is generally not considered limiting for pyrite formation. We, therefore, interpret these results as indicating that reactive iron was probably not limiting for pyrite formation in these sediments. At Peru Site 680, DOP averages 0.87 and iron may limit pyrite formation in these sediments.

The relationship between organic carbon flux to sediments and sulphate reduction rates is largely independent of the availability of reactive iron to form iron sulphide minerals from the H_2S that is produced as a result of bacterial sulphate reduction. It is consequently reasonable to expect that nearly total reduction

of sulphate should occur in sediments from beneath highly productive waters receiving a relatively large supply of marine organic matter, as is characteristic of the sediments examined in this investigation. This is indeed observed at Oman Margin and Peru Site 688 (see Fig. 4), but complete sulphate reduction does not occur at the Benguela and Peru 680 sites.

At the Benguela site, between about 50 mbsf to approximately 100 mbsf the concentration of dissolved sulphate decreases in a nearly linear manner; at greater depths, the dissolved sulphate concentration varies irregularly between 5 to 10 mM over a depth range of close to 200 m. At Peru Site 680, dissolved sulphate de-

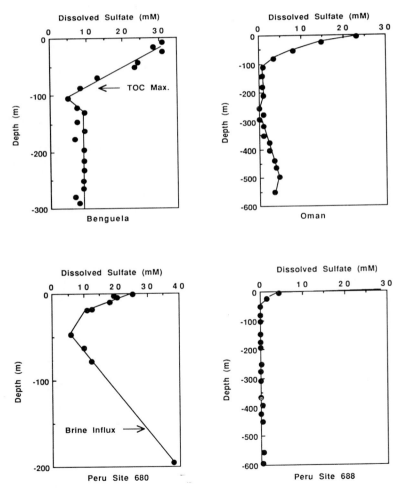

Fig. 4. Dissolved sulphate depth distributions at the sites studied. Dissolved sulfate data for these sites was obtained from Gieskes *et al.* (1984), Prell *et al.* (1989) and Suess *et al.* (1988) Benguela (+), Oman (△), Peru 680 Site (●) and Peru 688 Site (○).

creases to 6 mM at 48 mbsf and then increases with increasing depth due to the influx of a sulphate bearing brine.

Discussion

The summary of results of this study indicate that carbon and reduced sulphur relationships in sediments from major centres of coastal upwelling exhibit significant differences from normal marine sediments (e.g. Berner 1970, 1984) and have local characteristics. The most important differences exist in sulphate concentration gradients, average TOC concentrations and C/S ratios. Examination of possible reasons for these differences is of importance for understanding variability in the carbon–sulphur system of hemipelagic sediments underlying upwelling regions and their general relationship with marine sediments from regions of lower biological productivity.

C/S relationships

We do not note a strong relationship between TOC and TRS (Fig. 5). However, if the sediments are grouped according to organic carbon range (<2, 2–3, >3 wt%) trends in average C/S ratios from beneath the zone of apparent active sulphate reduction are evident (Fig. 6). Sediments from Peru Margin Site 680 do not fit this trend pattern because of possible iron limitation and the complex behaviour of dis-

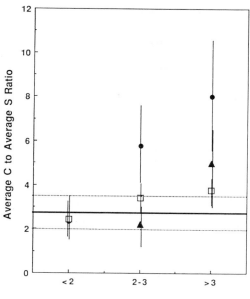

Fig. 6. A plot of the average C/S ratios for three different ranges in TOC concentration. Solid horizontal line is average C/S ratio for normal marine sediments and dotted horizontal line is the standard deviation for these sediments. Solid vertical lines are one standard deviation for C/S ratios. (■) Benguela; (▲) Peru Site 688; (●) Oman.

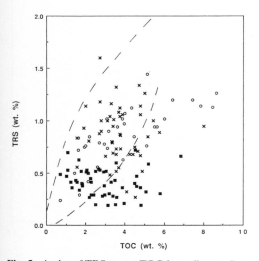

Fig. 5. A plot of TRS versus TOC for sediments from Benguela (○), Oman (■) and Peru Site 688 (×). Dashed lines are data envelope for normal marine sediments of Berner & Raiswell (1983).

solved sulphate complicate interpretation and are not included in Fig. 5. Sediments at the Benguela and Oman sites with 'normal' organic contents (i.e. <2 wt%) have an average C/S ratio close to, but slightly below, that of the average for normal marine sediments. Sediments from the Peru Site 688 do not fall into this category. Sediments with moderately high organic contents (2–3 wt%) are close to the 'normal' marine sediment average C/S ratio at Peru Site 688 and in the Benguela upwelling area. C/S ratios are about twice average in sediments from the Oman Margin.

C/S ratios in highly organic-rich sediments (>3 wt% organic carbon) from the Benguela upwelling area average about 30% higher (C/S = 3.8 ± 0.7) and from the Peru Magin about 80% (C/S = 5.0 ± 1.9) higher than those of normal marine sediments. The highly organic-rich sediments from the Oman Margin have an average C/S ratio (8.0 ± 2.5) that approaches the range generally characteristic of freshwater environments. Even at these uncharacteristically high C/S ratios for marine sediments, DOP is less than 0.4. The high C/S ratios in the

Oman Margin sediments are, therefore, probably not the result of iron-limiting pyrite formation.

Dissolved sulphate−carbon relationships

The dissolved sulphate concentration profiles (Fig. 4) provide insights into the differences in diagenetic processes at the upwelling sites studied. These profiles are dominantly the result of diffusive transport of sulphate into the sediments supplying dissolved sulphate and sulphate removal via reduction by bacteria. Given the generally high TOC concentrations dissolved sulphate would be expected to be completely and rapidly reduced based on the general observation that in near-shore sediments typically containing ~1 wt% TOC, sulphate is often completely reduced in the upper metre of sediment.

The expected distribution of dissolved sulphate is only approached at Peru Site 688. Although dissolved sulphate is completely reduced at the Oman Site, the ~100 m depth interval over which sulphate reduction occurs is large. Incomplete sulphate reduction occurs at the Benguela site and shallow Peru Site 680, indicating that organic matter is limiting for the process. At the shallow Peru Site, complete sulphate reduction would probably have occurred in the upper 100 m without the influx of additional dissolved sulphate from depth, yielding a profile similar to that observed in the Oman sediments.

Types of organic matter

Westrich et al. (1984) have demonstrated that not simply the quantity, but also the type of organic matter, determines the pool of metabolizable TOC in sediments. Therefore, a reasonable hypothesis to explain the lower sulphate gradient in the Benguela upwelling sediments is that the organic matter in these sediments is less readily metabolized than that of the other sites. This could possibly occur because the sedimentation rate is substantially lower in Benguela sediments and the organic matter is exposed to microbial attack for longer periods of time. Canfield (1989), for example, has discussed the strong correlation between the efficiency of organic matter burial and sedimentation rate (see also Müller & Suess 1979). Their results indicate that organic matter burial efficiency at the Benguela upwelling site should be only about a quarter of that of the other sites due to its probable longer exposure to oxic respiration.

Although still somewhat controversial, the organic matter Rock-Eval hydrogen index (HI; amount of hydrocarbons released during pyrolysis per gram of TOC) is gaining increased use as at least a qualitative measure of the extent of organic matter degradation (e.g. Pratt et al. 1986; Davis et al. 1988; Dean et al. 1989). The basic concept in utilizing this approach is that the more hydrogen-rich portions of the organic matter are preferentially metabolized, resulting in a decrease in the HI with increasing extent of degradation.

Figure 7 summarizes the HI data for the organic matter from all sites except Peru Site 680. Although there is considerable scatter in the data, it is clear that the HI values from the Benguela upwelling sediments are generally lower than those from the other sites. The averages for Benguela upwelling, Oman and deep Peru Margin sediments (with >2 wt% TOC) are, respectively, 291, 367 and 381. The increasing trend in the HI of these sites matches their increasing sulphate concentration gradients. In the sediments from below 100 mbsf at the Benguela upwelling site, where the dissolved sulphate concentration is close to constant, the average HI is only 238. In contrast, the Oman and Peru Margin sites have HI's in excess of 380 over a similar depth interval. The HI at the

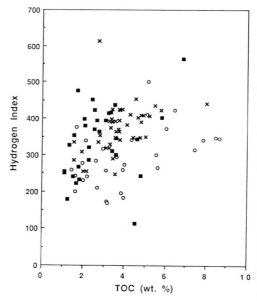

Fig. 7. The relationship between the hydrogen index and TOC in sediments from Benguela (○), Oman (■) and Peru Site 688 (×). Data from Emeis et al. (1990) and Emeis & Morse (1990).

shallow Peru site has a high average of 452 but cannot be interpreted with regard to sulphate gradients because of the influx of brine-associated sulphate. At the Benguela site, the co-existence of substantial dissolved sulphate concentrations with relatively high TOC concentrations for millions of years is certainly supportive of our hypothesis that organic matter is of a type not readily susceptible to being metabolized by sulphate-reducing bacteria.

Relation of TOC and TRS to sedimentation rates

A general correlation has been observed in TOC and TRS concentrations or accumulation rates with the rate at which sediments are deposited (e.g. Heath *et al.* 1977; Toth *et al.* 1977; Berner 1978; Müller *et al.* 1979; Berner *et al.* 1989; Canfield 1989). We will, therefore, examine the results of this study in the context of these general observations.

Logarithms of the C and S accumulation rates are plotted against the logarithms of sediment accumulation rate for the results of this study in Fig. 8, excluding Peru Site 680 for reasons previously discussed. Data from other sediments with similar accumulation rates are included from the summary of Berner & Canfield (1989) for comparison. The TOC accumulation rates in the sediments from the Peru and Oman margins are similar to, but slightly higher than, those observed in other sediments, and they are distinctly higher in the sediments from the Benguela upwelling area. Because the sediments in this study come from beneath highly productive surface waters, the observation that they have higher than normal TOC concentrations is not surprising.

The TRS accumulation rates can also be compared with those observed by Berner & Canfield for sediments with similar accumulation rates. They are about the same in the Oman Margin sediments, slightly higher in the Peru Margin sediments, and distinctly higher in the Benguela upwelling area sediments. These differences in TRS accumulation rates roughly reflect those of the TOC accumulation rates.

C/S ratios have also been plotted versus the logarithm of the sediment accumulation rates in Fig. 8C. Included in this figure is a trend line for normal marine sediments derived from the least-squares fits of the TOC and TRS data of Berner & Canfield (1989). This relation indicates that C/S ratios in normal marine sediments tend to deviate increasingly from the average C/S ratio for normal marine sediments with decreasing sediment accumulation rate indicating that the

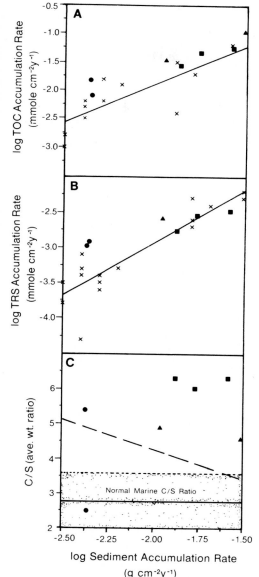

Fig. 8. The relationship of the log of the TOC accumulation rate (A) and log of the TRS accumulation rate (B), and the C/S ratio (C) to the log of the sediment accumulation rate. X's are data of Berner & Canfield (1989), and the solid line in A and B is the least-squares fit to their data over the range of sediment accumulation rates presented. In C the dashed line represents the C/S ratio derived from least-squares fits in A and B. The stippled area represents ±0.8 about the normal marine C/S ratio of 2.8. (●) Benguela; (▲) Peru Site 688; (■) Oman. Only data from below the zone of apparent sulphate reduction are shown.

C/S ratio may be dependent on sedimentation rate. However, the C/S ratios from the three upwelling sites exhibit little relationship to sediment accumulation rates and are, with one exception from Benguela, higher than would be expected.

The role of iron

When this research was initiated we hypothesized that, in the organic-rich sediments below upwelling areas, iron would be limiting for pyrite formation rather than metabolizable organic matter. However, our results indicate that generally only low to moderate DOP values are obtained in most of these sediments. At Peru Site 680 addition of sulphate via brine intrusion at depth results in high DOP values and, therefore, iron may limit pyrite formation at this site. This observation further substantiates the idea that iron is probably not limiting in the other sediments studied where low to moderate DOP values are observed.

Controls on C/S ratios

A major factor that can influence C/S ratios is the 'openness' of a system. In shelf sediments where bioturbation and bioirrigation rates are generally high, over 90% of the sulphide which is produced can be lost via transport and reoxidation (e.g. Goldhaber et al. 1977; Jørgensen 1978). Biologically mediated transport has a general tendency to decrease with increasing water depth (e.g. Berner 1980). This is a result of both the tendency of deeper sediments to have lower organic matter concentrations and the influences of temperature and pressure on biological processes.

The organic-rich sediments from the Oman Margin have anomalously high C/S ratios, even though they have the lowest average TOC concentration and reactive iron does not appear to be limiting for pyrite formation. This site is the shallowest studied and may, therefore, have the highest rates of bioturbation and bioirrigation. This could possibly result in the loss of a greater fraction of the reduced sulphur, leading to higher C/S ratios. This explanation for the observed intersite differences in C/S ratios is necessarily highly speculative, but could be tested by investigation of processes near the interfacial region of sediments in the different areas studied. It is obvious from a plot (Fig. 8) of TRS and TOC accumulation rates, however, that upwelling sediments deviate systematically from other marine sediments.

Conclusions

The hemipelagic sediments underlying productive oceanic regions from the Benguela upwelling area and Oman and Peru Margins have highly variable organic carbon and reduced sulphur concentrations and remarkably different distributions of dissolved sulphate. The influx of a sulphate-bearing brine at the shallow Peru Site (680) has a major influence on sediment chemistry that makes traditional diagenetic interpretations largely inapplicable.

C/S ratios for sediments, containing less than 2 wt% TOC exclusive of Peru Site 680, are close to the average for normal marine sediments. C/S ratios increase with increasing TOC. Sediments with greater than 3 wt% TOC have C/S ratios which average about one and a half times those of normal marine sediments for the Benguela upwelling area and Peru Site 688 sediments, whereas sediments with similar TOC concentrations from the Oman Margin have C/S ratios approaching those characteristic of freshwater sediments.

The low degree of pyritization, at all sites except Site 680, indicates that iron is probably not limiting pyrite formation. Rates of sulphate reduction appear to be related more to the susceptibility of organic matter to metabolism by sulphate reducing bacteria than to its concentration or water depth. We hypothesize that both the nature of organic matter which is buried and the openness of the system to exchange of reduced sulphur and oxidants strongly influence C/S ratios in these hemipelagic, organic-rich sediments.

This research was supported by the National Science Foundation Chemical Oceanography Program (Morse) and USSAC (Emeis). We thank P. A. Meyers for his helpful comments.

References

BERNER, R. A. 1970. Sedimentary pyrite formation. American Journal of Science, 268, 1–23.
—— 1978. Sulphate reduction and the rate of deposition of marine sediments. Earth and Planetary Science Letters, 37, 492–498.
—— 1980. Early diagenesis: a theoretical approach. Princeton University Press.
—— 1982. Burial of organic carbon and pyrite sulphur in the modern ocean: its geochemical and environmental significance. American Journal of Science, 282, 451–473.
—— 1984. Sedimentary pyrite formation: an update: Geochimica et Cosmochimica Acta, 48, 605–615.
—— & RAISWELL, R. 1983. Burial of organic carbon and pyrite sulphur in sediments over Phanerozoic

time: a new theory. *Geochimica et Cosmochimica Acta*, **47**, 855–862.

—— & CANFIELD, D. E., 1989. A new model for atmospheric oxygen over Phanerozoic time. *American Journal of Science*, **289**, 333–361.

CANFIELD, D. E. 1989. Sulphate reduction and oxic respiration in marine sediments: implications for organic carbon preservation in euxinic environments. *Deep-Sea Research*, **36**, 121–138.

——, RAISWELL, R., WESTRICH, J. T., REEVES, C. M. & BERNER, R. A. 1986. The use of chromium reduction in the analysis of reduced inorganic sulphur in sediments and shale. *Chemical Geology*, **54**, 149–155.

DAVIS, H. R., BYERS, C. W. & DEAN, W. E. 1988. Pyrite formation in the Lower Cretaceous Mowry shale: Effect of organic matter type and reactive iron content. *American Journal of Science*, **288**, 873–890.

DEAN, W. E. & ARTHUR, M. A. 1989. Iron-sulphur relationships in organic-carbon-rich sequences I: Cretaceous western interior seaway. *American Journal of Science*, **289**, 708–743.

EMEIS, K. C. & MORSE, J. W. 1990. Organic carbon and sulphur relations in sediments of the Peru Margin-ODP Sites 680 and 688. *In*: SUESS, E., VON HUENE, R. *et al.* (eds) Proceedings ODP, Scientific Results, 112: College Station, Ocean Drilling Program, 441–453.

——, —— & MAYS, L. L. 1991. Organic carbon, reduced sulphur and iron in Neogene and Quaternary upwelling sediments from the Oman and Benguela upwelling systems. *In*: PRELL, W. D., NIITSUMA, N. *et al.* (eds) Proceedings ODP, Scientific Results, 117: College Station, Ocean Drilling Program, 517–527.

GOLDHABER, M. B. R., ALLER, R. C., COCHRAN, J. K., ROSENFELD, J. K., MARTENS, C. S. & BERNER, R. A. 1977. Sulphate reduction, diffusion and bioturbation in Long Island sound sediments: report from the FOAM group: American Journal of Science, **227**, 193–237.

HAY, W. W., SIBUET, J.-C. *et al.* 1984. Initial Reports, DSDP, 75, Washington, Government Printing Office.

HEATH, G. R., MOORE, T. C., JR. & DAUPHIN, J. P. 1977. Organic carbon in deep-sea sediments. *In*: ANDERSEN, N. R. & MALAHOFF, A. (eds) *The Fate of Fossil Fuel CO_2 in the Oceans*, Plenum New York, 605–625.

JØRGENSEN, B. B. 1978. A comparison of methods for the quantification of bacterial sulphate reduction in coastal marine sediments. III. Estimation from chemical and bacteriological field data. *Geomicrobiology Journal*, **1**, 49–64.

LEVENTHAL, J. & TAYLOR, C. 1990. Comparison of methods to determine degree of pyritization.

Geochimimica et Cosmochimica Acta, **54**, 2621–2625.

MEYERS, P. A., BRASSELL, S. C. & HUC, A. Y. 1984. Geochemistry of organic carbon in South Atlantic Sediments from DSDP Leg 75. *In*: HAY, W. W., SIBUET, J.-C. *et al.* (eds) Initial Reports, DSDP 75/2, Washington, Govt. Printing Office, 967–981.

——, ——, ——, BARRON, E. J., BOYCE, R. E., DEAN, W. E., HAY, W. W., KEATING, B. H., MCNULTY, C. L., NOHARA, M., SCHALLREUTER, R. E., SIBUET, J., STEINMETZ, J. C., STOW, D., and STRADNER, H. 1983. Organic geochemistry of sediments recovered by DSDP/IPOD Leg 75 under the Benguela Current. *In*: THIEDE, J. & SUESS, E. (eds) *Coastal Upwelling: Its Sediment Record*, Part B, Plenum, New York, 453–466.

MÜLLER, P. J. & SUESS, E. 1979. Productivity, sedimentation rate, and sedimentary organic matter in the ocean. *Deep-Sea Research*, **26A**, 1347–1362.

PRATT, L. M., CLAYPOOL, G. E. & KING, J. D. 1986. Geochemical imprint of depositional conditions on organic matter in laminated-bioturbated interbeds from fine-grained marine sequences. *Marine Geology*, **70**, 67–84.

PRELL, W. D., NIITSUMA, N. *et al.* 1989. Proceedings, Initial Reports, ODP, 117: College Station, Ocean Drilling Program.

RAISWELL, R. 1982. Pyrite texture, isotopic composition and the availability of iron. *American Journal of Science*, **282**, 1244–1263.

—— & BERNER, R. A., 1985. Pyrite formation in euxinic and semi-euxinic sediments. *American Journal of Science*, **285**, 710–724.

——, BUCKLEY, F., BERNER, R. A. & ANDERSON, T. F. 1988. Degree of pyritization of iron as a paleoenvironmental indicator of bottom-water oxygenation. *Journal of Sedimentary Petrology*, **58**, 812–819.

SUESS, E., VON HUENE, R. *et al.* 1988. Proceedings, Initial Reports, ODP, 112: College Station, Ocean Drilling Program.

TOTH, D. J. & LERMAN, A. 1977. Organic matter reactivity and sedimentation rates in the ocean. *American Journal of Science*, **277**, 265–285.

WESTRICH, J. T. & BERNER, R. A. 1984. The role of sedimentary organic matter in bacterial sulphate reduction: the G model tested. *Limnology and Oceanography*, **29**, 236–249.

ZHABINA, N. N. & VOLKOV, I. I. 1978. A method of determination of various sulphur compounds in sea sediments and rocks. *In*: KRUMBEIN, W. E. (ed.) *Environmental biogeochemistry and geomicrobiology, vol. 3: Methods, metals and assessment*. Ann Arbor Science Publications, 735–746.

Organic geochemistry as a tool to study upwelling systems: recent results from the Peru and Namibian shelves

DANIEL J. REPETA, MARK A. McCAFFREY[1] & JOHN W. FARRINGTON

Chemistry Department, Woods Hole Oceanographic Institution, Woods Hole, MA 02543, USA

[1] *Present address: Chevron Oil Field Research Company, PO Box 1627, Richmond, CA 94802, USA*

Abstract: Organic geochemists are currently developing new, molecular-based tools for studying the historical record of coastal upwelling. Several hundred biomarkers, organic compounds with known biological sources, have been identified in sediments underlying the world's major upwelling systems. Studies completed over the last two decades show that the distribution of many biomarkers in sediments is heavily impacted by the oceanographic and ecological conditions that prevail at the time of sediment deposition. Therefore, these biomakers have the potential to serve as useful palaeoenvironmental indicators. In order to decipher the sedimentary record on the molecular level, a better understanding of early diagenesis, and the coupling between water column biology, chemistry and biomarker distribution in sediments, is needed. Upwelling environments provide excellent sites to conduct such studies. High sediment accumulation rates and good preservation of organic matter in sediments relative to other depositional environments permit high-resolution time-series studies. We summarize here some recent research on early diagenesis, the effect of dysaerobic conditions on biomarker preservation, and the impact of El Nino Southern Oscillation (ENSO) events on the organic geochemical record. We further suggest some specific areas of future research that could substantially enhance our understanding of upwelling environments.

Organic geochemical studies of coastal upwelling areas have provided much of our current understanding of organic matter cycling in contemporary and ancient marine systems. The high primary productivity and shallow water column associated with coastal upwelling results in rapid accumulation and good preservation of organic matter in the underlying sediments; making high-resolution time-series studies of processes in the water column and sediments feasible. In the 1970s and early 1980s research focused on characterizing the complex suite of organic biomarkers present in the water column and sediments and on relating biomarkers to likely sources of organic matter (Wardroper *et al*. 1978; Lee *et al*. 1980; Smith *et al*. 1982, 1983*a*, *b*; Volkman *et al*. 1983, 1987; Wakeham *et al*. 1983). As a more complete understanding of the extractable organic matter became available, it was apparent that, although the sediments and water column particulate matter were geologically young, the biomarker distribution was heavily overprinted by diagenesis and by contributions from bacteria. Transformation products that had been previously observed in geologically more ancient deposits, and had been assumed to be formed over very long timescales, were observed in surface sediments. Therefore, initial studies aimed at identifying the source of biomarkers in upwelling environments were rapidly followed by studies of early diagenesis (Gagosian & Farrington 1978; Gagosian & Smith, 1979; Gagosian *et al*. 1980; Lee & Cronin 1982; Brassell & Eglinton 1983; Henrichs & Farrington 1984*a*, *b*; Repeta & Gagosian 1984, 1987; Repeta 1989). More recently, studies have begun to focus on the impact of changing environmental conditions on organic matter production and preservation in sediments, and on the reconstruction of palaeo-upwelling environments (Farrington *et al*. 1988; McCaffrey *et al*. 1990; Farrimond *et al*. 1990*b*; ten Haven *et al*. 1990*b*; Poynter *et al*. 1990). These studies, although relatively new, have yielded new tools with which to study the historical record of upwelling. Such studies would not be possible without the understanding of source and the effect of early diagenesis on the sedimentary record provided by the previous two decades of research.

Studies of biomarkers in Recent sediments were stimulated by the identification of stable, lipid-class compounds in organic-rich shales and oils. The similarity of these compounds to extant

From SUMMERHAYES, C. P., PRELL, W. L. & EMEIS, K. C. (eds), 1992, *Upwelling Systems: Evolution Since the Early Miocene*. Geological Society Special Publication No 64, pp 257–272.

functionalized biomarkers invariably led to questions of their source and the depositional conditions under which they were preserved (Hunt 1979; Tissot & Welte 1984). Of the world's major coastal upwelling systems, the Peru−Chile and Namibian shelf upwelling systems have been the most thoroughly analyzed by organic geochemists. Biomarker lipids identified in Peruvian and Namibian shelf sediments include sterols and pigments characteristic of diatoms, dinoflagellates, silicoflagellates, and zooplankton (Smith *et al.* 1982, 1983*a*; Ridout *et al.*, 1984; Repeta & Gagosian 1987), alkenones (Volkman *et al.* 1983; McCaffrey *et al.* 1990) characteristic of prymnesiophytes, iso- and anteiso-fatty acids from bacteria (Smith *et al.* 1983*b*; Farrington *et al.* 1988, 1990), and hydrocarbons and alkenols from vascular plants (Volkman *et al.* 1983; McCaffrey *et al.* 1991). These findings are in agreement with the record of input derived from oceanographic observations, mineralogical and palaeontological analyses: both systems receive large inputs from diatoms and silicoflagellates that are rapidly consumed by zooplankton in the water column and further remineralized by bacteria in sediments. Although both regions are adjacent to very arid coastlines, there is a significant aeolian and perhaps fluvial input of clastic material that may serve to transport small amounts of terrestrially-derived organic matter. The organic geochemical record also reveals significant inputs from dinoflagellates (Smith *et al.* 1982, 1983*a*), cryptophytes, purple non-sulphur photosynthetic bacteria (Repeta & Gagosian 1987), and perhaps cyanobacteria (McCaffrey *et al.* 1991; ten Haven *et al.* 1990*a*) that have not been identified by other types of sedimentological analyses.

Although organic geochemical analyses have identified a wide variety of sources for organic matter in sediments from upwelling areas, no unique set of sedimentary biomarkers or molecular indices have been shown to be diagnostic of marine coastal upwelling environments. In addition to those studies of lipids in Recent sediments cited above, Farrimond *et al.* (1990*a*, *b*) and ten Haven *et al.* (1990*a*) have made extensive investigations of lipids in Quaternary to Pliocene age sediments recovered during ODP Leg 112 from the Peru margin (11°S), and ten Haven *et al.* (1990*b*) and Poynter *et al.* (1990) have compared sediments from upwelling and non-upwelling areas of the eastern North Atlantic (ODP Leg 108). Quantitatively, sediments underlying upwelling systems tend to have higher organic carbon contents and accumulation rates than other coastal marine sediments. Qualitatively, the distribution of alkenones, sterols, hydrocarbons, pigments and other lipid-class biomarkers do not differ in a unique way from non-upwelling systems (Volkman 1986; ten Haven *et al.* 1990*b*). However, differences in the relative abundances of alkanes, alkenes and sterenes are apparent when comparing sediments from upwelling areas with coastal sediments collected from non-upwelling areas (e.g. Farrington *et al.* 1977; Gagosian & Farrington 1978; Volkman *et al.* 1983; ten Haven *et al.* 1990*a*, *b*; Poynter *et al.* 1990). It is unclear to what extent such comparisons can be made either globally or over time due to the lack of comparable sampling. Recently, organic geochemical studies have targeted lipids from source organisms unique to upwelling environments (McCaffrey *et al.* 1989). These studies may ultimately provide a means for identifying upwelling environments using molecular tracers.

In order to recognize upwelling systems in the sedimentary record, and to reconstruct palaeoenvironmental conditions that prevailed at the time of deposition (e.g. palaeoproductivity, palaeodysoxia), a more complete understanding of early diagenesis and the effects of short-term environmental changes on organic matter preservation in sediments is needed. Upwelling systems provide good sites to carry out these studies: recycling processes can be conveniently studied by water, sediment trap, and finely sectioned core samples to provide high-resolution time-course measurements of changes in organic matter composition as it transits the water column and is incorporated into surface sediments. In this paper, we summarize some of our recent research on early diagenesis, the impact of dysaerobic conditions on biomarker transformation and preservation in sediments, and the impact of short-term climatic fluctuations on the organic geochemical record. Furthermore, we suggest some specific areas of future research that could substantially enhance our understanding of the sedimentary signature of these depositional environments.

Early diagenesis

The high production and flux of organic matter associated with upwelling systems, coupled with a very rapid rate of remineralization at the sediment−water interface, results in bottom water dysoxia and anoxic conditions in sediments (Henrichs & Farrington 1984*a*, *b*; Fossing 1990). At the site 15°S, 75°W studied by organic geochemists from the Woods Hole Oceanographic Institution, Fossing (1990) measured sulphate reduction rates and found they were equivalent to 10–30% of the primary production in the overlying water column. Greater than 50% of the sulphate reduction occurs in the top 20 cm of the sediment column, representing <50 years of sediment deposition. As a result, post-depositional alteration and remineralization of biomarker compounds may, on a timescale of only a few years, result in the complete loss of some biomarkers that are abundant near the sediment–water interface. Unless degradation pathways and stable alteration products for important biomarkers can be identified, the palaeoenvironmental information associated with these compounds is lost from the sedimentary record.

Early diagenesis of photosynthetic pigments in Peru surface sediments

A very clear example of diagenetic overprinting is illustrated in Fig. 1 which details the distribution of carotenoids in seawater, sediment trap, and surface sediment samples collected in the Peru upwelling region. Seawater and sediment trap samples have high concentrations of the carotenoids fucoxanthin and diadinoxanthin from diatoms, reflecting the overwhelming

quantitative importance of these algae to total phytoplankton in this region (de Mendolia 1981). The distribution of pigments in surface sediments is, however, quite different. Fucoxanthin and diadinoxanthin are virtually absent from surface sediments (Fig. 2). Quantitatively abundant pigments in sediments are all derived from zooplankton, cryptophytes and bacteria, even though these organisms are only minor contributors to the total organic carbon. Biomarker pigments in surface sediments would, therefore, incorrectly suggest that diatoms are a relatively minor source for organic matter in Peru sediments, and that inputs from zooplankton, cryptophytes and bacteria dominate the organic carbon flux from the euphotic zone.

A quantitative reconstruction of the original phytoplankton pigment input to sediments could be made if pigment degradation rates and products were better understood. Through the use of high-resolution sampling on the millimetre scale (representing 1–2 months of sediment accumulation), a degradation pathway for carotenoids in Peru sediments was proposed by Repeta (1989). The pathway quantitatively accounts for the distribution of pigments in surface sediments, and allows an assessment of the original diatom input. Flocculant material at and immediately below the sediment–water interface has a pigment distribution very similar

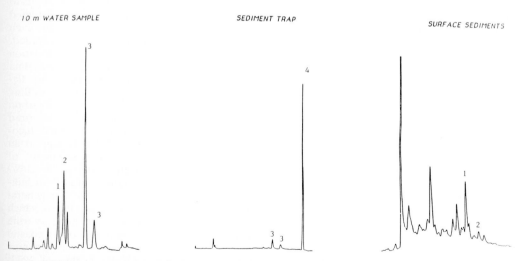

10 m WATER SAMPLE   SEDIMENT TRAP   SURFACE SEDIMENTS

Fig. 1. High-pressure liquid chromatograms of (a) seawater particulate matter, (b) sediment trap sample and (c) surface sediment (0–2 cm) collected at 15°S, 75°W in the Peru upwelling area. Peak identifications are as follows: (1) diatoxanthin, (2) diadinoxanthin, (3) fucoxanthin and (4) fucoxanthinol. The figure illustrates the rapid loss of fucoxanthin and other highly polar carotenoid epoxides from sediments, and the increase in chromatogram complexity that results from diagenetic overprinting. No fucoxanthin could be detected in sediments. Samples were analyzed on a 5 μm amino-bonded silica column eluted with a gradient of hexane and methylene chloride/methanol.

D. J. REPETA *ET AL.*

ng/gdw

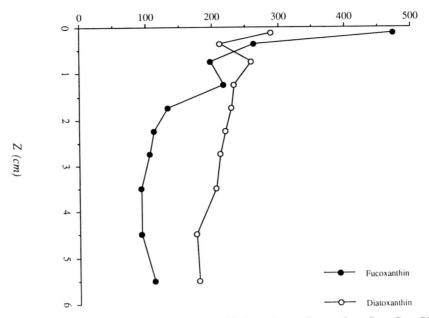

Fig. 2. The concentration of diatoxanthin and fucoxanthin in surface sediments from Peru Core SC-2 (11°S, 78°W). Like other β,β-bicyclic carotenes and xanthophylls the concentration of diatoxanthin is relatively constant down core, while fucoxanthin and other 5,6-epoxides degrade rapidly in surface sediments.

to seawater and sediment trap samples (Fig. 1; Ridout *et al.* 1984; Repeta 1989). Within the 0−1 cm interval, major xanthophylls character-istic of diatoms, dinoflagellates and prymnesio-phytes are removed. However, some pigments, for example β-carotene and diatoxanthin, undergo very little apparent degradation (Fig. 2). Pigments that degrade are structurally distinct in having a 5,6-epoxide (Fig. 3), an observation that led Repeta & Gagosian (1987) to suggest that the degradation rate of any pigment is determined by the rate of epoxide formation and rearrangement.

Epoxide rearrangement leads to rapid frag-mentation of the molecule and subsequent for-mation of low molecular weight products. Klok *et al.* (1984a, b) identified a series of loliolides as major constituents of the organic matter in Namibian shelf sediments, and suggested these compounds represent end-products in the degra-dation of carotenoids. This hypothesis was tested by Repeta (1989) who analyzed very finely sectioned Peru surface sediments for both loliolide and fucoxanthin. Results, summarized in Table 1, illustrate the near-quantitative cor-respondence between the loss of fucoxanthin and the production of loliolide in sediments.

The original contribution of diatom pigments to surface sediments can therefore be calculated by the sum of fucoxanthin and loliolide, even when >90% of the original pigment is degraded. As illustrated in Table 1, when degradation products are taken into account, pigment data support the overwhelming importance of dia-toms as a source for organic matter in upwelling sediments. Assuming a fucoxanthin/carbon mass ratio of 0.006 as measured in cultured algae, the calculated amount of 'original' fuco-xanthin in our core SC-2 (Table 1) support an organic carbon value for these sediments of 16%, close to the measured value of 18−20%.

Studies of pigment degradation in Peru sedi-ments led to the formulation of the very general degradation pathway illustrated in Fig. 3, which is thought to be operative in all anoxic marine sediments. Studies of numerous other coastal marine sediments and of the Black Sea now support this pathway (Watts & Maxwell 1977; King & Repeta 1991, unpublished results). Aside from a quantitative method for deter-mining phytoplankton input to sediments, two other results are of interest. The pathway suggests that pigments which cannot form un-stable 5,6 epoxides are likely to be stable over

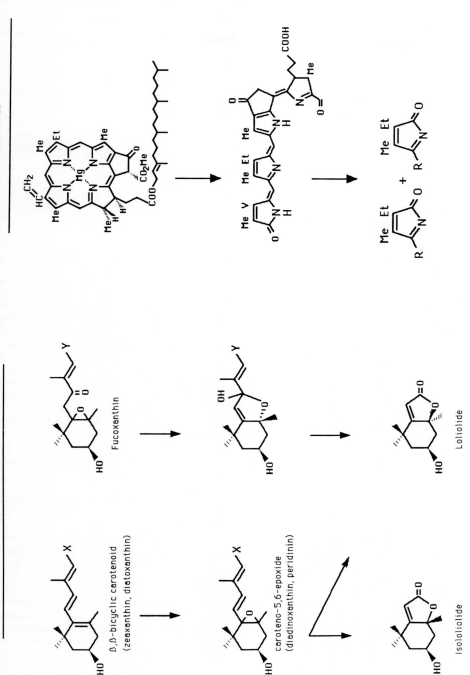

Fig. 3. General diagenetic pathway for carotenoids and chlorophylls in anoxic marine sediments.

Table 1. The degradation of fucoxanthin to loliolide in Peru core SC-2 (Repeta 1989). Mole equivalents of fucoxanthin and loliolide. Total fucoxanthin in Column 3 is in $\mu g/g$ dry weight and represents the estimated fucoxanthin at $t = 0$.

Depth (cm)	Fucoxanthin	Loliolide	Total Fucoxanthin
0–0.25	0.72	0.95	1100
0.25–0.5	0.40	0.99	921
0.5–1.0	0.30	1.16	960
1.0–1.5	0.33	1.37	1020
1.5–2.0	0.20	1.38	1040
2.0–2.5	0.17	1.46	1072
2.5–3.0	0.16	1.55	1125
3.0–4.0	0.14	1.30	948
4.0–5.0	0.14	1.28	869
5.0–6.0	0.17	1.31	974
6.0–8.0	ND	1.38	1007*
8.0–10.0	ND	1.85	1316*
12.0–14.0	ND	1.35	987*

* Assumes 0.15 μmole fucoxanthin/g dry weight

very long periods of time, and therefore persist as biomarkers in sediments. This was tested in an analysis of Recent to Miocene age sediments recovered from the Peru margin during Leg 112 of the Ocean Drilling Program (Repeta 1990). Pleistocene sediments have a complex distribution of carotenoids very similar to that found in surface sediments. However, Miocene age sediments have a very simple distribution of carotenoids. Carotenoids that do persist do not have a 5,6 epoxide and cannot be degraded by the route shown in Fig. 3. Thus the proposed degradation pathway is useful for choosing which pigments are potentially valuable biomarkers.

A second result pertains to the sequence of reactions by which large and complex organic molecules are degraded to small, easily metabolizable substrates. The carotenoid degradation pathway suggests that only a small number of steps, operating at key points within the molecule, may be the preferred diagenetic route, and that the web of reactions hypothesized to explain the complex distribution of biomarker degradation products reported for other classes of biomarkers in sediments may be quantitatively insignificant. For example, we suggest that chlorophyll is degraded by only a few simple steps that are relatively insensitive to the small structural features which distinguish chlorophylls-*a*, -*b*, and -*c* (Fig. 3). The large number of chlorophyll degradation products observed in recent and ancient sediments would therefore represent only a small fraction of the total chlorophyll input, and will probably be of little value in quantitatively estimating palaeo-productivity. High concentrations of as yet

unidentified chlorophyll degradation intermediates have been isolated from the floc and the 0–2 mm interval of Peru surface sediments (Simpson & Repeta, unpublished). Spectroscopic data suggests these compounds are a linear tetrapyrroles derived from oxidation of chlorophyll-*a* at a meso position. An understanding of this degradation route, and the associated terminal degradation products, may ultimately permit quantitative estimates of chlorophyll deposition. Due to the very high concentrations of organic carbon and high accumulation rates that characterize upwelling sediments, this intermediate can be isolated in sufficient quantity for full structural characterization, and for its degradation rate to be studied. Such studies are not possible in coastal or open ocean sediments.

Early diagenesis of sterols in Peru surface sediments

Sterol transformation reactions have been very widely studied because of the important role steroidal hydrocarbons have as biomarkers in ancient sediments and petroleum. Like pigment degradation products, recognizable sterol transformation products constitute only a small fraction of the total sterol input to sediments (Gagosian *et al.* 1983). Most sterols are degraded by as yet unidentified pathways. However, the structural diversity manifest in the sterol carbon skeleton make even trace quantities of sterol transformation products valuable as biomarkers (see next section). A large number of sterols and sterol degradation products have been identified in surface sediments from the Namibian and Peru upwelling systems (Gagosian & Farrington 1978; Gagosian & Smith 1979; Gagosian et al. 1980; Smith et al. 1982, 1983a; McCaffrey 1990). Of particular interest is the observation that many transformation products that had been thought to form over much longer periods of time and under more severe geothermal gradients, are in fact, present in surface sediments (see for example Hussler & Albrecht 1983; Farrington et al. 1988).

The 4-desmethylsteroids are biosynthesized as stenols and, to a lesser extent, as stanols (Nishimura & Koyama 1977). Three distinct transformation pathways have been elucidated for cholesterol in upwelling sediments: (1) rearrangement to 14 $\alpha(H)-1(10-> 6)-$abeo-chloesta-5,7,9(10)-triene (hereafter C_{27} anthrasteroid) (Fig. 4, pathway I), (2) dehydration and formation of cholestadienes and cholestatrienes (Fig. 4, pathway II), and (3) reduction to cholestanol via cholestenone (Fig. 4, pathway III). Many of the degradation products shown in Fig. 4 have been found in surface sediments (0–1 cm) recovered from either the Peru or Namibian upwelling systems. Transformation reactions are therefore very rapid, occurring in the water column and/or at the sediment–water interface. It is interesting to note that down-core changes in sediment chemistry and burial time do not result in an accumulation of the transformation products suggested in Fig. 4. Figure 5 shows the concentration of cholesterol and cholesterol alteration products in the top 100 cm of Peru core SC-3 (McCaffrey et al. 1991), and illustrates the rapid decrease in the sum of these compounds below the sediment–water interface. Greater than 90% of cholesterol degradation occurs in the top 2–3 centimetres of the core, representing <10 years of diagenesis. Transformation of cholesterol to the products shown in Fig. 4 is obscured by an equally rapid removal of the degradation products.

The C_{27} anthrasteroid defined in the previous paragraph has been reported in Cretaceous black shales (Hussler & Albrecht 1983) and immature sediments recovered as part of the Deep Sea Drilling Program (Rullkötter & Welte 1983; Hussler & Albrecht 1983; Brassell et al. 1984). Gagosian & Farrington (1978), Farrington et al. (1988) & McCaffrey et al. (1991) have reported this compound in recent sediments from the Peru and Namibian upwelling systems. The proposed precursor is a cholestadiene or cholestatriene formed from dehydration and oxidation of cholesterol or cholestanol (Brassell et al. 1984). Profiles of the

C_{27} anthrasteroid are relatively constant with depth in SC3, implying that formation occurs primarily in the water column or at the sediment–water interface, and that very little degradation follows deposition. Farrington et al. (1988) noted that the highest concentrations of C_{27} anthrasteroid occurred in sections of a Peru core that correspond to high sea surface water temperature and (by implication) low productivity time periods. Minor to moderate fluctuations of this type were also observed in Peru core SC-3 as shown in Fig. 5. Therefore, fluctuations in water column chemistry and biology may impact the distribution of specific transformation products in sediments and the extent of early diagenesis.

At some point in the diagenesis of anoxic marine sediments, reduced inorganic sulphur (S^o, H_2S, polysulphides) from sulphate reduction forms steroid thiophenes and crosslinks sterols (or sterenes) to macromolecular organic matter (Mossman et al. 1990). Steroids with thiophene side chains have been observed in crude oils (Sinninghe Damsté et al. 1987, 1988, 1989), and pyrolyses of asphaltenes and kerogens have yielded alkylthiophenes presumed to be derived from bound steroids (Sinninghe Damsté et al. 1988, 1989). Production of steranes by Raney–Ni desulphurization of resins indicates that steranes are bound to these substances by sulphide or polysulphide bonds. Mossmann et al. (1990) showed that sulphur is incorporated into Peru margin kerogens and bitumens in the surface 15 m of ODP Leg 112 core 680 (250 m water depth, 11°S) and core 686 (450 m water depth, 11°S), but no assessment has been made of the importance of sulphur cross-linking of sterols into macromolecular material, or the formation of steroid thiophenes at the sediment–water interface. The rapid decrease in total sterols in the most recent sediments, and the observation that most transformation products are already present in the 0–1 cm fraction suggests the sediment–water interface may be an important site for sulphur incorporation. This question has not been addressed by studies completed to date, but the distribution of steroidal sulphur compounds is a potentially significant tool in palaeoenvironmental reconstruction, recording both the distribution of sterols and the presence of reduced sulphur at the time of deposition.

Organic geochemical indicators of dysaerobic depositional conditions

Coastal upwelling regimes are frequently mentioned as modern analogues to the depo-

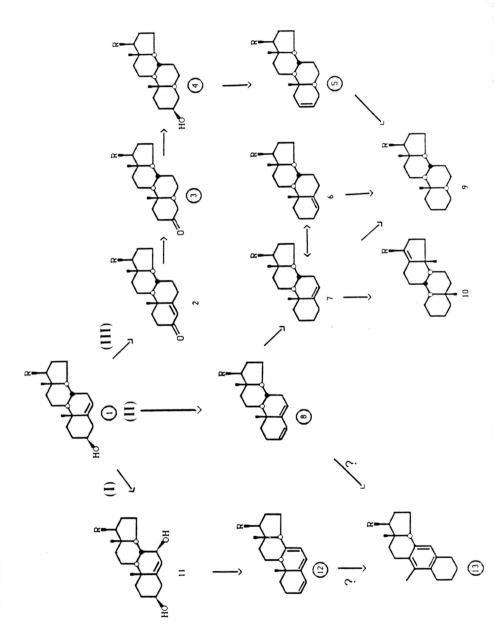

Fig. 4. Diagenetic alteration pathways of 4-desmethyl Δ^5 stenols in recent sediments. Circled compound numbers indicate cholesterol [R = 2-(6-methylhepatane)] transformation products found in core SC3 sediments from the Peru upwelling system. The unsaturations depicted in cholestatriene (compound 12) are nuclear, but the exact double bond positions are only tentative.

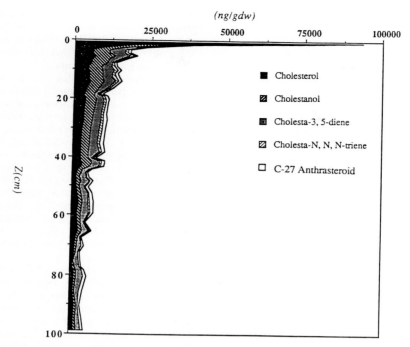

Fig. 5. Concentration profiles of cholesterol and cholesterol degradation products in Peru core SC-3, 0–100 cm.

sitional environments of certain important petroleum source rocks, such as the Miocene Monterey Formation of the California Borderland (Soutar *et al.* 1981), and the Permian Phosphoria Formation of Wyoming and Montana (Maughan 1984). Deposition of organic carbon-rich sediments in coastal upwelling areas is generally believed to be the result, in part, of dysoxic (<0.1 ml O_2/l) and anoxic depositional conditions conducive to organic matter preservation (Demaison & Moore 1980). Recently, however, the importance of dysoxia to the preservation of organic carbon-rich sediments has been questioned (Pedersen & Calvert 1990; Calvert & Pedersen 1991). The resulting controversy has stimulated renewed interest in developing methods to determine the relative oxygenation of a depositional environment from a sediment or an oil.

Physical characteristics of a sediment, such as sediment laminations, the absence of macrofauna, or the distribution of benthic foram tests, can serve as indicators of dysoxic depositional conditions (e.g. Rhoads & Morse 1971; Douglas 1981). Recent sediments recovered from the oxygen minimum zone of the Peru upwelling system often display microlaminations on visual inspection and X-ray analysis. However, formation of laminae requires a seasonality of sediment input, which is not always present at low latitudes. Furthermore, bioturbation during infrequent, brief periods of bottom water oxicity may periodically destroy laminations laid down over much longer periods of bottom water dysoxia. Large sequences of diatomaceous ooze recovered from the Peru and Namibian selves and presumably deposited under low oxygen conditions, do not exhibit lamination by visual inspection. Benthic foram tests from species inhabiting low oxygen depositional environments have also been suggested as a means for identifying dysoxic depositional conditions, but in highly corrosive fluids of organic carbon-rich sediments carbonate tests may dissolve. These methods, which rely on physical characteristics of a sediment, are of no use in characterizing the oxicity of the depositional environment from an oil, a problem that often arises when trying to characterize the source-rock of a migrated oil. Organic geochemical biomarkers may ultimately provide a resolution to these problems, since numerous organic geochemical parameters have been suggested as indicators of bottom water oxygenation during sediment deposition.

Sedimentary profiles of the hydrogen index,

HI (the mg of hydrocarbons produced by pyrolysis of 1 g sedimentary TOC), have been interpreted to reflect the degree of oxidative reworking of the sediments. Whelan *et al.* (1990) provide HI profiles for several Recent sediment cores from the Peru upwelling area. Fluctuations in sedimentary profiles of HI in a given basin may have utility as an indicator of the history of bottom-water oxygenation. However, because the HI is also affected by the type of sedimentary organic matter present (e.g. terrestrial vs. marine organic matter) it may be difficult to interpret differences in HI values between basins or across facies changes. Like the physical methods described in the preceding paragraph, the hydrogen index may only be applied to a sediment, and not an oil.

A number of molecular organic geochemical indices have also been proposed to identify low oxygen environments in the sedimentary record. Most represent empirical formulations of degradation product ratios. The ratio of pristane/phytane as an indicator for low oxygen environments has been discussed by Didyk *et al.* (1978). Under reducing conditions, sedimentary phytol (C_{20}) derived from chlorophyll is reduced primarily to phytane (C_{20}); whereas under oxidative conditions, phytol is converted primarily to pristane (C_{19}) through oxidation (to a carboxylic acid) followed by decarboxylation (Volkman & Maxwell 1986). Didyk *et al.* (1978) suggested that oxic depositional environments are characterized by pristane/phytane ratios >1. Sediments with ratios <1 were thought to be deposited under dysaerobic or anoxic conditions. Unfortunately, it seems as though the pristane/phytane ratio cannot be so easily interpreted. Sedimentary phytane is derived not only from phytol diagenesis, but also from *de novo* synthesis by certain archaebacteria. Additionally, a large number of sediments have pristane/phytane ratios that are inconsistent with the general pattern described by Didyk *et al.* (1978). Problems with using the pristane/phytane ratio as an indicator of relative oxicity of the depositional environment have recently been reviewed by ten Haven *et al.* (1987).

Two promising molecular indicators of oxygenation in a depositional environment are the Ni-porphyrin/V-porphyrin ratio (Lewan 1984) and the 'homohopane index' (Peters & Moldowan 1991) in sediments and oils. Nickel and vanadyl porphyrins, diagenetic alteration products of chlorophyll, are formed by complexation of Ni^{2+} and VO^{2+} with free-base porphyrins. Under anoxic depositional conditions, the production of free sulphide (from the reduction of porewater sulphate) may lead

to precipitation of nickel sulphides, allowing a greater proportion of the free-base porphyrins to be complexed by VO_2^+. High Ni-porphyrin/V-porphyrin ratios are therefore indicative of oxic depositional environments.

The homohopane index [C_{35} homohopane/$\Sigma(C_{31}$ to C_{35} homohopanes)] likewise depends on differences in the distribution of degradation products under oxic and anoxic conditions. The $C_{31}-C_{35}$ homohopanes are diagenetic alteration products of C_{35} polyhydroxyhopanoids produced by many bacteria. Oxidative cleavage of the side chain results in $C_{31}-C_{34}$ hopanols (Rohmer *et al.* 1980, 1984) that can be reduced to hopanes. Under dysoxic depositional conditions, the C_{35} hopanol may be reduced directly to C_{35} homohopane, yielding a higher value for the homohopane index (Peters & Moldowan 1990). The Ni-porphyrin/V-porphyrin ratio and the homohopane index in sediments and oils show promise as indicators of the relative oxygenation in the original depositional environment, but these parameters must be measured in Recent sediments from well-characterized depositional environments in order to confirm their utility. We are unaware of any applications of these two techniques to the Peru or Namibian coastal upwelling areas. Such a study would be a significant contribution to the implementation of molecular indices in determining palaeo-oxicity.

McCaffrey *et al.* (1989) proposed a novel method for identifying sediments deposited under low oxygen conditions in coastal upwelling regimes. They suggested using biomarkers specific for the sulphur-oxidizing bacteria, *Thioploca* spp., marine species of bacteria that have been found *only* in dysoxic surface sediments of coastal upwelling regimes (McCaffrey *et al.* 1989) as indicators for palaeoupwelling conditions. Fossilized bacterial mats believed to be from similar bacteria have been found in sections of the Miocene Monterey Formation of the California Borderland (Williams & Reimers 1983), a formation deposited in a coastal upwelling regime (Soutar *et al.* 1981). *Thioploca* may therefore serve as a diagnostic organism for upwelling regimes. Detailed lipid analysis of bacteria picked from freshly sampled surface sediments had high concentrations of cyclolaudenol (24-methyl-9, 19-cyclolanost-25-en-3β-ol), an unusual 4,4-dimethyl C_{31} sterol. No marine source of cyclolaudenol other than *Thioploca* has ever been identified, making this sterol or its degradation products promising biomarkers for palaeodysaerobic depositional conditions. The potential of this compound as a palaeoenvironmental indicator is, however, currently unknown, since cyclolaudenol appears to be rapidly degraded in surface sediments (McCaffrey et al. 1989), and the diagenetic alteration pathway of cyclolaudenol in sediments has not been elucidated. Gas chromatographic–mass spectrometric analysis of extracts from Peru margin surface sediments sampled in the OMZ (core SC7, 100 m; core KNSC6, 268 m) for degradation products expected to be formed from cyclolaudenol by reactions illustrated in Fig. 4 (e.g., 24-methyl-9,19-cyclolanosta-2,25-diene and 24-methyllanost-9(14), 25-dien-3β-ol) suggest that only trace quantities of these compounds could be present. Our comparison of the mass spectrum and retention time of authentic cyclolaudenone with GCMS data from the sterone fraction also suggested that cyclolaudenone was not present in significant quantities in these sediments.

Cyclolaudenol may undergo a series of rapid alterations in the sediments, with none of the initial alteration products accumulating. Another intriguing possibility is that cyclolaudenol, or an alteration product of this compound, is converted into a bound form either by cross-linking or by incorporation of sulphur. Investigation of these possibilities will determine the potential utility of cyclolaudenol alteration products as palaeoenvironmental indicators.

Constructing an organic geochemical record of changing depositional conditions

Several studies have attempted to derive palaeoenvironmental records from the geochemistry of Peru margin sediments. Reimers & Suess (1983a) proposed that profiles of the elemental and isotopic composition of kerogen from these sediments reflect changes in circulation, upwelling, and bottom-water oxygenation during the last 16000 years. Reimers & Suess (1983b) correlated changes in the climate and physical oceanography of this area since the Late Pleistocene with two depositional hiatuses and with changes in regional TOC accumulation. Farrimond et al. (1990b) interpreted a sedimentary profile of the C_{37} alkenone unsaturation index (U_{37}^k) as indicating changes in the intensity of upwelling along the Peru margin over the last 350000 years. Construction of these long-term records of depositional conditions for the Peru margin is frequently hampered by sedimentary uncomformities caused by slumping in this seismically active region.

Interest in the El Niño phenomenon has pro-

vided substantial impetus for constructing much more detailed records of the Peruvian palaeoclimate. El Niño events are climatic disturbances of variable intensity that last from several months to a year and affect the eastern tropical Pacific once every 2–10 years (Quinn et al. 1987). During El Niño conditions, relaxation of the strong southeast trade winds causes deepening of the thermocline, nutricline, and mixed layer along the Peru margin. These periods are further characterized by a 5–20 fold reduction in primary productivity (Barber & Chavez, 1983, 1986), and increased sea-surface temperature, rainfall, and continental runoff (Deser & Wallace 1987; Quinn et al. 1987). The persistence of low primary productivity associated with prolonged El Niño events may cause widespread mortality of anchovy and sea-bird populations (Barber & Chavez 1983, 1986) along the Peru coast. In addition, the El Niño phenomenon has been implicated in short-term climatic events that extend beyond the Pacific basin (e.g. Barber & Chavez 1986).

Efforts to construct an organic geochemical record of El Niño events have included examination of Peru margin sediment profiles of TOC, C_{37} alkenones, odd-carbon-chain-length n-alkanes and even-carbon chain length n-alkanols. Henrichs & Farrington (1984a) and Farrington et al. (1988) found that a sedimentary TOC profile of a core deposited over the last 130 years, was inversely correlated with periods of greater and lesser El Niño activity, an observation that these studies attributed to the reduction of primary productivity associated with El Niño conditions. The relative unsaturation of sedimentary C_{37} alkenones, a function of the historical record of changing sea-surface temperature (Brassell et al. 1986), was measured in Peru margin sediments by Farrington et al. (1988) and McCaffrey et al. (1990). These studies found the relative unsaturation of these compounds to be positively correlated with periods of greater and lesser El Niño activity, an observation attributed to the increase in sea surface temperature associated with El Niño conditions (Fig. 6). Since El Niño events are associated with increases in continental runoff along the Peru coast (Quinn et al. 1987; Deser & Wallace 1987) sedimentary profiles of biomarkers for higher plant input might also be expected to have potential as indicators of an El Niño record. However, at 15°S, McCaffrey et al. (1991) found a poor correlation between the historical El Niño record and sedimentary profiles of odd-carbon-number n-alkanes and even-carbon number n-alkanols (biomarkers for higher plant input). McCaffrey attributed this

Alkenone temperature (°C) in SC3

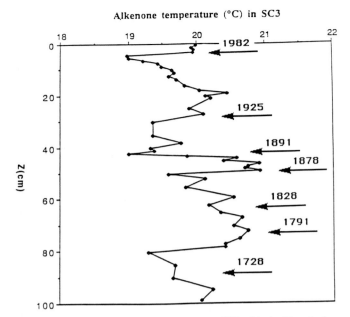

Fig. 6. Comparison of the alkenone temperature record in core SC3 with the historical record of 'very strong' ENSO events complied by Quinn *et al.* (1987). Very strong events are defined as having sea surface temperature anomalies of 7–12°C.

lack of correlation to a poor temporal coupling between terrigenous sediment deposition near shore, and offshore transport and redeposition of terrigenous sediment in the OMZ.

In a given core, the maximum time resolution of the organic geochemical record of depositional conditions depends on several factors including: (1) the core sectioning interval, (2) the sedimentation rate, (3) the depth of the sediment mixed layer, (4) the quality of the core dating, and (5) the time scale over which there is variability in the input of the organic constituents being measured. McCaffrey *et al.* (1990) discussed in detail the factors affecting the resolution of the sedimentary C_{37} alkenone record and concluded that periods of frequent El Niño activity can be more readily identified in the sediment record than isolated El Niño events in periods of less frequent El Niño activity; however, they also concluded that the sedimentary U_{37}^k could be used to identify individual, very strong El Niño events (SST anomalies of 7–12°C) in the Peru margin sedimentary record.

The U_{37}^k-derived sea-surface temperature anomaly at 11°S for the 1982–1983 ENSO event found by McCaffrey was 2°C, a lower value than the measured sea surface temperature anomaly of 7–9°C. McCaffrey *et al.* (1990)

explained this difference by suggesting that the U_{37}^k-derived ENSO temperature may be attenuated in some way from the actual value. However, information has recently come to our attention which suggests that prymnesiophytes, the putative source for C_{37} alkenones in Peru sediments, may have a productivity maximum that is temporally offset from the time of maximum sea surface temperature (Chavez (1985); as noted in Mitchell-Innes & Winter 1987). What we failed to note earlier (McCaffrey *et al.* 1990) was that the maximum in the coccolithophore population during the 1982–1983 ENSO occurred in September–October 1982; at a time of year when the sea surface temperature would only have been 2–3°C above normal. The U_{37}^k-derived 2°C temperature anomaly for 1982–1983 reported by McCaffrey *et al.* (1990) might therefore be expected if the signal is biased from large contributions of coccolithophores deposited in the fall of 1982. While this interpretation is speculative, it suggests that measurements of U_{37}^k may allow better representations of intense ENSO events than previously thought. Comparison of U_{37}^k-derived sea surface anomalies from finely-sectioned gravity and piston core samples collected on the Peru margin with records of ENSO events recorded in the Quelcaya ice cap

(Thompson *et al.* 1984; 1986) would provide a test of this concept.

Conclusions

There has been good progress towards understanding the influence of biological source, early diagenesis, and environmental conditions on the distribution of biomarkers in sediments underlying upwelling systems. Despite the inherent complexities of the processes involved, carefully collected samples coupled with quantitative measurements have yielded important insights into the organic geochemical record. Biomarker pigments show promise as potential indicators of palaeoproductivity, while U^k_{37}-derived sea surface temperature measurements provide a means for distinguishing periods of intense ENSO activity from periods characterized by normal upwelling conditions. Early diagenetic transformation reactions of sterols and hopanols have added to our knowledge of factors controlling the distribution of these important biomarkers in ancient sediments, petroleum source rocks and oils.

The scene has now been set for more comprehensive studies aimed at collecting three-dimensional data sets for biomarker distributions in sediments from Peru, Namibia and elsewhere; both in the upper one metre of sediments and in deeper gravity and piston core samples. These studies will help to assess the spatial variability and regional differences in productivity and organic matter cycling associated with upwelling and will serve to connect organic geochemical studies of the very surface sediments with studies of geologically older samples collected as part of the Ocean Drilling Program.

This work was supported by grants OCE-88–11409 and OCE-88–14398 from the National Science Foundation. We thank Carl Johnson for assistance with GCMS and probe MS, and the officers and crew of R/V Moana Wave 87–08 for assistance with sample collection. This is Woods Hole Oceanographic Institution contribution number 7711.

References

BARBER, R. T. & CHAVEZ, F. P. 1983. Biological consequences of El Niño. *Science*, **222**, 1203–1210.

—— & —— 1986. Ocean variability in relation to living resources during the 1982–83 El Niño. *Nature*, **319**, 279–285.

BRASSELL, S. & EGLINTON, G. 1983. The potential of organic geochemical compounds as sedimentary indicators of upwelling. *In*: SUESS E. & THIEDE, J. (eds) *Coastal Upwelling. Its Sediment Record, Part A*. Plenum, New York, 545–571.

——, ——, MARLOWE, I. T., PFLAUMANN, U. & SARNTHEIN, M. 1986. Molecular Stratigraphy: a new tool for climatic assessment. *Nature*, **320**, 129–133.

——, McEVOY, J., HOFFMANN, C. F., LAMB, N. A., PEAKMAN, T. M. & MAXWELL, J. R. 1984. Isomerization, rearrangement, and aromatisation of steroids in distiguishing early stages of diagenesis. *Organic Geochemistry*, **6**, 11–23.

CALVERT, S. E. & PEDERSEN, T. F. 1991. Organic carbon accumulation and preservation in marine sediments: How important is anoxia? *In*: WHELAN, J. & FARRINGTON, J. W. (eds) *Productivity, accumulation and Preservation of Organic Matter: Recent and Ancient Sediments*, Columbia University Press, New York.

CHAVEZ, F. P. 1985. Ocean variability and phytoplankton community structure: Onset of the 1982–1983 El-Nino in the Peruvian upwelling region. *In*: *Preprints of the symposium on vertical motion in the equatorial upper ocean and its effects upon living resources and the atmosphere*. SCOR-UNESCO.

DEMAISON, G. J. & MOORE, G. T. 1980. Anoxic environments and oil source bed genesis. *AAPG Bulletin*, **64**, 1179–1209.

DE MENDIOLA, B. R. (1981) Seasonal phytoplankton distribution along the Peruvian coast. *In*: RICHARDS, F. A. (ed.) *Coastal Upwelling*. Am. Geophys. Union, Wash. DC, 348–356.

DESER, C. & WALLACE, J. M. 1987. El Niño events and their relation to the Southern Oscillation: 1925–1986. *Journal of Geophysical Research*, **92**, 14 189–14 196.

DIDYK, B. M., SIMONEIT, B. R. T., BRASSELL, S. C. & EGLINTON, G. 1978. Organic geochemical indicators of palaeoenvironmental conditions of sedimentation. *Nature*, **272**, 216–222.

DOUGLAS, R. G. 1981. Paleoecology of continental margin basins: a modern case history from the borderland of southern California. *In*: DOUGLAS, R. G., COLBURN, I. P. & GORSLINE, D. S. (eds) *Depositional Systems of Active Continental Margin basins: SEPM Pacific Section Short Course Notes*, 121–156.

FARRIMOND, P., POYNTER, J. G. & EGLINTON, G. 1990a. Molecular composition of sedimentary lipids off the Peru margin, Leg 112. *In*: SUESS, E., VON HUENE, R. *et al.* (eds) *Proceedings of the Ocean Drilling Program, Scientific Results, Vol. 112*. Ocean Drilling Program, College Station, TX, 539–546.

——, —— & —— 1990b. A molecular stratigraphic study of Peru margin sediments, Hole 686B, Leg 112. *In*: SUESS, E., VON HUENE, R. *et al.* (eds) *Proceedings of the Ocean Drilling Program, Scientific Results, Vol. 112*. Ocean Drilling Program, College Station, TX, 547–553.

FARRINGTON, J. W., DAVIS, A. C., SULANOWSKI, J., McCAFFREY, M. A., McCARTHY, M., CLIFFORD, C. H., DICKINSON, P. & VOLKMAN, J. K. 1988. Biogeochemistry of lipids in surface sediments of the Peru upwelling area — 15°S. *In*: MATTAVELLI, L. & NOVELLI, L. (eds) *Advances in Organic Geochemistry 1987 Organic Geochemistry*, **13**, 607–617.

——, FREW, N. M., GSCHWEND, P. M. & TRIPP, B. W. 1977. Hydrocarbons in cores of north-western Atlantic coastal and continental margin sediments. *Estuarine and Coastal Marine Science*, **5**, 793–808.

——, MCCAFFREY, M. A. & SULANOWSKI, J. 1990. Early diagenesis of organic matter in Peru upwelling area sediments. *In*: ITTEKKOT, V., KEMPE, S., MICHAELIS, W. & SPITZY, A. (eds) *Facets of Modern Biogeochemistry*. Springer, New York, 353–364.

FOSSING, H. 1990. Sulfate reduction in self sediments in the upwelling region off central Peru. *Continental Shelf Research*, **10**, 355–367.

GAGOSIAN, R. B. & FARRINGTON, J. W. 1978. Sterenes in surface sediments from the southwest African shelf and slope. *Geochimica et Cosmochimica Acta*, **42**, 1091–1101.

—— & SMITH, S. O. 1979. Steroid ketones from the southwest African shelf. *Nature*, **254**, 287–289.

——, SMITH, S. O., LEE, C., FARRINGTON, J. W. & FREW, N. M. 1980. Steroid transformations in Recent sediments. *In*: DOUGLAS, A. G. & MAXWELL, J. R. (eds) *Advances in Organic Geochemistry 1979*, 407–419.

GAGOSIAN, R. G., VOLKMAN, J. K. & NIGRELLI, G. E. 1983. The use of sediment traps to determine sterol sources in coastal sediments off Peru. *In*: BJORØY, M. *et al.* (eds) *Advances in Organic Geochemistry 1981*. Wiley, 369–379.

HENRICHS, S. M. & FARRINGTON, J. W. 1984*a*. Peru upwelling region sediments near 15°S. 1. Re-mineralization and accumulation of organic matter. *Limnology and Oceanography*, **29**, 1–19.

—— & ——. 1984*b*. Peru upwelling region sediments near 15°S. 2. Dissolved free and total hydrolyz-able amino acids. *Limnology and Oceanography*, **29**, 20–34.

HUNT, J. M. 1979. *Petroleum Geochemistry and Geology*. Freeman, San Francisco.

HUSSLER, G. & ALBRECHT, P. 1983. $C_{27}-C_{29}$ Mono-aromatic anthrasteroid hydrocarbons in Cretaceous black shales. *Nature*, **304**, 262–263.

KLOK, J., BAAS, M., COX, H. C., DE LEEUW, J. W., RIJPSTRA, W. I. C. & SCHENCK, P. A. 1984*a*. Qualitative and quantative characterization of the total organic matter in a recent marine sediment II. *In*: SCHENCK, P. A. *et al.* (eds) *Advances in Organic Geochemistry 1983. Organic Geochemistry*, **6**, 265–278.

——, ——, ——, ——, & ——. 1984*b*. Loliolides and dihydroactinidiolides in a recent marine sediment probably indicate a major transformation pathway of carotenoids. *Tetra. Letters*, 5577–5580.

LEE, C. & CRONIN, C. 1982. The vertical flux of particulate organic nitrogen in the sea: decomposition of amino acids in the Peru upwelling area and equatorial Atlantic. *Journal of Marine Research*, **40**, 227–251.

——, GAGOSIAN, R. B. & FARRINGTON, J. W. 1980. Geochemistry of sterols in sediments from the Black Sea and southwest African shelf and slope. *Organic Geochemistry*, **2**, 103–113.

LEWAN, M. D. 1984. Factors controlling the proportionality of vanadium to nickel in crude oils. *Geochimica et Cosmochimica Acta*, **48**, 2231–2238.

MAUGHAN, E. K. 1984. Geological setting and some geochemistry of petroleum source rocks in the Permian Phosphora Formation. *In*: WOODWARD, J., MEISSNER, F. F. & CLAYTON, J. L. (eds) *Hydrocarbon Source Rocks of the Greater Rocky Mountain Region* Rocky Mountain Assoc. of Geologists, 281–294.

MCCAFFREY, M. A. 1990. *Sedimentary lipids as indicators of depositional conditions in the coastal Peruvian upwelling regime*. PhD Thesis, Woods Hole Oceanogr. Inst./Mass. Inst. Tech.

——, FARRINGTON, J. W. & REPETA, D. J. 1989. Geochemical implications of the lipid composition of *Thioploca* spp. from the Peru upwelling region — 15°S. *Organic Geochemistry*, **14**, 61–68.

——, —— & ——. 1990. The organic geochemistry of Peru margin surface sediments — I. A comparison of the C_{37} alkenone and historical El Niño records. *Geochimica et Cosmochimica Acta*, **54**, 1671–1682.

——, —— & ——. 1991. The organic geochemistry of Peru margin surface sediments — II. Paleoenvironmental implications of hydrocarbon and alcohol profiles *Geochimica et Cosmochimica Acta*, **55**, 483–498.

MITCHELL-INNES, B. A. & WINTER, A. 1987. Coccolithophores: a major phytoplankton component in marine upwelled waters off the Cape Peninsula, South Africa in March, 1983. *Marine Biology*, **95**, 25–30.

MOSSMAN, J. -R., APLIN, A. C., CURTIS, C. D. & COLEMAN, M. L. 1990. Sulfur Geochemistry at sites 680 and 686 on the Peru Margin. *In*: SUESS, E., VON HUENE *et al.* (eds) *Proceedings of the Ocean Drilling Program, Scientific Results, Vol. 112* Ocean Drilling Program, College Station, TX, 455–464.

NISHIMURA, M. & KOYAMA, T. 1977. The occurrence of stanols in various living organisms and the behavior of sterols in contemporary sediments. *Geochimica et Cosmochimica Acta*, **41**, 379–385.

PETERS, K. E. & MOLDOWAN, J. M. 1991. Effects of source, thermal maturity, and biodegradation on the distribution and isomerization of homo-hopanes in petroleum. *Organic Geochemistry*, **17**, 47–61.

PEDERSEN, T. F. & Calvert, S. E. 1990. Anoxia vs. productivity: what controls the formation of organic-carbon-rich sediments and sedimentary rocks? *AAPG Bulletin*, **74**, 454–466.

POYNTER, J. G., FARRIMOND, P., BRASSELL, S. C., EGLINTON, G. 1990. Molecular stratigraphic study of sediments from holes 658A and 660A, Leg 108. *In*: RUDDIMAN, W., SARNTHEIN, M. *et al.* (eds) *Proceedings of the Ocean Drilling Program,*

Scientific Results, Vol. 108 Ocean Drilling Program, College Station, TX, 387–396.

QUINN, W. H., NEAL, V. T. & ANTUNEZ DE MAYOLO, S. E. 1987. El Niño occurrences over the past four and a half centuries. *Journal of Geophysical Research*, **92**, 14449–14461.

REPETA, D. J. 1989. Carotenoid diagenesis in recent marine sediments: II. Degradation of fucoxanthin to loliolide. *Geochimica et Cosmochimica Acta*, **53**, 699–707.

—— 1990. Carotenoid diagenesis in Pleistocene to Miocene sediments from the Peru margin. *In*: SUESS, E., VON HUENE, R. *et al.* (eds) *Proceedings of the Ocean Drilling Program, Scientific Results, Vol. 112* Ocean Drilling Program, College Station, TX, 567–572.

—— & —— 1984. Transformation reactions and recycling of carotenoids and chlorins in the Peru upwelling region (15°S, 75°W). *Geochimica et Cosmochimica Acta*, **48**, 1265–1277.

—— & —— 1987. Carotenoid diagenesis in recent marine sediments; I. The Peru continental shelf (15°S, 75°W). *Geochimica Cosmochimica Acta*, **51**, 1001–1009.

REIMERS, C. E. & SUESS, E. 1983a. Late Quaternary fluctuations in the cycling of organic matter off central Peru: A proto-kerogen record. *In*: SUESS, E. & THIEDE, J. (eds) *Coastal upwelling and its sedimentary record, Part A*. Plenum, New York, 497–526.

—— & —— 1983b. Spatial and temporal patterns of organic matter accumulation on the Peru continental margin. *In*: THIEDE, J. & SUESS, E. (eds) *Coastal upwelling and its sedimentary record, Part B*. Plenum, New York, 311–345.

RHOADS, D. C. & MORSE, J. W. 1971. Evolutionary and ecological significance of oxygen-deficient marine basins. *Lethaia*, **4**, 413–428.

RIDOUT, P. S., TIBBETTS, P. J. C. & MORRIS, R. J. 1984. Novel carotenoid pigments in organic-rich sediments from the Peru continental shelf. *Oceanologica Acta*, **7**, 363–367.

ROHMER, M., BOUVIER-NAVE, P. & OURISSON, G. 1984. Distribution of hopanoid triterpenes in prokaryotes. *Journal of General Microbiology*, **130**, 1137–1150.

——, DASTILLUNG, M. & OURISSON, G. 1980. Hopanoids from C_{30}–C_{35} in Recent muds. *Naturwissenschaften*, **67**, 456–458.

RULLKÖTTER, J. & WELTE, D. H. 1983. Maturation of organic matter in areas of high heat flow – a study of sediments from DSDP leg 63, offshore California, and leg 64, Gulf of California. *In*: BJORØY, M. *et al.* (eds) *Advances in Organic Geochemistry*. Wiley, New York, 338–438.

SINNINGHE DAMSTÉ, J. S., DE LEEUW, J. W., KOCK-VAN DALEN, A. C., DE ZEEUW, M. A., DE LANGE, F., RIJPSTRA, W. I. C. & SCHENCK, P. A. (1987) The occurrence and identification of a series of organic sulphur compounds in oils and sediment extracts. I. A study of Rozel Point oil (U.S.A.). *Geochimica et Cosmochimica Acta*, **51**, 2369–2391.

——, RIJPSTRA, W. I. C., DE LEEUW, J. W. &

SCHENCK, P. A. 1988. Origin of organic sulphur compounds and sulphur-containing high molecular weight substances in sediments and immature crude oils. *In*: NOVELLI, L. & MATTAVELLI, L. (eds) *Advances in Organic Geochemistry 1987, Organic Geochemistry*, **13**, 593–606.

——, Eglinton G., DE LEEUW, J. W. & SCHENCK, P. A. 1989. Organic sulfur in macromolecular sedimentary organic matter: I. Structure and origin of sulphur containing moieties in kerogen, asphaltenes and coal as revealed by flash pyrolysis. *Geochimica et Cosmochimica Acta*, **53**, 873–889.

SMITH, D. J., EGLINTON, G., MORRIS, R. J. & POUTANEN, E. L. 1982. Aspects of steroid geochemistry of a diatomaceous sediment from the Namibian Shelf. *Oceanologica Acta*, **5**, 365–378.

——, ——, —— & —— 1983a. Aspects of steroid geochemistry of an interfacial sediment from the Peruvian upwelling. *Oceanologica Acta*, **6**, 211–219.

——, —— & —— 1983b. Interfacial sediment and assessment of organic input from a highly productive water column. *Nature*, **304**, 259–261.

SOUTAR, A., JOHNSON, S. R. & BAUMGARTNER, T. R. 1981. In search of modern depositional analogs to the Monterey Formation. *In*: *The Monterey Formation and Related Siliceous Rocks of California*; SEPM, Los Angeles, 123–147.

TEN HAVEN, H. L., DE LEEUW, J. W., RULLKÖTTER, J. & SINNINGHE DAMSTÉ, J. S. 1987. Restricted utility of the pristane/phytane ratio as a palaeoenvironmental indicator. *Nature*, **330**, 641–643.

——, LITTKE, R., RULLKÖTTER, J., STEIN, R. & WELTE, D. H. 1990a. Accumulation rates and composition of organic matter in late Cenozoic sediments underlying the active upwelling area off Peru. *In*: SUESS, E. & VON HUENE, R. *Proceedings of the Ocean Drilling Program, Scientific Results, Vol. 112*. Ocean Drilling Program, College Station, TX, 591–606.

——, RULLKÖTTER, R. & STEIN, R. 1990b. Preliminary analyses of extractable lipids in sediments from the eastern north Atlantic (leg 108): A comparison of a coastal upwelling (Site 658) and a non-upwelling area (Site 659). *In*: RUDDIMAN, W., SARNTHEIN, M. *et al.* (eds) *Proceedings of the Ocean Drilling Program, Scientific Results, Vol. 108*. Ocean Drilling Program, College Station, TX, 351–360.

THOMPSON, L. G., THOMPSON, E. M. & ARANO, B. M. 1984. El Niño-southern oscillation events recorded in the stratigraphy of the tropical Quelecaya ice cap, Peru. *Science*, **226**, 50–52.

——, THOMPSON, E. M., DANSGAARD, W. & GROOTES, P. M. 1986. The little ice age as recorded in the stratigraphy of the tropical Quelecaya ice cap, Peru. *Science*, **226**, 361–364.

TISSOT, B. P. & WELTE, D. H. 1984. *Petroleum formation and occurrence*. Springer, New York.

VOLKMAN, J. K. 1986. A review of sterol biomarkers for marine and terrigenous organic matter. *Organic Geochemistry*, **9**, 83–99.

—— & MAXWELL, J. R. 1986. Acyclic isoprenoids as

biological markers. *In*: Johns, R. B. (ed.) *Biological Markers in the Sedimentary Record* 1–42. Elsevier, Amsterdam.

——, Farrington, J. W., Gagosian, R. B. & Wakeham, S. G. 1983. Lipid composition of coastal marine sediments from the Peru upwelling region. *In*: Bjorøy, M. *et al.* (ed.) *Advances in Organic Geochemistry 1981*. Wiley, New York, 228–240.

——, Farrington, J. W. & Gagosian, R. B. 1987. Marine and terrigenous lipids in coastal sediments from the Peru upwelling region at 15°S: Sterols and triterpene alcohols. *Organic Geochemistry*, **11**, 463–477.

Wakeham S. G., Farrington, J. W. & Volkman, J. K. 1983. Fatty acids, wax esters, triglycerides, and glyceryl esters associated with particles collected in sediment traps in the Peru upwelling area. *In*: Bjorøy, M. *et al.* (eds) *Advances in*

Organic Geochemistry 1981. Wiley, New York, 185–197.

Wardroper, A. M. K., Maxwell, J. R. & Morris, R. J. 1978. Sterols of a diatomaceous ooze from Walvis Bay. *Steroids*, **32**, 203–221.

Watts, C. D. & Maxwell, J. R. 1977. Carotenoid diagenesis in a marine sediment. *Geochimica et Cosmochimica Acta*, **41**, 493–497.

Whelan, J. K., Kanyo, Z., Tarafa, M. & McCaffrey, M. A. 1990. Organic Matter in Peru upwelling sediments — analysis by pyrolysis-GC and GCMS. *In*: Suess, E., von Huene, R. *et al.* (eds) *Proceedings of the Ocean Drilling Program, Scientific Results, Vol. 112*, 573–590, Ocean Drilling Program, College Station, TX.

Williams, L. A. & Reimers, C. 1983. Role of bacterial mats in oxygen-deficient marine basins and coastal upwelling regimes: Preliminary report. *Geology*, **11**, 267–269.

Water depth and diagenetic constraints on the use of barium as a palaeoproductivity indicator

MARTA T. VON BREYMANN[1], KAY-CHRISTIAN EMEIS[2] & ERWIN SUESS[3]

[1] Ocean Drilling Program, Texas A&M University, College Station, TX 77840, USA
[2] Geologisch-Paläontologisches Institut, Universität Kiel, Olshausenstrasse 40/60,
2300 Kiel, Germany
[3] GEOMAR, Wischhofstrasse 1–3, 2300 Kiel, Germany

Abstract: Sediments underneath the high productivity areas of the coastal upwelling and equatorial divergence zones in the Pacific and Indian oceans are enriched in barium, and on this basis the barium content of the sediments has long been suggested as a potential palaeoproductivity indicator. Analyses of sediments from the Peru margin corroborate the pattern of enhanced barium accumulation in areas of high primary productivity in the deep ocean, but also show that this pattern cannot be extended to shallow-water deposits. Sediments from the Peru shelf lack any barium enrichment, whereas this element is significantly enriched in slope and basinal deposits in water columns deeper than 2000 m. This depth effect is further illustrated at Site 682 located in the rapidly subsiding Lima Basin. The Quaternary sequence deposited at water depths >3000 m is enriched in organic carbon, opal and biogenic barium. The Miocene sediments, although deposited under highly productive waters associated with a coastal upwelling centre, do not show an enrichment in the barium record corresponding to the very high organic carbon and opal levels; a pattern that is consistent with deposition in shallow basins.

In addition to the effect of water depth on the barium distribution, overprinting of primary signals can be observed in sediments from upwelling areas undergoing strong anoxic diagenesis. Microcrystalline barite is partly dissolved in intervals depleted in interstitial sulphate as shown for sediments from the Peru margin. Dissolution of barite in sulphate depleted intervals of deep water sections leads to high barium concentrations near the termination of the sulphate reducing zone, where downward sulphate and upward barium diffusion foster local barite precipitation in diagenetic fronts.

The barium distribution in sedimentary oxic and suboxic environments at deep water depositional sites has a high potential as a palaeoproductivity indicator; however, barium accumulation as a proxy for ocean fertility should be used with caution in areas of varying water depths and in anoxic diagenetic environments where sulphate depletion undersaturates the interstitial waters with respect to barite.

The reconstructions of past climates, productivity patterns and chemical characteristics of the oceans from sedimentary records necessitates the identification of biological, mineralogical and chemical indicators, i.e. proxies, that record changes in the depositional environment. A major effort of palaeoceanographers in recent years has been devoted to finding such indicators that permit detailed reconstruction of productivity as a key factor in the global carbon cycle (e.g. Sarnthein *et al.* 1987; Boyle 1988; Berger *et al.* 1989). Biogenic carbonate and opal, often used directly to assess past productivities, undergo severe dissolution during passage through the water column and in the sediments. The organic matter in sinking detritus and in sediments, although long thought to be a good semiquantitative indicator (e.g. Müller & Suess 1979; Sarnthein *et al.* 1988) is remineralized in the water column, at the sediment–water interface, and within the sediment column to a significant extent (e.g. Cho & Azam 1988), leaving a small residual signal for extrapolation. Furthermore, productivity reconstructions based on organic carbon accumulation rates have considerable limitations in continental margin settings, where input from terrigenous sources and downslope transport of exhumed organic matter complicate the interpretation (Ittekkot 1988; Prahl *et al.* 1989). Other chemical parameters as proxies for productivity are thus needed to confirm inferences based upon organic carbon distributions and actual productivity measurements.

The good correlation between dissolved barium and silica in the water column has been taken as an indicator for a common biogenic mechanism controlling their distribution in the ocean (Dehaires *et al.* 1980). Sediments underneath the equatorial divergence in the Pacific and Indian Oceans are enriched in barium, and on this basis the barium content of the sediments

From SUMMERHAYES, C. P., PRELL, W. L. & EMEIS, K. C. (eds), 1992, *Upwelling Systems: Evolution Since the Early Miocene.* Geological Society Special Publication No 64, pp 273–284.

has long been suggested as a potential palaeo-productivity indicator (e.g. Revelle 1944; Goldberg & Arrhenius 1958). Recent measurements of barium flux in sediment trap samples strongly support this observation and serve as further evidence for a link between upper ocean biological processes and barium flux to the seafloor (Dymond *et al.* in press).

Lea & Boyle (1990) have suggested a relationship between the barium distribution in benthic foraminifers and water mass characteristics of glacial oceans. The variations in the Ba/Ca ratio of benthic foraminifers are thought to reflect changes in dissolved barium resulting from bottom-water ventilation (Lea & Boyle 1990). On the other hand, Bishop (1988) has shown that high particulate barium concentrations are associated with regions of intense organic matter regeneration. The effects of productivity, transport and the concentration of dissolved barium in bottom water have been evaluated by Dymond *et al.* (in press). They have shown that; (1) there is a direct link between particulate barium and ocean fertility; (2) at a given site the systematic variations of the C_{org}/Ba ratio in the particle rain can be estimated as a function of water depth; and (3) site-to-site changes in the decrease rate of the C_{org}/Ba values with depth seem to be related to the dissolved barium content of deep water.

Within the sediments the association of barium with productivity has been reasonably well established. Non-clastic barium concentrations in sediments from the Indian Ocean have been used to reconstruct Palaeogene and Neogene productivity underneath the equatorial divergence and to trace the northward movement of the Indian plate underneath this high productivity zone (Schmitz 1987). Likewise, Shimmield & Mowbray (1991) and Weedon & Shimmield (1991) showed that non-clastic barium concentrations in sediments from the Owen Ridge underneath the Arabian Sea upwelling area correlate highly with the $\delta^{18}O$ records of planktonic foraminifers, and found that highest barium levels, interpreted as highest productivity occurred at the heights of the interglacials. The correlation of isotope records and sedimentary barium contents is taken as an indicator that the supply of nutrients, productivity and high barium accumulation rates are linked to global changes in ocean fertility on glacial/interglacial timescales.

Barium in biogenically precipitated barite has great advantages over either organic matter, opal or carbonate as a primary productivity indicator because a larger percentage of the original signal is preserved in the sediment record (Dymond *et al.* in press). However, some caveats emerge from our work on upwelling sediments of the Peru margin and the equatorial Pacific which defines certain water-depth and diagenetic constraints on the indiscriminate use of barium as a productivity proxy. In the Peru margin, the eastern boundary coastal upwelling interacts with a tectonically controlled margin morphology (Thornburg 1981; Suess *et al.* 1987), providing a unique scenario to illustrate the depth and diagenetic considerations in using barium for palaeo-productivity reconstructions.

In this study we present results showing that depositional and tectonic history as well as possible diagenetic effects must be considered when interpreting the sedimentary barium record. For this we draw on published results of chemical analysis of sediments and pore waters documented by von Breymann *et al.* (in prep.), Emeis *et al.* (1990) and von Breymann *et al.* (1990). Analytical methods and results are described in these publications. Table 1 lists sites, water depths and sedimentary facies of the sediments considered for this study.

Regional patterns of barium accumulation in surface sediments

The sediments used in this study come from areas characterized by high biological productivity, but differ in their proximity to clastic sources, water depth and sedimentation rates. They offer the opportunity to examine the depositional, tectonic and diagenetic effects on the biogenic barium record because the general abundance of organic carbon and opal in these sediments characterize the type-facies commonly associated with barium enrichment in the sediments.

Comparison of barium concentration in surface sediments from the Bauer basin with the coastal upwelling area in the Peru margin (Fig. 1) show an enrichment of this element underneath the equatorial divergence that illustrates the general nature of barium association with high productivity sediments. The enhanced barium contents in the Bauer Basin sediments correspond to the well known region of oceanic upwelling and enhanced biological productivity underneath the equatorial divergence. These sediments are also enriched in biogenic opal, a relationship commonly observed in marine pelagic sediments (Goldberg & Arrhenius 1958). The deeper water levels and reduced sedimentation rates in these sediments relative to the Peru shelf result in significantly lower accumulation of organic carbon.

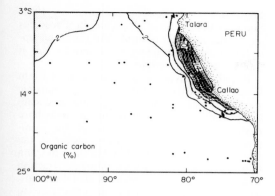

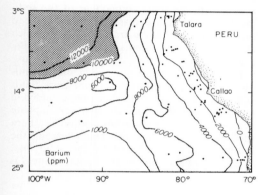

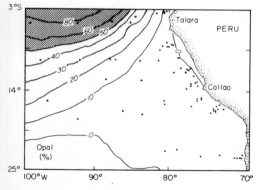

Fig. 1. Isolines of the concentrations of organic carbon, barium and opal in a carbonate free basis in surface sediments of the Bauer basin and Peru margin.

In contrast, no barium enrichment is observed in the organic-rich facies associated with coastal upwelling (Fig. 1). This sedimentary province, which extends for more than 1200 km along the Peru margin in water depths between 50 and 500 m, and its relation to high primary productivity has been extensively documented

(Reimers & Suess 1981). A series of surface sediment samples from these oceanic and coastal upwelling areas was selected to illustrate this apparent effect of water depth in the accumulation of barium (Fig. 2). Samples with similar organic carbon and opal contents show a significant increase in the barium content with water depth from 365 to 4581 m, whereas the organic carbon and opal concentrations in these sediments merely fluctuate between 2 and 5%.

That the influence of water depth on barium concentration in the sediments is an ubiquitous feature of many coastal upwelling areas is further illustrated by surface sediment analyses of the northwest Arabian Sea by Shimmield *et al.* (1990) and Hermelin & Shimmield (1990). Their results, complemented by analysis of surface sediments from the same area (Sirocko & Emeis, pers. comm.), also show an increase in barium with water depth (Fig. 3). Similarly, Calvert & Price (1983) reported a lack of barium enrichment in the opal-rich sediments of the shallow Namibian Shelf, a pattern that contrasts the higher levels of barium measured in the calcareous ooze sediments of the upper slope (Fig. 4).

These observations suggest that, besides siliceous-biogenic productivity, water depth may also contribute to the accumulation of barium in marine sediments. This is consistent with the mechanism proposed by Bishop (1988) for barite formation during decay, aggregation and settling of organic-rich detritus, where barite abundance increases during vertical transport below the thermocline. Sediment trap samples also show an increase in the particulate barium flux with depth (Dymond *et al.* in prep.), and provide additional evidence for a syngenetic origin for sedimentary barite.

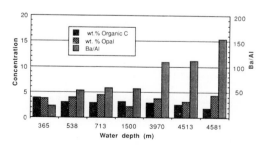

Fig. 2. Concentrations of organic carbon, opal, and barium normalized to aluminum for seven surface sediments of the Peru margin. Note that concentrations of organic carbon and opal are roughly comparable in all samples, while barium normalized to aluminum increases with water depth.

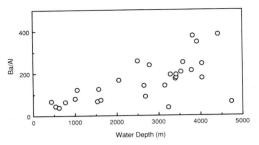

Fig. 3. Water depth versus barium normalized to aluminum for surface sediments of the northwestern Arabian Sea. Data from Shimmield *et al.* (1990), Hermelin & Shimmield (1990) and Sirocko & Emeis (unpublished).

Significance of the barium record in palaeoproductivity reconstructions

To evaluate the effects of varying water depths in the barium record and its significance in palaeoproductivity reconstructions, we analyzed cores from the shelf and slope areas between 11° and 16°S in the Lima Basin. This basin has been subsiding continuously at rates of 275 m/Ma during Pliocene to middle Pleistocene time, and at 500 m/Ma during the late

Pleistocene and Miocene (Kulm *et al.* 1981, Suess, von Huene *et al.* 1988) and thus provides an unique scenario to study the effects of upwelling-induced primary productivity in a rapidly subsiding margin.

In pelagic environments particulate barium fluxes are usually dominated by biogenic sources, whereas the detrital aluminosilicate component may be significant in nearshore environments. Factor analysis of the composition of sediment samples recovered in the Peru margin during ODP Leg 112 show thorium to be a good indicator for the lithogenic fraction in this region (von Breymann *et al.* 1990); thus, we have utilized the thorium abundance to estimate the biogenic component of the sedimentary barite. The excess of barium relative to the detrital signal is illustrated in Fig. 5, which also includes data from ODP Site 677 in the Equatorial Pacific for comparison. Because barium preservation in the sediments depends on the degree of saturation in the pore fluids with respect to barite, we have only included in this figure samples above the depth of sulphate depletion. Samples from Site 680 on the Peru shelf cluster along the line characterizing the detrital signal represented by the solid line, suggesting that at this site the barium content is

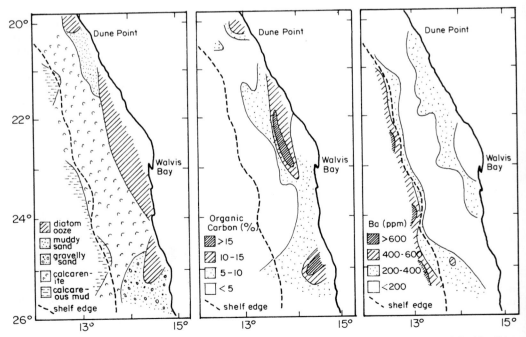

Fig. 4. Distribution of sediment lithofacies, organic carbon and barium in surface sediments of the Namibian continental shelf (Modified from Calvert & Price 1983).

Table 1. Site details.

Site	Location	Water Depth (m)	Sediment Type	Average TOC (%)	Average opal-Si (%)	Average Ba (ppm)	Reference
680	11°03.90'S/78°04.67'W	272	Foraminifer-siliceous mud	4.70	4.8	385	1,2
682	11°15.99'S/79°03.73'W	3801	Foraminifer-diatomaceous mud	7.80	9.6	717	1,2
685	9°06.78'S/80°35.01'W	5093	Diatomaceous mud	5.99	6.0	937	1,2
688	11°32.28'S/78°56.6'W	3836	Diatomaceous mud	3.80	4.4	1568	1,2
677	1°12.138'N/83°44.22'W	3472	Siliceous nannofossil ooze	0.42	n.d.	2656	3,4

1: Suess, von Huene et al. (1988)
2: Emeis et al. (1990)
3: Becker, Saito et al. (1988)
4: von Breymann (unpublished)

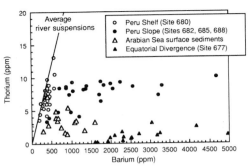

Fig. 5. Barium to thorium ratios of sediments from three upwelling areas compared to the ratio in average riverine suspended matter (Martin & Maybeck 1979). For water depth and sediment type refer to Table 1. Note that sediments from the Peru shelf (Site 680) follow the trend of clastic lithogenic material, while deeper sites from the Peru shelf deviate systematically towards higher barium content. Surface sediments from the northern Arabian Sea are enriched in barium over thorium, a trend that is seen most clearly in sediments from Site 677 underneath the Equatorial Divergence.

almost exclusively associated with the clastic fraction of the sediment. By contrast, samples from Sites 682, 685, and 688 of the Peru slope are significantly enriched in barium, reflecting the input from the biogenic component. This trend is even more pronounced in samples from Site 677, underneath the equatorial-upwelling zone.

The depth dependence of the biogenic barium content of the Peru slope and shelf sites is clearly apparent in Fig. 6. This figure shows biogenic barium and total organic carbon in a sequence of cores across the Peru margin. Core W7706−44 and ODP Site 680 are located beneath the strongest wind-driven upwelling areas, underneath present productivity levels as high as 1 gC/m^2/a (Chavez & Barber 1987). These sediments record deposition of diatom frustules and high concentrations of organic matter characteristic of upwelling facies; however, no significant accumulation of biogenic barium is associated with these deposits. Contrasting this scenario, sediments currently deposited in the slope and trench axis (Cores W7706−49, W7706−50) record high levels of biogenic barium that increase seaward. Core W7706−69 has the highest concentration of barium in the sediments. This core is located closer to the equator, where higher productivity coupled with waters deeper than 2000 m lead to barium levels as high as 7000 ppm.

Sites 682 and 688 lie on the lower slope of the

Peru trench, seaward of the mud lens associated with present-day upwelling. The Site 688 sequence depicted in Fig. 6 comprises Quaternary diatomaceous muds that were deposited at water depths greater than 3000 m (Suess, von Huene *et al.* 1988). These sediments are enriched in barium even though they were deposited in a lower productivity regime relative to the shelf sites; again reflecting the effect of water depth in the barium distribution. Samples from Site 682 comprise sequences that span from middle Eocene to the Holocene, and record significant fluctuations in water depth (Fig. 7). Benthic foraminifer assemblages indicate that the Pliocene to Holocene sediments were deposited at water depths similar to the present-day water depth of 3788 m. The Miocene assemblages, on the other hand, reflect upper shelf to middle bathyal depths of approximately 500−1500 m (Suess, von Huene *et al.* 1988). The effect of tectonically driven changes in water depth and depositional regimes is reflected in the sediment record. Sediments between 0 and 114 mbsf consist of hemipelagic muds having abundant biogenic components very rich in organic carbon (5 to 18%) and opaline silica (3 to 15%). This sequence shows a biogenic barium enrichment similar to that measured in Core W7706−49 and even though some of these enhanced barium levels represent localized enrichments related to barite remobilization (see next section), the general profile indicates concentrations higher than 1000 ppm; levels that are indicative of water depths >1000 m. The section ranging from 114 to 311 mbsf (late middle to late Miocene age) consists of diatomaceous muds, with diatom contents reaching 40% (Suess, von Huene *et al.* 1988), and represents deposition under the upper Miocene upwelling centre in shallow water (Fig. 7). The organic carbon values and the opal contents are higher than in the Pleistocene deposits; however, this unit is characterized by very low barium levels. Deposition at Site 682 during the Miocene occurred in a scenario comparable to that of the present day Peru shelf (Core W7706−44, Site 680) where sediments accumulating underneath the upwelling centre do not reflect the high biogenic productivity in the barium record, due to deposition in waters shallower than 1000 m.

Diagenetic overprinting of barium distribution in sediments

The pronounced diagenetic processes in organic-rich coastal upwelling sediments impose another constraint that may limit the usefulness of this element in anoxic sedimentary environ-

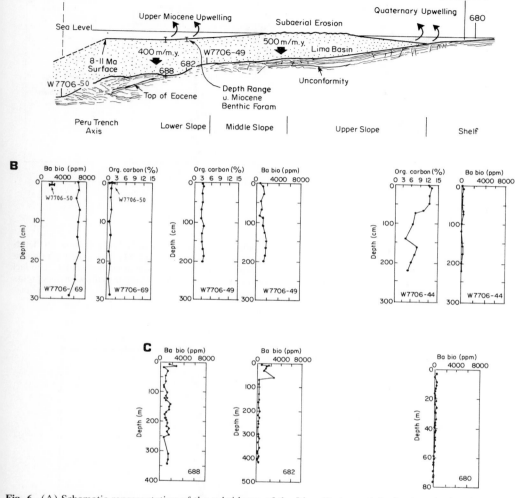

Fig. 6. (A) Schematic representation of the subsidence of the Lima Basin, and the landward migration of upwelling centers between upper Miocene and present times modified from Suess, von Huene *et al.* (1988). Subsidence is based on benthic foraminifer assemblages, coastal upwelling facies and the hiatus associated with the 8–11 Ma unconformity. (B) Distribution of organic carbon and biogenic barium in kasten cores from the Peru middle slope (W7706–49) and shelf (W7706–44). (C) Distribution of biogenic barium in ODP drill-sites on the lower slope (688), middle slope (682) and shelf (680). Core W7706–69 is located in the trench axis, closer to the high productivity associated with the equatorial divergence. It shows higher biogenic barium levels characteristic of deposition underneath fertile, deep-water environments.

ments. In spite of the low solubility and hence high stability of barite (BaSO$_4$) in seawater, this mineral is dissolved under conditions of sulphate depletion during microbial sulphate reduction when sulphate concentrations in the interstitial waters approach zero:

$$BaSO_4 \rightarrow Ba^{2+} + SO_4^{2-}$$
$$2CH_2O + SO_4^{2-} \rightarrow H_2S + 2HCO_3^-.$$

Such conditions frequently occur in upwelling sediments accumulating at high rates. Figure 8 depicts the downhole distribution of the barium to thorium ratio in solids and of dissolved barium and sulphate in the sediment pore waters of Sites 680, 688 and 677. As stated before, the barium excess relative to the detrital ratio as indicated by the deviation from the average river suspension for Sites 688 and 677 is very

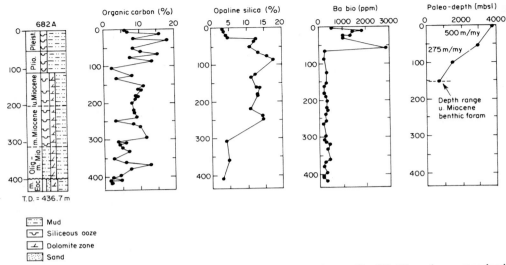

Fig. 7. Lithologic units, organic carbon, opaline silica, biogenic barium at Site 682. The palaeo-water-depth depicted by the solid line is based on subsidence rates reported by Kulm *et al.* (1981). Note the high opaline silica concentration of the Miocene deposits, consistent deposition under a coastal upwelling centre. The lack of biogenic barium enrichment in the Miocene sequence is consistent with deposition in shallow environments.

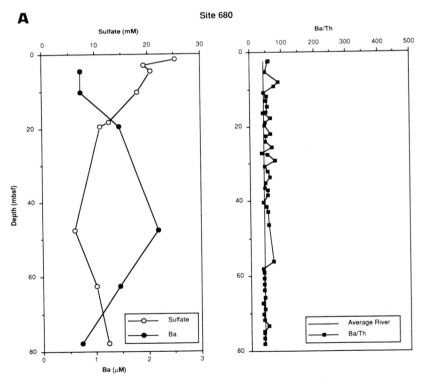

Fig. 8. Downhole profiles of dissolved barium and sulphate concentrations in interstitial waters and barium normalized to thorium in sediments at (A) Site 680 and (B) Site 688 drilled on the Peru margin, and at (C) Site 677. Also given is the average ratio of barium to thorium for shales (Wedepohl 1970) as a solid line where appropriate. Note different scales for dissolved Ba and Ba/Th in the individual profiles!

B

Site 688

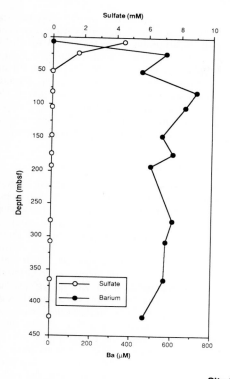

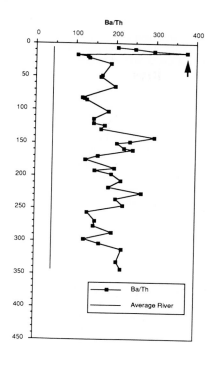

C

Site 677

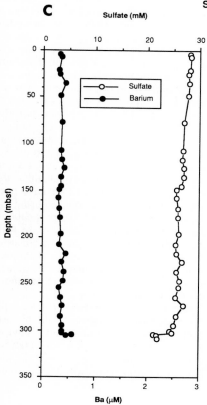

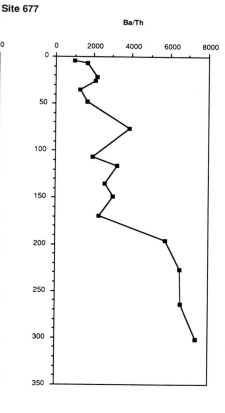

likely the result of biogenic or epigenetic accumulation of barium at these sites. The steep increase in dissolved barium at Site 688, where values reach up to 800 μM, greatly exceeds the seawater equilibrium concentration relative to barite solubility of 0.36 μM (Church & Wolgemuth 1972). The high concentrations of barium in the interstitial waters of the deep slope site, contrary to the lack of biogenic particulate and dissolved barium that is evident at Site 680 (Fig. 8), must result from dissolution of some portion of this biogenic barite under conditions of complete sulphate exhaustion.

Dissolution of barite in the sulphate-depleted intervals of deep-water sections, diffusion and reprecipitation leads to an enrichment of particulate barite near the termination of the sulphate reduction zone at Site 688. At this level downward sulphate diffusion and upward barium transport foster local barite precipitation. The diagenetic barite front is marked with an arrow in Fig. 8b. The same pattern of sulphate, dissolved barium, and particulate barium concentrations was also encountered at Sites 682 and 685 on the Peru slope and is described elsewhere (von Breymann *et al.* 1990).

The barium distributions at the Peru slope sites contrast markedly with those observed at Site 677 underneath the Equatorial Divergence (Fig. 8c). Pore waters at this site do not show evidence for barium mobilization, even though the sediments are enormously enriched in biogenic barium (see Fig. 5). The reason for the differing behaviour of dissolved barium in comparison to the margin sites lies in the ubiquitous presence of high concentrations of interstitial sulphate in the sediments. The contents of both sulphate and dissolved barium barely deviate from those of seawater (Fig. 8c). Under these conditions, the pore waters remain supersaturated with respect to barite during diagenesis and barite is not dissolved. We can be reasonably certain that any productivity signal encoded in the barium record at Site 677 is largely unaffected by remobilization and dissolution and that it has not been erased or overprinted by post-depositional diagenesis. On the other hand, sulphate at Site 688 is completely exhausted at approximately 40 m below the seafloor and a portion of the sedimentary barite is dissolved, giving rise to high concentrations of dissolved barium in pore waters of this site.

These results imply that the development of 'barite fronts' requires a labile barium source, which is not likely to be the barium associated with the clastic detritus but rather draws from the syngenetically formed barite flux and hence degrades the productivity signal. The development of 'barite fronts', a phenomenon similar to the well known metalliferous redox fronts in pelagic sediments, was proposed by Goldberg & Arrhenius (1958) and restated by Brumsack (1986) as a mechanism leading to the formation of barite enrichment at chemical boundaries and in lag deposits. It is not immediately clear if the loss of syngenetic barite can be corrected for, or whether this kind of diagenetic overprinting degrades the signal beyond correction.

Conclusions

Results from geochemical sediment analysis are consistent with sediment trap studies of barium fluxes (Dymond *et al.* in press); observations that indicate that the barium productivity signal is amplified during transport through the water column. The processes by which barium is transported to the sediments, although not completely clear, are likely to be related to a syngenetic mechanism during decay, aggregation and settling of organic-rich detritus (Bishop 1988). The barium flux to the ocean floor is probably a function of the dissolved barium concentration, primary productivity and type of substrate. The sediment data clearly show a lack of biogenic barium enrichment in shallow environments; however, the results do not constrain this phenomenon to processes in the water column. Differences in preservation and bioturbation, both processes occurring at the sediment water interface, could also contribute to the observed barium distribution.

The sedimentary barium distributions presented here corroborate the pattern of enhanced barium accumulation in areas of high primary productivity in the deep ocean, but also show that this pattern cannot be extended to shallow-water environments. This observation is of utmost significance when attempting comparison of palaeoproductivity regimes among sites underlying water columns of significantly different depths or in regions that have undergone significant uplift or subsidence during their geological history. The fact that particulate barium flux shows an exponential increase with water depth (Dymond *et al.* in press) is consistent with the lack of biogenic barium accumulation in sediments shallower than 1000 m; an observation that may be useful in tracing palaeodepths in marginal basins.

Our data also show that barium as a proxy for siliceous biogenic input should be used with caution in anoxic diagenetic environments where sulphate depletion undersaturates the interstitial waters with respect to barite, as barium remobilization will degrade the palaeoproductivity signal. On the other hand, buried and partially dissolved diagenetic barite fronts may offer a novel way of tracking changes in diagenesis, i.e. intensity of sulphate reduction and deviations from uniform sedimentation rates. The reconstruction of productivity from barium concentrations and accumulation rates is only advised in deep pelagic sediments with low rates of sulphate reduction during early diagenesis. The barium distributions in the sediment record must be interpreted in light of the particular depositional and diagenetic conditions at each site before attempting a direct application of this tracer to palaeoproductivity reconstructions.

We would like to thank the Ocean Drilling Program and Oregon State University for the samples used in this study. Comments by G. B. Shimmield and an anonymous reviewer greatly improved the manuscript. We gratefully acknowledge financial support from USSAC to each of the authors.

References

BECKER, K., SAKAI, H. et al. 1988. Proceedings of the Ocean Drilling Program, Scientific Results. Ocean Drilling Program, College Station, TX, 111.

BERGER, W. H., SMETACEK, V. S. & WEFER, G. (eds) 1989. Productivity of the Ocean: Present and Past. Wiley, Chichester, 471.

BISHOP, J. K. B. 1988. The barite-opal-organic carbon association in oceanic particulate matter. Nature, 332, 341–363.

BOYLE, E. A. 1988. Cadmium: Chemical tracer of deepwater paleoceanography. Palaeoceanography, 3/4, 471–489.

BRUMSACK, H. J. 1986. The inorganic geochemistry of Cretaceous black shales (DSDP Leg 41) in comparison to modern upwelling sediments from the Gulf of California. In: SUMMERHAYES, C. P. & SHACKLETON, N. J. (eds) North Atlantic Paleoceanography. Geological Society, London, Special Publication, 21, 447–462.

BRUMSACK, H. J. & GIESKES, J. M. 1983. Interstitial water trace element chemistry of laminated sediments from the Gulf of California, Mexico. Marine Chemistry, 14, 89–106.

CALVERT, S. E. & PRICE, N. B. 1983. Geochemistry of Namibian Shelf sediment. In: THIEDE, J. & SUESS, E. (eds) Coastal Upwelling: Its Sedimentary Record. Plenum, New York, 337–375.

CHAVEZ, F. P. & BARBER, R. T. 1987. Estimates of new production in the Equatorial Pacific. Deep-Sea Research, 34, 1229–1243.

CHURCH, T. M. & WOLGEMUTH, K. 1972. Marine barite saturation. Earth and Planetary Science Letters 15, 35–44.

CHO, B. C. & AZAM, F. 1988. Major role of bacteria in biogeochemical fluxes in the ocean's interior. Nature, 332, 441–43.

DEHAIRES, F., CHESSELET, R. & JEDWAB, J. 1980. Discrete suspended particles of barite and the barium cycle in the ocean. Earth and Planetary Science Letters, 49, 528–550.

DYMOND, J., SUESS, E. & LYLE, M. Barium in deep-sea sediments: a geochemical indicator of palaeoproductivity. Paleoceanography (in press).

EMEIS, K.-C., BOOTHE, P. N., KATZ, B. J., MORSE, J. W., PRESLEY, B. J. & VON BREYMANN, M. T. 1990. Geochemical data report for Peru margin sediments from Sites 680, 682, 685, and 688. In: SUESS, E., VON HUENE, R., et al. (eds) Proceedings of the Ocean Drilling Program, Scientific Results. Ocean Drilling Program, College Station, TX, 683–692.

GOLDBERG, E. D. & ARRHENIUS, G. O. S. 1958. Chemistry of Pacific pelagic sediments. Geochimica et Cosmochimica Acta, 13, 153–212.

HERMELIN, J. O. R. & SHIMMIELD, G. B. 1990. The importance of the oxygen minimum zone and sediment geochemistry in the distribution of Recent benthic foraminifers in the Northwest Indian Ocean. Marine Geology, 91, 1–29.

ITTEKKOT, V. 1988. Global trends in the nature of organic matter in river suspensions. Nature, 332, 436–438.

KULM, L. D., SCHRADER, H., RESIG, J. M., THORNBURG, T. M., MASIAS, A. & JOHNSON, L. 1981. Late Cenozoic carbonates on the Peru continental margin: Lithostratigraphy, biostratigraphy, and tectonic history. In: KULM, L. D. et al. (eds) Nazca Plate: Crustal Formation and Andean Convergence, Geological Society of America, Memoir 154, 445–468.

LEA, D. W. & BOYLE, E. A. 1990. Foraminiferal reconstruction of barium distributions in water masses of the glacial oceans. Paleoceanography, 5, 719–742.

MARTIN, J.-M. & MEYBECK, M. 1979. Elemental mass-balance of material carried by major rivers. Marine Chemistry, 7, 173–206.

MÜLLER, P. J. & SUESS, E. 1979. Productivity, sedimentation rate, and sedimentary organic carbon in the ocean – I. Organic carbon preservation. Deep-Sea Research, 26A, 1347–1362.

PRAHL, F., MUEHLHAUSEN, L. & LYLE, M. 1989. An organic geochemical assessment of oceanographic conditions at MANOP Site C over the past 26 000 years. Paleoceanography, 4, 495–510.

REIMERS, C. E. & SUESS, E. 1981. Spatial and temporal patterns of organic matter accumulation on the Peru continental margin. In: THIEDE, J. & SUESS, E. (eds) Coastal Upwelling: Its Sedimentary Record. Plenum, New York, 311–346.

REVELLE, R. 1944. Marine bottom samples collected in the Pacific by the Carnegie on its seventh cruise. Carnegie Inst. Washington Publ. 556, 1–180.

SARNTHEIN, M., WINN, K. & ZAHN, R. 1987. Palaeoproductivity of oceanic upwelling and the effect on atmospheric CO_2 and climate change during deglaciation times. In: BERGER, W. H. & LABEYRIE, L. D. (eds) Abrupt Climate Change. Dordrecht (D. Reidel), 311–337.

——, WINN, K., DUPLESSY, J.-C. & FONTUGNE, R. 1988. Global variations of surface ocean productivity in low and mid-latitudes: Influence on CO_2 reservoirs of the deep ocean and atmosphere during the last 21 000 years. *Paleoceanography*, **3/3**, 361–399.

SCHMITZ, B. 1987. Barium, equatorial high productivity and the northward wandering of the Indian continent. *Paleoceanography*, **2**, 63–77.

SHIMMIELD, G. B. & MOWBRAY, S. R. 1991. The inorganic geochemical record of the northwestern Arabian Sea: A history of productivity variation over the last 400 ka from Sites 722 and 724. *In*: PRELL, W. L., NIITSUMA, N. *et al.* (eds) *Proceedings of the Ocean Drilling Program, Scientific Results*. Ocean Drilling Program, College Station, TX, **117**.

SUESS, E., KULM, L. D. & KILLINGLEY, J. S. 1987. Coastal upwelling and the history of organic-rich mudstone deposition off Peru. *In*: BROOKS, J. & FLEET, A. J. (eds) *Marine Petroleum Source Rocks*. Geological Society, London, Special Publication, **26**, 181–197.

SUESS, E., VON HUENE, R. *et al.* 1988. *Proceedings of the Ocean Drilling Program, Initial Reports*. Ocean Drilling Program, College Station, TX, **112**.

THORNBURG, T. M. 1981. *Sedimentary basins of the Peru continental margin: Structure, stratigraphy and Cenozoic tectonics from 6°S to 16°S latitude*, MS thesis, Oregon State University, Corvallis.

VON BREYMANN, M., EMEIS, K.-C. & CAMERLENGHI, A. 1990. Geochemistry of Sediments from the Peru upwelling area: results from ODP Sites 680, 682, 685, and 688. *In*: SUESS, E., VON HUENE, R. *et al.* (eds) *Proceedings of the Ocean Drilling Program, Scientific Results*. Ocean Drilling Program, College Station, TX, **112**, 491–503.

VON BREYMANN, M. T., SUESS, E., LYLE, M. & DYMOND, J. submitted. Enrichment of barium and copper in deep-water sediments of the Peru margin and Nazca Plate: Implications for palaeoproductivity reconstructions. *Paleoceanography*.

WEDEPOHL, K. H. 1970. Environmental influences on the chemical composition of shales and clays. *In*: AHRENS, L. H., PRESS, L. *et al.* (eds) *Physics and Chemistry of the Earth*. Pergamon, Oxford 307–333.

WEEDON, G. & SHIMMIELD, G. B. 1991. Late Pleistocene upwelling and productivity variations in the northwest Indian Ocean deduced from spectral analyses of geochemical data from ODP Sites 722 and 724. *In*: PRELL, W. L., NIITSUMA, N. *et al. Proceedings of the Ocean Drilling Program, Scientific Results*. Ocean Drilling Program, College Station, TX, **117**.

Strong deglacial minimum in the $\delta^{13}C$ record from planktonic foraminifera in the Benguela upwelling region: palaeoceanographic signal or early diagenetic imprint?

R. SCHNEIDER, A. DAHMKE, A. KÖLLING, P. J. MÜLLER, H. D. SCHULZ & G. WEFER

Fachbereich Geowissenschaften, Universität Bremen, Klagenfurter Straße, 2800 Bremen 33, Germany

Abstract: A strong deglacial decrease in the $\delta^{13}C$ values of the planktonic foraminifera *G. inflata* and *G. bulloides*, spanning a 1000-year period, was measured in a core from the Benguela upwelling region. The deglacial $\delta^{13}C$ minimum exceeds background values by more than $-1‰$, and is between -1.6 to $-2.0‰$ below Holocene values. The unusual low $\delta^{13}C$ values could reflect a change in the isotopic composition of the upwelled South Atlantic Central Water (SACW) and/or changes in the stratification of the surface waters in the Benguela coastal upwelling region. The observed $\delta^{13}C$ decrease correlates with a proposed zone of authigenic $CaCO_3$ precipitation at 6 m depth in the anaerobic sediments. This raises the question whether the $\delta^{13}C$ minimum was caused by diagenetic alteration of the $\delta^{13}C$ record or not. Calculations based on estimated interstitial water $\delta^{13}C_{TCO_2}$ values and flux rates of Ca predict a 5% authigenic $CaCO_3$ precipitation additional to the primary $CaCO_3$ content in the sediment, which could account for an average diagenetic imprint of $-1.0‰$ $\delta^{13}C_{CaCO3}$ if precipitated on foraminiferal tests. However, missing visual evidence (SEM) for authigenic $CaCO_3$ phases greatly weakens the case for diagenetic causes for the negative $\delta^{13}C$ spike. The deglacial negative $\delta^{13}C$ spike is therefore assumed to be a primary palaeoceanographic signal.

In many palaeoceanographic studies, stable oxygen and carbon isotopes of planktonic foraminiferal tests have been used to evaluate past temperatures, global ice cover changes and the TCO_2 budget of the surface ocean during Quaternary glacial and interglacial times. In particular $\delta^{13}C$ changes in planktonic foraminiferal records from sediment cores collected worldwide have been useful in identifying ancient variations in carbon reservoirs (Shackleton 1977), nutrient conditions and circulation changes (Shackleton & Pisias 1985; Williams 1985; Curry & Crowley 1987; Oppo & Fairbanks 1989), upwelling intensity and productivity (Berger *et al.* 1978; Berger & Vincent 1986; Sarnthein *et al.* 1984) or atmospheric-ocean gas exchange rates (Charles & Fairbanks 1990). To date few palaeoceanographic studies dealing with stable isotopes on foraminifera have examined the alteration of the stable isotope signal through early diagenetic processes (see references in Longstaffe 1983). Other studies are mostly focused on diagenetic processes within older sediments (Irwin *et al.* 1977; Killingley 1983; Showers *et al.* 1987).

In 1988, sediment cores were recovered by RV Meteor from the eastern Angola Basin in order to reconstruct the late Quaternary palaeoceanography of the surface waters and to evaluate the early diagenetic processes in the sediments (Wefer *et al.* 1988). At Site GeoB

1023 ($17°09.5'S/11°00.5'E$, water depth 1980 m, Fig. 1), two gravity cores were taken next to each other: GeoB 1023-4 was sampled for geochemical and interstitial water studies, and GeoB 1023-5 for investigations of faunal assemblages, isotopic measurements, and evaluation of accumulation rates of biogenic bulk parameters (total organic carbon (TOC), opal, $CaCO_3$).

Site GeoB 1023 is placed beneath the high productivity area off Namibia (Fig. 1). Today strong SE-Trades induce coastal upwelling of the SACW (South Atlantic Central Water) from depths of 200 to 400 m up to 15° S during austral winter (Hart & Currie 1960; Hagen *et al.* 1981; Nelson & Hutchings 1983). North of the coastal upwelling area, the surface waters are marked by the convergence of the northward flowing Benguela Coastal Current and the southward flowing Angola Current (BCC and AC, Fig. 1) (Moroshkin *et al.* 1970). The convergence changes its position seasonally between 17° and 14° S. North of the convergence, warm and nutrient poor surface waters of the AC superimpose subsurface cold and nutrient rich water masses of the BBC. A strong thermocline is established between 20 and 30 m water depth during the whole year (Shannon *et al.* 1987).

In this contribution, we present the $\delta^{18}O$ and $\delta^{13}C$ records of planktonic foraminifera for the last deglaciation in the Benguela upwelling sys-

From SUMMERHAYES, C. P., PRELL, W. L. & EMEIS, K. C. (eds), 1992, *Upwelling Systems: Evolution Since the Early Miocene*. Geological Society Special Publication No 64, pp 285–297.

285

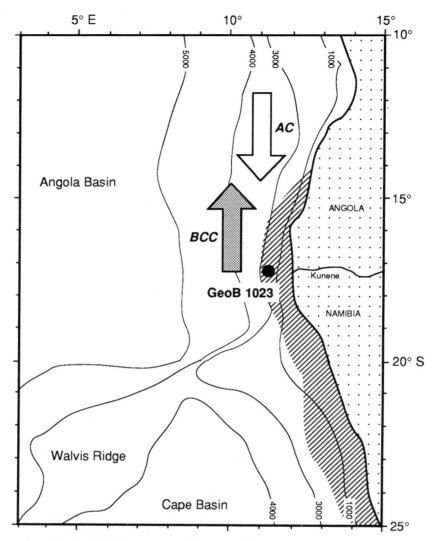

Fig. 1. Location of Site 1023 in the coastal upwelling area off Namibia (hatched). The arrows show direction of the main surface currents: AC, Angola Current; BCC, Benguela Coastal Current. Depth contours are given in metres.

tem and discuss them first in a palaeoceano-graphic sense. Second, we estimate the amount of authigenic $CaCO_3$ precipitation from the interstitial water geochemistry and discuss the possible diagenetic overprint on the isotopic signals.

Methods

Stratigraphic control was established by ^{14}C determinations on total organic carbon (TOC) in core GeoB 1023–4. The ^{14}C determinations

were made on TOC using the benzol-syntheses (TASK benzene synthesizer), and were measured with a PACKARD Tri-Carb 1050 liquid scintillation counter. The ^{14}C ages were calculated with a half-life time of 5568 years. The $\delta^{13}C$ correction was according to Faure (1986).

Stable oxygen and carbon isotope measurements were made on *Globorotalia inflata* (d'Orbigny) and *Globigerina bulloides* d'Orbigny using a manual carbonate preparation line attached to a FINNIGAN MAT

Table 1. Content (wt%) and $\delta^{13}C$-values (%O vs PDB) of total organic carbon (TOC) and ^{14}C determinations for core GeoB 1023−4.

Depth in core (m)	TOC content	$\delta^{13}C$ TOC	^{14}C age* (years B.P.)
0.41−0.45	4.2	−20.04	1 910 ± 60
1.45−1.48	2.7	−20.33	5 860 ± 150
2.44−2.48	2.8	−20.16	9 530 ± 360
2.95−2.99	3.8	−20.36	10 580 ± 110
4.44−4.48	3.4	−19.87	11 240 ± 190
5.94−5.97	2.8	−19.84	13 860 ± 140
8.12−8.15	2.2	−19.91	14 580 ± 280
9.14−9.17	2.5	−20.07	18 220 ± 260

* To calculate the ^{14}C ages a half-life time of 5568 years was used. The $\delta^{13}C$ correction was according to Faure (1986).

251 mass spectrometer. Both species displayed continuously high abundances throughout the core, suitable to measure duplicates and to sample within a small size range (200−350 μm). Calibration to the PDB standard was via the NBS18, NBS19 and NBS20 standards. Analytical precision was better than ±0.08‰ and ±0.05‰ for $\delta^{18}O$ and $\delta^{13}C$, respectively.

$\delta^{13}C$-measurements on TOC were carried out with a FINNIGAN trapping box, combined with a furnace system of a HERAEUS CHN analyzer and attached to a FINNIGAN DELTA mass spectrometer. Calibration to the PDB standard was via the PEF-1 and sucrose ANU standards. Analytical precision was better than ±0.1‰.

The contents of TOC and $CaCO_3$ in core GeoB 1023−4 were measured with a LECO CS 125 (F. GINGELE, unpublished data). In core GeoB 1023−5 the TOC contents were determined with a HERAEUS CHN analyzer. For this purpose we run duplicate samples, one for the total carbon (TC) and a second decalcified with 6 N HCL for TOC. The $CaCO_3$ content was calculated from the difference of both $(CaCO_3) = (TC − TOC) \times 8.333$, assuming that the total inorganic carbon comes from $CaCO_3$. The analytical error was less then 3% for TOC and between 5 and 10% for $CaCO_3$.

The interstitial water preparation and analyses were done with standard methods (Grasshoff et al. 1983) and are described in Kölling (1991).

Stratigraphy

The chronology for core GeoB 1023−4 is based on the ^{14}C ages shown in Table 1 and Fig. 2. No correction for surface water "^{14}C age" was performed. The age-depth plot (Fig. 2) indicates average sedimentation rates of 30 cm/ka for the Holocene and for the last Glacial, and 110 cm/

ka for the deglaciation phase. The age model from core GeoB 1023−4 was converted to core GeoB 1023−5 using the $CaCO_3$ records (Fig. 3). The $CaCO_3$ records of the two cores are identical in both amplitude and pattern, which allows a correlation between the cores. The presented age model shows a continuous sedimentation pattern without erratic changes for both cores, which is consistent with the $\delta^{18}O$ records of the planktonic foraminifera in core GeoB 1023−5 (see below). This observation applies in particular to the depth interval, which is the focus in this study.

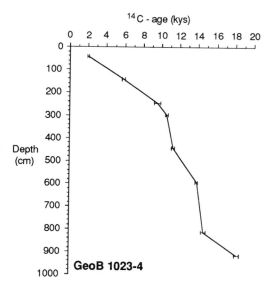

Fig. 2. Age-depth plot for core GeoB 1023−4 based on uncorrected ^{14}C ages of the total organic carbon (Table 1). Error bars show 1 sigma deviation.

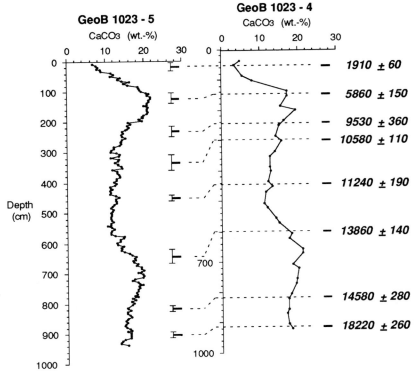

Fig. 3. Dating of the sediments in core GeoB 1023−5 with the correlation of the CaCO₃ records. The ¹⁴C ages from core GeoB 1023−5 were transfered to depth in core GeoB 1023−5 by identifying comparable events in the pattern of both CaCO₃ records. Error bars show uncertainties in the alignment due to different sample intervals between the two cores.

Results

Figure 4 shows the Ca^{2+} and SO_4^{2-} concentrations, and the alkalinity of interstitial waters versus depth in core GeoB 1023−4. From these profiles two principal zones can be deduced, in which early diagenetic reactions took place (Kölling 1991). The first zone, at a depth of 2.5 to 3.5 m, is controlled by oxidation processes coupled with the fixation of HCO_3^- (expressed as alkalinity), and the release of Ca^{2+}. The second zone, which is located between 6 and 7 m depth, is mainly controlled by the reduction of SO_4^{2-} and the fixation of Ca^{2+} as $CaCO_3$, as can be deduced from the Ca^{2+} profile.

Figure 4 also shows the results of the $\delta^{18}O$ and $\delta^{13}C$ measurements on planktonic foraminifera from core GeoB 1023−5. According to the ¹⁴C age model the depth profiles are divided into a glacial, deglacial and Holocene section. For the deglacial phase we take the period between 8.5 and 14.5 ka (Fairbanks 1989). The $\delta^{18}O$ records for both species, *G. inflata* and

G. bulloides, exhibit a trend from high glacial to low interglacial values, as expected for Termination I. While the curve for *G. inflata* documents steplike changes during deglaciation, the curve for *G. bulloides* indicates a more linear change in surface water conditions from the last glacial maximum (LGM) to the Holocene (HOL). Delta $\delta^{18}O_{LGM-HOL}$ values are 2.3‰ for *G. bulloides* and 1.6‰ for *G. inflata*.

The $\delta^{13}C$ records from both species are marked by a large negative peak at 6 m depth in core GeoB 1023−5 (Fig. 4). Above and below this event, they also reveal generally lower values for the time of deglaciation (DEGL) compared to Holocene (HOL) levels. The deficit relative to Holocene values (delta $\delta^{13}C_{DEGL-HOL}$) amounts to −0.4‰ for *G. inflata*, and −0.8‰ for *G. bulloides* above and below the negative peak, and to −1.6‰ and −2.0‰ at the centre of the peak. In the interval corresponding to the LGM, $\delta^{13}C$ values of *G. bulloides* are comparable to Holocene data, while those from *G. inflata* remain lower.

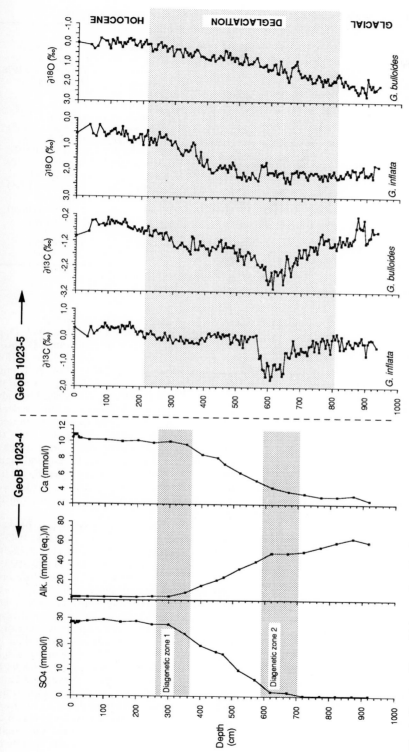

Fig. 4. Results of interstitial water investigations and isotopic measurements versus depth in the sediment. Columns 1 to 3: Interstitial water profiles for SO_4^{2-}, alkalinity, and Ca^{2+} from core GeoB 1023–4. Shaded areas show sediment layers where proposed diagenic reactions occur (s. text). Columns 4 to 7: $\delta^{13}C$ and $\delta^{18}O$ records of *G. inflata* and *G. bulloides* from core GeoB 1023–5. The differentiation of the sediments into the glacial, deglacial and Holocene section was according to the transferred ^{14}C ages (Fig. 3). Note the strong $\delta^{13}C$ minimum for both species from 5.80 to 6.60 m depth in the core GeoB 1023–5. It occurs where the steep gradients of Ca and alkalinity flatten to more stable concentrations downcore in core GeoB 1023–4.

Table 2. Holocene to Deglaciation differences at Termination I from other planktonic records.

delta $\delta^{13}C$ (HOL-DEGL)	Age (ka)	Core	Region	Species	Reference
0.4	?	M12372	NW-Africa	*G. ruber*	Berger *et al.* (1978)*
0.4−0.8	6−18	M12392	NW-Africa	*G. inflata* *G. ruber* *G. bulloides*	Zahn (1986)
0.4−0.5	6−13	V28−122	Caribbean Sea	*G. sacculifer*	Oppo & Fairbanks (1989)
0.4−0.5	8−16	KNR110−43 KNR110−82	W-Equatorial Atlantic	*G. sacculifer*	Curry & Crowley (1987)
0.5	8−18	M13519	E-Equatorial Atlantic	*G. sacculifer*	Sarnthein *et al.* (1984)
0.7	6−17	GeoB1008	Congo Fan	*G. ruber*	Schneider (1991)
0.7	8−?	RC13−271	South Atlantic	*N. pachyderma*	Charles & Fairbanks (1990)
1.2	12−14[†]				
0.4	6−13	RC11−120	S-Indian Ocean	*G. bulloides*	Shackleton & Pisias (1985)
0.4	6−17	V19−30	Pacific	*G. dutertrei*	Shackleton & Pisias (1985)

* No age given, Termination I related to TOC content and foraminiferal counts.
† Short additional depletion of −0.5 ‰ O for 2000 years.

Deglacial $\delta^{13}C$ minimum as a Palaeoceanographic signal

Variations in the $\delta^{13}C$ values of planktonic foraminifera should provide a means of reconstructing the palaeoceanography and palaeoproductivity of surface waters of the Benguela coastal upwelling regime. In the following paragraphs we compare the strong $\delta^{13}C$ decrease in core GeoB 1023−5 with $\delta^{13}C$ minima reported from other sediment cores in the Atlantic Ocean at Termination I, and we examine alternative models which could explain the observed minimum in the Benguela upwelling area.

Isotopic composition of planktonic foraminifera from low and mid-latitude sediments of the Atlantic Ocean, show a prominent minimum at Termination I with delta $\delta^{13}C_{DEGL-HOL}$ values of −0.4 to −0.8‰ (references to Table 2). Cores from areas south of 43°S exhibit values from −0.7 to −1.2‰ (Table 2). To our knowledge, values more negative than −1.2‰ for delta $\delta^{13}C_{DEGL-HOL}$ have not been observed in records from planktonic foraminifera. In Fig. 5 the $\delta^{13}C$ records of *G. inflata* and *G. bulloides*, interpolated to 200 year time intervals, are compared with the stacked $\delta^{13}C$ record from planktonic foraminifera (*Globigerinoides sacculifer* (Brady)) in sediment cores from the western equatorial Atlantic Ocean (Curry & Crowley 1987). This record is believed to represent the $\delta^{13}C$ signal of the surface waters in the low productivity, tropical and subtropical Atlantic Ocean (Curry & Crowley 1987; Oppo & Fairbanks 1989). Based on our ^{14}C chronology, the $\delta^{13}C$ minimum in core GeoB 1023−5 correlates well with the timing of the $\delta^{13}C$ minimum in this stacked record. This seems also the case for the other Atlantic cores cited in Table 2. However, the magnitude of the deglacial $\delta^{13}C$ decreases observed in these Atlantic sediment cores is only comparable to the Deglaciation-to-Holocene difference, which is observed between 10 and 12 ka and again between 14 and 16 ka in core GeoB 1023−5 (Fig. 5). The additional decrease of −1.2‰ at 13 ka in core GeoB 1023−5 is not seen in the other records.

The difference in the $\delta^{13}C_{DEGL-HOL}$ between the two measured species *G. inflata* (−0.45‰) and *G. bulloides* (−0.85‰) averages 0.4‰ for the deglacial sediments in core GeoB 1023−5 (Fig. 5) and is comparable to the difference between the same species found in the Northwest African upwelling centre (Zahn 1986). Whether this interspecific difference is a result of different seasonal abundance maxima or of slightly different depth habitats during their life cycle in the upper mixed layer (Fairbanks *et al.* 1980; Deuser & Ross 1989) is not obvious for this coastal upwelling region. Nevertheless, the interspecific difference is expected to reflect different seasonal variations in the hydrography and $\delta^{13}C_{TCO2}$ in the surface water between the Holocene and the Deglaciation. Of greater interest for this study is the fact that, despite the

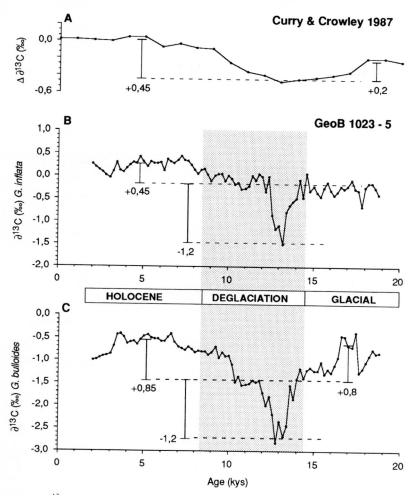

Fig. 5. Interpolated $\delta^{13}C$ values of *G. inflata* (B) and *G. bulloides* (C) in core GeoB 1023−5 versus time (200 year intervals). (A) shows the stacked $\delta^{13}C$ record of *G. sacculifer* from the western Equatorial Atlantic (Curry & Crowley 1987). Positive numbers indicate the $\delta^{13}C$ difference of Holocene and glacial values relative to the deglacial minimum values (GeoB 1023−5 outside the negative spike). Negative numbers show the additional $\delta^{13}C$ decrease in core GeoB 1023−5 in relation to deglacial values from 10 to 12 ka and from 14 to 16 ka.

interspecific difference, the additional $\delta^{13}C$ decrease at 13 ka has the same magnitude of −1.2‰ (Fig. 5) for both species. This may indicate a short intensification (about 1000 years) of the effect responsible for the broader deglacial $\delta^{13}C$ minimum observed in core GeoB 1023−5 (between 10 and 16 ka), and also seen in other Atlantic cores (Table 2).

Oppo & Fairbanks (1989) offered two hypotheses which could explain the widespread deglacial minimum. One proposes that an enhanced upwelling rate caused the deglacial $\delta^{13}C$ minimum by transporting more

^{12}C-enriched deeper water to the surface. GEOSECS data from our investigation area show an average decrease of −1.4‰ in $\delta^{13}C$ of total CO_2 and a temperature difference of about −5 to −10°C for the upper boundary of the intermediate water (400 to 500 m) compared to surface water (Kroopnick 1985; Bainbridge 1981). If, however, the additional −1.2‰ $\delta^{13}C$ decrease at 13 ka was caused by increasing upwelling rates of deeper and colder waters, the $\delta^{18}O$ records of foraminiferal tests must display outstanding positive $\delta^{18}O$ values. Anomalously positive $\delta^{18}O$ values are not associated with the

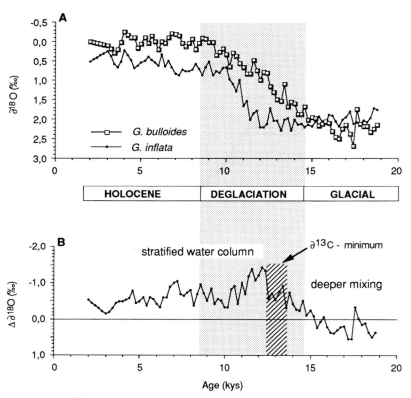

GeoB 1023-5

Fig. 6. (A) Interpolated $\delta^{18}O$ values of *G. inflata* (B) and *G. bulloides* (C) in core GeoB 1023−5 versus time (200-year intervals). (B) Difference between $\delta^{18}O$ values of *G. bulloides* and *G. inflata*, indicating deeper mixing of the surface waters during the glacial and a more stratified water column within the deglaciation phase and the Holocene (s. text). The lined area gives the time interval for the negative $\delta^{13}C$ spike from Fig. 5.

$\delta^{13}C$ decrease at 13 ka in our records (Fig. 6A).

If we assume for the Benguela region that *G. bulloides* lives in shallow water depths of the surface layer where high productivity occurs, and that *G. inflata* lives within or below the thermocline (Van Leeuwen 1989), then the $\delta^{18}O$ record of these species suggests a more stratified water column during the deglaciation compared to the glacial period. During the glacial period *G. bulloides* shows comparable or higher $\delta^{18}O$ values than *G. inflata*, indicating a mixing of thermocline or deeper waters up to the surface layer. At 15 ka the $\delta^{18}O$ values of *G. bulloides* start to decrease, while the values of *G. inflata* remain on the glacial level for the following 3000 years. If the difference of the $\delta^{18}O$ values from *G. bulloides* and *G. inflata* reflect the magnitude of stratification of the surface waters,

then the delta $\delta^{18}O_{\text{bull-infl}}$ record (Fig. 6B) shows an increasing stratification from 15 ka until 12 ka and a slow decrease during the Holocene. A stronger stratification in the Benguela upwelling system at 17°S around 12 ka could be the result from a stronger influence of the AC (Fig. 1), which moves the convergence of the AC and BCC southwards and thickens the warm and nutrient-poor surface layer. This concept coincides with results from other investigations of the surface water palaeoceanography in that area. During the period between 9 and 12 ka an intensified stratification was reported for the region north of 10°S (Van Leeuwen 1989) and a stronger influence of warm surface waters was assumed in the upwelling area at 22°S south of the Walvis Ridge (Charles & Morley 1988). The $\delta^{13}C$

minimum in our records occurs at that time when the stratification was increasing (Fig. 6B). Regarding the $\delta^{18}O$ records of G. bulloides and G. inflata, we have to reject the model that intensified upwelling caused the strong $\delta^{13}C$ minimum at 13 ka.

Thus, we prefer the second hypothesis presented by Oppo & Fairbanks (1989) to explain the deglacial $\delta^{13}C$ minimum in planktonic foraminiferal records. They pointed out that the $\delta^{13}C$ minimum may be caused by changes in the $\delta^{13}C_{TCO2}$ composition of the source water feeding the surface mixed layer. $\delta^{13}C$ changes could be produced by variations in the mixing of source waters or changes in the input and degradation of terrestrial organic carbon into the ocean and do not require an increase in upwelling intensity. If this scenario accounts for the short additional negative event in the $\delta^{13}C$ planktonic record observed in our core from the Benguela coastal upwelling area, then $\delta^{13}C$ data from benthic foraminifera living in the depth range of intermediate waters must show similar $\delta^{13}C$ deviations during deglaciation. Possibly, a strong -1.6 to $-2.0‰$ deglacial $\delta^{13}C$ minimum has not been observed for the South Atlantic until now, because of the lack of sediment cores with high resolution.

Unfortunately, so far there are no data available for intermediate waters from the southeastern South Atlantic. Only further investigations on sediment cores from shallow water depths (200–1000 m), which provide high resolution $\delta^{13}C$ records of benthic and planktonic foraminifera, will help to determine whether the magnitude of the deglacial $\delta^{13}C$ decrease observed in core GeoB 1023–5 could be caused by lower $\delta^{13}C$ values in the source water (SACW) feeding the Benguela upwelling system off Southwest Africa.

Deglacial $\delta^{13}C$ minimum and authigenic CaCO$_3$ precipitation

The magnitude of the $\delta^{13}C$ decrease in our records is not comparable to other observed $\delta^{13}C$ minima at Termination I in the Atlantic Ocean (see above) and the negative spike occurs at a depth in the sediment (Fig. 7) where new authigenic CaCO$_3$ precipitation is proposed from interstitial water geochemistry. This coincidence raised the question of the extent to which carbon and oxygen isotope signals may be affected by early diagenesis.

This problem is especially pronounced in sediments with high organic carbon contents under coastal upwelling regions. In these sediments, degradation of organic carbon leads to anoxic conditions and steep concentration gradients in the interstitial waters, thus producing high flux rates of interstitial water components, often associated with precipitation of authigenic minerals. In the following chapter we estimate the amount of possible authigenic CaCO$_3$ precipitation in the sediment layer where the prominent $\delta^{13}C$ spike occurs in our records and discuss the evidence that we have for an early diagenetic imprint on our $\delta^{13}C$ records.

Under existing geochemical steady state conditions, Fick's first law must be applied in order to calculate the fluxes of components in the interstitial water. Therefore, the constant concentration gradients between the two diagenetic zones (Fig. 4) imply that components are transported, but that no transformation processes such as precipitation or dissolution take place between the two zones. A chemical process in a steady state system controlled by diffusion is always associated with a change in the interstitial water concentration gradient. Because the gradient of Ca^{2+} in our profile remains uniform over the interval from 3 to 5.5 m, the calcite precipitation front must begin at a depth near 6 m, where the constant concentration gradient for Ca^{2+} evens out to a constant level. The rate of precipitated authigenic calcite was estimated to be 1% of the total sediment and 5% of the total CaCO$_3$ within a 50 cm thick precipitation zone beginning at 5.90 m depth in core GeoB 1023–4 (Fig. 7). The boundary conditions for this calculation are given in Table 3. This estimate might be afflicted with a great uncertainty, because we are not able to determine exactly the time interval during which the observed gradient has existed. Nevertheless, the calculations with our boundary conditions and the time constant of 5000 years show that the observed Ca^{2+} concentration gradient is able to precipitate 5% new authigenic CaCO$_3$ in relation to the total CaCO$_3$ at that depth in the sediment. As we will show next, 5% authigenic CaCO$_3$ could produce a decrease of $-1‰$ in the $\delta^{13}C$ signal when precipitated on the foraminiferal tests.

Assuming a closed interstitial water system at 6 m depth in the sediment, the $\delta^{13}C$ value of the total CO$_2$ ($\delta^{13}C_{TCO2}$) of this water is determined by the $\delta^{13}C_{TOC}$ of the degraded marine organic matter (Table 1). Within the sulphate reduction zone, $\delta^{13}C_{TCO2}$ of the interstitial water is expected to have values between -20 and $-25‰$ (Presley & Kaplan 1968; Nissenbaum et al. 1972; Irwin et al. 1977). Fractionation of $\delta^{13}C$ during the precipitation of authigenic CaCO$_3$ from interstitial waters would only have minor effects on the $\delta^{13}C$ composition of the

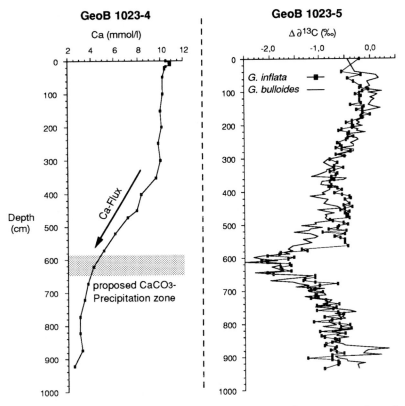

Fig. 7. Coexistence of the modelled diagenetic CaCO$_3$ precipitation and the strong negative spike in the deglacial δ^{13}C minimum. Column 1 indicates the modelled Ca flux to a 50 cm thick zone of authigenic CaCO$_3$ precipitation in core GeoB 1023–4. Column 2 shows the deglacial δ^{13}C spikes of *G. inflata* and *G. bulloides* in core GeoB 1023–5, having the same magnitude and coexisting with the proposed CaCO$_3$ precipitation at the same depth in the sediment. In order to normalize the data, the average Holocene δ^{13}C values (0.40 to 1.80 m depth in core GeoB 1023–5) were set to zero.

solid phase (Emrich *et al.* 1970: +1.85‰ at 20°C, −0.035‰/°C). Thus the δ^{13}C$_{CaCO3}$ from authigenic calcium carbonate will be equivalent to the δ^{13}C$_{TCO2}$ of the interstitial water.

The δ^{18}O values of the authigenic CaCO$_3$ depend on temperature–salinity related fractionation (Epstein *et al.* 1953; Craig & Gordon 1965), which occurs in equilibrium with the interstitial water. Based on the measured δ^{13}C$_{TOC}$ (Table 1) and sediment temperatures (4°C), we would expect authigenic CaCO$_3$ to have δ^{13}C and δ^{18}O values of −20‰ and +3‰, respectively. Isotopic measurements of authigenic calcium carbonate crystals in sediments from the Congo Fan (7°S) provide values of −25 to −29‰ for δ^{13}C, and of +2 to +4‰ for δ^{18}O (Jansen *et al.* 1987). The sediments in this investigation were extracted from 3040 and

4270 m water depth and contained 3 to 4% TOC with δ^{13}C$_{TOC}$ values of −25 to −27‰.

Taking our calculated values as the end-member for 100% authigenic CaCO$_3$, an additional decrease of −1‰ in delta δ^{13}C$_{DEGL-HOL}$ at 6 m depth in core GeoB 1023–5 (Fig. 7) accounts for 5% authigenic CaCO$_3$ on calcareous foraminiferal tests. This is within the range estimated from the interstitial water flux rate of Ca^{2+}. Regarding the δ^{18}O values, a 5% authigenic CaCO$_3$ precipitation on the measured foraminiferal tests would shift the primary values only by +0.1 to +0.2‰. This is within the noise level of the δ^{18}O variations in core GeoB 1023–5, and would not obviously change the δ^{18}O record indicating a diagenetic imprint.

Despite the good 'fit' of the calculations from

Table 3. Estimation of the calcite precipitation (D_{Ca}-value was taken from Li & Gregory 1974).

assumptions	
time	5000 years
gradient	2×10^{-5} (mmol cm^{-4}) and no change over time
zone of precipitation	50 cm thick
D_{Ca}	4.4×10^{-6} (mmol cm^{-2} s^{-1})
density of the sediment	2 (g cm^{-3})
calcite content of the sediment	20%
calculations	
flux$_{Ca}$	8.8×10^{-11} (mmol cm^{-2} s^{-1})
Ca sink for 5000 years and in a zone of 50 cm	0.27 (mmol cm^{-3}) $\approx$ 10 (mg cm^{-3})
calcite precipitation for 5000 years and in a zone of 50 cm	25 (mg cm^{-3})
% of calcite precipitation related to the calcite mass in the sediment	5%

the additional $-1‰$ $\delta^{13}C$ decrease and from the interstitial water component flux rates resulting in a 5% authigenic $CaCO_3$ precipitation, there are some doubts regarding a diagenetic alteration of the $\delta^{13}C$ record from planktonic foraminifera. These are based mainly on the fact that no visual evidence (scanning electron microscopy) for solid diagenetic authigenic $CaCO_3$ precipitates on foraminiferal tests exists. In addition, we have no explanation of why this authigenic $CaCO_3$ precipitation should be restricted to a 50 cm thick layer in the sediments characterized by the decrease in the $\delta^{13}C$ signal which does not extend to sediments further downcore. In summary, our interstitial water data show evidence for authigenic $CaCO_3$ precipitation and a diagenetic alteration of the $\delta^{13}C$ record of planktonic foraminifera in the range of about $-1‰$. However, these precipitates have not been observed with scanning electron microscope investigations. Thus to date, the diagenetic model is unable to explain the strong deglacial $\delta^{13}C$ decrease observed in our records from the Benguela upwelling system.

Conclusions

We have shown that a strong negative spike exists in the deglacial $\delta^{13}C$ minimum of planktonic foraminiferal $\delta^{13}C$ records from the Benguela upwelling region. The long-term $\delta^{13}C$ minimum (10–16 ka) with the negative spike at 13 ka in the record of *G. bulloides* and *G. inflata* correlates well with a global deglacial $\delta^{13}C$ minimum, assumed to be caused by ^{12}C enrichment of intermediate water which had exchanged with the surface mixed layer. Subtracting the magnitude of the deglacial $\delta^{13}C$

minimum widely observed in other Atlantic cores from our record, an additional decrease of about $-1‰$ restricted to a sediment interval corresponding to 1000 years remains to be explained. We have no data which indicate that these changes in source water $\delta^{13}C_{TCO2}$ could also account for the entire magnitude of the strong decrease in the delta $\delta^{13}C_{DEGL-HOL}$ values of planktonic foraminifera from the Benguela current region at 13 ka.

Calculations from flux rates of interstitial water components and the additional decrease of $-1‰$ in the $\delta^{13}C$ record of *G. inflata* and *G. bulloides* can account for a 5% authigenic $CaCO_3$ precipitation relative to the total $CaCO_3$ content in the sediments. An examination of whether this additional decrease was caused by an early diagenetic imprint revealed no evidence for authigenic $CaCO_3$ precipitates by scanning electron microscopy. A diagenetic imprint also cannot explain why the $\delta^{13}C$ records return downcore to values comparable to levels above the precipitation zone.

Due to the lack of significant evidence for the diagenetic authigenic $CaCO_3$ precipitation, we believe that the strong deglacial $\delta^{13}C$ decrease in the record from planktonic foraminifera in core GeoB 1023–5 is a primary paleoceanographic signal. This interpretation must be supported by investigations on $\delta^{13}C$ records of benthic and planktonic foraminifera from sediments covering the interglacial–glacial depth range of the intermediate water in the southeast South Atlantic.

The authors thank Captain Bruns and the crew of the METEOR for their dedicated services during the cruise M 6–6. We thank R. Henning for executing the ^{14}C analyses and S. Hinrichs for her assistance preparing the interstitial water analyses. We gratefully acknowledge the support of T. Bickert and F. Gingele during the SEM investigations. The manuscript has greatly benefited from reviews by K. Emeis, G. Ganssen and D. Kroon. We acknowledge the valuable comments on our manuscript by W. H. Berger. We thank M. Botros and S. Middendorf for improving the english. This research was funded by the Deutsche Forschungsgemeinschaft (Sonderforschungsbereich 261 at Bremen University, Contribution 30).

References

BAINBRIDGE, A. (Ed.) 1981. GEOSECS Atlantic Expedition Hydrographic Data Vol. 1., U.S. Government Printing Office, Washington, D.C.

BERGER, W. H., DIESTER-HAAS, L. & KILLINGLEY, J. S. 1978. Upwelling off North-West Africa: the Holocene decrease as seen in carbon isotopes and sedimentological indicators. *Oceanologica Acta*, **1** (1), 3–7.

—— & VINCENT, E. 1986. Deep-sea carbonates: reading the carbon-isotope signal. *Geologische Rundschau*, **75**, 249–269.

CHARLES, C. D. & FAIRBANKS, R. G. 1990. Glacial to interglacial changes in the isotopic gradients of Southern Ocean surface water. In: BLEIL, U. & THIEDE, J. (eds) *Geological History of the Polar Oceans: Arctic versus Antarctic*. NATO ASI Series C, **308**, 519–538, Kluwer, Dordrecht.

—— & MORLEY, J. J. 1988. The paleoceanographic significance of the radiolarian *Didymocyrtis tetrathalamus* in eastern Cape Basin sediments. *Paleogeography, Paleoclimatology, Paleoecology*, **66**, 113–126.

CRAIG, H. & GORDON, L. I. 1965. Deuterium and oxygen-18 variations in the ocean and marine atmosphere. *In*: TONGIORGI, E. (ed.) *Stable isotopes in oceanographic studies and paleotemperatures*. Spoleto, **9**, 1–22, Consiglio Nazionale delle Ricerche, Laboratorio di Geologica Nucleare, Pisa.

CURRY, W. B. & CROWLEY, T. J. 1987. The $\delta^{13}C$ of equatorial Atlantic surface waters: Implications for ice age pCO_2 levels. *Paleoceanography*, **2**(5), 489–517.

DEUSER, W. G. & ROSS, E. H. 1989. Seasonally abundant planktonic foraminifera of the Sargasso Sea: Succession, deep-water fluxes, isotopic compositions, and paleoceanographic implications. *Journal of Foraminiferal Research*, **19**(4), 268–293.

EMRICH, K., EHHALT, D. H. & VOGEL, J. C. 1970. Carbon isotope fractionation during the precipitation of calcium carbonate. *Earth and Planetary Science Letters*, **8**, 363–371.

EPSTEIN, S., BUCHSBAUM, R., LOWENSTAM, H. A. & UREY, H. C. 1953. Revised carbonate-water isotopic temperature scale. *Geological Society of America Bulletin*, **64**, 1315–1326.

FAIRBANKS, R. G. 1989. A 17000-year glacio-eustatic sea level record: Influence of glacial melting rates on the Younger Dryas event and deep-ocean circulation. *Nature*, **342**, 637–642.

——, WIEBE, P. H. & BE, A. W. H. 1980. Vertical distribution and isotopic composition of living planktonic foraminifera in the Western North Atlantic. *Science*, **207**, 61–63.

FAURE, G. (ed.) 1986. *Principles of Isotope Geology* (2nd edition). Wiley, New York.

GRASSHOFF, K., EHRHARDT, M. & KREMLING, K. 1983. *Methods of Seawater Analysis* (2nd edition). Verlag Chemie, Weinheim.

HAGEN, E., SCHEMEINDA, R., MICHELCHEN, N., POSTEL, L., SCHULZ, S. & BELOW, M. 1981. Zur küstensenkrechten Struktur des Kaltwasserauftriebs vor der Küste Namibias. *Geod. Geophys. Veröffentl.*, **IV** (36), 1–99.

HART, T. J. & CURRIE, R. I. 1960. The Benguela Current. *Discovery Rep.*, **31**, 123–298.

IRWIN, H., CURTIS, C. & COLEMAN, M. 1977. Isotopic evidence for source of diagenetic carbonates formed during burial of organic-rich sediments. *Nature*, **269**, 209–213.

JANSEN, J. H. F., WOENSDREGT, C. F., KOOISTRA, M. J., VAN DER GAAST, S. J. 1987. Ikaite pseudomorphs in the Zaire deep-sea fan: An intermediate between calcite and porous calcite. *Geology*, **15**, 245–248.

KILLINGLEY, J. S. 1983. Effects of diagenetic recrystallization on $^{18}O/^{16}O$ values of deep-sea sediments. *Nature*, **301**, 594–597.

KÖLLING, A. 1991. *Frühdiagenetische Prozesse und Stoff-Flüsse in marinen und ästuarinen Sedimenten*. PhD Thesis, Berichte, Fachbereich Geowissenschaften, Universität Bremen (in press).

KROOPNICK, P. M. 1985. The distribution of carbon-13 in the world oceans. *Deep-Sea Research*, **32**, 57–84.

LI, Y.-H. & GREGORY, S. 1974. Diffusion of ions in sea water and in deep-sea sediments. *Geochimica et Cosmochimica Acta*, **38**, 703–714.

LONGSTAFFE, F. J. 1983. Stable isotope studies of diagenesis in clastic rocks. *Geoscience Canada*, **10**, 43–58.

MOROSHKIN, K. V., BUBNOV, V. A. & BULATOV, R. P. 1970. Water circulation in the eastern South Atlantic. *Oceanology*, **10**, 27–34.

NELSON, G. & HUTCHINGS, L. 1983. The Benguela upwelling area. *Prog. Oceanogr.*, **12** (3), 333–356.

NISSENBAUM, A., PRESLEY, B. J. & KAPLAN, I. R. 1972. Early diagenesis in a reducing fjord, saanich inlet, British Columbia — I. Chemical and isotopic changes in major components of interstitial water. *Geochimica et Cosmochimica Acta*, **36**, 1007–1027.

OPPO, D. W. & FAIRBANKS, R. G. 1989. Carbon isotope composition of tropical surface water during the past 22000 years. *Paleoceanography*, **4** (4), 333–351.

PRESLEY, B. J. & KAPLAN, I. R. 1968. Changes in dissolved sulfat, calcium and carbonate from interstitial water from near-shore sediments. *Geochimica et Cosmochimica Acta*, **32**, 1037–1048.

SARNTHEIN, M., ERLENKEUSER, H., GRAFENSTEIN, R. VON & SCHROEDER, C. 1984. Stable-isotope stratigraphy for the last 750000 years: 'METEOR' core 13519 from the eastern equatorial Atlantic. *METEOR Forschungsergebnisse*, Reihe C, **38**, 9−24.

SHACKLETON, N. J. 1977. Carbon-13 in Uvigerina: tropical rainforest history and the Equatorial Pacific carbonate dissolution cycles. *In:* ANDERSEN, N. R. & MALAHOFF, A. (eds) *The Fate of Fossil Fuel CO_2 in the Oceans*. Plenum, New York, 401−428.

—— & PISIAS, N. G. 1985. Atmospheric carbon dioxide, orbital forcing, and climate. *In:* SUNDQUIST, E. T. & BROECKER, W. S. (eds) *The Carbon Cycle and Atmospheric CO2: Natural Variations Archaen to Present*. Geophysical Monograph Series, **32**, 412−417, AGU, Washington, D.C.

SHANNON, L. V., AGENBAG, J. J. & BUYS, M. E. L. 1987. Large- and mesoscale features of the Angola-Benguela front. *In:* PAYNE, A. I. L., GULLAND, J. A. & BRINK, K. H. (eds) The Benguela and comparable ecosystems. *S. Afr. J. Mar. Sci.*, **5**, 11−34.

SHOWERS, W. J., LENT, R. M. & MARGOLIS, S. V. 1987. BSEM evaluation of carbonate diagenesis: Benthic foraminifera from the Miocene Pungo River Formation, North Carolina. *Geology*, **15**, 731−734.

SCHNEIDER, R. 1991. *Spätquartäre Produktivitätsände-rungen im östlichen Angola-Becken: Reaktion auf Variationen im Passat-Monsun-Windsystem und in der Advektion des Benguela Küstenstroms*. PhD Thesis, Berichte, Fachbereich Geowissenschaften, Universität Bremen.

WEFER, G., BLEIL, U. *et al.* 1988. *Bericht über die METEOR-Fahrt M6−6*, Libreville-Las Palmas, 18.2.1988−23.3.1988. Berichte, Fachbereich Geowissenschaften, Universität Bremen, 3.

WILLIAMS, D. F. 1985. Carbon isotopic variations in surface waters of the Gulf of Mexico on time scales of 10000, 30000, 150000 and 2 million years. *In:* SUNDQUIST, E. T. & BROECKER, W. S. (eds) *The Carbon Cycle and Atmospheric CO2: Natural Variations Archaen to Present*, Geophysical Monograph Series, **32**, 329−341, AGU, Washington, D.C.

VAN BENNEKOM, A. J. & BERGER, G. W. 1984. Hydrography and silica budget of the Angola Basin. *Netherlands Journal of Sea Research*, **17** (2−4), 149−200.

VAN LEEUWEN, R. J. W. 1989: Sea-floor distribution and Late Quaternary faunal patterns of planktonic and benthic foraminifers in the Angola Basin. *Utrecht Micropaleontol. Bull.*, **38**.

ZAHN, R. 1986. *Spätquartäre Entwicklung von Küstenauftrieb und Tiefenwasserzirkulation im Nordost-Atlantik. Rekonstruktion anhand stabiler Isotope kalkschaliger Foraminiferen*. PhD Thesis, Christian-Albrechts-Universität Kiel.

The geological record of
upwelling evolution

Late Pliocene and Pleistocene climatic oscillations and monsoon upwelling recorded in sediments from the Owen Ridge, northwestern Arabian Sea

DAVID W. MURRAY & WARREN L. PRELL

Department of Geological Sciences, Brown University, Providence, RI 02912, USA

Abstract: Pelagic sediments recovered during Leg 117 of the Ocean Drilling Program (ODP) from the Owen Ridge, northwestern Arabian Sea, record regional upwelling variations and global climatic oscillations since the Late Neogene. Miocene to Recent deposits exhibit characteristic light and dark cycles (0.5–1.0 m thick) that are well correlated to calcium carbonate concentration; light layers are carbonate-rich and dark layers carbonate-poor. The deposits are largely composed of biogenic calcite and eolian derived terrigenous materials. Opaline silica and organic carbon comprise less than 10% of the sediment composition. Within the last 370 000 years, the major compositional oscillations are synchronous with global ice volume changes. These cycles result from terrigenous dilution rather than changes in carbonate production or dissolution. Non-carbonate concentration characterizes these cycles and is a good approximation of temporal changes in terrigenous input for the past 3.4 My. Prior to 2.5 Ma, the major compositional oscillations are dominated by high-frequency cycles possibly related to earth's precessional changes. Within the past 2.5 My there is a shift in variance to much longer periods characteristic of high-latitude climatic variations. Based on late Pleistocene associations between lithogenic grain size and accumulation, the sedimentary cycles produced by changes in the lithogenic flux are attributed to changes in source area aridity rather than monsoon wind strength.

Calcite, opal and organic carbon accumulation rates, commonly used to infer palaeoproductivity, are compared to records of monsoon wind strength in the Arabian Sea. Changes in calcite accumulation by as much as 3 mg/cm^2/a between glacial and interglacial intervals are attributed to dissolution rather than calcite production. The accumulation of organic carbon matches the changes in sedimentation rate. We attribute this high correlation to enhanced preservation of organic carbon by increased sedimentation rate, not to palaeoproductivity variations. Opal accumulation provides a good match to other indices of monsoon wind strength and upwelling intensity. These monsoon indices exhibit a strong concentration of variance in the precessional band, but lag the expected forcing by ~9 ky.

Major variations in the mean accumulation rates of sediment components, thought to reflect large changes in monsoon-driven upwelling, are quantified for the late Pliocene to Present. The average rate of calcium carbonate accumulation increases from 1 to 3 mg/cm^2/a and organic carbon accumulation decreases from 75 to 30 μg/cm^2/a. The long-term increase in carbonate accumulation is the result of enhanced preservation of Recent deposits compared to the upper Pliocene. The high rate of organic carbon accumulation between 1.5 and 3.0 Ma, also observed at Oman Margin sites, implies that oceanographic conditions were more favourable for high production and preservation of organic carbon in the Arabian Sea during the Late Pliocene compared to the Present.

The strong winds associated with the Indian Ocean summer monsoon cause the upwelling of nutrient-rich waters along the coast of Arabia. These nutrient-rich waters sustain high levels of oceanic productivity from June to September, making the northwestern Arabian Sea one of the world's most productive oceanic areas. Recent studies of foraminifers, pollen, and wind-borne detritus (Prell 1984*a*, *b*; Prell & van Campo 1986; Sirocko & Sarnthein 1989; Clemens & Prell 1990; Prell, Niitsuma *et al.* 1991) indicate that the deep-sea sediments in the northwestern Arabian Sea contain records of monsoon variability from terrestrial and marine sources.

Pelagic sediments on the Owen Ridge (Fig. 1) lie beneath the area affected by monsoon-driven upwelling and should record long-term variations in the strength of the monsoon and local upwelling. Preliminary results from ODP Leg 117 noted that Owen Ridge sediments exhibited a strong cyclicity in properties such as colour, magnetic susceptibility, wet-bulk density and calcium carbonate content (Prell, Niitsuma *et al.* 1989). Analysis of these data (Busch 1991; Murray & Prell 1991;

From SUMMERHAYES, C. P., PRELL, W. L. & EMEIS, K. C. (eds), 1992, *Upwelling Systems: Evolution Since the Early Miocene*. Geological Society Special Publication No 64, pp 301–321.

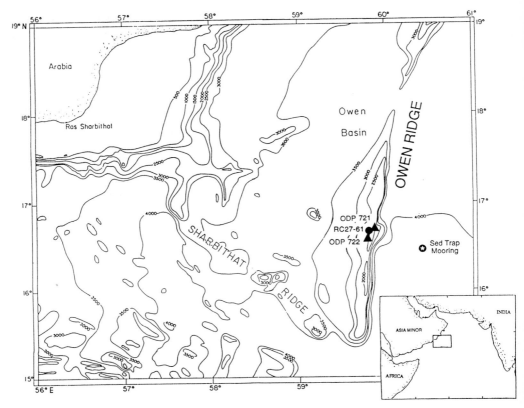

Fig. 1. Bathymetric map of the northwest Arabian Sea and location of ODP Sites 721 and 722, piston core RC27–61, and the western Arabian Sea trap of Nair *et al.* (1989). Contours in metres.

Clemens & Prell 1991; Weeden & Shimmield 1991) revealed a pervasive cyclicity of about 1 m or about 23 ky, the period associated with Earth's precessional radiation changes. Other periodicities related to the Earth's orbital variations were also identified. Previous studies on the large-scale features of the monsoon using atmospheric circulation models (Kutzbach & Guetter 1986; Prell & Kutzbach 1987) indicate that the variation of northern hemisphere summer insolation caused by the cyclic precession of the equinoxes is a primary forcing for changes in the strength of the summer monsoon. In this study, we examine variations in the major sediment components (biogenic calcite and terrigenous materials) from the crest of the Owen Ridge to determine if they record variations in the intensity of the monsoon as inferred from atmospheric circulation simulations. The terrigenous material on the Owen Ridge is largely eolian dust from near-by land areas (Sirocko & Sarnthein 1989; Clemens & Prell

1990). Terrigenous input to the deep sea should be controlled by changes in wind direction and strength, and source area aridity. Biogenic calcite is mostly derived from the shells of coccolithophores and foraminifers. Since the crest of the Owen Ridge is above the calcium carbonate saturation horizon, the accumulation of calcite at this site should be controlled by the balance between shell production and carbonate dissolution resulting from organic matter degradation. In addition to these major components, records of organic carbon and opal accumulation are evaluated for their potential as palaeoproductivity indices in sediments from this region.

Data and methods

ODP Site 722 (16°37.3'N, 59°47.8'E; 2027 m water depth) and near-by piston core RC27–61 (16°36.5'N, 59°51.4'E; 1893 m water depth) were obtained near the crest of the Owen Ridge beneath the high productivity region of the northwestern Arabian Sea (Fig. 1). Of the total 15.97 m recovered in core RC27−61, only the top 11.20 m (0 to 370 ka) were studied because the lower portion of the core was disturbed by coring. A total of 12 cores comprise the top 110 m (0 to 3.4 Ma) of Site 722. To ensure that the Site 722 record was complete, a composite section was constructed using material recovered from Hole 722B and filling in coring gaps with material from adjacent Hole 722A and near-by Hole 721B. High-quality shipboard volume magnetic susceptibility data measured at 5 cm intervals and visual marker layers (Prell, Niitsuma *et al.* 1989) were used to correlate the holes and recognize data gaps. Detailed hole-to-hole correlations revealed gaps as large as 1.90 m across core breaks, even though reported core recoveries were greater than 100% (Prell, Niitsuma *et al.* 1989). The composite depth model for Hole 722B was constructed by assigning the sediment−water interface a depth of 0 mbsf and successively adding each spliced sediment section down through the sediment column. This follows the approach of Ruddiman *et al.* (1989) in their construction of a composite depth model for DSDP Sites 607 and 609. The composite depth reconstruction for Hole 722B Cores 1H through 12X is documented in Murray & Prell (1991) and summarized in Fig. 2 and Table 1.

Hole 722B was sampled at 20 cm intervals in Cores 1H through 12X (0.01−105.51 metres below seafloor (mbsf)). Core RC27−61 was sampled at 10 cm intervals. The Site 722B sedimentation rates are about 30% higher than those in the corresponding section of RC27−61; 11.20 m in RC27−61 equals 15.30 m in Site 722B. The greater sedimentation rate in Site 722 helps to offset the possible aliasing attributed to a coarser sampling interval. Each sample was freeze-dried and two thirds of the dried sample was separated for faunal and isotope analysis. The remaining one third was ground for the chemical analyses reported here and in Murray & Prell (1991). The Site 722 data used in this study are listed in Murray & Prell (1991) and Clemens & Prell (1991). The RC27−61 data are given in Clemens & Prell (1990) and the Appendix.

Calcium carbonate content was measured on a gasometric apparatus similar to that described by Jones & Kaiteris (1983). The Brown University system uses a differential pressure gauge in place of a vacuum gauge and carbonate reactions are measured at atmospheric pressure. The carbonate was digested in 3 ml of 34% phosphoric acid (a 1:1 mixture of concentrated acid and deionized water). Replicate analyses of both

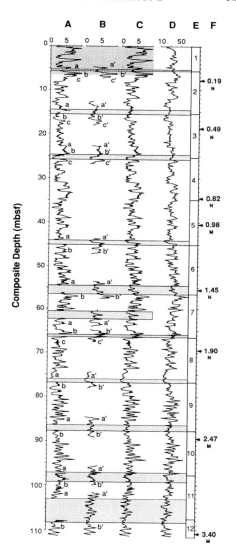

Fig. 2. (A) Hole 722B volume magnetic susceptibility (10^{-6} cgs) versus composite depth for Cores 1H-12X. Light shaded intervals denote data gaps at core breaks and disturbed intervals. Magnetic susceptibility values above 6.60 mbsf (heavy shading) were divided by two for plotting. (B) Magnetic susceptibility in the spliced sections used to fill data gaps and suspect intervals obtained from offset Holes 722A and 721B. Data above and below the splices are presented to show the excellent correlation between holes. (C) Composite magnetic susceptibility record for Site 722. (D) Non-carbonate contents ($100-CaCO_3\%$) for Hole 722B. Regressions between magnetic susceptibility and non-carbonate % were used to estimate values for the data gaps. (E) Hole 722B cores. (F) Site 722 nannofossil (N) and magnetic reversal (M) events. See Table 2 for listing.

Table 1. Composite depth model for Hole 722B.

	From sample	To sample	Original depth (mbsf)		Composite depth (mbsf)	
			From	To	From	To
722 B	1H-1, 1 cm	1H-4, 19 cm	0.01	5.19	0.01	5.19
722 A	1H-3, 80 cm	1H-3, 130 cm	3.80	4.30	5.20	5.70
722 B	2H-1, 21 cm	2H-7, 9 cm	5.71	14.59	5.71	14.59
722 A	2H-3, 90 cm	2H-4, 34 cm	13.70	14.64	14.60	15.54
722 B	3H-1, 3 cm	3H-7, 54 cm	15.45	24.64	15.55	24.74
721 B	3H-4, 25 cm	3H-4, 130 cm	23.85	24.90	24.75	25.80
722 B	4H-1, 86 cm	5H-7, 59 cm	25.56	43.89	25.81	44.14
721 B	5H-3, 30 cm	5H-3, 120 cm	41.80	42.70	44.15	45.05
722 B	6H-1, 6 cm	6H-7, 34 cm	43.96	53.24	45.06	54.34
721 B	6H-3, 40 cm	6H-4, 105 cm	51.50	53.65	54.35	56.45
722 B	7H-1, 26 cm	7H-3, 150 cm	53.46	57.65	56.46	60.70
[a]721 B	7H-1, 75 cm	7H-2, 60 cm	58.15	59.50	60.85	62.20
722 B	7H-5, 1 cm	7H-7, 70 cm	59.25	62.90	62.21	65.90
721 B	7H-4, 146 cm	7H-5, 54 cm	63.36	63.94	65.91	66.49
722 B	8H-1, 5 cm	8H-7, 64 cm	62.95	72.54	66.50	76.09
721 B	8H-4, 130 cm	8H-5, 55 cm	72.70	73.45	76.10	76.85
722 B	9H-1, 11 cm	9H-7, 79 cm	72.61	82.29	76.86	86.54
721 B	9H-5, 80 cm	9H-6, 45 cm	83.20	84.35	86.55	87.70
722 B	10H-1, 11 cm	10H-7, 69 cm	82.81	92.39	87.71	97.29
721 B	10X-6, 20 cm	10X-6, 110 cm	94.20	94.60	97.30	97.70
722 A	10X-3, 90 cm	10X-4, 90 cm	90.40	91.90	97.75	99.25
722 B	11X-2, 31 cm	11X-4, 119 cm	93.71	97.59	99.26	103.14
721 B	11X-4, 70 cm	11X-6, 20 cm	100.80	103.30	103.15	105.65
722 A	11X-3, 40 cm	11X-4, 145 cm	99.60	102.15	105.70	108.25
722 B	12X-1, 96 cm	12X-3, 105 cm	102.46	105.55	108.26	111.35

[a] No magnetic susceptibility data available for Section 722B-7H-4.

samples and standards routinely give an analytical precision of better than 0.5% by weight. Organic carbon measurements were made on a Carlo Erba NA1500 carbon analyser after removal of calcium carbonate. We followed the technique described by Verardo *et al.* (1990) for removal of the inorganic carbon fraction. Five to ten milligrams of dried sample were placed in aluminum sample holders and treated with sulphurous acid (8% reagent grade) until the reaction was complete. The residue was then analysed for carbon and nitrogen. All analyses were duplicated and the differences were generally less than 5% by weight. Opal was extracted from the sediments following the technique of Mortlock & Froelich (1989) except that buffered 0.5 M acetic acid, rather than hydrochloric acid, was used to remove the carbonate fraction. A hot (80°C) 2M Na_2CO_3 leach was used to extract opal from the sediment samples. Measurements were made on a Spectronics 601 spectrophotometer and the precision based on replicates was within ±1% by weight.

Dry bulk density data needed to determine mass accumulation rates were derived from the dry weight in a known volume for RC27−61 samples and from the shipboard GRAPE wet bulk density measurements for Site 722. Hole 722B shipboard GRAPE data (1.8 cm-spaced measurements) was first smoothed with a cubic spline and then sampled at depths corresponding to the discrete shipboard bulk density measurements for the top 100 m. A linear regression based on GRAPE wet bulk density (GWBD) and discrete shipboard dry bulk density (DBD) data [DBD = −1.2664 + 1.3481 (GWBD); r = 0.84] was used to estimate dry bulk density values for Hole 722B samples. GRAPE values were obtained for individual samples used in this study by linearly interpolating between adjacent 1.8 cm-spaced measurements. GRAPE data gaps due to coring and unmeasured short core sections were filled with data from the offset holes used to construct the composite depth model (Murray & Prell 1991).

An age model for the past 3.4 My of Hole 722B (Table 2) is based on the shipboard magnetic-reversal stratigraphy and nannofossil datums. With the exception of the upper limit of *Discoaster pentaradiatus* (2.40 Ma), which

Table 2. Magnetic and Nannofossil datums for Hole 722B[a].

Event[a]	Age (Ma)	Composite Depth[b] (mbsf)
B *Emiliania huxleyi*	0.19	7.95
T *Pseudoemiliania lacunosa*	0.49	18.90
T *Reticulofensestra* sp. A	0.82	34.65
B Jaramillo	0.98	40.35
T *Calcidiscus macintyrei*	1.45	55.55
T *Discoaster brouweri*	1.90	69.50
T *Discoaster pentaradiatus*	2.40	80.05
Matuyama/Gauss	2.47	89.40
Gauss/Gilbert	3.40	110.80

[a] From Shipboard Scientific Party (1989, Tables 4 and 7).
[b] The hole-to-hole correlation based on magnetic susceptibility was used to obtain Hole 722B composite depths for the nannofossil datums that were originally identified in Hole 722A.

was excluded in this age model, the nannofossil datums lie along the linear rates between magnetic events (Fig. 3). This coarse resolution age model provides mean sedimentation rates covering approximately 500 000-year intervals. In Hole 722B, these rates range from 23 m/My (2.5–3.4) to 41 m/My (0–1 Ma).

Oxygen isotope stratigraphy provides a common chronostratigraphic framework that has higher resolution (10^3 years) than magnetic and nannofossil datums (Imbrie *et al.* 1984). We used oxygen isotope stratigraphy to construct high-resolution ($\sim 10^3$ years) age models for Site 722 from 0 to 1.0 Ma and for RC27–61 from 0 to 0.37 Ma (Clemens & Prell 1990; 1991). These models rely on identification of oxygen isotope

events (Prell *et al.* 1986) and their assigned ages in the SPECMAP stack (Imbrie *et al.* 1984). We assume a linear sedimentation rate between 81 identified isotope events in RC27–61 and 51 events in Site 722B to derive ages for individual samples. Sedimentation rates (S) for the individual samples (i) were derived from the difference in age (T) and depth (D) of adjacent samples: $S_i = (D_{i+1} - D_{i-1})/(T_{i+1} - T_{i-1})$. The higher-resolution chronology requires sedimentation rates to be greater in the glacial stages compared to interglacials. This pattern is illustrated in RC27–61 by the relatively expanded depth intervals of glacial stages compared to the corresponding time within an interglacial (Fig. 4). These results indicate that the assumption of a constant sedimentation rate between relatively widely-spaced magnetic reversal and biostratigraphic datums does not accurately reflect the temporal changes in the input of major sedimentary components on glacial/interglacial timescales.

Results and discussion

Major sedimentary cycles

Upper Neogene sediments recovered from core RC27–61 and Site 722 are largely foraminifer–nannofossil oozes comprised of 33–83% calcium carbonate ($\bar{x} = 66\%$) and 12–63% terrigenous material. Opal and organic carbon generally comprise <10%. The major compositional changes associated with oscillations of sediment type ᴀ the past 370 000 years are shown in Fig. 5. Within this time interval, we use the oxygen isotope stratigraphy to provide a chronology. Thus, high-frequency ($\sim 10^3$ years) variations in sedimentation rate can be determined. Potential influences of dilution by carbonate or lithogenic material can be removed

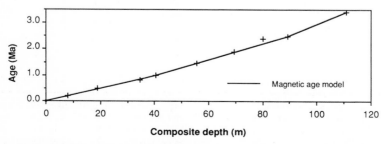

Fig. 3. Age vs. depth plot of the coarse resolution (magnetic reversal) age model for 0–120 m in Site 722. Crosses are the nannofossil and magnetic reversal data listed in Table 2.

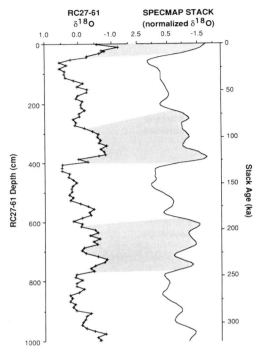

Fig. 4. Comparison of plots of the oxygen isotope composition of *G. sacculifer* in core RC27−61 versus depth and the SPECMAP stack versus age. Shaded intervals highlight interglacial intervals. Note that glacial intervals are expanded in RC27−61 compared to interglacials with similar time lengths.

by expressing the variations in terms of mass accumulation (MAR); where MAR (g/cm^2/ky or mg/cm^2/year) = concentration (g/g) × sedimentation rate (cm/ky) × dry bulk density (g/cm^3). Since these Owen Ridge sediments are largely a two-component mixture, $CaCO_3$ and terrigenous content have an inverse relationship. Non-carbonate concentration (100−$CaCO_3$%) exhibits variations similar to the terrigenous (%) record of Clemens & Prell (1990) (Fig. 5C). The only significant differences occur in interglacial stages where non-carbonate values are higher. This difference exists because opal and organic carbon comprise approximately 5% of the interglacial sediment that is not accounted for in the 100-$CaCO_3$% measurements. The MAR records (Fig. 5D) exhibit strong glacial/interglacial variations which have almost opposite phase compared with carbonate percent (Table 3). High carbonate concentrations associated with interglacial stages correspond to intervals with substantially larger numbers of planktonic foraminifer fragments (Fig. 5E) and lower carbonate accumulation rates (Fig. 5D) as compared to glacial intervals. We conclude that much of the variation in carbonate content is due simply to terrigenous dilution, so that $CaCO_3$ content is not, at this site, a simple monitor of the carbonate system. These results imply that the major sedimentary cycles in the western Arabian Sea are controlled by variations in the input of lithogenic material.

Table 3. Summary of cross spectral analysis[a].

Time Series[a]	100 ky		41 ky		23 ky	
	Phase	Coherency	Phase	Coherency	Phase	Coherency
−δ^{18}O (‰) (min ice)	−5 ± 9°	0.96	−75 ± 9°	0.96	−81 ± 9°	0.96
G. bulloides (%)	—	—	+2 ± 20°	0.83	−120 ± 25°	0.74
Lithogenic grain size	—	—	—	—	−147 ± 9°	0.96
Lithogenic (%)	−177 ± 12°	0.93	+164 ± 15°	0.89	+94 ± 11°	0.94
Lithogenic MAR	+161 ± 15°	0.90	+113 ± 20°	0.83	+89 ± 15°	0.90
$CaCO_3$ (%)	+6 ± 9°	0.92	−16 ± 10°	0.91	−80 ± 13°	0.85
$CaCO_3$ MAR	+140 ± 18°	0.86	+59 ± 16°	0.89	—	—
Fragments (%)	−32 ± 5°	0.98	−126 ± 8°	0.96	−132 ± 13°	0.92
Opal (%)	—	—	−10 ± 14°	0.91	−130 ± 10°	0.95
Opal MAR	+165 ± 21°	0.81	+31 ± 14°	0.91	−129 ± 9°	0.95
C-org (%)	—	—	—	—	+170 ± 25°	0.76
C-org MAR	+148 ± 18°	0.86	+53 ± 20°	0.84	+155 ± 15°	0.88
Müller and Suess	—	—	—	—	+162 ± 28°	0.73
Sarnthein *et al.*	+155 ± 16°	0.89	+47 ± 16°	0.89	+162 < 17°	0.92

[a] Summary of phase spectra between RC27−61 time series and ETP for Milankovitch frequency bands. Positive values indicate that the record leads ETP, and negative values indicate a lag. Record length = 6−370 ky; sample interval = 2 ky; # of lags = 90; bandwidth = 0.007; only statistically significant phases are reported and the test statistic for non-zero coherency at the 80% confidence level = 0.524. Müller and Suess and Sarnthein *et al.* refer to the paleoproductivity estimates from equations in the respective papers.

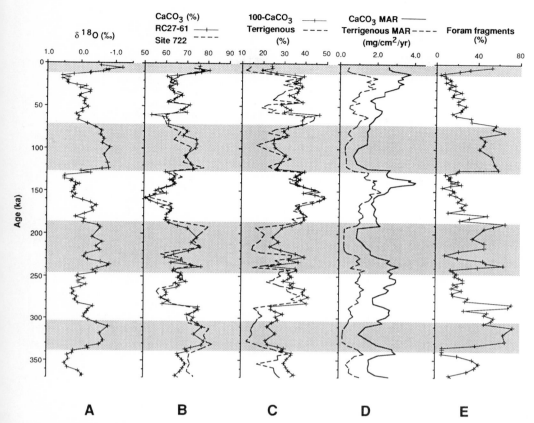

Fig. 5. Time series for core RC27−61 of (A) oxygen isotope composition of *G. sacculifer*, (B) CaCO₃ concentration, (C) non-carbonate and terrigenous concentration, (D) CaCO₃ and terrigenous MAR, and (E) >150 μm foraminifer fragment/(fragments + whole foraminifers). Also shown (B) is the CaCO₃ concentration time series from Site 722 for comparison to RC27−61. Interglacial stages are highlighted.

Clemens & Prell (1990) and deMenocal *et al.* (1991) have previously demonstrated that terrigenous content is highly correlated to terrigenous accumulation rate and that terrigenous content is a good index of temporal changes in lithogenic input. The close correspondence between terrigenous and noncarbonate concentration (Fig. 5E) implies that $100-\text{CaCO}_3\%$ is a reliable monitor of the input of terrigenous material to the Owen Ridge as long as opal content is relatively low (<10%). If this relationship persisted over the past 3.4 My, the non-carbonate concentration data (Fig. 2D) can be used to examine the variations of terrigenous input to the Arabian Sea in response to major climatic events during the late Pliocene and Pleistocene. This time interval includes the 'initiation' or rapid expansion of northern hemi-sphere glaciation near 2.4 Ma (Bachman 1979; Shackleton *et al.* 1984).

To document the major variations in non-carbonate content over the past 3.4 My, we have used standard time series analysis (Jenkins & Watts 1968; Imbrie *et al.* 1989) to examine 500 000-year intervals of this Plio/Pleistocene sedimentary record. Unfortunately, the precision of this approach is limited by the low-resolution bio-magneto stratigraphy and chronology. However, the change in dominance from variance near 31 ky prior to 2.5 Ma to variance concentrated at lower frequencies after 2.5 Ma is clearly evident (Fig. 6). Here, we note that no 'tuning' of the record was done. Hence, the low resolution of our age estimates and the bandwidth of our analysis likely incorporate the 23 ky precessional insolation variations into the

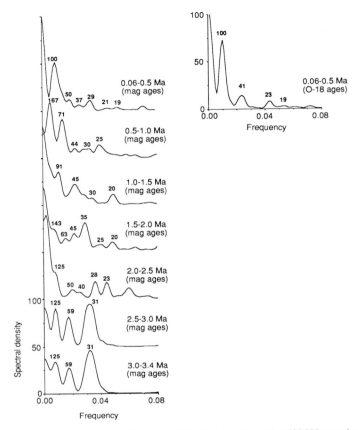

Fig. 6. Power spectra of non-carbonate % data in Site 722 calculated for 500 000-year intervals ($\Delta t = 2$ ka, bandwidth $= 0.004$). The mag ages refer to time series based on the magnetic reversal chronology. Periods corresponding to each of the major peaks in variance are indicated. Also shown is the spectrum for the 6–500 ka interval in Site 722 using the high-resolution oxygen isotope chronology (Clemens & Prell 1991). Note that the general characteristics of the spectra are independent of the age models in the 6–500 ka time interval (i.e. both have a high concentration of variance in the low frequencies).

31 ky period. Bloemendal & deMenocal (1989) & deMenocal *et al.* (1991) used magnetic susceptibility records as a measure of terrigenous content to examine a similar interval of time in Site 721. Using a chronostratigraphy tuned to the Earth's precessional cycle, they showed that magnetic susceptibility was dominated by high-frequency (1/23 ky) variations relative to longer periods prior to 2.4 Ma and that since 2.4 Ma, the magnetic susceptibility oscillations are dominated by 41 ky and longer periods. Although we have not resolved the 23 ky periodicity as clearly in our 'untuned' records, the non-carbonate and magnetic susceptibility data both show the shift from higher to lower frequency variation at about 2.4 Ma. DeMenocal *et al.*

(1991) suggest that the increase in 41 ky variation reflects increases in source area aridity associated with the expansion of northern hemisphere ice sheets. This interpretation is consistent with that of Clemens & Prell (1990) for the lithogenic data from RC27–61 (Fig. 5C,D). Within the past 370 000 years, terrigenous input to the Owen Ridge has a strong positive correlation with the size of northern hemisphere ice sheets ($\delta^{18}O$) at periods of 100, 41 and 23 ky; these are the so-called Milankovitch periods associated with late Pleistocene climatic change. However, Clemens & Prell (1990) note that maxima in accumulation of terrigenous material do not coincide with maxima in median grain size of the lithogenic component (Table 3). This difference occurs because median grain size is thought to reflect monsoon wind strength and the timing of its maxima and minima corresponds with other indicators of palaeomonsoon strength. Clemens & Prell (1991) documented the difference in phase of in terrigenous accumulation and indices of monsoon wind strength (including grain size) in records spanning the past one million years. Assuming these relationships persisted throughout the past 3.4 My, the major cycles of sediment composition on Owen Ridge reflect variations in source area aridity rather than variations in monsoonal upwelling.

Monsoonal upwelling (0–370 ka)

Previous results. Although bulk sediment composition does not reflect the upwelling process, other indicators clearly show its role in the western Arabian Sea. The planktonic foraminifer *Globigerina bulloides* has been used extensively as an index of monsoonal upwelling in the Arabian Sea (Prell 1984a, b). Prell & Curry (1981) showed that *G. bulloides* abundance is correlated with lower summer surface temperatures which, in turn, are correlated with wind-induced upwelling (Prell & Streeter 1982).

More recently, time series of a monsoon pollen index (Prell & van Campo 1986) and median lithogenic grain size (Clemens & Prell 1990) have been compared to the *G. bulloides* records from the Arabian Sea. The time series of *G. bulloides* and lithogenic grain size (measured in core RC27–61 for the past 370 000 ky) are remarkably similar (Fig. 7), although some differences are evident, especially in terms of peak amplitudes. Large peaks are apparent in both time series near 50, 210 and 260 ka. Importantly, these records do not exhibit significant variation at the broad 100 or 41 ky glacial/interglacial periods characteristic of the oxygen isotope (global ice volume) time series (Fig. 7) or the bulk carbonate and terrigenous components (Fig. 5). Thus, the monsoonal variation is not correctly characterized in terms of glacial and interglacial cycles or periods.

To quantify the relationships between terrigenous and monsoonal indicators, Clemens & Prell (1990) used cross spectral analysis to define their coherency and phase with respect to ETP (an index of orbital variation, Imbrie *et al.* 1984). We summarize their results in Table 3 and for the 23 ky precessional cycle on a phase wheel (Fig. 8) (see Imbrie *et al.* 1989; Clemens

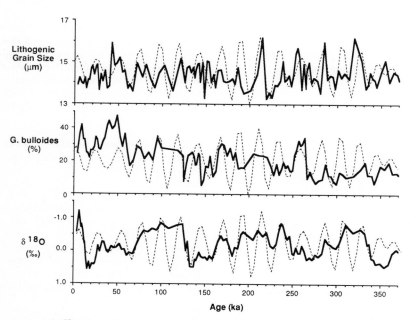

Fig. 7. Time series of $\delta^{18}O$ (ice volume), *G. bulloides* (monsoon upwelling index), and lithogenic grain size (monsoon wind index) for 6–370 ky from core RC27–61. The dashed line on each plot shows the precessional radiation changes lagged 9 ky for grain size and *G. bulloides* and 5 ky for $\delta^{18}O$.

& Prell 1990 for further discussion of phase wheels). Since precessional changes in northern hemisphere summer radiation are an important forcing of the monsoon, we focus on the 23 ky band. The phase wheel summary displays the phases of statistically important variations of the numerical indices. Phase differences between a particular index and maximum radiation in the precessional band (-P referenced to June 21 perihelion) are reported as vectors on the phase wheel where a full 360° rotation corresponds to 23 ky. Negative phase differences in Table 3 reflect a lag with respect to the maximum precessional radiation and a clockwise angular direction (Fig. 8). Both *G. bulloides* and lithogenic grain size lag the proposed forcing by about 140° (9 ky). If monsoon wind strength was directly forced by radiational heating, the observed response should approximately coincide with the forcing. The 9 ky lag suggests that internal feedbacks within the climate system are necessary to explain the temporal variations observed in the deep-sea record. Conceptual models which consider these feedbacks are discussed by Prell (1984*b*) and Clemens & Prell (1990). Prell (1984*b*) suggested that snow cover over Asia that persists into the summer season delays the low-level heating of the Tibetan plateau. If these conditions were synchronous with the waxing and waning of the major northern hemisphere ice sheets, the monsoon response to increased precessional radiation would be lagged by as much as 5 ky. However, Clemens & Prell (1990) note that albedo changes associated with snow in Tibet cannot account for the 9 ky lag observed in the monsoon indices. They suggest that latent heat supplied by the southern Indian Ocean, which strengthens the monsoon in the modern environment, is responsible for the lag in the precessional band. They link the amount of latent heat to sea−surface temperature changes in the southern Indian Ocean and note that these changes are statistically in phase with changes in monsoon strength. However, the 9 ky lag is not consistent with the modelling results of Prell & Kutzbach (1987). Work in progress by Clemens & Olgesby (in prep.) will evaluate this discrepancy with additional atmospheric and coupled ocean−atmosphere modelling experiments. In addition, Anderson *et al.* (this volume) examine changes in the structure of the wind field and the importance of curl-driven versus coastal upwelling as a possible explanation of different temporal and spatial patterns of biological response to the monsoon. Nevertheless, the terrigenous grain size and *G. bulloides* indices of monsoon strength on the Owen Ridge are in phase and provide a similar coherent response to which other biogenic components deposited beneath the zone of upwelling can be compared.

Calcium carbonate, opaline silica, and organic carbon are the major biogenic components produced as a result of monsoon upwelling and preserved in Owen Ridge sediments. Here we evaluate the palaeoproductivity signal contained in each of these components in light of the lithogenic grain size and *G. bulloides* results (Fig. 9).

Calcium carbonate. Our understanding of the response of carbonate productivity to monsoonal upwelling is complicated by variable carbonate preservation. Although RC27−61 (1897 m) and ODP Site 722 (2027 m) lie well above the top of the calcite hydrographic and foraminiferal lysoclines (~3500 m) (Fig. 10; Cullen & Prell 1984), both exhibit variable carbonate preservation/dissolution. Currently the sites are bathed by waters that are 5 to 10 μM above calcite saturation (Fig. 10). Most scenarios of glacial to interglacial changes in ocean chemistry (e.g. Boyle 1988; Kallel *et al.* 1988) indicate lower nutrients and CO_2 in intermediate waters during glacials intervals and imply even greater $[CO_3^{2-}]$. Thus, the waters bathing these sites during the past 370000 years

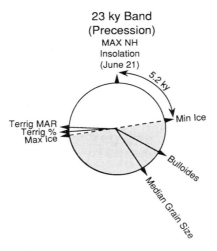

Fig. 8. Phase wheel summary of cross spectral analyses in the 23 ky band, referenced to insolation maximum corresponding to June 21. Data are from Clemens & Prell (1990). Hemisphere of ice growth is shaded. Movement in a clockwise direction reflects a lag with respect to the insolation forcing.

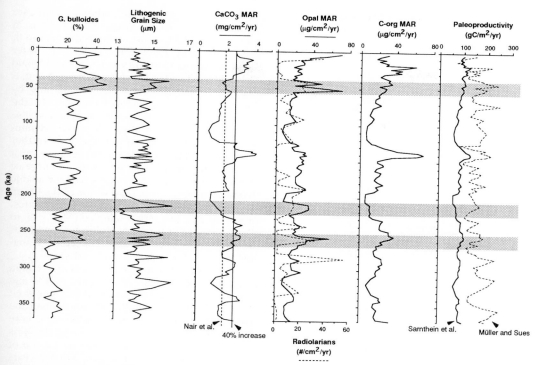

Fig. 9. Time series of monsoon indices and major biogenic components for 6–370 ka in core RC27–61. Strong monsoon events are highlighted. Dashed line on the CaCO₃ MAR plot is the rate measured in the western Arabian Sea trap (Nair *et al.* 1989) and the solid line reflects a 40% increase. The radiolarian flux is based on counts from slides containing the >63 μm size fraction. Palaeoproductivity estimates based on the equations of Müller & Suess (1979) and Sarnthein *et al.* (1988) are shown.

are unlikely to be undersaturated with respect to carbonate (i.e. the sites remain above the lysocline). If dissolution was minimal at these sites, then calcium carbonate accumulation should reflect the surface water calcium carbonate (planktonic foraminifer and coccolith) production. Other biogenic carbonate components such as pelagic aragonite (pteropods) and benthic foraminifers are not significant in Owen Ridge sediments. The abundance of detrital (eolian) calcite and dolomite is thought to be small (<10%) at these offshore sites (Sirocko *et al.* 1991). Furthermore, detrital phases of carbonate are unlikely to react completely with the phosphoric acid used in the CaCO₃ measurement and are underrepresented in this study. If the observed range of calcite accumulation rates (0.74 to 4.0 mg/cm²/y) does reflect surface production, the changes in carbonate MAR do not coincide with changes in lithogenic grain size and *G. bulloides* (Fig. 9) nor does carbonate MAR have significant variation within the pre-

cessional band. These relationships indicate that dissolution may have modified the record of surface carbonate productivity.

The close correspondence between CaCO₃ MAR and the foraminiferal fragment index (Fig. 5D, E) supports the inference that carbonate dissolution is at least partly responsible for the observed carbonate cycles. Since these sediments are well above the lysocline, degradation of organic carbon in the surface sediments must be supplying the acid to dissolve the carbonate. As the flux of organic carbon increases relative to carbonate carbon, more calcite will dissolve. The amount of carbonate preserved will depend upon the water column carbonate ion concentration $[CO_3^{2-}]$, and the organic carbon and calcite input to the sediments. These relationships can be quantified with models that consider porewater and solid phase carbonate reactions in near-surface sediments. Using the diffusion-reaction model of Emerson & Bender (1981), Archer (1991) obtained a family of curves that

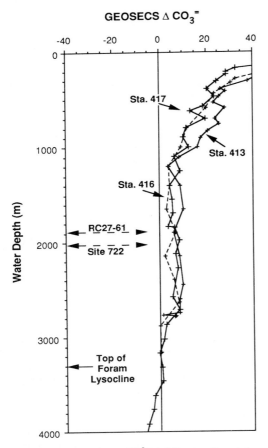

Fig. 10. Water column CO_3^{2-} (μM) saturation state based on data in Takahashi *et al.* (1980) from GEOSECS stations 413, 416, and 417 from the northwest Arabian Sea. The relative positions of core RC27−61 and Site 722 and the top of the foraminifer lysocline (Cullen & Prell 1984) are shown. $\Delta[CO_3^{2-}]$ values approach 200 μM near the sea surface.

reflect calcite accumulation in response to a given water column saturation ($\Delta[CO_3^{2-}]$), the initial calcite rain rate, and the associated organic carbon input to the sediments. This model assumes that reaction order for calcite dissolution is 4.5 (Keir 1980), the calcite rate constant is 100%/day (Keir 1980; Archer 1991), and that dissolved oxygen is the only significant electron acceptor for respiration (Bender & Heggie 1984).

We used the Archer (1991) model to evaluate whether organic carbon input and decay can account for the range of $CaCO_3$ MAR in RC27−61. The results are presented in Fig. 11 as a

comparison of the initial carbonate rain rate to the $CaCO_3$ accumulation for variations in the C-org/$CaCO_3$ input to the sediments (0.0, 0.5, 0.67, and 1.0 molar ratios) and water column carbonate saturation levels (5, +5, and +15 μM). When the C-org/$CaCO_3$ input equals 0.0, carbonate dissolution is driven only by changes in water column saturation. In the modern setting, water column saturation is close to +5 μM (Fig. 10) and the Holocene accumulation is about 2.6 mg/cm²/y (Fig. 9). To further evaluate the Holocene (modern) case, we must estimate the initial input of calcite and organic carbon to the surface sediments. Data available from sediment traps deployed east of the Owen Ridge (Nair *et al.* 1989) provide these estimates, assuming that the period sampled (May 1986 to April 1987) reflects typical Holocene conditions and the traps were efficient collectors of material falling through the water column.

The sediment traps in the western Arabian Sea recorded annual calcite fluxes of 1.9 mg/cm²/y from May 1986 to April 1987 (Nair *et al.* 1989). This rate is significantly lower than the Holocene rate (2.6 mg/cm²/y) measured in core RC27−61 (Fig. 9). In fact, 1.9 mg/cm²/y is lower than the mean $CaCO_3$ flux to the top of the Owen Ridge over the past 370 000 years (2.1 mg/cm²/y, Fig. 9). Compared to other Owen Ridge cores, the rates in RC27−61 are considered to be typical or slightly lower (Clemens 1990; Murray & Prell 1991). Taken together, these data suggest that the fluxes reported by Nair *et al.* (1989) underestimate of the modern flux to the Owen Ridge. More recent data on the foraminifera fluxes measured during both the 1986 and 1987 monsoons indicate that the 1986 monsoon was relatively weak and fluxes were relatively low (Curry *et al.* this volume). Within the time interval considered by Nair *et al.* (1989), foraminifera fluxes in the >150 μm size fraction from the western Arabian Sea site averaged close to 1700 shells/m²/day (Curry *et al.* this volume). During the following year, the average flux of foraminifera (>150 μm) increased by about 40% to over 2300 shells/m²/day. A comparable increase in bulk carbonate content provides a better match between the rates measured in the sediment traps and the Holocene rates for RC27−61 (Fig. 9). However, for this trap flux to be characteristic of Holocene carbonate sedimentation on the Owen Ridge, all the calcite input to the sediments must be preserved. Foraminifera fragment data from the top of core RC27−61 (Fig. 5E) indicates that substantial dissolution has occurred [fragments/(fragments + whole foraminifers) = 53%]. Mooring experiments in

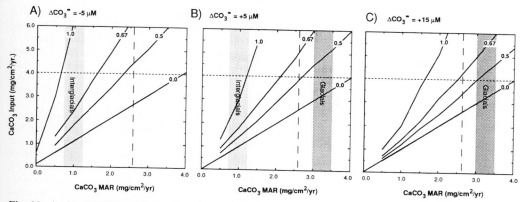

Fig. 11. Archer (1991) model output of $CaCO_3$ input versus accumulation for C-org/$CaCO_3$ input (molar) of 0.0, 0.5, 0.67, and 1.0 for $\Delta[CO_3^{2-}]$ of −5, 5, and 15 μM. Horizontal dashed lines denote a $CaCO_3$ rain rate of 4 mg/cm²/y. Vertical dashed line is the measured flux of $CaCO_3$ at the top of RC27−61. Light shading shows the range of carbonate accumulation in the low carbonate interglacial intervals. The heavy shading denotes the range of accumulation rates from high carbonate glacial intervals.

the Panama Basin (Thunell & Honjo 1981) and equatorial Pacific (Metzler *et al.* 1982) show a general correspondence between weight loss (i.e. dissolution) and fragmentation. Thus, the observed Holocene ratio (about 50:50) of whole foraminifers to fragments in the >150 μm fraction implies a loss of carbonate. These data indicate that Holocene calcite production had to be greater than 2.6 mg/cm²/y and that the trap-measured fluxes for 1986 and 1987 underestimate the biogenic calcite input.

Well preserved, low-foraminifer fragment sections of core RC27−61 provide alternative estimates of modern calcite rain rates to the Owen Ridge. Well preserved intervals near 10, 140 and 260 ka have calcite accumulation rates between 3 and 4 mg/cm²/y (Fig. 5D, E). These intervals contain both a low relative abundance (compared to whole foraminifers) and flux of foraminifer fragments and may reflect the preservation spikes associated with changing climatic regimes and water column chemistry (Boyle 1988). Assuming that little carbonate has been lost from maxima of $CaCO_3$ MAR, these intervals, which are associated with both moderate and strong monsoon-driven upwelling (Figs 7 & 9), may provide a better estimate of the biogenic calcite rain to the top of the Owen Ridge. If carbonate production increased in association with extremely strong monsoons, the calcite input to the sediments might be greater than 4 mg/cm²/y. Calcium carbonate fluxes of this magnitude are not common in the pelagic marine environment, but have been

measured as annual rates in sediment traps and sediments in the Santa Barbara and Panama Basins (Honjo 1982; Dunbar 1983).

Given an initial flux of 4 mg $CaCO_3$/cm²/yr, a C-org/$CaCO_3$ flux ratio of about 0.55 (0.264 mgC/cm²/y) is required to dissolve $CaCO_3$ and account for the Holocene accumulation rate of 2.6 mg/cm²/y (Fig. 11B). Trap-derived estimates of the C-org/$CaCO_3$ ratio in the western Arabian Sea average about 0.8 (Nair *et al.* 1989). However, some of the organic carbon rain will degrade rapidly at the sediment−water interface and not influence dissolution in the pore waters (Emerson & Bender 1981; Emerson *et al.* 1985; Martin & Bender 1989). Thus a Holocene C-org/$CaCO_3$ input of 0.55 is reasonable and accounts for a 35% loss of the primary biogenic calcite flux. The higher estimate of $CaCO_3$ input, more than twice the flux reported Nair *et al.* (1989), requires a greater organic carbon rain than that measured in the sediment traps. The empirical relationships of Suess (1980) and Berger *et al.* (1988) for organic carbon flux and water depth, allow us to evaluate whether our estimated fluxes of organic carbon are realistic for the Arabian Sea. The sediment trap-measured organic carbon flux of 0.18 mgC/cm²/y (1.8 gC/m²/y) at 3020 m is associated with a surface production of 11.5 to 13.1 mgC/cm²/y (115 to 131 gC/m²/y); a low range for this region (Krey & Babenerd 1976). In contrast, an organic carbon flux of 0.384 mgC/cm²/y to 3020 m (the flux associated with 4 g $CaCO_3$/cm²/y and a

C-org/CaCO₃ molar ratio of 0.8) yields a surface production of 24.5 to 27.9 mgC/cm²/y. These high annual production rates are within the range reported for this region (Smith 1984; Berger et al. 1988). This analysis supports our assertion that the biological production associated with both the 1986 and 1987 monsoons was relatively low compared to average Holocene rates or that the traps were inefficient collectors of the particulate flux. Longer time series of monsoon wind, biological production, and organic carbon flux in this region are necessary to evaluate these differences.

Invoking organic carbon degradation to account for the low carbonate accumulation rates (~0.8–1.3 mg CaCO₃/cm²/y) in interglacial stages 5, 7 and 9 (Fig. 9) with a calcite input of 4 g/cm²/y, requires either an increase in the C-org/CaCO₃ input to a value more than 1.0 (Fig. 11B) or a substantial (30–35 μM) decrease in [CO₃²⁻] (Archer 1991). Alternatively, a decrease in both carbonate and organic carbon productivity by more than a factor of two, and an input ratio of 0.55 (modern) could account for low accumulation rates of calcium carbonate during interglacials (Fig. 11B). Other sediment indices (Fig. 9) imply that these intervals of low carbonate accumulation are associated with moderate to strong monsoons. Therefore both biogenic calcite and organic carbon were probably the same as or higher than modern levels and a combination of decreased water column saturation and increased C-org/CaCO₃ input is the most likely scenario to account for the low calcite accumulation (Fig. 11A). The associated high levels of organic carbon production are currently found closer to the Arabian coast, and we suggest that these conditions were more widespread during the strong monsoon intervals.

During glacial intervals the [CO₃²⁻] in intermediate waters is thought to have increased as much as ~10 μM (Boyle 1988). Without changing other factors, this increase in [CO₃²⁻] would cause only an additional 0.4 mg/cm²/y of calcite to accumulate (Fig. 11C), which is only a small portion of the glacial to interglacial range of carbonate accumulation. The flux of foraminifera fragments is low in these intervals implying that the foraminifera assemblage has undergone little dissolution. If the foraminifera reflect preservation of the whole carbonate portion of the sediments, these data suggest that, rather than an increase in biogenic calcite production, the effect of organic carbon degradation for dissolving carbonate was diminished to account for the full range of CaCO₃ accumulation rates during glacial intervals. This can

be accomplished by either a substantial (40–45 μM) increase of [CO₃²⁻] in intermediate Arabian Sea intermediate waters compared to modern values, a decrease in the input of organic carbon to carbonate in the sediment mixed layer, or a combination of these factors. We cannot differentiate between these effects with the present data.

Although the quantification of processes affecting carbonate dissolution in near surface sediments is poorly constrained, even in the modern setting, these modelling results show that biogenic calcite fluxes could be high during strong monsoons but result in low carbonate accumulation rates if organic carbon production also increased substantially. In this case, increased dissolution and foraminifer fragmentation would occur during strong monsoons. In support of this hypothesis, the 23 ky variations in foraminifera fragmentation are synchronous with other indices of monsoon wind strength and upwelling (Table 3; Fig. 12).

Opal. Very little opal is preserved in the Owen Ridge sediments and most of the observed peaks are composed of well preserved radiolarians (Fig. 9). Changes in opal accumulation match other monsoon indices, especially in the 23 ky

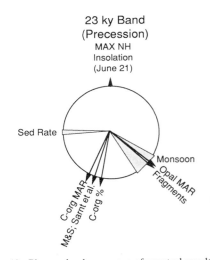

Fig. 12. Phase wheel summary of spectral results listed in Table 3 for the 23 ky precessional band. The shaded monsoon sector is based on phase lags of the grain size and *G. bulloides* time series. The Sed Rate sector corresponds to phase of high sedimentation rates associated with lithogenic input. The M&S and Sarnt et al. vectors refer to palaeoproductivity estimates for the Müller & Suess (1979) and Sarnthein et al. (1988) equations, respectively.

precessional band (Figs 9 and 12). Although some alteration of the opal signal is likely due to post-depositional diagenesis, the original variations in productivity and input seem to be preserved, as most of major peaks in the other monsoon indices are also observed in opal, or radiolarian accumulation (Fig. 9). Thus opal appears to be a reliable monsoon index in the Owen Ridge sediments, and its association with high production of organic carbon (Margalef 1978; Dymond & Lyle 1985) provides additional support for increased C-org/CaCO$_3$ rain ratios during strong monsoonal upwelling that result in low accumulation of biogenic calcite in these intervals.

Organic carbon. A number of studies have focused on the use of organic carbon preserved in deep-sea sediments as a palaeoproductivity index (Müller & Suess 1979; Sarnthein *et al.* 1988; Lyle *et al.* 1988). However, other studies (Emerson 1985; Emerson & Hedges 1988) question the reliability of this index because of the numerous factors, unrelated to surface productivity, which affect organic carbon preservation. For example, increased sedimentation rates enhance organic carbon preservation in marine sediments (Heath *et al.* 1977; Müller & Suess 1979; Sarnthein *et al.* 1988). In most environments, surface production and sedimentation rate are positively correlated and organic carbon-based palaeoproductivity estimates attempt to eliminate this sedimentation rate enhancement. However, in the western Arabian Sea, the sedimentation rate increases are not synchronous with increases in monsoonal upwelling and its associated surface productivity. As noted previously, the sedimentation rates increase as a result of terrigenous input, and this input reflects changes in the source area, not monsoonal upwelling. Maxima in the monsoonal indices occur in the lower sedimentation rate intervals. The 23 ky variations in organic carbon accumulation and concentration in core RC27-61 are not synchronous with indices of monsoonal upwelling (Fig. 12). The timing of maxima in organic carbon accumulation lies between maxima in the monsoon indices and sedimentation rate (that is between an index of production and preservation) (Fig. 12). This intermediate phase implies that organic carbon accumulation on the Owen Ridge reflects both the influence of monsoon upwelling and enhanced preservation attributed to sedimentation rate. To assess the role of sedimentation rate on the structure of the C-org MAR, we used the equations of Müller & Suess (1979) and Sarnthein *et al.* (1988), who try to remove the

rate-dependent component (Fig. 9). If the effect of sedimentation rate is removed we expect that the phase of C-org MAR would be similar to other indices of monsoonal upwelling and high productivity. Although differences exist between the two palaeoproductivity curves (Fig. 9), the phase of the 23 ky variations does not change (Fig. 12) and we conclude that either sedimentation rate still imposes a major influence on the preservation of organic carbon in this area or that the oceanic carbon production is not directly linked to monsoonal upwelling. Until the non-biogenic sedimentation rate effect can be removed, we do not consider organic carbon to be a reliable index of high-frequency changes in monsoonal upwelling in the Owen Ridge cores.

Long-term changes 0–3.4 Ma

The detailed relationships discussed above can also be used to interpret the long-term variations of monsoonal upwelling from records of planktonic $\delta^{18}O$ (ice volume), non-carbonate concentration (terrigenous flux), calcium carbonate and organic carbon MAR, and coarse fraction content (mostly shells of foraminifers) (Fig. 13). Because a coarse resolution age model based on magnetic-reversal stratigraphy was used (note control points in Fig. 13), only large-scale changes are significant in the MAR records. The Pliocene section that begins nears 3.4 Ma is characterized by low CaCO$_3$ fluxes (about 1 mg/cm^2/y) that increase by a factor of three from the late Pliocene to the Present (note that the step at 2.4 Ma is due to the age model control). Organic carbon exhibits a different pattern of change over the past 3.4 My. From 3.4 to 3.8 Ma, the average rates were low and close to present values of 20 to 30 μg/cm^2/y. After about 3.0 Ma, the accumulation rates increase to a maximum of 125 μg/cm^2/y near 2.4 Ma. This increase in organic carbon accumulation precedes the rise in calcium carbonate accumulation near 2.4 Ma and is not associated with age model picks. The average organic carbon MAR decreases from the late Pliocene to the Pleistocene with present values near 30 μg/cm^2/y for the top of the Owen Ridge. Since the high carbon accumulation rates near 2.4 Ma are associated with an interval of lower mean sedimentation rate compared to the Present, the high organic carbon accumulation rates in the late Pliocene cannot be attributed to sedimentation rate-enhanced preservation. Coarse fraction (>150 μm) content exhibits a trend similar to that of the carbonate mass accumulation rate and generally opposite to

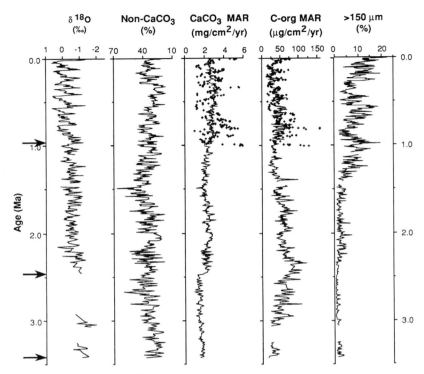

Fig. 13. Time series of *G. sacculifer* $\delta^{18}O$, non-carbonate concentration, calcium carbonate and organic carbon mass accumulation rates, and coarse fraction ($>150\ \mu m$) abundance from Hole 722B composite data. Note that non-carbonate content is plotted with higher values to the left. The ages for the isotope data are derived from the low-resolution magnetic reversal chronology. The arrows correspond the identified magnetic reversal events listed in Table 2. Data represented by the solid lines in the MAR profiles use chronologies based on magnetic stratigraphy, and the crosses represent values calculated using the oxygen isotope-based age model of Clemens & Prell (1991).

that of the organic carbon profile. Examination of the coarse fraction in Site 722 samples indicates that prior to 1.5 Ma the foraminifer assemblage is more fragmented and dissolved than younger material, and low coarse fraction is a good index of high dissolution. Taken together, these data imply that oceanographic conditions were more favourable for organic carbon production and preservation in the late Pliocene compared to the Present, due either to the local influence of monsoonal upwelling or regional oceanographic changes which provide more nutrients to the surface waters. Evidence of high productivity in the late Pliocene is also noted in the near-by sites on the Oman margin (Prell, Niitsuma *et al.* 1989; Prell *et al.* 1990), where laminated sediments that are rich in opal and organic carbon occur in the interval between 1.5 and 3.4 Ma. The presence of these laminae

at the margin sites implies that the oxygen minimum zone was intensified during the late Pliocene. Such an intensification could be attributed to surface production rather than to a regional or more global decrease of oxygen in the intermediate waters. If the production was monsoon induced, our data suggest that the late Pliocene was a time of stronger monsoons compared to the Present. Prell & Kutzbach (1987) showed that glacial conditions had a dampening effect on the monsoon circulation. The lack of substantial northern hemisphere ice sheets and glacial boundary conditions in the late Pliocene could contribute to a strong monsoon circulation. However, further study is necessary to isolate local monsoon-induced changes in surface production from the changes in productivity or preservation related to regional oceanographic variations.

Conclusions

This study of the major sediment components of the Pliocene–Pleistocene deposits from the Owen Ridge reveals that non-carbonate concentration is a good proxy of lithogenic input. Prior to 2.5 Ma, this input had significant high frequency (<31 ky) variation, but since that time variance is concentrated in longer periods. The longer periods may reflect high latitude forcing of source area aridity rather than local monsoon dynamics; a similar conclusion was obtained by deMenocal *et al.* (1991).

Our study of the high frequency changes in the major sediment components reveals that increases in $CaCO_3$ and organic carbon MAR do not coincide with strong monsoons. We show that the calcite changes can be driven by dissolution even though the crest of the Owen Ridge is well above the regional lysocline. These carbonate dissolution cycles may be driven by organic matter degradation and require greater organic carbon production during the inter-glacial with relatively lower production during glacial episodes. Over the past 370 000 years, a group of monsoon indices, including the relative abundance of *G. bulloides*, opal MAR, and terrigenous grain size, give a coherent signal of strong monsoons that lags the proposed forcing by about 9 ky in the 23 ky precessional band. Organic carbon accumulation does not follow this pattern. Until we can fully remove the effects of sedimentation rate-enhanced preservation of organic carbon, organic matter accumulation cannot be used as a reliable index of monsoon variability.

Large-scale changes in the mean accumulation rates of organic carbon and calcium carbonate on the Owen Ridge suggest that oceanographic conditions were more favorable for biological production and/or preservation between 1.5 and 3.4 Ma. The lack of large northern hemisphere glaciers may in part be responsible for this increase.

This research was supported by grants from the National Science Foundation (OCE-8511571 and OCE-8911874. We gratefully acknowledge P.B. ($CaCO_3$), A. deCharon (opal), W. Kang (c-org and opal), T. Saha (coarse fraction), A. Martin (faunal counts) and J. Farrell (isotopes) for their technical help on RC27–61 samples. We thank S. Clemens for his extensive work on the RC27–61 and Site 722B isotope age models and for providing files of the published terrigenous data. The manuscript benefited from helpful reviews by L. Krissek, F. Sirocko, S. Clemens and W. Howard. Special thanks to W. Curry who provided files of the foram data published in this volume and D. Archer who provided preprints of the papers discussing the dissolution model.

References

ARCHER, D. 1991. Modelling the calcite lysocline. *Journal of Geophysical Research*, in press.

BACHMAN, J. 1979. Pliocene biostratigraphy of DSDP sites 111 and 116 from the North Atlantic Ocean and the age of northern hemisphere glaciation. *Stockholm Contributions in Geology*, **32**, 115–137.

BENDER, M. L. & HEGGIE, D. T. 1984. Fate of organic carbon reaching the sea floor: a status report. *Geochimica et Cosmochimica Acta*, **81**, 977–986.

BERGER, W. H., FISCHER, K., LAI, C. & WU, G. 1988. Ocean carbon flux: global maps of primary production and export production. *In*: AGEGIAN, C. (ed.), *Biogeochemical Cycling and Fluxes between the Deep Euphotic Zone and Other Oceanic Realms*, NOAA National Undersea Research Program, Res. Rpt. 88–1, 137–176.

BLOEMENDAL, J. & DEMENOCAL, P. 1989. Evidence for a change in the periodicity of tropical climate cycles at 2.4 Myr from whole-core magnetic susceptibility measurements. *Nature*, **342**, 897–900.

BOYLE, E. A. 1988. The role of vertical chemical fractionation in controlling late Quaternary atmospheric carbon dioxide. *Journal of Geophysical Research*, **93**, 15 701–15 714.

BUSCH, W. H. 1991. Analysis of wet-bulk density and sediment color cycles in Pliocene-Pleistocene sediments of the Owen Ridge (Site 722) and Oman Margin (Site 728). *In*: PRELL, W. L., NIITSUMA, N. *et al. Proceedings of the Ocean Drilling Program, Scientific Results*. Ocean Drilling Program College Station, TX **117**, 239–253.

CLEMENS, S. C. 1990. *Quaternary Variability of Indian Ocean Monsoon Winds and Climate*. PhD thesis, Brown University.

—— & PRELL, W. L. 1990. Late Pleistocene variability of Arabian Sea summer-monsoon winds and dust source-area aridity: Eolian records from the lithogenic component of deep-sea sediments. *Paleoceanography*, **5**, 109–145.

—— & —— 1991. One million year record of summer monsoon winds and continental aridity from the Owen Ridge (Site 722), northwest Arabian Sea. *In*: PRELL, W. L., NIITSUMA, N. *et al. Proceedings of the Ocean Drilling Program, Scientific Results*, Ocean Drilling Program, College Station, TX **117**, 365–388.

CULLEN, J. L. & PRELL, W. L. 1984. Planktonic foraminifers in northern Indian Ocean surface sediments: distribution and preservation. *Marine Micropaleontology*, **9**, 1–52.

DEMENOCAL, P., BLOEMENDAL, J. & KING, J. 1991. A rock-magnetic record of monsoonal dust deposition to the Arabian Sea: Evidence for a shift in the mode of deposition at 2.4 Ma. *In*: PRELL, W. L., NIITSUMA, N. *et al. Proceedings of the Ocean Drilling Program, Scientific Results*, Ocean

D. W. MURRAY & W. L. PRELL

Appendix: RC27−61 data.

Depth (cm)	Age (ka)	Sed Rate (cm/ky)	Dry density (g/cm^3)	CaCO$_3$ (%)	Opal (%)	C-org (%)	G. bull. (%)	Frags (%)	>150 μm (%)
2	3.7	4.33	0.792	75.93	2.058	0.888	25	53	22
12	6.0	4.33	0.806	75.55	1.566	0.611	36	32	24
22	8.3	4.33	0.806	80.54	1.020	0.497	42	22	35
32	10.2	5.70	0.800	76.58	0.801	0.602	33	8	31
42	12.0	5.70	0.887	73.74	0.510	0.399	33	4	28
52	13.7	5.70	0.929	65.09	0.539	0.502	25	9	24
62	15.5	5.70	0.948	60.59	0.555	0.558	25	9	15
72	17.3	5.70	0.949	62.39	0.545	0.511	22	13	20
82	19.0	5.60	0.878	62.59	0.480	1.226	26	14	19
92	20.8	5.49	0.875	64.62	0.378	1.021	26	9	19
102	22.6	5.49	0.992	62.55	0.490	0.598	29	14	19
112	24.5	5.49	0.890	65.08	0.466	0.922	35	18	25
122	26.3	5.49	0.928	61.80	0.426	0.738	33	13	18
132	28.1	5.49	0.922	61.59	0.505	0.884	27	12	18
142	29.9	4.64	0.963	63.33	0.610	0.583	27	18	22
152	32.4	4.02	0.929	63.66	0.500	0.572	32	24	22
162	34.9	4.02	0.917	64.12	0.574	0.705	34	17	20
172	37.4	4.02	0.866	67.83	0.488	0.923	42	15	23
182	39.9	3.66	0.797	65.40	0.985	1.046	45	26	22
192	42.9	3.34	0.758	63.68	1.946	1.368	40	21	18
202	45.8	3.35	0.908	61.32	0.649	0.693	41	21	15
212	48.8	3.35	0.784	71.41	1.705	1.068	47	28	19
222	51.8	3.40	0.806	69.26	2.601	0.969	35	25	19
232	54.7	3.47	0.964	67.03	0.530	0.673	29	23	14
242	57.6	3.47	0.916	70.01	0.602	0.625	37	15	23
252	60.5	3.46	1.128	53.45	0.555	0.537	26	19	6
262	63.4	3.00	1.046	60.31	0.526	0.529	17	33	14
272	67.1	2.48	1.155	61.57	0.485	0.555	20	34	13
282	71.4	2.33	1.075	61.39	0.562	0.897	29	57	7
292	75.7	2.33	0.994	67.99	0.680	0.574	27	54	12
302	80.0	2.21	0.933	70.20	0.674	0.585	21	65	16
312	84.8	2.11	1.039	68.42	0.660	0.456	25	42	16
322	89.5	2.11	0.929	74.43	0.892	0.735	20	47	17
332	94.3	2.11	0.917	74.92	1.084	0.623	34	45	17
342	99.0	1.39	0.948	74.29	0.646	0.577	28	41	17
352	108.6	1.04	1.029	69.19	0.600	0.575	27	53	12
362	118.2	1.28	1.012	72.06	0.813	0.540	26	56	12
372	124.2	2.00	1.034	73.28	0.770	0.606	23	59	16
376	125.2	4.00	0.925	72.89	0.545	0.429	8	22	23
386	127.7	4.08	1.052	60.16	0.578	0.501	18	19	4
396	130.1	4.08	0.985	62.00	0.415	0.645	23	9	12
406	132.6	4.08	0.977	64.72	0.473	0.895	24	14	15
416	135.0	5.00	0.895	64.22	0.435	0.925	26	12	20
426	136.6	6.25	0.980	62.18	0.514	1.026	22	14	13
436	138.2	6.25	0.931	63.24	0.556	1.139	17	21	15
446	139.8	6.25	1.016	63.95	0.464	1.094	18	15	18
456	141.4	6.25	0.972	64.75	0.550	1.033	25	24	19
466	143.0	5.00	1.052	63.48	0.493	0.679	23	14	19
476	145.4	4.17	1.072	60.76	0.608	0.603	5	6	14
486	147.8	4.17	1.103	57.08	0.665	0.419	8	16	9
496	150.2	4.17	1.126	55.30	0.605	0.405	17	18	14
506	152.6	4.17	0.956	60.57	0.760	0.627	16	13	20
516	155.0	3.57	1.034	55.41	0.693	0.701	23	19	14
526	158.2	3.12	1.161	50.93	0.620	0.513	11	25	11
536	161.4	3.12	1.103	53.04	0.825	0.475	14	21	13
546	164.6	3.12	0.976	56.56	0.899	0.750	27	29	15
556	167.8	3.12	0.947	62.49	0.835	0.734	31	24	19
566	171.0	3.08	0.996	63.30	0.699	0.580	30	27	21
576	174.3	3.03	0.998	61.99	0.712	0.524	23	12	22

Depth (cm)	Age (ka)	Sed Rate (cm/ky)	Dry density (g/cm³)	CaCO₃ (%)	Opal (%)	C-org (%)	G. bull. (%)	Frags (%)	>150 μm (%)
586	177.6	3.03	1.004	60.84	0.702	0.654	28	49	9
596	180.9	3.08	1.069	60.73	0.679	0.763	21	32	15
606	184.1	3.08	1.063	60.13	0.818	0.536	26	23	18
616	187.4	3.03	1.092	61.71	0.991	0.611	15	66	8
626	190.7	3.03	1.098	66.15	0.842	0.473	16	55	11
636	194.0	1.40	0.991	70.46	0.858	0.443	16	46	17
646	205.0	1.21	1.024	74.98	0.696	0.470	25	35	19
656	210.5	1.82	0.919	72.35	2.161	0.659	24	46	14
666	216.0	2.11	0.887	76.60	1.957	0.557	23	46	17
676	220.0	2.50	0.946	71.23	1.249	0.493	22	22	20
686	224.0	2.50	1.040	64.40	0.579	0.410	17	9	14
696	228.0	2.90	1.191	60.03	0.582	0.427	11	21	12
706	230.9	3.51	1.142	67.57	0.502	0.642	18	45	10
716	233.7	3.51	1.153	63.02	0.504	0.587	12	48	6
726	236.6	3.70	1.044	71.91	0.602	0.586	16	64	8
736	239.1	4.08	1.004	77.07	0.660	—	19	40	15
746	241.5	4.08	1.036	64.45	0.615	0.526	16	14	13
756	244.0	4.00	1.016	63.70	0.504	0.588	18	17	16
766	246.5	4.08	1.028	67.71	0.531	0.772	14	20	21
776	248.9	4.08	0.982	67.24	0.484	0.808	15	18	25
786	251.4	4.17	0.971	66.18	0.536	0.811	24	22	20
796	253.7	4.35	1.032	67.69	0.604	0.837	27	26	20
806	256.0	4.35	0.997	70.02	1.368	0.797	33	26	22
816	258.3	4.35	1.042	65.12	0.789	0.597	30	17	17
826	260.6	3.92	0.987	66.91	0.868	0.599	31	21	18
836	263.4	3.57	1.020	65.47	0.926	0.712	34	15	17
846	266.2	3.57	1.239	59.84	0.574	0.415	10	25	9
856	269.0	3.57	1.152	60.87	0.608	0.483	14	16	9
866	271.8	3.03	1.177	60.74	0.529	0.439	10	17	10
876	275.6	2.63	1.180	58.29	0.542	0.530	7	31	9
886	279.4	2.63	1.107	61.85	0.514	0.594	9	28	9
896	283.2	2.63	1.188	59.12	0.557	0.790	9	72	4
906	287.0	2.94	1.067	75.77	0.866	0.795	18	69	8
916	290.0	3.33	1.082	75.89	0.496	0.714	11	27	10
926	293.0	3.33	1.090	73.76	0.480	0.586	11	49	8
936	296.0	3.33	1.147	70.20	0.476	0.623	8	46	5
946	299.0	2.99	1.132	73.61	0.553	0.573	6	55	3
956	302.7	2.74	1.035	72.43	1.015	0.628	13	53	6
966	306.3	2.74	1.126	75.44	0.605	0.627	12	46	8
976	310.0	1.65	1.112	77.49	0.527	0.742	10	73	10
986	318.4	1.19	1.200	73.70	0.550	0.545	11	64	7
996	326.8	1.49	—	78.49	1.829	0.743	16	66	6
1006	331.8	2.67	0.985	77.44	0.727	0.526	19	38	12
1016	334.3	4.00	—	72.55	0.451	0.405	12	7	13
1026	336.8	4.00	1.022	69.80	0.520	0.553	11	7	7
1036	339.3	3.92	1.041	70.79	0.528	0.545	12	7	6
1046	341.9	3.92	1.178	65.96	0.457	0.526	7	6	7
1056	344.4	2.78	1.137	66.45	0.464	0.522	10	21	8
1066	349.1	2.13	1.094	68.21	0.454	0.643	17	35	12
1076	353.8	2.11	1.092	69.79	0.500	0.865	15	41	13
1086	358.6	2.11	1.061	68.66	0.490	0.796	19	37	10
1096	363.3	2.13	1.093	67.46	0.509	0.725	13	30	11
1106	368.0	2.74	1.108	64.85	0.498	0.633	13	13	12
1116	370.6	3.92	1.092	67.22	0.442	0.876	11	16	13

Drilling Program, College Station, TX 389–407.

DUNBAR, R. B. 1983. Stable isotope record of upwelling and climate from Santa Barbara Basin, California. In: THIEDE, J. & SUESS, E. (eds), Coastal Upwelling its Sediment Record, Part B, NATO conference series. Plenum, New York, 217–246.

DYMOND, J. & LYLE, M. 1985. Flux comparisons between sediments and sediment traps in the eastern tropical Pacific: Implications for CO$_2$ variations during the Pleistocene. Limnology and Oceanography, 30, 699–712.

EMERSON, S. 1985. Organic carbon preservation in marine sediments. In: SUNDQUIST, E. T. & BROECKER, W. S. (eds), The Carbon Cycle and Atmospheric CO$_2$: Natural Variations Archean to Present. Geophys. Monog., 32, Washington D.C. (Am. Geophys. Union), 78–89.

—— & BENDER, M. L. 1981. Carbon fluxes at the sediment-water interface of the deep sea: calcium carbonate preservation. Journal of Marine Research, 39, 139–162.

——, FISCHER, K., REIMERS, C. & HEGGIE, D. 1985. Organic carbon dynamics and preservation in deep-sea sediments. Deep-Sea Research, 32, 1–21.

—— & HEDGES, J. 1988. Processes controlling organic carbon content of open ocean sediments. Paleoceanography, 3, 621–634.

HEATH, G. R., MOORE, T. C. & DAUPHIN, J. P. 1977. Organic carbon in deep sea sediments. In: ANDERSON, N. R. & MALAHOFF, A. (eds), The Fate of fossil fuel CO$_2$ in the Oceans, Plenum, New York, 605–628.

HONJO, S. 1982. Seasonality and interaction of biogenic and lithogenic particulate flux at the Panama Basin. Science, 218, 883–884.

IMBRIE, J., HAYS, J. D., MARTINSON, D. G., MCINTYRE, A., MIX, A. C., MORELY, J. J., PISIAS, N. G., PRELL, W. L. & SHACKLETON, N. J. 1984. The orbital theory of Pleistocene climate: Support from a revised chronology of the marine oxygen isotopic record. In: BERGER, A. L., IMBRIE, J., HAYS, J., KUKLA, G. & SALTZMAN, B. (eds), Milankovitch and Climate, Part 1, Reidel, Dordrecht, 269–305.

——, MCINTYRE, A. & MIX, A. 1989. Oceanic response to orbital forcing in the Late Quaternary: observational and experimental strategies. In: DUPLESSY, J. C. et al. (eds), Climate and Geoscience, Boston (Klewer), 105–120.

JENKINS, G. M. & WATTS, D. G. 1968. Spectral Analysis and its Applications, Oakland (Holden Day).

JONES, G. A. & KAITERIS, P. 1983. A vacuum-gasometric technique for rapid and precise analysis of calcium carbonate in sediments and soils. Journal of Sedimentary Petrology, 53, 655–660.

KALLEL, N., LABEYRIE, L. D., JUILLET-LECLERC, A., DUPLESSY, J-C. 1988. A deep hydrological front between intermediate and deep-water masses in the glacial Indian Ocean. Nature, 333, 651–655.

KEIR, R. S. 1980. The dissolution kinetics of biogenic calcium carbonates in seawater. Geochimica et Cosmochimica Acta, 44, 241–252.

KREY, J. & BABENERD, B. 1976. Phytoplankton Production Atlas of the International Indian Ocean Expedition. Keil (Landesvermessungsamt Schleswig-Holstein).

KUTZBACH, J. E. & GUETTER, P. J. 1986. The influence of changing orbital parameters and surface boundary conditions on climate simulations for the past 18 000 years. Journal of Atmospheric Science, 43, 1726–1759.

LYLE, M., MURRAY, D. W., FINNEY, B. P., DYMOND, J., ROBBINS, J. M. & BROOKSFORCE, K. 1988. The record of Late Pleistocene biogenic sedimentation in the eastern tropical Pacific Ocean. Paleoceanography, 3, 39–60.

MARGALEF, R. 1978. Life forms of phytoplankton as survival alternatives in an unstable environment. Oceanologica Acta, 1, 493–509.

MARTIN, W. R. & BENDER, M. L. 1988. The variability of benthic fluxes and sedimentary remineralization rates in response to seasonally variable organic carbon rain rates in the deep sea: a modelling study. American Journal of Science, 288, 561–574.

METZLER, C. V., WENKAM, C. R. & BERGER, W. H. 1982. Dissolution of foraminifera in the eastern equatorial Pacific: an In Situ experiment. Journal of Foraminifera Research, 12, 362–368.

MÜLLER, P. J. & SUESS, E. 1979. Productivity, sedimentation rate, and sedimentary organic matter in the oceans-I. Organic carbon preservation. Deep-Sea Research, Part A, 26, 1347–1362.

MURRAY, D. W. & PRELL, W. L. 1991. Pliocene to Pleistocene variations in calcium carbonate, organic carbon, and opal on the Owen Ridge, Northern Arabian Sea. In: PRELL, W. L., NIITSUMA, N., et al. Proceedings of the Ocean Drilling Program Scientific Results, 117, College Station, TX (Ocean Drilling Program), 343–355.

MORTLOCK, R. A. & FROELICH, P. N. 1989. A simple method for the rapid determination of biogenic opal in pelagic marine sediments. Deep-Sea Research, 36, 1415–1426.

NAIR, R. R., ITTEKKOT, V., MANGANINI, S. J., RAMASWAMY, V., HAAKE, B., DEGENS, E. T., DESAI, B. N. & HONJO, S. 1989. Increased particle flux to the deep ocean related to monsoons. Nature, 338, 749–751.

PRELL, W. L. 1984a. Variation in monsoonal upwelling: a response to changing solar radiation. In: HANSEN, J. E. & TAKAHASHI, T. (eds), Climate Processes and Climate Sensitivity: Washington (American Geophysical Union), Geophysics Monogram, 29, Maurice Ewing Series, 5, 48–57.

—— 1984b. Monsoonal climate of the Arabian Sea during the late Quaternary: A response to changing solar radiation. In: BERGER, A., IMBRIE, J., HAYS, J., KUKLA, G. & SALTZMAN, B. (eds), Milankovitch and Climate, Part 1, D. Reidel, Dordrecht, Holland 349–366.

PRELL, W. L. & CURRY, W. B. 1981. Faunal and isotopic indices of monsoonal upwelling: Western Arabian Sea. Oceanologica Acta, 4, 91–98.

PRELL, W. L., IMBRIE, J., MARTINSON, D. G., MORELY, J. J., PISIAS, N. G., SHACKLETON, N. J., STREETER, H. F. 1986. Graphic correlation of oxygen isotope stratigraphy: Application to the late Quaternary. *Paleoceanography*, **1**, 137−162.

PRELL, W. L. & KUTZBACH, J. E. 1987. Monsoon variability over the past 150 000 years. *Journal of Geophysical Research*, **92**, 8411−8425.

PRELL, W. L., NIITSUMA, N., *et al.* 1989. *Proceedings of the Ocean Drilling Program, Init. Repts.*, Ocean Drilling Program, College Station, TX **117**.

PRELL, W. L., NIITSUMA, N., *et al.* 1991. *Proceedings of the Ocean Drilling Program Scientific Results*, Ocean Drilling Program, College Station, TX **117**.

PRELL, W. L. & shipboard party of ODP Leg 117, 1990. Neogene tectonics and sedimentation of the SE Oman continental margin: results from ODP Leg 117. *In*: ROBERTSON, A. H. F., SEARLE, M. P. & RIES, A. C. (eds), *The Geology and Tectonics of the Oman Region*. Geological Society, London, Special Publication, **49**, 745−758.

PRELL, W. L. & STREETER, H. F. 1982. Temporal and spatial patterns of monsoonal upwelling along Arabia: A modern analogue for the interpretation of Quaternary SST anomalies. *Journal of Marine Research*, **40**, 143−155.

PRELL, W. L. & VAN CAMPO, E. 1986. Coherent response of Arabian Sea upwelling and pollen transport to late Quaternary monsoonal winds. *Nature*, **323**, 526−528.

RUDDIMAN, W. F., RAYMO, M. E., MARTINSON, D. G., CLEMENT, B. M. & BACKMAN, J. 1989. Pleistocene evolution; Northern hemisphere ice sheets and north Atlantic Ocean. *Paleoceanography*, **4**, 353−412.

SARNTHEIN, M. & WINN, K., DUPLESSY, J-C. & FONTUGNE, M. R. 1988. Global variations of surface ocean productivity in low and mid latitudes: Influence on CO_2 reservoirs of the deep ocean and atmosphere during the last 21 000 years. *Paleoceanography*, **3**, 361−399.

SHACKLETON, N. J., BACHMAN, J., ZIMMERMAN, H., KENT, D. V., HALL, M. A., ROBERTS, D. G., SCHNITKER, D. & BALDAUF, J. 1984. Oxygen isotope calibration of the onset of ice-rafting and history of glaciation in the North Atlantic region. *Nature*, **307**, 429−432.

Shipboard Scientific Party, 1989. Site 722. *In*: PRELL, W. L., NIITSUMA, N., *et al. Proceedings Ocean Drilling Program Init. Repts.*, College Station, TX (Ocean Drilling Program), **117**, 255−317.

SIROCKO, F. & SARNTHEIN, M. 1989. Wind-borne deposits in the northwest Indian Ocean: Record of Holocene sediments versus modern satellite data. *In*: LEINEN, M. & SARNTHEIN, M. (eds), *Paleoclimatology and Paleometerology: modern and past patterns of global atmospheric transport*, NATO ASI Series, Boston (Kluwer), 401−433.

SIROCKO, F., SARNTHEIN, M., LANGE, H. & ERLENKEUSER, H. 1991. Atmospheric summer circulation and coastal upwelling in the Arabian Sea during the Holocene and last glaciation. *Quaternary Research*, **36**, 72−93.

SMITH, S. L. 1984. Biological indications of active upwelling in the northwestern Indian ocean in 1964 and 1979, and a comparison with Peru and northwest Africa. *Deep-Sea Research*, **31**, 951−967.

SUESS, E. 1980. Particulate organic carbon flux in the oceans — surface productivity and oxygen utilization. *Nature*, **288**, 260−263.

TAKAHASHI, T., BROECKER, W. S., BAINBRIDGE, A. E. & WEISS, R. F. 1980. Carbonate chemistry of the Atlantic, Pacific, and Indian Oceans: The results of the GEOSECS Expeditions, 1972−1978. Lamont-Doherty Geol. Obs. Tech. Rept. 1, CU−1−80.

THUNELL, R. C. & HONJO, S. 1981. Calcite dissolution and the modification of planktonic foraminiferal assemblages. *Marine Micropaleontology*, **6**, 169−182.

VERARDO, D., FROELICH, P. N., MCINTYRE, A. 1990. Determination of organic carbon and nitrogen in marine sediments using the Carlo Erba NA-1500 Analyzer, *Deep-Sea Research*, **37**, 157−165.

WEEDON, G. P., SHIMMIELD, G. B. 1991. Late Pleistocene upwelling and productivity variations in the northwest Indian Ocean deduced from spectral analysis of geochemical data from Sites 722 and 724. *In*: PRELL, W. L., NIITSUMA, N. *et al. Proceedings Ocean Drilling Program Scientific Results*, Ocean Drilling Program, College Station, TX **117**, 431−443.

Organic matter variations in sediments from DSDP sites 362 and 532: evidence of changes in the Benguela Current upwelling system

PHILIP A. MEYERS

Department of Geological Sciences, The University of Michigan, Ann Arbor, Michigan 48109–1063, USA

Abstract: Diatom-rich nannofossil oozes from DSDP Sites 362 and 532 on the Walvis Ridge continental terrace contain light–dark cycles which are related to fluctuations in upwelling intensity over these sites from Middle Miocene to Holocene times. The dark intervals in the alternations result from dissolution of carbonates and addition of clastic components. Oxidation of marine-derived organic matter is important to dissolution of carbonates in these sediments. Concentrations of organic matter in the dark sections are enhanced by larger contributions of both marine and land-derived material than in light sections. The dark sections appear to correlate with periods of greater Antarctic ice volumes, suggesting that regional upwelling was intensified and that transport of organic matter from Africa by winds and possibly rivers was increased during these times.

Sediments recovered by the Deep Sea Drilling Project (DSDP) from the continental terrace of the Walvis Ridge, Southwest African margin, record the history of upwelling and enhanced biological productivity associated with the Benguela Current. Siesser (1980) concluded from concentrations of organic carbon and from diatom species assemblages in rotary drilled cores from DSDP Site 362 (Fig. 1) that the onset of upwelling over this location dates from ~10 Ma and that productivity has gradually increased since the Late Miocene. A less disturbed and more complete record of the upwelling history since ~6 Ma (Hay *et al.* 1982) was obtained by hydraulic piston coring at DSDP Site 532. Dean *et al.* (1984) noted that concentrations of biogenic silica and diatom microfossils have maxima in the lower Pleistocene and upper Pliocene parts of the Site 532 record, evidently the result of a productivity maximum during this time. The concentration of organic carbon generally reflects this period of higher productivity, but it varies in response to Milankovitch-type cycles which are manifested as cyclic light–dark variations in sediment colour and carbonate content (Gardner *et al.* 1984).

A number of possible explanations have been suggested for the cycles in sediment colour and composition. Sancetta (1984) described variations in diatom assemblage compositions which indicate that the location and intensity of the Benguela Current shift cyclically. Glacial–interglacial sea-level changes may have produced lateral relocation of the current axis (Dean *et al.* 1984; Diester-Haass *et al.* 1986). Gardner *et al.* (1984) suggested that glacial–interglacial climate changes caused fluctuations in the delivery of land-derived clastic sediments, diluting the largely biogenic sediments to varying degrees and creating the light–dark cycles. Diester-Haass *et al.* (1986, 1990) combined the glacial–interglacial current shifts, alternations in sea level, and changes in contributions of land-derived sediment components to explain the cycles. They concluded, moreover, that carbonate dissolution, caused by oxidation of marine organic matter, has been the dominant factor in producing the light–dark cycles. Marine organic matter is more susceptible to oxidation to CO_2 and to contributing to carbonate dissolution than is continental organic matter (cf. Berger 1970; Thunnell 1976).

If oxidation of marine organic matter is central to the origin of the light–dark cycles found at Sites 362 and 532, variations in the proportions of marine and continental organic matter should exist in the sediments. Changes in the rate of marine productivity, in the amount of continental material transported to the sea and in the degree of preservation impact these proportions. I describe here the results of organic geochemical analyses done to assess the amounts of marine and continental contributions of organic matter contained in sediments deposited from the Middle Miocene to the early Pleistocene at DSDP Sites 362 and 532.

Experimental

Samples

Three sets of relatively closely spaced samples in light–dark cycles from DSDP Sites 362 and

From SUMMERHAYES, C. P., PRELL, W. L. & EMEIS, K. C. (eds), 1992, *Upwelling Systems: Evolution Since the Early Miocene.* Geological Society Special Publication No 64, pp 323–329.

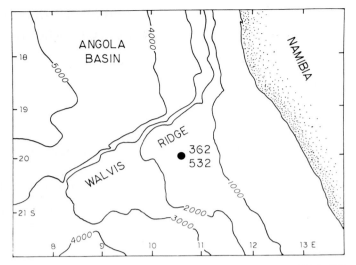

Fig. 1. Locations of DSDP Sites 362 and 532 on the continental terrace of the Walvis Ridge, South Atlantic Ocean. The two sites are actually about 1 km apart. Site 362 was sampled by rotary coring during DSDP Leg 40 in 1975 and is in 1325 m of water. Site 532 was sampled by hydraulic piston corer during DSDP Leg 75 in 1980. Water depth at this site is 1331 m. Depth contours are given in metres.

532 were selected. The three cored lengths of sediments provide close examination of organic matter compositions deposited during different phases of the growth of upwelling over the Walvis Ridge (Table 1). Sediment in Core 532B-17 is a diatom-rich nannoplankton ooze having pronounced light−dark cycles. This core, at about 69 to 73 metres below sea floor (mbsf), is close to the Plio-Pleistocene boundary (1.8 Ma). Sections 3, 4 and 5 from Core 362−16 contain sediment made up of upper Miocene (c. 5.3 Ma) calcareous nannoplankton ooze. These sections are from 200 to 205 mbsf. Sections 1 and 2 from Core 362−33 were deposited in the Middle Miocene (14 Ma) and contain a light-coloured marly nannoplankton chalk having weakly developed colour cycles. The sub-bottom depth of these sections is from 520.5 to 523.5 mbsf. Full descriptions of the Site 362 cores are provided by Bolli *et al.* 1978) and of the Hole 532B core by Hay *et al.* (1984). Sample spacing in the three cores varied between 10 and 20 cm.

Procedures

Samples were freeze-dried, and their calcium carbonate concentrations were measured by treatment with 3 N HCl using the carbonate bomb procedure of Müller & Gastner (1971). Total organic carbon (TOC) was determined with a Hewlett-Packard 185 CHN analyzer which quantified the carbon remaining in the sediment samples after the carbonate bomb analyses. Organic matter atomic C/N values were calculated from the residual carbon CHN analytical results.

Oxygen and carbon isotopic ratios of bulk carbonates were determined with a VG Micromass 602 mass spectrometer calibrated with the NBS-20 carbonate standard. Organic carbon isotope ratios were determined by combusting the carbonate-free residues of the carbonate bomb analyses and analyzing the CO_2 produced from the TOC. Data are presented relative to the PDB standard.

Results and discussion

Organic carbon concentrations in sediments reflect the rate of supply of organic matter, the degree of its preservation and the amount of dilution by other sediment components. Diester-Haass *et al.* (1986, 1990) attempted to compensate for the effects of variable dissolution of calcium carbonate, which concentrates TOC to varying degrees, in sediments of Sites 362 and 532 so that organic matter supply and preservation could be assessed. Their adjusted TOC values reveal enhanced contributions of organic carbon to dark-coloured sediments. Carbonate oxygen isotope data indicate that the dark intervals correspond to periods of greater continental ice volumes, presumably Antarctic

Table 1. General descriptions of intervals of closely-spaced samples of nannoplankton oozes and chalks selected for study from Deep Sea Drilling Project sites on the Walvis Ridge.

Hole-Core-Sections	Depth (mbsf)	Age
532−17−1, 2 and 3	69 to 73	early Pleistocene
362−16−3, 4 and 5	200 to 205	Late Miocene
362−33−1 and 2	520.5 to 523.5	Middle Miocene

glaciers, (Diester-Haass *et al.* 1986, 1990). TOC variations evidently arose from the combination of enhanced supply and improved preservation of organic matter during glacial times and of concordant greater dissolution of calcium carbonate in the dark intervals.

The organic matter in ocean sediments is a mixture containing variable proportions of residual material produced by marine algae and of detrital material from plant production and erosion on continents. The contributions from the marine and land sources of organic matter can be distinguished from each other by their characteristic elemental and isotopic compositions. Marine algae produce organic matter which is normally high in protein and lipid content relative to its carbohydrate content, and they utilize dissolved HCO_3^- as their carbon source. Organic matter synthesized by algae typically has C/N atomic ratios which approximate the Redfield ratio of 6.7 (cf. Goldman *et al.* 1979) and a stable carbon isotopic ratio averaging −21‰ (cf. Peterson *et al.* 1985). Land-derived organic matter is generally dominated by the cellulosic tissues of C3 plants, hence C/N ratios are 25 or more (cf. Meyers 1990). Under conditions of nutrient depletion, the C/N ratios of marine algal matter rise (e.g.

Goldman 1979), but they never reach the elevated values characteristic of land plants. The source of carbon for land plants is atmospheric CO_2 which is isotopically lighter than marine bicarbonate, and so the organic matter isotope signature of continental organic carbon is typically about −28‰ (cf. Peterson *et al.* 1985). These distinctions in the elemental and isotopic compositions of marine and land organic matter are well preserved in marine sediments for periods of 100 ka (e.g. Jasper & Gagosian 1989). The results of the present study of Walvis Ridge sediments suggests that these characteristics remain intact for times as long as 14 Ma.

The three intervals selected for high-resolution study of the light−dark cycles differ substantially in period of upwelling history, concentration of organic carbon, and sediment colour. They consequently illustrate some of the changes in contributions of organic matter to light−dark cycles from times of different palaeoproductivities.

Core 362−33 (Middle Miocene − 14 Ma). Sections 362−33−1 and 362−33−2 include a weakly developed light−dark−light colour change with accompanying shifts in calcium carbonate contents from ~50% in the light portions to ~40% in the dark part (Fig. 2).

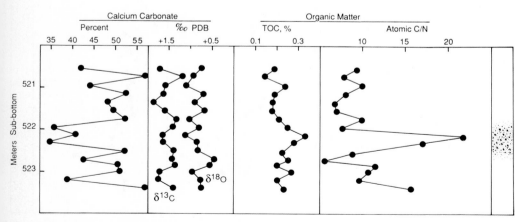

Fig. 2. Calcium carbonate concentrations and $\delta^{18}O$ and $\delta^{13}C$ values, total organic carbon (TOC), and atomic C/N ratios of sediments from Middle Miocene Core 362−33. Light−dark colour variations are indicated on right.

Organic carbon concentrations are low, maximizing at only ~0.3% in the dark interval. The low concentrations of organic matter, coupled with the absence of biogenic opal, show that upwelling-enhanced productivity had not yet developed over the Walvis Ridge at this time (Diester-Haass *et al.* 1990).

The organic matter C/N ratios are generally between 5 and 10, which are typical of most marine sediments low in TOC (cf. Müller 1977; Premuzic *et al.* 1982; Jasper & Gagosian 1989; Keswani *et al.* 1984). Several sediment samples within these sections have C/N values above 15, most notably the samples from the dark portion (Fig. 2). Diester-Haass *et al.* (1990) conclude that the colour changes in the low-TOC sediment of Core 362–33 are created by variations in dilution of carbonates by continental sediments components; marine organic matter is not sufficiently available to cause significant carbonate dissolution. The higher C/N values in the darker portions of this core are consistent with larger proportions of land-derived organic matter being incorporated into these sediments along with larger amounts of clastic material from Africa. The coastal regions bordering the Walvis Ridge areas of the Atlantic evidently were arid during the Middle Miocene (van Zinderen-Bakker 1984; Diester-Haass *et al.* 1990), so eolian transport is a probable route by which the continental materials were delivered

to Site 362. Furthermore, river valleys along the Namibian coast are ten to twenty times wider than the rivers now flowing through them, suggesting that flow volumes may have been larger at times in the past. It is possible that climate was somewhat more humid during glacial times, adding a fluvial component to the eolian transport of continental materials to the offshore sediments. The light–dark cycles suggest that climate changes, involving intensified wind velocities and perhaps moister conditions in southwest Africa, occurred during times of expanded Antarctic ice volumes.

Core 362–16 (Late Miocene −5.3 Ma). A well developed dark–light–dark colour cycle exists in Sections 362–16–3, 4, and 5 (Fig. 3). Percentages of calcium carbonate peak at 70% in the light sediment and range between about 55 to 62% in the dark portions. Organic carbon concentrations remain around 1% in Sections 362–16–3 and 4 but reach over 2% in the darker Section 362–16–5. The increase in TOC and the presence of opal indicate that upwelling was developed over Site 362 by the Late Miocene (Siesser 1980; Diester-Haass *et al.* 1990). Furthermore, inorganic $\delta^{13}C$ values are lighter by *c.* 0.5‰ in Core 362–16 than in Core 362–33. These data are for bulk carbonate, which is made up mostly the remains of coccolithophores wherein species composition changes can cause isotopic shifts (Paull &

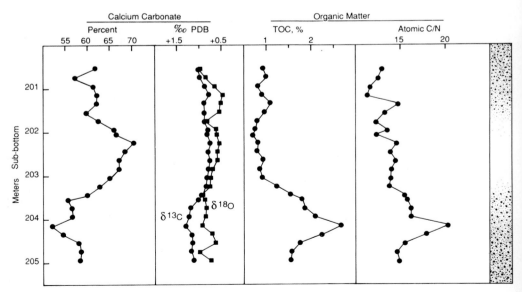

Fig. 3. Calcium carbonate concentrations and $\delta^{18}O$ and $\delta^{13}C$ values, total organic carbon (TOC), and atomic C/N ratios of sediments from Upper Miocene Core 362–16. Light–dark colour variations are indicated on right.

Thierstein 1987). Nonetheless, the global shift at 6 Ma of more than 0.5‰ to lighter $\delta^{13}C$ values in benthic forams (Haq *et al.* 1980) may be recorded in the difference between these two sedimentary intervals. Woodruff & Savin (1985) showed that lowered sea level and locally enhanced marine productivity can combine to produce lighter carbonate isotopic ratios as seen in Core 362–16 in benthic forams. More isotopically light organic carbon reaches these animals under these conditions. Recycling of organic carbon in the water column can similarly affect the carbonate isotope compositions of planktonic organisms. The shift to the lighter values in the bulk carbonate of Core 362–16 may be at least partly caused by oxidation and reutilization in the photic zone of larger amounts of organic carbon created after the onset of enhanced productivity between the Middle Miocene and the Late Miocene (cf. Siesser 1980; Hay *et al.* 1982).

The pattern of the organic matter C/N values resembles the TOC pattern: highest C/N ratios correspond to samples having the highest TOC contents (Fig. 3). Like the TOC values, the C/N ratios are higher in Core 362–16 than in Core 362–33. The correspondence between TOC and C/N values could mean that sediments having higher organic carbon contents have received more land-derived organic matter, as is probably true for Core 362–33. The evidence

of enhanced marine productivity (Diester-Haass *et al.* 1990), however, suggests that most of the increase from ~0.2% TOC in Core 362–33 to 1 to 2% TOC in Core 362–16 is from the additional accumulation of marine organic matter in the sediments. The overall increase in C/N values, especially evident in the dark intervals, cannot be solely from land-derived organic matter. Instead, the appearance of upwelling evidently resulted in nitrogen depletion in the photic zone over the Walvis Ridge and production of marine organic matter poor in nitrogen (e.g. Goldman *et al.* 1979). The C/N signature of the small amount of continental organic matter in these sediments is evidently overwhelmed by the elevated C/N values of marine organic matter produced in the upwelling regime since ~6 Ma.

Core 532B-17 (Late Pliocene – 1.8 Ma). Core 532B-17 is from the zone of maximum opal content in the sedimentary record on the Walvis Ridge of the Benguela Current upwelling system. Carbonate concentrations are diluted by the opal. Sediment colour is generally buff to tan, darker than in older sediments. Light–dark cycles are well developed and correspond with cyclical variations in concentrations of calcium carbonate and organic carbon (Fig. 4).

Organic $\delta^{13}C$ values of range between −19.7‰ and −21.3‰ and average − 20.6 ± 0.4‰ (Fig. 4). This mean value indicates that

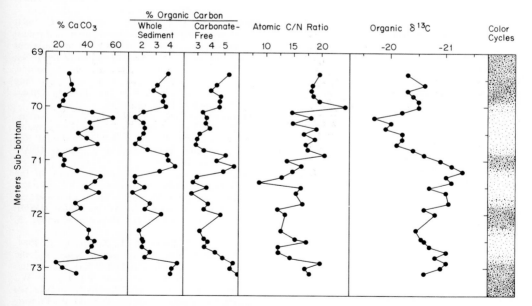

Fig. 4. Calcium carbonate concentrations, total organic carbon (TOC), atomic C/N ratios, and organic carbon $\delta^{13}C$ values of sediments from Upper Pliocene Core 532B-17. Light–dark colour variations are indicated on right.

the overwhelming source of the organic matter is from algal production. C/N values are high for marine organic matter (Fig. 4), indicating that nitrogen depletion accompanied upwelling-enhanced marine productivity. Fluctuations in $\delta^{13}C$ and C/N values do not coincide with TOC cycles (Fig. 4). The cause of these fluctuations is not known. Variations in contributions of land-derived organic matter may combine with variations in availability of supply of dissolved nitrogen to create the C/N fluctuations. The isotopic variations appear to be cyclical, although unrelated to sediment colour. This lack of correspondence implies that currently unidentified cyclical processes influence organic deposition in this upwelling system.

Carbonate $\delta^{13}C$ values in Section 532B-17-2 are between -0.5 and $-1.0‰$, although slightly lighter carbonate $\delta^{13}C$ values are found in the darker intervals of Section 532B-17-2 (Meyers et al. 1986), concordant with the higher rates of accumulation of marine organic matter evident in these intervals (Diester-Haass et al. 1986). Oxidative recycling of marine organic matter in the photic zone would lead to the lighter carbonate isotope values while improving the preservation of the surviving organic matter. The higher accumulation rate of organic carbon in the dark cycles of Core 532B-17 supports the hypothesis that oxidation of marine organic matter at the sea bottom contributes to the creation of carbonate dissolution cycles.

Summary and conclusion

Study of the type and amount of organic matter in closely spaced samples of sediments deposited at DSDP Sites 362 and 532 on the Walvis Ridge shows aspects of the Middle Miocene to early Pleistocene history of enhanced marine production in the Benguela Current upwelling system.

1. The light−dark cycles which are found throughout these sediments appear to record fluctuations in upwelling intensity which correspond to variations in Antarctic continental ice volumes.

2. The light−dark cycles represent variations in the dissolution of sedimentary carbonate and in the delivery of land-derived sedimentary materials. Dissolution of carbonate results from oxidation of marine organic matter in the dark intervals.

3. Accumulation of total organic matter in dark intervals is enhanced by greater production of marine material. The contribution of continental material also increases in dark intervals, possibly as wind strengths increased during these

times. Increased fluvial contributions of organic matter from Namibia may have further augmented the total organic matter in the dark intervals.

4. Fluctuations in the proportions of marine and continental organic matter are superimposed on the overall increase in production of marine organic matter since the Late Miocene which accompanied the development of the Benguela Current.

Comments from M. T. von Breymann and W. E. Dean were important in improving this paper. I thank the International Program of Ocean Drilling, Deep Sea Drilling Project, for providing the samples described in this study and for the opportunity to participate in Leg 75 offshore of Namibia. Isotope measurements were done by the Stable Isotope Laboratory of The University of Michigan. Parts of this study were supported by the U.S. National Science Foundation (Grant Number OCE 8214605).

References

BERGER, W. H. 1970. Planktonic foraminifera: selective solution and the lysocline. *Marine Geology*, **8**, 111−138.

BOLLI, H. M., RYAN, W. B. F., McKNIGHT, B. K., KAGAMI, H., MEGUEN, M., SIESSER, W. G., NATLAND, J. H., LONGORIA, J. F., PROTO DECIMA, F., FORESMAN, J. B. & HOTTMAN, W. E. 1978. Walvis Ridge − Sites 362 and 363. *In*: BOLLI, H. M., RYAN, W. B. F. et al. *Initial Reports of the Deep Sea Drilling Project*, vol. 40. U.S. Govt. Printing Office, Washington, D.C., 183−356.

DEAN, W. E., HAY, W. W. & SIBUET, J. -C. 1984. Geological evolution, sedimentation, and paleoenvironments of the Angola Basin and adjacent Walvis Ridge: Synthesis of results of Deep Sea Drilling Project Leg 75. *In*: HAY, W. W., SIBUET, J. -C. et al. *Initial Reports of the Deep Sea Drilling Project*, vol. 75. U.S. Govt. Printing Office, Washington, D.C., 509−544.

DIESTER-HAASS, L., MEYERS, P. A. & ROTHE, P. 1986. Light−dark cycles in opal-rich sediments near the Plio-Pleistocene boundary, DSDP Site 532, Walvis Ridge continental terrace. *Marine Geology*, **73**, 1−23

——, —— & —— 1990. Miocene history of the Benguela Current and Antarctic ice volumes: Evidence from rhythmic sedimentation and current growth across the Walvis Ridge (DSDP Sites 362 and 532). *Paleoceanography*, **5**, 685−707.

GARDNER, J. V., DEAN, W. E. & WILSON, C. 1984. Carbonate and organic-carbon cycles and the history of upwelling at DSDP Site 532, Walvis Ridge, South Atlantic Ocean. *In*: HAY, W. W., SIBUET, J.-C. et al. *Initial Reports of the Deep Sea Drilling Project*, vol. 75. U.S. Govt. Printing Office, Washington, D.C., 905−921.

GOLDMAN, J. C., McCARTHY, J. J. & PEAVEY, D. G. 1979. Growth rate influence on the chemical composition of phytoplankton in oceanic waters. *Nature*, **279**, 210−215.

HAQ, B. U., WORSLEY, T. R., BURCKLE, L. H., DOUGLAS, R. G., KEIGWIN, L. D., Jr. OPDYKE, N. D., SAVIN, S. M., SOMMER, M. A., II, VINCENT, E. & WOODRUFF, F. 1980. Late Miocene marine carbon-isotopic shift and synchroneity of some phytoplanktonic biostratigraphic events. *Geology*, **8**, 427−431.

HAY, W. W. *et al.* 1982. Sedimentation and accumulation of organic carbon in the Angola Basin and on the Walvis Ridge: Preliminary results of Deep Sea Drilling Project Leg 75. *Geological Society of America Bulletin* **93**, 1038−1050.

HAY, W. E. *et al.* 1984. Site 532: Walvis Ridge. *In*: HAY, W. W., SIBUET, J.-C. *et al.*, *Initial Reports of the Deep Sea Drilling Project*, vol. 75. U.S. Govt. Printing Office, Washington, D.C., 295−445.

JASPER, J. P. & GAGOSIAN, R. B. 1989. Glacial-interglacial climatically-forced sources of sedimentary organic matter to the late Quaternary northern Gulf of Mexico. *Nature*, **342**, 60−62.

KESWANI, S. R., DUNHAM, K. W. & MEYERS, P. A. 1984. Organic geochemistry of late Cenozoic sediments from the subtropical South Atlantic. *Marine Geology*, **61**, 25−42.

MEYERS, P. A. 1990. Impacts of late Quaternary fluctuations in water level on the accumulation of sedimentary organic matter in Walker Lake, Nevada. *Palaeogeography, Palaeoclimatology, Palaeoecology*, **78**, 229−240.

MEYERS, P. A., DUNHAM, K. W. & RAU, G. H. 1986. Organic geochemical character of opal-rich sediments in light−dark cycles near the Plio-Pleistocene boundary in DSDP site 532, Walvis Ridge. *Paleoceanography*, **1**, 567−575.

MÜLLER, G. & GASTNER, M. 1971. The 'Karbonat-Bombe', a simple device for the determination of the carbonate content in sediments, soils and other materials. *Neues Jb. Mineralogie*, **10**, 466−469.

MÜLLER, P. J. 1977. C/N ratios in Pacific deep-sea sediments: Effect of inorganic ammonium and organic nitrogen compounds sorbed by clays. *Geochimica et Cosmochimica Acta*, **41**, 765−776.

PAULL, C. K. & THIERSTEIN, H. R. 1987. Stable isotopic fractionation among particles in Quaternary coccolith-sized deep-sea sediments. *Paleoceanography*, **2**, 423−429.

PETERSON, B. J., HOWARTH, R. W. & GARRITT, R. H. 1985. Multiple stable isotopes used to trace the flow of organic matter in estuarine food webs. *Science*, **227**, 1361−1363.

PREMUZIC, E. T., BENKOVITZ, C. M., GAFFNEY, J. S. & WALSH, J. J. 1982. The nature and distribution of organic matter in the surface sediments of world oceans and seas. *Organic Geochemistry*, **4**, 63−77.

SANCETTA, C. 1984. Diatoms from Leg 75, Deep Sea Drilling Project. *In*: HAY, W. W., SIBUET, J.-C. *et al. Initial Reports of the Deep Sea Drilling Project*, vol. 75. U.S. Govt. Printing Office, Washington, D.C., 755−759.

SIESSER, W. G. 1980. Late Miocene origin of the Benguela Upwelling System of northern Namibia. *Science*, **208**, 283−285.

THUNELL, R. C. 1976. Calcium carbonate dissolution history in Late Quaternary deep-sea sediments, Western Gulf of Mexico. *Quaternary Research*, **6**, 281−297.

WOODRUFF, F. & SAVIN, S. M. 1985. $\delta^{13}C$ values of Miocene Pacific benthic foraminifera: Correlations with sea level and biological productivity. *Geology*, **13**, 119−122.

VAN ZINDEREN-BAKKER, E. M. 1984. Palynological evidence for late Cenozoic arid conditions along the Namibia coast from Holes 532 and 530A, Leg 75, Deep Sea Drilling Project. *In*: HAY, W. W., SIBUET, J.-C. *et al. Initial Reports of the Deep Sea Drilling Project*, vol. 75. U.S. Govt. Printing Office, Washington, D.C., 763−768.

The Benguela Current and associated upwelling on the southwest African Margin: a synthesis of the Neogene−Quaternary sedimentary record at DSDP sites 362 and 532

LISELOTTE DIESTER-HAASS[1], PHILIP A. MEYERS[2] & PETER ROTHE[3]

[1] Alfred-Wegener-Institut 2850 Bremerhaven, Germany

[2] The University of Michigan Ann Arbor, Michigan, USA

[3] Universität Mannheim 6800 Mannheim, Germany

Abstract: Sediments cored at DSDP Sites 362 and 532 on the Walvis Ridge provide a Neogene−Quaternary history of the development of the upwelling system on the south-west African margin. Upwelling occurs principally on the landward side of the Benguela Current. The upwelling centres have shifted northward since the Middle Miocene as the current has intensified and has flowed farther to the north. Changes in productivity are recorded in the types, proportions and preservation of foraminifera, radiolaria, diatoms, organic matter, and clay minerals in the sedimentary record. Prior to the Late Miocene (10 Ma), the Benguela Current did not reach the Walvis Ridge, and enhanced productivity is not evident in the sediments at this location. Between 10 to 5.2 Ma, upwelling was recorded in the DSDP sites in glacial periods, indicating that the Benguela Current intensified during glacial periods and transported evidence of upwelling to Sites 362/532 from near-coastal areas. During interglacial periods the current was not as strong and did not reach the Walvis Ridge, turning instead to the west within the Cape Basin. Strengthening of the current continued such that by the Pliocene and Quarternary the upwelling signal is contained in interglacial sediments. Sediments deposited in these more recent glacial times contain a weak or absent upwelling signal because glacial intensification shifts the Benguela Current system northward to reach the Angola Basin before it turns westward away from its coast-parallel direction.

The Benguela Current constitutes the eastern boundary of the South Atlantic subtropical gyre. The development of the Benguela Current system is an important component in the evolution of the southern hemisphere Neogene climate and of South Atlantic surface circulation patterns. Long-term and short-term variations in the Benguela Current system and related upwelling since the Middle Miocene are mainly driven by changes in Antarctic ice mass with its growth and fluctuations, which are reflected in oxygen isotope data.

The major upwelling systems of the modern oceans began to develop in the Middle Miocene as evolution of deep and intermediate cold water masses led to the thermal stratification that typifies the oceans of today (cf. Kennett 1977). The record of the history of upwelling-enhanced productivity associated with the Benguela Current is provided by the biogenous sediments deposited on the Walvis Ridge, which rises above the calcite compensation depth on the continental margin of southwest Africa. The history of this system may in a general way be a surrogate for the records of other coastal upwelling systems, where water depths and submarine topography often preclude local preservation of the upwelling signals.

A synthesis of the history of the Benguela Current system and its related upwelling as provided from studies of the sediment records of Deep Sea Drilling Project (DSDP) Sites 532 and 362 is given here, based on information given in Siesser (1980), Diester-Haass (1985, 1988), Diester-Haass et al. (1986, 1988, 1990), Diester-Haass & Rothe (1987), Oberhänsli (1991) and references therein.

Present-day upwelling and indicators of past upwelling on the southwest African coastal margin

Modern upwelling off southwest Africa at the latitude of the Walvis Ridge, 20°S, is on the inner shelf and at the shelf edge (Summerhayes 1983), or about 150 km east of the DSDP sites. The upwelling is produced by the prevailing SE−NW blowing Trade Winds, which are subject to seasonal N−S migrations. The Trade Wind migrations arise from the shift of the subtropical high-pressure zone towards the equator during austral winters and away from the equator during summers. The Benguela Current, which flows parallel to the coast off southwest Africa, turns to the west over the

From SUMMERHAYES, C. P., PRELL, W. L. & EMEIS, K. C. (eds), 1992, *Upwelling Systems: Evolution Since the Early Miocene*. Geological Society Special Publication No 64, pp 331−342.

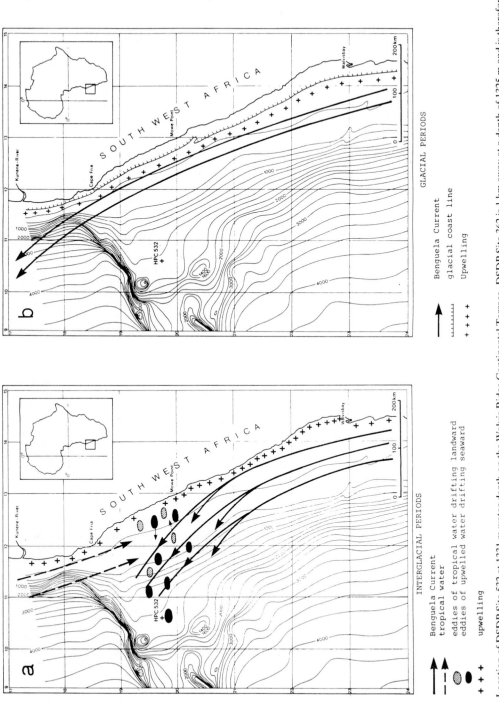

Fig. 1. Location of DSDP Site 532 at 1331 m water depth on the Walvis Ridge Continental Terrace. DSDP Site 362 is 1 km away at a depth of 1325 m and is therefore at essentially the same location. Surface currents and upwelling off southwest Africa today (a) and during the last glacial periods (b). Depth contours in metres. After van Zinderen-Bakker (1976).

Walvis Ridge. Tropical water meets the cool Benguela Current water in the latitude of about 20°S, where eddies of upwelled water are formed and carried westward as the Benguela Current turns away from the coast (Hart & Currie 1960; Hagen et al. 1981) (Fig. 1). These eddies transport a high signal of productivity to the ridge, but the main core of upwelling and high productivity remains close to the coast.

During the last glacial period the Benguela Current continued farther northward close to the continent in a SE−NW direction to about 17°S in the southern Angola Basin, where it turned westward (Fig. 1) (van Zinderen-Bakker 1976). Northerly intensification of the Benguela Current during times of greater continental ice volumes appears to be a consistent feature of its history.

Reconstruction of the Neogene and Quaternary history of upwelling off southwest Africa is complicated by the absence of long sediment cores from directly under the main upwelling areas. Sites 360, 364 and 365 from DSDP Leg 40 are too far offshore to provide good records of upwelling, and they suffer from drilled and therefore disturbed sediment records (Bolli et al. 1978). Sites 362 (Leg 40, Bolli et al. 1978) and 532 (Leg 75, Hay et al. 1984) in ~1300 m water depth on the Walvis Ridge are approximately 200 km from the coast, well outside the main upwelling areas. The sediment records from the latter two sites, however, do provide fairly well preserved carbonate microfossil records, and the use of hydraulic piston coring at Site 532 yielded minimally disturbed cores.

Although the history of the Benguela Current and associated upwelling cannot be interpreted directly from samples from the two Walvis Ridge DSDP sites, reconstruction is made possible by their sedimentary records of biological productivity from the eddies of upwelled water which are transported to the west by the Benguela Current. The principal upwelling signal used in this reconstruction is the opal content of the sediment sand fraction. Skeletons of radiolaria and diatoms were produced in the eddies of upwelled water (Schuette & Schrader 1981); some were carried west by the Benguela Current, where they sank to the sea floor over the Walvis Ridge.

The history of the flow of the Benguela Current, that is the change in the location where it turns from the coast to flow westward, can be reconstructed from the Walvis Ridge DSDP sites by means of the opal signal and also by use of the clay mineral assemblages advected to the Walvis Ridge. The present-day clay mineral assemblage is characterized by low amounts (<10%) of kaolinite from areas of tropical weathering in the north, illite (~50%) from the arid Namib area (Bremner 1975) and montmorillonite, supplied mainly by the Orange River in South Africa and transported northwards by the Benguela Current (Bornhold 1973). Montmorillonite/illite ratios (M/I) are useful indicators of the varying influence of local illite versus distant montmorillonite supply and thus of the varying path of the Benguela Current over time (Diester-Haass et al. 1990).

The Late Quaternary sediment record

Late Quaternary sediments from Site 532 contain two types of alternating facies (Fig. 2): interglacial sediments with higher opal contents supplied to the Walvis Ridge by the Benguela Current as it turns west, and glacial sediments characterized by heavier $\delta^{18}O$ values and with very low or absent opal contents (Diester-Haass 1985). Moreover, glacial−interglacial cycles are recorded as dark−light colour variations in the Walvis Ridge sediments (Diester-Haass et al. 1986). Glacial sediments are characterized by strong dissolution of carbonate tests of planktonic foraminifera. Ratios of benthic foraminifera to planktonic foraminifera are therefore considerably greater in glacial than in interglacial sediments.

Carbonate dissolution on continental margins in water depths above the oceanic lysocline or carbonate compensation depth can only be produced by decomposition of organic matter and thus production of pore water CO_2 (Berger 1970; Berger et al. 1982; Emerson & Bender 1982). This dissolution is controlled by two processes: (a) surface water productivity (Berger 1970; Thunell 1976) and (b) lateral supply of organic matter from the shelf/upper slope (Parker & Berger 1971; Swift & Wenkam 1978; Diester-Haass et al. 1986). With the glacial−interglacial migrations of the shoreline, organic matter supply from the continental slope can change: an increased supply during regressions and a reduced supply during transgressions (Thunell 1976; Berger & Vincent 1981; Broecker 1982; Diester-Haass et al. 1986). Furthermore, productivity on continental margins was generally increased in glacial periods as compared to interglacial times. For the eastern Atlantic a factor of 2−3 for the Quaternary has been calculated (Müller et al. 1983).

The two effects — increase in surface water productivity and increase in lateral supply of marine organic matter from shallow continental shelf/upper slope areas in glacial periods —

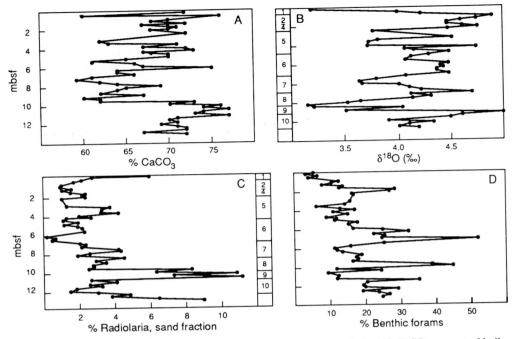

Fig. 2. Late Quaternary Cores 532–1, 2, and 3 (0 to 13 m subbottom, mbsf). (A) CaCO₃ content of bulk sediment. (B) $\delta^{18}O$ of *Uvigerina* spp. (measured by N. Shackleton); more positive values record glacial stages. Left side: $\delta^{18}O$ stages (after Oberhänsli, 1991). (C) percent radiolaria in the sand fraction (>63 µm). Right: d¹⁸O stages. (D) Benthos/plankton foraminiferal ratio, calculated as (% benthics/% benthics + % planktonics) × 100; high values indicate greater carbonate dissolution.

cannot be separated quantitatively. Both lead to an increase in net organic matter accumulation rates and thus enhanced carbonate dissolution. Carbon isotope data indicate that the organic matter present in sediments on the Walvis Ridge remains predominantly marine in origin in both glacial and interglacial intervals (Meyers *et al.* 1986) and consequently it can be easily oxidized. The enhanced carbonate dissolution during glacial times, combined with larger contributions of continental clastic material, produces darker coloured sediments in the Walvis Ridge sites.

The presumed correlation between strong carbonate dissolution and higher organic matter supply during glacial periods with lowered sea level has been documented by means of oxygen isotope data in several sedimentary sequences from Sites 532 and 362 (Diester-Haass 1985; Diester-Haass *et al.* 1986; 1990). We conclude that this is a genetically linked relationship and postulate that all carbonate dissolution maxima in this continental margin are originated in glacial periods with lowered sea level and that all carbonate preservation maxima originated in

interglacial periods. Thus, carbonate dissolution profiles can help to define glacial–interglacial cycles.

The opal contents in these sediments from the Walvis Ridge are a signal of the near-coastal upwelling and are supplied by the Benguela Current turning west in the latitude of the investigated sites. The concentration of organic matter, however, which increases in glacial periods, has been found not to be a valid indicator of glacial–interglacial variations of upwelling in this area. Organic carbon concentrations do not consistently follow opal concentrations (Diester-Haass *et al.* 1986). This suggests that the two principal indicators of enhanced marine productivity, opal and organic matter, must have sources that are not identical along the African margin. Opal originates from the surface waters and is supplied by the Benguela Current to these sites. Organic matter, however, originates not only from surface waters, but also from near-bottom downslope transport from coastward upper slope and shelf areas during periods of ice volume maxima and lowered sea level.

Quaternary and Pliocene sediment record

The glacial–interglacial variability described for the Late Quaternary evidently existed in the same qualitative way throughout the Quaternary and Pliocene and produced multiple small-scale changes in sediment composition similar to those in the Late Quaternary, summarized in Table 1, with a cyclicity of <100 000 years (Diester-Haass & Rothe 1987). The variability present in Pliocene and older sediments must be related to Antarctic glaciation in view of the absence of northern hemisphere glacial cycles until about 2.4 Ma (Rea & Schrader 1985) and the presence of major Antarctic glaciation since the Middle Miocene (Shackleton & Kennett 1975). The large-scale trends in carbonate dissolution, opal contents and eustatic sea level superimposed upon the small-scale cycles in the Quaternary–Pliocene sequence are summarized in Fig. 3.

The clay mineral composition throughout the Plio-Pleistocene sequence shows rhythmic fluctuations with higher M/I ratios in interglacial periods than in glacial ones (Fig. 4).

Late Miocene sediment record

Highest opal concentrations correspond to glacial periods, as identified by heavy $\delta^{18}O$ values (Fig. 5), in sediments deposited in the Late Miocene at the Walvis Ridge sites, and they are related to organic matter concentration maxima and strongest carbonate dissolution (Diester-Haass et al. 1990). The relationship between opal content as an upwelling signal and carbonate dissolution/organic matter content as a signal of sea-level lowering is reversed relative to the Quaternary–Pliocene period. The first opal occurrence at 10 Ma coincides with a major regression (Haq et al. 1987).

The clay minerals show higher glacial M/I ratios than interglacial ones in the early Late Miocene (Fig. 4B), whereas between 9 to 5.2 Ma local illite supply from the Namib during glacial periods depresses the M/I ratios (Fig. 4C).

Middle Miocene sediment record

Opal is absent from sediments older than 10 Ma from Site 362 (Figs 4 & 6). Organic matter content is very low (<0.3%), but nevertheless shows a cyclicity which is related to carbonate $\delta^{18}O$ values. Sediments with heavier $\delta^{18}O$ values have slightly higher organic carbon concentrations than do interglacial sediments. Carbonate dissolution is consistently weak, reflecting

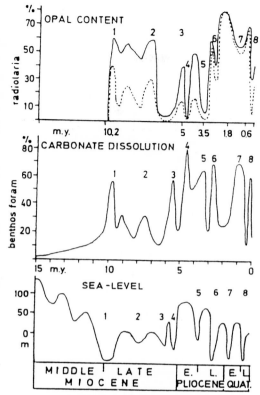

Fig. 3. Schematic summary of variations in opal content and carbonate dissolution in Walvis Ridge sediments and global eustatic sea-level changes during the last 15 Ma. Opal content: plotted as percent radiolaria plus diatoms (>63 μm) of the sand fraction (dotted line) and as percent radiolaria of the sum of radiolaria plus benthonic foraminifera (solid line). Note that percentages are sensitive to varying dilution by planktonic foraminifera as their dissolution varies; ratios with benthonic foraminifera exclude this effect (see Diester-Haass & Rothe 1987; Diester-Haass 1988). Carbonate dissolution: plotted as percent benthonic foraminifera in the sum benthonic plus planktonic foraminifera, see Diester-Haass (1988). Sea-level curve from Haq et al. (1987). Numbers 1–8: major regressions since the Late Miocene. Regressions 1–3 are simultaneous with high opal content and strong carbonate dissolution, whereas regressions 4–8 are simultaneous with low opal content and strong carbonate dissolution.

the absence of much CO_2 from oxidation of marine organic matter. M/I ratios are higher in the units with heavier $\delta^{18}O$ values. Variations in $CaCO_3$ content are principally controlled by variations in clastic input (Diester-Haass et al. 1990).

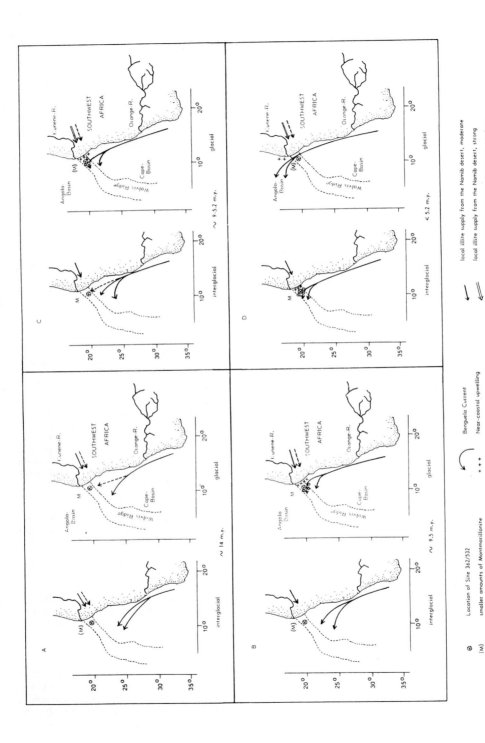

Fig. 4. Reconstruction of the evolution of the Benguela Current system since the Middle Miocene.

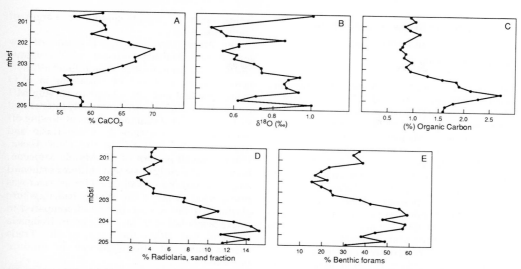

Fig. 5. Late Miocene Sections 362–16–3, 4, and 5 (200.5 to 205 m subbottom, mbsf). (A) percent CaCO₃ of bulk sediment. (B) δ¹⁸O of bulk carbonate. (C) percent organic carbon of bulk sediment. (D) percent radiolaria of sand fraction. (E) benthos/plankton foraminiferal ratio calculated as (% benthics/% benthics + % planktonics) × 100; high values indicate greater carbonate dissolution.

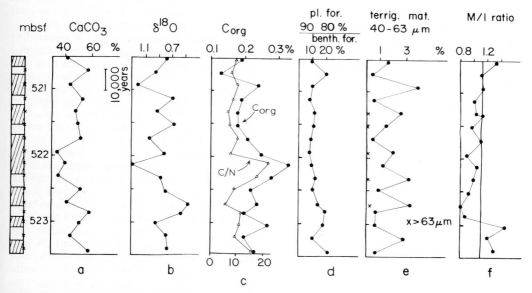

Fig. 6. Middle Miocene Sections 362–33–1 and 2 (520.5 to 523.5 m subbottom). Alternations of marly chalks (hatched intervals) and chalks (open intervals) are indicated near depth scale (from Bolli *et al.* 1978). (a) percent CaCO₃ of bulk sediment. (b) δ¹⁸O of bulk carbonate. (c) percent organic carbon and organic matter C/N ratios. (d) benthos/plankton foraminiferal ratio, calculated as (% benthics/% benthics + % planktonics) × 100; high values indicate greater carbonate dissolution. (e) percent terrigenous matter in the 40–63 and >63 μm fraction. (f) montmorillonite/illite ratios (M/I).

Reconstruction of the history of the Benguela Current and related upwelling off southwest Africa

Analyses of Neogene to Quaternary sediments from DSDP Sites 362 and 532 on the Walvis Ridge continental terrace for coarse fraction contents, organic carbon concentrations, oxygen and carbon isotopes and clay mineral assemblages reveal rhythmic patterns of sedimentation. Darker marls record times of Antarctic ice-volume maxima (heavier $\delta^{18}O$ values), and light-coloured chalks and chalky marls were deposited during ice-volume minima. These sediment patterns reflect different phases in the development of the Benguela Current and its associated upwelling.

Our synthesized reconstruction of the history of the flow pattern of the Benguela Current system from the Middle Miocene to the present is based on several criteria. The essential factors are as follows:

1. The cored sites are too far away from the coast to be influenced directly by upwelling. They receive an indirect opalline signal of the near-coastal upwelling when the Benguela Current turns away from the coast over the Walvis Ridge and supplies eddies of upwelled water to the Walvis Ridge. When the current turns towards the west either north or south of the Walvis Ridge, there is no upwelling signal in the sediment record of the Walvis Ridge sites.

2. The history of carbonate dissolution is genetically linked to, and thus is synchronous with, the history of sea-level variations caused by changes in continental ice volume.

3. The upwelling signal of opal content is not consistently followed by variations in organic matter content. Both opal and organic matter originate from coastal upwelling areas *via* surface lateral transport and sink over the Walvis Ridge; additional organic carbon is supplied by near-bottom downslope transport processes during regressions.

4. The Orange River is the main source of montmorillonite today and we assume this to be true throughout all the Neogene, based on the information from Dingle & Hendey (1984). The variations in the M/I ratios reflect the local contribution of illite from the Namib Desert versus more-distant montmorillonite supply by the Benguela Current.

From these factors, established from modern and Late Quaternary conditions, we reconstruct the following history of the Benguela Current system since the Middle Miocene. We consider this history to be a hypothesis for testing by future deep-sea drilling along the margin of southwest Africa.

The *Middle Miocene* was a period of low fertility as evidenced by no opal, <0.3% organic carbon, and no upwelling signal. Glacial/glacial cycles, reflected by variations in $\delta^{18}O$ values, existed and are related to varying M/I ratios. These findings are tentatively interpreted as a system with a Benguela Current flowing off southwest Africa within the Cape Basin and turning to the west within the Cape Basin. During glacial periods of the Middle Miocene, however, the current system shifted northward and montmorillonite from the Orange river was transported as far as the Walvis Ridge, where glacial M/I ratios were increased compared to interglacial ones (Fig. 4a). This 'proto-Benguela Current' was either too weak or the Trade Winds were not strong enough to produce upwelling.

In the *Late Miocene*, at 10 Ma, when a major regression (Haq *et al.* 1987) points to a major Antarctic cooling event, a first opal maximum in sediments at the Walvis Ridge sites indicates the beginning of upwelling phenomena in the Walvis Ridge area. From 10 to 5.2 Ma sediments show numerous fluctuations between glacial sediments with high contents of opal and organic matter and strong carbonate dissolution and interglacial sediments with small or absent opal contents and good carbonate preservation.

The Benguela Current system is assumed to have shifted northwards during Antarctic glacial periods of the Late Miocene, reaching the Walvis Ridge, producing upwelling in the near-coastal areas, and turning west over the Walvis Ridge, thus supplying the upwelling signal to the sites. In the interglacial periods, however, the Benguela Current turned to the west within the Cape Basin (Figs 4b and 4c).

The M/I ratios of the early Late Miocene show the same pattern as in the Middle Miocene: higher glacial M/I ratios than in interglacial periods (Table 1) as a consequence of the glacial northward migration of the current axis as far as the Walvis Ridge. Starting at about 9 Ma, however, the interglacial M/I ratios are higher than glacial ones (Table 1). This is probably due to a glacially induced increase in wind velocity and thus in local supply of illite from the adjacent Namib desert, depressing the M/I ratios as found in Plio-Pleistocene sediments (Diester-Haass & Rothe 1987).

At 5.2 Ma a major change occurred: sediments from interglacial periods started to have the higher opal contents, whereas glacial sediments had small amounts or were void of opal during the *Pliocene and Quaternary*.

Table 1. Summary of the main sedimentary and oceanographic parameters related to the Benguela Current and associated upwelling in interglacial and glacial intervals of Antarctica for the three main periods of 0–5.2, 5.2–10 and 10–14 Ma. Ages in parentheses are subperiods when clay contents changed as the current strengthened.

Sedimentary or oceanographic parameter	Interglacial			Glacial Periods			Primary controlling factor
	0–5.2 Ma	5.2–10 Ma	10–14 Ma	0–5.2 Ma	5.2–10 Ma	10–14 Ma	
carbonate $\delta^{18}O$	lower	lower	lower	higher	higher	higher	ice volume
sea level	high	high	high	low	low	low	ice volume
CaCO$_3$ amount	high	high	high	lower	lower	lower	dissolution/dilution
% organic carbon	low	low	very low	high	high	lower	sealevel
carbonate dissolution	weak	weak	very weak	strong	strong	very weak	sealevel
opal content	high	low	absent	low	high	absent	upwelling/transport
mont./illite ratio	higher	higher lower (5.2–9) (9–10)	lower	lower	lower higher (5.2–9) (9–10)	higher	transport
area where current turns to the west	Walvis Ridge	Cape basin	Cape Basin	Angola Basin	Walvis Ridge	Cape Basin	Polar front(?)

Consequently, beginning at 5.2 Ma high opal concentrations are related to good carbonate preservation and low organic matter content.

A fluctuating, northward expansion of the Benguela Current system over time is indicated by the sedimentary record. In the present interglacial period the current reaches the Walvis Ridge, where it departs from its SE−NW alignment along the Namibian coast to flow more to the west. Signals of strong upwelling on the inner shelf are transported as eddies by the Benguela Current to the Walvis Ridge.

Interglacial M/I ratios are high at the Walvis Ridge DSDP sites due to steady supply of montmorillonite by the Benguela Current from the Orange River and lower local illite supply. In glacial periods, however, the Benguela Current shifts farther north, flowing parallel to the coast as far as the Angola Basin and only here turning to a western direction. The signal of increased fertility is not deposited on the Walvis Ridge but instead in the Angola Basin, as described for the Late Quaternary by Jansen *et al.* (1984) and by van Zinderen-Bakker (1976). The current shift is accompanied by the lowering of M/I ratios in glacial times relative to interglacial ones as more terrigenous material is blown in from the Namib Desert (Diester-Haass *et al.* 1986). These results do not provide direct information about upwelling intensity on the shelf during glacial periods because Sites 362 and 532 are too distant from the shelf.

In the Plio-Pleistocene sedimentary record, the described small-scale variability with a periodicity of <100 000 years is overprinted by large-scale fluctuations (Fig. 3) which show an increase in opal content on the Walvis Ridge in the Late Pliocene and subsequent decrease in the late Quaternary. Northward migration of the polar front in the Late Pliocene (Wise *et al.* 1985) might have temporarily intensified Benguela Current velocities and upwelling strength, or the axis of the Benguela Current system might have shifted in an E−W direction during this time.

The long-term variations in intensity of the upwelling signal suggest that the strength, and possibly the axis, of the Benguela Current is strongly influenced by the position of the polar front in the Southern Ocean. The Peru Current hypothetically would be similarly affected by changes in the southern hemisphere polar front, either directly by north−south relocations in the position of the surface water masses or indirectly by induced modifications in atmospheric circulation. Schrader & Sorknes (1990) estimate from diatom contents of sediments from Sites 681 and 686 that productivity doubled during late Quaternary interglacial periods in the waters over these locations on the Peru Margin. This pattern resembles the record of higher productivity found in late Quaternary interglacial sediments at Site 532 on the Walvis Ridge. The shallow water depths over the Peru Margin sites (150 m and 450 m, respectively), however, make them particularly sensitive to onshore−offshore movement of the upwelling core as sea level fell and rose during glacial−interglacial transitions (Oberhänsli *et al.* 1990). The similarity in enhanced interglacial productivity signals consequently cannot be used to determine that these two upwelling systems respond similarly to glacial−interglacial changes.

Conclusion

The Benguela Current has progressively strengthened since the Middle Miocene. The current has experienced a long-term northward migration from the Cape Basin to the Walvis Ridge and the Angola Basin. Throughout this process, small-scale, cyclic north−south migrations of the system have occurred. These originate in southern hemisphere glacial−interglacial cycles over the past 14 Ma. Antarctic continental ice volumes evidently have been important to the history of this eastern-boundary current upwelling system. Upwelling offshore of southwest Africa has intensified and shifted with the growth and cyclicity of the Benguela Current system.

We thank W. W. Hay, W. E. Dean and W. L. Prell for their comments which improved this contribution. The Deep Sea Drilling Project provided the sediment samples described in this paper. Parts of this work were supported by grants from the Deutsche Forschungsgemeinschaft, North Atlantic Treaty Organization and the U.S. National Science Foundation.

References

BERGER, W. H. 1970. Planktonic foraminifera: selective solution and the lysocline. *Marine Geology*, **8**, 111−138.
——, BONNEAU, M.-C. & PARKER, F. L. 1982. Foraminifera on the deep-sea floor: lysocline and dissolution rate. *Oceanologica Acta*, **5**, 249−258.
—— & VINCENT, E. 1981. Chemostratigraphy and biostratigraphic correlation: exercises in systematic stratigraphy. *Oceanologica Acta*, Proceedings 26th International Geological Congress, Geology of Oceans. Paris, 115−127.
BOLLI, H. M., RYAN, W. B. F. *et al.* (eds) 1978. *Initial Reports of the Deep Sea Drilling Project*, vol. 40. U.S. Government Printing Office, Washington, D.C.

BORNHOLD, B. D. 1973. *Late Quaternary Sedimentation in the Eastern Angola Basin*. Technical Report, Woods Hole, WHOI 773–8.

BREMNER, J. M. 1975. *Mineralogy and Distribution of Clay Minerals on the southwest African Continental Shelf and Adjacent Hinterland*. Technical Report no. 7, Geology Department, University of Cape Town, 46–55.

BROECKER, W. S. 1982. Glacial to interglacial changes in ocean chemistry. *Progress in Oceanography*, **11**, 151–198.

DIESTER-HAASS, L. 1985. Late Quaternary sedimentation on the eastern Walvis Ridge, SE Atlantic (HPC 532, IPOD Leg 75) and neighboured piston cores. *Marine Geology*, **65**, 145–189.

—— 1988. Sea-level changes, carbonate dissolution and history of the Benguela Current in the Oligocene-Miocene off Southwest Africa (DSDP Site 362, Leg 40). *Marine Geology*, **79**, 213–242.

——, HEINE, K., ROTHE, P. & SCHRADER, H.-J. 1988. Late Quaternary history of continental climate and the Benguela Current off Southwest Africa. *Palaeogeography, Palaeoclimatology, Palaeoecology*, **65**, 81–91.

——, MEYERS, P. A. & ROTHE, P. 1986. Light-dark cycles in opal-rich sediments near the Plio-Pleistocene boundary, DSDP Site 532, Walvis Ridge Continental Terrace. *Marine Geology*, **73**, 1–23.

——, —— & —— 1990. Miocene history of the Benguela Current and Antarctic ice volumes: evidence from rhythmic sedimentation and current growth across the Walvis Ridge (DSDP Sites 362 and 532). *Paleoceanography*, **5**, 685–707.

—— & ROTHE, P. 1987. Plio-Pleistocene sedimentation on the Walvis Ridge, Southeast Atlantic (DSDP Site 532) – Influence of surface currents, carbonate dissolution and climate. *Marine Geology*, **77**, 53–85.

DINGLE, R. V. & HENDEY, Q. B. 1984. Late Mesozoic and Tertiary sediment supply to the eastern Cape Basin (SE Atlantic) and paleo-drainage systems in southwestern Africa. *Marine Geology*, **56**, 13–26.

EMERSON, S. & BENDER, M. 1982. Carbon fluxes at the sediment-water interface of the deep-sea: Calcium carbonate preservation. *Journal of Marine Research*, **39**, 139–162.

HAGEN, E., SCHEMAINDA, R., MICHELSEN, N., POSTEL, L., SCHULZ, S. & BELOW, M. 1981. Zur küstensenkrechten Struktur des Kaltwasserauftriebs vor der Küste Namibias,. *Geod. Geophys. Veroff.*, **36**.

HAQ, B. U., HARDENBOL, J. & VAIL, P. R. 1987. Chronology of fluctuating sea-levels since the Triassic (250 Million years ago to present). *Science*, **235**, 1156–1167.

HART, T. J. & CURRIE, R. T. 1960. The Benguela Current. *Discovery Reports*, **31**, 123–298.

HAY, W. W., SIBUET, J.-C. *et al.* 1984. Initial Reports of the Deep-Sea Drilling Project, vol. 75. U.S. Government Printing Office, Washington D.C.

JANSEN, J. H. F., VAN WEERING, T. C. E., GIELES, R. & VAN IPEREN, J. 1984. Middle and Late Quaternary oceanography and climatology of the Zaire-Congo fan and the adjacent Angola Basin. *Netherlands Journal of Sea Research*, **17**, 201–249.

KENNETT, J. P. 1977. Cenozoic evolution of Antarctic glaciation, the circum-Antarctic ocean, and their impact of global palaeoceanography. *Journal of Geophysical Research*, **82**, 3843–3859.

MEYERS, P. A., DUNHAM, K. W. & RAU, G. H. 1986. Organic geochemical character of opal-rich sediments in light–dark cycles near the Pliocene–Pleistocene boundary in Deep-Sea Drilling Project Site 532, Walvis Ridge. *Paleoceanography*, **1**, 567–575.

MÜLLER, P. J., ERLENKEUSER, H. & VON GRAFENSTEIN, R. 1983. Glacial–interglacial cycles in oceanic productivity inferred from organic carbon contents in eastern North Atlantic sediment cores. *In*: THIEDE, J. & SUESS, E. (eds) *Coastal Upwelling: its Sediment Record*, Part B, Plenum, New York, 365–398.

OBERHÄNSLI, H. 1991. Upwelling signals at the northeastern Walvis Ridge during the past 500 000 years. *Paleoceanography*, **6**, 53–71.

——, HEINZE, P., DIESTER-HAASS, L. & WEFER, G. 1990. Upwelling off Peru during the last 430 000 yr and its relationship to the bottom-water environment, as deduced from coarse grain-size distributions and analyses of benthic foraminiferas at Holes 679D, 680B, and 681B, Leg 112. *Proceedings Ocean Drilling Project, Scientific Reports*, **112**, 369–390.

PARKER, F. L. & BERGER, W. H. 1971. Faunal and solution patterns of planktonic foraminifera in surface sediments of the South Pacific *Deep-Sea Research*, **18**, 73–107.

REA, D. K. & SCHRADER, H.-J. 1985. Late Pliocene onset of glaciation: ice-rafting and diatom stratigraphy of North Pacific DSDP cores. *Palaeogeography, Palaeoclimatology, Palaeoecology*, **49**, 313–325.

SCHRADER, H. & SORKNES, R. 1990. Spatial and temporal variation of Peruvian coastal upwelling during the latest Quaternary. *Proceedings Ocean Drilling Program, Scientific Results*, vol. 112, 391–409.

SCHUETTE, G. & SCHRADER, H.-J. 1981. Diatom taphocoenoses in the coastal upwelling area off Southwest Africa. *Marine Micropaleontology*, **6**, 131–155.

SHACKLETON, N. J. & KENNETT, J. P. 1975. Paleotemperature history of the Cenozoic and initiation of Antarctic glaciation. *Initial Reports, Deep Sea Drilling Project*, vol. 29, 743–755.

SIESSER, W. G. 1980. Late Miocene origin of the Benguela upwelling system off northern Namibia. *Science*, **208**, 283–285.

SUMMERHAYES, C. P. 1983. Sedimentation of organic matter in upwelling regimes. *In*: THIEDE, J. & SUESS, E. (eds) *Coastal upwelling, its sediment record* (NATO Conf. Ser., vol. IV, 10b, Plenum Press, New York, 29–72.

SWIFT, S. A. & WENKAM, C. 1978. Holocene accumulation rates of calcite in the Panama Basin: lateral and vertical variations in calcite dissolution. *Marine Geology*, **27**, 67–77.

THUNELL, R. C. 1976. Optimum indices of calcium carbonate dissolution in deep-sea sediments. *Geology*, **4**, 525–528.

VAN ZINDEREN-BAKKER, E. M. 1976. The evolution of Late Quaternary paleoclimates of Southern Africa. *In*: VAN ZINDEREN-BAKKER, E. M. &

COETZEE, J. A. (eds) *Paleoecology of Africa*, vol. IX, Balkema, Cape Town, 160–202.

WISE, S. W., GOMBOS, A. M. & MUZA, J. P. 1985. Cenozoic evolution of polar water masses, southwest Atlantic Ocean. *In*: HSU, K. J. & WEISSERT, H. J. (eds) *South Atlantic Paleoceanography*. Cambridge University Press, 283–324.

Calcareous nannofossils of Plio-Pleistocene sediments from the northwestern margin of tropical Africa

ANNICK PUJOS

Institut de Géologie du Bassin d'Aquitaine (I.G.B.A.), CNRS (U.R.A. 197), Université de Bordeaux 1, Talence, France

Abstract: Coccoliths are skeletal remains of organisms living in the uppermost part of the oceans, so they reflect the climatological and hydrological variations of the uppermost water layers. The main goal of the present study is to use their fossil remains (calcareous nannofossils) to capture information about the environment where they lived for the last 700 000 years. The work is based on a study of sediment from Site 658, ODP Leg 108 located in a major upwelling area in the northeastern tropical Atlantic, close to the African continent. The hydrological and atmospherical conditions of the area are complex: seasonally windy and alternatively humid and arid. Downcore the effects of these changes are complicated by the presence of climatic stages including various glacial/interglacial alternations.

The interpretation of Plio-Pleistocene climatic history at Site 658 is based on analysis of abundance matrices (calcareous nannofossils as well as other <25μm organic and inorganic elements) and of two nannofossil-based transfer functions (giving estimates for summer–winter temperatures, summer–winter salinities and productivity). The nannofossils most useful for paleoecological interpretation proved to be *Rhabdosphaera* (related to increased temperature and decreased productivity), *Coccolithus pelagicus* (related to sharp decreases in temperature and inversely to salinity), *Syracosphaera* (related to increased salinity) and *Helicopontosphaera* (related to sharp decreases in salinity and increased productivity).

A tentative paleoenvironmental and paleoecological model is given for a typical glacial/interglacial alternation. During *glacial* periods the African continent was arid, with seasonal winds blowing towards the ocean, and the uppermost oceanic waters showing increased salinity. At first oceanic temperatures were low, and organic matter linked with fecal pellets was abundant due to wind-induced upwelling; temperature then increased slightly, before decreasing at the end of the glacial period under the influence of northern ice sheets. At the *glacial/interglacial boundary*, rainy monsoons caused strong and sudden increased runoff, which lowered salinity; *interglacial* time was characterized by low salinity surface waters. As interglacials began, fluvial outflows supplied abundant inorganic and organic matter, while the Canary Current brought cooler waters south from northern latitudes, and there was a short record of upwelling. Then, temperature increased slowly, as the area became dominated by tropical waters.

The main goal of the present study is to try to capture as much information as possible from calcareous nannofossils so as to use them to tell us about the upper/middle Pleistocene history of a particular part of the Atlantic ocean. The section studied (ODP Site 658) is located in a tropical area and was chosen because similar work in another tropical area (the Caribbean) has produced satisfying palaeo-environmental and -climatological results (Pujos 1987 and in press; Giraudeau & Pujos 1990; Giraudeau 1986, 1990). The hydrology of the northeastern tropical Atlantic, off the Casamance coast, is complicated by the presence of upwelling. Changes in the hydrology from glacial to interglacial periods must have influenced the nannoplankton populations living there. One goal of this study was to determine as precisely as possible the main periods of upwelling within

the last 700 000 years, in relation to Atlantic oceanography, African climate, and glacial/interglacial alternations.

Calcareous nannofossils are small calcitic elements forming pieces of the skeleton of planktonic algae (*Coccolithophoridae*) living in most of the modern oceans. They belong to the phytoplankton and their distribution at the oceanic surface has been related to the main climatic zones (McIntyre & Bé 1967; Okada & McIntyre 1977) and to the temperature of superficial waters (McIntyre *et al.* 1972). Because their assemblages can reflect the physico-chemical character of their environment (like planktonic foraminifera and, on a smaller scale, diatoms and radiolarians), it appears possible to use them to derive transfer functions that can be used to estimate the physical properties of Pleistocene oceanic waters (Roche *et al.*

From SUMMERHAYES, C. P., PRELL, W. L. & EMEIS, K. C. (eds), 1992, *Upwelling Systems: Evolution Since the Early Miocene*. Geological Society Special Publication No 64, pp 343–359.

1975; Climap Project Members 1984; Pujos 1987 and in press; Giraudeau & Pujos 1990; Giraudeau 1986, 1990). The transfer function developed here takes this previous work into account and is adapted to the specific upwelling problem considered in this paper.

In making analyses not only coccoliths are considered, but also other components of the <25μm fraction, including small diatoms and other organic/inorganic elements; these were observed, determined and counted (or semi-quantitatively evaluated) on smear slides by using an optical microscope. Having been tested on the Pleistocene assemblages, the same methods and selected nanno-taxa were used for the Pliocene section.

Oceanic area and material studied

Because the chosen oceanic area is the eastern part of the tropical−equatorial Atlantic some of the results already obtained in tropical oceanic areas can be taken into account in the present work, especially for periods when the in situ tropical waters supplied by the western equatorial warm water reservoir (McIntyre et al. 1989) were present. Other hydrological influences complicate palaeoenvironmental studies: for instance the influx of cooler waters in the northern Canary Current; the influx of local fresh waters from seasonal river runoff; and the development of a complex upwelling regime that is permanent offshore from Cap Blanc between 20° and 25°N and restricted to the winter-spring period between 12 and 20°N. The location of Site 658 at the boundary between these two upwelling regimes (about 20°N) complicated the problem. Upwelling generates zonal negative temperature anomalies in oceanic surface waters, the impact of which on the tropical nannoplanktonic associations has to be taken into account.

The area is also influenced by a complex system of seasonal winds (Fig. 1), with meridional trade winds at the oceanic surface and mid-tropospheric zonal winds in the Saharan Air Layer (SAL). There are prominent seasonal winds, the Harmattan in winter and monsoon in summer. The dominant air currents bring characteristic mineralogical and/or biogenic particles to the study area; these eolian and fluviatile components indicate the history of 'cyclical North African aridity and monsoonal humidity' (Ruddiman, Sarnthein et al. 1989a).

The sediments studied come from Site 658 from ODP Leg 108 (20°44.95'N, 18°34,85'W, 2263 m depth). This Site was considered as the 'upwelling Site' of Leg 108 (Ruddiman,

Sarnthein et al. 1989a). I looked at the Quaternary sediments of the uppermost 96 m, which extend back to 700 ka. The main climatic stages and substages of this section have been established by Sarnthein & Tiedeman (1989) on the basis of isotope data ($\delta^{18}O$ and $\delta^{13}C$) in shells of planktonic and benthonic foraminifera. Samples for nannofossil study were taken at 30 cm intervals. Sedimentation was continuous and regular, but there were three hiatuses in sedimentation and/or sampling (1) between 27 and 96 ka; (2) in the middle of stage 11; (3) in the middle of stage 15. The distribution of calcareous nannofossils and a preliminary transfer function have been already partly published for this section (Pujos in press).

For the second part of my study, I chose to compare results obtained from the Pleistocene section of Site 658 with those from two Pliocene sections at the same Site. Nannofossil sampling was made at about 2 m intervals in the two Pliocene sections, which date from 2090 to 2490 ka and from 2950 and 3120 ka.

Methods of nannofossil study

Coccoliths were counted on smear slides with an optical microscope. Like Backman & Shackleton (1983), I used two kinds of counting methods depending on the purpose of the study:

(1) Stratigraphic species were counted on one view-field (×1200); counts were transformed into percentages; species appearances and disappearances, as well as acmes were recorded.

(2) For ecological species the method of counting was more complicated, because abundance matrices have to reflect nanno-

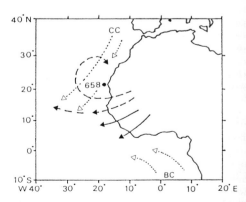

Fig. 1. Locations of Site ODP 108−658. . . . oceanic currents: CC: Canary Current, BC: Benguela Current, --- dominant atmospheric currents.

plankton associations as they were in life and also because the method has to be applicable to fossil series. Data have been deposited as Supplementary Publication no SUP 18076 (7pp) with the British Library Document Supply Centre, Boston Spa, Wetherby, W. Yorkshire, UK and with the Geological Society Library, Burlington House, Piccadilly, London, UK.

Coccoliths are pieces of the exoskeleton of a monocellular algae that cover the surface of coccoliths cells like the roof tiles of houses. When the algae die the coccoliths are usually dissociated from each other and fall to the bottom of the sea. Thus, when coccoliths are counted on sediment smear slides, these counts do not represent cell counts. Coccolith counts have to be transformed into cell (= sphera) counts by taking the usual number of coccoliths per cell for each taxon into account (Giraudeau & Pujos 1990); the number of coccoliths per cell has been deduced from nannosphera drawings (Lecal 1953), and SEM photos (McIntyre & Bé 1967; Okada & Honjo 1973; Okada & McIntyre 1977) and from a personal communication by Kleine (1987). These new abundance matrices will be used as taxa abundances for transfer functions. Only eight ecological taxa were counted for the transfer function. They were selected because they must have lived for most of Pleistocene time and so they can be found as fossils in most of the Pleistocene sediments.

From their transfer functions, Giraudeau & Pujos (1990) and Pujos (1988a, b, and in press) deduced that the best procedure would be to count 150 coccoliths of seven of the eight ecological taxa, to note the number of view-fields necessary to obtain this count, and to count the eight taxon (= Florisphaera div. sp.) in the same number of fields. The abundance matrices could then be converted into sphera numbers and into percentages. The last step would be to transform the sphera percent matrices into five ranks, following the method used for Southern Ocean diatoms (Pichon et al. 1967); each transfer function has its own rank matrix, depending on the highest percentage of the taxa.

Stratigraphical methods

Before studying paleoenvironments, a chronology as precise as possible had to be established for each section. For Pliocene sediments, ages are given according to the interpretation of the isotopic curves (Sarnthein & Tiedeman 1989). For Pleistocene sections, isotopes measured in shells of benthic and planktonic Foraminifera (Sarnthein & Tiedeman 1989) define climatic

stages and can be used to date them precisely by using the SPECMAP curve (Imbrie et al. 1984).

Nannofossil datums can confirm some stage numbers, and nannofossil markers can be used for dating samples where isotopic data were not available because of calcite dissolution for example. These datums and markers are obtained from the 'stratigraphical' nannofossils taxa, described above (method published by Pujos 1988c). Based on the abundance and distribution of selected taxa, their higher (HO) and lower (LO) occurrences and their higher (HA) and lower (LA) acmes can be used as stratigraphic controls.

In the last 700 ka of the Pleistocene at Site 658 it is possible to recognize the following dated events.

15 ka	HO of *Gephyrocapsa aperta*
25 ka	HO of *Gephyrocapsa ericsonii*
115 ka	LO of *Umbellosphaera irregularis*
125 ka	LA of *Emiliania huxleyi*
160 ka	HA of *Gephyrocapsa caribbeanica* and *G. lumina*
225 ka	HA of *G. aperta*
290 ka	LA of *G. aperta*
275 ka	LA of *G. carribbeanica/G. lumina*
340 ka	LO of *G. ericsonii*
440 ka	HO of *Pseudoemiliania lacunosa*
365–540 ka	HO of *Gephyrocapsa doronicoides* (depending on variants)

Paleoecological methods

Nannofossil species choice

Eight taxa have been chosen for palaeoecological studies (Giraudeau & Pujos 1990; Pujos, in press). These species are almost always present throughout the studied cores, and they are still living in the Atlantic Ocean:

Coccolithus pelagicus
Cyclococcolithina leptopora
Florisphaera div. sp.
Helicopontosphaera div. sp.
Rhabdosphaera clavigera and *Discosphaera tubifera*
Scapholithus fossilis
Syracosphaera div. sp.
Umbilicosphaera sibogae

The percentage of all the ecological taxa (i.e. counts of the eight taxa above) is shown in the Supplementary Publication; also those of the other less abundant taxa: *Coccolithus pataecus*, *Thoracosphaera* spp., *Pontosphaera* spp., *Emiliania annula* and *Ceratolithus* spp. Using a restricted number of taxa for a transfer function is also the basis of the method of Karlin et al. (1989), who used seven species of planktonic Foraminifera from the same ODP Leg 108.

It is not possible to explain palaeoenvironmental history by using only the abundance of these taxa, because very few papers focus on large-scale palaeoenvironmental interpretations of calcareous nannoplankton data, except for McIntyre & Bé who established a climatic nanno-zonation in the Atlantic ocean (1967). *Coccolithus pelagicus* is generally taken as a 'cold' species; for example, it is present in glacial stages of the Mediterranean Sea (Noel & Panigel 1985), and it is taken as a subarctic species by McIntyre *et al.* (1970). *Cyclococcolithina leptopora* is an eurythermal species (McIntyre *et al.* 1970). *Florisphaera* div. sp. is present in all the oceans, but restricted to equatorial–tropical waters (Okada & McIntyre 1977). *Helicopontosphaera* is widespread in the tropical and subtropical areas, with various species (McIntyre & Bé 1967); according to Noel & Panigel (1985), this genus could be more abundant during low-salinity periods in the Mediterranean Sea. *Rhabdosphaera clavigera* and *Discosphaera tubifera* are named here as '*Rhabdosphaera*'; these two species have a similar morphology, and for McIntyre *et al.* (1967 & 1970) they have the same tropical–subtropical distribution at the surface of the oceans; according to Berger (1973) they could be related to poor-nutrient waters. No environmental interpretation could be found for *Scapholithus fossilis*; it is perhaps a ubiquitous genus. *Syracosphaera* div. sp. is present in the studied area with two main species: *S. histrica* is well known in all the oceans; it is more abundant in tropical to transitional areas (Okada & McIntyre 1977); Weaver & Pujol (1988) established a relation between high abundance of this species and low salinity periods in the Mediterranean Sea. *S. pulchra* is present in all the oceans, mostly in tropical to transitional areas (Borsetti & Cati 1972; McIntyre & Bé 1967; Okada & McIntyre 1977) and in waters poor in nutrients (Roth & Coulbourn 1977; Berger 1973). Coccoliths of *Umbilicosphaera sibogae* are more abundant in subtropical–tropical (McIntyre & Bé 1967; Okada & Honjo 1973; Okada & McIntyre 1977) and nutrient-poor waters (Roth & Coulbourn 1982).

It is evident that little is known about the relationships between calcareous nannoplankton and environment. Most of the knowledge concerns climatic zones. For the relations between salinity and nutrients and nannoplankton populations almost nothing has been proved. That is why nannofossil-based transfer functions were attempted.

Nannofossil-based transfer functions

The *transfer function method* of Imbrie & Kipp (1971; Imbrie *et al.* 1973) has been used with calcareous nannofossil matrices by Giraudeau (1986). Giraudeau & Pujos (1990); Chalié (1988) and Pujos (1988a, b, in press). Its principle is now well known, with three main programmes being available for calculating the functions.

CABFAC: a Q mode factor analysis made on sphera count matrices in ranks from recent core top sediments

REGRESS: a linear or curvilinear regression analysis (here a curvilinear regression is used) linking associations from CABFAC with parameters of superficial waters (winter and summer temperatures and salinities, from the U.S. Naval Atlas 1967; productivity from Berger 1989).

THREAD: final step of the method links the two previous step results to sphera count matrices in ranks from fossil sections; it ends up giving parameter estimates that are smoothed by using a three-running average technique.

I first used sediment samples from the whole Atlantic ocean for my transfer function database, but it became evident that it was difficult to apply the same 'formula' to associations from all latitudes. In fact, the choice of a restricted oceanic area seems to give the best results (see the different papers from Pujos and Giraudeau for tropical areas); once the method is set up for a given latitude (here: tropical areas), it should be easier to extend it over a whole ocean.

This is why after a first study of sediments for estimating temperatures from the Caribbean Sea (Giraudeau & Pujos 1990), a second one was set up for estimating salinities and temperatures for tropical sites from the eastern Atlantic (Pujos, in press). The present paper also concerns sites from the eastern Atlantic. The method used here is close to that of a preceding paper (Pujos, in press), but it has been refined in relation to the complex hydrology of the area, and completed by an attempt to estimate productivity.

Two main transfer functions were used for the present paper, depending on the chosen parameter and on the core location. They differ from each other in the choice of the core tops used for the factor analysis, and one was used for temperature estimations and the other for salinity and productivity estimations. Varimax factor score matrices of both functions are given in the Supplementary Publication. The communality, for the core top as well for the core assemblages, is always >0.82. Only three samples of the studied Site 658 obtained a communality <0.82. These could be due to increased dissolution or to a counting problem: the corresponding estimates were removed from the results.

In Fig. 2, comparisons between the three chosen parameters (temperature, salinity and productivity data) show that there is a linear relation between temperatures and salinities for samples located north of 35°N, where temperatures are lower than 18°C in summer and 14°C in winter (Fig. 2a, b). For these core tops, salinity does not vary much (1‰ in winter and 1,5‰ in summer) while temperature fluctuates between 6 and 18°C in summer and between 2 and 14°C in winter. South of 35°N, there is not such a clear relation between temperatures and salinities. If all the recent samples had been kept for the salinity transfer function the strong temperature variations might have influenced the weak salinity estimates. For that reason the northernmost core tops were removed from the salinity/productivity transfer function. This decision is also borne out in Fig. 2d, where obvi-

ously there is no relation between salinity and productivity for the samples South of 35°N.

For estimating *temperatures*, the corresponding transfer function takes in account nanno-associations from the whole northern Atlantic Ocean, where temperatures vary from 2 to 27°C in February and from 7 to 28°C in August (according to the U.S. Naval Atlas, 1967). 179 recent core tops are used. Nannofossil associations are well diversified; they are dominated either by *C. pelagicus* or *Florisphaera*, depending on cooler or warmer temperatures. Corresponding standard errors for estimated temperatures are: 1.03°C for the February estimates and 0.91°C for the August ones.

This new transfer function, named 'Atl-T' (see the ATL-T characteristics in the Supplementary Publication) is applied to the Pleistocene and Pliocene sections of Site 658.

For interpreting temperature estimations, it is necessary to know what water masses were likely to be present in the area of Site 658 during the Pleistocene. Two main oceanic water masses succeed one another: warm *in situ* tropical waters, and the cooler waters of the northern

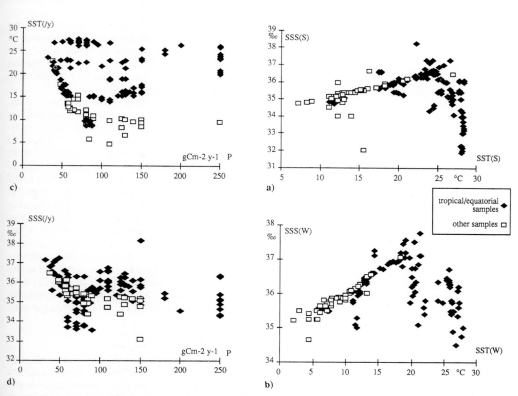

Fig. 2. Core Top samples: relations between temperatures (W, S and annual), Salinities (W, S and annual) and productivity.

Canary Current. Winter as well as summer temperatures are linked to these main surface waters, but are also affected by seasonal upwelling which brings low-temperature waters to the surface in the study area.

For estimating *salinity and productivity*, a single transfer function was established for both parameters. Salinity data were taken from the U.S. Naval Atlas (1967) and productivity data from Berger (1989). Tropical and equatorial salinities of superficial oceanic waters are usually high in the Atlantic Ocean, except off the big river mouths (Amazon, Congo, Niger) which pour huge amounts of fresh water into the ocean. Seasonal African river runoff brings fresh water inflow to the area of Site 658. Productivity maps (Berger, 1989, Fig. 11) show highest values near African tropical rivers. The greatest variances for salinity and productivity are located in the northern hemisphere, between 35°N and the equator. North of about 35°N these two parameters do not vary much (Fig. 2). Thus, for estimating these properties, I restricted selection of the core tops for CABFAC and REGRESS to 109 subtropical and equatorial samples. These new transfer functions are named 'Trop-S' for salinity and 'Trop-P' for productivity; and their characteristics for the factor analysis (which is the same for Trop-S and Trop-P) are shown in the Supplementary Publication.

At present salinity varies between 33 and 37.5‰ (U.S. Naval Atlas 1967) and productivity between 25 and more than 250 g C m^{-2} a^{-1} (Berger, 1989). Nanno-associations are dominated by *Florisphaera*. Standard errors for estimated salinities are 0.30‰ for February estimates and 0.34‰ for August estimates; and 12 g C m^{-2} a^{-1} for productivity.

These transfer functions were used for estimating salinities and productivity for the Plio-Pleistocene sections of Site 658.

'Climatic reconstruction'

On the basis that temperature and salinity are the main parameters influenced by climatic change, a 'climatic reconstruction' is attempted with a simple empirical formula:

cl.rec. = ((SSS(y) − 35) + (SST(y) − 26))/4
cl.rec. = 'climatic reconstruction'
SSS(y) = sea annual salinity
     = (SST(S) + SST(W))/2
SST(y) = sea annual temperature
     = (SST(S) + SST(W))/2

The curve drawn from the values obtained is compared to the isotopic curves, when possible (Fig. 4: Pleistocene of Site 658).

Components other than nannofossils

Other organic or inorganic elements <25μm can be determined and counted on the same smear slides used for counting nannofossils. Their abundances are presented schematically in Fig. 7.

Diatom abundance was estimated in one view field (× 1200), even when they were broken, which was their general condition. No taxonomical distinction was made. The most important peaks are located mainly at the glacial/interglacial boundaries (14/13, 12/11, 10/9, 8/7, 6/5, 2/1). At the beginning of some glacial stages (16, 14) broken and/or dissolved diatoms are abundant. Diatom abundance was more difficult to estimate in most glacial stages, where they occurred as diffuse clouds of very small pieces. Diatoms are taken as indicators of nutrient-rich water.

The non-biogenic *silts* consisted of small pieces of quartz (usually ≤10μm), which were too small to enable their origin to be determined. They may have had two main origins, being either wind blown or brought in by rivers in flood. Silt was most abundant at the glacial/interglacial boundaries (16/15, end of stage 12, 10/9, 8/7, 2/1), when they were brought to the ocean by strong river flows at the beginning of periods of monsoon rainfall. They were also abundant during most of stage 6, and during two interglacial stages (15 and 7) which may have been exceptionally rainy.

A *colloidal* brownish substance was commonly seen coating and hiding nannofossils on smear slides. Analysed with SEM, this constituent was found to be amorphous and composed of silica and organic matter. Colloids were abundant at the beginning of most of the glacial/interglacial boundaries (16/15, 14/13, 12/11, 10/9, 8/7, 2/1 and at the beginning of stage 5), when waters were nutrient-rich due to upwelling and/or runoff. When remains of broken diatoms were abundant, colloids glued them into compact aggregates. Sometimes these aggregates had a more or less cylindrical shape, probably representing fecal pellets. These occurred at the beginning of the glacial stages (16, 14, 12, 8, 6, 2), when nutrient-rich waters were brought to the surface by upwelling linked to strong winds.

Pleistocene results

The abundances of the Pleistocene ecological taxa in Site 658 are given in the Supplementary Publication. They are represented graphically on Figs 3–7, in relation to the alternation of glacial/interglacial stages (see also Pujos, in

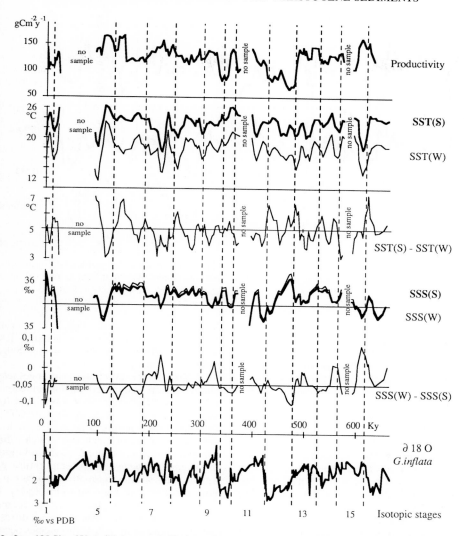

Fig. 3. Leg 108 Site 658 A (Pleistocene). Estimated temperatures, salinities and productivity (from calcareous nannofossils) and isotopic stages (from planktonic Foraminifera)

press), to the abundances of components other than the nannofossils, and to temperature−salinity−productivity estimations. Some curves are associated on the same figure for comparing them more easily:

nannofossil-based estimates of temperature, salinity and productivity (Fig. 3);

foraminifera-based δ^{18}O and nannofossil-based 'climatic reconstruction' (Fig. 4);

some nannofossil taxa and estimated temperatures (Fig. 5) and salinities (Fig. 6);

main events occurring at stage limits, in relation to productivity (Fig. 7).

Temperature (Figs 3.5 & 7)

There is no close relationship between SST(W)/SST(S) and the alternation of climatic stages. In a near-equatorial area, Karlin *et al.* (1989) produced planktonic foraminifera-based estimates of temperature that reflected only partially the variation in temperature of superficial oceanic waters; they explain these perturbations by the presence of organisms from deeper water layers. That cannot be the case here, because calcareous nannofossils are algae and live in the upper-most oceanic layers (the photic zone),

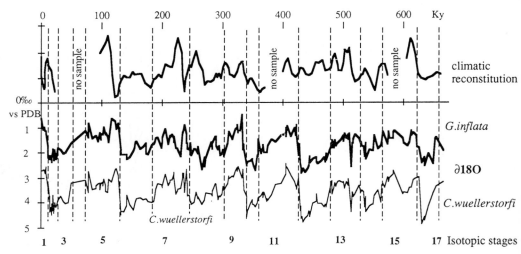

Fig. 4. Leg 108 Site 658 A (Pleistocene). $\delta^{18}O$ measured in shells of benthic and planktonic Foraminifera (Sarnthein & Tiedeman 1989). Climatic reconstruction from estimated SST(y) and SSS(y) from calcareous nannofossils.

where they receive the solar radiation necessary for their photosynthesis. The irregular fluctuations in nannofossil-based temperature estimates may be linked to periodic arrivals of different kinds of water, disturbing the relationship expected between estimated temperatures and climatic stages.

SST(W) varies between 12 and 20°C, and SST(S) between 20 and 26°C (Fig. 3); the maxima and minima of these two kinds of estimates parallel one another. Seasonality (SST(S)−SST(W), Fig. 3) fluctuates between 3.5 and 7°C, with a mean of 5°C, which matches well with results obtained by Prell *et al.* (1976) and by Climap Project Members (1981).

A complex link can be established between estimated temperatures and the alternation of climatic stages, especially for the last 300 ka; it is presented in Fig. 9 and can be described as follows.

At the beginning of *interglacial stages*, superficial waters are warm (*in situ* tropical waters); they are quickly replaced by cooler waters from the Canary Current, the influence of which is first very strong, then weakens gradually. At the same time, temperatures increase to reach tropical values at the interglacial−glacial stage limits.

During most of the *glacial stages*, temperatures are moderately low, which is due either to seasonal upwelling that explains the first (lowermost) cooling or to the global influence of northern ice sheets that explains the second (uppermost) cooling within the even stages. In the middle of glacial stages, temperatures (SST(S) more than SST(W)) increase. Ruddiman *et al.* (1989b) attribute this to Sahelian aridity.

On Fig. 5, the abundances of *two selected nanno-taxa* are compared to temperature estimates. The *Rhabdosphaera* abundance curve varies in the same way as that of SST(S)− SST(W), corroborating what is already known about the ecology of this taxon, which is linked to warm climates. At Site 658, the relationship of *Coccolithus pelagicus* to temperature is not regular. This species is usually abundant at cool temperatures and high latitudes today (McIntyre *et al.* 1970), but here it seems to be influenced mostly when temperatures are extreme: more than 50% of the species occurred during the short periods of temperature minima; species minima are located when temperatures are highest, at the beginning of the interglacial stages.

Salinity (Figs 3, 6 & 7)

Figure 6 shows clear relationship between SSS(W)/SSS(S) and climatic stages for the last 700 Kyr. 'Salinity seasonality' (= SSS(W) − SSS(S)) is always weak (= 0,05 ± 0,05%) and does not fluctuate much, though it shows some peaks in interglacials. These peak values are much lower than the standard error of the transfer functions (= 0.30%); the absolute values are less important than the variations between them which imply that summer sal-

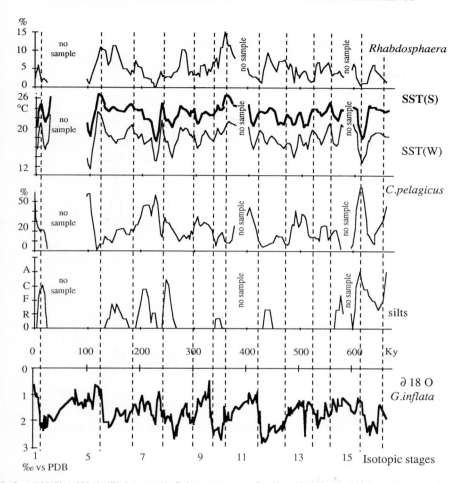

Fig. 5. Leg 108 Site 658 A (Pleistocene). Calcareous nannofossils and estimated temperatures

nities are lower than winter salinities during interglacial stages.

The relation between salinity estimates and the climatic stages is as follows:

During *glacial stages*, salinity increases up to 36‰, due to intensified aridity in the Sahel Morzadec-Kerfourn 1988; Gasse *et al*. 1989). At the same time, winds blow offshore from the near-by continent (Harmattan in winter and monsoon in summer) bringing various continental particles to the ocean: dusts (= 'silts' on smear slides, at the end of glacial stages) and broken diatoms (at the beginning of some glacial stages). The link between wind-transported diatoms and 'a given arid period' was noted by Gasse *et al*. (1989). Some rare undamaged diatoms are also found in the same sediments. They belong to the species *Thalassionema niztschioides*, an upwelled water indicator.

During *interglacial stages*, salinity drops to 35 to 35.5‰; then increases slightly to about 35.75‰. These low salinities relate to tropical humidity during the warm periods of the northern hemisphere (Morzadec-Kerfourn 1988; Gasse *et al*. 1989). This wetness induces strong rains and raises river levels bringing fresh water to the ocean from the Niger or even from the Congo.

At the boundary between glacial and interglacial stages the sea level is very low, and the continental shelf is partially or totally exposed. The sudden rise of the rivers supplies large amounts of inorganic ('silts') and organic particles (fresh water diatoms, such as *Melosira*) from the exposed shelf and from the hinterland to the ocean.

On Fig. 6, the abundances of *two selected nanno-taxa* are compared with salinity esti-

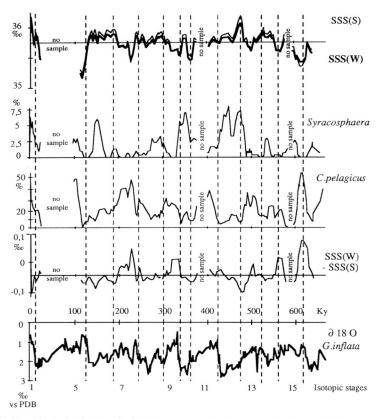

Fig. 6. Leg 108 Site 658 A (Pleistocene). Calcareous nannofossils and estimated salinities

mates. *Coccolithus pelagicus* was almost absent and *Syracosphaera* was very abundant during glacial stages when salinity was high. This contradicts the results of Weaver & Pujol (1988) who found a possible relation between an increase in the abundance of *Syracosphaera* and 'lowered salinity by increased run-off' in the Mediterranean Sea. *Helicopontosphaera* is also abundant when salinity decreases suddenly at the beginning of the interglacial stages; its correlation with low salinity was observed by Noel & Panigel (1985). In spite of the difficulty in using absolute values of seasonal salinity (SSS(W)−SSS(S)) the maxima of these estimates can be linked to the minima of *C. pelagicus* suggesting a relation between abundant *C. pelagicus* and low salinity.

'Climatic reconstruction' (Fig. 4)

Comparison of the 'climatic reconstruction' curve, derived from the annual temperature and salinity estimates, with $\delta^{18}O$ measurements

shows strong similarities. The main minima and maxima of the 'climatic reconstruction' curve fit well with those of the $\delta^{18}O$ curve, and the glacial/interglacial alternation is obvious, as are most of the substages.

Productivity (Figs 3 & 7)

Productivity fluctuations roughly follow the alternation of climatic stages. Productivity increases markedly at the beginning of most of the interglacial stages (= stages 5, 7, 11, 13 15).

Comparison of estimated productivity with the distribution of colloids, silts, *Helicoponto-sphaera* and diatoms (Fig. 7) helps to understand the distribution of organic components.

At the beginning of *interglacial stages* productivity estimates, colloids, silts and small diatoms increase at the same time, or more precisely they follow one another in a short time, from the end of the glacial period to the beginning of the interglacial one. This is due to

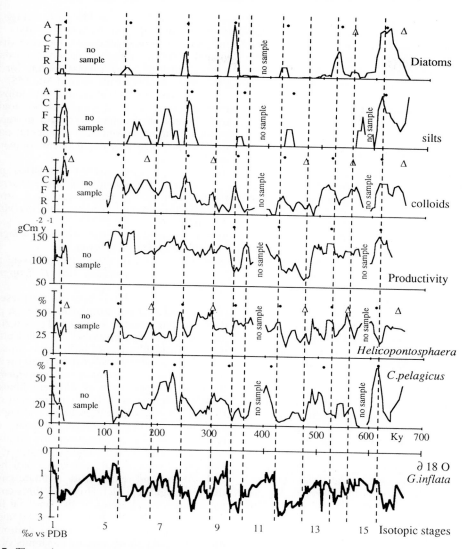

Fig. 7. The main events at glacial/interglacial (△) and interglacial/glacial (●) stage limits.

the onset of the period of decreased salinity of the warm wet season and to the sudden arrival of nutrient- and silicate- rich fresh waters from rivers. At first, rivers lay down their sediment load (→ silts at the even end of glacial stages), then silica and organic matter (→ colloids and highly productive waters at the glacial/interglacial limits). These productive waters are the best environment for diatoms, which find organic matter and silica necessary to build their frustules: it explains why diatoms lag behind the silt peak. *Helicopontosphaera* is abundant at about the same time as diatoms: it is not

clear whether these abundances are linked to low salinity or to high productivity.

At the beginning of *glacial stages*, productivity estimates and silt abundances have no maximum; but colloids and diatoms (mostly broken and/or dissolved unidentified diatoms) are abundant. Colloids and diatoms form compact masses which look like the remains of fecal pellets. This suggests the presence of nutrient-rich waters brought to the surface by upwelling, as the Harmattan begins to blow. The poor preservation of the diatoms can be explained by their presence within the fecal pellets. Dissolution of silicous organisms is also common at the beginning of the arid period, when waters are undersaturated in silica. Just after the colloid-diatom peak, there is a peak in the abundance of *Helicopontosphaera*, linked either to nutrient-rich waters or to low salinity. It is followed by abundant *Rhabdosphaera*, representing depletion of surface waters in nutrients.

Pliocene results (Fig. 8)

The study of Pliocene sections from Site 658 give less precise results, mostly because of the small sample density (about one sample every 2 m). Nevertheless, global results and correlations are similar to those in the Pleistocene. For instance, the same abundances of ecological nanno-taxa can be found (Fig. 8a), with *C. pelagicus* varying like (SSS(W)−SSS(S)) and in opposition to estimated temperatures; *Syracosphaera* showing inverse behaviour. *Syracosphaera* abundances are not related to estimated salinities.

Diatoms, silts and colloids are commonly very abundant and fluctuate in the same way as in the Pleistocene. However, because of the wide sample spacing it is not possible to see if these properties follow one another as they do in the Pleistocene.

Colloids and estimated productivity vary in the same way as in the Pleistocene.

Nannofossil-based estimates (Fig. 8b, d): estimated temperatures at Site 658 fluctuate between the same minima and maxima in the Pliocene as in the Pleistocene, in spite of the presence of large amounts of *Coccolithus pelagicus*, a 'cold' taxon in the Pliocene. The 'climatic reconstruction' also fits well with isotopic measurements, providing that the same sample spacing is used for both graphs.

Palaeoenvironmental and palaeoclimatological conclusions

The study of calcareous nannofossils and some organic and inorganic components of the <25μm sediment at Site 658 provides indications about the palaeoecological use of nannofossils, and on their usefulness for reconstructing the hydrological history of an area through Pleistocene glacials and interglacials. While most of the glacial stages are alike, as are most of the interglacial ones, there are some discrepancies due either to special climatic conditions (e.g. silts in stage 7 and 15) or to possible sedimentary hiatuses (e.g. sediments from the latest period of stage 10?) or to lack of samples (e.g. most of

stages 11, 5 and 2, the middle part of stage 15, stages 4 and 3). On balance the data are sufficient to permit conclusive palaeoenvironmental interpretations of nannofossil abundances and lead to a synthetic scheme for the Pleistocene history of the area of Site 658.

As a first step, calcareous nannofossils themselves are clearly a good palaeoecological tool. Simple taxa abundances help to reconstruct variations in some environmental parameters and even global palaeoenvironmental conditions such as:

higher temperatures and/or decreased productivity: e.g. abundant *Rhabdosphaera*;

sudden decreases of temperature: e.g. strong and time-limited increase in *Coccolithus pelagicus*;

higher salinities: e.g. rare *Coccolithus pelagicus* and abundant *Syracosphaera*;

sudden decreases of salinity: e.g. strong and time-limited increase in *Helicopontosphaera*.

There is also a relation between the presence of abundant *Helicopontosphaera* and high productivity; but, because salinity and productivity are sometimes synchronous, it is difficult to dissociate the influence of both parameters.

Calcareous nannofossils can be used for *estimating salinity, temperature and productivity* through the application of different kinds of transfer functions related to environment controls. There is no special problem in using and explaining transfer functions, but some parameters show such strong and sharp variations that one parameter may influence another. An example of such an influence may occur here, with salinity and temperature estimate curves that are roughly parallel. However, these coarse correlations break down at the seasonal level which is strongly influenced by physical and/or hydrological features. This differentiation at different scales shows one of the limits of the method.

In spite of coarse scale sampling in the Pliocene sections, this study proved that the same transfer functions give satisfying estimates of environmental change in sections older than the Pleistocene. They now have to be tested in other oceanic areas and in uninterrupted lower Pleistocene and Pliocene sections.

The 'climatic reconstruction' presented here is an experiment in using estimates of temperature and salinity, the two main parameters of oceanic waters, to represent climate history. The results obtained suggest that it could provide a new 'method' for identifying the main climatic variations, even in

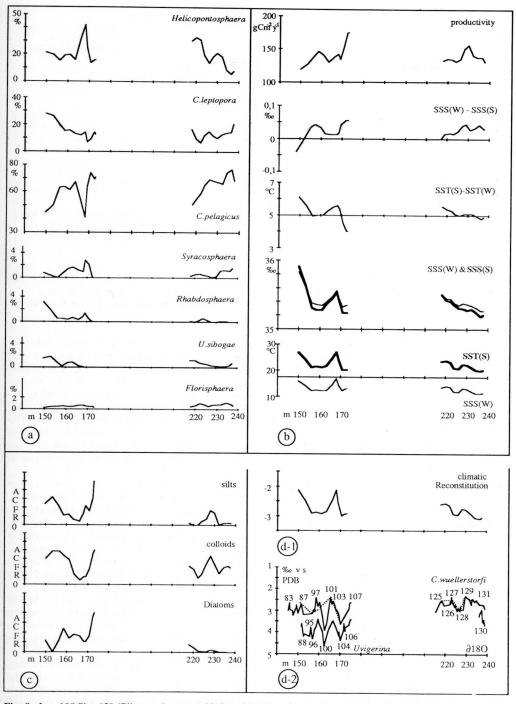

Fig. 8. Leg 108 Site 658 (Pliocene between 2090 and 2490 ka, and between 2950 and 3120 ka): (a) distribution of the ecological taxa of calcareous nannofossils; (b) estimated temperatures, salinities and productivity; (c) distribution of silts, colloids and diatoms in the <25μm fraction; (d1) climatic reconstruction from nannofossils; (d2) --- $\delta^{18}O$ measured in shells of benthic and planktonic Foraminifera (from Sarnthein & Tiedeman 1989); ... curve of $\delta^{18}O$ (p.F.) by using only the same samples as for the nannofossils study.

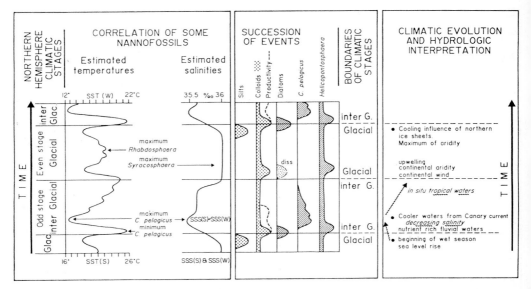

Fig. 9. Pleistocene synthetic scheme of nannofossil-based estimates, nannofossil ecological taxa, other <25 μm elements and climatic interpretation for a glacial/interglacial alternation (area of ODP Site 658).

hydrologically complex areas. The reconstructions are not as reliable as isotopic measurements, but they ought to be useful when there is no isotope data available.

As a second step, calcareous nannofossils reflect and reveal the history of hydrology of surface waters in a given area. For instance, it is possible to differentiate between cooling events of different cause. Of the various estimated *temperature decreases*, some are due to the arrival of the Canary Current that brings cooler waters from northern latitudes; some are caused by upwelling; and others, during glacial stages, reflect the cooling influence of northern ice sheets. Periods of *increasing productivity* are explained either by increased upwelling, or by the arrival of nutrient-rich river water; it is not always possible to distinguish one from the other. Using *salinity estimates* and the main abundances of some organic (nanno-taxa; total diatom abundance) and inorganic material (colloids = organic matter; silts) we can identify the main hydrological features of the glacial/interglacial alternations. This applies both to the Pleistocene and the Pliocene.

Taking all of the available information together it is possible to construct a Pleistocene synthetic scheme (Fig. 9), starting *at the end of a glacial period*, just before the glacial/interglacial boundary. First a tropical wet season begins on the African continent and generates strong rains (= monsoon rainfall) and raises the river levels (here mostly the Niger, but also many temporary smaller rivers). The consequences are decreased salinity in the oceanic waters, especially in summer (SSS(S) < SSS(W)), the arrival of inorganic silts brought by rivers, and increases in productivity and in the abundance of small diatoms. All these increases are momentary, except for the low salinity, which will last for the whole interglacial period, which is continuously rainy.

During *interglacial stages*, temperature maxima are evident only at the glacial/interglacial and at the interglacial/glacial boundaries, due to the presence of *in situ* tropical waters only during these short periods. At the beginning of the interglacial period, a sudden decrease of temperature is explained by the arrival of the Canary Current bringing cooler North Atlantic Central Water; these waters are also less salty than the *in situ* tropical waters, so can amplify the low salinities induced by increased river runoff. Clearly, cool and nutrient-rich water can be brought to the study area either by rivers or by upwelling; it is not really possible to separate both phenomena and very likely they act at the same time (see also Stein *et al.* (1989)). At the end of the interglacial stage, the influence of the Canary Current diminishes slowly, and its cool waters are replaced gradually by tropical waters.

At the boundary between the interglacial and

the following glacial stage, the tropical waters are re-established. They are warm, and, because this is the beginning of the dry period, inducing evaporation, the salinity is higher. During the whole *glacial stage*, the African continent is arid and surface waters are more salty. At least at the beginning of the period, a continental wind (Harmattan) blows offshore causing upwelling to bring nutrient-rich and silica-undersaturated waters to the surface. At the middle of the glacial stage upwelling decreases, probably because wind strength drops. Towards the end of the period, when glaciation is maximum in the northern hemisphere, the area is influenced by the northern ice sheets, and surface waters cool. This last cooling is directly followed by the beginning of the tropical wet season, which was the starting point of the synthetic scheme.

I thank co-chief scientists, the whole staff, and particularly Helene Manivit who gave me the opportunity to obtain and study many samples from the ODP Leg 108. I am especially grateful to W. L. Prell, A. McIntyre and E. M. Pokras for their detailed review and to C. P. Summerhayes for editorial assistance. The research was supported by an 'Action de Soutien' of the CNRS.

References

BACKMAN, J. & SHACKLETON, N. J. 1983. Quantitative biochronology of Pliocene and early Pleistocene calcareous nannofossils from the Atlantic, Indian and Pacific oceans. *Marine Micropaleontology*, 8, 141–170.

BERGER, W. H. 1973. Biogenous Deep-Sea Sediments. Production, Preservation and Interpretation *In*: RILEY, J. P. & CHESTER, R. (eds), *Chemical Oceanography*, New York, Academic, 5, 265–386.

—— 1989. Appendix: global maps of ocean productivity. *In*: BERGER, W. H. SMETACEK, V. S. & WEFER, G. (eds) *Productivity of the Ocean: Present and Past*, Wiley, New York, 429–455.

BORSETTI, A. M. & CATI, F. 1972. Il nannoplancton calcareo vivente nel Tirreno Centro-Meridionale. *Giornale di Geologia*, (2), 43, 1, 157–174.

CHALIE, F. 1988. Les nannofossiles calcaires du Pleistocène supérieur et de l' Holocène de deux carottes profondes de l'océan Atlantique Sud Systématique–Biostratigraphie–Paléoécologie. D.E.A., Univ. Bordeaux I.

CLIMAP PROJECT MEMBERS 1981. Seasonal reconstructions of earth's surface at the last glacial maximum. *The Geological Society of America, Map and Chart Series*, MC-36.

GASSE, F., STABELL, B., FOURTANIER, E. & VAN IPEEREN, Y. 1989. Freshwater Diatoms influx in intertropical Atlantic: relationship with continental records from Africa. *Quaternary Research*, 32, 229–243.

GIRAUDEAU, J. 1986. Les nannofossiles de trois carottes de l'Atlantique Nord-Est et de la Méditerrannée: influence de la dernière déglaciation. Mem. DUSEO, Univ. de Bordeaux I

—— & PUJOS, A. 1990. Fonction de Transfert basée sur les nannofossiles calcaires du Pléistocène des Caraïbes. *Oceanologica Acta*, 10, 4, 453–469.

IMBRIE, J., HAYS, J. D., MARTINSON, D. G., MCINTYRE, A., MIX, A. C., MORLEY, J. J., PISIAS, N. G., PRELL, W. L. & SHACKLETON, N. J. 1984. The orbital theory of Pleistocene climate: support for a revised chronology of the marine δ^{18}O record. *In*: BERGER, A., IMBRIE, J., HAYS, J., KUKLA, G. & SALTZMAN, B. *Milankovitch and Climate*. Reidel, Dordrecht, 269–306.

—— & KIPP, N. G. 1971. A new micropaleontological method for quantitative paleoclimatology: application to a late Pleistocene Caribbean core. *In*: TUREKIAN, K. K. (ed) *The late Cenozoic glacial ages*, New Haven, Connecticut, Yale University Press, 71–181.

——, VAN DONK, J. & KIPP, N. G. 1973. Paleoclimatic investigation of a late Pleistocene Caribbean deep-sea core: comparison of isotopic and faunal methods. *Quaternary Research*, 3, 10–38.

KARLIN, K., RUDDIMAN, W. F. & MCINTYRE, A. 1989. Comparison of late Pliocene and late Pleistocene sea-surface temperatures in the equatorial Atlantic divergence. *Proceedings of the Ocean Drilling Program, Scientific Results*, Ocean Drilling Program, College Station, TX, 108, 187–210.

MCINTYRE, A. & BE, A. W. H. 1967. Modern Pacific Coccolithophorida: a paleontologic thermometer. New York Academy of Science Transactions, Ser. II, 32, 720–731.

——, —— & ROCHE, M. B. 1970. Modern Pacific Coccolithophoridae: a palaeontologic thermometer New York Academy of Science Transactions, Ser. II, 32, 720–731.

——, RUDDIMAN, W. F. & JANTZEN, R. 1972. Southward penetrations of the North Atlantic polar front: faunal and floral evidence of large-scale surface water masses movements over the last 225 000 years. *Deep-Sea Research*, 19, 1, 61–77.

——, ——, KARLIN, K. & MIX, A.C. 1989. Surface water response of the equatorial Atlantic Ocean to orbital forcing. *Paleoceanography*, 4, 1, 19–55.

MORZADEC-KERFOURN, M. T. 1988. Distribution des kystes de Dinoflagellés dans les sédiments pleistocènes de la marge guinéenne de l'Afrique (Equamarge I, 1983) *Palaeogeography, Palaeoclimatology, Palaeoecology*, 65, 201–216.

MULLER, C., BLANC-VERNET, L., CHAMLEY, H. & FROGET, C. 1974. Les Coccolithophoridés d'une carotte méditerranéenne. Comparaison paléoclimatologique avec les Foraminifères, Ptéropodes et les argiles. *Tethys*, 6, 4, 805–828.

NOEL, D. & PANIGEL, M. 1985. Les sapropels de Méditerranée orientale dans leur contexte sédimentologique; données sur les nannofossiles et les nannofaciès. *Coll. Gréco* 52, 7–8.

OKADA, H. & HONJO, S. 1973. The distribution of oceanic coccolithophorids in the Pacific. *Deep-*

Sea Research, **20**, 355–374.

—— & McIntyre, A. 1977. Modern cocco lithophores of the Pacific and North Atlantic oceans. *Micropaleontology*, **23**, 1, 1–55.

Pichon, J. J., Labracherie, M., Labeyrie, L. D. & Duprat, J. 1987. Transfer Functions between diatom assemblages and surface hydrology in the southern Ocean. *Palaeogeography, Palaeoclimatology, Palaeoecology*, **61**, 79–95.

Prell, W. L., Gardner, J. V., Be, A. W. H. & Hays, J.D. 1976. Equatorial Atlantic and Carribean foraminiferal assemblages, temperatures, and circulation: interglacial and glacial comparisons. *In*: Cline, R. M. & Hayes, J. D. (eds) *Investigation of Late Quaternary Paleoceanography and Paleoclimatology*, Geol. Soc. Amer. Mem., New York, **145**, 247–266.

Pujos, A. 1987. The use of a transfer function from coccolith assemblages: estimation of Quaternary temperature and salinity in the Caribbean and tropical Atlantic. *I.N.A. Newsletter*, **9**, 60–61.

—— 1988a. Stratigraphical and paleoecological distribution of calcareous nannofossils throughout the Quaternary in the Caribbean Sea. *11th Conference of the Caribbean, Barbados, Juillet 1987*.

—— 1988b. Stratigraphical and paleoecological distribution of calcareous nannofossils throughout the Quaternary in the Caribbean Sea. *In*: *Transactions of the 11th Caribbean Geological Conf., Barbados, 20–26 Juillet 1986*, **8**, 1–8–13.

—— 1988c. Spatio-temporal distribution of some Quaternary coccoliths. *Oceanologica Acta*, **11**, 1, 65–77.

—— 1989. Hydrological interpretation of the Quaternary and Neogene calcareous nannofossils and the mineralogical fraction <25µ in the eastern subtropical Atlantic Ocean. *28th International Geological Congress, Washington, July 1989*.

—— in press. Calcareous nannofossils and the <25 µm fraction in Quaternary sediments of the subtropical N.E. Atlantic ocean. Mem. Sci. Geol., Mem. Ist. Geol. e Min., Univ. Padova, Sp. Publ., INA

Meeting, Firenze, Sept. 1989.

Roth, P. H. & Coulbourn, W. T. 1982. Floral and solution patterns of coccoliths in surface sediments of the North-Pacific. *Marine Micropaleontology*, **7**, 1–52.

Ruddiman, W., Sarnthein, M. *et al.* 1989a. *Proceedings of the Ocean Drilling Program, Scientific Results*, College Station, TX, **108**.

——, ——, *et al.* 1989b. Late Miocene to Pleistocene evolution of climate in Africa and the low-latitude Atlantic: overview of Leg 108 results. *In*: Ruddimann, W., Sarnthein, M. *et al. Proceedings of the Ocean Drilling Program, Scientific Results*, Ocean Drilling Program, College Station, TX, **115**, 463–484.

Sarnthein, M. & Tiedeman, R. 1989. Towards a high-resolution stable isotope stratigraphy of the last 4 million years, ODP Sites 658 and 659 off northwest Africa. *In*: Ruddiman, W., Sarnthein, M. *et al. Proceedings of the Ocean Drilling Program, Scientific Results*, Ocean Drilling Program, College Station, TX, **108**, 167–185.

Stein, R., ten Haven, L. H., Littke R., Rullkotter, J. & Welte, D. H. 1989. Accumulation of marine and terrigenous organic carbon at upwelling Site 658 and nonupwelling Sites 657 and 659: implications for the reconstruction of paleoenvironments in the eastern subtropical Atlantic through late Cenozoic times. *In*: Ruddimann, W., Sarnthein, M. *et al. Proceedings of the Ocean Drilling Program, Scientific Results*, Ocean Drilling Program College Station, TX, **108**, 361–385.

Weaver, P. P. E. & Pujol, C. 1988. History of the last deglaciation in the Alboran sea (western Mediterranean) and adjacent North Atlantic as revealed by coccolith floras. *Palaeogeography, Palaeoclimatology, Palaeoecology*, **64**, 35–42.

U.S. Naval Oceanographic Office 1967. *Oceanographic Atlas of the North Atlantic Ocean*, Sec. II, Physical Properties. U.S. Naval Oceanographic Office, Washington, Pub. No. 700.

Evidence for aridity-driven dust flux to the northwest Arabian Sea and for decoupling of the dust and upwelling systems

L. A. KRISSEK[1] & S. C. CLEMENS[2]

[1] Department of Geological Sciences, Ohio State University, Columbus, OH 43210-1398, USA

[2] Department of Geological Sciences, Brown University, Providence, RI 02912-1846, USA

Abstract: Late Quaternary records of dust grain size, dust flux (mass accumulation rate; MAR) and dust mineralogy from ODP Site 722 on the Owen Ridge, northwest Arabian Sea, have been used to: (1) infer environmental conditions in the continental source areas; (2) determine the spectral response (frequency and phase relationships) of dust MAR and mineralogy to environmental changes associated with global ice volume variations and orbital insolation patterns and (3) evaluate potential associations between the continental (dust) and marine (upwelling) systems over the past 800 ky. The terrigenous dust component is composed of smectite, illite, palygorskite, kaolinite, chlorite, quartz, plagioclase feldspar and dolomite. This is consistent with the composition of source areas currently supplying sediment to the Arabian Sea. An R-mode factor analysis identifies four mineral assemblages: three reflect arid continental source conditions and one reflects more humid conditions. Total dust MAR, two of the three 'arid' factor assemblages, and six of the seven minerals associated with the 'arid' factors are coherent with the marine isotopic record of global ice volume over at least one primary orbital frequency, with input maxima during glacial (arid) hemicycles. In contrast, wind strength and upwelling intensity indicators exhibit maxima during the interglacial (humid) hemicycles, indicating a decoupling of the continental (dust MAR) and monsoon-driven upwelling systems.

In the Arabian Sea, upwelling within the water column is driven seasonally by the southwestern (summer) monsoon winds (e.g. Wyrtki 1971; Smith & Bottero 1977). These winds, in turn, are driven by the combination of two effects: differential sensible heating of southern Asia relative to the Indian Ocean and direct latent heating of the troposphere over southern Asia resulting from the condensation of water vapour evaporated from the Indian Ocean (Webster 1987). Most studies of the monsoon history over geological time scales have concentrated on records of the biological response to productivity associated with monsoon-driven upwelling, as preserved in sediments of the Arabian Sea. Such work includes studies of the faunal response using *Globigerina bulloides* (Prell & Curry 1981; Prell 1984a, b; Anderson 1990; Prell 1990; Anderson & Prell 1991; Kroon et al. 1991) and of accumulation rates of biogenic carbonate, biogenic silica and organic carbon (Murray & Prell 1990; Pedersen & Zahn 1990; Murray & Prell 1991; Steens et al. 1991; Zahn & Pedersen 1991). These studies have generally identified the importance of orbitally forced insolation changes on monsoon-induced upwelling, demonstrating cyclical episodes of increased productivity/preservation. The monsoon upwelling record has also been tied

to fluctuations in continental climates by comparing foraminiferal and pollen assemblages in marine sediments (Van Campo et al. 1982; Prell & Van Campo 1986; Van Campo 1986). These data suggest increased humidity and strong southwest monsoons during interglacial intervals and more arid conditions and weakened monsoons during glacial intervals. These interpretations generally agree with African lake-level data (Street & Grove 1979) and the results of palaeoclimatic modelling efforts for the last glacial maximum (Kutzbach 1981; Kutzbach & Otto-Bleisner, 1982; COHMAP Members 1988).

Another important sediment component is terrigenous material transported to the Arabian Sea by summer monsoon winds, predominantly the southwest monsoon and the northwest Shamal winds (Sirocko & Lange 1991). Chester et al. (1985) sampled aerosols over the northern Arabian Sea and determined that the aerosols were compositionally similar to the underlying marine sediments and to the material derived from the arid regions of Iran—Makran. Sediment trap data from the western Arabian Sea (Nair et al. 1989) demonstrate that 80% of the dust MAR is provided by eolian transport during the summer monsoon months (June to August). The effects of eolian input on timescales of

From SUMMERHAYES, C. P., PRELL, W. L. & EMEIS, K. C. (eds), 1992, *Upwelling Systems: Evolution Since the Early Miocene*. Geological Society Special Publication No 64, pp 359–378.

centuries to millenia have been examined using the accumulation rates of terrigenous components over the past 8 ky, which outline major sediment sources in Oman and central Arabia. The average annual fluxes of these components over the past 8 ky compare well with estimates of transcoastal dust flux derived from satellite data for 1979 (Sirocko & Sarnthein 1989).

Longer-term dust records from the Arabian Sea were reported by Clemens & Prell (1990, 1991) and by Bloemendal & deMenocal (1989) and deMenocal et al. (1991). Over the past million years, the mass accumulation rate (MAR; $g/cm^2/ky$) of land-derived dust correlates positively with global ice-volume as indicated by the marine oxygen isotope record (Clemens & Prell 1990, 1991). This relationship was interpreted to reflect the effect of global climate on aridity and vegetation cover in the continental source areas, with maximum deflation potential (maximum aridity, minimum vegetation) and resulting maximum dust transport during glacial intervals. In contrast, the record of dust grain size is not well correlated to either the marine oxygen isotope record or the dust MAR record, but does show good correlation between increased dust grain size and increased abundance of G. bulloides, the indicator of monsoon-induced upwelling. The dust grain size is thus interpreted as a wind strength indicator, thereby recording a different process than the dust MAR (Clemens & Prell 1990). Bloemendal & deMenocal (1989) and deMenocal et al. (1991) demonstrated the usefulness of magnetic susceptibility data as a proxy for dust content in a record to 3.2 Ma from the Owen Ridge, and identified the increased importance of 41 ky cycles in that record since 2.4 Ma. Because 2.4 Ma also marks a time of major increase in Northern Hemisphere ice volume, the increased importance of 41 ky cycles was interpreted to record increased aridity in the dust source areas in response to global climate changes associated with increased Northern Hemisphere ice volume (Bloemendal & deMenocal 1989; deMenocal et al. 1991).

Because the mineralogical composition of the dust may also carry a climatic signal, Krissek & Clemens (1991) analyzed the dust mineralogy in a record to 500 ka. Minerals present in the Arabian Sea sediments include smectite, illite, palygorskite, chlorite, kaolinite, quartz, plagioclase feldspar and dolomite. This composition is consistent with the compositions of source areas which currently supply sediment to the area (Kolla et al. 1976, 1981; Chester et al. 1985; Sirocko & Sarnthein 1989; Debrabant et al.

1991). An R-mode factor analysis identified four mineral assemblages present throughout the past 500 ky; three of the factors are interpreted as mineral assemblages derived from arid source regions, and one is interpreted to record more humid source regions. In the time domain, each factor is dominated by variability on time scales of 10 to 100 ky, with little obvious correlation to isotopically defined glacial/interglacial stages. When viewed in the frequency domain, however, each factor contains spectral peaks with concentrations of variance at or near primary Milankovitch frequencies. In addition, each 'arid' factor is coherent and in phase with the dust MAR record over a single primary Milankovitch frequency band. These relationships indicate that the increased dust MAR during glacial intervals is a complex result of increased dust supply from specific sources (or types of weathering regimes) that respond to environmental changes at distinct timescales. The physical reasons for coherency between each factor and dust MAR at a single Milankovitch frequency are not known, but may include differences in the susceptibilities of minerals to varying timescales of weathering, and/or preferential development of suitable continental source environments by climatic changes at various Milankovitch frequencies.

In this paper, we expand the study of Krissek & Clemens (1991) in two ways. Firstly, we expand the spectral investigation to study the relationship between insolation, global ice volume, dust MAR and the abundance of individual minerals (and factor assemblages); secondly, we consider more explicitly the relationships between the responses of the dust system and the responses of the upwelling system to changes in the same forcing functions (insolation) and boundary conditions (global climatic conditions related to ice volume). By doing so, we recognize more clearly the physical linkages between insolation, global climate (as related to ice volume), total dust MAR and the fluxes of individual minerals and mineral assemblages. Individual components of the dust flux signal (individual minerals and mineral assemblages), as well as the total dust MAR signal, respond strongly to environmental conditions that accompanied maximum global ice volume at the eccentricity (100 ky), obliquity (41 ky) and, to a lesser extent, the precession (23 ky) bands. These responses, however, are strongly out of phase with those of the upwelling system.

Krissek & Clemens (1991) have demonstrated that comparisons of the mineral data to the dust MAR record are more readily conducted in the frequency than in the time domain. Here we concentrate primarily on frequency domain comparisons. We begin by presenting the mineral abundance records to 800 ka, and then discuss the mineral assemblages identified by an R-mode factor analysis and their palaeoenvironmental/palaeoclimatic implications. Further discussions consider the data in the frequency domain, first by briefly summarizing the major relationships between insolation, global ice volume and the total dust MAR in the Arabian Sea. We then proceed to examine the relation-

ships, in frequency and phase, between the record of global ice volume and the records of individual minerals and mineral assemblages.

Methods

The sediments analyzed in this study were recovered at ODP Hole 722B, which was drilled on the Owen Ridge at 16°37′N, 59°48′E, at a water depth of 2027 m, during ODP Leg 117 (Fig. 1). Samples were analyzed from the upper

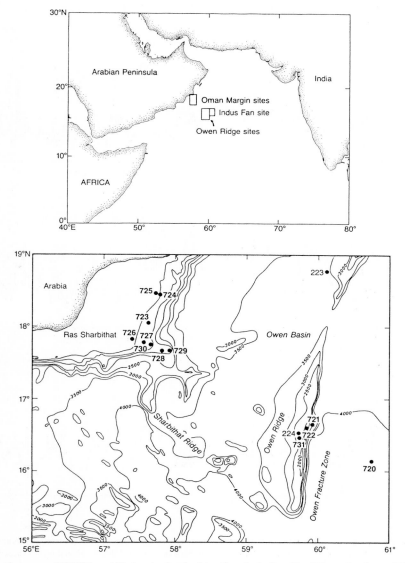

Fig. 1. Location map of ODP Leg 117 sites in the Arabian Sea, including Site 722 on the Owen Ridge (From Prell, Niitsuma *et al.* 1989).

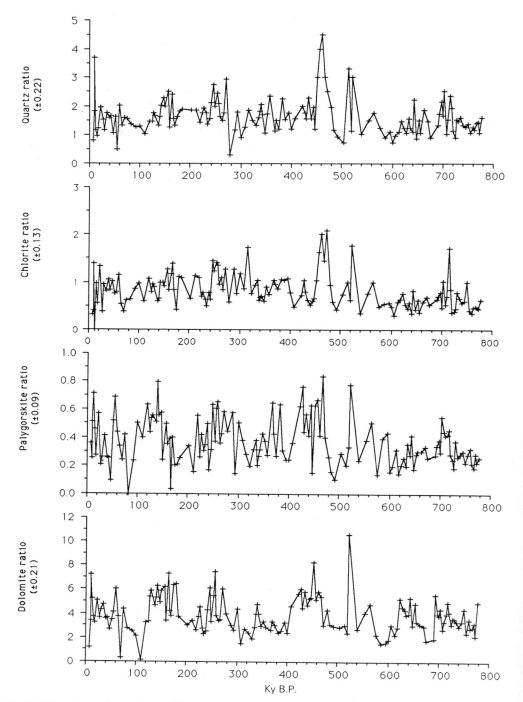

Fig. 2. Mineral abundances (mineral/boehmite peak area ratios) at ODP Site 722, plotted as a function of age. Value given in parenthesis along mineral ratio axis is standard deviation of the peak area ratio (absolute value), based on replicate analyses.

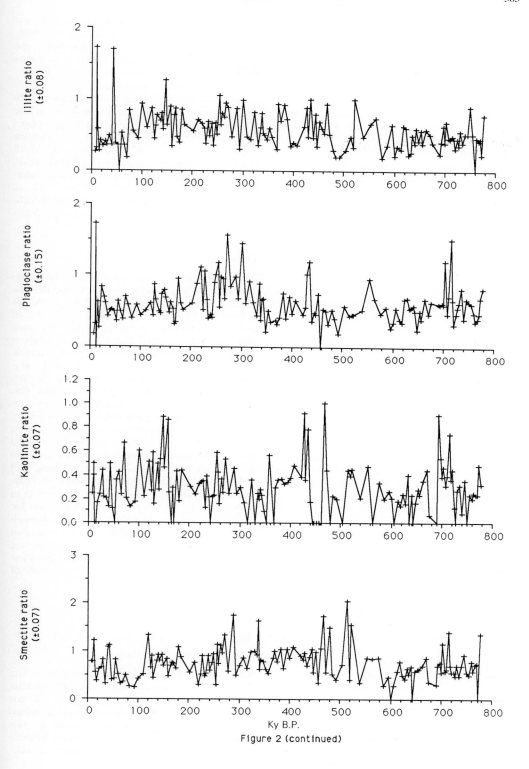

Figure 2 (continued)

40 m of sediment, which are contained within lithological Unit I (Shipboard Scientific Party 1989). Lithological Unit I is composed of alternating light and dark beds of foraminifer-bearing nannofossil ooze, nannofossil ooze/chalk, and marly nannofossil ooze/chalk. Sampling interval for the study was 20 cm, which is equivalent to a 4.3 ky sampling interval at an average sedimentation rate of 4.5 cm/ky (Clemens & Prell 1991).

Dust grain size and dust MARs were determined following the techniques of Clemens & Prell (1990). Mineral abundances were determined by X-ray diffraction analysis of pressed powder mounts (random grain orientation) of the terrigenous fraction after removing carbonate with buffered acetic acid, organic matter with sodium hypochlorite, and opal with sodium carbonate. An internal standard (10% boehmite by weight) was added to each pressed powder, and X-ray diffraction analyses were performed as described by Krissek & Clemens (1991). Mineral abundances are expressed as the ratio of the area of a mineral diffraction peak (e.g. quartz) to the area of the boehmite (020) peak. The diffraction peaks used here are the smectite (001), palygorskite (110), illite (001), quartz (100), plagioclase (201), kaolinite (002), chlorite (004), and dolomite (104) peaks. Because the peak area ratios have not been converted to absolute abundances, only downcore variations in the abundances of individual minerals can be evaluated; absolute abundances of two or more minerals cannot be compared. Relative abundances of multiple minerals are also difficult to estimate realistically, since using pressed powder (random orientation) mounts and analyzing the entire fine terrigenous fraction violates the basic assumptions of the most widely used semiquantitative techniques (e.g. Biscaye 1965).

The peak area ratio data were examined for variable-to-variable relationships by R-mode factor analysis, using the procedure of the StatView 512+ software package (Brainpower Inc. 1986). The final results were obtained by an Orthotran (oblique) refinement of a Varimax solution. The Varimax solution is an adjustment of the initial factor analysis results, so that each variable is either very important or unimportant in defining a factor (Davis 1986). This type of solution simplifies interpreting the geological significance of each factor in terms of the original variables. The Orthotran refinement is also used to define more geologically interpretable factors by allowing the factors to intercorrelate slightly; all factor intercorrelations following the Orthotran refinement were less than 0.45. The

terminology employed here is that of StatView (Brainpower, Inc., 1986) and Davis (1986), which labels the coefficients that indicate the importance of each variable within a factor as 'loadings' and the coefficients of factor importance to each sample as 'scores'.

Ages for these samples were obtained from the age model constructed for 0 to 780 ka at Site 722 by Clemens & Prell (1991). This age model is based on correlation of the oxygen isotope record from Hole 722B to the SPECMAP stacked oxygen isotope record of Imbrie et al. (1984). Records were interpolated at 4 ky intervals for the cross-spectral analyses, and all analyses were conducted using standard techniques (Imbrie et al. 1989; Jenkins & Watts 1968).

Data

Mineral/boehmite peak area ratios, dust concentration (%), dust grain sizes (median diameter, microns), and dust MAR are plotted as a function of age in Figs 2 & 3. Each record exhibits significant variability over the past 800 ka, but none of the records exhibits a consistent long-term trend over that interval. Variance of the quartz, chlorite, and palygorskite records exhibits a small step-like decrease at approximately 520 ka. Despite this change, the palygorskite record contains consistent cycles of variation approximately 100 ky in duration; similar patterns are also evident in the dolomite record, the dust abundances and the dust MARs. Because palygorskite tends to form small fibrous grains (<30 μm long and <5 μm wide), the apparent increase in palygorskite abundance in sediments younger than approximately 520 ka may partially account for the decrease in median dust grain size through the same interval. The difference in timing of the palygorskite increase and the grain size decrease, however, indicates that the decrease in median grain size is not solely a result of increased palygorskite abundance.

Discussion

Mineral assemblages and their palaeoclimatic implications

The clay and silt-sized terrigenous dust at Site 722 is composed of smectite, illite, palygorskite, kaolinite, chlorite, quartz, plagioclase feldspar and dolomite, all of which have been identified as important terrigenous constituents in previous studies of Holocene and modern Arabian Sea sediments. Associations of these minerals,

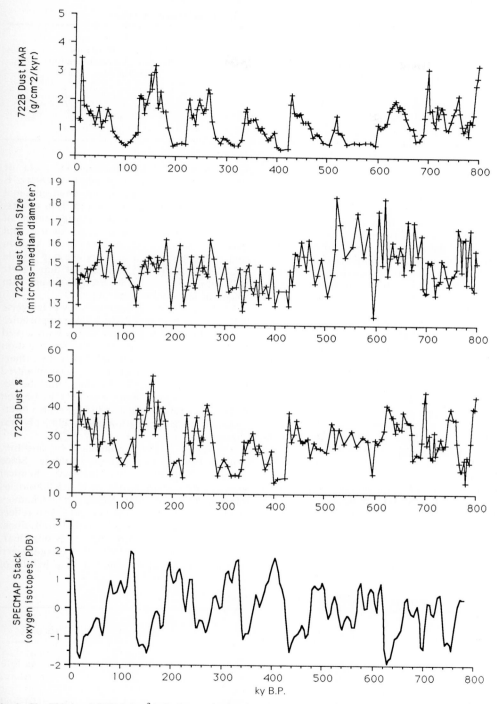

Fig. 3. Site 722 dust MAR (g/cm² ky), dust grain size (median diameter μm), dust concentration (%) and the SPECMAP stacked oxygen isotope record (Imbrie *et al.* 1984). Note the strong inverse correlation between the dust MAR and the SPECMAP stack and the absence of correlation between the dust grain size record and the SPECMAP stack.

Table 1. Variance distribution in R-mode factor analysis of 722B mineralogical data.

Factor	Proportion of original variance (%)	Proportion of variance: Orthotran/Varimax solution (normalized to 100%)
1	42%	38%
2	13%	23%
3	11%	17%
4	09%	22%

which may carry clearer palaeoclimatic or palaeoenvironmental signals than abundances of individual minerals, have been identified by performing an R-mode factor analysis of the mineral abundance data. Four factors are required to account for approximately 75% of the original data variance. The contributions of the four factors to explaining the original variance, and their proportionate contributions following the Orthotran/Varimax solution, are listed in Table 1. Loadings of each variable on each of the four factors are listed in Table 2.

The mineral assemblages identified by this factor analysis of the mineral record to 800 ka are essentially the same as those identified for the record to 500 ka (Krissek & Clemens 1991). The similarity of these two analyses indicates that the mineralogical signal from 500 to 800 ka is not significantly different from that between 0 and 500 ka. The palaeoenvironmental/provenance interpretations of these assemblages closely follow those of Krissek & Clemens (1991) and are summarized as follows.

(1) Factor 1 (F1) is an association of chlorite, quartz, and, to a lesser extent, dolomite. Because chlorite is only stable under conditions of very minimal chemical weathering (Dixon & Weed 1989; Velde 1985; Chamley 1989), its importance in Factor 1 suggests that this assemblage formed in, or was recycled from, relatively arid source regions. This interpretation is supported by the importance of dolomite, which

is recycled from older sedimentary rocks or produced by desiccation of sabkhas. Quartz is not particularly useful as an environmental indicator, since it can be derived from quartz-bearing source rocks under a wide range of conditions. The importance of quartz and dolomite as terrigenous components in Arabian Sea sediments was also demonstrated by de Menocal et al. (1991), who found that quartz and dolomite abundances strongly covary with magnetic susceptibility at Site 722.

(2) Factor 2 (F2) is dominated by plagioclase feldspar and kaolinite, with a lower importance of illite. Plagioclase feldspars are best preserved under conditions of limited precipitation (Chamley 1989) and minimal chemical weathering where formation of illite is also favoured (Dixon & Weed 1989); kaolinite may be recycled from older, more intensely weathered rocks. As a result, this assemblage is also interpreted to reflect formation under relatively arid conditions.

(3) Factor 3 (F3) is dominated by smectite, with a lower importance of kaolinite. Since smectite is produced by moderate chemical weathering of a wide variety of source lithologies (Dixon & Weed 1989; Velde 1985; Chamley 1989), this assemblage is interpreted to reflect formation under relatively humid conditions. The source area of this smectite is not clear, however; Kolla et al. (1976, 1981) emphasized the importance of the Deccan Trap basalts of

Table 2. Factor loadings for Hole 722B mineralogical data.

Variable	Factor Loadings			
	Factor 1	Factor 2	Factor 3	Factor 4
Smectite	0.27	0.01	0.88	−0.05
Palygorskite	−0.01	0.07	0.01	0.89
Illite	0.28	0.40	0.14	0.30
Quartz	0.81	−0.01	0.17	0.10
Plagioclase	0.24	0.80	−0.19	−0.06
Kaolinite	−0.27	0.75	0.38	0.13
Chlorite	0.82	0.08	0.12	0.00
Dolomite	0.48	−0.04	−0.11	0.58

the Indian subcontinent as a smectite source, whereas Sirocko & Lange (1991) also identified smectite supply from the west or northwest via winds. Despite the tendency for smectite to form under more humid conditions, we find little evidence linking this factor to periods of humid environmental conditions on orbital timescales.

(4) Factor 4 (F4) is dominated by palygorskite and, to a lesser extent, dolomite. The abundance of palygorskite throughout the Neogene section at Site 722 (Debrabant *et al*. 1991) and in surface sediments across the Arabian Sea (Kolla *et al*. 1976, 1981; Sirocko & Sarnthein 1989; Sirocko & Lange 1991) indicates that palygorskite is a detrital component, not an authigenic phase. In continental settings, palygorskite is formed in alkaline lakes and calcrete/caliche profiles, and is present in a wide variety of carbonate and evaporite deposits. Because palygorskite is extremely susceptible to decomposition by subsequent chemical weathering, (Dixon & Weed 1989; Velde 1985; Chamley 1989), its importance in this assemblage indicates derivation from an arid source region.

Time series of scores (Fig. 4) for each factor (mineral assemblage) are dominated by variability on time scales of 10 to 100 ky, with no evidence of significant long-term trends and limited evidence of major step-like discontinuities. The only observable change is in the palygorskite/dolomite assemblage (F4), where variance decreases in sediments older than approximately 520 ka. Despite this step-like decrease, shorter-term variability is most obvious in the scores on the palygorskite/dolomite assemblage (F4), where cycles of approximately 100 ky duration are overlain by fluctuations of even shorter duration. The presence of this cyclicity in the scores for the palygorskite/dolomite assemblage (F4) is expected, since the abundance records of palygorskite and dolomite both exhibited cyclicity at approximately 100 ky (Fig. 2).

Analysis in the frequency domain

Background. Krissek & Clemens (1991) demonstrated that the mineral assemblages are seemingly not well correlated to the marine oxygen isotope record when compared visually in the time domain, but that statistically significant relationships are observed when the records are compared in the frequency domain. Such apparent discrepancy may arise because each factor record is a complex mix of signals. The various signals, in turn, may develop for a variety of reasons: (1) weathering assemblages

do not respond instantaneously to climate changes; (2) weathering reactions and assemblages may respond in a nonlinear fashion to climate change; (3) pre-existing weathering assemblages may be recycled from older rocks and mixed with the assemblage formed under extant climate, and (4) weathering assemblages do not respond solely to climate (e.g. bedrock, relief, drainage effects).

Each factor record is influenced by these potentially complex relationships in amplitude and phase, each of which varies independently over each orbital band. As a result, frequency domain analysis of the mineral abundance and factor score records has aided interpretation of this complex record by identifying similar distributions of variance within the oxygen isotope, dust MAR, dust grain size, mineral abundance, and factor score records (Krissek & Clemens 1991). The total dust MAR at Site 722 has been shown to vary at orbital frequencies that are synchronous with glacial–interglacial cyclicity as defined by the marine oxygen isotope record (Clemens & Prell 1991), with increased dust MAR during times of increased aridity (increased global ice volume). We spectrally analyzed the mineral abundance and the factor score records over the past 800 ka to determine: (1) which individual minerals and/or mineral assemblages contribute to the increase in total dust MAR during glacials and (2) the timing of increased input for each mineral and mineral assemblage over glacial/interglacial cycles.

Insolation/global ice volume and global ice volume/Arabian Sea dust MAR relationships. Comparisons in this study employ a standard time series of orbital insolation variations known as ETP (Imbrie *et al*. 1984), which is a normalized summation of changes in the eccentricity (e), obliquity (tilt; t), and negative precession ($-P$) of the Earth's orbit. The signs for obliquity and precession are chosen to give maximum summer insolation in the Northern Hemisphere. We also employ a standard marine oxygen isotope record; the SPECMAP stacked oxygen isotope record of Imbrie *et al*. (1984), which effectively represents changes in past global ice volume (Fig. 4). Cross-spectral comparison of these two records illustrates that the records are strongly coherent, with significant phase differences over the obliquity and precessional frequencies and a near-zero phase difference over the eccentricity band (Imbrie *et al*. 1984; Fig. 5). Given these strong, consistent relationships, the comparison of a given climate record to either of these two standards can be used to characterize the phase response of that

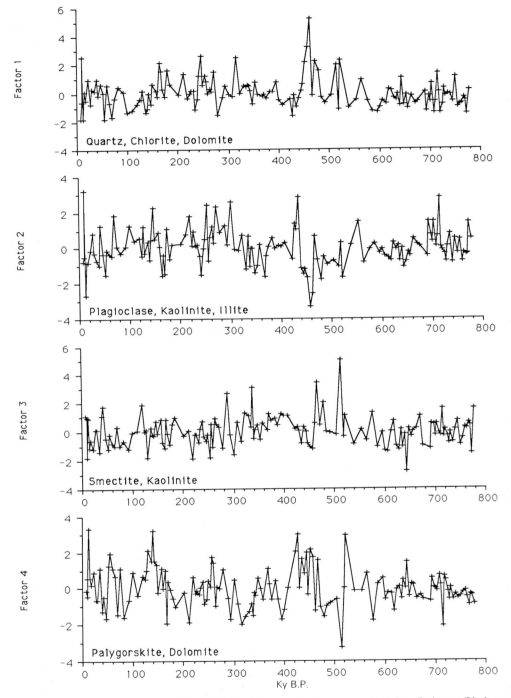

Fig. 4. Scores for the four factors at Site 722 defined by R-mode factor analysis and an Orthotran/Varimax solution refinement. Loadings of each variable on each factor are listed in Table 2. Factors 1, 2 and 4 are interpreted as indicators of arid source conditions, whereas Factor 3 is interpreted as an indicator of more humid weathering.

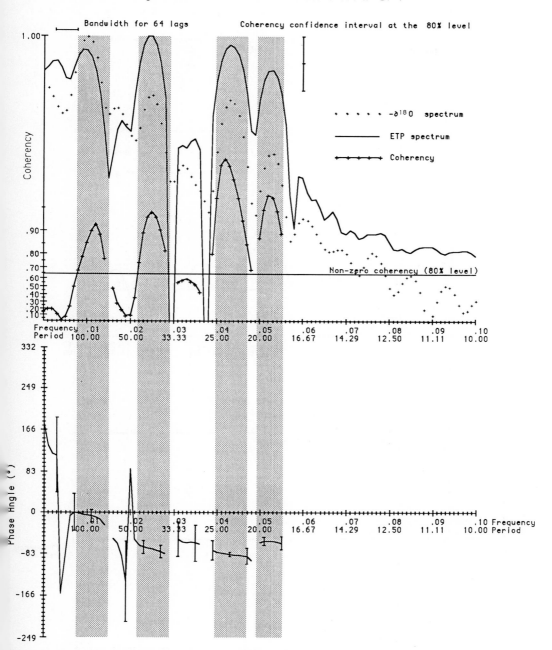

Fig. 5. Normalized variance spectrum of the SPECMAP stacked oxygen isotope record (crosses) and the insolation record (ETP as a solid line; Imbrie *et al.* 1984) for the interval 0 to 774 ka. The variance spectrum is plotted on an arbitrary log scale and the coherency spectrum is plotted on a hyperbolic arctangent scale. Frequencies are in cycles/ky. Sampling interval is interpolated to 4 ky. Frequency bands characterized by strong cross correlation between the two records are highlighted by shaded bars. The SPECMAP stack is multiplied by minus one such that large values correspond to minimum ice volume. As a result, negative phase values indicate that minimum ice volume lags maximum eccentricity, obliquity and precession.

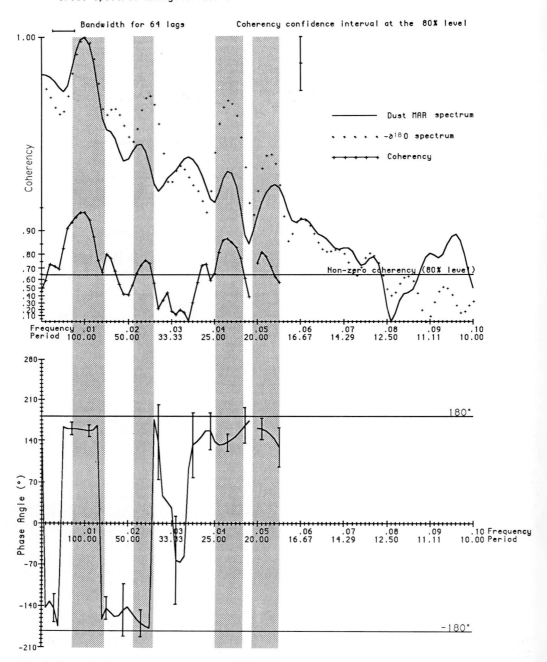

Fig. 6. Normalized variance spectrum of the SPECMAP stacked oxygen isotope record (crosses) and the Site 722 dust MAR (Clemens & Prell 1991), for the interval 6 to 774 ka. Presentation as in Fig. 5. Phase values near ±180° indicate that maxima in dust MAR occur near glacial maxima.

record with respect to changes in insolation and global ice volume (and the accompanying changes in global climate). Previous studies (e.g. Berger 1978) have demonstrated that the obliquity (41 ky) cycles are the dominant control on high-latitude insolation patterns, the precessional (23 ky) cycles have a major effect on low-latitude insolation patterns and the eccentricity (100 ky) cycles have negligible effect on incoming insolation. Despite the negligible effect of eccentricity on incoming insolation, the largest fluctuations in the ice volume record occur at 100 ka cycles; the physical processes responsible for producing the 100 ka cycles in the ice-volume record remain unknown. As we describe below, dust flux to the Arabian Sea is driven, in part, by climatic and environmental changes that accompany these cyclical ice-volume changes.

The response of Arabian Sea dust flux to changes in insolation patterns and changes in global climate during major fluctuations in ice volume can be evaluated by comparing the records in either the time domain or the frequency domain. Visual comparison of the dust MAR and oxygen isotope records (Figs 3 & 4) reveals a strong inverse correlation, with high dust input during glacial intervals (intervals with low $\delta^{18}O$ values; Clemens & Prell 1990, 1991). The same relationship is displayed in the frequency domain by cross-spectral comparison (Fig. 6). Similar coherence and phase relationships were documented for a shorter Arabian Sea record by Clemens & Prell (1990) who invoked increased aridity, decreased vegetation cover and increased surface deflation during times of increased global ice volume to explain the increase in dust MAR. Supporting evidence for decreased vegetation cover, which results in increased dust MAR during times of increased aridity (including glacial periods), has been provided from loess sequences in central China (Kukla et al. 1989), lake levels in Africa (Street-Perrot & Harrison 1985), and modern dust flux over the Atlantic during periods of drought in Africa (Prospero & Nees 1986).

Relationships between ice volume, Arabian Sea dust MAR, and mineral dust components. The preceding comparisons have demonstrated that dust flux to the Arabian Sea increases during times of increased global ice volume, which is taken to indicate the effects of climate change on source area aridity during glacial episodes. The next step, then, is to examine the response of the individual minerals and mineral assemblages (factors) to aridity forcing over glacial/interglacial cycles. Instead of presenting these

comparisons in a large number of cross-spectral plots, the statistically significant (coherent) spectral associations are summarized on phase wheels (Imbrie et al. 1989; Clemens & Prell 1990) as phase differences with respect to the SPECMAP stack over each of the fundamental orbital frequencies (100 ky, 41 ky, and 23 ky; Fig. 7). Only the relationships that are significantly coherent above the 80% confidence interval (CI) are presented on the phase wheel plots. For convenience, the zero phase on the respective wheels is set at maximum eccentricity, obliquity and precession (referenced to June 21 perihelion), thereby relating zero phase to maximum insolation due to obliquity and precession. Vectors are then used to represent the timing of maximum and minimum ice volumes, maximum dust MAR and maximum mineral abundances through an orbital cycle, with angular values from zero representing the phase differences (as referenced to the timing of minimum ice volume in the SPECMAP stack). Parameters with positive phase differences are considered to 'lag' minimum ice volume within a cycle, whereas parameters with negative phase differences are considered to 'lead' minimum ice volume within a cycle.

A phase wheel for each orbital frequency is shown in Fig. 7, and the phase angles, coherency values and spectral density contributions for statistically significant, well resolved spectral peaks are listed in Tables 3 & 4. At the 100 ky band, the palygorskite/dolomite/illite assemblage (F4) and its major mineral components are all coherent with the ice volume record. In addition, the palygorskite/dolomite/illite assemblage (F4) and each of its major mineral components plot within the glacial hemicycle, near the time of maximum ice volume and dust MAR. Although quartz is not an important component in Factor 4, its maximum input within the 100 ky band also lies within the glacial hemicycle.

At the obliquity (41 ky) band, the plagioclase/kaolinite/illite assemblage (F2) and its two most important mineral components (plagioclase and kaolinite) are coherent with the ice volume record. These vectors plot within the glacial hemicycle, near maximum ice volume and maximum dust MAR. In contrast, illite is not coherent with the ice volume record at the 41 ky band, although illite is coherent with the ice volume record at approximately the 38 ky band with a large phase angle. Causes for the difference in behavior of illite and plagioclase/kaolinite are unknown, but may reflect the response of illite-forming processes to climatic changes at both the 41 ky and 23 ky bands.

a

Maximum eccentricity (100 kyr)

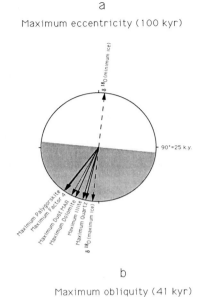

c

−Precession (23 kyr)
(June 21 perihelion)

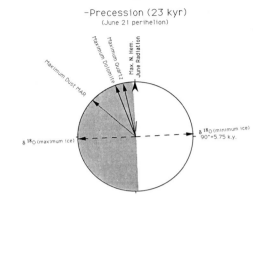

b

Maximum obliquity (41 kyr)

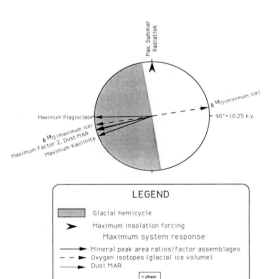

Fig. 7. Phase wheel summaries of insolation, global ice volume, dust MAR and dust mineral abundances at Site 722. Each wheel illustrates statistically significant cross-coherence and associated phase relationships over a specific orbital band (referenced to the SPECMAP stack). Maximum insolation forcing over the obliquity and precession bands occurs at the top of the respective phase wheels. Phase differences between the maxima in a given record are plotted as vectors whose angular positions are measured clockwise (+, lagging) or counter clockwise (−, leading) from a given reference (insolation or ice volume). For example, over the obliquity cycle, maximum kaolinite input to the Arabian Sea occurs at $-12°$ (~1.4 ky; $12°/360° \times 41$ ky) before (leads) maximum ice volume. Within the error of the phase estimate, maximum kaolinite input occurs synchronously with maximum global ice volume, dust MAR and Factor 2. The shaded area indicates the glacial hemicycle in each case. Maxima in the total dust MAR, mineral component abundances and factor assemblages all occur within the glacial hemicycles, reflecting the effect of glacially induced aridity on dust supply and the formation of minerals and mineral assemblages. See Table 3 for tabulated phase values.

At the precessional (23 ky) band, quartz and dolomite abundances are coherent with the ice volume record; these minerals are two of the major components in the chlorite/quartz/dolomite assemblage (F1). However, the lack of coherency between chlorite and the ice volume record at all bands prevents the chlorite/quartz/dolomite assemblage (F1) itself from being coherent with the ice volume record over

the 23 ky band. In contrast, Krissek & Clemens (1991) demonstrated coherency at the 23 ky band between total dust MAR and a chlorite/quartz/dolomite assemblage and deMenocal et al. (1991) identified a strong and coherent precessional signal in a 3.2 My magnetic susceptibility record dominated by quartz and dolomite. The loss of such coherency in the record examined here is interpreted to result from the

Table 3. Phase table of all coherent parameters.

Parameter	Minimum Ice Volume ($-\delta^{18}O$) with respect to ETP ($coh^2 > 0.41297$ @ 80% CI; + = lag)		
	100 k	41 k	23 k
722B $-$ $\delta^{18}O$	006° ± 18	081° ± 17	088° ± 7
SPECMAP	006° ± 15	072° ± 9	084° ± 4
	Lithogenic parameters with respect to SPECMAP stack (Maximum Ice volume) (Hole 722B; $coh^2 > 0.41297$ @ 80% CI; + = lag)		
Eolian MAR	022° ± 9	−006° ± 21	044° ± 14
Factor 1	—	—	—
Factor 2	—	−005° ± 17	—
Factor 3	—	—	—
Factor 4	030° ± 11	—	—
Quartz	007° ± 17	—	080° ± 28
Chlorite	—	—	—
Plagioclase	—	008° ± 19	—
Illite	010° ± 27	—	—
Kaolinite	—	−012° ± 22	—
Smectite	—	—	—
Palygorskite	031° ± 24	—	—
Dolomite	017° ± 12	—	072° ± 26

decreased variances in chlorite abundance and chlorite/quartz/dolomite assemblage importance between 500 and 800 ka. The quartz and dolomite vectors still plot within the glacial hemicycle, but not near the time of maximum ice volume, as were the cases for minerals and mineral assemblages in the 100 ky and 41 ky (obliquity) bands.

In summary, the three phase wheels (Fig. 7) and the spectral density values (Table 4) illustrate relatively consistent relationships between the global ice volume signal and a portion of the supply of two 'arid' mineral assemblages (plagioclase/kaolinite/illite and palygorskite/dolomite/illite) and six minerals over at least one of the primary orbital insolation bands for each mineral/mineral assemblage. The consistency of these relationships is demonstrated by the similarity of relative variance distributions between the SPECMAP stack and all of the terrigenous indicators (Table 4), with relative variance values ranging from 28% to 50% in the 100 ky band, from 5% to 18% in the 41 ky band, and from 3% to 9% in the 23 ky band. For each coherent relationship, maximum input of the mineral or mineral assemblage occurs during the respective glacial hemicycle. The maximum dust MAR is also located in the glacial hemicycle of each frequency, indicating that the record of total dust MAR, a portion of the record of dust input expressed as 'arid' mineral assemblages, and a portion of the record of dust input expressed as individual minerals respond consistently to global climatic changes

associated with changes in global ice volume. This response is strongest in the 100 ky and 41 ky (obliquity) bands (Fig. 7), where the maximum inputs cluster most closely to the time of maximum ice volume and maximum dust MAR. The response in the 23 ky (precessional) band also falls within the glacial hemicycle, but lags significantly behind the time of maximum ice volume and dust MAR. Reasons for the less constrained response over the precessional cycle are not known, but the larger phase difference may indicate that the time required to produce a weathering assemblage is relatively long compared to a precessional hemicycle.

Table 4. Percent of total spectral density (summed over a bandwidth of 64 lags).

Parameter	Frequency Band		
	100 k	41 k	23 k
SPECMAP	50	12	09
Eolian MAR	48	05	03
Factor 1 (F1)	—	—	05
Factor 2 (F2)	—	12	—
Factor 3 (F3)	—	—	—
Factor 4 (F4)	31	—	—
Quartz (F1)	—	—	07
Chlorite (F1)	—	—	03
Plagioclase (F2)	—	07	—
Illite (F2)	—	12	—
Kaolinite (F2)	—	18	—
Smectite (F3)	—	—	—
Palygorskite (F4)	28	—	—
Dolomite (F4)	37	—	—

Krissek & Clemens (1991) have discussed possible explanations for the coherence between total dust MAR and mineral assemblages over orbital frequencies. In general, those explanations invoke either differences in the susceptibilities of minerals to varying timescales of weathering or preferential development of suitable continental source environments by climatic changes associated with ice volume variations at the various orbital frequencies. Although the relationships observed here do not further constrain those hypotheses, the same physical explanations are still applicable. For example, the maximum inputs of quartz, illite, dolomite and palygorskite are more closely linked to variations in the 100 ky band than to the 41 ky (obliquity) band, suggesting that continental environments/climates appropriate for the formation/deflation of these minerals developed preferentially in response to global climatic changes during the 100 ky ice volume fluctuations. Such climatic/environmental changes might include aridity effects on weathering rates, effects of sea-level changes on exposure of source areas such as the Persian Gulf region (Sirocko & Lange 1991), or other effects. Within the group of minerals that respond to variations at the 100 ky band, however, the phase of maximum input relative to maximum ice volume (and, presumably, maximum aridity) may reflect the effects of weathering/formation kinetics. The maximum inputs of quartz, illite and dolomite occur soon after the time of maximum aridity, whereas the maximum palygorskite input lags further behind. Quartz, illite and dolomite are produced with little or no chemical weathering, so they may be mobilized rapidly as regional aridity increased and vegetation cover decreased (i.e. deflation potential increased). In contrast, palygorskite may have been formed under relatively arid conditions early in a glacial hemicycle and then have been mobilized later in the same cycle. This sequence would account for the greater lag of palygorskite within the 100 ky cycle. While this scenario may be tenable, we point out that, within the error of our phase estimates (Table 3), we cannot readily resolve the exact lead/lag relationships.

Kaolinite and plagioclase inputs respond strongly to climate variations at the 41 ky (obliquity) band, whereas quartz and dolomite inputs respond strongly at the 23 ky (precessional) band. Within the obliquity band the separation of input maxima for kaolinite and plagioclase may also reflect differences in formation history. Maximum kaolinite supply occurs within the glacial hemicycle of the obliquity band (Fig. 7), but leads maximum ice volume.

Since kaolinite is formed under warm, humid conditions (Dixon & Weed 1989, Chamley 1989), this material was probably produced during the preceding humid interglacial, if not earlier (which might include kaolinite inherited from the parent material). With the onset of more arid conditions and the loss of vegetation, the kaolinite-bearing surficial cover was eroded and transported to the Arabian Sea early in the glacial hemicycle. The kaolinitic cover was depleted as deflation continued, so that less heavily weathered and therefore more feldspar-rich, material was supplied later in the glacial hemicycle. As a result, a compositional inversion is produced in the Arabian Sea sediments during the obliquity cycle by the preferential supply of successively less-weathered material.

The strong response of quartz and dolomite input at the 23 ky (precessional) band is consistent with the observations of deMenocal et al. (1991), who identified the importance of a 23–19 ky periodicity, coherent with precessional indices, throughout a 3.2 My record of magnetic susceptibility from the Owen Ridge. In that record, semiquantitative quartz and dolomite abundances and the total terrigenous content covaried strongly with the susceptibility values, indicating that the susceptibility record was a good proxy of terrigenous fraction (dust) variations. The magnetic susceptibility record of deMenocal et al. (1991) also exhibited strong periodicity at the 41 ky band, coherent with obliquity indices, over the past 2.4 My. Equivalent variations have not been observed in the mineral abundances and mineral assemblage data presented here, however. The differences in the results of this study and those of deMenocal et al. (1991) may have several causes, including: (1) differences in the mineral abundance data, resulting from the difference between the semiquantitative analytical technique of deMenocal et al. (1991) and the internal standard technique used in this study; (2) the fact that deMenocal et al. (1991) performed spectral analysis only on the magnetic susceptibility record, which is not perfectly correlated with their estimates of dolomite and quartz abundances, whereas this study examined each component individually. Despite these differences in the details of results, both deMenocal et al. (1991) and this study recognize the major effect that changes in source area aridity have on dust supply to the Arabian Sea in response to changes in global ice volume.

Finally, we note that the smectite factor (F3) shows no significant coherence at any of the orbital frequencies. This suggests that, while smectite is produced under relatively humid conditions, the formation and transport of smectite in this region are not closely linked to environmental changes over orbital timescales. As a result, the supply of smectite from India (Kolla *et al.* 1976, 1981) and/or the Arabian Peninsula (Sirocko & Lange 1991) may be relatively constant through time.

Relationships between the upwelling (oceanic) system and the dust (continental) system. Clemens & Prell (1990, 1991) have interpreted the dust MAR record in the Arabian Sea as an indicator of continental source area aridity and the dust grain size record as an indicator of monsoon wind strength. Since the monsoon winds are also the physical forcing mechanism for coastal upwelling and the associated biological productivity, dust grain size might be expected to covary with indices of the oceanic upwelling system. At the same time, moisture transfer from the ocean to the continents is generally expected to increase with the monsoon wind strength, so that some common responses might be expected in the monsoon-induced upwelling system and the continental aridity system. The available records from the Arabian Sea, however, do not indicate such linkages; the dust MAR and some of its components (minerals and mineral assemblages) respond to increased continental aridity over each orbital insolation band, whereas wind strength/upwelling indicators (dust grain size, foraminiferal faunal indicators and opal MARs) show little response at the 100 ky band and have maxima within the interglacial (humid) hemicycles of the obliquity and precession bands (Prell 1984*a*; Clemens & Prell 1990; Murray & Prell 1991). These differences indicate that the continental (dust) and the marine (upwelling) systems respond differently to the combined effects of changes in monsoon strength and precipitation. The explanation for this decoupling may lie in the fact that the moisture delivered by the monsoon is precipitated predominantly over the Indian subcontinent, whereas the Arabian Peninsula, East Africa and Iran/Makran are the major suppliers of terrigenous dust to the Arabian Sea. For whatever reasons, the supply of dust is more sensitive to conditions of source area aridity than to transport competence due to monsoon intensification.

Summary

Terrigenous eolian sediments deposited on the Owen Ridge during the past 800 ky are composed of smectite, illite, palygorskite, kaolinite, chlorite, quartz, plagioclase feldspar and dolomite. This mineralogy is consistent with the composition of sediment presently found in the Arabian Sea, which is a mixture of material supplied from East Africa, the Arabian Peninsula, Iran/Makran and the Indian subcontinent. An R-mode factor analysis of the mineral abundances has identified four mineral assemblages present throughout the record at Site 722: a chlorite/quartz/dolomite assemblage (F1), a plagioclase/kaolinite/illite assemblage (F2), a smectite/kaolinite assemblage (F3) and a palygorskite/dolomite/illite assemblage (F4). On the basis of their mineral compositions, the chlorite/quartz/dolomite, plagioclase/kaolinite/illite and palygorskite/dolomite/illite assemblages are interpreted to reflect arid continental source conditions, whereas the smectite/kaolinite assemblage is interpreted to record relatively humid source conditions. These results are consistent with those determined for the dust record from 0 to 500 ka by Krissek & Clemens (1991).

Previous work has demonstrated that global ice volume responds, in part, to changes in solar insolation and that total dust MAR in the Arabian Sea increases during times of increased global ice volume, increased continental aridity and decreased vegetation cover. Abundances of the palygorskite/dolomite/illite assemblage, illite, palygorskite, dolomite and quartz vary coherently with global ice volume over the 100 ky band, with maximum input during the glacial hemicycle. Maximum palygorskite abundance lags behind maxima of the other mineral components, perhaps reflecting the time required to produce palygorskite within the glacial hemicycle. At the 41 ky (obliquity) band, the plagioclase/kaolinite/illite assemblage, plagioclase and kaolinite are coherent with the ice volume record, with abundance maxima during the glacial hemicycle. Maximum kaolinite abundance leads the plagioclase maximum, perhaps recording the initial removal of material that was heavily weathered during the preceding humid interglacial, followed by exposure and removal of relatively unweathered plagioclase. Quartz and dolomite are coherent with the ice volume record in the 23 ky (precessional) band, with abundance maxima occurring in the glacial hemicycle. The abundance maxima in the precessional band do not cluster with maximum ice volume or maximum dust MAR, perhaps reflecting the large portion of a precessional glacial hemicycle required to generate an assemblage of weathering products.

The total dust MAR and most of its mineral components (six individual minerals and two mineral assemblages) respond to increased continental aridity in at least one of the three orbital insolation bands, whereas wind strength/upwelling indicators show little response at the 100 ky band and have maxima within the interglacial hemicycles of the obliquity and precession bands. These differences indicate that the continental (dust MAR) and marine (upwelling) systems respond to insolation forcing and global ice volume boundary conditions in very different ways, perhaps because the supply of dust from inland source areas of Arabia, East Africa, and Iran/Makran is more sensitive to continental aridity than transport competence.

We wish to thank the officers and crew of the drilling vessel SEDCO BP 471 and the ODP technical staff for their efforts during Leg 117. T. C. Horner assisted with sample preparation. This research was supported by Joint Oceanographic Institutions subgrants to L. Krissek, S. Clemens and W. Prell.

References

ANDERSON, D. M. 1991. *Foraminifer Evidence of Monsoon Upwelling off Oman During the Late Quaternary*. PhD Dissertation, Providence RI (Brown University).

—— & PRELL, W. L. 1991. Coastal upwelling gradient during the late Pleistocene. *In*: PRELL, W. L., NIITSUMA, N. *et al. Proceedings of the Ocean Drilling Program, Scientific Results*, Ocean Drilling Program, College Station, TX, **117**, 265–276.

BERGER, A. L. 1978. Long-term variations in caloric insolation resulting from the Earth's orbital elements. *Quaternary Research*, **9**, 139–167.

BISCAYE, P. E. 1965. Mineralogy and sedimentation of recent deep sea clay in the Atlantic Ocean and adjacent seas and oceans. *Geological Society of America Bulletin*, **76**, 803–832.

BLOEMENDAL, J. & DEMENOCAL, P. 1989. Evidence for a change in the periodicity of tropical climate cycles at 2.4 Myr from whole-core magnetic susceptibility measurements. *Nature*, **342**, 897–900.

BRAINPOWER, Inc., 1986. *Statview 512+*. Calabasas, CA (Brainpower, Inc.).

CHAMLEY, H. 1989. *Clay Sedimentology*. Springer, New York.

CHESTER, R., SHARPLES, E. J. & SANDERS, G. S. 1985. The concentration of particulate aluminum and clay minerals in aerosols from the northern Arabian Sea. *Journal of Sedimentary Petrology*, **55**, 37–41.

CLEMENS, S. C. & PRELL, W. L. 1990. Late Pleistocene variability of Arabian Sea summer monsoon winds and continental aridity: Eolian records from the lithogenic component of deep-sea sediments. *Paleoceanography*, **5**, 109–145.

—— & PRELL, W. L. 1991. One million year record of summer monsoon winds and continental aridity from the Owen Ridge (Site 722), northwest Arabian Sea. *In*: PRELL, W. L., NIITSUMA, N. *et al. Proceedings of the Ocean Drilling Program, Scientific Results,*, Ocean Drilling Program, College Station, TX, **117**, 365–388.

COHMAP Members, 1988. Climatic changes of the last 18000 years: Observations and model simulations. *Science*, **241**, 1043–1052.

DAVIS, J. C. 1986. *Statistics and Data Analysis in Geology*: Wiley, New York.

DEBRABANT, P., KRISSEK, L., BOQUILLON, A. & CHAMLEY, H. 1991. Clay mineralogy of Neogene sediments of the western Arabian Sea: Mineral abundances and paleoenvironmental implications. *In*: PRELL, W. L., NIITSUMA, N. *et al. Proceedings of the Ocean Drilling Program, Scientific Results*, Ocean Drilling Program, College Station, TX, **117**, 183–196.

DEMENOCAL, P., BLOEMENDAL, J. & KING, J. 1991. A rock-magnetic record of monsoonal dust deposition to the Arabian Sea: evidence for a shift in the mode of deposition at 2.4 Ma. *In*: PRELL, W. L., NIITSUMA, N. *et al. Proceedings of the Ocean Drilling Program, Scientific Results*, Ocean Drilling Program, College Station, TX, **117**, 398–408.

DIXON, J. B. & WEED, S. B. 1989. *Minerals in Soil Environments*: Madison, WI (Soil Science Society of America).

IMBRIE, J., HAYS, J. D., MARTINSON, D. G., MCINTYRE, A., MIX, A. C., MORLEY, J. J., PISIAS, N. G., PRELL, W. L. & SHACKLETON, N. J. 1984. The orbital theory of Pleistocene climate: Support from a revised chronology of the marine oxygen isotope record. *In*: BERGER, A. IMBRIE, J., HAYS, J., KUKLA, G. & SALTZMAN, B. (eds) *Milankovitch and Climate, Part 1*: Reidel, Dordrecht, 269–305.

——, MCINTYRE, A. & MIX, A. 1989. Oceanic response to orbital forcing in the late Quaternary: Observational and experimental strategies. *In*: DUPLESSY, J. C. (ed.) *Climate and Geosciences*: Reidel, Boston.

JENKINS, G. M. & WATTS, D. G. 1968. *Spectral Analysis and its Applications*. Holden Day, Oakland.

KOLLA, V., HENDERSON, L. & BISCAYE, P. E. 1976. Clay mineralogy and sedimentation in the western Indian Ocean. *Deep-Sea Research*, **23**, 949–961.

——, KOSTECKI, J. A., ROBINSON, F., BISCAYE, P. E. & RAY, P. K. 1981. Distributions and origins of clay minerals and quartz in surface sediments of the Arabian Sea. *Journal of Sedimentary Petrology*, **51**, 563–569.

KRISSEK, L. A. & CLEMENS, S. C. 1991. Mineralogic variations in a Pleistocene high-resolution eolian record from the Owen Ridge, western Arabian Sea (Site 722): Implications for sediment source conditions and monsoon history. *In*: PRELL, W. L., NIITSUMA, N. *et al. Proceedings of the Ocean Drilling Program Scientific Results*, Ocean

Drilling Program, College Station, TX, **117**, 197−214.

KROON, D., STEENS, T. N. F. & TROELSTRA, S. R. 1991. Onset of monsoonal related upwelling in the western Arabian Sea as revealed by planktonic foraminifers. *In*: PRELL, W. L., NIITSUMA, N. *et al. Proceedings of the Ocean Drilling Program, Scientific Results*, Ocean Drilling Program, College Station, TX, **117**, 257−264.

KUKLA, G., HELLER, F., MING, L. X., CHUN, X. T., SHENG, L. T. & SHENG, A. Z. 1988. Pleistocene climates in China dated by magnetic susceptibility. *Geology*, **16**, 811−814.

KUTZBACH, J. E. 1981. Monsoon climate of the Early Holocene: Climate experiment with the Earth's orbital parameters for 9000 years ago. *Science*, **214**, 59−61.

—— & OTTO-BLEISNER, B. L. 1982. The sensitivity of the African-Asian monsoonal climate to orbital parameter changes for 9000 years B.P. in a low-resolution General Circulation Model. *Journal of Atmospheric Science*, **39**, 1177−1188.

MURRAY, D. W. & PRELL, W. L. 1990. Biogenic sedimentation on the Owen Ridge, northwestern Arabian Sea during the past one million years: Evidence for changes in monsoon-induced upwelling. *Transactions of the American Geophysical Union*, **71**, 1397.

—— & —— 1991. Pliocene to Pleistocene variations in calcium carbonate, organic carbon, and opal on the Owen Ridge, northern Arabian Sea. *In*: PRELL, W. L., NIITSUMA, N. *et al. Proceedings of the Ocean Drilling Program, Scientific Results*, Ocean Drilling Program, College Station, TX, **117**, 343−364.

NAIR, R. R., ITTEKKOT, V., MANGANINI, S. J., RAMASWAMY, V., HAAKE, B., DEGENS, E. T., DESAI, B. N. & HONJO, S. 1989. Increased particle flux to the deep ocean related to monsoons. *Nature*, **338**, 749−751.

PEDERSEN, T. F. & ZAHN, R. 1990. Bimodal wind vs. nutrient forcing of Arabian Sea biological productivity: The paleoproductivity record at ODP site 724. *Transactions of the American Geophysical Union*, **71**, 1397.

PRELL, W. L. 1984*a*. Monsoonal climate of the Arabian Sea during the late Quaternary: A response to changing solar radiation. *In*: BERGER, A., IMBRIE, J., HAYS, J., KUKLA, G. & SALTZMAN, B. (eds) *Milankovitch and Climate, Part 1*: Reidel, Dordrecht, 349−366.

—— 1984*b*. Variation of monsoonal upwelling: A response to changing solar radiation. *In*: HANSEN, J. E. & TAKAHASHI, T. (eds) *Geophysical Monograph Series, vol.* **29**: *Climate Processes and Climate Sensitivity*, Washington, D.C. (AGU), 48−57.

—— 1990. The amplitude and phase of monsoon upwelling indices: A key to the identification of atmospheric and oceanic mechanisms in the paleoceanographic record. *Transactions of the American Geophysical Union*, **71**, 1376.

—— & CURRY, W. B. 1981. Faunal and isotopic

indices of monsoonal upwelling: western Arabian Sea. *Oceanologica Acta*, **4**, 91−98.

——, NIITSUMA, N. *et al.* 1989. *Proceedings of the Ocean Drilling Program, Initial Reports*, Ocean Drilling Program, College Station, TX, **117**.

—— & VAN CAMPO, E. 1986. Coherent response of Arabian Sea upwelling and pollen transport to Late Quaternary monsoonal winds. *Nature*, **323**, 526−528.

PROSPERO, J. M. & NEES, R. T. 1986. Impact of the North African drought and El Niño on mineral dust in the Barbados trade winds. *Nature*, **320**, 735−738.

Shipboard Scientific Party, 1989. Site 722. *In*: PRELL, W. L., NIITSUMA, N. *et al. Proceedings of the Ocean Drilling Program, Initial Reports*, Ocean Drilling Program, College Station, TX, **117**, 255−318.

SIROCKO, F. & LANGE, H. 1991. Clay-mineral accumulation rates in the Arabian Sea during the late Quaternary. *Marine Geology*, **97**, 105−119.

—— & SARNTHEIN, M. 1989. Wind-borne deposits in the northwest Indian Ocean: Record of Holocene sediments versus modern satellite data. *In*: LEINEN, M. & SARNTHEIN, M. (eds) *Paleoclimatology and Paleometeorology: Modern and Past Patterns of Global Atmospheric Transport*, NATO ASI Ser., V. 282: Boston (Kluwer), 401−433.

SMITH, R. L. & BOTTERO, J. S. 1977. On upwelling in the Arabian Sea. *In*: Marting & Angel (eds) *A Voyage of Discovery*, Pergamon, Oxford 291−303.

STEENS, T. N. F., KROON, D., TEN KATE, W. G. & SPRENGER, A. 1991. Late Pleistocene periodicities of oxygen isotope ratios, calcium carbonate contents, and magnetic susceptibilities of western Arabian Sea Margin Hole 728A. *In*: PRELL, W. L., NIITSUMA, N. *et al. Proceedings of the Ocean Drilling Program, Scientific Results*, Ocean Drilling Program, College Station, TX, **117**, 309−320.

STREET, A. F. & GROVE, A. T. 1979. Global maps of lake-level fluctuations since 30 000 yr. B.P. *Quaternary Research*, **12**, 83−118.

STREET-PERROTT, F. A. & HARRISON, S. P. 1985. Lake levels and climate reconstruction. *In*: HECHT, A. D. (ed.) *Paleoclimate Analysis and Modeling*, Wiley, New York 291−340.

VAN CAMPO, E. 1986. Monsoon fluctuations in two 20 000-yr B.P. oxygen-isotope/pollen records off southwest India. *Quaternary Research*, **26**, 376−388.

——, DUPLESSY, J. C. & ROSSIGNOL-STRICT, M. 1982. Climatic conditions deduced from a 150-kyr oxygen isotope-pollen record from the Arabian Sea. *Nature*, **296**, 56−59.

VELDE, B. 1985. *Clay Minerals: A Physico-Chemical Explanation of their Occurrence*: Elsevier, Amsterdam.

WEBSTER, P. J. 1987. The elementary monsoon. *In*: FEIN, J. S. (ed.) *Monsoons*: Wiley, New York 3−32.

WYRTKI, K. 1971. Oceanographic atlas of the International Indian Ocean Expedition, Washington D.C. (National Science Foundation).

ZAHN, R. & PEDERSEN, T. F. 1991. Late Pleistocene evolution of surface and mid-depth hydrography at the Oman Margin: planktonic and benthic isotope records at Site 724. In: PRELL, W. L., NIITSUMA, N. et al. Proceedings of the Ocean Drilling Program, Scientific Results, Ocean Drilling Program, College Station, TX, 117, 291−308.

Variation of South Somalian upwelling during the last 160 ka: radiolarian and foraminifera records in core MD 85674

JEAN PIERRE CAULET[1], MARIE-THÉRÈSE VÉNEC-PEYRÉ[2], COLETTE VERGNAUD-GRAZZINI[3] & CATHERINE NIGRINI[4]

[1] *Laboratoire de Géologie, Muséum, URA 723 du CNRS, 43 rue Buffon, 75005 Paris, France*

[2] *Laboratoire de Paléontologie, Muséum, URA 12 du CNRS, Paris, France*

[3] *Université P. et M. Curie, LODYC du CNRS, Paris, France*

[4] *510 Papyrus Dr., La Habra Heights, Ca. 90631, USA*

Abstract: Indicators of upwelling activity and surface-water productivity for the last 160 ka have been studied in the 'Marion Dufresne' core MD 85674 taken off Somalia (3°11, 2 N−50°26, 3 E; 4875 m depth). Quantitative changes in the abundances of radiolarian species which are restricted to upwelling areas (*A. murrayana*, *C. irregularis*, *D. infabricatus*, *L. nigriniae*, *P. caryoforma*, *P. crustula*, and *P. minythorax*) were used to monitor the variation of vertical advection of deep water. These changes are compared with those recorded by the stable carbon isotopes of a foraminiferal thermocline dweller, *N. dutertrei*, and with quantitative variations of some planktonic foraminifers (*N. dutertrei*, *G. bulloides*, *G. menardii*, *G. sacculifer* and *G. glutinata*). Taken together, our data indicate that, under the south Somalian gyre, upwelling activity was maximal during transition between isotope stages 6 and 5, isotope stage 3, and transition between isotope stages 2 and 1 (respectively at about 130 ka, 65 to 25 ka, and 15 to 10 ka). These data also suggest that, at least during the last 60 ka, periods of increased activity in the Somalian, Arabian and Peruvian upwelling systems were synchronous.

The biogeochemistry of the oceans is governed, in large part, by coastal processes involved in upwelling systems. High productivity areas are generally related to upwelling zones where deep nutrient-rich waters are brought to the surface, resulting in very high rates of carbon fixation through photosynthesis. Distinct chemical, physical and biological patterns characterize the rising water column. Sediments that accumulate directly beneath upwelling zones preserve a record of these patterns. Thus, the sediment record of coastal upwelling provides a memory bank of important climate controlling functions (Suess & Thiede 1983; Thiede & Suess 1983).

Fluctuations in the intensity of upwelling systems were first related to climatic variations by Arrhenius (1952), who suggested that increased planetary temperature gradients during glacial periods bring increased wind velocities which stimulate upwelling of nutrient-rich thermocline water. Temperature reconstructions (CLIMAP 1976; CLIMAP 1981) also suggest increased coastal upwelling in glacial oceans. Using the quantity of organic matter in sediments off northwest Africa as an index of Pleistocene productivity, Müller & Suess (1979) found that oceanic productivity was today approximately the same as during past interglacial stages, but was higher by a factor of 2 or 3 during glacial stages. The higher productivity of the glacial ocean was attributed to increased coastal upwelling, as well as to generally increased mixing due to stronger temperature gradients, winds and currents (Berger *et al.* 1989). The increased activity of low-latitude upwelling systems appears to have been widespread all over the eastern boundary settings, and has probably contributed to the reduction of atmospheric pCO_2 during glacial times.

Conversely, recent studies of planktonic microfossil changes in Pleistocene sediments from the Peru and Oman margins suggest decreased upwelling intensity during the last glacial period. Although evidence of a persistent upwelling phenomenon during the last 400 ka has been reported at ODP 112 Sites 681 and 868 off Peru, the strongest upwelling seems to have occurred during interglacial stages, with weaker upwelling during glacial period (Schrader & Sorknes 1990). Coarse-fraction analysis and benthic foraminiferal assemblages at ODP 112 Holes 679D, 680B and 681B indicate that Peru upwelling intensity was higher during the early parts of isotope stage 1, stage 3, the later part of stage 5 and during the early parts of stages 6 and 7. Conversely, decreased upwelling is documented within isotope stage 1, the later part of stages 2 through 4 and 7, the middle part

From SUMMERHAYES, C. P., PRELL, W. L. & EMEIS, K. C. (eds), 1992, *Upwelling Systems: Evolution Since the Early Miocene*. Geological Society Special Publication No 64, pp 379–389

of stage 6, and during stage 9 (Obërhansli et al. 1990). To Prell et al. (1980), the nature of faunal change and the estimates of sea surface temperature (CLIMAP 1981) indicated warmer conditions or weaker upwelling conditions south of Arabia at 18 ka BP. Such observations are consistent with independant records of monsoon variability based on the time distribution of pollen in both terrestrial and deep sea sediments (van Campo et al. 1982), and from records of lake level changes (Street-Perrot & Harrison 1984). Together, these observations seem to indicate that the Peru and Arabian Sea upwelling systems went through a somewhat similar evolution during the late Pleistocene.

The purpose of this paper is to present some preliminary results based on a study of the variations of radiolarians, planktonic foraminifera and oxygen and carbon stable isotopes in core MD 85674 (Fig. 1), and to test whether the evolution of the Somalian upwelling system is similar to that recorded along the Arabian and Peruvian margins.

Oceanographic setting and material studied

In the northwestern Indian Ocean, a number of distinct upwelling systems are associated with the southwest monsoon winds that occur from April to September. These systems are found in the Somali Current, off southwest Arabia, and off the Malabar coast of India (see summary in Cushing 1971). In contrast to upwelling systems located in the regions of eastern boundary currents, the upwelling off Somalia during the southwest monsoon is in a western boundary region and is related to a strong western boundary current (Warren et al. 1966). Detailed studies of modern upwelling processes linked to the Somali current began with the Indian Ocean Experiment, an oceanographic survey conducted during the onset of the southwest monsoon in 1979 (Swallow 1980). Results of this and other studies indicate that the Somali Current develops two clockwise gyres near 5°N and 10°N, inducing two areas of upwelling off Somalia. The chemical and biological description of these two gyres suggests stronger upwelling at 10°N. Surface samples of phytoplankton are dominated numerically by diatoms which are also common in the upwelling off Peru (Smith & Codispoti 1980). During the southwest monsoon, primary productivity increases all along the Somali coast with areas of upwelling being up to ten times more productive than oligotrophic areas (Smith & Codispoti 1980). At 5°N, during a full strength monsoon (for example in July and August 1979), primary productivity of carbon was 1.7 ± 0.8 g/m^2/day (Smith & Codispoti 1980). At intermediate depths (550 to 1000 m), high salinity waters are associated with a pronounced oxygen minimum layer (Warren et al. 1966). These high salinity waters, overflowing from the Gulf of Aden, are mainly flowing southwestward, at least between 3°N and 4°S (Leetmaa et al. 1980). It is not yet clear how the oxygen minimum is related to the high productivity of surface waters. Below 2500 m, cold deep waters with high oxygen content flow northward (Warren et al. 1966), but these have been known to reverse during summer (Fieux et al. 1986).

During the 'MD 44-INDUSOM' cruise of the Marion Dufresne (April–May 1985), 21 piston cores were collected along four transects located on the East African Margin and in the Somali Basin between the Equator and Socotra Island (Caulet 1987). Beneath the two upwelling areas (5°N and 10°N), the sediments are characterized by large biogenous silica fractions and high sedimentation rates, and carbonate cycles were observed in the deepest cores, below 4000 m (Caulet et al. 1988). A detailed study of this material has been undertaken in order to reconstruct the evolution of the south Somalian upwelling during the late Pleistocene.

Core MD 85674 (3°11, 2 N−50°26, 3 E; 4875 m depth) was selected for the present study because of its location just beneath the south gyre at 5°N (Fig. 1), its high rate of sedimentation (more than 8.5 cm/1000 yr for the last 130 ka), and the lack of hiatuses or important turbiditic layers. Downcore carbonate content in this core exhibits some cyclic changes, and some foraminiferal species appear to be dissolved in a few levels (Caulet et al. 1988). Carbonate dissolution is less pronounced in other cores collected from shallower depths on the continental slope, but many of these contain hiatuses and numerous turbiditic layers that probably result from winnowing by strong underwater currents related to the Somali Current, thus making them unsuitable for palaeoenvironmental studies (Caulet et al. 1988).

Methods

A lithological description of core MD 85674, based on smear slides and carbonate content, is given in Caulet (1987). For this study, carbonate content was measured in samples taken at 5 to 10 cm intervals. Foraminiferal studies and stable isotope measurements were done on the same samples at 20 cm intervals. Radiolarians were studied at the same levels, plus additional samples every 10 cm.

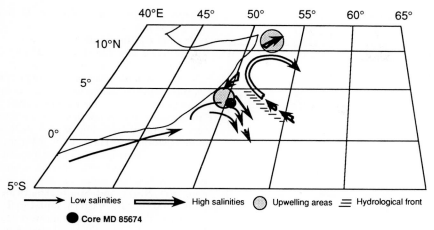

Fig. 1. Location of Core MD 85674. Surface circulation patterns during full strength monsoon (July and August), after Fieux (1987).

Radiolarian slides were prepared according to the standard method described by Sanfilippo *et al.* (1985). For each sample, 32 radiolarian species, including stratigraphical and upwelling markers, were counted in a total population of 6000 to 20 000 radiolarian skeletons. Radiolarian species considered to be upwelling markers are those whose presence or abundance in tropical sediments are restricted to well known upwelling areas such as the Peru Current or Arabian Margin (Nigrini & Caulet in press). Upwelling radiolarian species off Somalia include representatives of *Acrosphaera murrayana*, *Cypassis irregularis*, *Dictyophimus infabricatus*, *Lamprocyrtis nigriniae*, *Phormocyrtis caryoforma*, *Phormostichoartus crustula* and *Pterocorys minythorax*. Relative abundances of these species were added together to give an 'upwelling radiolarian index' (URI).

Relative abundances of planktonic foraminifera were estimated for the fraction of sediment coarser than 125 μm. For each sample level, representatives of 18 species (work in progress) were counted in a total of 300 individuals, except in a few samples where foraminiferal assemblages are extremely rare. Detailed counts of radiolarians and foraminifera are available from the authors on request.

The plankton foraminiferal species *Neogloboquadrina dutertrei* was chosen (from the size fraction comprised between 500 μm and 125 μm) for oxygen and carbon isotope analysis. This species, which is rare or absent in oligotrophic waters, is generally well represented in eutrophic waters (Bé & Hamelin 1967; Tolderlund & Bé 1971; Schott 1966 and others). Its representatives are relatively abundant throughout the core and so permitted us to reconstruct a nearly complete record (Fig. 2). Standard techniques for isotope analyses were used. Some 30 to 35 specimens per sample were ultrasonically cleaned to remove adhering particles (clays or coccoliths), and then roasted under vacuum at 350°C for one hour. CO_2 for isotope analyses was extracted by reaction with 100% phosphoric acid at 50°C in an oven. Evolved gas samples, after two on-line distillation steps to obtain pure CO_2, were analyzed in a VG Isogas Sira 9-triple collector mass spectrometer. All isotope data are calibrated to the PDB reference in the standard D notation through the use of intercalibrated standards. Internal reproducibility is ±0.01 for $\delta^{18}O$ and $\delta^{13}C$. The analytical precision of analyses of the carbonate standard run during the period of investigation is 0.06‰ for $\delta^{18}O$ and 0.04‰ for $\delta^{13}C$. Standard deviation of separated analyses of the same foraminiferal species are 0.10‰ for $\delta^{18}O$ and 0.06‰ for $\delta^{13}C$.

Results and discussion

Chronological framework

Continuous occurrence of rare representatives of the radiolarian species *Buccinosphaera invaginata* gives an age younger than 180 to 160 ka to the base of Core MD 85674. First appearance of *B. invaginata* was dated at 0.16/0.18 Ma in the central Indian Basin (Johnson *et al.* 1989). A more precise chronological framework was obtained for Core MD 85674 by using the stable oxygen isotope record of *N. dutertrei*. Isotope data were obtained for

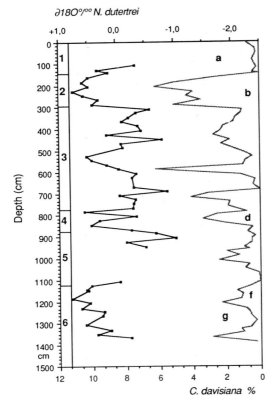

∂18O‰ *N. dutertrei*

Fig. 2. Oxygen isotope stratigraphy based on analysis of *N. dutertrei*, and changes in the content of *C. davisiana* (percentages versus total radiolarian species). Letter designation of maxima and minima of the *C. davisiana* curve after Morley & Hays (1979).

Stage 5/Stage 6 transition at 1110 cm = 129.84 ka.
Additional control points were used:
    Sub-stage 2.2 at 226 cm = 17.85 ka
    Sub-stage 4.2 at 783 cm = 65 ka.

Variations in the abundance of the radiolarian *Cycladophora davisiana* were used to calibrate the missing parts of the isotope curve. Abundance cycles of this species in the Pleistocene were calibrated by using oxygen isotope variations (Morley & Hays 1979; Morley 1983). Usually rare in tropical and subtropical areas, *C. davisiana* is a subpolar species, abundant in sediments beneath areas of coastal upwelling along the North and South American continents, and in the eastern equatorial Pacific where the thermocline is shallowest (Lombari & Boden 1985). The relatively high abundance of this species in Core MD 85674 allows us to produce a high-quality *C. davisiana* record (Fig. 2). Prominent maxima and minima in the *C. davisiana* pattern show the same relationship to oxygen isotope variations as in previously studied cores (Morley 1983), and permit us to calibrate the missing parts of the oxygen isotope record. Various maxima and minima of the *C. davisiana* curve have been given letter designations to facilitate comparison with the oxygen isotope stages (Morley & Hays 1979). It is clear from Fig. 2 that the low relative abundance zone (a) at the top of the core corresponds to isotope stage 1 with the underlying high relative abundance (b) occurring within isotope stage 2. All published *C. davisiana* curves exhibit low abundance level in the topmost samples with the highest abundance level occurring immediately below these low *C. davisiana* values (Morley 1983).

Variations in the upwelling radiolarian index (URI)

Radiolarian abundance in sediments is a valuable indicator of fertility changes. Diatoms dominate in high fertility areas, whereas maximum radiolarian occurrences are reported from areas surrounding these high fertility zones (Molina-Cruz 1984). Fossil remains of radiolarian assemblages are well preserved under high productivity zones and reflect their life distribution patterns (Casey 1971; Petrushevskaya 1971). Characteristic radiolarian assemblages closely related to upwelling areas have been described in the eastern Pacific by Molina-Cruz (1977, 1984), and Romine & Moore (1981). Radiolarian fractions in sediments deposited under the Somalian gyres are 5 to 10 times greater than in sediments deposited

most samples, with the exception of the intervals between 1000 cm and 945 cm, and between 100 cm and the top core where representatives of *N. dutertrei* were too rare.

As reported on Fig. 2, isotope stage 1, which should correspond to the upper 100 cm, is not recorded. Stage 2 extends from approximately 120 cm to 270 cm, stage 3 from approximately 270 cm to 775 cm, stage 4 from 775 cm to 875 cm, stage 5 from 875 cm to 1110 cm (with sub-stage 5e not being represented), stage 6 from 1110 cm downcore. Interpolated ages were calculated after the following age assignments (Martinson *et al.* 1987):
    Stage 1/Stage 2 transition at 120 cm = 12.05 ka
    Stage 2/Stage 3 transition at 270 cm = 24.1 ka
    Stage 3/Stage 4 transition at 775 cm = 58.96 ka
    Stage 4/Stage 5 transition at 875 cm = 73.9 ka

under the equatorial area of the Indian Ocean (Caulet 1987). However, total radiolarian abundance (in percent of all material in coarse fractions) does not vary by much down Core MD 85674, suggesting persistent high fertility since at least isotope stage 6. This is corroborated by the presence of radiolarian species characteristic of upwelling (Nigrini & Caulet in press) in almost all core levels (radiolarians were absent only in the sample at 681 cm). Rapid changes in the abundance of the upwelling species throughout glacial and interglacial episodes give rise to rapid fluctuations of the URI, indicating high frequency activity of the south Somalian gyre (Fig. 3). Strong maxima in the URI curve between 1200–1100 cm, 800–700 cm, 450–400 cm and 150–100 cm suggest that vertical advection of subsurface water was important at the end of stage 6, during stage 3, and at the transition between stage 2 and 1. In addition, detailed analysis of radiolarian assemblages (see MD 85674 range chart in Nigrini and Caulet in press) indicates that the diversity of the upwelling fauna also increased during these episodes.

There is evidence to suggest that peak values of the CaCO$_3$ curve and maxima of the URI curve are synchronous (Fig. 3). This close relationship suggests that intense surface productivity enhanced by upwelling processes was the main factor controlling the carbonate sedimentation at Core MD 85674 location.

Variations of the foraminiferal assemblages

Core MD 85674 was taken in 4875 m of water which is normally below the CCD in the Indian Ocean (Leclaire 1974); however, carbonate is quite abundant, amounting, at intervals, to nearly 60% of the sediment. In addition, calcium carbonate content appears to be very variable (between 1% and 75% of the sediment). Downcore, calcium carbonate contents increase or decrease regularly, excluding any strong and rapid input of shallow carbonate import through turbiditic processes. Occurrence of shallow benthic foraminifers (work in progress) at level 1192 cm suggests, however, that the high CaCO$_3$ percentage measured in this sample could be related to turbidite inputs.

Higher calcium carbonate fractions (more than 40% of the sediment) are made of coccoliths and foraminifers. They were found only in sediments deposited during the isotope transitions 6/5 and 4/3, the late part of stage 3 and stage 2, and the transition 2/1. As compared to planktonic forms, very well preserved benthic foraminifers are small and rare, confirming that the major part of the calcium carbonate was

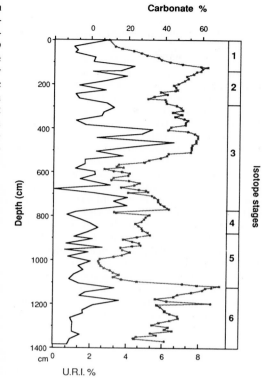

Fig. 3. Upwelling radiolarian index (URI) curve and CaCO$_3$ content curve versus depth. Isotope stages are reported from Fig. 2.

produced in the surface layer (work in progress).

Because of selective dissolution, relative percentages of dissolution resistant planktonic foraminifers are expected to increase during episodes of important dissolution, obliterating the fluctuations of the pelagic inputs strictly related to changes in the upwelling intensity. The cumulated percentages of the resistant species (*N. dutertrei, Globorotalia menardii, Globorotalia tumida* and *Pulleniatina obliquiloculata*) are always higher than 60% throughout core MD674. One may, therefore, argue that dissolution has been effective throughout the time interval recorded in the core. This could be consistent with the great water depth of the core. In that view, we have computed a dissolution index (SI) based on the relative variations of dissolution resistant species such as *N. dutertrei, G. menardii, G. tumida* and *P. obliquiloculata* and susceptible species such as *Globigerina bulloides, Globigerinoides sacculifer* and *Globigerinita glutinata* (Cullen & Prell 1984).

SI = (*N. dutertrei* + *G. menardii* + *G. tumida* + *P. obliquiloculata*/*N. dutertrei* + *G. menardii* + *G. tumida* + *P. obliquiloculata* + *G. bulloides* + *G. sacculifer* + *G. glutinata*) × 10.

For all levels, values of this index are high (fluctuating between 8 and 9), compared to published values calculated for Indian, Pacific and Atlantic cores located at shallower depths (Volat *et al.* 1980). However, lower values of this index are recorded during isotope transition 5e/6, stage 5a and stage 3, suggesting a lower intensity of the dissolution during these intervals (Fig. 4). Maximal values are recorded during isotope stage 2 and stage 4. The classical glacial−interglacial changes in the intensity of the dissolution that one would expect for the Indian Ocean (for instance a close correspondence between interglacials and higher dissolution periods (see Volat *et al.* 1980 and Peterson & Prell 1985) is not clearly reflected in this record. The fluctuations of SI are independent of those of the calcium carbonate content (excepted the high value recorded in stage 4), which supports our previous statement that the CaCO₃ content reflects the surficial production. The same observation has also been done for surficial sediment samples from the western continental margin of India (Divakar Naidu 1990) where a higher concentration of $CaCO_3$ is related to high productivity in the upwelling regions. These observations are corroborated by the strong correlation existing between the fluctuations of the URI and those of the $CaCO_3$ content throughout core MD674. Thiede (1975) also mentioned that the presence in the upwelling assemblage of foraminiferal species highly resistant to dissolution relative to other species might give the false impression that there was important dissolution near the foraminiferal lysocline.

Previous studies of foraminiferal populations in highly productive areas such as the northwestern Indian Ocean, or the continental margin of west Africa, have shown that some species or assemblages can be related to upwelling conditions. For example, the abundance of *N. dutertrei*, *G. bulloides* and *G. menardii* in both living and fossilized assemblages of the northwestern Indian Ocean have been demonstrated to reflect nutrient-rich waters related to tropical upwelling (Duplessy *et al.* 1981; Prell & Curry 1981; Kroon 1988). In the eastern

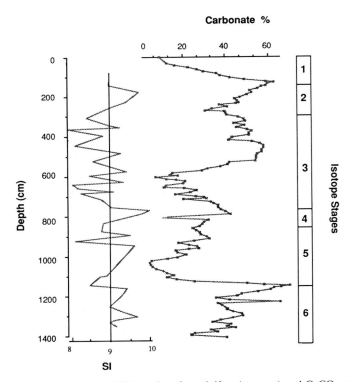

Fig. 4. Variations of the solution index (SI) based on foraminifers (see text) and CaCO₃ curve.

Arabian sea, Zhang (1985) reported a tropical upwelling assemblage characterized by *N. dutertrei* and *G. bulloides*. In the Peruvian coastal upwelling area, *N. dutertrei* is also the most frequent species (Wefer *et al.* 1983). From plankton tows off western Africa, Thiede (1975) reported an upwelling assemblage dominated by *N. dutertrei*, *Globorotalia inflata* and *Globigerina quinqueloba*, the former two being considered as 'subsurface dwellers'.

Relative abundances of *G. bulloides* throughout Core MD 85674 are lower than 10% (Fig. 5), in good agreement with values published for recent surficial sediments of equatorial areas of the northwestern Indian Ocean (Cullen & Prell 1984; Prell 1984*a*). An attempt has been done to reconstruct time series of upwelling variability, using the variations in the relative abundance of the surface species *G. bulloides* (work in progress). Data were compared to the *G. bulloides* curves previously published by Prell (1984*b*) and Prell & Kutzbach (1987). The fluctuations in abundance recorded for the last 60 ka display a pattern rather similar to that reported for the Core V34−88 off Arabia (Prell 1984*b*), maximal percentages being recorded, at both locations, during isotope stage 3, at about 50 ka. It should be noted, however, that in the Somalian core, this maximum predates the maximum values of the URI by about 15 ka (Fig. 5). Such discrepancy cannot yet be explained, but it appears that in some cases the relationship of the species *G. bulloides* to the varying intensity of an upwelling system should be questioned.

In Core MD 85674, *N. dutertrei* and *G. menardii* are well represented. Their cumulative percentage versus total planktonic foraminifers is always between 10% and 15% in all levels (except between 1100 and 990 cm and between 100 cm and the top, where only very rare foraminifers were observed) (Fig. 5). The almost continuous and high abundance of these thermocline dwellers confirms that upwelling was a persistant phenomenon during the greater part of the last 160 ka. Moreover, the cyclic variations of these two species are roughly in phase with variations of the URI (Fig. 5).

Two other species, such as *G. sacculifer* and *G. glutinata*, are less abundant (usually less than 10% of the foraminiferal population), but the variations of their abundances exhibit a close relationship (peak to peak) with the variations of the URI. The maximum abundances of this assemblage occur in isotope stage 6, transition between isotope stages 5 and 4, stage 3, and between transition between stages 2 and 1. Thus, *N. dutertrei*, *G. menardii*, *G. sacculifer*

and *G. glutinata* appear to be the best foraminiferal markers for upwelling activity in the 5°N Somalian area.

Carbon isotope analysis

As a result of biological fractionation during photosynthesis and respiration, the $\delta^{13}C$ distribution of the total dissolved inorganic carbon ($\Sigma \, CO_2$) strongly fluctuates in the euphotic layer of the ocean. Carbonate producers such as planktonic foraminifers incorporate these carbon isotopes in their shells and should, therefore, record the $\delta^{13}C$ values of the $\Sigma \, CO_2$ of the sea water where they live and calcify.

As previously shown in the northern part of the Indian Ocean (Kroon & Ganssen 1988), upwelling and subsequent primary production produce a lateral $\delta^{13}C$ gradient from the upwelling centre to the fringes, and finally to a 'normal' environment. It has been shown that species living at intermediate depths, such as *G. menardii* or *N. dutertrei*, exhibit negative relationships with the $\delta^{13}C$ in the upwelling zones; i.e. low $\delta^{13}C$ values are recorded during maximum upwelling periods (Kroon & Ganssen 1988). The $\delta^{13}C$ changes recorded by *N. dutertrei* through time in the sedimentary record of Core MD 85674 were also investigated as an index of relative changes in the intensity of the Somalian upwelling system.

Today, $\delta^{13}C$ values of living representatives of this species in the Arabian Sea vary from about 0‰ to +1.0‰, the lowest values being recorded close to the centre of the Arabian upwelling (Kroon & Ganssen 1988). In Core MD 85674, the $\delta^{13}C$ values of this species range from about 0‰ to more than +1.5‰ (Fig. 5). Although mean values are higher by about 0.5‰ than in the Arabian Sea upwelling, the temporal variation in the record of the Somalian upwelling is of the same order as the present day geographical variation in the northwestern Indian Ocean. Modern values of the Somalian system are unknown because no δ^{13} data are available for the most recent sediments.

The $\delta^{13}C$ variations recorded throughout Core MD 85674 suggests that minimal values roughly correlate with peak values of the URI. The correlation between the most depleted $\delta^{13}C$ values and maximum values of the URI during stage 3 is particularly striking (Fig. 5). Together, these data suggest that the intensity of the south Somalian upwelling was at a maximum at that time and place. In the lower part of stage 3, elevated values of the URI correlate with higher values of $\delta^{13}C$, and a lower calcium carbonate content, suggesting that the thermocline was

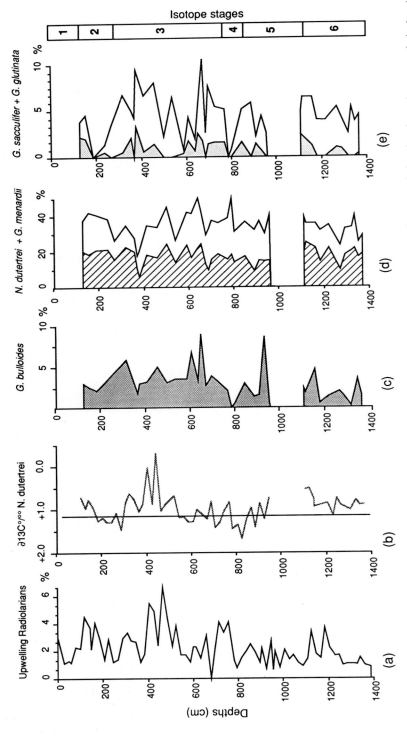

Fig. 5. (a) URI curve; (b) carbon isotope curve (mean $\delta^{13}C$ calculated around +1.03) based on analysis of *N. dutertrei*; relative abundance (versus total planktonic foraminifers) of (c) *G. bulloides*, (d) *N. dutertrei* + *G. menardii*, and (e) *G. sacculifer* + *G. glutinata*.

not so depleted in ^{13}C, probably as a result of somewhat lower primary production. As major vertical advection of deep water is recorded by upwelling radiolarian species at the same time, this relatively weak primary surface productivity could be explained by a shift of the south Somalian gyre. Complementary studies are, however, necessary to explore this hypothesis.

Late Pleistocene evolution of the Somalian upwelling

Radiolarian and foraminiferal records in Core MD 85674, combined with calcium carbonate measurements and oxygen and carbon stable isotope analyses, do not allow at this time a detailed history of the south Somalian upwelling system to be reconstructed for the last 160 ka. However, some important trends of the glacial/interglacial patterns of upwelling and surface fertility can be recognized. We propose here a simple scenario for the first-order variations of the south Somalian upwelling to serve as a basis for further studies.

The consistent occurrence of typical upwelling radiolarian species and the common occurrence of 'upwelling foraminifers', such as *N. dutertrei* and *G. menardii*, throughout Core MD 85674 indicate that vertical advection of cold, nutrient-rich deep water, resulting in increased sea surface productivity, was persistent over the last 160 ka. Upwelling off Somalia appears, thus, to be a persistent process in time, as are the Arabian and Peruvian upwelling systems (Prell 1984b; Schrader & Sorknes 1990). It is not yet clear if the Somalian gyre located at 5°N was also stable in space given discrepancies between the carbon isotope record and the variations of the URI observed in some portions of the Core.

High-frequency variations in the URI show, however, that many rapid changes in the vertical advection of deep water took place during relatively short periods. Prominent maxima in URI curve and synchronous increases in the relative abundances of *G. sacculifer* and *G. glutinata* suggest maximum upwelling activity at the transition between stages 6 and 5, during most of stage 3, and at the base of stage 1. Maximum values of the upwelling index published by Prell (1984b) for two cores (V34−88 and V34−87) of the Arabian sea were recorded during isotope stage 3 and termination 1. Minimum values were recorded during glacial stages 6, 4 and 2. Between 130 ka and 60 ka, values of the same index display a more regular pattern with fluctuations of lower amplitude. Episodes of increased activity of both the Somalian and Arabian upwelling systems appear, thus, to have

been synchronous, at least during the last 60 ka, with a peak activity during isotope stage 3.

Coarse fraction studies and benthic foraminiferal assemblages at ODP 112 Holes 679D, 680B, and 681B (Obërhansli *et al.* 1990) have shown that periods of strong upwelling activity on the Peruvian margin were approximately synchronous with those reported in the northwestern Indian Ocean during the last 60 ka. Increased upwelling conditions during stage 5, reported from the Peruvian upwelling area (Schrader & Sorknes 1990), are not observed in the Somalian and Arabian upwelling areas.

These data suggest a common climatic control of upwelling activity in both the Pacific and Indian Oceans during the Late Pleistocene.

Financial support for this study was provided by CNRS-INSU-DBT grant no 292. The authors are much indebted to M. Tamby who carefully picked out the foraminifers for isotope studies, and to M. J. Urrutiaguer who processed the samples for isotope analysis. D. J. Schneider and A. Sournia are thanked for constructive discussions and remarks. We are grateful to two anonymous reviewers whose suggestions resulted in substantial improvements to an earlier version of this paper.

References

ARRHENIUS, G. OS. 1952. *Sediment cores from the east Pacific*. Report Swedish Deep Sea Expedition, 1947−48, **55**, 1−288.

BÉ, A. W. H. & HAMELIN, W. H. 1967. Ecology of recent planktonic foraminifera. Part 3: distribution in the North Atlantic during the summer of 1962. *Micropaleontology*, **13**, 87−106.

—— & TOLDERLUND, D. S. 1971. Distribution and ecology of living planktonic foraminifera in surface waters of the Atlantic and Indian Oceans. *In*: FUNNELL, B. M. & RIEDEL, W. R. (eds) *Micropaleontology of the Oceans*, Cambridge University Press, 105−149.

BERGER, W. H., SMETACEK, V. S. & WEFER, G. 1989. Ocean productivity and paleoproductivity. An overview. *In*: *Productivity of the ocean: present and past*. Dahlem Workshop Reports. Life Sciences Research Report 44.

CASEY, R. E. 1971. Radiolarians as indicators of past and present water-masses. *In*: FUNNELL, B. M. & RIEDEL, W. R. (eds) *Micropaleontology of the Oceans*, Cambridge University Press, 331−341.

CAULET, J.-P. 1987. 45° Campagne Océnographique du MS 'Marion Dufresne'. Publications des Campagnes à la Mer. Terres Australes et Antarctiques Françaises, 1−95.

——, DEBRABANT, P. & FIEUX, M. 1988. Dynamique des masses d'eaux océaniques et sédimentation quaternaire sur la Marge de l'Afrique de l'Est et dans le Bassin de Somalie. Résultats préliminaires de la Mission MD-44 INDUSOM du Marion Dufresne. *C. R. Acad. Sc. Paris*, **307**, Sér. II: 281–288.

CLIMAP 1976. The surface of the ice-age. *Earth Science*, **191**.

CLIMAP 1981. Seasonal reconstructions of the Earth's surface at the last glacial maximum. Geological Society of America, Chart Series MC-36.

CULLEN, J. L. & PRELL, W. L. 1984. Planktonic foraminifera of the northern Indian Ocean: distribution and preservation in surface sediments. *Marine Micropaleontology*, **9**, 1–52.

CUSHING, D. H. 1971. Upwelling and the production of fish. *Advanced Marine Biology*, **9**, 255–334.

DIVAKAR NAIDU, P. 1990. Distribution of upwelling index planktonic foraminifera in the sediments of the western continental margin of India. *Oceanologica Acta*, **13**, 327–333.

DUPLESSY, J.-C., BÉ, A. W. H. & BLANC, P. L. 1981. Oxygen and carbon isotopic composition and biogeographic distribution of planktonic foraminifera in the Indian Ocean. *Paleogeography, Paleoclimatology, Paleoecology*, **33**, 9–46.

FIEUX, M. 1987. Océan Indien et Mousson. Conférence à la Mémoire d'Anton Bruün, 14° session de la C.O.I., UNESCO, Mars 1987, 1–15.

——, SCHOTT, F. & SWALLOW, J. C. 1986. Deep boundary currents in the western Indian Ocean revisited. *Deep-Sea Research*, **33**, 415–426.

JOHNSON, D. A., SCHNEIDER, D. A., NIGRINI, C. A., CAULET, J. P. & KENT, D. V. 1989. Pliocene-Pleistocene radiolarian events and magnetostratigraphic calibrations for the tropical Indian Ocean. *Marine Micropaleontology*, **14**, 33–66.

KROON, D. 1988. Distribution of extant planktic foraminiferal assemblages in Red Sea and northern Indian Ocean surface waters. *In*: BRUMMER, G. J. A. & KROON, D. (eds) *Planktonic Foraminifers as Tracers of Ocean Climate History*. Free University Press, Amsterdam, 225–267.

—— & GANSSEN, E. 1988. Northern Indian Ocean upwelling cells and the stable isotope composition of living planktic foraminifers. *In*: BRUMMER, G. J. A. & KROON, D. (eds) *Planktonic Foraminifers as Tracers of Ocean Climate History*. Free University Press, Amsterdam, 299–319.

LECLAIRE, L. 1974. Late cretaceous and cenozoic deposits. Paleoenvironments and paleoceanography of the central western Indian Ocean. *In*: SIMPSON, E. S. W., SCHLICH, R. *et al. Initial Reports of the DSDP*, Washington **25**, 481–513.

LEETMAA, A., ROSSBY, H. T., SAUNDERS, P. M. & WILSON, P. 1980. Subsurface circulation in the Somali current. *Science*, **209**, 590–592.

LOMBARI, G. & BODEN, G. 1985. *Modern Radiolarian Global Distributions*. Cushman Science Foundation for Foraminiferal Research, Special Publication 16A.

MARTINSON, D. G., PISIAS, N. G., HAYS, J. D., IMBRIE, J., MOORE, T. C. & SHACKLETON, N. J. 1987. Age dating and the orbital theory of the ice ages: development of a high resolution 0 to 300 000-year chronostratigraphy. *Quaternary Research*, **27**, 1–29.

MOLINA-CRUZ, A. 1977. Radiolarian assemblages and their relationship to the oceanography of the subtropical Southeastern Pacific. *Marine Micropaleontology*, **2**, 315–352.

—— 1984. Radiolarian as indicators of upwelling processes: the Peruvian connection. *Marine Micropaleontology*, **9**, 53–75.

MORLEY, J. J. 1983. Identification of density-stratified waters in the Late Pleistocene North Atlantic: a faunal derivation. *Quaternary Research*, **20** 374–386.

—— & HAYS, J. D. 1979. *Cycladophora davisiana*: a stratigraphic tool for Pleistocene North Atlantic and interhemispheric correlation. *Earth and Planetary Science Letters*, **44**, 383–389.

MORLEY, J. J. & HAYS, J. D. 1983. Oceanographic conditions associated with high abundances of the radiolarian *Cycladophora davisiana*. *Earth and Planetary Science Letters*, **66**, 63–72.

MÜLLER, P. J. & SUESS, E. 1979. Productivity, sedimentation rate, and sedimentary organic matter in the oceans. I. Organic carbon preservation. *Deep-Sea Research*, **26A**, 1347–1362.

NIGRINI, C. & CAULET, J.-P. 1992. Late Neogene radiolarian assemblages unique to Indo-Pacific areas of upwelling. *Micropaleontology*.

OBERHÄNSLI, H., HEINZE, P., DIESTER-HAASS, L. & WEFER, G. 1990. Upwelling off Peru during the last 430 000 yr and its relationship to the bottom-water environment, as deduced from coarse-grain size distributions and analyses of benthic foraminifera at Holes 679D, 680B, and 681B, Leg 112. *In*: SUESS, E., VON HUENE *et al.* 1990. Proceedings of the Ocean Drilling Program, Scientific Results, College Station, TX, **112**, 369–390.

PETERSON, L. C. & PRELL, W. L. 1985. Carbonate preservation and rates of climatic change: an 800 kyr record from the Indian Ocean. *In*: SUNDQUIST, E. T. & BROECKEN, W. S. (eds) *The Carbon Cycle and Atmospheric CaCO₃: natural variations, Archean to Present*. American Geophysical Union Monograph, **32**, 251–270.

PETRUSHEVSKAYA, M. G. 1971. Spumellarian and Nassellarian radiolaria in the plankton and bottom sediments of the central Pacific. *In*: FUNNELL, B. M. & RIEDEL, W. R. (eds) *Micropaleontology of the Oceans*, Cambridge University Press, 309–317.

PRELL, W. L. 1984a. Variation of monsoonal upwelling: a response to changing solar radiation. *In*: HANSEN, J. E. & TAKAHASHI, T. (eds) Climatic processes and climate sensitivity, Geophysical Monograph, **29**, 48–57.

—— 1984b. Monsoonal climate of the Arabian Sea during the late Quaternary: a response to changing solar radiation. *In*: BERGER, A. L. *et al.* (eds) *Milankovitch and Climate*. Part 1, 349–366. Reidel, Dordrecht.

—— & CURRY, W. B. 1981. Faunal and isotopic indices of monsoonal upwelling: Western Arabian Sea. *Oceanologica Acta*, **4**, 91–98.

——, HUTSON, W. H., WILLIAMS, D. F., BÉ, A. W. H., GEITZENAUER, K. & MOLFINO, B. 1980. Surface circulation of the Indian Ocean during the last

Glacial maximum, approximately 18000 yr BP. *Quaternary Research*, **14**, 309–336.

—— & KUTZBACH, J. E. 1987. Monsoon variability over the past 150000 years. *Journal of Geophysical Research*, **92**, 8411–8425.

ROHLING, E. J. & GIESKES, W. W. C. 1989. Late Quaternary changes in mediterranean intermediate water density and formation rate. *Paleoceanography*, **4**, 531–545.

ROMINE, K. & MOORE, T. C. Jr. 1981. Radiolarian assemblage distributions and paleoceanography of the eastern Equatorial Pacific Ocean during the last 127000 years. *Palaeogeography, Palaeoclimatology, Palaeoecology*, **350**, 281–314.

SANFILIPPO, A., WESTBERG-SMITH, M. J. & Riedel, W. R. 1985. Cenozoic Radiolaria. *In*: BOLLI, H. M., PERCH-NIELSEN, K. & SAUNDERS, J. B. (eds) *Plankton Stratigraphy*, Cambridge University Press, 631–712.

SCHOTT, W. 1966. *Foraminiferenfauna und Stratigraphie der tiefsee Sedimente im nordatlantischen Ozean*. Report Swedish Deep-Sea Research Expedition, 1947–1948, sediment cores North Atlantic Ocean, **8**, 357–469.

SCHRADER, H. & SORKNES, R. 1990. Spatial and temporal variation of peruvian coastal upwelling during the latest Quaternary. *In*: SUESS, E., VON HUENE *et al*. 1990. *Proceedings of the Ocean Drilling Program, Scientific Results*, College Station, TX, **112**, 391–406.

SMITH, S. L. & CODISPOTI, L. A. 1980. Southwest monsoon of 1979: chemical and biological response of Somali coastal waters. *Science*, **209**, 597–599.

STREET-PERROT, F. A. & HARRISON, S. P. 1984. Temporal variations in lake levels since 30000 yr B.P. — an index of the global hydrological cycle. *In*: HANSEN, J. E. & TAKAHASHI, T. (eds) *Climate Processes and Climate Sensitivity*. Geophysical Monographies Series, AGU, **29**, 118–129.

SUESS, E. & THIEDE, J. 1983. Coastal upwelling: its sedimentary record. Part A: Responses of the sedimentary regime to present coastal upwelling.

SWALLOW, J. C. 1980. The Indian Ocean Experiment: Introduction. *Science*, **209**, 588.

THIEDE, J. 1975. Distribution of foraminifera in surface waters of a coastal upwelling area. *Nature*, **253**, 712–714.

—— & SUESS, E. 1983. *Coastal upwelling, its sediment record. Part B: Sedimentary records of ancient coastal upwelling*.

THUNNELL, R. C. & REYNOLDS, L. A. 1984. Sedimentation of planktonic foraminifera: seasonal changes in species flux in the Panama Basin. *Micropaleontology*, **30**, 241–260.

TOLDERLUND, D. S. & BÉ, A. W. H. 1971. Seasonal distribution of planktonic foraminifera in the western North Atlantic. *Micropaleontology*, **17**, 297–329.

VAN CAMPO, E., DUPLESSY, J. C. & ROSSIGNOL-STRICK, M. 1982. Climatic conditions from a 150-ka oxygen isotope-pollen record from the Arabian Sea. *Nature*, **296**, 56–59.

VOLAT, J.-L., PASTOURET, L. & VERGNAUD-GRAZZINI, C. 1980. Dissolution and carbonate fluctuations in Pleistocene deep-sea cores: a review. *Marine Geology*, **34**, 1–28.

WARREN, B., STOMMEL, H. & SWALLOW, J. C. 1966. Water masses and patterns of flow in the Somali Basin during the southwest monsoon of 1964. *Deep-Sea Research*, **13**, 825–860.

WEFER, G., DUNBAR, R. B. & SUESS, E. 1983. Stable isotopes of foraminifers off Peru recording high fertility and changes in upwelling history. *In*: *Coastal upwelling, its sediment record. Part B: Sedimentary records of ancient coastal upwelling*, 295–308.

ZHANG, J. 1985. Living planktonic foraminifera from the eastern Arabian Sea. *Deep-Sea Research*, **32**, 789–798.

Peruvian coastal primary palaeo-productivity during the last 200 000 years

HANS SCHRADER

Geological Institut B, University of Bergen, Allégt. 41, 5007 Bergen, Norway

Abstract: Two times series of primary palaeo-productivity off the Peruvian coast over the last 200 000 years are presented for Ocean Drilling Leg 112 Sites: Site 681, Hole 681A at 11° and Site 686A, Hole 686A at 13° southern latitude. Estimates of primary palaeo-productivity are based on the transfer function PDU-3 that uses marine planktonic diatom assemblage distribution from surface sediment samples and a ten-year average primary productivity map over the area with a range of 37 to 365 $gC/m^2/year$. Primary palaeo-productivity does not follow a simple glacial–interglacial mode; the record is more complex and above average palaeo-productivity occurred in Sites 681 and 686 over the following time intervals: 12 to 28, 60 to 68, and 148 to 160 ka; major increases in productivity were found during peak glaciations, and significant decreases occurred at 8, 24, 72 to 80, 112 to 128, and 160 to 168 ka. The averaged palaeo-productivity curve of 681A and 686A over the last 160 000 years is in inverse phase with the Vostok ice core atmospheric CO_2 indicating that part of the atmospheric CO_2 variations is linked to changes in the biological pump activities of the eastern Pacific boundary current system.

The physical and biological aspects of the coastal upwelling phenomenon off the Peruvian coast is relatively well known (Barber & Smith 1981; Blasco 1971; De Mendiola 1981). The physical upwelling process triggered by the equatorward trade wind system does not by itself control primary production off the coast of Peru (Canby 1984); the presence of different water masses and their nutrient content that get upwelled together with the southern trade wind system are the primary factors controlling primary production in the surface waters.

Marine planktonic diatoms are the main inhabitants of these freshly upwelled water masses (Blasco 1971; Richert 1975); therefore diatoms in sediments underlying present and past coastal upwelling areas have the potential to reflect the magnitude and extent of the variations in primary productivity (Schuette & Schrader 1981*a, b*).

Due to the fragile nature of the frustules of common upwelling diatoms (*Skeletonema costatum*, *Chaetoceros* species, *Ditylum* species, *Nitzschia* species and *Thalassiosira* species) these species are very sensitive to bottom transport after they have settled to the sea floor. They will be dissolved or broken up when transported on the sea floor and therefore sediment assemblages containing large proportions of these species are more likely to be autochthonous sediment assemblages (Schrader & Schuette 1981).

Schrader & Sorknes (1990, 1991) presented preliminary results that tried to reconstruct palaeo-productivity based on the development

of a transfer function by relating marine planktonic diatoms from sediment surface samples off Peru to measured primary productivity in surface waters of that area (Zuta & Guillén 1970) and applying that relationship to a *few* samples from two ODP Leg 112 Sites: Holes 681A and 686A (Suess *et al.* 1988).

This paper contains palaeo-productivity estimates from two complete sections, sampled in 7 cm wide increments, over the top 16 metres of ODP Leg 112 Holes 681A and 686A and from discrete samples from 680B (Fig. 1) covering the last 200 000 years and is part of the debate about past variations of the oceanic biological pump (Berger & Vincent 1986). The biological pump incorporates carbon from the CO_2 pool dissolved in surface waters into tissues or into carbonate shells and thus lowers the partial pressure of CO_2 in surface waters and enhances the partial pressure in deep water not in contact with the atmosphere. The lowered partial pressure of CO_2 in surface waters will enhance diffusion of atmospheric CO_2 across the air/sea interface and thus uptake of CO_2 in surface waters (Moore & Bolin 1986).

Definition of transfer function PDU-3

The CABFAC (Imbrie & Kipp 1971) analysis of the surface samples (original data matrix from Schuette & Schrader 1979) was used as defined in Schrader & Sorknes (1990). The varimax factor score matrix (Table 1) displays the resulting eight factors. Seven factors explained 97% of the variance contained in the 48

From SUMMERHAYES, C. P., PRELL, W. L. & EMEIS, K. C. (eds), 1992, *Upwelling Systems: Evolution Since the Early Miocene*. Geological Society Special Publication No 64, pp 391–409.

391

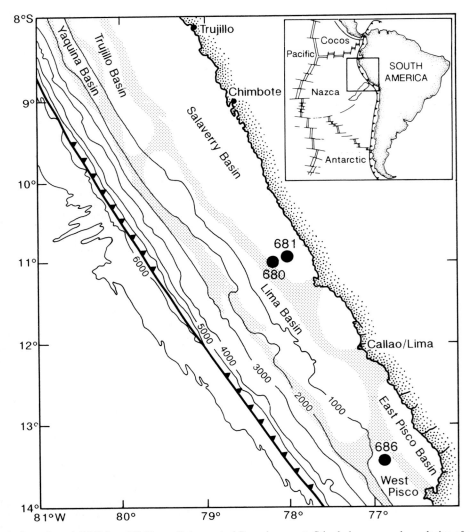

Fig. 1. Location of ODP Leg 112 Sites off the central Peruvian coast. Stippled areas are boundaries of shelf and upper slope sedimentary basins; depth contours are in metres; the Peru–Chile Trench is marked by the toothed lined (from Suess *et al.* 1988).

surface samples (Table 2) with communalities generally higher than 0.9 except for samples 1 and 27.

Ten-year average primary productivity values were assigned to each surface sample from the map of Zuta & Guillén (1970) and a stepwise multiple regression analysis (REGRESS program, Imbrie & Kipp 1971) was run on the mapped productivity and varimax factor components matrix. The resulting Peru Diatom Upwelling transfer function 'PDU-3' (Table 3) includes five factors and has a standard error of estimate of 18.7 gC/m²/year (Fig. 2). Values of

mapped and calculated productivity and their residuals are tabulated in Table 4.

Stratigraphy

Various stratigraphic interpretations have been proposed to establish a chronology for the various ODP Leg 112 drill sites including Sites 680, 681 and 686 (Fig. 1). The oxygen isotope stratigraphy of the benthic foraminifera *Bolivina seminuda* from Wefer *et al.* (1990) was adopted here with modifications of the placements of the stage boundaries (ages of boundaries from

Martinson *et al.* 1987) as proposed by Heinze (1990) for 680B (Fig. 3B and Table 5).

The occurrence of distinct horizons in all three holes with increased abundances of marine planktonic warm water oceanic species (percentage sum of *Thalassionema nitzschioides* var. *parva*, *Azpeitia nodulifer*, *Coscinodiscus radiatus*, *Rhizosolenia bergonii*, *Pseudoeunotia doliolus*, *Roperia tesselata*) (Table 6) and horizons with marked decreases in palaeoproductivity were numbered 1 through 12 in 680B (Figure 3A) using the same samples that were used to extract benthic foraminifera for oxygen isotope analysis.

The approach to correlate from this 'standard section 680B' to 681A and 686A presumes that all records from Sites 680, 681 and 686 are continuous and contain no major long lasting breaks and disturbances except for not recovered near sea–surface sediments and disturbances at the tops and bottoms of cores indicated by black triangles in figures. The placement of these correlation points (1 through 12) in 680B, 681A and 686A (the top two metres were not recovered at 686A) is illustrated in Fig. 4 (depth versus percent abundance of warm water diatom species) and in Fig. 5 (depth versus calculated primary productivity). No stable oxygen isotope stratigraphies are available for 681A (some oxygen isotope analyses were run on samples from 681B, though, but two metres of surficial sediments were not recovered at that hole) and 686A (no foraminifera present in the top 20 metres).

Contemporaneous lows in palaeo-primary productivity and highs in abundances of warm water diatom species at all three sites were labelled (Fig. 5) assuming that the atmospheric and oceanic driving forces that control these variations with long lasting warm water intrusions off central Peru influence both the northern Sites 680 and 681 and the southern Site 686 simultaneously.

The age–depth relationship at 680B (Fig. 6) is based on the placement of the oxygen isotopic stage boundaries (Heinze 1990). The depth occurrence of correlation points based on diatom warm water assemblage occurrences displays linear trends comparing the 'standard section 680B' to 681A and 681A to 686A (Fig. 7). This correlation may be supported by the occurrence of light coloured horizons, of phosphorite horizons and of dolomite horizons at respective intervals (Table 7).

The last occurrence and mass abundance of selected diatom species further down core in 681A and 680B supports the proposed correlation: (1) The last occurrence of *Nitzschia*

fossilis at 22.75 mbsf in 680B and at 21.5 mbsf in 681A. (2) The last occurrence of a large centrally constricted *Delphineis* species that has not been formally described at 23.25 mbsf in 680B and at 22.0 mbsf in 681A. (3) The mass occurrence of *Delphineis* species (same species as above) at 26.5 mbsf in 680B and at 26.0 mbsf in 681A. (4) A common occurrence of a large and coarsely structured *Skeletonema costatum* at 18.2 mbsf in 681A and at 17 mbsf in 681A.

The last occurrence of *Nitzschia fossilis* ranges higher off Peru to around 300 ka compared to its last occurrence off Japan where it becomes extinct at 550 ka (Koizumi & Tanimura 1985). Part of this discrepancy might be related to less accurate stratigraphies in the DSDP Leg 86 drill sites that is primarily based on calibration of microfossil events to the palaeomagnetic stratigraphy.

The age–depth model of 680B was used to convert the depth scale into a time scale using the programs AGER and TIMER (SPECMAP statistical package, N. Pisias, Oregon State University) adopting a linear age depth relationship between data points. The resulting ages of diatom horizon 1 through 12 of 680B (Table 5) was used to date contemporaneous horizons in 681A and 686A. These horizon ages then were used in the AGER and TIMER program runs to convert the depth scale in 681A and 686A into a time scale of evenly spaced sample points (spacing 1 ka) over the last 200 000 years (Figs 8 & 9).

Samples

Site 681A at 11° southern latitude is located today within an active upwelling plume with primary productivity values approaching 220 gC/m^2/year; it is situated in 150 m water depth (Fig. 1).

The southern Site 686, Hole 686A is located at 13° southern latitude in an area with primary productivity values approaching 180 gC/m^2/year (Zuta & Guillén 1970); this Hole has a water depth of 446.8 m (Fig. 1).

Two different types of samples were analyzed from the three holes (for sedimentological description see Suess *et al.* 1988). These are:

(1) Very tiny, pea-sized samples from 680B that represented splits of the Wefer *et al.* (1990) and Heinze (1990) sample set that was used for benthic foraminifera oxygen isotope and organic carbon analysis.

(2) 7 to 7.5 cm long channel samples that were scraped perpendicular to the core axis from cleaned surfaces of 681A and 686A. The channel samples did slightly overlap at their

Table 1. Varimax factor score matrix from CABFAC (CABFAC-CLIMAP program from N. Pisias, Oregon State University) on 48 surface sediment samples and 15 marine planktonic diatom species/groups categories (for definition of species and species groups and weighing of *Skeletonema costatum* and *Delphineis karstenii* see Schrader & Sorknes 1990, 1991).

Varimax factor score matrix

Variable	Factor 1	Factor 2	Factor 3	Factor 4	Factor 5	Factor 6	Factor 7	Factor 8
Thalassionema nitzschioides var. *parva*	0.011	0.136	−0.046	−0.017	−0.105	0.277	0.002	0.002
Thalassionema nitzschioides	0.097	0.121	0.219	0.117	−0.043	*0.892*	0.055	−0.151
Thalassiosira excentrica	0.203	0.024	0.108	0.039	−0.169	−0.065	0.234	0.032
Thalassiosira oestrupii	0.019	0.045	−0.003	0.022	−0.086	−0.004	0.210	0.200
Coscinodiscus radiatus Azpeitia nodulifer	−0.045	*0.942*	−0.014	0.061	0.237	−0.156	−0.005	−0.135
Delphineis karstenii	*0.943*	0.053	0.004	−0.031	−0.110	−0.103	−0.220	−0.044
Skeletonema costatum	−0.002	−0.068	−0.059	*0.981*	−0.080	−0.103	−0.029	−0.072
Rhizosolenia bergonii	−0.009	0.055	−0.013	0.005	−0.032	0.106	−0.007	0.017
Actinoptychus undulatus/splendens	0.211	−0.072	0.041	0.046	0.407	−0.031	*0.830*	0.061
Pseudoeunotia doliolus	0.015	0.168	0.029	0.062	−0.115	0.014	−0.065	*0.721*
Stephanopyxis turris/palmeriana	0.036	−0.003	0.022	−0.015	−0.021	−0.013	0.113	0.035
Actinocyclus ehrenbergii	−0.069	0.009	0.956	0.018	−0.097	−0.193	−0.029	0.012
Thalassiothrix longissima	0.007	0.070	−0.057	0.038	−0.061	0.129	0.009	*0.570*
Roperia tesselata	−0.003	0.003	0.018	0.051	0.039	0.044	−0.047	0.194
Cyclotella striata/stylorum	0.080	−0.170	0.116	0.075	*0.826*	0.095	−0.374	0.152

Table 2. Varimax factor components matrix from CABFAC (CABFAC-CLIMAP program from N. Pisias, Oregon State University) run on 48 surface samples and 15 diatom species/groups.

Varimax factor components matrix

Sediment surface samples	Communality	Factor 1	Factor 2	Factor 3	Factor 4	Factor 5	Factor 6	Factor 7
SAMP 1	0.691	0.053	0.275	0.204	0.152	0.616	0.227	0.341
SAMP 2	0.904	−0.021	0.888	0.138	0.117	0.245	−0.002	0.152
SAMP 3	0.953	0.094	0.343	0.272	0.126	0.072	0.856	0.002
SAMP 4	0.952	0.234	−0.018	0.055	0.059	0.431	0.060	0.838
SAMP 5	0.967	0.068	0.702	0.114	0.130	0.157	0.643	0.027
SAMP 6	0.921	0.090	0.915	0.038	0.094	0.110	0.231	−0.008
SAMP 7	0.989	0.176	0.960	0.025	0.079	0.161	0.030	−0.055
SAMP 8	0.978	0.545	0.399	0.110	0.097	0.602	0.124	−0.351
SAMP 9	0.965	0.952	0.089	0.093	0.038	0.132	0.140	−0.056

SAMP 10	0.994	0.410	0.105	0.422	0.140	0.413	0.659	−0.113
SAMP 11	0.991	0.445	0.425	0.208	0.123	0.724	0.163	0.045
SAMP 12	0.990	0.728	0.261	0.186	0.104	0.508	0.284	−0.097
SAMP 13	0.985	0.486	0.182	0.475	0.227	0.623	0.221	0.043
SAMP 14	0.994	0.312	0.101	0.780	0.118	0.399	0.316	−0.073
SAMP 15	0.975	0.496	0.383	0.482	0.302	0.386	0.330	0.031
SAMP 16	0.994	0.393	0.746	0.127	0.123	0.292	0.408	−0.036
SAMP 17	0.975	0.201	0.352	0.363	0.142	0.714	0.231	0.308
SAMP 18	0.950	0.191	0.475	0.102	0.342	0.744	0.038	0.077
SAMP 19	0.995	0.709	0.274	0.410	0.097	0.435	0.089	0.206
SAMP 20	0.897	0.768	0.006	0.120	0.043	0.159	−0.067	0.511
SAMP 21	0.987	0.891	0.060	0.117	0.363	0.036	0.165	0.122
SAMP 22	0.982	0.170	0.223	0.285	0.166	0.706	0.524	0.149
SAMP 23	0.971	0.415	0.773	0.110	0.118	0.375	0.179	0.055
SAMP 24	0.989	0.288	0.471	0.045	0.802	0.087	0.173	−0.030
SAMP 25	0.981	0.281	0.623	0.147	0.141	0.527	0.399	0.187
SAMP 26	0.995	0.369	0.698	0.133	0.137	0.415	0.395	−0.078
SAMP 27	9.873	0.083	0.444	0.396	0.182	0.564	0.402	0.020
SAMP 28	0.982	0.363	0.685	0.115	0.124	0.324	0.392	0.307
SAMP 27	0.990	0.096	0.344	0.169	0.799	0.422	0.032	0.126
SAMP 30	0.980	0.401	0.197	0.612	0.146	0.352	0.488	0.146
SAMP 31	0.978	0.050	0.056	0.969	0.086	0.086	0.080	0.115
SAMP 32	0.961	0.295	0.410	0.363	0.163	0.654	0.339	0.069
SAMP 33	0.962	0.093	0.598	0.224	0.161	0.441	0.569	−0.026
SAMP 34	0.987	0.070	−0.001	0.252	0.946	0.076	0.120	0.067
SAMP 36	0.995	0.059	0.114	0.907	0.112	0.287	0.244	−0.024
SAMP 37	0.987	0.313	0.266	0.668	0.175	0.545	0.202	0.060
SAMP 38	0.983	0.722	0.409	0.189	0.216	0.293	0.324	0.144
SAMP 39	0.932	0.411	0.068	0.266	0.128	0.348	0.718	0.187
SAMP 40	0.959	0.277	0.343	0.135	0.168	0.797	0.068	0.280
SAMP 41	0.970	0.322	0.553	0.429	0.141	0.489	0.321	0.120
SAMP 42	0.922	0.527	0.246	0.383	0.112	0.600	0.235	0.096
SAMP 43	0.997	0.577	0.251	0.300	0.269	0.551	0.296	0.216
SAMP 44	0.976	0.571	0.180	0.494	0.301	0.477	0.222	0.074
SAMP 45	0.985	0.176	0.087	0.954	0.129	0.036	0.101	0.086
SAMP 46	0.989	0.422	0.047	0.129	0.805	0.303	0.230	0.022
SAMP 47	0.987	0.042	0.957	0.031	0.102	0.188	0.150	0.006
SAMP 48	0.994	0.111	0.384	0.191	0.144	0.158	0.867	0.034
SAMP 49	0.977	0.527	0.258	0.296	0.213	0.596	0.380	0.006
Variance		17.146	20.636	14.276	8.444	19.591	12.539	3.894
Cumulative variance		17.146	37.782	52.059	60.503	80.094	92.634	96.528

Table 3. Statistics of Peru Diatom Upwelling (PDU-3) transfer function from output of stepwise multiple regression analysis (REGRESS-CLIMAP program from N. Pisias, Oregon State University). Productivity values in gC/m²/year.

Variable no	Variable name	Mean	Standard deviation
1	Productivity (gC/m²/year)	185.06250	71.4427
2	Factor 1 (Delphineis karstenii)	0.33858	0.24080
3	Factor 2 (Azpeitia nodulifer)	0.36681	0.27087
4	Factor 3 (Actinocyclus ehrenbergii)	0.29235	0.24189
5	Factor 4 (Skeletonema costatum)	0.20838	0.20471
6	Factor 5 (Cyclotella striata/stylorum)	0.38867	0.21403
7	Factor 6 (Thalassionema nitzschioides)	0.28325	0.21475
8	Factor 7 (Actinoptychus undulatus)	0.09017	0.17744

```
**  Sum of squares reduced in this step . . . . . . . . . . .    5449.474
**  Proportion reduced in this step . . . . . . . . . . . . . . .    0.023
**  Cumulative sum of squares reduced . . . . . . . . . .226400.600
**  Cumulative proportion reduced. . . . . . . . . . . . . .    0.944   of    239890.800
**  For 5 variables entered
 *  Multiple correlation coefficient . . . . . . . . . . . . .    0.971
    (adjusted for degrees of freedom) . . . . . . . . . . .    0.969
 *  F-value for analysis of variance . . . . . . . . . . . . .  140.973
 *  Standard error of estimate . . . . . . . . . . . . . . . . .   17.922
    (adjusted for degrees of freedom) . . . . . . . . . . .   18.737
```

Variable number	Variable name	Regression coefficient	Std.error of regression coefficient	Computed t-value
1	Factor 1	0.73416	12.98621	−0.057
2	Factor 2	−143.51840	13.67018	−10.499
3	Factor 3	157.03180	14.09319	11.142
4	Factor 4	81.35053	14.49537	5.612
5	Factor 5	51.10340	12.40674	4.119

Intercept   155.23290

```
*  Mean absolute value of residuals . . . . . . . . . . . . . . . . . . . 13.7934
*  Standard deviation of absolute value of residuals . . . . . .  9.6292
*  Maximum absolute value . . . . . . . . . . . . . . . . . . . . . . . . 37.6016
*  Minimum absolute value . . . . . . . . . . . . . . . . . . . . . . . .  0.5430
```

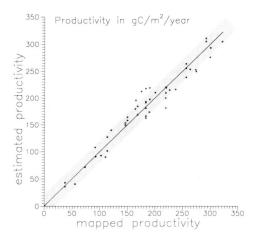

Fig. 2. Primary productivity values from the Zuta & Guillén (1970) map versus estimated productivity based on the transfer function PDU-3. The hatched area represents the standard error of estimate of 18.7

Table 4. Sediment surface samples (column 1) and their respective productivity values (column 2) from the map of Zuta and Guillén (1970). Calculated productivity based on PDU-3 transfer function (column 3), residual (column 4), maximum and minimum calculated productivity (column 5 and 6) and standard error of estimate (column 7).

Surface sample no	mapped prod. (gC/m²/year)	calc. prod.	Residual	max y value (gC/m²/year)	min y value	Standard error
1	183.00000	191.60590	−8.60594	217.36220	165.84970	19.81250
2	73.00000	71.51272	1.48728	97.09937	45.92608	19.68203
3	183.00000	162.57940	20.42062	188.19170	136.96710	19.70178
4	183.00000	193.10650	−10.10649	220.82960	165.38330	21.32550
5	92.00000	90.93353	1.06647	116.22570	65.64139	19.45549
6	37.00000	43.08304	−6.08304	68.94588	17.22020	19.89449
7	37.00000	35.90617	1.09383	61.74714	10.06520	19.87767
8	146.00000	153.49770	−7.49773	178.43900	128.55650	19.18557
9	183.00000	166.20180	16.79817	193.12840	139.27530	20.71274
10	256.00000	238.62470	17.37527	263.31150	213.93800	18.98983
11	189.00000	173.57850	15.42148	198.64470	148.51240	19.28164
12	183.00000	180.86910	2.13094	205.99570	155.74240	19.32821
13	263.00000	253.64990	9.35013	278.61830	228.68150	19.20648
14	300.00000	292.98300	7.01703	318.38190	267.58410	19.53760
15	219.00000	219.88440	−0.88437	245.12340	194.64530	19.41466
16	102.00000	92.75104	9.24896	117.82480	67.67731	19.28748
17	219.00000	209.60910	9.39093	234.70050	184.51760	19.30111
18	168.00000	168.78150	−0.78154	194.29870	143.26440	19.62858
19	200.00000	209.89240	−9.89243	235.09810	184.68680	19.38894
20	168.00000	184.27530	−16.27534	210.85650	157.69420	20.44707
21	165.00000	195.71040	−30.71040	222.39230	169.02850	20.52454
22	183.00000	217.44080	−34.44078	242.88490	191.99660	19.57241
23	110.00000	90.02517	19.97483	115.18830	64.86205	19.35625
24	150.00000	164.17990	−14.17989	191.13300	137.22670	20.73319
25	113.00000	127.10030	−14.10026	151.81810	102.38240	19.01373
26	91.00000	108.02430	−17.02435	132.86700	83.18169	19.10974
27	190.00000	197.26260	−7.26256	222.13720	172.38790	19.13434
28	113.00000	101.35990	11.64005	126.17460	76.54535	19.08816
29	190.00000	218.89520	−28.89525	245.56880	192.22170	20.51815
30	273.00000	252.63450	20.36551	277.50810	227.76090	19.13356
31	292.00000	310.71410	−18.71408	337.76850	283.65970	20.81107
32	219.00000	199.85810	19.14186	224.67630	175.04000	19.09088
33	120.00000	140.14980	−20.14981	164.89100	115.40860	19.03171
34	299.00000	275.73860	23.26144	303.89440	247.58270	21.65834
36	292.00000	305.03430	−13.03433	331.27040	278.79830	20.18158
37	256.00000	263.81220	−7.81219	289.03330	238.59110	19.40088
38	150.00000	158.22790	−8.22787	183.51170	132.94410	19.44910
39	226.00000	215.13930	10.86072	240.28550	189.99300	19.34326
40	219.00000	181.39840	37.60164	206.98280	155.81390	19.68036
41	164.00000	179.45750	−15.45749	204.37550	154.53950	19.16767
42	220.00000	219.45700	0.54300	244.26370	194.65030	19.08205
43	237.00000	215.93700	21.06296	240.76240	191.11170	19.09642
44	256.00000	255.41700	0.58304	280.50350	230.33050	19.29731
45	321.00000	304.75990	16.24008	331.67080	277.84900	20.70071
46	274.00000	249.40640	24.59363	276.06520	222.74760	20.50677
47	55.00000	40.62816	14.37184	66.46950	14.78683	19.87795
48	146.00000	149.82230	−3.82228	175.14870	124.49590	19.48184
49	175.00000	212.08500	−37.08501	236.83630	187.33380	19.03942

boundaries and represent a complete section of 16.05 metres at 681A and 15.35 metres at 686A only interrupted and possibly disturbed at both the top and at the bottom of the hydraulic piston cores (illustrated in Figs 3 & 5 by the black triangles). Each sample covers roughly a time span of a minimum of 400 (top) to 1200 years (at 15 mbsf); therefore the time series of 681A and 686A contain a 'sampling filter of 400 to 1200 years.

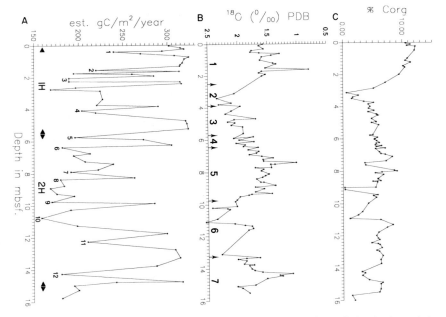

Fig. 3. Hole 680B. A, estimated primary productivity of discrete samples and correlation horizons 1 through 12. B, $\delta^{18}O$ of *Bolivina seminuda* digitized from Heinze (1990) and oxygen isotope stage boundaries as defined by Wefer *et al.* (1990) and Heinze (1990). C, weight percent of dry weight of organic carbon from Wefer *et al.* (1990) and Suess (pers. comm. 1989). Black triangles along the depth axis in A represent core tops and core breaks of hydraulic piston cores 1H through tops of 3H.

The increasing filter width with depth and thus time in 681A and 686A is responsible for the general decrease in productivity from the surface to the bottom (Fig. 5). This trend is an artefact and is most dramatically expressed at the top of 681A. The sample size is also responsible for the 'higher and lower' productivity in 680B (mean = 246; minimum = 109; maximum = 324 gC/m²/year) in comparison to the nearby 681A (mean = 209; minimum =

Table 5. Hole 680B: Depth of oxygen isotope stage boundaries and ages in ka from Heinze (1990).

Stage	Depth in mbsf	Age in ka
1	2.50	12.05
2	3.91	24.11
3	5.72	58.96
4	6.51	73.91
5	9.79	129.84
6	13.30	189.61
7	16.60	244.18
8	19.42	303.00
9	23.23	339.00
10	24.73	362.00
11	30.60	423.00
12	31.61	478.00
13	35.86	531.00
14	37.11	565.00
15	41.00	620.00

Table 6. Occurrences (in metres below the sea-floor) of stratigraphic horizons 1 through 12 in Holes 680B, 681A, and 686A and their ages (in ka).

Horizon no	680B depth	681A depth	686A depth	Age (ka)
1	0.40	1.06	NC	2
2	1.55	2.01	NC	7
3	2.04	2.52	0.60	10
4	4.09	4.13	2.27	28
5	5.75	5.29	3.41	59
6	6.37	5.89	4.01	72
7	7.88	7.42	6.41	97
8	8.35	7.86	6.67	106
9	9.75	9.27	8.17	129
10	10.75	10.59	8.92	146
11	12.25	11.86	10.17	172
12	14.25	13.98	12.64	205

NC = not recovered

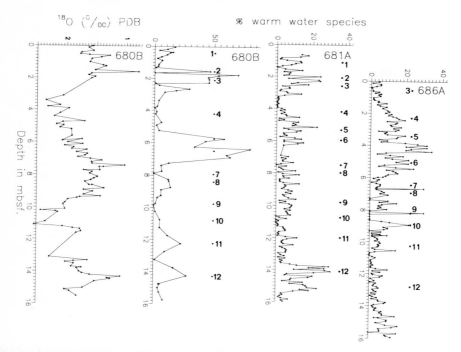

Fig. 4. Delta [18]O of *Bolivina seminuda* digitized from Heinze (1990) of 680B. Percent warm water marine planktonic diatom species in 680B, 681A and 686A. Small dots represent correlation horizons. Note that 686A did not recover approximately the top two metres of surficial sediments.

144; maximum = 275 gC/m²/year) (Fig. 5). Sample points of the 7 cm wide samples are plotted at midpoints in all figures.

Palaeo-primary productivity estimates

A pseudo factor components matrix was produced using THREAD (CLIMAP-THREAD, N. Pisias, Oregon State University; Imbrie & Kipp 1971) and primary palaeo-production determined using the transfer function PDU-3 and the THREAD output. The resulting downcore estimates of primary palaeo-productivity are plotted in Figs 3A (Hole 680B) and 5 (Holes 680B, 681A, and 686A). The raw data of 681A and 686A are tabulated in Table 8.

Time series analysis

Based on the proposed correlation of the diatom horizons 1 through 12 at 680B to equivalent horizons in 681A and 686A and using the oxygen isotope stage boundary ages (Prell *et al.* 1986; Martinson *et al.* 1987, data for 680B from Wefer *et al.* 1990; Heinze 1990) a time series of estimated primary palaeo-productivity over the last

200 000 years was computed for 681A and Site 686A (Figs 8 & 9).

Disturbances and missing sections do occur over the tops and bottoms of the hydraulic piston cores, notably over the intervals 0 to 0.5, 6.35 to 6.80, and 14.90 mbsf to the base of Core 2H at Hole 681A (Suess *et al.* 1988) and over the intervals 0 to 0.1, 5.1 to 5.3, and 14.60 to 14.80 mbsf at Hole 686A (Figs 3 & 5). The two time series of estimated primary productivity are plotted along the same time scale on Fig. 8. This figure also contains the SPECMAP stack (Imbrie *et al.* 1984) and the oxygen isotope curve of 680B (Heinze 1990). The trend in decreased average productivity in both 681A and 686A is due to the increase in filter width from 400 years at the top to 1200 years at the bottom. Productivity during the most recent times also is biased due to the fact of non-sampling and/or non-recovery of near surface sediments. A gap exists in the series of 681A over the interval 80 000 to 88 000 years represented by the transition between Cores 1H and 2H (Figs 5, 8 & 9).

The two time series represent raw data and are not filtered. The average palaeo-

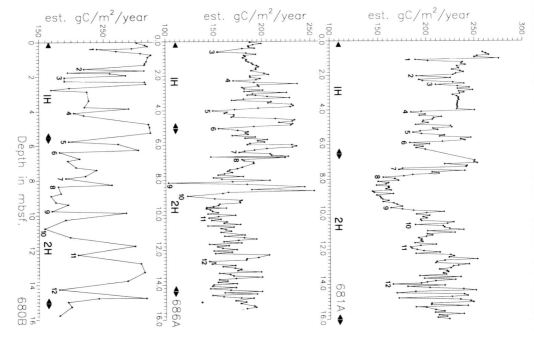

Fig. 5. Estimated primary productivity versus depth in 680B with distant discrete samples, in 686A and in 681A both with continuous channel samples. Sample points for 681A and 686A are plotted as midpoints. Numbers along the left-hand side of curves are correlation horizons 1 through 12. The black triangle in 681A and 686A represent tops and bottoms of the hydraulic piston cores.

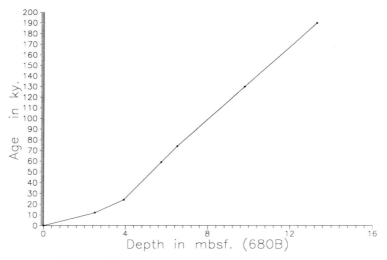

Fig. 6. Age versus depth in 680B based on oxygen isotope stratigraphy (from Wefer *et al.* 1990 and Heinze 1990). Sedimentation rate of the top 4 metres is 16 cm/10^3 years and it is 6 cm/10^3 years over the interval 4 to 14 mbsf.

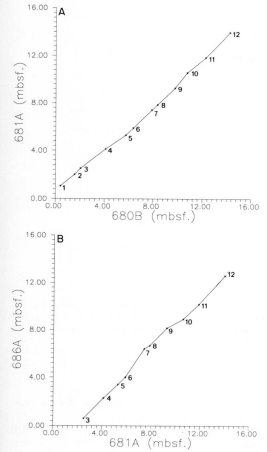

Fig. 7. A, diatom correlation horizons 1 through 12 and their respective depth down core in the 'standard section' 680B versus 681A. B, diatom correlation horizons 3 through 12 and their respective depth in 681A versus 686A.

productivity over the last 200 000 years is 209 $gC/m^2/year$ at 681A with a minimum value of 144 and a maximum value of 275; the average is 180 $gC/m^2/year$ at 686A with a minimum value of 103 and a maximum value of 254. Productivity was generally high in both locations; high levels of productivity are common during the maximum glaciations (see SPECMAP stack on Fig. 8) at 12 to 28, 60 to 68 and 148 to 160 ka. Productivity decreases did occur during major interglacials at 72 to 80, 112 to 128 and 160 to 168 ka. Increases and decreases are not restricted to the above-mentioned intervals, though. A major decline in palaeo-productivity did occur over the interval 108 to 128 ka. (Fig. 8).

Two palaeo-productivity highs in 686A, *one* at 132 to 140 ka and *two* at 80 ka, are not recorded in 681A. The 'missing' peak *two* is due to the core break between cores 1H and 2H.

The intervals with substantial decreases in productivity are characterized by the abundant occurrence of moderately to poorly preserved diatom assemblages containing abundant oceanic warm water diatoms (*Azpeitia no-dulifer*, *Pseudoeunotia doliolus*, *Rhizosolenia bergonii*, *Thalassionema nitzschioides* var. *parva* a. o.) or abundant robust neritic species including *Coscinodiscus asteromphalus*, *Actinoptychus undulatus*, *A. splendens* and *Actinocyclus ehrenbergii*.

During peak glacials with large drops in sea level well preserved delicate diatom assemblages accumulated in this shallow water (present water depth 150 m) shelf environment at Site 681. Extremely well preserved diatom assemblages are today being sedimented and preserved in the sedimentary record off the Namibia coast (Southwest Africa) in water depth of less than 50 m (Schuette & Schrader

Table 7. Occurrence of 'white', phosphorite and or dolomite horizons in 680B, 681A, and 686A in metres below the sea-floor. Observed depth and calculated depth based on relationship illustrated in Fig. 7.

680B depth	681A (depth) calculated	observed	686A (depth) calculated	observed
1.5	1.7	1.7	—	—
3.0	3.2	3.1	1.4	1.5
3.5	3.6	3.6	1.9	1.8
6.3	6.2	6.3	4.7	4.3
7.9	7.8	7.5	5.8	5.9
9.1	8.8	8.8	7.3	7.2
11.1	10.7	10.7	9.3	9.2
13.6	13.0	13.1	11.8	11.8
14.8	14.1	14.0	12.8	12.6
15.6	14.8	14.8	13.6	13.7
680B−681A	$y = 0.38 + 0.93x$			
681A−686A	$y = 1.9 + 1.05x$			

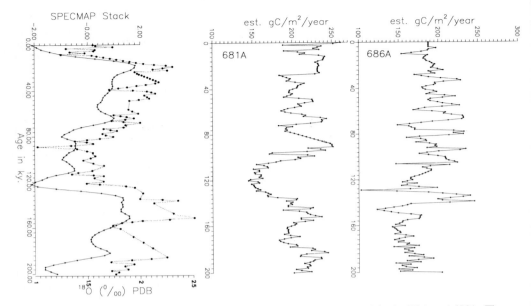

Fig. 8. Time series over the last 200 000 years of estimated primary productivity in 681A and 686A. The SPECMAP stack (from Imbrie *et al.* 1984) and the $\delta^{18}O$ of 680B (digitized from Heinze (1990) and modified through AGER and TIMER) are plotted along the same time scale. Note the data gap in 681A over the interval 80 to 84 ka.

1981*b*) indicating that shallowing during major sea-level drops might not prevent accumulation of fine-grained, organic-matter-rich hemipelagic mud with well preserved delicate diatom assemblages in case no strong bottom currents existed.

The high palaeo-productivity values of the latest Pleistocene to Holocene in 681A (Fig. 8) are not found in 686A since the top two metres of surficial sediment was not recovered at this hole. These high values at 681A are most likely due to an artefact that is caused by coring disturbance, counting bias or scaling problems. The equivalent section from a gravity core collected at the Site 681 clearly shows a gradual decrease in palaeo-productivity after a major peak at the Termination I that corresponds to data presented by DeVries & Schrader (1981).

The discrepancies in the direct comparison of the productivity values of 680B with those of 681A and 686A (Fig. 5) are primarily due to the wide spacing of the discrete samples and their small size at 680B that does not permit a complete resolution of all the variations contained in the depth series. The interval of common *Skeletonema costatum* between horizon 3 to 4 (Fig. 5) in 681A is not present at 680B and might be due to a stronger Peru Counter Current

actively removing these delicate diatom frustules from the bottom.

The organic carbon values from 680B (Fig. 3C, from Wefer *et al.* 1990 and Suess, pers. comm. 1989) are on the average 4.8 wt% of dry sample with higher values in the top three metres reaching >12% and lower values at 3, 7.5, 9, 11, 14.4 mbsf. These low organic carbon values correspond to lows in the estimated palaeo-primary productivity curve (Fig. 3) and indicate that both proxies are in phase over comparable intervals.

Discussion

Palaeo-productivity is used here as a direct expression of primary productivity as it occurs in the photic zone; it is based on the direct calibration of sedimented recent planktonic marine diatom assemblages to a ten-year average primary productivity map off coastal Peru. The transfer function (PDU-3) cannot be directly applied in other areas because of differences in diatom species compositions: *Skeletonema costatum* and *Delphineis karstenii* do not occur or are not preserved in sediments from other coastal upwelling areas.

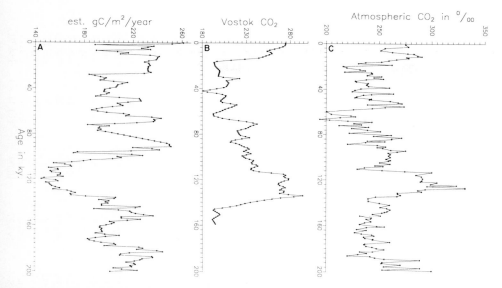

Fig. 9. Time series over the last 200 000 years of estimated primary productivity at 681A, atmospheric CO_2 content from air bubbles in the Vostok ice core in the Antarctic (original data from Barnola *et al.* 1987, modified only through TIMER) and $\Delta\delta^{13}C$ of core V19–30 in the eastern equatorial Pacific (digitized from Shackleton & Pisias 1985).

Due to the expanded nature of the Holocene record at 681A and the uncertainty of recovery of most recent sediments at both 681A and 686A the Holocene variations should not be over interpreted. At both Sites 681 and 686 a British expedition (Price & Kemp, Universities of Edinburgh and Southampton pers. comm.) has recently collected undisturbed gravity cores. These cores are now been analyzed for their diatom assemblages and they will provide the latest Pleistocene to Holocene details. Preliminary analysis of the top 4 m of the Site 681 gravity core displays a gradual decrease of palaeoproductivity during the Holocene to the Present and not an increase (Schrader, in preparation).

No palaeo-productivity time series derived from cores of comparable shallow water depth (100–400 m) from the world's major coastal upwelling areas such as the California, the Benguela and the Canary current system is accessible for comparison. Most palaeo-productivity studies have used cores taken at greater water depth and greater distance from the actual upwelling plumes.

Marine diatoms in sediment assemblages, their state of preservation and the abundance of special species were utilized to assess produc-

tivity qualitatively (DeVries & Schrader 1981; Diester-Haass *et al.* 1973, Schuette & Schrader 1979, 1981*a*, *b*; Donegan & Schrader 1982). However, none of these analysis has used the direct calibration technique as it is presented here.

Only a few time series of reconstructed coastal upwelling variations exist in the literature, most studies having focused on the last peak glaciation at 20 ka BP and on open acean areas (Mix 1989*a*, *b*). The area off North West Africa has been the focus of several studies using the accumulation of organic carbon in sediments (Müller *et al.* 1983) and the variation of $\Delta\delta^{13}C$ extracted from both planktonic and benthic foraminifera (Sarnthein *et al.* 1988) as measures of productivity.

Comparing the record off Peru with similar time series from other coastal upwelling areas that use the estimated flux of organic carbon as a primary production measure, the following consistent pattern emerge. Off Northwest Africa (Müller *et al.* 1983; Sarnthein *et al.* 1987), for instance, the estimated productivity curves of three cores dated by oxygen isotopic stratigraphy, display similar upwelling variations to those found off Peru. Early oxygen isotope stage 5 there is also characterized by lowered

Table 8. A, Hole 681A estimated primary productivity data. B, Hole 686A estimated primary productivity data. Depth (in mbsf) are midpoints of the 7 cm wide channel samples, ages (in ka) are based on respective age depth models as defined in the 'Stratigraphy' section, and estimated productivity is based on transfer function PDU-3 and is in gC/m²/year.

681A Depth	Age	Prod.	681A Depth	Age	Prod.	686A Depth	Age	Prod.	686A Depth	Age	Prod.
0.63	0.05	258.62	8.60	118.07	163.06	0.04	3.96	187.57	7.35	116.43	173.90
0.70	0.11	261.95	8.67	119.21	143.68	0.05	4.07	187.57	7.42	117.50	166.26
0.78	0.53	265.11	8.74	120.36	145.49	0.12	4.83	199.28	7.50	118.73	163.61
0.84	0.84	253.15	8.81	121.50	165.28	0.19	5.58	190.73	7.57	119.80	168.67
0.91	1.21	250.09	8.89	122.80	147.93	0.26	6.34	185.71	7.65	121.03	160.48
0.99	1.63	275.39	8.97	124.11	151.66	0.32	6.98	186.50	7.72	122.10	153.99
1.06	2.00	188.73	9.05	125.41	152.34	0.39	7.74	192.45	7.80	123.33	179.96
1.14	2.42	201.75	9.12	126.55	154.23	0.41	7.95	179.44	7.87	124.40	149.11
1.20	2.74	237.86	9.20	127.86	160.64	0.6	10.00	153.71	7.95	125.63	157.82
1.28	3.16	236.43	9.27	129.00	154.53	0.61	10.11	153.71	8.02	126.70	207.81
1.35	3.53	240.74	9.34	129.90	165.69	0.67	10.75	183.72	8.10	127.93	168.94
1.43	3.95	231.96	9.42	130.93	169.11	0.74	11.51	193.53	8.17	129.00	102.76
1.55	4.58	233.82	9.54	132.48	174.51	0.8	12.16	181.04	8.25	130.81	184.11
1.63	5.00	226.94	9.62	133.51	162.74	0.86	12.80	182.91	8.40	134.21	243.82
1.71	5.42	235.23	9.69	134.41	174.56	0.94	13.66	179.93	8.55	137.61	188.96
1.77	5.74	238.66	9.77	135.44	186.20	1.04	14.74	184.12	8.62	139.20	253.56
1.86	6.21	230.83	9.84	136.34	217.92	1.12	15.60	183.53	8.70	141.01	164.62
1.94	6.63	227.89	9.91	137.24	199.75	1.18	16.25	185.96	8.77	142.60	158.71
2.01	7.00	189.85	9.99	138.27	189.29	1.25	17.01	189.52	8.92	146.00	122.58
2.12	7.65	224.97	10.06	139.17	202.94	1.32	17.76	190.62	9.07	149.12	150.34
2.23	8.29	192.22	10.14	140.21	195.99	1.39	18.52	194.50	9.15	150.78	178.50
2.30	8.71	196.24	10.21	141.11	200.06	1.46	19.27	196.58	9.22	152.24	176.23
2.38	9.18	227.79	10.29	142.14	193.45	1.54	20.13	193.61	9.30	153.90	176.76
2.45	9.59	239.29	10.36	143.04	194.34	1.61	20.89	193.83	9.37	155.36	155.59
2.52	10.00	209.63	10.44	144.07	228.27	1.69	21.75	188.69	9.45	157.02	154.17
2.60	10.89	232.49	10.52	145.10	221.38	1.84	23.37	202.33	9.52	158.48	149.08
2.68	11.79	244.71	10.59	146.00	188.11	1.91	24.12	206.90	9.57	159.52	142.07
2.75	12.57	232.64	10.66	147.43	216.96	1.99	24.98	187.58	9.60	160.14	162.23
2.83	13.47	248.30	10.73	148.87	218.33	2.06	25.74	187.69	9.64	160.98	141.67
2.91	14.36	233.88	10.81	150.50	223.87	2.14	26.60	198.16	9.71	162.43	145.77
2.97	15.03	239.16	10.88	151.94	238.46	2.21	27.35	193.85	9.79	164.10	148.12
3.04	15.81	234.63	10.95	153.37	200.83	2.27	28.00	169.99	9.87	165.76	153.82
3.11	16.60	227.28	11.04	155.21	229.51	2.36	30.45	191.75	9.94	167.22	143.24
3.19	17.49	231.74	11.12	156.85	200.41	2.44	32.62	236.60	10.01	168.67	171.75
3.27	18.39	233.64	11.19	158.28	205.79	2.51	34.53	195.27	10.09	170.34	154.10

3.34	19.17	233.27	11.26	159.72	199.49	2.59	36.70	196.90	10.17	172.00	144.43
3.41	19.95	234.08	11.34	161.35	191.45	2.66	38.61	179.05	10.24	172.94	156.66
3.49	20.84	232.54	11.42	162.99	194.65	2.74	40.78	181.68	10.31	173.87	147.21
3.57	21.74	232.54	11.49	164.43	193.72	2.81	42.68	200.77	10.39	174.94	163.01
3.64	22.52	232.24	11.56	165.86	195.71	2.89	44.86	181.61	10.47	176.01	159.90
3.71	23.30	232.01	11.63	167.29	187.51	2.96	46.76	225.44	10.54	176.94	176.89
3.78	24.09	232.21	11.71	168.93	209.67	3.04	48.94	190.15	10.62	178.01	143.20
3.85	24.87	232.54	11.78	170.36	193.53	3.11	50.84	184.62	10.69	178.95	170.11
3.94	25.88	231.81	11.86	172.00	182.93	3.12	51.11	193.33	10.77	180.02	156.72
4.01	26.66	250.20	11.93	173.09	184.57	3.19	53.02	205.42	10.84	180.95	161.84
4.09	27.55	194.64	12.01	174.34	189.81	3.26	54.92	228.46	10.92	182.02	167.38
4.13	28.00	183.94	12.08	175.43	196.82	3.34	57.10	180.79	10.99	182.96	156.69
4.25	31.21	198.73	12.16	176.67	213.56	3.41	59.00	168.35	11.14	184.96	181.72
4.32	33.08	192.66	12.23	177.76	188.61	3.49	60.73	209.42	11.21	185.90	160.52
4.39	34.95	215.58	12.30	178.85	224.59	3.56	62.25	206.08	11.29	186.96	181.00
4.46	36.82	207.47	12.37	179.94	228.57	3.64	63.98	230.34	11.37	188.03	193.71
4.54	38.96	206.25	12.44	181.03	223.12	3.72	65.72	232.38	11.44	188.97	174.91
4.61	40.83	196.78	12.55	182.74	252.71	3.79	67.23	229.13	11.52	190.04	159.71
4.69	42.97	195.87	12.62	183.83	218.69	3.86	68.75	196.07	11.59	190.97	178.14
4.74	44.30	201.66	12.69	184.92	210.32	3.94	70.48	171.44	11.67	192.04	144.80
4.84	46.97	188.84	12.77	186.17	209.11	4.01	72.00	148.74	11.74	192.98	164.99
4.91	48.84	224.94	12.84	187.26	244.02	4.09	72.83	163.45	11.81	193.91	153.22
4.99	50.98	226.66	12.91	188.34	232.98	4.16	73.56	160.75	11.89	194.98	158.56
5.06	52.85	206.75	12.95	188.97	227.81	4.24	74.40	170.67	11.97	196.05	173.17
5.14	54.99	211.67	13.06	190.68	224.88	4.31	75.13	170.45	12.04	196.98	149.50
5.22	57.13	193.42	13.13	191.77	213.08	4.39	75.96	167.91	12.11	197.92	168.09
5.29	59.00	185.98	13.21	193.01	221.04	4.47	76.79	213.79	12.19	198.99	150.96
5.37	60.73	194.75	13.28	194.10	222.38	4.54	77.52	233.80	12.27	200.06	206.84
5.45	62.47	218.51	13.35	195.19	216.99	4.62	78.35	231.26	12.42	202.06	195.75
5.52	63.98	213.65	13.42	196.28	220.00	4.69	79.08	217.48	12.49	203.00	183.64
5.59	65.50	246.15	13.50	197.53	192.40	4.77	79.92	231.73	12.56	203.93	183.22
5.67	67.23	235.67	13.57	198.62	235.35	4.84	80.65	229.57	12.64	205.00	144.90
5.74	68.75	240.21	13.65	199.86	197.27	4.92	81.48	191.49	12.72	206.07	150.93
5.82	70.48	216.53	13.72	200.95	229.83	5.04	82.73	154.75	12.79	207.00	147.47
5.89	72.00	182.68	13.80	202.20	209.24	5.14	83.77	174.57	12.87	208.07	171.53
5.96	73.14	202.99	13.87	203.29	200.22	5.22	84.60	185.46	12.94	209.01	158.77
6.04	74.45	187.19	13.93	204.22	193.97	5.29	85.33	182.63	13.02	210.08	171.12
6.11	75.59	196.19	13.98	205.00	164.90	5.37	86.17	185.42	13.09	211.01	177.82
6.18	76.74	189.15	14.05	206.09	218.57	5.44	86.90	168.80	13.17	212.08	173.93
6.27	78.21	198.62	14.12	207.18	179.87	5.52	87.73	192.71	13.24	213.02	198.61
6.90	88.50	250.25	13.19	208.27	202.82	5.59	88.46	182.30	13.32	214.09	155.03
6.98	89.81	249.35	14.26	209.36	238.28	5.67	89.29	205.30	13.39	215.02	166.20

Table 8. *Contd.*

681A Depth	Age	Prod.	681A Depth	Age	Prod.	686A Depth	Age	Prod.	686A Depth	Age	Prod.
7.05	90.95	252.83	14.34	210.60	251.16	5.74	90.02	195.32	13.47	216.09	169.83
7.11	91.93	218.72	14.41	211.69	188.09	5.81	90.75	202.33	13.54	217.02	199.59
7.20	93.41	242.21	14.49	212.94	168.78	5.89	91.58	187.39	13.62	218.09	172.37
7.27	94.55	241.27	14.56	214.03	238.85	5.96	92.31	184.42	13.69	219.03	155.01
7.35	95.86	175.10	14.64	215.27	242.58	5.97	92.42	230.77	13.77	220.10	163.40
7.42	97.00	170.99	14.71	216.36	226.20	6.04	93.15	235.60	13.84	221.03	153.68
7.49	98.43	239.76	14.79	217.61	170.88	6.11	93.88	231.18	13.92	222.10	173.14
7.57	100.07	205.63	14.87	218.85	235.00	6.19	94.71	205.04	13.99	223.04	149.19
7.64	101.50	212.81	14.94	219.94	245.51	6.27	95.54	192.05	14.07	224.11	147.75
7.71	102.93	185.49	15.01	221.03	248.63	6.34	96.27	181.81	14.14	225.04	172.25
7.79	104.57	176.14	15.09	222.28	204.94	6.41	97.00	175.79	14.21	225.98	145.75
7.86	106.00	154.87	15.16	223.37	204.54	6.49	99.77	208.15	14.29	227.05	166.70
7.94	107.31	166.86	15.23	224.46	242.70	6.57	102.54	209.77	14.37	228.11	199.36
8.04	108.94	170.68	15.30	225.55	188.59	6.64	104.96	226.98	14.44	229.05	160.71
8.11	110.08	149.43	15.32	225.86	199.35	6.67	106.00	146.49	14.51	229.98	194.23
8.18	111.22	160.43	15.46	228.04	209.09	6.71	106.61	223.65	14.59	231.05	147.90
8.25	112.36	157.78	15.54	229.28	218.21	6.83	108.45	178.77	14.67	232.12	159.45
8.32	113.50	147.81	15.61	230.37	208.45	6.9	109.53	181.08	14.74	233.06	177.61
8.39	114.65	160.36	15.69	231.62	238.54	6.97	110.60	190.72	14.75	233.19	190.67
8.40	114.81	160.52	15.76	232.71	212.59	7.05	111.83	191.25	14.90	235.19	171.87
8.46	115.79	160.95	15.84	233.95	220.97	7.27	115.20	179.00	14.97	236.13	183.00
8.53	116.93	157.76	15.90	234.89	211.20	7.35	116.43	173.90	15.05	237.20	177.23
			15.98	236.13	223.32				15.20	239.20	191.40
			16.05	237.22	227.44				15.27	240.14	193.37
									15.35	241.21	183.62

productivity values, and maximum productivity was observed within oxygen isotope stages 2, parts of 3, and parts of 6. The resolution of the time series in Müller *et al.* (1983) is lower than the Peruvian series. The palaeo-productivity estimates from a Meteor core off the Spanish Sahara (Müller *et al.* 1983, Berger *et al.* 1989) covering oxygen isotope stages 1 to 6 display a very similar variation of productivity change except for oxygen isotope stage 1 where considerably reduced values were found off North-West Africa.

Coastal upwelling off Northwest Africa is controlled by the trade wind activities that cause through Ekman transport upwelling of nutrient-rich deeper waters. Variations of the trade wind strength have been interpreted by Dupont *et al.* (1989) to have been high during oxygen isotope stage 2 and low during the early part of oxygen isotope stage 5 (5e) and the middle part of stage 6.

Several studies have tried to reconstruct productivity in the eastern Equatorial Pacific (Pedersen 1983; Pedersen *et al.* 1988; Lyle 1988; Lyle *et al.* 1988); these reconstructions seem to indicate higher flux of organic carbon to the sea floor and thus higher sediment accumulation rates of organic carbon during oxygen isotope stage 2 or during the peak of the last glacial maximum at around 20 ka BP. These higher accumulation rates of sedimented organic carbon were related to higher new production which in turn is related to increased primary production in the photic zone.

The Peruvian record also shows higher values in the upper part of oxygen isotope stage 2. Over this interval most records of palaeo-productivity from both coastal upwelling areas in the Atlantic and in the Pacific show similar trends than the open ocean records from both the Atlantic (Mix 1989*a*) and the Pacific.

Two main hypothesis, the biological pump and the high-latitude alkalinity hypothesis (Broecker & Peng 1989) try to explain the variations in atmospheric CO_2 during the late Pleistocene and Holocene.

Mix (1989*b*) discusses the close relationship of atmospheric CO_2 measured in the Vostok ice core (Barnola *et al.* 1987) and the planktonic/benthic foraminiferai $\Delta\delta^{13}C$ from an equatorial Pacific core (Shackleton & Pisias 1985) as an expression of the size and effectiveness of the biological pump: both records seem to be coherent and in antiphase (Mix 1989*b*, his Fig. 1, Shackleton & Pisias 1985); the open ocean difference of deep sea $\delta^{13}C$ of benthic foraminifera and $\delta^{13}C$ of planktonic foraminifera are inter-

preted to be indications of primary productivity in the photic zone.

The Peruvian palaeo-productivity over the last 200 ka is compared with the atmospheric CO_2 content of the Antarctic Vostok ice core (Barnola *et al.* 1987, time scale from their Table 1, mean age of air) and with the $\Delta\delta^{13}C$ curve of Shackleton & Pisias (1985) all plotted along a common time scale in Fig. 9. Highest Peruvian palaeo-productivity occurs during peak glacials (except for the most Recent Holocene part) and both Perivian primary palaeo-productivity and atmospheric CO_2 are in antiphase; no significant lead or lags between the two signals could be detected except the increase of CO_2 in the most recent times. This relationship agrees with the open ocean relationship that is based on different palaeo-productivity proxies except the simple glacial—interglacial alteration does not exist in both the equatorial eastern Pacific Ocean (core V19—30, Shackleton & Pisias 1985) and the equatorial Atlantic (cores V32—08 and V30—36, Mix 1989*b*).

Two different oceanic biological pump systems can be distinguished: the oceanic (blue water) and the neritic (green water). The 'neritic' pump will effectively remove CO_2 from the atmosphere by extracting carbon and lowering the partial CO_2 pressure in surface waters via primary productivity and it will permanently store on the shelf and upper slopes organic carbon in the underlaying organic carbon rich, hemipelagic sediments. The 'oceanic' pump, on the other hand, will enhance CO_2 removal from the atmosphere, it will settle organic carbon as export productivity to the deep oceans, where the major part of the organic carbon will be oxidized and recycled. Therefore it is less effective in permanently removing carbon from the atmosphere/ocean system.

The Peruvian upwelling system represents an important area where the 'neritic' pump is extremely effective and where during glaciations, with lowered sea level and restricted narrower shelfs, high primary palaeo-productivity prevailed. Here also organic-rich, hemipelagic sediments were deposited on the shelf and on the upper slope during both high and low sea-level stands.

The Peruvian upwelling system is globally linked to the eastern boundary current systems and to the trade wind systems (Baumgartner & Christensen 1985, Philander 1983), it should be subjected and react similarly to both oceanic and atmospheric circulation changes as the northern and southern hemisphere boundary current system, that is the areas along western North America, western South America and the equatorial Eastern Pacific. Thus the Peruvian record might be used as a proxy for Pacific wide eastern boundary current system changes.

The combined open ocean and coastal Pacific Ocean constitutes 41% of today's global ocean productivity (Berger *et al.* 1987); this 41% can be further divided into 26% representing open ocean Pacific and 15% representing coastal Pacific productivity. The Pacific eastern boundary current system accounts for more than one half of the coastal Pacific primary production (Berger *et al.* 1987). Therefore palaeo-productivity changes as they are recorded in shallow shelf and slope sediments off Peru represent a substantial part of world ocean primary productivity variations.

This high primary productivity coupled with a shallow water oxygen minimum zone results in deposition of hemipelagic sediments that have high sedimentation rates (16 to 5.7 cm/10^3 years) and high accumulation rates of organic carbon. Heinze (1990) calculated accumulation rates of organic carbon at 680B of 35 in the Holocene to an average of 10 gC/m^2/year during oxygen isotope stages 1 to 8.

The northern shallow 681A and the southern, deeper 686A have similar primary palaeo-productivity records over the last 200 000 years. Extensive and long lasting intrusions of warm water represented by oceanic diatom floral elements occur in both sites simultaneously, as do intervals which contain high primary palaeo-productivity indicators represented by *Skeletonema costatum*, *Delphineis karstenii*, and mass occurrences of delicate remains of *Chaetoceros* species bristles. Major transitions from high palaeo-productivity to low palaeo-productivity occur primarily across the oxygen isotope stage boundaries. The early part of oxygen isotope stage 5 (= stage 5e) is characterized by a long-lasting decrease in palaeo-productivity. Palaeo-productivity over the last 200 000 years along the central Peruvian coast has been relatively high: it varied between 144 to 275 gC/m^2/year (average 209) at 681A and 103 to 254 gC/m^2/year (average 180) at 686A. Primary palaeo-productivity increased by a maximum of 76% and decreased by a minimum of 69% from the average at 681A and it increased by a maximum of 71%, decreased by a minimum of 57% from the average at 686A.

Samples of ODP Leg 112 were made available through the Ocean Drilling Program; they were collected by the author during Leg 112. Tim Schrader (Tulane University) helped with computer programming and wrote good documentations for the CLIMAP and SPECMAP (obtained in source code from Pisias and Mix, OSU) programs. I appreciate the exchange of data and ideas with Peter Heinze, Gerold Wefer (University of Bremen), and Erwin Suess (GEOMAR). The reviews of Lyle, Thunnell, Abrantes, and Prell helped to sharpen some of the conclusions. This project is funded through NAVF (Norges allmennvitenskapelige forskningsråd).

References

BARBER, R. T. & SMITH, R. L. 1981. Coastal upwelling systems. *In*: LONGHURST, A. R. (ed.) *Analyses of Marine Ecosystems*. Academic, New York, 31–68.

BARNOLA, J. M., RAYNAUD, D., KOROTKEVICH, Y. S. & LORIUS, C. 1987. Vostok ice core provides 160 000-year record of atmospheric CO_2. *Nature*, **329**, 408–414.

BAUMGARTNER, T. R. & CHRISTENSEN, N. JR. 1985. Coupling of the Gulf of California to large-scale interannual climatic variability. *Journal of Marine Research*, **43**, 825–848.

BERGER, W. H., FISCHER, K., LAI, C. & WU, G. 1987. Ocean productivity and organic carbon flux. I. Overview and maps of primary production and export production. University of California, Scripps Institution of Oceanography, Reference 87–30.

——, SMETACEK, V. S. & WEFER, G. 1989. Ocean productivity and paleoproductivity-an overview. *In*: BERGER, W. H., SMETACEK, V. S. & WEFER, G. (eds) *Productivity of the ocean: present and past*. John Wiley, Chichester, Life Science Research Reports, 1–34.

—— & VINCENT, E. 1986. Deep-sea carbonates: reading the carbon isotope signal. *Geologische Rundschau*, **75**, 249–269.

BLASCO, D. 1971. Composition and distribution of phytoplankton in the region of upwelling off the coast of Peru. *Investigacion Pesquera*, **35**, 61–112.

BROECKER, W. S. & PENG, T.-H. 1989. The cause of the glacial to interglacial atmospheric CO_2 change: A polar alkalinity hypothesis. *Global Biogeochemical Cycles*, **3** (3), 215–139.

CANBY, T. Y. 1984. El Niño's ill wind. *National Geographic*, **165**, 144–183.

DE MENDIOLA, B. R. 1981. Seasonal phytoplankton distribution along the Peruvian coast. *In*: RICHARDS, F. A. (ed.), *Coastal Upwelling, Coastal and Estuarine Sciences* 1, American Geophysical Union, Washington DC, 348–356.

DE VRIES, T. & SCHRADER, H. 1981. Variation of upwelling/oceanic conditions during the latest Pleistocene through Holocene off the Peruvian coast: A diatom record. *Marine Micropaleontology*, **6**, 157–167.

DIESTER-HAASS, L., SCHRADER, H.-J. & THIEDE, J. 1973. Sedimentological and paleo-climatical investigations of two pelagic ooze cores off Cape Barbas, North West Africa. Meteor Forschungsergebnisse, Reihe C, **16**, *19–66*.

DONEGAN, D. & SCHRADER, H. 1982. Biogenic and abiogenic components of laminated hemipelagic sediments in the central Gulf of California. *Marine Geology*, **48**, 215–237.

DUPONT, L. M., BEUG, H.-J., STALLING, H. & THIEDEMANN, R. 1989. First palynological results from Site 658 at 21°N off Northwest Africa: Pollen as climate indicators. *In*: RUDDIMAN, W., SARNTHEIN, M. *et al.* 1989. *Proceedings of the ODP, Scientific Research*, **108**, 93–111.

HEINZE, P. 1990. Das Auftriebsgeschehen vor Peru im Spätquartär: Ocean Drilling Program (ODP) Forschungsfahrt Nr. 112: Bohrungen 679D, 680B, 681B, 686B. PhD Thesis, Universität Bremen, Bremen.

IMBRIE, J., HAYS, J. D., MARTINSON, D. G., McINTYRE, A., MIX, A. C., MORLEY, J. J., PISIAS, N. G., PRELL, W. L. & SHACKLETON, N. J. 1984. The orbital theory of Pleistocene climate: Support from a revised chronology of the marine $\delta^{18}O$ record. *In*: BERGER, A. L. *et al.* (eds) *Milankovitch and Climate*, part 1. Reidel, Dordrecht, 269–305.

—— & KIPP, N. G. 1971. A new micropaleontological method for quantitative paleoclimatology: Application to a late Pleistocene Caribbean core. *In*: TUREKIAN, K. K. (ed.) *The Late Cenozoic Glacial Ages*. Yale University Press, New Haven, 71–181.

KOIZUMI, I. & TANIMURA, Y. 1985. Neogene diatom biostratigraphy of the middle latitude western north Pacific, Deep sea drilling project Leg 86. *In*: HEATH, G. R., BURCKLE, L. H. *et al.* Initial Reports DSDP, 86: Washington (U.S. Government Printing Office), 269–300.

LYLE, M. 1988. Climatically forced organic carbon burial in equatorial Atlantic and Pacific Oceans. *Nature*, **335**, 529–532.

——, MURRAY, D. M., FINNEY, B. P., DYMOND, J., ROBBINS, J. M. & BROOKSFORCE, K. 1988. The record of Late Pleistocene biogenic sedimentation in the Eastern Tropical Pacific Ocean. *Paleoceanography*, **3**, 39–59.

MARTINSON, D. G., PISIAS, N. G., HAYS, J. D., IMBRIE, J., MOORE, T. C. JR. & SHACKLETON, N. J. 1987. Age dating and the orbital theory of the ice ages: Development of a high resolution 0 to 300 000 year chronostratigraphy. *Quaternary Research*, **27**, 1–29.

MIX, A. C. 1989a. Influence of productivity variations on long term atmospheric CO_2. *Nature*, **337**, 541–544.

—— 1989b. Pleistocene paleoproductivity: Evidence from organic carbon and foraminiferal species. *In*: BERGER, W. H., SMETACEK, V. S. & WEFER, G. (eds) *Production of the Oceans: Present and Past*, Wiley, Chichester, Life Science Research Reports, 225–269.

MOORE III, B. & BOLIN, B. 1986. The oceans, carbon dioxide, and global climate change. *Oceanus* 1986, 9–15.

MÜLLER, P. J., ERLENKEUSER, H. & VON GRAFENSTEIN, R. 1983. Glacial-interglacial cycles in ocean pro-

ductivity inferred from organic carbon contents in eastern North Atlantic sediment cores. *In*: THIEDE, J. & SUESS, E. (eds) *Coastal Upwelling Part B*. Plenum, New York, 365–398.

PEDERSEN, T. F. 1983. Increased productivity in the eastern equatorial Pacific during the last glacial maximum (19 000 to 14 000 yr B.P.). *Geology*, **11**, 16–19.

——, PICKERING, M., VOGEL, J. S., SOUTHON, J. N. & NELSON, D. E. 1988. The response of benthic foraminifera to productivity cycles in the eastern equatorial Pacific: Faunal and geochemical constraints on glacial bottom water oxygen levels. *Paleoceanography*, **3**, 157–168.

PHILANDER, S. G. H. 1983. El Niño Southern Oscillation phenomena. *Nature*, **302**, 295–301.

PRELL, W., IMBRIE, J., MARTINSON, D. G., MORLEY, J. J., PISIAS, N. G., SHACKLETON, N. J. & STREETER, H. F. 1986. Graphic correlation of oxygen isotope stratigraphy application to the late Quaternary. *Paleoceanography*, **1**, 137–162.

RICHERT, P. 1975. *Die räumliche Verteilung und zeitliche Entwicklung des Phytoplanktons, mit besonderer Berücksichtigung der Diatomeen, im N. W.-Afrikanischen Auftriebswassergebiet*. PhD Thesis, Christian Albrechts Universität, Kiel.

SARNTHEIN, M., WINN, K., DUPLESSY, J.-C. & FONTUGNE, M. R. 1988. Global variations of surface ocean productivity in low and mid latitudes: Influence on CO_2 reservoirs of the deep ocean and atmosphere during the last 21 000 years. *Paleoceanography*, **3** (3), 361–399.

——, WINN, K. & ZAHN, R. 1987. Paleoproductivity of oceanic upwelling and the effect on atmospheric CO_2 and climatic change during deglaciation times. *In*: BERGER, W. H. & LABEYRIE, L. D. (eds) *Abrupt Climatic Change*. Reidel, Dordrecht, 311–337.

SCHRADER, H. & SCHUETTE, G. 1981. Marine Diatoms. *In*: EMILIANI, C. (ed.) *The Oceanic Lithosphere*. Wiley, New York, 1179–1232.

—— & SORKNES, R. 1990. Spatial and temporal variation of Peruvian coastal upwelling during the latest Quaternary. *In*: SUESS, E., VON HUENE, R. *et al.* ODP, *Scientific Results*, 112: College Station, TX (Ocean Drilling Program), 391–406.

—— & SORKNES, R. 1991. Peruvian coastal upwelling: Late Quaternary productivity changes revealed by diatoms. *Marine Geology*, **97**, 233–249.

SCHUETTE, G. & SCHRADER, H. 1979. Diatom taphocoenoses in the coastal upwelling area off Western South America. *Nova Hedwigia, Beihefte*, **64**, 359–378.

—— & —— 1981a. Diatoms in surface sediments: A reflection of coastal upwelling. *In*: RICHARDS, F. A. (ed.) *Coastal Upwelling*. Washington (American Geophysical Union), 372–380.

—— & —— 1981b. Diatom taphocoenoses in the coastal upwelling area off Southwest Africa. *Marine Micropaleontology*, **6**, 131–155.

SHACKLETON, N. J. & PISIAS, N. G. 1985. Atmospheric carbon dioxide, orbital forcing, and climate. *In*: SUNDQUIST, E. T. & BROECKER, W. S. (eds), *The Carbon Cycle and Atmospheric CO_2: Natural*

Variations Archean to Present, Geophysical Monographs, 32, American Geophysical Union, Washington D. C., 303–317.

SUESS, E., VON HUENE, R., EMEIS, K. and shipboard scientific party 1988. *Proceedings of the Ocean Drilling Program, Initial Reports*, 112, College Station, TX (Ocean Drilling Program).

SUESS, E., VON HUENE, R. *et al*. 1990. *Proceedings ODP, Scientific Results*, 112, College Station, TX (Ocean Drilling Program).

WEFER, G., HEINZE, P. & SUESS, E. 1990. Stratigraphy and sedimentation rates from oxygen isotope composition, organic carbon content, and grain-size distribution at the Peru upwelling region: Holes 680B and 686B. *In*: SUESS, E., VON HUENE, R. *et al*. 1990. *Proceedings ODP, Scientific Results*, 112: College Station, TX (Ocean Drilling Program), 355–367.

ZUTA, S. & GUILLÉN, O. 1970. Oceanografia de las aguas costeras del Peru. *Boletin Instituto del Mar del Peru*, 2, 161–323.

Transfer functions to reconstruct ocean palaeoproductivity: a comparison

M. SARNTHEIN, U. PFLAUMANN, R. ROSS, R. TIEDEMANN & K. WINN

University of Kiel, Olshausenstr. 40, W-2300 Kiel, Germany

Abstract: Oceanic plankton (export) productivity contributes to the control of glacial-to-interglacial changes in atmospheric CO_2 concentration. The extent of this contribution may be deciphered from global reconstructions of palaeoproductivity. We quantitatively estimate palaeoproductivity over the last 350 000 years in the eastern equatorial Atlantic, using equations based on foraminiferal assemblages and marine organic carbon accumulation rates; and make qualitative estimates using diatom and radiolarian accumulation rates. These proxydata are calibrated to data on modern primary production. When applied to the same set of marine sediment samples, the various reconstruction techniques produce productivity estimates with similar temporal productivity oscillations and a long-term similar absolute productivity level, suggesting that each provides a good signal of productivity changes.

The established glacial-to-interglacial changes in atmospheric CO_2 (Barnola *et al.* 1987) resulted to a large degree from variations in the CO_2 exchange between the atmosphere and the ocean (Broecker & Takahashi 1984; Sundquist 1985 and summary of literature in Sundquist & Broecker 1985). This exchange rate is controlled to a large, but unknown, extent by the export of organic carbon from the surface ocean to the deep sea, i.e. by the export production or 'biological pump' (Berger & Keir 1984; Berger *et al.* 1989a). Other influential factors are deepwater alkalinity, especially as a result of differential $CaCO_3$ dissolution (Berger & Keir 1984; Boyle 1986, 1988), changes in oceanic deepwater circulation and the downwelling of preformed nutrients accompanying deep-water formation (Mix & Fairbanks 1985).

The details of the modern distribution patterns of oceanic production and their interannual variations are being investigated by the Joint Global Ocean Flux Study (JGOFS) project (1990) in order to assess the significance of the modern biological pump. Likewise, the precise reconstruction of palaeoproductivity budgets has become increasingly important for the understanding of the past changes in atmospheric $p CO_2$, since oceanic productivity has varied over short time spans and on the small scales of upwelling cells, both of which are difficult to estimate by computer modelling.

During recent years, a number of approaches have been published, trying to develop quantitative empirical transfer formulae for reconstructing palaeoproductivity based on the deep-sea sediment record. Since Müller & Suess (1979) and Suess (1980) several authors have based their palaeoproductivity estimates on the rates of organic carbon accumulation in oxic ocean basins (Betzer *et al.* 1984; Sarnthein *et al.* 1987, 1988; Pedersen 1988; Finney *et al.* 1988; Lyle *et al.* 1988; Lyle 1988; Stein 1990). Other authors have tried to obtain their quantitative estimates from the floral composition (Schrader & Karpuz 1989) and the accumulation rates of siliceous fossils (Abrantes 1990; Lyle *et al.* 1988), from the faunal composition of planktonic foraminifers and the comparison of faunal and carbon-based evidence (Mix 1989a, b), or from benthic/planktonic ratios in foraminifers (Berger & Diester-Haass 1988). Most principal aspects of plankton productivity and reconstructing paleoproductivity were recently summarized in Berger *et al.* (1989a, b). Many aspects, however, remained controversial, due especially to caveats concerning the use of carbon accumulation rates, which were used to estimate productivity for the first budgets of past global organic carbon fluxes (Sarnthein *et al.* 1988; Sarnthein & Winn 1990).

In this paper, we present a simple comparison of the results from various transfer equations based on carbon accumulation rates, each based on different assumptions and/or different sets of modern sediment data for the calibration of the equations. These estimates are compared with results from a planktonic foraminiferal transfer function and from accumulation rates of siliceous microfossils (Abrantes 1990). All transfer equations were applied to a set of four well investigated cores in the East Atlantic. It can be demonstrated that the results from the various approaches are fairly robust with regard to the major productivity oscillations.

Precise sedimentation rates play an important role in the quality of the carbon and silica-based

From SUMMERHAYES, C. P., PRELL, W. L. & EMEIS, K. C. (eds), 1992, *Upwelling Systems: Evolution Since the Early Miocene.* Geological Society Special Publication No 64, pp 411–427.

palaeoproductivity estimates. Hence we carefully re-examined the surface–sediment ages and the sedimentation rates for the last 30 000 years in about 40 Atlantic deep-sea cores and present a new version of an organic carbon based transfer formula, accounting for almost 80% of the variance between measured and estimated export productivity data. A new transfer function based on planktonic foraminifer assemblages can explain as much as 63% of the variance of modern export productivity.

Empirical equations for palaeoproductivity: methods

The age control of our Atlantic cores for the last 30 000 years is described in detail by Winn *et al.* (1991). It was based on oxygen and carbon stable isotope stratigraphy, in most cases obtained from the benthic foraminifer *Cibicidoides wuellerstorfi*, the absolute $\delta^{18}O$ values of which can be traced across large parts of the Atlantic at a given stratigraphic level. A number of pronounced events in these $\delta^{18}O$ curves were dated by means of 'AMS-^{14}C analogue ages', determined by comparison with benthic $\delta^{18}O$ records from several high-resolution cores dated by a series of AMS-^{14}C ages (e.g. Bard *et al.* 1987; Duplessy *et al.* 1986). In addition, conventional ^{14}C ages were used for a number of cores. All the radiocarbon ages were converted into astronomical ages by means of dendrochronological conversion tables (Suess 1969) and the U/Th datings of Bard *et al.* (1990). Wherever possible, $\delta^{18}O$ records of gravity, kasten, and piston cores were spliced with records from companion box cores, which are most likely to preserve undisturbed surface sediment of zero age (Winn *et al.* 1991).

Prior to 30 000 years BP the $\delta^{18}O$ records were age calibrated to the SPECMAP timescale (Martinson *et al.* 1987), except for $\delta^{18}O$ event 5.53, which was re-adjusted to 131 000 years BP (Sarnthein & Tiedemann 1990).

Derivation of palaeoproductivity estimates from sedimentary organic carbon data

Extending the model of Müller & Suess (1979), Sarnthein *et al.* (1987, 1988) have shown that estimates of ocean palaeoproductivity (P) may be deduced from the accumulation rates of organic carbon in deep-sea sediments deposited in oxic environments with more than about 50–100 micromol O_2/kg in the bottom water. The principles of this transfer function are:

$$C_A = k \, F_C \, S_{B-C}^a \tag{1}$$

where carbon accumulation rates (C_A: based on concentrations of organic carbon, bulk sedimentation rates and dry bulk density) are considered as a function of both the water-depth dependent flux of organic carbon (F_C) to the sea floor and the (organic carbon free) sedimentation rate (S_{B-C}), which acts as some kind of 'sealing factor'. a and k are constants. This feedback relationship may be due primarily to an increasing proportion of sulphate reduction relative to oxic respiration in the early diagenetic organic carbon oxidation when sedimentation rates increase (Canfield 1989), but is not fully explained yet. The feedback model is little affected by the arguments of Emerson (1985) and Emerson *et al.* (1987), taking the 'sealing' too literally as a fast burying of carbon by high sedimentation rates. Recently, Calvert *et al.* (1991) showed that 'sealing', not the lack of oxygen, is the dominant factor for carbon preservation even in the euxinic sediments of the Black Sea.

Based on sediment trap data, Suess (1980) first defined an empirical relationship between F_C, primary productivity P and water depth z as

$$F_C = P/(0.0238 \, z + 0.212)$$
$$n = 33, \, r^2 = 0.79. \tag{2}$$

Suess used estimates of modern primary productivity from Koblentz-Mishke *et al.* (1970). Sarnthein *et al.* (1988) extended this concept by applying multiple regression analysis with a least-squares fit to an almost doubled database, arriving at

$$F_C = P^{1.22}/2.29 \, z^{0.5}$$
$$n = 67, \, r^2 = 0.86. \tag{3}$$

Betzer *et al.* (1984) had obtained a similar result from enlarging the data set of Suess (1980) with data from the central Pacific:

$$F_C = P^{1.41}/2.44 \, z^{0.63}$$
$$n = 26, \, r^2 = 0.94. \tag{4}$$

An evaluation of past changes in oceanic carbon budgets, however, requires not a reconstruction of P, but of the export production P_{exp} from the ocean surface layer across the thermocline to the deep ocean. This variable can be obtained from the empirical relationship $P_{exp} = P^2/400$ for primary production below 200 g C/m²a, and $P_{exp} = P/2$ for $P > 200$ g/m²a (Eppley & Peterson 1979), modifying equation (3) into:

$$F_C = 20.563 \, P_{exp}^{0.665}/z^{0.554}$$
$$n = 67, \, r^2 = 0.85. \tag{5}$$

We are aware that the database of this equation

is inadequate with regard to both the *modern estimates of P* as deduced from the FAO map (1981; mainly based on Koblentz-Mishke et al. 1970), and those of P_{exp}. JGOFS will add a lot to our understanding in the near future. At present, however, we still consider this as one of the best approximations available. We supplemented the data off northwest Africa by the detailed production values of Schemainda et al. (1975) and in the equatorial Atlantic by estimates of Corcoran & Mahnken (1969).

For reconstructing palaeoproductivity, the early approach of Müller & Suess (1979) did not include the water–depth relationship between flux and primary production. Based on a global set of surface–sediment data from 26 cores, by substituting P for F_c in equation (1), they obtained:

$$P = C \text{ DBD } 333.3 \ S_B^{-0.30}$$
$$(g \ m^{-2} \ a^{-1}) \qquad (6)$$

calculated against observed values: $n = 26$, $r^2 = 0.64$.

Expanding on Suess (1980, modified), Sarnthein et al. (1988) substituted equation (3) for F_C in equation (1) and subjected an enlarged global and $\log_{10}$ transformed data set of 57 sites for Recent C_A and S_{B-C} to a linear multiple regression analysis with total forcing (least-square fit) that resulted in:

$$P = 2.975 \ C^{0.306} \ S_B^{1.625} \ \text{DBD}^{0.28} \ z^{0.41} \ S_{B-C}^{-1.30}$$
$$(7)$$

calculated against observed values: $n = 57$, $r^2 = 0.70$ (Fig. 1a); standard error $= 36.0$.

The coefficient for depth (z) was predetermined to equal 0.41, based on sediment trap data (summarized in Sarnthein et al. 1988), thus z is not one of the regressor variables. A replacement of P by P_{exp} and the use of equation (5) instead of equation (3) led to equation (8):

$$P_{exp} = 0.0238 \ C^{0.6429} \ S_B^{0.8575} \ \text{DBD}^{0.5364} \ z^{0.8292}$$
$$\times \ S_{B-C}^{-0.2392} \qquad (8)$$

calculated against observed values: $n = 58$, $r^2 = 0.61$ (Fig. 1b); standard error $= 26.5$.

In a recent approach (Winn et al. 1991), we carefully re-examined the age control of 48 Atlantic sediment cores (Fig. 2a), thereby much improving the precision of sedimentation rates and the estimates of the actual surface sediment age in the input file for the transfer formula. The main evidence for our new rates stems from a better definition of the actual sediment surface age, based on a number of additional fits between $\delta^{18}O$ records from gravity or kasten cores and neighbour box cores, containing a well preserved sediment surface. Moreover,

more high-resolution oxygen-isotope records were available. Finally, for calculating rates the radiocarbon datings of the isotopic curves were now converted into calendar years via the nonlinear age corrections suggested by Bard et al. (1990) and Stuiver et al. (1991).

The depth coefficient z was also recalculated in a way predicting the export productivity based on flux values from sediment trap data, the reverse of the approach in Sarnthein et al. (1988). As a result, applying linear regression to $\log_{10}$-transformed data, we arrived at equations (9) and (10), which provide much better estimates than equations (7) and (8):

$$P = 61.390 \ C_A^{0.250} \ S_{B-C}^{-0.049} \ z^{0.150} \qquad (9)$$

calculated against observed values: $n = 45$, $r^2 = 0.74$ (Fig. 1c); standard error $= 17.4$.

$$P_{exp} = 9.354 \ C_A^{0.493} \ S_{B-C}^{-0.105} \ z^{0.300} \qquad (10)$$

calculated against observed values: $n = 45$, $r^2 = 0.79$ (Fig. 1d) standard error $= 9.7$.

Three outliers (about two standard deviations from estimated values) were removed from altogether 48 data; explanations of these anomalies reflect several potential biases in the estimation of palaeoproductivity.

(1) In a core proximal to the mouth of the Congo river, $\delta^{13}C$ values of organic matter amounting to -21 to $-22‰$ (Jansen et al. 1984) indicated a significant proportion of terrigenous organic carbon, much higher than in our samples from elsewhere (Westerhausen et al. 1991; Müller et al. 1983).

(2) In the only core from the top of a low seamount, detailed grain-size studies and ^{14}C datings suggested a loss of fine-grained organic sediment due to local winnowing.

(3) At one site, sedimentation rates were not trustworthy due to believed mishandling of the core.

Generally, at a number of sites it was difficult to define precisely the average values of modern productivity from the literature (e.g. Berger et al. 1987; FAO 1981; Koblentz-Mishke et al. 1970; Schemainda et al. 1975) because of the great local and seasonal variance of rates (Berger & Wefer 1990). For example, the amount of explained variance in palaeoproductivity values sank from 79% to less than 50% using the modern productivity estimates of Berger et al. (1987) for the calibration of our (palaeo-) productivity regression. Note, this latter data set served as a reference base for the foraminifer-based transfer function of Mix (1989a).

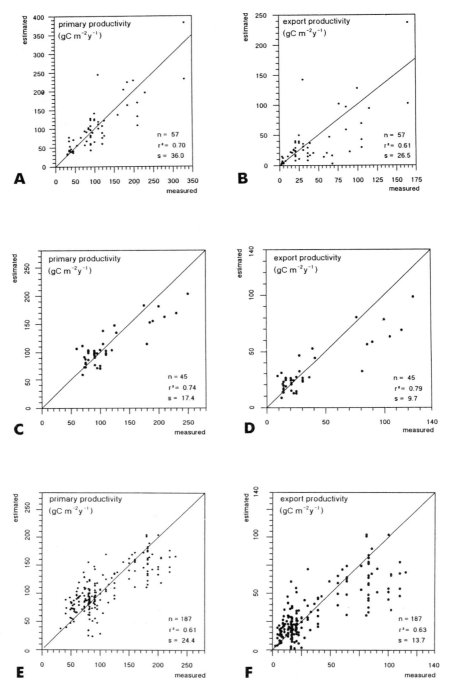

Fig. 1. Calibration data for paleoproductivity equations (primarily using modern productivity values of Koblentz-Mishke *et al.* 1970). (A) Equation (7) (from Sarnthein *et al.* 1988). (B) Equation (8) (from Sarnthein *et al.* 1988). (C) Equation (9), based on bulk sediment carbon and accumulation rates. (D) Equation (10), based on bulk sediment and carbon accumulation rates. (E) Formula 187−6−27, based on planktonic foraminifer samples. (F) Formula 187−6−27, based on planktonic foraminifer samples, calculated from the estimates of primary productivity (Fig. 1E) using the empirical formula of Eppley & Peterson (1979).

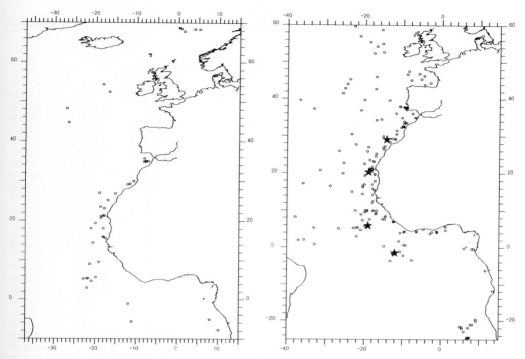

Fig. 2. Core-top sites used for paleoproductivity equations (9) and (10) (A) and 189−6−27 (B). Stars in Fig. 2B mark four deep-sea core sites 12392, 658, 13519, and 16772 (from N to S).

Generalizations and possible pitfalls of these palaeoproductivity equations were discussed in detail by Sarnthein *et al.* (1988) and Mix (1989*a*). A main problem is linked to the long-term averages that the sediment-based productivity values present. In reality, the export of organic matter to the deep sea is dominated by pulsating plankton blooms, especially with respect to the long-term persistent background drizzle of organic matter in low-productivity regions (Lochte & Turley 1988; Wefer 1989). Further problems resulting from different local marine and terrestrial carbon sources will be discussed further below. Finally, precise sedimentation rates are still controversial for numerous sediment cores, as shown by Mix (1989*a*), e.g. for his core V 32−08. This applies particularly to the rates of the last 20 000 years, where the U/Th datings of Bard *et al.* (1990) and varve counts of Lotter (1991) demonstrate that ^{14}C age scales must be corrected considerably. High-resolution dating is still needed for many other sections of the SPECMAP time scale such as $\delta^{18}O$ event 5.5 (Martinson *et al.* 1987; Chen *et al.* 1991).

Derivation of paleoproductivity estimates from planktonic foraminiferal species

Expanding on ideas of previous authors (Berger & Killingley, 1977, and others), Mix (1989*a, b*) used planktonic foraminiferal species to estimate quantitatively (palaeo-)productivity in the Atlantic using standard transfer function techniques (Imbrie & Kipp 1971). His transfer function model is

$$P = \Sigma \, (a_i \, X_i) + c. \tag{11}$$

Here X_i are the foraminiferal assemblages and their non-linear combinations as defined by Q-mode factor analysis. a_i and c are constants, found by multiple regression of the core-top foraminiferal assemblages on the modern productivity rates from each site (modern rates were obtained from Berger *et al.* 1987). The quantitative palaeoproductivity index of Mix (1989), named FAP-6, explained more than 60% ($n = 356$) of the modern variance in total primary productivity. A comparison of the statistical qualities of the various transfer functions, discussed in this paper, is given in Table 3.

Table 1. Factor description matrix of 187 core-top foraminifera.

Species	1 Coastal upwell.	2 Tropical	3 Subtr. center	4 Sub- polar	5 Trop. upwell.	6 Trop. infertil
1 *Aequilateralis*	0.0044	0.0909	0.0631	0.0135	0.0252	0.0210
2 *Bulloides*	0.9880	−0.0721	−0.0117	−0.0235	0.0925	−0.0420
3 *Calida*	0.0118	0.0024	0.0272	0.0125	−0.0066	0.0309
4 *Conglobatus*	−0.0007	0.0117	0.0030	0.0019	0.0124	0.0226
5 *Crassaformis*	−0.0103	0.0270	0.0623	0.0189	0.0252	−0.0430
6 *Dehiscens*	−0.0019	0.0020	0.0067	0.0015	0.0067	0.0113
7 *Digitata*	0.0031	0.0061	0.0173	0.0052	0.0135	0.0292
8 *Dutertrei*	−0.0502	0.0672	0.2725	−0.1193	0.6156	−0.5208
9 *Falconensis*	0.0254	0.0009	0.0108	0.0164	−0.0019	0.0240
10 *Glutinata*	0.0440	0.1285	0.1055	−0.1391	−0.0482	0.2030
11 *Hirsuta*	0.0332	−0.0001	0.0442	0.0218	−0.0377	0.0615
12 *Humilis*	0.0064	0.0071	−0.0016	−0.0145	−0.0167	0.0184
13 *Inflata*	0.0189	−0.0254	0.8995	0.0864	−0.2273	0.0223
14 *Menardii*	−0.0546	0.0769	0.1836	0.0716	0.4211	0.2218
15 *Obliquiloculata*	0.0036	0.0314	−0.0068	0.0071	0.0812	0.0744
16 *Pachyderma dext.*	−0.0278	−0.0240	0.0587	−0.9666	−0.0294	0.0573
17 *Quinqueloba*	0.0131	−0.0089	−0.0098	−0.0863	0.0044	0.0075
18 *Ruber white*	0.0797	0.8770	−0.0316	−0.0404	−0.2938	−0.1260
19 *Rubescens*	0.0037	0.0136	0.0081	0.0044	−0.0101	0.0088
20 *Trilobus tril.*	0.0115	0.3750	−0.0305	0.0497	0.4931	0.4114
21 *Scitula*	0.0347	0.0043	0.0415	−0.0155	−0.0286	0.0699
22 *Tumida*	−0.0175	0.0299	0.0292	0.0083	0.1138	0.0504
23 *Truncatulinoides*	0.0679	0.0173	0.2174	0.0350	−0.1399	0.2866
24 *Universa*	0.0124	0.0218	0.0618	0.0057	0.0242	−0.0082
25 *Tenellus*	0.0050	0.0147	0.0355	0.0074	−0.0209	0.0329
26 *Ruber pink*	−0.0043	0.1596	0.0111	0.0627	−0.0566	−0.5562
27 *Trilobus sacc.*	−0.0144	0.1381	0.0036	0.0052	0.0568	0.1801
% Variance explained	27.466	33.450	14.366	13.410	4.875	2.175

Since foraminiferal estimates are frequently too low at high productivities (constant $a \leq 1$ in Table 3), Mix (1989) has assumed limits in the response of foraminifera to high-productivity water regimes, where the species assemblage remains constant. Note that the carbon-based equations (9) and (10) (and the foraminifera-based equation, described below) may show the same feature (Fig. 1).

Following the concept of Mix, we present a new productivity transfer function for the East Atlantic, which covers with greater detail the zones of intense upwelling than did the data set of Mix (1989). Moreover, we employed the same modern productivity estimates as used for equations (9) and (10) instead of those by Berger *et al.* (1987), because the latter data produce markedly less consistent results. The transfer function, named 187−6−27 (Tables 1 & 2), is based on 187 core top samples (top 1 cm) from 60°N to 25°S (Fig. 2b), obtained from Kiel and Bremen core collections and supplemented by a number of CLIMAP data (Kipp 1976). This equation uses 27 foraminiferal species, grouped into 6 Q-mode factor assemblages. We only

allowed terms into the equation (Table 2) that were significant at the 1-alpha = 0.8 level, and left the rest as zeros. The statistical qualities of the equation ($r^2 = 0.61/0.63$) are presented in Table 3 and Fig. 1e and f.

Using the 'Dahlem' productivity map of Berger (1989) for calibration, equation 187−6−27 explains also 61% of the variance.

A possible bias of the modern foraminiferal species composition and thus the productivity estimates by calcium carbonate dissolution can be largely excluded, because species sensitive to dissolution such as *G. bulloides* characterize just the high-productivity areas where $CaCO_3$ dissolution is particularly strong. This is shown by the fact that there is no correlation between the relative abundances of *G. bulloides* and the carbonate content of the sediment in core 16772 ($r = 0.15$).

Likewise, Mix (1989) demonstrated a lack of correlation between foraminifera-based productivity estimates and dissolution-associated water depths in his core-top samples from 200−5800 m. As with the results of Mix (1989), formula 187−6−27 produces productivity esti-

Table 2. Foraminiferal transfer function for primary productivity in the Atlantic Ocean (g C m^{-2} y^{-1}). Term(I) = Index of Regression coefficient; X(I) = Foraminiferal assemblage combination; A(I) = Coefficient found by multiple regression.

Term(I)	X(I)	A(I)
31	F6	−894.82730
17	F2F4	233.29125
25	F5F6	513.76634
18	F2F5	459.94645
19	F2F6	612.59204
23	F4F5	284.40186
8	F4SQ	−82.66828
22	F3F6	469.87363
11	F1F2	230.95852
26	F1	−195.22649
10	F6SQ	−289.30306
14	F1F5	228.05799
21	F3F5	283.47471
30	F5	−380.72448
7	F3SQ	−113.13392
27	F2	−176.18259
5	F1SQ	0.00000
6	F2SQ	0.00000
9	F5SQ	0.00000
12	F1F3	0.00000
13	F1F4	0.00000
15	F1F6	0.00000
16	F2F3	0.00000
20	F3F4	0.00000
24	F4F5	0.00000
28	F3	0.00000
29	F4	0.00000
Intercept c =		278.38611

mates independent from local sea surface temperatures ($r = 0.14$).

Palaeoproductivity estimates based on siliceous microfossils and biogenic opal

Results from sediment traps indicate that in general the fluxes of diatoms, radiolarians, and biogenic opal are strongly correlated with ocean productivity (Takahashi 1986). Hence accumulation rates of these variables may also serve as valuable companion evidence for tracing past variations in productivity, although an equation does not exist for reconstructing absolute productivity estimates from the siliceous sediment record.

In this paper, accumulation rates of biogenic opal are from Tiedemann *et al.* (1989) and Tiedemann (1990). Accumulation rates of diatoms and radiolarians are from Abrantes (1990).

We may summarize that the quality of the various sediment-based estimates of modern productivity has become increasingly accurate with an improved database over the past ten years. The total variance explained in the regression data has increased from a modest original value of about 60 to 80%. The main improvements include (i) the high-precision age control for deducing sedimentation rates, (ii) the inclusion of sufficient samples from upwelling zones with high production into the set of modern sediment data, and (iii) the careful assignment of foraminiferal species such as *pachyderma−dutertrei* intergrades and their grouping into factor assemblages. Eppley & Peterson's (1979) conversion factor from primary productivity rates into rates of export production remains, of course, no more than a first, but most necessary, approximation of the relationships between true carbon budgets and the biological pump.

Pleistocene time series

The various transfer functions for palaeoproductivity were applied to Pleistocene time series from four core sites (Fig. 2), selected from different productivity regimes in the low latitudinal East Atlantic.

(1) Ocean Drilling Project (ODP) Site 658 was drilled off Cape Blanc below a persistent upwelling cell with extremely high productivity rates (Fig. 3).

(2) Core M 13519 was obtained, for contrast, from the Sierra Leone Rise, which is characterized by persistently low productivity rates (Fig. 4).

(3) Coring Site M 12392 lies off the northwestern Sahara, where the coastal upwelling regime strongly oscillated in its productivity from glacial to interglacial times (Fig. 5).

(4) Core M 16772 was obtained below the strongly oscillating upwelling regime of the equatorial eastern Atlantic (Fig. 6).

The four sediment records have precise and detailed time control based on age-calibrated benthic and planktonic $\delta^{18}O$ curves (Figs 3−6) (Kähler 1990; Sarnthein & Tiedemann 1990; Sarnthein *et al.* 1984; Winn *et al.* 1991; Zahn *et al.* 1986).

A comparison among the various foraminifera- and carbon-based productivity records obtained from the same sites reveals the following features. The general correlation between the two different productivity records, based on equation (9) and formula 187−6−27, is unexpectedly good in the joint data set of cores

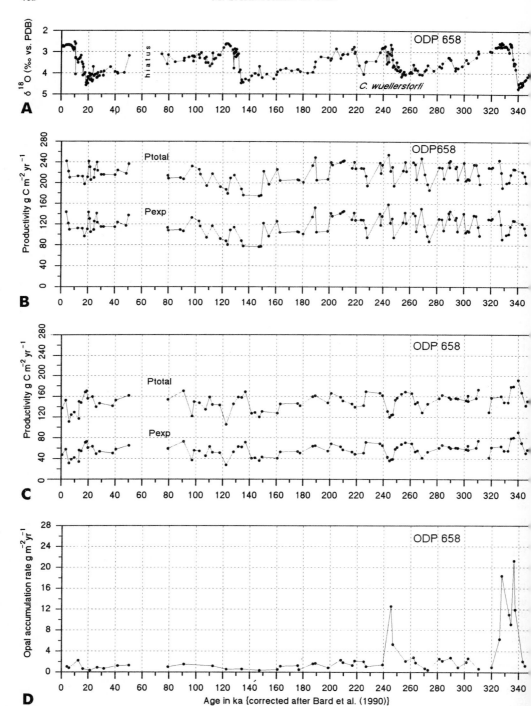

Fig. 3. ODP Site 658 results, (A) Down-core ^{18}O stratigraphy curve of *Cibicidoides wuellerstorfi.*
(B) Accumulation rates of organic carbon (equations (9) and (10)). Data from Tiedemann *et al.* (1989).
(C) Planktonic foraminifera formula 187−6−27. (Foraminifera counts from Niebler 1990). (D) Qualitative
estimates based on accumulation rates of biogenic opal (Tiedemann 1990).

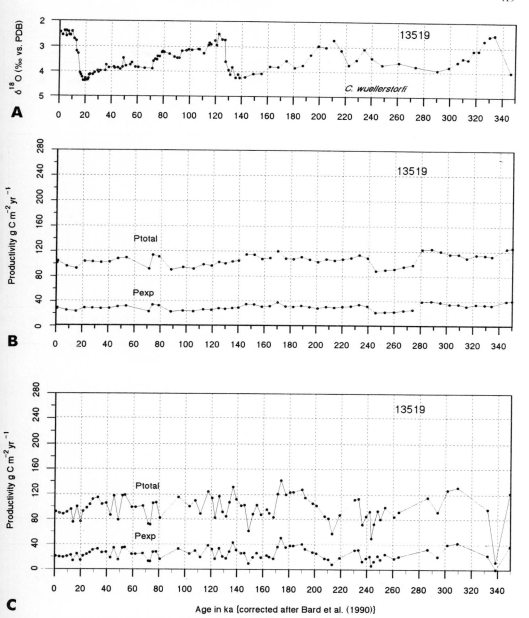

Fig. 4. Down-core δ^{18}O stratigraphy and productivity records from core M 13519. Caption as for Fig. 3(A–C). %C_{org} and DBD values from Müller *et al.* (1983).

12392, 13519, and Site 658 ($r^2 = 0.51$; scatter plot in Fig. 7), when considering the complex derivation of the formulas used. This implies that the general ranges of palaeoproductivity can be estimated by the two different techniques with a fair reliability. The carbon-based values appear generally more sensitive (and closer to modern productivity measures in the surface sediments) in the medium- and high-productivity range and the foraminifera-based estimates higher and possibly more reliable in the low-productivity zones. The data in Core

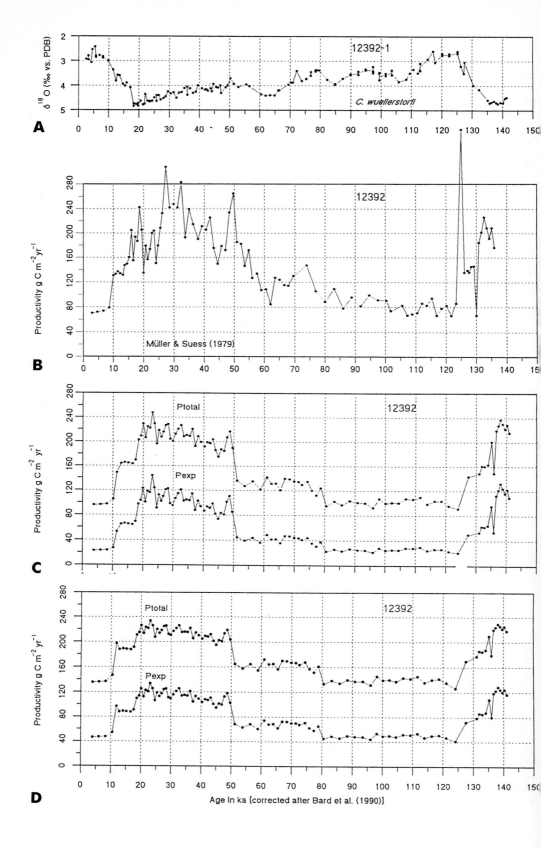

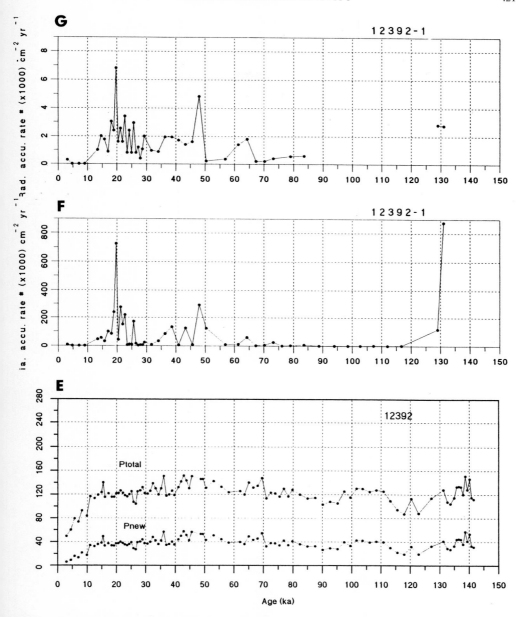

Fig. 5. Down-core $\delta^{18}O$ stratigraphy and productivity records from core M 12392. (A) $\delta^{18}O$ curve of *Cibicidoides wuellestorji*. Figs B–D. Productivity estimates based on accumulation rates of organic carbon using (B) the formula of Müller & Suess (1979). (C) of Sarnthein *et al.* (1988), equations (7) and (8), and (D) equations (9) and (10). % C_{org} and DBD values from Müller & Suess (179). (E) Estimates based on planktonic foraminifera assemblages using eq. 187−6−27. Counts from Thiede (1977). (F) Accumulation rates of diatoms (Abrantes 1990). (G) Accumulation rates of radiolarians (Abrantes 1990).

16772 from the equatorial upwelling belt, however, do not fit into this regression pattern. Possibly, this is related to the productivity oscil- lations in this core, which are too high in fre- quency and amplitude to be able to match two different records precisely. The explained vari-

Table 3. Statistics of transfer functions for estimates of palaeoproductivity.

	Sample number	Explained variance (%)	Standard error of estimates[1] (g C m^{-2} a^{-1})	Parameter of the Linear Regression $y = ax + b$		Authors
				a	b	
Equation (6) (bulk productivity)	26	64	?	1.1	−6.9	Müller & Suess (1979)
Equation (7) (bulk productivity)	57	70	36.0	0.71	36.5	Sarnthein *et al.* (1988)
Equation (8) (export productivity)	57	61	26.5	0.84	4.7	Sarnthein *et al.* (1988)
Equation (9) (bulk productivity)	45	74	17.5	0.62	39.0	this paper
Equation (10) (export productivity)	45	79	9.7	0.59	10.7	this paper
FAP-6 (bulk productivity)	356	>60	12.0	?<1.0	?	Mix 1989*a*
187–6–27 (bulk productivity)	187	61	24.4	0.61	41.4	this paper
187–6–27 (export productivity)	187	63	13.7	0.57	12.4	this paper

[1] mean absolute value of residuals

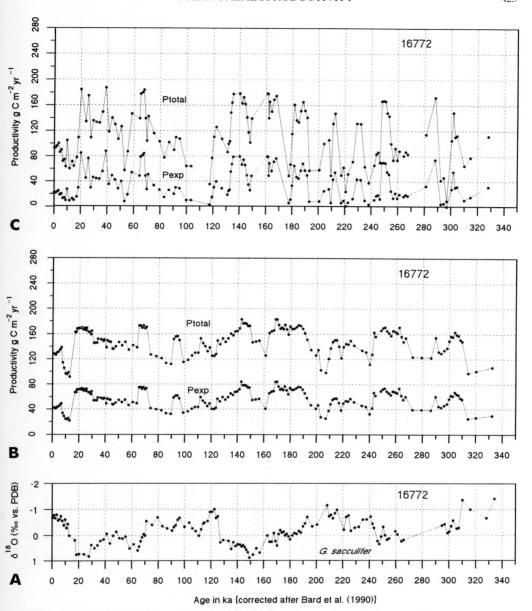

Fig. 6. Down-core $\delta^{18}O$ stratigraphy and productivity records from core M 16772. (A) $\delta^{18}O$ curve of *Globigerinoides trilobus sacculifer*. Productivity estimates based on (B) accumulation rates of organic carbon (equations (9) and (10)). Data from Westerhausen (1991). (C) Planktonic foraminifera formula $187-6-27$. (Foraminifera counts from Kähler 1990).

ance for the comparison of the two data sets obtained from this core only reaches slightly below 30%.

As compared with the foraminiferal estimates the oscillations of the carbon-based records have lower amplitudes in low latitudes, but are higher at mid-latitude core 12392 and Site 658. The lower amplitudes of the carbon-based productivity values may be an artifact of too widely spaced age control points resulting in spuriously

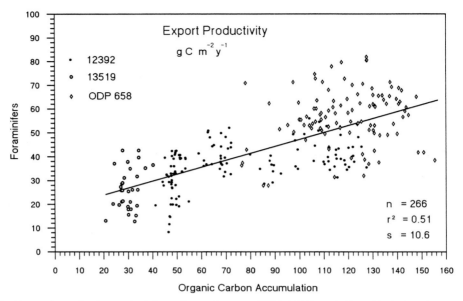

Fig. 7. Comparison of paleoproductivity estimates in cores 12392, 13519, and ODP 658 derived from carbon accumulation rates and planktonic species distribution.

constant sedimentation rates across different climatic regimes. Based on $\delta^{13}C$ values of the organic carbon content (recent calibration in East Atlantic modern sediments by Westerhausen *et al.* 1991), the proportion of terrestrial carbon is generally low at all four sites, apart from Site 658 where it occasionally reaches 25–30% (Müller *et al.* 1983; Westerhausen, 1991).

At ODP Site 658 (Fig. 3), which is characterized by high productivity, the record of opal accumulation rates is completely unrelated to the other productivity records (Fig. 3D).

At the northermost Core 12392, the variations in opal and diatom and radiolarian accumulation rates (Figs 5F and G) highlight some major trends in the carbon-based productivity records of Core 12392, but follow a different temporal oscillation pattern in detail.

The data of Core 12392 (cited as M12392) indicate that Müller & Suess (1979), using equation (6), had already found the basic trends and levels of productivity variation that we find using the refined equations. Their results seem to contain more noise than results obtained using the more recent equations (7) and (9), and a better recent age control. The corrections of the radiocarbon timescale by Bard *et al.* (1990) proved to be crucial. Equations (9) and (10) produced generally lower amplitudes in the productivity variations than (7) and (8); the course of the palaeoproductivity curves based

on these two pairs of equations, however, matches precisely.

The productivity level remained nearly constant in both the subtropical low-productivity zone at Site 13519 and the upwelling cell at Site ODP 658 over the last 350 000 years. At the two other tropical core sites cold stages paralleled an extreme increase in export productivity by a factor of three and more, depending on the equations used. At the site near the equator (16772), productivity shows cycles of about 20 000 and 40 000 years and at site 12392 off the northwestern Sahara there is a pronounced 100 000-year cycle. These variations indicate the importance of low-latitudinal productivity variations and upwelling cycles for the understanding of changes in the global CO_2 cycle.

Conclusions

Expanding on the concepts of several authors, transfer functions for the reconstruction of total and export palaeoproductivity estimates were based on both planktonic foraminiferal species assemblages and accumulation rates of organic carbon.

The quality of the transfer functions derived from the planktonic foraminiferal species groups was improved by (i) including samples from upwelling areas with high productivity; and (ii) a careful assignment and grouping of the foraminiferal species, based on their ability to predict sea surface temperatures. In this way, the total variance of modern productivity explained by the sediment foraminiferal data (r^2) increased up to 63% for export productivity, with a standard error of 13.7 g C m^{-2} a^{-1}.

The quality of the transfer equation based on carbon accumulation rates improved through (i) a more accurate age control for deducing sedimentation rates; (ii) a more precise definition of the surface age in sediment cores; (iii) a δ^{13} C$_{org}$-based distinction of the proportions of terrigenous organic matter and (iv) a recalculated water—depth coefficient. Accordingly, the explained variance for export productivity went up from earlier figures of 61 to 79%.

With respect to both equation groups, the modern productivity data of Koblentz—Mishke et al. (1970), FAO (1981), and similar studies, seemingly less trustworthy because of their more patchy distribution patterns, nevertheless yielded a better correlation with the sediment record than the generalized productivity patterns published, e.g., by Berger et al. (1987).

Silica, diatom, and radiolarian accumulation rates provide qualitative palaeoproductivity records whose patterns match only the highest productivity oscillations of the other records. However, silica production, in detail, follows rules different from those of carbon production as is also reflected by sediment trap data (Takahashi 1986).

Pleistocene palaeoproductivity time series from the eastern Atlantic 5°–21°N show an encouraging similarity ($r^2 = 0.51$) between the carbon-accumulation rate (C_A)-based estimates and the independently derived values from the Atlantic foraminiferal formula 187–6–27. This similarity is not observed in Core 16772, probably because the palaeoproductivity at this location oscillated at too high frequency beyond the temporal resolution for this core. In general, the long-term productivity oscillations derived from different C_A-based equations at any one site are strongly similar, when employing the same time control, demonstrating that the transfer functions are basically robust.

Productivity is estimated to have strongly varied over the last 350 000 years below the equatorial divergence zone and along the margin of the NW African coastal upwelling belt. These variations parallel the orbitally forced cycles of global climate as depicted in the δ^{18} O curves. In contrast, in both in low-productivity subtropical gyres (core 13519) and the high-productivity persistent upwelling cells (ODP Site 658), productivity estimates have remained nearly constant through geological time.

We gratefully acknowledge the thorough and constructive reviews of D. McCorckle, A. Mix, and W. Prell. H. Hensch and K. Kissling helped with careful laboratory analyses. This study was supported by the National Climate Project of the German Ministry of Research and Technology (BMFT), grant 07 KF 021.

References

ABRANTES, F. 1991. Variability of upwelling off NW Africa during the latest Quaternary: diatom evidence. *Palaeoceanography*, **6**, 431–460.

BARD, E., ARNOLD, M., MAURICE, P., DUPRAT, J., MOYES, J. & DUPLESSY, J.-C. 1987. Retreat velocity of the North Atlantic polar front during the last deglaciation determined by ^{14}C accelerator mass spectrometry. *Nature*, **328**, 791–794.

——, HAMELIN, B., FAIRBANKS, R. G. & ZINDLER, A. 1990. Calibration of the ^{14}C timescale over the past 30 000 years using mass spectrometric U–Th ages from Barbados corals. *Nature*, **342**, 405–410.

BARNOLA, J. M., RAYNAUD, D., KOROTKEVICH, Y. S. & LORIUS, C. 1987. Vostok ice core provides 160 000-years record of atmospheric CO$_2$. *Nature*, **329**, 408–414.

BERGER, W. H. & DIESTER-HAASS, L. 1988. Palaeoproductivity: the benthic/planktonic ratio in foraminifera as a productivity index. *Marine Geology*, **81**, 15–25.

——, FISCHER, K. & LAI, G. 1987. Ocean carbon flux: global maps of primary production and export production. *In*: AGEGIAN, C. (ed.) *Symposium on Ocean Productivity*. Hawai Dec. 1986. Scripps Institute of Oceanography Ref. 87–30.

—— & KEIR, R. S. 1984. Glacial-Holocene changes in atmospheric CO$_2$ and the deep-sea record. *In*: HANSEN, J. E. & TAKAHASHI, T. (eds), *Climate Processes and Climate Sensitivity*. Geophysics Monograph **29** (AGU), 337–351.

—— & KILLINGLEY, J. B. 1977. Glacial-Holocene Transition in Deep-Sea Carbonates: Selective Dissolution and the Stable Isotope Signal. *Science*, **197**, 563–566.

——, SMETACEK, V. S. & WEFER, G. (eds). 1989a. Productivity of the Ocean: present and past. *Dahlem Workshop Report*, **44**, Wiley, New York.

——, —— & —— 1989b. Ocean productivity and paleoproductivity — an overview. *In*: BERGER, W. H., SMETACEK, V. S. & WEFER, G. (eds) *Productivity of the Ocean: present and past*. Dahlem Workshop Report, **44** (Wiley-Interscience Publ.), 1–34.

—— & WEFER, G. 1990. Export production: seasonality and intermittency, and paleoceanographic implications. *Paleogeography, Paleoclimatology, Paleoecology*, **89**, 245–254.

BETZER, R. R., SHOWERS, W. J., LAWS, E. A., WINN, C. D., DiTULLIO, G. R. & KROOPNICK, P. M. 1984. Primary productivity and particle fluxes on a transect of the equator at 153°W in the Pacific Ocean. *Deep-Sea Research* **31**, 1–11.

BOYLE, E. A. 1986. Deep ocean circulation, preformed nutrients, and atmospheric carbon dioxide: theories and evidence from organic sediments. *In*: Hsü, K. J. (ed.) *Mesozoic and Cenozoic Oceans*. AGU Geodynam. Series **15**, 49−59.

—— 1989. The role of vertical chemical fractionation in controlling Late Quaternary atmospheric carbon dioxide. *Journal of Geophysical Research* **93**, 15 701−15 714.

BROECKER, W. S. & TAKAHASHI, T. 1984. Is there a tie between atmospheric CO_2 content and ocean circulation? *AGU Geophysical Monograph* 29 (Maurice Ewing Vol. 5), 314−326.

CALVERT, S. E., KARLIN, R. E., TOOLIN, L. J., DONAHUE, D. J., SOUTHON, J. R. & VOGEL, J. S. 1991. Low organic carbon accumulation rates in Black Sea sediments. *Nature*, **350**, 692−695.

CANFIELD, D. E. 1989. Sulfate reduction and oxic preservation in euxinic environments. *Deep-Sea Research* **36** (1), 121−138.

CHEN, J. H., CURRAN, H. A., WHITE, B. & WASSERBURG, G. J. 1991. Precise chronology of the last interglacial period: ^{234}U-^{238}Th-data from fossil coral reefs in the Bahamas. *Geological Society of America Bulletin*, **103**, 82−97.

CORCORAN, E. F. & MAHNKEN, C. V. W. 1969. Productivity of the tropical Atlantic Ocean. *In*: Actes Symp. Ocean. Resources Halieut. Atlant. Trop., Abidjan, 20−28 Oct. 1966. *Unesco*. 57−67.

DUPLESSY, J.-C., ARNOLD, M., MAURICE, P., BARD, E., DUPRAT, J. & MOYES, J. 1986. Direct dating of the oxygen-isotope record of the last deglaciation by ^{14}C accelerator mass spectrometry. *Nature*, **320**, 350−352.

EMERSON, S. 1985. Organic carbon preservation in marine sediments. *In*: SUNDQUIST, E. T. & BROECKER, W. S. (eds). The carbon cycle and atmospheric CO_2: Natural variations Archean Present. *Geophysics Monograph*, **32**, 78−87.

——, STUMP, D. *et al.* 1987. Estimates of degradable organic carbon in deep-sea surface sediments from ^{14}C concentrations. *Nature*, **329**, 51−53.

EPPLEY, R. & PETERSON, B. J. 1979. Particulate organic matter flux and planktonic new production in the deep ocean. *Nature* **282**, 677−680.

FAO Fisheries Department 1981. Atlas of living resources of the seas. *FAO Rome*, 4th Edition.

FINNEY, B. P., LYLE, M. W. & HEATH, G. R. 1988. Sedimentation at MANOP Site H (eastern equatorial Pacific) of the past 400 000 years: Climatically induced redox variations and their effects on transition metal cycling. *Paleoceanography*, **3** (2), 169−189.

JANSEN, J. H. F., van WEERING, T. C. E., GIELES, R. & van IPEREN, J. 1984. Middle and Late Quaternary oceanography and climatology of the Zaire-Congo fan and the adjacent eastern Angola Basin. *Netherlands Journal of Sea Research*, **17**, 201−249.

KÄHLER, G. 1990. *Oberflächentemperaturen im äquatorialen Atlantik während der letzten 330 000 Jahre (Meteor-Kern 16772)*. MSc Thesis, University of Kiel.

KOBLENTZ-MISHKE, O. J., VOLKOWINSKY, V. V. & KABANOVA, J. G. 1970. Plankton primary production of the World Ocean. *In*: WOOSTER, W. S. (ed.) *Scientific Exploration of the South Pacific*, 183−193.

LOCHTE, K. & TURLEY, C. M. 1988. Bacteria and cyanobacteria associated with phytodetritus in the deep sea. *Nature*, **333**, 67−69.

LOTTER, A. F. 1991. Absolute dating of the Late-Glacial period in Switzerland using anually laminated sediments. *Quaternary Research*, **35**, 321−330.

LYLE, M. 1988. Climatically forced organic carbon burial in equatorial Atlantic and Pacific Oceans. *Nature*, **335**, 529−532.

——, MURRAY, D. W., FINNEY, B. P., DYMOND, J., ROBBINS, J. M. & BROOKSFORCE, K. 1988. The record of Late Pleistocene biogenic sedimentation in the eastern tropical Pacific Ocean. *Paleoceanography*, **3** (1), 39−59.

MARTINSON, D. G., PISIAS, N. G., HAYS, J. D., IMBRIE, J., MOORE, T. C. & SHACKLETON, N. J. 1987. Age dating and the orbital theory of the ice ages: development of a high-resolution 0 to 300 000-year chronostratigraphy. *Quaternary Research*, **27**, 1−29.

MIX, A. C. 1989*a*. Pleistocene paleoproductivity: Evidence from organic carbon and foraminiferal species. *In*: BERGER, W. H., SMETACEK, V. S. & WEFER, G. (eds) *Productivity of the Ocean: Present and Past*, Wiley, Chichester, 313−340.

—— 1989*b*. Productivity of the Pleistocene Atlantic ocean estimated from foraminiferal species: Implications for paleo-CO_2. *Nature*, **337**, 541−544.

—— & FAIRBANKS, R. G. 1985. North Atlantic surface-ocean control of Pleistocene deep-ocean circulation. *EPSL*, **73**, 231−243.

MÜLLER, P. J., ERLENKEUSER, H. & VON GRAFENSTEIN, R. 1983. Glacial-interglacial cycles in oceanic productivity inferred from organic carbon contents in eastern North Atlantic sediment cores. *In*: THIEDE, J. & SUESS, E. (eds), *Coastal Upwelling: Its Sediment Record, Part B*, Plenum, New York, 365−398.

MÜLLER, P. J. & SUESS, E. 1979. Productivity, sedimentation rate, and sedimentary organic matter in the oceans − I. Organic carbon preservation. *Deep-Sea Research* **26**, 1347−1362.

NIEBLER, H. S. 1990. Geschichte der Meeresoberflächentemperaturen in einem Auftriebsgebiet vor Nordwest-Afrika (ODP-Station 658). *Unveröff. Dipl. Arbeit Univ. Kiel*, 61 S. plus Datenanhang.

PEDERSEN, T. F., PICKERING, M., VOGEL, J. S., SOUTHON, J. N. & NELSON, D. E. 1988. The response of benthic foraminifera to productivity cycles in the eastern equatorial Pacific: faunal and geochemical constraints on glacial bottom-water oxygen levels. *Palaeoceanography*, **3**, 157−168.

SARNTHEIN, M., ERLENKEUSER, H., v. GRAFENSTEIN, R. & SCHRÖDER, C. 1984. Stable isotope stratigraphy for the last 750 000 years: 'Meteor' core 13519 from the eastern equatorial Atlantic. *Meteor Forschungs-Ergebn*, **C38**, 9−24.

—— & TIEDEMANN, R. 1990. Younger Dryas-style cooling events at glacial Terminations I-VI:

associated benthic $\delta^{13}C$ anomalies at ODP Site 658 constrain meltwater hypothesis. *Palaeoceanography*, **5**, 1041–1055.

—— & WINN, K. 1990. Reconstruction of low and mid latitude export productivity, 30000 y B.P. to Present: Implications for global carbon reservoirs. *In*: SCHLESINGER, M. (ed.) *NATO Advanced Research Workshop 'Climate-Ocean-Interaction'*. Oxford, 26–30 Sep. 88, 319–342.

——, ——, DUPLESSY, J.-C. & FONTUGUE, M. R. 1988. Global variations of surface ocean productivity in low and mid latitudes: influence on CO_2 reservoirs of the deep ocean and atmosphere during the last 21000 years. *Palaeoceanography*, **3** (3), 361–399.

——, —— & ZAHN, R. 1987. Palaeoproductivity of oceanic upwelling and the effect on atmospheric CO_2 and climatic change during deglaciation times. *In*: BERGER, W. H. & LABEYERIE, L. (eds) *Abrupt Climatic Change*. Proceedings of the NATO/NSF A.R.W. Symposium at Biviers/Grenoble 1985. Reidel, Dordrecht, 311–337.

SCHEMAINDA, R., NEHRING, D. & SCHULZ, S. 1975. Ozeanologische Untersuchungen zum Produktionspotential der nordwestafrikanischen Wasserauftriebsregion 1970–1973. *Geod. Geophys. Veröff.* **4**.

SCHRADER, H. & KARPUZ, N. K. 1989. *Norwegian-Iceland Seas: Transfer functions between marine planktonic diatoms and surface water temperature*. *In*: KARPUZ, N. K., *Cand. Scient. Thesis*. University of Bergen. Sect. B. POC-NAVF-Contribution 5, 20–55.

STEIN, R. 1990. Organic carbon content/sedimentation rate relationship and its paleoenvironmental significance for marine sediments. *Geo-Marine Letters*, **10**, 37–44.

STUIVER, M., BRAZIUNAS, T., BECKER, B. & KROMER, B. 1991. Climatic, solar, oceanic and geomagnetic influences on Late-Glacial and Holocene atmospheric $^{14}C/^{12}C$ change. *Quaternary Research*, **35**, 1–24.

SUESS, E. 1980. Particulate organic carbon flux in the oceans — Surface productivity and oxygen utilization. *Nature*, **288**, 260–263.

SUESS, H. E. 1969. Die Eichung der Radiokarbonuhr. *Bild der Wissenschaft*, 121–127.

SUNDQUIST, E. T. 1985. Geological perspectives on carbon dioxide and the carbon cycle. *In*: SUNDQUIST, E. T. & BROECKER, W. S. (eds) *The*

Carbon Cycle and Atmospheric CO_2: Natural Variations Archean to Present. A.G.U. Geophysical Monograph, **32**, 5–60.

—— & BROECKER, W. S. (eds) 1985. The Carbon Cycle and Atmospheric CO_2: Natural Variations Archean to Present. *Geophysical Monograph*, 32 (AGU, Washington D.C.).

TAKAHASHI, K. 1986. Seasonal fluxes of pelagic diatoms in the Subarctic Pacific. *Deep-Sea Research*, **33**, 1225–1251.

THIEDE, J. 1977. Aspects of variability of the Glacial and Interglacial North Atlantic eastern boundary current (last 150000 years). *'Meteor' Forsch. Ergebn.* **C28**, 1–36.

TIEDEMANN, R. 1991. *Acht Millionen Jahre Klimageschichte von Nordwest-Afrika und Paläo-Ozeanographie des angrenzenden Atlantiks: Hochauflösende Zeitreihen von ODP Sites 658–661*. PhD Thesis University of Kiel.

—— SARNTHEIN, M. & STEIN, R. 1989. Climatic changes in the western Sahara: aeolo-marine sediment record of the last 8 M.y. (ODP-Sites 657–661). *In*: RUDDIMAN, W., SARNTHEIN, M., BALDAUF, J. *et al*. (eds) *Proceedings of the Ocean Drilling Program*, **108**. Ocean Drilling Program, College Station, TX.

WEFER, G. 1989. Particle flux in the ocean: effects of episodic production. *In*: BERGER, W. H., SMETACEK, V. S. & WEFER, G. (eds) *Productivity of the Ocean: Present and Past*. Wiley, Chichester, 139–153.

WESTERHAUSEN, L. 1991. *Organische Sedimente in equitoriales Ostatlantik: Einflusse von Herkurff, Transportmustern, Diagense und Klimaschwankungen*, PhD Thesis, University of Kiel.

——, POYNTER, J., EGLINGTON, G., ERLENKEUSER, H. & SARNTHEIN, M. 1992. Marine and terrigenous origin of organic matter in modern sediments of the equatorial east Atlantic: The $\delta^{13}C$ and molecular record. *Deep-Sea Research*, in press.

WINN, K., SARNTHEIN, M., & ERLENKEUSER, H. 1991. $\delta^{18}O$ stratigraphy and age control of Kiel sediment cores and some ODP sites in the East Atlantic. *Berichte-Reports, Geol. Paläont. Inst. Univ. Kiel*, **45**, 1–99.

ZAHN, R., WINN, K. & SARNTHEIN, M. 1986. Benthic foraminiferal $\delta^{13}C$ and accumulation rates of organic carbon: Uvigerina peregrind group and Cibicidoides wuellerstorf. *Palaeoceanography*, **1**, 27–42.

Miocene intensification of upwelling along the California margin as recorded in siliceous facies of the Monterey Formation and offshore DSDP sites

LISA D. WHITE[1], ROBERT E. GARRISON[2] & JOHN A. BARRON[3]

[1] Department of Geosciences, San Francisco State University, San Francisco, CA 94132, USA

[2] Earth Sciences Board, University of California, Santa Cruz, CA, 95064, USA

[3] U.S. Geological Survey, 345 Middlefield Road MS 915, Menlo Park, CA, 94025, USA

Abstract: Diatomaceous sediments and their diagenetic equivalents in the Monterey Formation record a variable history of upwelling along the California margin. Distinctive dark opal-CT and quartz cherts found in distal basins of the Monterey Formation are the result of burial diagenesis of pure biosiliceous oozes (biosiliceous oozes without significant admixtures of clay) and are therefore evidence of intensified coastal upwelling during the early middle Miocene. Dating of six sections of the Monterey Formation, largely by diatom biostratigraphy, suggests that at the Point Reyes and Point Año Nuevo sections in north-central California, the age of the earliest chert intervals is between 13.8 and 15.0 Ma, and 14.3 and 14.8 Ma, respectively. In south-central California, ages from the Shell Beach, Mussel Rock, and Lions Head sections imply that the age of the base of the chert intervals is between 12.7 and 13.3 Ma. Both ages correlate to an early middle Miocene high latitude cooling step that resulted in more vigorous surface water circulation, upwelling of nutrient-rich waters, and increased biosiliceous sedimentation in the North Pacific. The north–south difference in age of the base of the chert interval probably reflects a progressive intensification of the California Current from 15.0 to 12.7 Ma.

The age of the onset of biosiliceous sedimentation at DSDP sites of the northeastern Pacific is also generally younger at the more southern sites; however, these particular DSDP sites were located some distance from the centres of coastal upwelling and are not as reliable indicators of the intensification of upwelling along the California margin.

Marine siliceous sedimentary deposits dominated by diatoms are commonly interpreted as products of high surface water fertility conditions that are brought about by intensified upwelling of nutrient-rich subsurface waters and lead to diatom blooms. For this reason, the belt of diatomaceous sedimentary rocks that typify uplifted Neogene basins along the margins of three quarters of the Pacific basin, from Chile and Peru on the southeast to Japan on the northwest, have been viewed as a reflection of intensified coastal upwelling beginning in Miocene time (Orr 1972; Garrison 1975; Ingle 1981; Dunbar *et al.* 1990). These units (and equivalent sections offshore) record biosiliceous accumulation that may reflect productivity and the history of Miocene coastal upwelling systems around the Pacific margin. The purpose of this paper is to document this history, with a focus on dating the onset of intensive Miocene upwelling along the California margin.

The middle to upper Miocene Monterey Formation and related Neogene units of western California are notable among the circum-Pacific siliceous sequences for their thick and extensive diatom-rich deposits (in places diagenetically transformed into cherts or porcelanites) and for the broad scope of previous investigations (due in part to the fact that the Monterey Formation is the major petroleum source in California). In this regard, one of the most significant advances has been the development of a diatom zonation for the NE Pacific that has allowed precise age dating (resolution of time is several hundred thousand years) and correlation for Monterey sequences (Barron 1986a, b).

Our focus is on six sections of the Monterey Formation (Fig. 1) that, in their lower parts, contain distinctive dark cherts which we interpret to signal the beginning of intensive and sustained upwelling during the Miocene. Our analysis also includes data from several DSDP sites in the NE Pacific (Fig. 1); we conclude, however, that several of the Monterey onland sections, because they were closer to the centres of intense Miocene coastal upwelling than the offshore DSDP sites, contain a better record of coastal upwelling history. In addition, we point out that a number of local stratigraphic complications (e.g. hiatuses, compositional variations)

From SUMMERHAYES, C. P., PRELL, W. L. & EMEIS, K. C. (eds), 1992, *Upwelling Systems: Evolution Since the Early Miocene*. Geological Society Special Publication No 64, pp 429–442

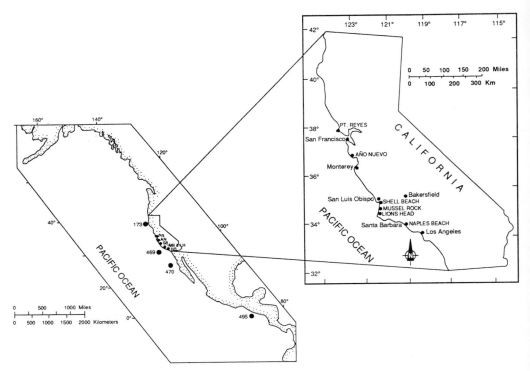

Fig. 1. Map of the northeastern Pacific, with detail of California, showing the location of the six sections of the Monterey Formation and the four DSDP sites investigated. Modified after Fig. 1 of Barron (1989) and Fig. 1 of White (1990).

may introduce difficulties to the interpretation of the sedimentary record of upwelling.

Nature of the Monterey Formation

Monterey and related hemipelagic/pelagic deposits accumulated in a series of relatively small, fault-bounded basins along the transform-dominated California margin. Many of these basins began to subside in late Oligocene to early Miocene time (Blake *et al.* 1978). The rather abrupt onset of Monterey deposition was between 18 and 17 Ma in many basins (Barron 1986*a*), perhaps due to a combination of rapid subsidence and a eustatic sea-level highstand, both of which acted to retard the influx of terrigenous sediment and to promote the accumulation of relatively undiluted pelagic or hemipelagic oozes and muds (Isaacs 1985).

The nature of Monterey sedimentary rocks has been determined by a combination of tectonic, paleoceanographic, and diagenetic factors (Ingle 1981; Pisciotto & Garrison 1981). Distal basins, located far from strandlines and shielded from terrigenous input by intervening proximal basins and submarine highs, accumulated bi-

ogenous pelagic oozes dominated by diatoms or coccolithophorids. Proximal basins, in contrast, were receptacles for detritus-rich hemipelagic muds, and, in some instances, for large turbidite fan systems.

The imprint of palaeoceanographic conditions on deposition of the Monterey was much more complex. The Monterey Formation can be generally divided into a lower calcareous facies (including coccolith limestones), a middle phosphatic facies which in many places is also quite calcareous and organic-rich, and an upper siliceous facies dominated by diatoms (Pisciotto 1978; Pisciotto & Garrison 1981). The change from generally calcareous sediments in the lower and middle Monterey to siliceous sediments in the upper part of the unit was attributed by Pisciotto & Garrison (1981) to the transition from a non-upwelling or low productivity regime to regime dominated by upwelling and high productivity following expansion of Antarctic glaciation during middle Miocene time (*c.* 16–14 Ma). However, as noted by Barron (1986*a*), Isaacs (1987*a*, *b*), and Isaacs & Lagoe (1987), pulses of siliceous (diatomaceous) sedimentation in the eastern Pacific and along the California margin also preceded the mid-Miocene glacial expansion (e.g. as early as 20 Ma in several basins). Moreover, the boundaries between the Monterey facies noted above are diachronous, and the lower calcareous and middle phosphatic facies do not occur in some basins.

These data cast doubt on a simple model in which major oceanographic changes left a precise and unambiguous imprint on these continental margin sediments. Instead, local factors such as differential preservation of siliceous and calcareous components, along with varying conditions of phosphatization (Garrison *et al.* 1990), may have been superimposed on the major palaeoceanographic trends. There is some evidence, for example, that the rates of dissolution of opal-A diatom frustules markedly increase in anoxic to suboxic pore waters, perhaps due to increases in alkalinity during sulphate reduction (von Stackelberg 1972; Loder *et al.* 1978; Boucher 1984). Pore water conditions of this kind (which also promote early diagenetic phosphatization (cf. Burnett 1977) are most common in organic-rich sediments deposited in anoxic or suboxic basins. Thus it is possible that silica-poor, calcareous-phosphatic sediments accumulated in low oxygen basins at the same time as siliceous sediments were being deposited in other, more oxygen-rich basins. In addition, preferential erosion and transport of diatom frustules in parts of some basins (e.g. middle Miocene of the Santa Barbara Basin: Arends & Blake 1986) has produced condensed sections where siliceous facies are missing, even though correlative siliceous facies are present in other parts of the same basin (Hornafius *et al.* 1989).

Though these factors complicate interpretation of Monterey sediments, the upper part of the Monterey is dominated by siliceous rocks everywhere, and this probably reflects more vigorous and sustained coastal upwelling of nutrient-rich waters, which probably followed middle Miocene expansion of Antarctic glaciation and the attendant intensification of boundary current systems (e.g. the California Current, cf. Ingle 1973, 1981). The earlier Miocene pulses of biosiliceous sedimentation may have been connected with other factors, e.g. expansion of North Atlantic Deep Water (Northern component water) in the Atlantic and intensified flow of silica-enriched Antarctic Bottom Water into the Indian and Pacific oceans (Keller & Barron 1983; Barron & Keller 1983; Barron 1986*a*); or to the nutrient enrichment of deep water in the North Pacific as a consequence of the increasing age of these deep waters as the source of saline outflow water in the Indian

Ocean is gradually shut off in the late early to middle Miocene (Woodruff & Savin 1989). In addition, these pulses probably record sporadic upwelling (as contrasted with the later sustained upwelling), and the sediments deposited commonly contained, in addition to diatoms, notable amounts of biogenic calcareous components (in contrast to the overwhelmingly siliceous nature of the upper Monterey).

Our concern in this article remains the timing of the major shift to almost exclusively biosiliceous (diatomaceous) sedimentation that appears to signal the onset of vigorous upwelling over time spans of millions of years. This shift seems to be marked in the Monterey distal basins by the occurrence of unusual dark, glassy quartz and opal-CT cherts at the base of the siliceous facies that lie stratigraphically above the calcareous and phosphatic facies. Judging by previous studies of the burial diagenesis of Monterey and other siliceous deposits, the precursor sediments for these cherts were nearly pure diatom oozes (less pure, clay-rich diatom muds of proximal basins, in contrast, became transformed into porcelanites and siliceous mudrocks during burial diagenesis: cf Isaacs 1980, 1982; Kastner 1981).

Studies by Isaacs (1980, 1982) and earlier investigations by Lancelot (1973) and Kastner *et al.* (1977) indicate clay-poor, diatomaceous oozes commonly alter to opal-CT and quartz cherts. Additional geochemical and stratigraphic studies by Isaacs (1981, 1982) and Isaacs *et al.* (1983) led her to propose that quartz cherts in particular form from clay-poor, carbonate-siliceous sediments with high Si/Al ratios. Furthermore, whole rock compositional analyses by Dunham & Blake (1987) suggest that opal-CT and quartz cherts form from the diagenetic alteration of oozes containing an average of 98% silica. In addition, Dunham & Blake (1987), citing textural, stratigraphic, and geochemical evidence from Santa Maria basin sections, concluded that quartz cherts have replaced nearly pure, relatively detritus-free diatom ooze.

If true, the first abundant occurrence of these cherts may indicate sustained deposition of pure diatom oozes, presumably the products of strong upwelling. Burial diagenesis, however, usually completely destroyed all diatom frustules, hence removing the primary means of assigning ages to the cherts. To overcome this difficulty, we have utilized dolomite lenses and layers within cherty and porcelaneous sequences that contain well preserved diatoms which can be recovered in acid-insoluble residues.

Methodology

Because of the poor preservation of planktonic foraminifers in the Monterey Formation and the time transgressive nature of benthonic foraminifers, diatoms have become an increasingly reliable group for age dating the Monterey Formation and similar sedimentary sequences in the eastern Pacific. Barron (1986*b*) presented an updated Miocene diatom zonation for the middle latitude northeastern Pacific in which he identified numerous primary and secondary diatom data useful for biostratigraphy. He also assigned numerical ages to the first and last occurrences of specific diatoms by correlating these with the low-latitude calcareous nanno-fossil and diatom zonations, which are directly correlated to the polarity and numerical time-scales. This timescale is based on graphical correlation and on the assumption that certain diatom events (first and last occurrences) are isochronous between middle and low latitudes. The occurrence of these zonal markers are often more limited in California, therefore secondary diatom data are utilized (Barron 1986*b*). Given refined Miocene diatom biochronology, which with good preservation can provide a resolution of approximately 100 000 years in the middle and late Miocene (Barron 1986*b*), the timing of important lithological changes and implied correlative palaeoceanographic events can be resolved within the time resolution of the biostratigraphy (Barron 1986*a*).

Figure 2 (after Barron 1989) shows a temperate to subarctic northeastern Pacific biostratigraphic timescale for the late Cenozoic, which includes the zonation of Barron (1986*b*). For reference, Fig. 2 also shows the diatom zonation of Koizumi (1985) for the subarctic and western North Pacific, as well as temperate radiolarian (Kling 1973; Riedel & Sanfilippo 1978; Wolfart 1981) and calcareous nannofossil zonations (Bukry 1973*a*, *b*, 1975). The correlation of these planktonic zonations to the palaeomagnetic timescale shown on Fig. 2 is largely indirect, and has been accomplished by assuming isochronous first and last appearance of diatoms and correlating diatom data of the temperate regions to tropical microfossil data that have been tied directly to the magnetic stratigraphy (Barron 1981, 1986*b*, 1989). The timescale follows the method of Barron *et al.* (1985) and Barron (1986*b*) in the correlation of palaeomagnetic chron 11 to palaeomagnetic anomaly 5 and placement of the middle/late Miocene boundary at 9.5 Ma instead of 10.4 Ma.

As noted above, the opal-A frustules of diatoms dissolve during silica diagenesis, but they may be preserved in some dolomite layers and concretions within cherty intervals (Lagle 1984; Wornardt 1986; White 1989). Diatom preservation occurs when the dolomite forms relatively early, before silica phase changes (Baker & Kastner 1981; Kastner *et al.* 1984), thereby protecting the delicate diatom frustule from dissolution during subsequent burial diagenesis. The technique for recovery, which is discussed more fully in White (1989), involves the dissolution of crushed dolomite samples in aqua regia (a combination of hydrochloric and nitric acids). The sample is then neutralized with sodium hydroxide and centrifuged to concentrate the diatoms. A strewn slide is then made from the insoluble residue and examined in its entirety for diatoms.

In order to pin-point the age of the transition from silica-poor to silica-rich rocks in the Monterey, we examine six onshore sections (Figs 1 & 3) that formed in distal basins and typically contain well developed cherty intervals with abundant dolomite layers. Our age assignments for these sections include the diatom work by White (1989) as well as other published dates based on diatoms, foraminifers, nanno-fossils, magnetostratigraphy and strontium isotopes (Table 1).

To supplement the onshore sections, stratigraphic data from four DSDP sites is included, simplified by Barron (1989) from site report information in the Initial Reports of the Deep Sea Drilling Program volumes. The generalized lithologic columns depicted in Fig. 4 show relative variations in biosiliceous (dominated by diatoms and radiolarians) sediment, porcelanite and chert (biosiliceous sediments that have undergone burial diagenesis), calcareous (dominated by foraminifers and nannofossils) sediment, clay, silt, and sandstone as depicted by Barron (1989). For a complete discussion of the lithologic description of the DSDP sites, the reader is referred to von Huene, Kulm, and others (1973); Yeats & Haq (1981); Aubouin & von Huene (1982). The biozonation of Fig. 2 was used by Barron (1989) to assign updated ages to the DSDP sites shown in Fig. 4. Both Figs 3 & 4 show only the northeastern Pacific temperate zonation of Barron (1986*b*) for reference.

Lithostratigraphy and biostratigraphy

Onshore Sections (see Fig. 1 for locations)

Pt. Reyes Section. The Point Reyes Peninsula, lying northwest of San Francisco and immediately adjacent to the San Andreas Fault, is an

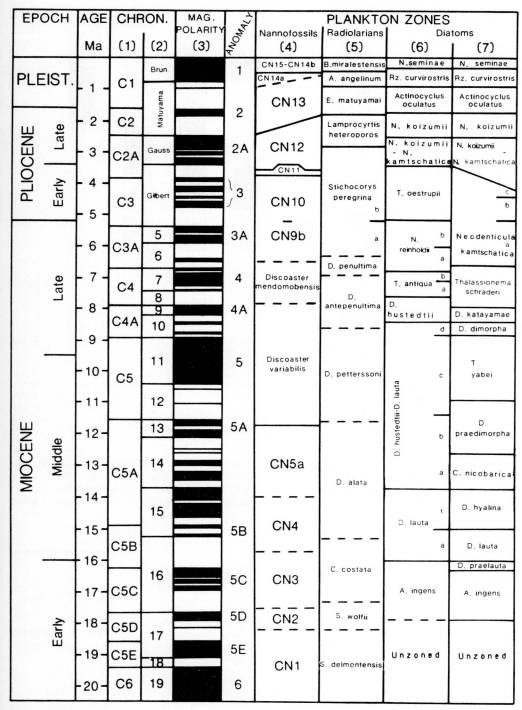

Fig. 2. Biostratigraphic time scale for the late Cenozoic of the temperate to subarctic northeastern Pacific, after Fig. 4 of Barron (1989). Numbers in parentheses refer to references: 1, Tauxe *et al.* (1983); 2, Theyer & Hammond (1974); La Brecque *et al.* (1977); 3, Berggren *et al.* (1985); polarity chrons after Barron *et al.* (1985); 4, Bukry (1973*a*, *b*, 1975); 5, Kling (1973); Riedel & Sanfilippo (1978); Wolfart (1981); 6, Barron (1981, 1986*b* (for temperate regions)); 7, Koizumi (1985), modified in part (for subarctic regions).

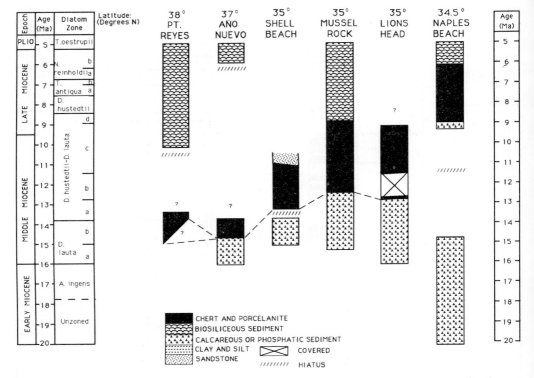

Fig. 3. Generalized chronostratigraphic diagram of six sections of the Miocene Monterey Formation from coastal California. Ages for Pt. Reyes, Pt. Año Nuevo, Mussel Rock and Lions Head after White (1989, 1990); age of Shell Beach after Khan *et al.* (1990); age of Naples Beach after Arends & Blake (1986); Barron (1986*b*); De Paolo & Finger 1987. Dashed lines connecting sections indicate time transgressive nature of dark chert and porcelanite intervals. Questions marks refer to the uncertain age of chert unit.

onshore portion of the largely offshore Bodega Basin. The Monterey Formation here is intensely folded and fractured so that accurate measurement of thicknesses are not possible.

However, sampling of several partial sections shows that the stratigraphically lowest chert-bearing rocks (the contact between calcareous–phosphatic rocks and chert-bearing rocks is not

Table 1. Age of earliest dominantly cherty facies in distal basins of the Monterey Formation.

Location	Latitude (degrees N)	Age (Ma)	Remarks	Source of data
Point Reyes	38	13.8–15.0	contact with calcareous facies not exposed	White (1989, 1990)
Año Nuevo	37	14.3–14.8	contact with calcareous facies obscured	White (1989) Omarzai *et al.* (1990)
Shell Beach	35	13.3	immediately above hiatus	Khan *et al.* (1990)
Mussel Rock	35	approximately 12.7	age not well constrained	White (1989)
Lions Head	35	approximately 12.7	age not well constrained	White (1989) Clark (1989)
Naples Beach	34.5	approximately 9.0	hiatus	Arends *et al.* (1986) Barron 1986*b* DePaolo *et al.* (1987)

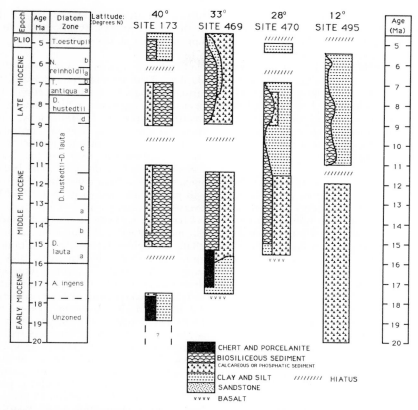

Fig. 4. Chronostratigraphic diagram of four northeastern Pacific DSDP sites. Ages from Barron (1989) and Barron & Baldauf (1990). Generalized litholigies of the sections after Barron (1989).

exposed) can be assigned to the *Denticulopsis lauta* Zone, subzone b implying an age of 13.8 to 15.0 Ma (Fig. 3; White 1989, 1990). No further constraint on the age of the oldest siliceous rocks at Pt. Reyes is possible at this time due to the limits of exposure in the field and the biostratigraphy.

Pt. Año Nuevo Section. Pt. Año Nuevo lies south of San Francisco and is an onshore fragment of the largely offshore Outer Santa Cruz Basin. Only the lower part of the Monterey is exposed at this locality where it consists largely of cherty and porcelaneous rocks. Dolomites within this section yield diatoms which are assigned to the *Denticulopsis lauta* Zone, subzone b. One specimen near the base of the siliceous facies contains the species *D. lauta*, *D. hyalina* and *Coscinodiscus praeyabei*, an assemblage suggesting an age of 14.7 to 14.3 Ma (based on the absence of *D. hustedtii*, Barron 1986b; White, 1989, 1990). However, recent

field and magnetostratigraphic investigations by Omarzai et al. (1990) suggests that the base of the cherty interval may extend slightly below the base of the section measured by White (1989) and may be therefore older in age. According to S. M. K. Omarzai (1990) the oldest porcelaneous rocks correlate to the lower part of paleomagnetic Chron 15 and are approximately 14.8 Ma.

Shell Beach Section. Shell Beach lies within the Pismo Basin in south−central coastal California and the Monterey Formation that crops out here has been dated by Khan et al. (1990) to a resolution of 50 000 years. Using a combination of magnetic polarity stratigraphy and diatom and nannofossil biostratigraphies, Khan et al. (1990) determined the Monterey Formation to be correlative to the lower part of magnetic polarity Chron 5B through the lower part of Chron 5r and has an age of 15.15 to 11.00 Ma. The Monterey Formation here consists of two general members or facies: a lower calcareous—phosphatic facies, about 75 metres thick, and an upper siliceous facies, about 212 metres thick. The boundary between these two lies immediately above a one-metre thick condensed phosphatic zone, shown by the dating of Khan *et al.* (1990) to represent a one million year period of slow sedimentation between 14.3 and 13.3 Ma. The base of the siliceous facies, which is marked by the first appearance of cherty rocks stratigraphically above the phosphatic conglomerate, is therefore 13.3 Ma (Fig. 3).

Mussel Rock Section. Mussel Rock is a coastal section lying within the Santa Maria Basin. A virtually complete Monterey section here includes the calcareous—phosphatic facies, a cherty member of the siliceous facies, and an upper section of the siliceous facies composed of interlayered diatomite and opal-CT porcelanite (Woodring & Bramlette 1950). The cherty member of the siliceous facies contains distinctive cycles consisting of intrastratally folded, dark, quartz cherts and laminated, organic-rich phosphatic—calcareous rocks; it is, in effect, a transitional unit between the lower calcareous-phosphatic facies and the upper siliceous facies. We interpret the stratigraphically lowest cherts at the base of the siliceous facies as recording the onset of intensive upwelling and biosiliceous sedimentation in a distal basin. Diatom assemblages recovered from dolomites in the cherty unit place it in the *Denticulopsis hustedtii—D. lauta* Zone, subzones b and c, suggesting this member spans the time interval between approximately 12.7 and 8.9 Ma (White 1989), but the lower boundary is not well constrained.

Lions Head Section. Like Mussel Rock, this is a coastal section within the Santa Maria Basin, but only a portion of the Monterey is exposed here. A lower calcareous—phosphatic facies underlies chert-bearing cycles similar to those of the middle member at Mussel Rock. Diatom assemblages dominated by *D. hustedtii, D. praedimorpha, D. lauta* and *Rhizosolenia barboi* from the chert-bearing interval at Lions Head, above the covered part of the section (Fig. 3), are equivalent to the *D. hustedtii—D. lauta* Zone, subzone c (Barron 1986*b*). This, combined with sedimentation rates estimated for the section from the diatom data, suggests an age range of from 11.4 Ma to 9.2 Ma (White 1989). The base of the chert-bearing interval below the covered interval is poorly exposed and associated dolomites contain no diatoms, but strontium isotope dating of these same dolomites

suggests an age of about 12.7 Ma for the base of the cherty interval (Clark 1989), somewhat similar to that at Mussel Rock.

Naples Beach Section. Lying within the Santa Barbara Basin west of Santa Barbara, this is a virtually complete Monterey section which has been dated using Foraminifera, diatoms, nannofossils, palaeomagnetic stratigraphy, and strontium isotopes. This section illustrates how erosion by bottom currents may act to complicate the sedimentary record of biosiliceous accumulation and productivity. The base of the siliceous facies (here consisting of porcelanites and muddy diatomites) is about 9.0 Ma. This overlies calcareous—phosphatic rocks which contain a remarkable condensed zone, about 8.5 metres thick and containing several phosphatic conglomerate layers. Foraminiferal and diatom studies by Arends & Blake (1986) suggest the condensed zone represents the time interval 14.8 to 9.3 Ma, diatom studies by Barron (1986*b*) indicate the interval was 14.3 to 9.3 Ma, and the strontium isotope work of DePaolo & Finger (1987) suggests it was 13.8 to 9.5 Ma. All of these time estimates span the age interval of the dark chert-bearing intervals at Mussel Rock and Lions Head; furthermore, although no dark quartz cherts occur in the Naples Beach section, this facies is present in wells drilled in oil fields about 10 kilometres or less offshore (Hornafius *et al.* 1989). Therefore middle Miocene submarine erosion at the Naples Beach locality has removed the sediment record of the onset of more or less continuous biosiliceous sedimentation making this section unsuitable as a record of the beginning of sustained coastal upwelling; we include discussion of this section to highlight one of the difficulties in interpreting the sedimentary record of upwelling.

Offshore sections (see Fig. 1 for locations)

Site 173. Site 173 was drilled off Cape Mendocino, California in a water depth of 2927 m (von Huene, Kulm and others 1973). The lower and middle Miocene units of this site are dominated by biosiliceous sediment, with minor amounts of calcareous sediment. Barron (1989) and Barron & Baldauf (1990), citing data from Ingle (1973), report that the earliest deposition of biosiliceous sediment (now porcelanite and chert) occurred between 18.7 to 17.6 Ma (Fig. 4). Above this, biosiliceous sediment continues to be a major component but the section is complicated by the presence of hiatuses. At

least three Miocene hiatuses have been identified by Keller & Barron (1983) who interpreted
them as the products of periods of erosion
caused by intensified bottom water activity
(Fig. 4; Barron 1989).

Site 469. Site 469 is located in the California
Continental Borderland in a water depth of
3790 metres (Yeats, Haq and others 1981).
The sediments are mixed terrigenous, calcareous, and siliceous (Fig. 4). The intensification of siliceous sedimentation at Site 469 is
estimated at to have occurred between 15.7–
17.5 Ma (Barron & Baldauf 1990), where chert
and porcelanite overlie clay and silt (Barron
1989). One hiatus is recognized near the
middle–late Miocene boundary and correlates
to hiatus NH4 of Keller & Barron (1983)
(Barron 1989).

Site 470. Site 470 was drilled off the coast of
Baja California in a water depth of 3549 metres
(Yeats, Haq and others 1981). The middle
through upper Miocene sediments, underlain
by basalt, consist of mixed biosiliceous, calcareous and terrigenous components. Lower
middle Miocene sediments above the basalt are
mixed calcareous and terrigenous (Fig. 4).
Though the appearance of biosiliceous sediment
in the middle Miocene is estimated to have
occurred between 13.8 and 15 Ma, the transition
from calcareous to siliceous sedimentation may
have been dissolution controlled (Barron &
Baldauf 1990). Two late Miocene hiatuses are
also recognized and correlate to hiatuses NH6
and NH7 of Keller & Barron (1983) (Barron
1989). The older hiatus, NH6, developed between approximately 7.0 to 6.0 Ma. This same
hiatus is present in the sections at Site 173 and
Año Nuevo. It correlates to a major sea-level
regression (Vail & Hardenbol 1979; Haq *et al.*

1988) and tectonic changes along the California
margin (Barron 1986a; Garrison & Ramirez
1989).

Site 495. Site 495 was drilled off the coast of
central America in the eastern equatorial Pacific
in 4140 metres of water (Aubouin & von Huene
1982). Calcareous sediments dominate the
middle Miocene portion of the section (Fig. 4).
A hiatus from 12.0 to 11.0 Ma (Barron 1989)
occurs at the contact between the dominantly
calcareous section and the overlying biosiliceous
and terrigenous sediments of the upper middle
Miocene through Pliocene (Fig. 4). This transition to carbonate-poor sediments probably
reflects the movement of this site to a depth
below the CCD as well as increasing silica
productivity during the late Miocene (Barron
1989).

Climatic implications

Temporal and spatial distribution of Miocene biosiliceous facies

Onshore sections. Figures 3 & 4 show the spatial
and temporal distribution of biosiliceous facies
and diagenetically derived cherts and porcelanites at selected onshore and offshore sites,
respectively. Of particular interest in these
chronostratigraphic diagrams is the stratigraphically lowest (earliest) occurrence of siliceous facies at each of the locations, which
theoretically should record the onset of vigorous upwelling and biosiliceous (diatomaceous) sedimentation. Interpretation of
the sediment record is complicated by sedimentological factors such as masking of diatomaceous sedimentation by detrital input and
hiatuses due to erosion and/or dissolution. How-

Table 2. Age of earliest dominantly siliceous facies at selected DSDP sites in the Northeastern Pacific (modified and expanded from Barron & Baldauf 1990).

Site	Latitude (degrees N)	Age (Ma)	Remarks	Source of data
173	40	17.6–18.7	Nature of contact uncertain	Ingle (1973) Barron (1989) Barron *et al.* (1980)
469	33	15.7–17.5	Associated with calcareous facies, overlies clastic facies	Yeats *et al.* (1981) Barron (1989) Barron *et al.* (1990)
470	28	13.8–15.0	Associated with calcareous facies, overlies clastic facies; dissolution contact	Yeats *et al.* (1981) Barron (1989) Barron *et al.* (1990)
495	12	11.0–12.0	Hiatus, associated with calcareous facies	Aubouin *et al.* (1982) Barron (1989)

ever, the data for the onshore and offshore regions shown in Tables 1 & 2, respectively, indicate the following general trends.

In the onshore California sections (excluding the Pt. Reyes and Naples Beach sections where the contact between the siliceous and calcareous facies is not exposed), the base of the siliceous facies (as documented by the appearance of distinctive dark cherts) lies in the range of 12.7 to 14.8 Ma, and there is an indication that this contact becomes younger from north (14.3 to 14.8 Ma at Pt. Año Nuevo) to south (13.3 at Shell Beach, and around 12.7 Ma at Mussel Rock and Lions Head) (see discussions in White 1989, 1990).

Therefore, an apparent age difference exists for the base of the siliceous facies between the Pt. Año Nuevo section at a latitude of 37°N, and sections in south–central California at a latitude of 35°N (Figs 1 & 3). Age estimates for the Shell Beach, Mussel Rock, and Lions Head sections suggest that the transition occurred at this latitudes between 12.7 to 13.3 Ma, i.e. up to 2 Ma younger than at Pt. Año Nuevo. This transition is obscured in the Naples Beach section by a hiatus that had a duration of 14.8 Ma to 9.3 Ma (Arends & Blake 1986; see also estimates by Barron 1986*b*; and DePaolo & Finger 1987). Although biosiliceous sedimentation may have begun earlier at this location, submarine erosion has removed this sediment and the stratigraphically lowest highly siliceous intervals in this section are dated as 9.0 Ma (Fig. 3 and Table 1).

Offshore sections. As noted by Barron & Baldauf (1990), the evidence from several North Pacific DSDP sites suggests that a major expansion of biosiliceous sedimentation in this region occurred between 18 and 15 Ma. Data in Fig. 4 and Table 2 appear to suggest that the base of the silica-bearing facies in the northeastern corner of the Pacific becomes younger toward the south, from a value of 17.6−18.7 Ma off northern California to values as young as 11 to 12 Ma off Central America. However, the biosiliceous record at the sites is complicated by the dilution of biosiliceous oozes by calcareous and clastic sediments. Thus, variation in the intensification of upwelling between offshore sites is more difficult to interpret because the sites may have been farther removed from upwelling centres.

Biosiliceous/porcelaneous sediments at Site 173 (40° North latitude) appeared between 17.6−18.7 Ma. DSDP Sites 469 and 470, are located near the southern end of the California Current (Yeats, Haq and others 1981) at lati-

tudes of 33°N and 28°N, respectively. The oldest biosiliceous and porcelaneous sediments at Site 469 are 15 to 17.5 Ma, and these are mixed with calcareous oozes. The oldest biosiliceous sediments at Site 470 are in the range 13.8 to 15 Ma, and also occur associated with calcareous and clay-rich sediments. At Site 495 in the eastern equatorial Pacific off Central America, the contact between calcareous sediments and the overlying mixed clastic and biosiliceous sediments is a hiatus which spans the estimated time interval 11 to 12 Ma (Barron 1989; Fig. 4). Thus, the interpretation of intensified upwelling is complicated at this tropical site both by a hiatus and by increasing amounts of calcareous and fine-grained clastic sediments which mask biogenic oozes.

Implications for the intensification of Miocene upwelling along the California margin and other parts of the northeastern Pacific

In the above discussions, we have distinguished between sediments and sedimentary rocks that contain minor biosiliceous components and those which are dominated by such components or their diagenetic equivalents, such as the upper siliceous facies of the Monterey Formation. It is the latter type of deposit that we interpret as recording the onset of strong and persistent coastal upwelling of nutrient-rich waters which promoted diatomaceous sedimentation. We noted at the outset that nearshore units like the Monterey Formation may provide a better record of coastal upwelling than offshore sites farther removed from upwelling plumes.

As noted by Barron & Baldauf (1990; see also Barron 1989), the major change in late Cenozoic sedimentation in the northeastern Pacific was the relatively abrupt onset of biosiliceous-rich sedimentation at about 16.0 to 17.5 Ma. Because this event preceded major middle Miocene cooling at high and middle latitudes, which occurred in the interval 14.9−12.4 Ma, Barron & Baldauf proposed it was the result of basin−basin fractionation of deep, silica-rich waters of the North Atlantic and those in the North Pacific. Subsequent Miocene diatomaceous sedimentation in the North Pacific, in their view, was a response to a series of middle to latest Miocene cooling steps. Polar cooling can significantly increase the latitudinal thermal gradient from the poles to the equator, thereby increasing surface water circulation. Stronger circulation could result in stronger upwelling, elevated nutrient levels, and sedimentation of pure diatom oozes. The diachronous distribution of the base of the cherty intervals in the Monterey Formation suggests that there may have been a latitudinal difference in upwelling, resulting in earlier and perhaps more intense upwelling in northern California than in southern California.

Coastal upwelling along the California margin is a result of southward winds parallel to the coast that drive the California Current (Huyer 1983). Due to Ekman transport, surface waters are deflected away from the coastline and nutrient-rich water upwells from beneath the surface layer. Wind strength, which is a function of pole to equator thermal gradients, would have a major influence on transport of the California Current and intensity of upwelling (Ingle 1973). Judging by onshore Monterey sections, coastal upwelling was vigorous only along the northern California margin between approximately 14 and 15 Ma, during the early phase of the 14.9 to 12.4 Ma cooling step. Between 14 and 12 Ma, following the latter phases of cooling, vigorous upwelling associated with the California Current reached the central and southern California region.

This model accords well with the interpretations of Barron & Keller (1983) who, based on interpretations of diatom floras and foraminiferal faunas in DSDP cores off California, recognized a dominance of California Current assemblages at both northern and southern latitudes starting between 12 and 13 Ma, whereas strong subtropical influences are present in older Miocene assemblages. They further proposed that coastal upwelling associated with the California Current was generally moderate prior to about 12.5 Ma.

Summary

The middle to upper Miocene Monterey Formation of California consists of thick and extensive diatom-rich deposits that record a sustained history of coastal upwelling along the California margin. In particular, the appearance of distinctive dark cherts in the Monterey Formation during the early middle Miocene reflects the beginning of intensified upwelling. The application of diatom biostratigraphy, in combination with other dating techniques, has resulted in a detailed chronology of Monterey sections from distal basins. This chronology suggests that the age of the base of the dark chert intervals is in the range of 12.7 to 14.8 Ma, but is strongly diachronous and becomes younger from north to south.

At the Point Año Nuevo section, at a latitude of 37°N, the age of the oldest cherts is 14.3 to 14.8 Ma. Between latitudes 35°N and 34.5°N are the Shell Beach, Mussel Rock, Lions Head, and Naples Beach sections. The age of the base of the chert intervals at these sections is between 12.7 to 13.3 Ma.

The nature of upwelling along the California margin, as recorded in the siliceous facies of the Monterey Formation, was complex and highly variable probably due to both changes in width and length of upwelling centres over time. Interpretation of the Monterey Formation and related offshore biosiliceous-rich units is hampered by tectonic and diagenetic factors discussed previously but, overall, onshore sections of the Monterey Formation may provide better records in which to model the intensification of upwelling during the Miocene than offshore DSDP sites. The latter were probably further from the locations of maximum coastal upwelling, and it may be more appropriate to measure intensification of the California Current in these sections by the dissolution of carbonate and the increase in cold-water microfossil assemblages (Barron & Keller 1983; Keller & Barron 1983).

The trends observed in the Monterey Formation are likely due to changes in the strength of the California current as a result of stepwise high latitude cooling. Vigorous coastal upwelling associated with the California Current was limited to the northern California margin between 14 and 15 Ma. Between 13 and 12 Ma, following the later stages of the 14.9 to 12.4 Ma cooling step, vigorous upwelling spread southward and began to affect the central and southern California margin.

This research was partially supported by a grant from the Petroleum Research Fund, administered by the American Chemical Society (Grant ACS-PRF No. 18439-AC2), and we express our gratitude to the donors of this fund. Travel support to attend the conference on upwelling was kindly provided by the United States Science Advisory Committee (USSAC) and JOI (Joint Oceanographic Institutions, Incorporated), and we gratefully acknowledge these organizations. The authors thank Jack Baldauf, Warren Prell and an anonymous reviewer for their very thorough review of the manuscript and for helpful suggestions for improvement.

References

ARENDS, R. A. & BLAKE, G. H. 1986. Biostratigraphy and paleoecology of the Naples Bluff coastal section based on diatoms and benthic foraminifera. *In*: CASEY, R. E. & BARRON, J. A. (eds) *Siliceous Microfossil and Microplankton Studies of the Monterey Formation and Modern Analogs.*

Pacific Section, Society of Economic Paleontologists and Mineralogists Special Publication, **45**, 121–135.

AUBOUIN, J. & VON HUENE, R. (eds) 1982. Initial reports of the Deep Sea Drilling Project, **67**. Washington, D.C., U.S. Government Printing Office.

BAKER, P. A. & KASTNER, M. 1981. Constraints on the formation of sedimentary dolomite. *Science*, **213**, 215–216.

BARRON, J. A. 1981. Late Cenozoic diatom biostratigraphy and paleoceanography of the middle-latitude eastern North Pacific, DSDP Leg 63. *In*: YEATS, R. S. & HAQ, B. U. (eds) Initial Reports of the Deep Sea Drilling Project. U.S. Government Printing Office, Washington, D.C., **63**, 507–538.

—— 1986a. Paleoceanographic and tectonic controls on deposition of the Monterey Formation and related siliceous rocks in California. *Palaeogeography, Palaeoclimatology, Palaeoecology*, **53**, 27–45.

—— 1986b. Updated diatom biostratigraphy for the Monterey Formation of California. *In*: CASEY, R. E. & BARRON, J. A. (eds) *Siliceous microfossil and microplankton studies of the Monterey Formation and modern analogs.* Pacific Section, Society of Economic Paleontologists and Mineralogists Special Publication, **45**, 105–119.

—— 1989. The late Cenozoic stratigraphic record and hiatuses of the northeast Pacific; Results from the Deep Sea Drilling Project. *In*: WINTERER, E. L., HUSSONG, D. M. & DECKER, R. W. (eds) *The Eastern Pacific Ocean and Hawaii.* Boulder, Colorado, Geological Society of America, The Geology of North America, v. N, 311–322.

—— & KELLER, G. 1983. Paleotemperature oscillations in the late and Late Miocene of the northeastern Pacific. *Micropaleontology*, **29**, 150–181.

——, KELLER, G. & DUNN, D. A. 1985. *A multiple microfossil biochronology for the Miocene.* Geological Society of America Memoir, **63**, 21–35.

—— & BALDAUF 1990. Development of biosiliceous sedimentation in the North Pacific during the Miocene and early Pliocene. *In*: TSUCHI, R. (ed.) *Pacific Neogene Events, Their Timing, Nature and Interrelationship.* University of Tokyo Press, 43–63.

BERGGREN, W. A., KENT, D. V., FLYNN, J. J. & VAN COUVERING, J. A. 1985. Cenozoic Geochronology. *Geological Society of America Bulletin.* **96**, 1407–1418.

BLAKE, M. C. JR., CAMPBELL, R. H., DIBBLEE, T. W. JR., HOWELL, D. G., NILSEN, T. H., NORMARK, W. R., VEDDER, J. G. & SILVER, E. A. 1978. Neogene basin formation in relation to plate-tectonic evolution of the San Andreas Fault system, California. *AAPG Bulletin*, **62**, 344–372.

BOUCHER, J. M. 1984. *Silica Dissolution and Reaction Kinetics in Southern California Borderland Sediments.* MSc Thesis, University of Southern California.

BUKRY, D. 1973a. Coccolith and silicoflagellate stratigraphy, Deep Sea Drilling Project Leg 18, eastern North Pacific. *In*: KULM, L. D. & VON HUENE, R. (eds) Initial Reports of the Deep Sea Drilling Project. U.S. Government Printing Office, Washington, D.C., **18**, 817–831.

—— 1973b. Low-latitude coccolith biostratigraphic zonation. *In*: EDGAR, N. T. & SAUNDERS, J. B. (eds) Initial Reports of the Deep Sea Drilling Project. U.S. Government Printing Office, Washington, D.C., **15**, 685–703.

—— 1975. Coccolith and silicoflagellate stratigraphy, northwestern Pacific Ocean, Deep Sea Drilling Project Leg 32. *In*: LARSON, R. L. & MOBERLY, R. (eds) Initial Reports of the Deep Sea Drilling Project. U.S. Government Printing Office, Washington, D.C., **32**, 677–701.

BURNETT, W. C. 1977. Geochemistry and origin of phosphorite deposits from off Peru and Chile: *Geological Society of America Bulletin*, **88**, 813–823.

CLARK, L. 1989. *Strontium isotopic variation and dating of dolomites in the Monterey Formation, California.* MSc thesis, California State University, Los Angeles.

DE PAOLO, D. J. & FINGER, K. L. 1987. Applications of strontium isotopes in correlating the Miocene Monterey Formation, California (abs.): Fourth International Congress on Pacific Neogene Stratigraphy, Berkeley, California, 16.

DUNBAR, R. B., MARTY, R. C. & BAKER, P. A. 1990. Cenozoic marine sedimentation in the Sechura and Pisco Basins, Peru. *Palaeogeography, Palaeoclimatology, Palaeoecology*, **77**, 235–261.

DUNHAM, J. B. & BLAKE, G. H. 1987. Guide to the coastal outcrops of the Monterey Formation of western Santa Barbara County, California. *In*: DUNHAM, J. B. (ed.) *Guide to the Coastal Outcrops of the Monterey Formation of Western Santa Barbara County, California.* Pacific Section SEPM Bok **53**, 1–36.

GARRISON, R. E. 1975. Neogene diatomaceous sedimentation in East Asia: A review with recommendation for further study. *United Nations ESCAP, CCOP Technical Bulletin*, **9**, 57–69.

—— & RAMIREZ, P. C. 1989. Conglomerates and breccias in the Monterey Formation and related units as reflections of basin margin history. *In*: COLBURN, I. & ABBOTT, P. (eds) *Conglomerates in Basin Analysis: A Symposium dedicated to A. O. Woodford.* Pacific Section, Society of Economic Paleontologists and Mineralogists, **67**, 189–206.

——, KASTNER, M. & REIMERS, C. E. 1990. Miocene phosphogenesis in California. *In*: BURNETT, W. C. & RIGGS, S. R. (eds) *Phosphate Deposits of the World*, **3**, *Neogene to Modern Phosphorites.* Cambridge University Press, 285–298.

HAQ, B. V., HARDENBOL, J. & VAIL, P. R. 1988. Chronology of fluctuate sea levels since the Triassic. *Science*, **235**, 1156–1157.

HORNAFIUS, S. J., ECHOLS, R. J. & FELBER, B. E. 1989. Paleogeographic implications of disconformities in the Monterey Formation, California (abs). *AAPG Bulletin*, **73**, 541.

HUYER, A. 1983. Coastal upwelling in the California Current system. *Progress in Oceanography*, **12**, 259–284.

INGLE, J. C., JR. 1983. Summary comments on Neogene biostratigraphy, physical stratigraphy, and paleoceanography in the marginal northeastern Pacific Ocean. *In*: KULM, L. D., VON HUENE, R. (eds) Initial Reports of the DSDP, **18**, 517–567. U.S. Government Printing Office, Washington, D.C., 949–959.

—— 1981. Origin of Neogene diatomites around the north Pacific rim. *In*: GARRISON *et al*. (eds) *The Monterey Formation and Related Siliceous Rocks of California*. Pacific Section, Society of Economic Paleontologists and Mineralogists Special Publication, 159–179.

ISAACS, C. M. 1980. *Diagenesis in the Monterey Formation Examined Laterally Along the Coast Near Santa Barbara, California*. PhD Dissertation, Stanford University.

—— 1981. Outline of diagenesis in the Monterey Formation examined laterally along the Santa Barbara Coast, California. *In*: ISAACS, C. M. (ed.) *Guide to the Monterey Formation in the California Coastal Area, Ventura to San Luis Obispo*. Pacific Section AAPG **52**, 25–58.

—— 1982. Influence of rock composition on kinetics of silica phase changes in the Monterey Formation, Santa Barbara area, California. *Geology*, **10**, 304–308.

—— 1983. Compositional variation and sequence in the Miocene Monterey Formation, Santa Barbara coastal area, California. *In*: LARUE, D. K. & STEEL, R. J. (eds) *Cenozoic Marine Sedimentation, Pacific Margin, U.S.A.* Pacific Section, Society of Economic Paleontologists and Mineralogists, **41**, 117–132.

—— 1985. Abundance versus rate of accumulation in fine-grained strata of the Miocene Santa Barbara Basin, California. *Geo-Marine Letters*, **5**, 25–30.

—— 1987a. *Field notes on the Monterey Formation, Santa Barbara area, California: The Miocene Monterey Formation — Depositional and Diagenetic Facies Along the Santa Barbara, California Coastal Area*. American Association of Petroleum Geologists Student Chapter Field Trip #1 Guidebook, 1–30.

—— 1987b. An overview of the Monterey Formation of California, USA (abs.). Fourth International Congress on Pacific Neogene Stratigraphy, Berkeley, California, 52–53.

—— & LAGOE, M. B. 1987. Mid-Tertiary biogenous silica deposition in California — the pre-Monterey record. *In*: TSUCHI, R. (ed.) *Pacific Neogene Event Studies*: Shizuoka University, Shizuoka, Japan, 39–42.

KASTNER, M. 1981. Authigenic silicates in deep-sea sediments: formation and diagenesis. *In*: EMILIANI, C. (ed.) *The Sea*, 7. Wiley, New York, 915–980.

——, KEENE, J. B. & GIESKES, J. M. 1977. Diagenesis of siliceous oozes — 1. Chemical controls on the rate of opal-A to opal-CT transformation — an experimental study. *Geochemica et Cosmo-*

chimica Acta, **41**, 1041–1059.

——, MERTZ, K. A., JR., HOLLANDER, D. & GARRISON, R. E. 1984. The association of dolomitite-phosphorite-chert: causes and possible diagenetic sequences. *In*: GARRISON, R. E., KASTNER, M. & ZENGER, D. H. (eds) *Dolomites of the Monterey Formation and other organic-rich units*. Pacific Section, Society of Economic Paleontologists and Mineralogists Book **41**, 75–86.

KELLER, G. & BARRON, J. A. 1983. Paleoceanographic implications of Miocene deep-sea hiatuses. *Geological Society of America Bulletin*, **94**, 590–613.

KHAN, S. M., COE, R. S. & BARRON, J. A. 1990. High-resolution magnetic polarity stratigraphy of the Miocene Monterey Formation at Shell Beach, Pismo Basin, California. *In*: GARRISON, R. E. (ed.) *Syllabus and Fieldtrip Guidebook, Japan-U.S. Seminar on Neogene Siliceous Sediments of the Pacific Region*, 106–117.

KLING, S. A. 1973. Radiolaria from the Eastern North Pacific, Deep Sea Drilling Project, Leg 18. *In*: KULM, L. D. & VON HUENE, R. (eds) Initial Reports of the Deep Sea Drilling Project. U.S. Government Printing Office, Washington, D.C., **18**, 617–671.

KOIZUMI, I. 1985. Diatom biochronology for late Cenozoic northwest Pacific. *Journal of the Geological Society of Japan*, **91**, 195–211.

LA BRECQUE, J. L., KENT, D. V. & CANDE, S. C. 1977. Revised magnetic polarity time scale for the Late Cretaceous and Cenozoic time. *Geology*, **5**, 330–335.

LAGLE, C. W. 1984. Recovery of siliceous microfossils by disaggregation of dolomite. *In*: GARRISON, R. E. *et al*. (eds) *Dolomites of the Monterey Formation and other organic-rich units*. Pacific Section Society of Economic Paleontologists and Mineralogists, **41**, 185–194.

LANCELOT, V. 1973. Chert and silica diagenesis in sediments from the central Pacific. *In*: Initial Reports of the Deep Sea Drilling Project, **17**, 377–405. U.S. Government Printing Office. Washington, D.C.

LODER, D. S., LYONS, W., MURRAY, S. & McGUINESS, H. D. 1978. Silicate in anoxic pore waters and oxidation effects during sampling. *Nature*, **273**, 373–374.

OMARZAI, S., KHAN, COE, R. & BARRON, J. 1990. Magnetic polarity stratigraphy of the Miocene Monterey Formation of California at Point Año Nuevo, Outer Santa Cruz Basin. EOS Transactions, American Geophysical Union, **71**, 1285.

ORR, W. N. 1972. Pacific Northwest siliceous phytoplankton. *Palaeogeography, Palaeoclimatology, Palaeoecology*, **12**, 95–114.

PISCIOTTO, K. A. 1978. *Basinal sedimentary facies and diagenetic aspects of the Monterey Shale, California*. PhD dissertation, University of California, Santa Cruz.

—— & GARRISON, R. E. 1981. Lithofacies and depositional environments of the Monterey Formation, California. *In*: GARRISON *et al*. (eds) *The Monterey Formation and Related Siliceous*

Rocks of California. Pacific Section Society of Economic Paleontologists and Mineralogists Special Publication, 97–122.

RIEDEL, W. R. & SANFILIPPO, A. 1978. Stratigraphy and evolution of tropical Cenozoic radiolarians. *Micropaleontology*, **24**, 61–96.

TAUXE, L., TUCKER, P., PETERSEN, N. P. & LABREQUE J. P. 1983. The magnetostratigraphy of Leg 73 sediments. *Palaeogeography, Palaeoclimatology, Palaeoecology*, **42**, 65–90.

THEYER, R. & HAMMOND, S. R. 1974. Paleomagnetic polarity sequence and radiolarian zones, Brunhes to Epoch 20. *Earth and Planetary Science Letters*, **22**, 307–319.

VAIL, P. R. & HARDENBOL, J. 1979. Sea-level changes during the Tertiary. *Oceanus*, **22**, 71–79.

VON HUENE, R., KULM, L. D. & SHIPBOARD SCIENTIFIC PARTY 1973. Site 173. *In*: KULM, L. D., VON HUENE, R. (eds) Initial Reports of the DSDP, **18**, 517–567. U.S. Government Printing Office, Washington, D.C., 31–95.

VON STACKELBERG, U. V. 1972. Faziesverteilung in Sedimenten des indischpakistanischen Kontinentalrandes (Arabisches Meer). 'Meteor' Forschungsergebnisse, Reihe C, **9**, 1–173.

WHITE, L. D. 1989. *Chronostratigraphic and Paleoceanographic Aspects of Selected Chert Intervals in the Miocene Monterey Formation, California.* PhD dissertation, University of California, Santa Cruz.

—— 1990. Stratigraphy and paleoceanographic history of the Monterey Formation at Pt. Reyes and Pt. Año Nuevo, California. *In*: GARRISON, R. E., GREENE, H. G. *et al.* (eds) *Geology and Tectonics of the Central California Coastal Region, San*

Francisco to Monterey. Pacific Section, American Association of Petroleum Geologists Volume and Guidebook, **67**, 91–104.

WOLFART, R. 1981. Neogene radiolarians from the eastern North Pacific (off Alta and Baja California), Deep Sea Drilling Project Leg 63. *In*: YEATS, R. S. & HAQ, B. U. (eds) Initial Reports of the Deep Sea Drilling Project. U.S. Government Printing Office, Washington, D.C., **63**, 473–506.

WOODRING, W. P. & BRAMLETTE, M. N. 1950. Geology and paleontology of the Santa Maria district, California. U.S.G.S. Professional Paper **222**, 1–142.

WOODRUFF, F., SAVIN, S. M. & DOUGLAS, R. G. 1981. Miocene stable isotope record: A detailed Pacific Ocean study and its paleoclimatic implications. *Science*, **212**, 665–668.

WOODRUFF, F. & SAVIN, S. M. 1989. Miocene deep-water oceanography. *Paleoceanography*, **4**, 87–140.

WORNARDT, W. W., JR. 1986. Diatom biostratigraphy from diatomaceous dolomites and shales in the Monterey Formation, Rodeo Canyon, Pt. Pedernales and Lions Head sections, southwestern Santa Barbara County, California. *In*: CASEY, R. E. & BARRON, J. A. (eds) *Siliceous microfossil and microplankton studies of the Monterey Formation and modern analogs*. Pacific Section Society of Economic Paleontologists and Mineralogists Special Publication, **45**, 141–147.

YEATS, R. S. & HAQ, B. U. (eds) 1981. Initial Reports of the Deep Sea Drilling Project (various site reports). U.S. Government Printing Office, Washington, D.C., **63**, 1–967.

Planktonic foraminifera of the coastal upwelling area off Peru during the Pleistocene

MASAKO IBARAKI

Geoscience Institute, Faculty of Science, Shizuoka University, Shizuoka 422, Japan

Abstract: Planktonic foraminifera of the coastal upwelling area off Peru during the Pleistocene have been quantitatively examined in ODP Leg 112 cores obtained from five sites beneath the upwelling area. Laminated diatomaceous facies in some cores suggest they had been in upwelling centres during the Pleistocene. The Pleistocene fauna dominantly consists of cold water and eurythermal elements, but also contains diverse tropical−subtropical species. The fauna is similar to the living one in the modern upwelling area, although the former seems to have much more cold-water elements. The most important species in the coastal upwelling area off Peru during the Pleistocene were *Globigerina quinqueloba*, concentrated in upwelling centres, *Neogloboquadrina dutertrei*, dominantly found in surrounding areas, and many kinds of tropical−subtropical species. Typical temperate water dwellers are rare.

The area off Peru is a typical coastal upwelling area, where phytoplankton propagate due to strong upwelling. In this upwelling centre with its low oxygen and rich organic matter, laminated diatomaceous muds accumulate and calcareous microfossils are rare. However, some living planktonic foraminifera such as *Globigerina bulloides* and *Neogloboquadrina dutertrei* are said to be important in the coastal upwelling water-mass off Peru (Thiede 1975, 1983).

During ODP Leg 112, ten sites were cored on the Peruvian margin to investigate the coastal upwelling system (Fig. 1). The drill sites are located beneath, or close to, modern upwelling centres. Quaternary and Neogene lithologies recovered from the cores mostly consist of diatomaceous mudstone. Diatom-rich facies have been predominant there since latest Early Miocene times.

In this paper an attempt is made to document features of planktonic foraminifera in the coastal upwelling area off Peru during the Pleistocene by examining ODP cores.

Working method

During ODP Leg 112, 24 holes were drilled at ten sites (Site 679 through 688) on the continental shelf and slope off Peru. Planktonic foraminifera were sporadic in occurrence, although obtained from 213 samples of the 655 examined. Quantitative analyses of planktonic foraminifera are presented from samples of core catchers of Cores 1 to 15 of seven holes from five sites. All samples are Pleistocene. Other core samples proved to be barren of planktonic foraminifera.

Samples of approximately 10 cm^3 were washed through a 250-mesh screen (0.062 mm) and dried in an oven. Planktonic foraminifera greater than 0.125 mm were selected from washed residues, and the frequency of occurrence of each species was calculated. The studied samples yielded 50 species and subspecies in total, and one sample contained as many as 1056 individuals (Fig. 2).

Geological setting and palaeoenvironments

The drill sites of Leg 112 are located within the present coastal upwelling centres and areas strongly influenced by upwelling. The dominant lithology is organic-rich diatomaceous mudstone. The beginning of diatomaceous sedimentation in the area is recorded in samples from Site 682A on the landward lower slope of the Peruvian Trench 11°15.99′S, 79°03.73′W at a water depth of 3788 m. The sediments recovered from the top through Core-34X-CC at Hole 682A consist of diatomaceous mudstone, and the content of diatoms decreases rapidly below this core. Sediments on Core-34X-CC are assignable to calcareous nannoplankton Zone NN4, the *Denticula nicobarica* diatom zone and the *Calocycletta costata*-Base *Dorcadospyris alata* radiolaria zone, being dated at about 17 Ma (Suess *et al.* 1988). Index planktonic foraminifera were found just below this in Core-35X-CC, which contained *Globigerina falconensis* and *Catapsydrax stainforthi* assignable to Zone N6−7 at 17−18 Ma (Ibaraki 1990). The beginning of coastal upwelling off Peru is therefore considered to be late Early Miocene in age.

Based on the planktonic foraminiferal biostratigraphy, the treated sections, Cores 1 to

From SUMMERHAYES, C. P., PRELL, W. L. & EMEIS, K. C. (eds), 1992, *Upwelling Systems: Evolution Since the Early Miocene*. Geological Society Special Publication No 63, pp 443−449.

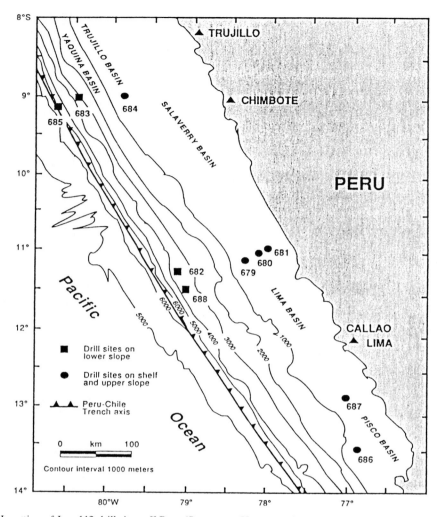

Fig. 1. Location of Leg 112 drill sites off Peru (Suess, von Huene *et al.* 1988).

15 of seven holes from the five sites, are all Pleistocene. A detailed correlation of the sections has been attempted by using planktonic foraminifera datum levels and magnetostratigraphy (Fig. 2). One of the key datum levels is the latest change of the coiling direction of *Pulleniatina* spp. from sinistral to dextral, which occurs shortly before the Brunhes normal polarity epoch at 0.73 Ma (Saito 1976). Six sites (Site 679, 680, 681, 684, 686 and 687) are located in modern coastal upwelling centres. Their lithologies are organic-rich diatomaceous mudstone, and the recovered Pleistocene sediments of these cores are frequently intercalated with laminated mudstone reflecting their deposition in the oxygen-minimum zone (Suess *et al.*

1988). Thus, these sites are considered to have been in upwelling centres during the Pleistocene. Four other sites (Site 682, 683, 685 and 688) are on the eastern lower slope of the Peru Trench. The Pleistocene sediments of these cores also consists of diatomaceous mudstone and are considered to have been under the influence of the coastal upwelling regime off Peru.

Planktonic foraminifera of the upwelling regime during the Pleistocene

Living planktonic foraminifera and their distribution pattern in coastal upwelling areas have been studied by Bé & Tolderland (1971), Bé

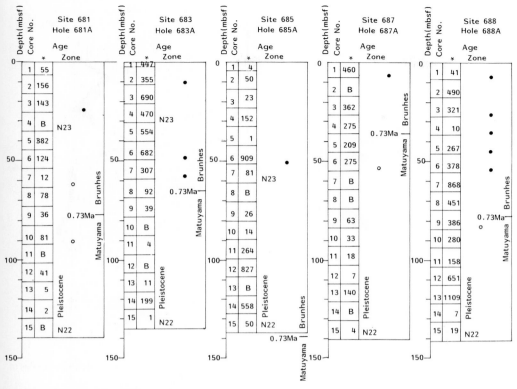

Fig. 2. Biostratigraphy and magnetostratigraphy of cores 1 to 15 at the examined five sites. *, number of planktonic foraminiferal specimens from respective samples. B; Barren. ●, Dextral-coiling *Pulleniatina* spp. ○, Sinistral-coiling *Pulleniatina* spp.

(1977) and Thiede (1975, 1983) for example. According to these studies, the dominant planktonic foraminifera in upwelling water masses are *Globigerina bulloides*, *Globigerinita glutinata*, *Neogloboquadrina dutertrei* and *Globigerinella aequilateralis*.

Globigerina bulloides is a cold water surface dweller of the temperate−subpolar region. Its concentration exceeds 50% of the total planktonic foraminifera specimens in the coastal upwelling area off Peru (Thiede 1983). *Globigerinita glutinata*, a eurythermal species tolerant to a wide range of temperature and extending from tropical to polar regions, is rare in upwelling water off Peru, although dominant in surrounding areas (Thiede 1983). *Neogloboquadrina dutertrei*, a eurythermal species living in temperate to tropical regions, is commonly found in upwelling water-masses (Bé 1977; Thiede 1983). *Globigerinella aequilateralis*, a common dweller in subtropical−tropical regions, prefers to live in boundary currents near the coast in upwelling areas (Bé &

Tolderland 1971). *Globigerinoides ruber* and *Globorotalia menardii* are locally important either in or near coastal upwelling (Thiede 1983). For instance *Globigerinoides ruber*, a typical subtropical dweller in surface water, commonly occurs in warm water masses associated with both the Canary and Peru Currents, but is rare in actual upwelling areas. *Globorotalia menardii*, a warm and deep water dweller, is commonly found in a part of the upwelling regime off northwest Africa, but is rare off Peru.

Faunal analyses of Pleistocene planktonic foraminifera are presented from core catcher samples of Holes 681A and 688A (Fig. 3). Hole 681A is located in 10°58.60′S, 77°57.46′W at a water depth of 150.5 m on the continental shelf in a modern coastal upwelling centre off Peru. The Pleistocene sequence of Hole 681A consists of diatomaceous mudstone, frequently intercalated with laminated mudstone suggesting deposition in an upwelling centre. Hole 688A is located in 11°32.26′S, 78°56.57′W at a water

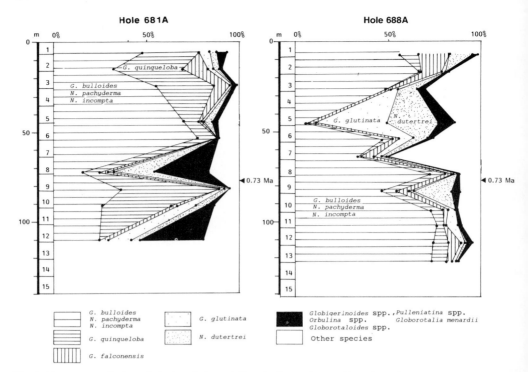

Fig. 3. Percentage of selected planktonic foraminifera in the total assemblage from the core catcher samples of Hole 681A (presumed upwelling centre) and Hole 688A (outside upwelling centre).

depth 3819.8 m on the landward lower slope of the Peru Trench and outside an upwelling centre. The Pleistocene sequence consists of diatomaceous mudstone. Both sites are situated at low latitude, however, their planktonic foraminiferal faunas are predominantly cold water and eurythermal dwellers. These include abundant cold water dwellers such as *Globigerina bulloides*, *Globigerina quinqueloba*, *Neogloboquadina incompta* and *Neogloboquadrina pachyderma*, and eurythermal species such as *Globigerina falconensis*, *Globigerinita glutinata* and *Neogloboquadrina dutertrei*. In addition, many kinds of tropical−subtropical dwellers such as *Globigerinoides ruber*, *Globigerinoides elongatus*, *Globigerinoides succulifer*, *Globorotalia menardii*, *Globorotalia tumida*, *Pulleniatina obliquiloculata*, *Globorotaloides hexagona* and *Sphaeroidinella dehiscens* were found to be present (Fig. 3).

Planktonic foraminifera in upwelling areas off Peru during Pleistocene are thus composed dominantly of cold and eurythermal elements, with lesser amounts of diverse warm water dwellers. Typical temperate water dwellers such as *Globorotalia crassaformis*, *Globorotalia*

inflata and *Globorotalia truncatulinoides* were rare.

Holes 681A, 681B, 687A, 687B are located beneath the present-day and presumed Pleistocene upwelling centres, and Holes 683A, 685A and 688A are located in surrounding areas strongly influenced by coastal upwelling since the Pleistocene. Comparing the Pleistocene planktonic foraminifera of both areas with each other it is clear that *Neogloboquadrina pachyderma* and *Globigerina bulloides* dominantly occur in and adjacent to upwelling centres. *Globigerina quinqueloba* is commonly found in upwelling centres (Fig. 4). *Neogloboquadrina dutertrei* is rich in adjacent areas rather than upwelling centres and varies inversely with *Neogloboquadrina pachyderma* (Fig. 5). *Globigerinella aequilateralis* was absent off Peru. *Globorotaloides hexagona*, a deep warm-water inhabitant limited to the tropical Pacific Ocean (Bé, 1977), occurred at many horizons, suggesting that the upwelling area has been affected by deep warm water currents.

Globigerinoides spp., were sporadic in general, but abundant in some horizons, where they exceeded 50% of the planktonic foramin-

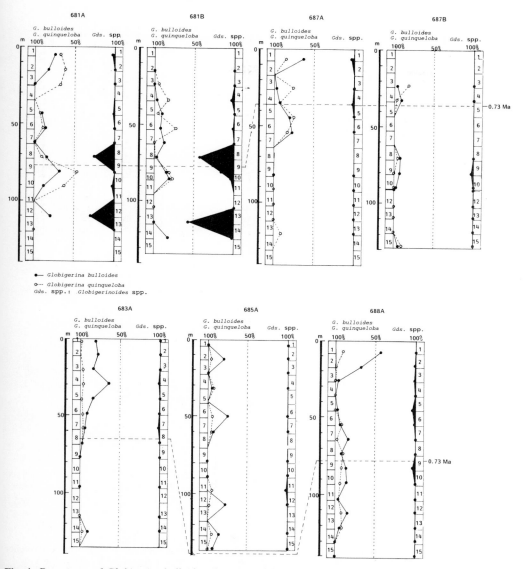

Fig. 4. Percentage of *Globigerina bulloides*, *G. quinqueloba* and *Globigerinoides* spp. in the total assemblage from core catcher samples of selected sites (681A, 681B, 687A, 687B: presumed upwelling centres), (683A, 685A, 688A: outside upwelling centres).

iferal assemblage (Fig. 4). This suggests the introduction of equatorial water caused by shifts in the upwelling centres, warm events, or El Niño events.

Conclusion

The Pleistocene sediments of ODP cores consist of diatomaceous mudstone suggesting depo-

sition in upwelling areas. The Pleistocene fauna is composed of 50 species and subspecies in total, although occurrences are sporadic in general. The fauna consists of such cold water species as *Globigerina bulloides*, *G. quinqueloba*, *Neogloboquadrina incompta* and *N. pachyderma*, such eurythermal species as *Globigerina falconensis*, *Globigerinita glutinata* and *Neogloboquadrina dutertrei*, and diversified

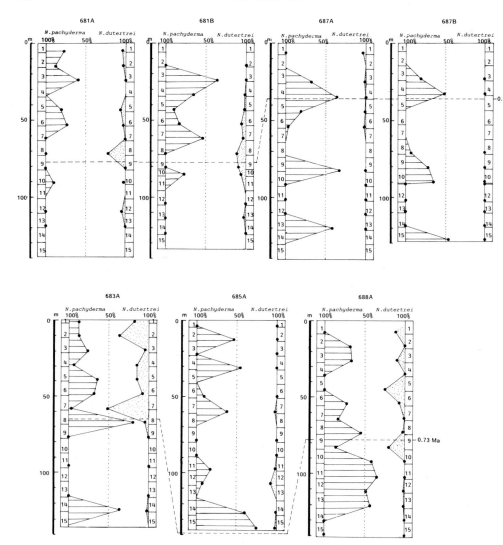

Fig. 5. Percentage of *Neogloboquadrina pachyderma* and *N. dutertrei* in the total assemblage from core catcher samples of selected sites (681A, 681B, 687A, 687B: presumed upwelling centres), (683A, 685A, 688A: outside upwelling centres).

tropical—subtropical species such as *Globigerinoides sacculifer*, *Globorotalia menardii* and *Pulleniatina obliquiloculata*. Typical temperate water dwellers such as *Globorotalia crassaformis* and *G. inflata* are rare. The fauna is similar in composition to the modern one off Peru, but the Pleistocene fauna has more cold-water elements than the modern one.

Of the above-mentioned species, the most important are *Globigerina quinqueloba*, *Neogloboquadrina dutertrei* and diverse tropical—

subtropical species. *Globigerina quinqueloba* is predominantly found in the upwelling centres themselves rather than in the surroundings; *Neogloboquadrina dutertrei* in contrast is dominantly found in the areas surrounding upwelling centres; specimens of *Globigerina bulloides* are abundant both in and adjacent to upwelling areas.

Globigerinoides spp., tropical—subtropical surface water inhabitants, are dominant in some horizons, which may be related to shifts of upwelling centres, to warm events, or to El Niño events.

The author is grateful to Professor R. Tsuchi of Shizuoka University for his kind reading of the manuscript. Warmest thanks are also owed to Professor W. L. Prell of Brown University for his critical review.

References

Bé, A. W. H. 1977. An ecological zoogeographical and texonomic review of Recent planktonic foraminifera. *In*: Ramsey, A. T. S. (ed.) *Oceanic Micropalaeontology*. Academic, London, **1**, 1–100.

—— & Tolderland, D. S. 1971. Distribution and ecology of living planktonic foraminifera in surface waters of the Atlantic and Indian Ocean. *In*: Funnell, B. M. & Riedel, W. R. (eds) *The Micropalaeontology of Oceans*. Cambridge University Press, 105–149.

Ibaraki, M. 1990. Eocene through Pleistocene plank-tonic foraminifers off Peru, Leg 112 -biostratigraphy and paleoceanography. *In*: Suess, E., von Huene, R. *et al. Proceedings of the Ocean Drilling Program, Scientific Results*. Ocean Drilling Program. College Station, TX, **112**, 239–262.

Saito, T. 1976. Geologic significance of coiling direction in the planktonic foraminifera *Pulleniatina*. *Geology*, **4**, 305–309.

Suess, E., von Huene, R., *et al.*, 1988. *Proceedings of the Ocean drilling Program. Initial Reports*. Ocean Drilling Program, College Station, TX, **112**.

Thiede, J. 1975. Distribution of foraminifera in surface water of a coastal upwelling area. *Nature*, **253**, 712–714.

—— 1983. Skeletal plankton and nekton in upwelling water masses of northwestern South America, *In*: Suess, E. & Thiede, J. (eds) *Coastal Upwelling: its sediments record, Part. A., Responses of the sedimentary regime to present coastal upwelling*. Plenum, New York, 183–207.

The history of coastal upwelling off Peru (11°S, ODP Leg 112, Site 680B) over the past 650 000 years

PETER-MATTHIAS HEINZE & GEROLD WEFER

Geowissenschaften, Universität Bremen, Postfach 330 440, 2800 Bremen 33, Germany

Abstract: The coarse sediment fraction (>63 μm) and benthic foraminiferal composition of Quaternary sediment cores from ODP LEG 112 Hole 680B (252.5 m water depth) were sampled from the upwelling area off Peru. High-resolution oxygen isotope stratigraphy based on analyses of the benthic foraminifera *Bolivina seminuda* allows a detailed reconstruction of the upwelling history since oxygen isotope Stage 16. Variations in the relative abundances of the benthic foraminiferal species *Nonionella auris*, *Bolivina costata*, and *Bolivina seminuda* document changes in fertility, which were found to be enhanced during interglacial Stages 1, 3, 5, 7, 9 and 11. Generally, bioturbated sediments are dominated by the genera *Cassidulina*, *Epistominella*, *Gyroidina*, *Trifarina* and *Valvulineria*. These benthic foraminifera are members of the 'Undercurrent Fauna', which is commonly associated with sediments that have a high terrigenous detrital component and a low organic carbon content (<3 wt%). These sedimentary deposits are indicative of high near-bottom current velocities of the Peruvian Undercurrent and well oxygenated bottom waters (0.5 to >6 ml/l O_2). The entire core interval investigated in Hole 680B appears to have been affected by the Peruvian Undercurrent. Generally, undercurrent-dominated sections were found to correspond with glacial oxygen isotope stages.

The ocean stores 60 times more carbon than the atmosphere; thus, small changes in oceanic CO_2 may produce large changes in atmospheric CO_2. Gas exchange between the ocean and the atmosphere is particularly intense in the upwelling regions along the equator, the western coasts of the continents, and in the southern polar ocean. Upwelling brings up CO_2-rich waters which release CO_2 to the atmosphere. Also, the high primary productivity in these areas results in increased fixation of atmospheric CO_2, acting to balance the budget. However, subsequent sedimentation of organic matter removes carbon from the atmospheric CO_2 cycle. In this manner, changes in the intensity of upwelling can exert a significant influence on the CO_2 budget of the atmosphere and consequently on the global climate (Berger *et al.* 1989). The focus of this paper is to reconstruct the history of the upwelling area off Peru, which is today one of the most productive regions in the oceans.

Sedimentation in the shallow upwelling regions of the continental shelves is primarily influenced by: changes in sea level due to climatic and tectonic processes; wind circulation and surface currents; and bottom currents (e.g. Krissek & Scheidegger 1983; Bremner 1983). Thus, an attempt to reconstruct fluctuations in upwelling faces the complex task of identifying the changing influences of these various factors.

Characteristics of the study area

Sediments

Hole 680B was drilled off Peru during Leg 112 of the Ocean Drilling Project at 11°03.90'S, 78°04.67W in a water depth of 252.5 m (Fig. 1). The sediments recovered exhibit a typical lithology comprised for the most part of dark-olive to grey-black hemipelagic muds intercalated with several decimetre- to metre-thick sandy sections which contain intervals of high concentrations of bivalve shell and phosphorite nodules (Suess, Huene *et al.* 1988).

Oceanographic setting

The upwelling centres, which are subjected to seasonal changes in intensity, are located at 6°S, 9°S, 11°S, and 15°S along the Peruvian coast. During the southern winter, the upwelling intensity is high and an area extending up to 60 km from the coast is affected. In the southern summer, however, upwelling is comparatively low in intensity and is limited to an area extending only 10−20 km from the coast (Maeda & Kishimoto 1970).

The hydrography in the shelf area off Peru is dominated by two main current systems: the Peru Current (PC) and the Peru Countercurrent

From SUMMERHAYES, C. P., PRELL, W. L. & EMEIS, K. C. (eds), 1992, *Upwelling Systems: Evolution Since the Early Miocene*. Geological Society Special Publication No 64, pp 451−462.

451

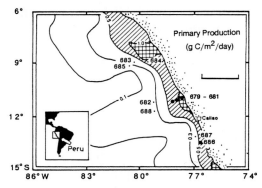

Fig. 1. Positions of the drill holes of ODP Leg 112 in the upwelling area off Peru (from Suess, Huene et al. 1988). Contour lines represent values of primary production in g C/m²/day.

(PCC) (Fig. 2), both of which are involved in the upwelling process. The PC flows along the surface in a northerly direction, while beneath it the PCC flows as an undercurrent to the south. In the following, the Peru Countercurrent will be termed undercurrent or UC. The mean velocities of both currents are approximately 20 km/day (Barber & Smith 1981). The PC is about 20 m thick and its main flow path lies 50–70 km from the coast. The subsurface UC, which is supplied by near-surface waters of the

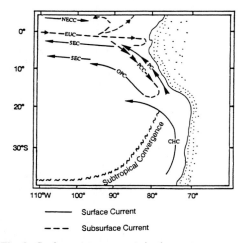

Fig. 2. Surface water currents in the eastern equatorial Pacific adapted from Wyrtki (1964, 1966, 1967). NECC, North Equatorial Counter Current; EUC, Equatorial Undercurrent; SEC, South Equatorial Current; PC, Peru Current; PCC, Peru Counter Current; OPC, Oceanic Peru Current; CHC, Chile Current.

Equatorial Counter Current, flows from 5°S to 20°S, at a depth of 50–100 m. However, due to the coastal morphology, the UC can reach water depths of 300 m in places (Brink et al. 1983).

Oxygen minimum zone

An oxygen minimum zone (OMZ) exists on the Peruvian shelf (Brockmann et al. 1980) (Fig. 3) within which the oxygen content of the water does not exceed 0.5 ml/l (Rosenberg et al. 1983; Mullins et al. 1985). The central portion of the Peruvian OMZ is distinguished by an oxygen content of <0.2 ml/l and lies between 100 and 400 m water depth (Burnett et al. 1980). Based on published data, the average oxygen content of the bottom water in the investigation area is assumed to be <0.3 ml/l.

El Niño events

The term 'El Niño event' is used for the seasonally unusually early appearance of warm surface waters along the coasts of Ecuador and Peru as far as 12°S (Quinn et al. 1987). During these events, anomalously warm equatorial waters with a high salinity (35.4‰) flow into the study area and cause both the 15°C isotherm and the 35‰ isohaline to descend from 70 m to 150 m depth (Leetmaa et al. 1987). Simultaneously, the bottom current velocity increases from <1 cm s⁻¹ to >36 cm s⁻¹ (Smith 1983) and the oxygen content of the bottom water rises. During these events, high values of between 2 ml/l and 5 ml/l oxygen, which are high enough to support macrobenthos, have been observed at depths down to 300 m (Tarazona et al. 1988).

The oceanographic changes accompanying El Niño events cause the phytoplankton production to decrease by a factor of about 10 (Barber & Chavez 1986). Although the upwelling intensity is not diminished, the upwelling area is less productive due to the deepening of the thermocline (Leetmaa et al. 1987). With respect to the circulation velocities, Enfield (1981) even observed an increase in coastal wind speeds during El Niño events. During these times, extreme rainstorms and floods combined with solifluctions affect the northern Peruvian coast.

Material and methods

The sediment cores were collected with an advanced hydraulic piston corer (APC). Individual samples were taken from the cores at an interval of about 25 cm. The samples, which had an average size of 20 cm³, were dissolved in a

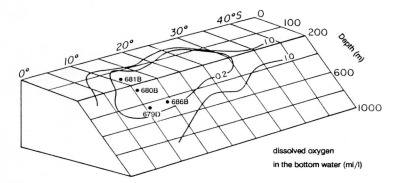

Fig. 3. Positions of the drill sites with respect to the oxygen minimum zone off Peru (after Resig, 1990). Holes 679D, 681B, and 686B are described in Heinze (1990).

Borax solution ($Na_2B_4O_7.10H_2O$, pH9) for 24 hours and subsequently wet-sieved through a 63 μm sieve to separate the sand/silt and the clay fractions. The collected residue was wet-sieved through 125 μm, 212 μm, and 300 μm screens, then dried and weighed. The selected size fractions correspond to those used by WEFER et al. (1983) and Dunbar & Wefer (1984). In order to determine the abundances of the terrigenous constituents (mainly quartz, feldspars, and mica) of the fraction >63 μm the method used by Sarnthein (1971) was employed, which is based on visual percentage estimates. The oxygen isotope mass ratios of the benthic foraminifera were measured using a Finnigan MAT 251 mass spectrometer. The results are reported in the usual delta notation relative to the PDB standard.

$$\delta(‰) = \frac{(R)\ \text{Sample-}(R)\ \text{Standard}}{(R)\ \text{Standard}} \times 1000$$

where $R = {}^{18}O/{}^{16}O$

The isotopic stratigraphy established in this study is based on stable oxygen isotope compositions of the benthic foraminifera *Bolivina seminuda*. Because of the small average weight of one individual (3 μg in the fraction 125–212 μm), it was necessary to measure at least 20 specimens per sample. However, in most cases, more than 40 individuals were analyzed per sample in the small size fraction. Only clean, whole specimens were selected following examination under the binocular microscope at 100× magnification. For the calculation of the average sedimentation rates the ages in Imbrie et al. (1984) were used.

The faunal analysis of the benthic foraminifera was conducted on samples from the fraction >125 μm. The benthic foraminifera were identified following Loeblich & Tappan (1964),

Cushman (1926, 1927, 1937), Uchio (1960), Smith (1963, 1964), Resig (1981), and Matoba & Yamaguchi (1982). The faunal diversity is reported in the Fisher-α-Index (Williams 1964). In order to group foraminifera displaying a similar sample composition, the percentages of the species were clustered using the Euclidian distance and the grouping algorithm by Ward (Deichsel & Trampisch 1985), which repeats the calculation of the distance matrix after each fusion. In order to validate the groupings established by the cluster analysis, a factor analysis was performed using the cosine-theta-coefficient. This calculation utilizes the absolute value and the parameter-specific variance, which is necessary in the investigation of interdependent parameters. The results of the factor analysis demonstrate essentially the same interrelationships between the species as the cluster analysis and therefore support the groupings established by this method. The data are reported in Heinze (1990).

Results

Stratigraphy

A stratigraphic section for Hole 680B was published by Wefer et al. (1990) on the basis of the oxygen isotope composition, the organic carbon content, and the grain size distribution. Since then, 40 additional oxygen isotope measurements were made on samples between 5 and 15 m core depth. The stratigraphy proposed herein is based solely on oxygen isotope data and incorporates 190 isotopic measurements of the benthic foraminifera *Bolivina seminuda*. According to Grossman (1984), *Bolivina seminuda* can be considered a typical foraminifera of the OMZ and exhibits a minimal vital

effect and precipitates oxygen isotopes in equilibrium with the ambient water.

A comparison with the standard isotope stratigraphy of Imbrie *et al.* (1984), Pisias *et al.*
(1984), Prell *et al.* (1986) and Martinson *et al.*
(1987), reveals that the global isotopic stages
and events can be identified. The calculation of
the sedimentation rates is based on the ages of
the isotopic stage boundaries and events. The
ages in Martinson *et al.* (1987) were adopted for
the interval between δ^{18}O-stage 8 and the
Holocene, while for older sediments the ages in
Imbrie *et al.* (1984) were used.

The isotopic data of *Bolivina seminuda* are
plotted versus time in Fig. 4, together with the
standard isotopic curve of Imbrie *et al.* (1984).
The standard curve reflects primarily global
δ^{18}O signals caused by alternating growth and
melting periods of the polar ice caps. However,
the effect of local temperature changes on this
curve can not be completely ruled out (Imbrie
et al. 1984). In general, the two curves in Fig. 4
demonstrate good agreement. The average sedimentation rate for the last 620 000 years was
determined to be 7.5 cm ka^{-1}.

Composition of Benthic foraminifera

In the investigated samples, 49 taxa of benthic
foraminifera were identified. The benthic foram
fauna was comprised for the most part of the
genera *Bolivina, Cassidulina, Epistominella,
Gyroidina,* and *Nonionella.* The fauna is dominated by the species *Bolivina seminuda.*

To establish relationships within the distribution pattern of the benthic foraminifera, a
cluster analysis of the species percentages was
performed. Species represented by only a few
individuals in a small number of samples, or
species which occurred only once, were excluded from the cluster analysis. The result of
the cluster analysis is presented in the form of a
dendrogram in Fig. 5.

The faunal groups G1 and G3 (undercurrent
fauna) (Fig. 6g) are dominated by the genera
Cassidulina, Epistominella, Gyroidina, Trifarina
and *Valvulineria* (Fig. 7). In general, these two
groups show an obvious affinity with the coarse-
grained sediment sections containing high
amounts of terrigenous detritus (Fig. 6b) and
little organic carbon (Fig. 6c). The faunal group
G1 reaches higher percentages (>50%) in
δ^{18}O-Stages 2, 4, 5, 9, 10, 11, 12, 13, 14 and 15.
Higher percentages (>20%) of group G3 can
be found within δ^{18}O-Stages 1, 11, 12 and 13
(Fig. 7a and b).

The species *Bolivina seminuda* was not included in any faunal group. *Bolivina seminuda,*

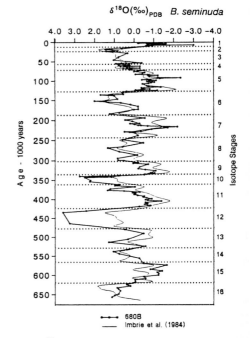

Fig. 4. δ^{18}O values of *Bolivina seminuda* from Hole
680B versus time, together with the standard curve of
Imbrie *et al.* (1984).

Nonionella auris and *Bolivina costata* (the latter
two species belonging to group G2) dominate
the foraminiferal assemblage in the fine-grained,
high organic-carbon sediments. *Bolivina
seminuda* reaches average percentages of about
50% (Fig. 6f). Maxima for this species are
observed within δ^{18}O-Stages 1 and 3, in the
middle of Stage 5, at the beginning of Stage 6,
and in sections of δ^{18}O-Stages 7, 10 and 16.
Higher percentages of *Bolivina costata* are observed within δ^{18}O-Stages 1, 3, 5, 7, 9, 11
and 13/14 (Fig. 6e). Maximum amounts of
Nonionella auris are observed in the lower parts
of δ^{18}O-Stages 5 and 9, and in δ^{18}O-Stage 8,
while smaller numbers of this species occur in
δ^{18}O-Stages 1, 7, 11 and 14 (Fig. 6d).

The group G4 never reaches proportions of
more than 10% (not shown in the figures).
Relative maxima are observed intermittently in
all δ^{18}O-Stages. Species characteristic of very
different types of facies, such as *Bolivina inter-
jucta bicostata, Cassidulina sublobosa,
Globobulimina spp, Uvigerina striata,* and
Virgulinella spp, occur together in this group.
The sparse appearance of each of these species
is the likely reason for their association in group
G4.

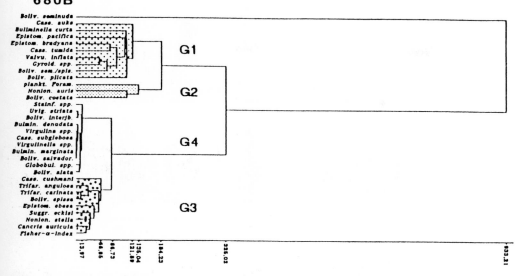

Fig. 5. Dendrogram showing results of the cluster analysis of benthic foraminifera for Hole 680B. Numbers represent the sums of the squares of the errors.

Discussion

Upwelling indicators

Organic carbon. The high organic carbon accumulation rate is typical of upwelling deposits (Fig. 6c). Organo-chemical analyses showed that the organic material in Hole 680B is generally of marine character (Suess, Huene *et al.* 1988). Generally, the relative abundances of organic carbon and terrigenous material show a negative correlation (Fig. 6b,c). Minimum amounts of organic carbon (<3 wt%) correspond to high amounts of coarse terrigenous material. These coarse-grained sediment sections are commonly bioturbated (Suess, Huene *et al.* 1988).

The negative correlation between organic material and terrigenous components points to a possible dilution effect and to a reworking of the fine-grained particulate organic material. The undercurrent (UC) off Peru would be the dominant force leading to such effects in the study area. According to Suess *et al.* (1986), the UC is responsible for the formation of the different sediment facies on the Peruvian Shelf.

Benthic foraminifera. The faunal composition of the benthos, in particular the benthic foraminifera living on and within the sediment, is a very sensitive tracer of environmental changes at the seafloor and thereby provides additional information about the productivity of the surface water (e.g. Resig 1981; Mullins *et al.* 1985; Mackensen, 1985; Lutze *et al.* 1986; Altenbach & Sarnthein 1989; Caralp 1989*a*).

The three species *Nonionella auris*, *Bolivina costata* and *Bolivina seminuda* comprise about 65% of the foram fauna in Hole 680B (Fig. 6d,e,f). In the more offshore located Hole 679D, *Nonionella auris* is completely absent, *Bolivina costata* is observed in trace amounts and *Bolivina seminuda* has low average values of about 15% (Oberhänsli *et al.* 1990). In the more landward located Hole 681B, the three species *Nonionella auris*, *Bolivina costata* and *Bolivina seminuda* comprise more than 95% of the benthic foram fauna (Heinze 1990). Taking also into consideration the results from Hole 679D (Oberhänsli *et al.* 1990) and Hole 681B (Heinze 1990), we assume that *Bolivina seminuda* is adapted to environmental conditions not directly influenced by upwelling (Hole 679D). Approaching the zone of upwelling, higher percentages of *Bolivina costata* are observed (Hole 680B). The upwelling centre is characterized by the highest abundances of *Nonionella auris*, which is best adapted to the extremely low oxygen conditions (Hole 681B). Bandy & Arnal (1957), Bandy & Rodolfo (1964) and Resig (1981) described a benthic foram fauna of similarly low diversity in organic-rich, fine-grained sediments off Central and South America. According to Ingle *et al.* (1980), the typical Oxygen Minimum Zone (OMZ) fauna is

680B

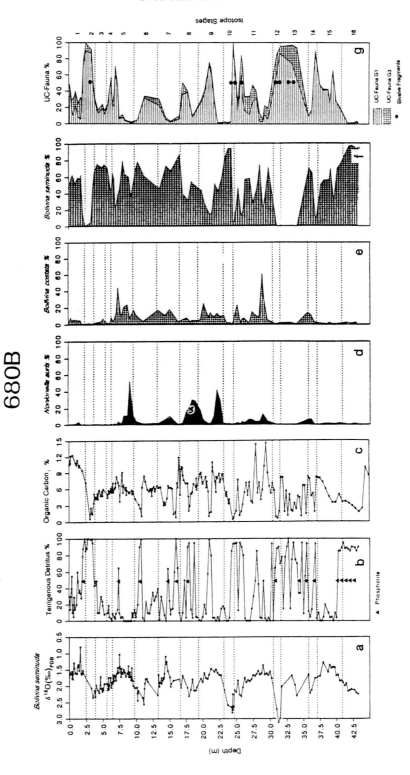

Fig. 6. Stratigraphy and upwelling indicators in Hole 680B. (a) $\delta^{18}O$ values of *Bolivina seminuda*; (b) content of terrigenous detritus in %; (c) organic carbon content in %; percentage contributions to the fauna of (d) *Nonionella auris*; (e) *Bolivina costata*; (f) *Bolivina seminuda*, (g) undercurrent fauna in %.

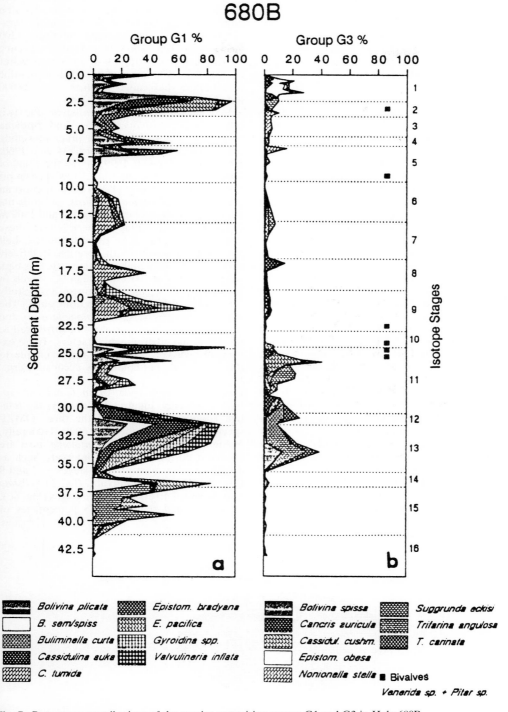

Fig. 7. Percentage contributions of the species comprising groups G1 and G3 in Hole 680B.

comprised primarily of *Bolivina seminuda* and *Bolivina costata*. Due to the dominance of these species together with *Nonionella auris* in the investigated habitat, this assemblage will henceforth be referred to as the Oxygen Minimum Zone Fauna (OMZF). *Bolivina seminuda* dominates the OMZF in Hole 680B (Fig. 6f), *Nonionella auris* and *Bolivina costata* are important contributors to the foram fauna in Hole 681B (Heinze 1990). In Fig. 8, it is shown which areas the three species occupy within the oxygen minimum zone of the upwelling cell off Peru. *Nonionella auris* is more common in Hole 681B than in Hole 680B (Heinze 1990). Considering that Hole 681B is today located in the centre of the upwelling cell, we assume that *Nonionella auris* is best adapted to low oxygen conditions which generally occur at sites with maximum flux rates of organic matter. We are aware that the regeneration of the bottom water with oxygen has to be taken into account. This is addressed in the section on bottom current indicators. We further assume that *Bolivina costata* lies in an intermediate position between the other two species with regard to its optimal living conditions.

Mullins *et al.* (1985), Vercoutere *et al.* (1987) and Quinterno & Gardner (1987) described distribution patterns of benthic foraminifera in the upwelling areas off California in the Point Sur and Russian River areas, between 500 to 1000 m water depth. These authors concluded that a decrease from 0.5 to 0.3 ml/l of the dissolved oxygen in the bottom water was responsible for the abundance increase of *Bolivina seminuda* in the centre of the OMZ. Oxygen concentrations in the bottom water of about 0.1 ml/l in coastal waters off Peru are not uncommon (Salzwedel *et al.* 1987). However, such concentrations do not appear to be limiting for benthic foraminifera (Phleger & Soutar

1973). Off Baja California, in the Santa Barbara Basin, and off Peru, these authors describe large standing stocks of living benthic foraminifera (>63 μm) ranging between 1200 individuals/20 cm^2 and 9500 individuals/20 cm^2, with oxygen concentrations in the bottom water of only 0.1 ml/l. The number of dead benthic foraminifera exceeded values of 22000 individuals/20 cm^2.

In contrast to *Bolivina seminuda*, the two other species *Nonionella auris* and *Bolivina costata* were not observed in other upwelling areas such as those off California (Uchio 1960; Douglas & Heitman 1979) or in the Gulf of Oman (Hermelin & Shimmield 1990). Even off Peru, Dunbar & Wefer (1984) did not report an occurrence of *Nonionella auris* or *Bolivina costata* in sediments between 600 m and 1500 m water depth. According to Resig (1981), these two species appear to be restricted to the shelf area off Central and South America. Relatively extreme environmental conditions, such as high water contents of 500% and high C_{org}-levels in the uppermost sediments, distinguish our study area from other OMZ environments. The abundant occurrences of *Nonionella auris* and *Bolivina costata* may therefore be attributed to these unusual environmental factors. These extremely high C_{org} values are rather unique to this site and do not commonly occur off Peru.

Oxygen minimum zone foram fauna and upwelling intensity. Figure 6d−f displays the relative abundance patterns of the three OMZF species versus depth for Hole 680B. Generally, maximum abundances of *Nonionella auris* are observed during interglacial intervals, such as displayed in sections of δ^{18}O-stages 5, 7 and 9 (Fig. 6d). In these intervals, *Bolivina costata* also shows relatively high percentages (Fig. 6e). It is suggested that the high percentages of

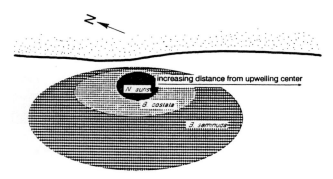

Fig. 8. Schematic distribution of the benthic foraminifera *Nonionella auris*, *Bolivina costata*, and *Bolivina seminuda* in the oxygen minimum zone off the coastal upwelling area off Peru.

Bolivina costata during δ^{18}O-stages 1, 3, 5, 7, 9 and 11 are considered to be the result of increased upwelling during interglacial stages.

Schrader & Sorknes (1990a) investigated the composition of the diatom flora in Holes 681A and 686A. Their results allowed them to identify variations in the upwelling intensity off Peru over the last 400 000 years. The stratigraphy was based on a correlation of the diatom compositions in Holes 681A and 686A, with the flora in Hole 680B, dated after Wefer *et al.* (1990) using oxygen isotopes. Time intervals with increased upwelling were found in sections of δ^{18}O-stages 3, 5, 7 and 8, while the upwelling intensity was reduced in δ^{18}O-stages 2, 6, and 10 (Schrader & Sorknes 1990a). These results largely correspond to the upwelling history interpreted from the distribution pattern of the OMZF in Hole 680B. In a more recent paper, Schrader & Sorknes (1990b) revised the stratigraphy and concluded from marine diatom assemblages that palaeoproductivity is not in phase with the general glacial−interglacial cycles and that the largest swings in the magnitude of palaeoproductivity seem to occur across oxygen isotope stage boundaries.

Bottom current indicators

In addition to tracing the history of upwelling off Peru, the investigated sediments document the activity of bottom currents. This information is reflected in the distribution patterns of terrigenous detritus and organic carbon, as well as the composition of the benthic foram fauna. On the Peruvian shelf, the undercurrent dominates the hydrographic regime and causes sediment movement and the redistribution of terrigenous detritus in a southerly direction (Suess *et al.* 1986).

Many studies of Recent benthic foraminifera provide information on the preferred environmental conditions (Table 1) of most of the foraminiferal species in faunal groups G1 and G3 (Fig. 7). Results of investigations on living benthic foraminifera led Corliss (1985) to conclude that a correlation exists between the genus and the substrate. Foraminifera with planoconvex shells (e.g. the genus *Gyroidina*), and those with biconvex shells (e.g. the genus *Cassidulina*), are well adapted to turbulent bottom water conditions. This is also supported by the ornamented shells of these genera, which serve to increase their stability. Analogous to their living counterparts (Table 1), the foraminifera of groups G1 and G3 indicate relatively fast-moving bottom water with high oxygen concentrations, as well as a coarse-grained substrate containing relatively low proportions of organic carbon. Such conditions are encountered today off Peru in areas influenced by the undercurrent. The groups G1 and G3 are therefore considered to be typical of a bottom water environment influenced by the undercur-

Table 1. Characteristic environmental conditions of benthic foraminifera in the study area. Most species belong to groups G1 or G3 of the cluster analysis. Corg = organic carbon content of the sediment in %C of dry sediment. Data from: (1) Ingle *et al.* (1980); (2) Resig (1990); (3) Douglas & Heitman (1979); (4) Mullins *et al.* (1985).

Species	Area	O$_2$ content (ml/l)	C$_{org}$	Reference
Bolivina interjuncta	Peru	1.0	0.2−2.0	(1)
B. plicata	Peru	undercurrent assoc.		(2)
B. spissa	Calif.	0.3−1.1	1.0−6.0	(3)
Bulimina denudata	Calif.	2.5−6.5	1.0	(3)
Cancris auricula	Calif.	2.5−6.5	0.9	(3)
Cassidulina auka	Calif.	2.5−6.5	0.9	(3)
C. cushmanni (delic.)	Calif.	0.3−1.1	1.0−6.0	(3)
C. tumida (tortuosa)	Calif.	0.8−5.5	1.1	(3)
Nonionella stella	Calif.	2.5−6.5	1.0	(3)
N. basispanata	Calif.	2.5−6.5	1.0	(3)
Suggrunda eckisi	Calif.	0.5−3.0	1.0−3.0	(3)
Trifarina angulosa	Calif.	2.5−6.6	0.9	(3)
T. carinata	Peru	undercurrent assoc.		(2)
Uvigerina striata	Peru	undercurrent assoc.		(2)
Valvulineria inflata	Calif.	1.0	0.2−2.0	(1)
Cassidulina spp.	Calif.	0.5−2.0	1.0	(4)
Epistominella spp.	Calif.	0.5−1.0	1.0−2.0	(4)
Gyroidina spp.		>0.5	1.0−2.0	(4)

rent and will henceforth be referred to as the Undercurrent Fauna (UCF).

The intervals characterized by increased terrigenous detritus and the presence of faunal groups G1 and G3, sometimes also contain molluscs with robust shells (Fig. 7b). Rosenberg *et al.* (1983) interpret the sturdy shells of the molluscs in layers with a high terrigenous component as representing a benthic environment in which the bottom water is moving and contains oxygen levels of more than 1 ml/l. Based on the literature data in Table 1, the species of groups G1 and G3 are interpreted to characterize more highly oxygenated bottom waters than do the species of the OMZF. The oxygen concentrations are generally greater than 0.5 ml/l and may exceed 1.0 ml/l in the sections containing mollusc shells.

The relative abundances of G1 and G3 in Hole 680B coincide generally with the presence of detrital material (Figs 6b and g). Based on the proposed relationship between the faunal groups G1 and G3 and the undercurrent, we conclude that the UC exerted a direct influence on the sediments of Hole 680B over the past 620 000 years. A stronger effect is expected during the glacial intervals (δ^{18}O-stages 2, 4, 6, 8, 10, 12, 14), but also during parts of stages 9, 11, 13 and 15.

Greatly increased bottom current velocities and an accompanying rise in oxygen concentrations have been observed during modern El Niño events off the coast of Peru (Brockmann *et al.* 1980, Pak *et al.* 1980, Shaffer 1982, Barber & Chavez 1986 and Suess *et al.* 1986). At these times, the intensity of the undercurrent is increased and its zone of influence may extend to the seafloor. Reimers & Suess (1983) emphasize that the energy of the UC in the horizontal direction is spatially limited and fluctuates strongly, so that only a portion of the shelf is affected at one time. Current environmental conditions during El Niño events favour molluscs and the foraminiferal species of the UCF. A strongly reduced surface water fertility is presently observed in association with El Niño events (Arntz 1986; Barber & Chavez 1986; Suess *et al.* 1986). Therefore, the UCF might be a possible indicator for El Niño type events.

Conclusions

Variations in the relative abundances of the benthic foraminiferal species *Nonionella auris*, *Bolivina costata*, and *Bolivina seminuda* show, that productivity was enhanced during interglacial periods.

The genera *Cassidulina*, *Epistominella*,

Gyroidina, *Trifarina* and *Valvulineria* are members of the 'Undercurrent Fauna' commonly associated with sediments having a high terrigenous detrital component and a low organic carbon content (<3 wt%). These sedimentary deposits are indicative of high near-bottom current velocities of the Peruvian Undercurrent (20–40 cm s^{-1}) and well oxygenated bottom waters (0.5–>6 ml/l O$_2$). The entire core interval investigated in Hole 680B appears to have been affected by the Peruvian Undercurrent. In general, undercurrent-dominated sections were found to correspond to glacial periods.

Samples were provided by the Ocean Drilling Project. G. F. Lutze, Kiel, verified the benthic foraminiferal species identifications. Part of the isotopic analyses was conducted in the C^{14} laboratory of the University of Kiel on a MAT 251 Mass Spectrometer with automatic carbonate preparation. M. Botros, W. H. Berger, H. Schrader, W. Prell and an anonymous colleague critically read the manuscript and made very valuable suggestions. We gratefully acknowledge the help and suppport provided by the individuals and institutions named above. This investigation was supported by the German Research Foundation (ODP/DSDP Schwerpunktprogramm).

References

ARNTZ, W. E. 1986. The two faces of El Niño 1982–83. *Meeresforsch.* **31**, 1–44.

ALTENBACH, A. V. & SARNTHEIN, M. 1989. Productivity record in benthic foraminifera. *In*: BERGER, W. H., SMETACEK, V. S. & WEFER, G. (eds) *Productivity of the Ocean: Present and Past* (Dahlem Konferenzen). John Wiley, New York, 255–269.

BANDY, O. L. & ARNAL, R. E. 1957. Distribution of recent foraminifera off west coast of Central America. *AAPG Bulletin*, **41**, 2037–2053.

——— & RODOLFO, K. S. 1964. Distribution of foraminifera and sediments, Peru-Chile trench area. *Deep-Sea Research*, **11**, 817–837.

BARBER, R. T. & CHAVEZ, F. P. 1986. Ocean variability in relation of the living resources during the 1982–1983 El Niño. *Nature*, **319**, 279–285.

——— & SMITH, R. L. 1981. Coastal Upwelling Ecosystems. *In*: LONGHURST, A. R. (ed) *Analysis of Marine Ecosystems*. London, Academic, 31–68.

BERGER, W. H., SMETACEK, V. S. & WEFER, G. 1989. Ocean productivity and paleoproductivity-an overview. *In*: BERGER, W. H., SMETACEK, V. S. & WEFER, G. (eds) *Productivity of the Ocean: Present and Past*. Wiley, New York, 1–34.

BREMNER, J. M. 1983. Biogenic sediments on the South-West-Africa (Namibia) continental margin. *In*: THIEDE, J. & SUESS, E. (eds) *Coastal Upwelling, Its Sedimentary Record* (Part B); 73–103. Plenum, New York.

BRINK, K. H., HALPERN, D. & SMITH, R. L. 1983. Circulation in the Peruvian upwelling system near 15°S. *Journal of Geophysical Research*, **85**,

4036–4048.

BROCKMANN, C., FAHRBACH, E., HUYER, A. & SMITH, R. L. 1980. The poleward undercurrent along the Peru coast: 5°S to 15°S. *Deep-Sea Research*, 27, 847–856.

BURNETT, W. C., VEEH, H. H. & SOUTAR, A. 1980. U-Series, oceanographic and sedimentary evidence in support of recent formation of phosphate nodules off Peru. SEPM Special Publication, 29, 61–71.

CARALP, M. H. 1989. Abundance of *Bulimina exilis* and *Melonis barleeanum*: Relationship to the quality of marine organic matter. *Geo-Marine Letters*, 9, 37–43.

CORLISS, B. H. 1985. Microhabitats of benthic foraminifera within deep-sea sediments. *Nature*, 314, 435–438.

CUSHMAN, J. A. 1926. Some new foraminifera from the Upper Eocene of the southeastern coastal plain of the United States. *Contr. Cush. Lab. Foram. Res.*, 2, 29–51.

—— 1927. Recent foraminifera from off the west coast of America. *Bull. Scripps Inst. Ocean. Tech. Ser.*, 1 (10), 119–188.

—— 1937. A monograf of the subfamily *Virgulininae* of the foraminiferal family *Buliminidae*. Cush. Lab. For. Res. Spec. Publ., 9, 1–228.

DEICHSEL, G. & TRAMPISCH, H. J. 1985. Cluster-analyse und Diskriminanz-analyse; 135 P. Stuttgart, Fischer.

DOUGLAS, R. G. & HEITMAN, H. L. 1979. Slope and borderland. SEPM Special Publication, 27, 231–246.

DUNBAR, R. B. & WEFER, G. 1984. Stable isotope fractionation in benthic foraminifera from the Peruvian continental margin. *Marine Geology*, 59, 215–225.

ENFIELD, D. B. 1981. Thermally driven wind variability in the planetary boundary layer above Lima, Peru. *Journal of Geophysical Research*, 86, C3, 2005–2016.

GROSSMAN, E. L. 1984. Carbon isotopic fractionation in live benthic foraminifera — comparison with inorganic precipitate studies. *Geochimica et Cosmochimica Acta*, 48, 1505–1512.

HEINZE, P. 1990. Das Auftriebsgeschehen vor Peru im Spätquartär. Berichte, Fachbereich Geowissenschaften, Universität Bremen.

HERMELIN, J. O. & SHIMMIELD, G. B. 1990. The importance of the oxygen minimum zone and sediment geochemistry in the distribution of recent benthic foraminifera in the Northwest Indian Ocean. *Marine Geology*, 91, 1–29.

IMBRIE, J., HAYS, J. D., MARTINSON, D. G., MCINTYRE, A., MIX, A. C., MORELEY, J. J., PISIAS, N. G., PRELL, W. L. & SHACKLETON, N. J. 1984. The orbital theory of Pleistocene climate: Support from a revised chronology of the marine ^{18}O record. *In*: BERGER, A. L. (ed.) *Milankovitch and Climate*, Part 1. Reidel, New York, 269–305.

INGLE, J., Jr, KELLER, G. & KOLPACK, R. L. 1980. Benthic foraminiferal biofacies, sediments and water masses of the southern Peru-Chile trench area, southeastern Pacific Ocean. *Micropaleon-*

tology, 26, 113–150.

KRISSEK, L. A. & SCHEIDEGGER, K. F. 1983. Environmental controls on the sediment texture and composition in low oxygen zones off Peru and Oregon. *In*: THIEDE, J. & SUESS, E. (eds) *Coastal Upwelling, Its Sediment Record* (Part B); 163–180. Plenum, New York.

LEETMAA, A., BEHRINGER, D. W., HUYER, A., SMITH, R. L. & TOOLE, J. 1987. Hydrographic conditions in the Eastern Pacific before, during and after the 1982/83 El Niño. Prog. *Oceanography*, 19, 1–47.

LOEBLICH, A. R. & TAPPAN, H. 1964. Protista 2. *In*: MOORE, R. C. (ed.) *Treatise on invertebrate paleontology* (C); 900 S. University of Kansas Press, Boulder.

LUTZE, G. F., PFLAUMANN, U. & WEINHOLZ, P. 1986. Jungquartäre Fluktuationen der benthischen Foraminferen in Tiefsee-Sedimenten vor NW-Afrika — Eine Reaktion auf Produktivitätsänderungen im Oberflächenwasser. *'Meteor' Forschungsergebn.*, 40 (C), 163–180.

MACKENSEN, A. 1985. *Verbreitung und Umwelt Benthischer Foraminiferen in der Norwegischen See* Dissertation, Universität Kiel.

MAEDA, S. & KISHIMOTO, R. 1970. Upwelling off the coasts of Peru. *Journal of the Oceanological Society of Japan*, 26, 300–309.

MARTINSON, D. G., PISIAS, N. G., HAYS, J. D., IMBRIE, J., MOORE, T. C. (jr.) & SHACKLETON, N. J. 1987. Age dating and the orbital theory of the ice ages: Development of a high-resolution 0–300 000-year chronostratigraphy. *Quaternary Research*, 27, 1–29.

MATOBA, Y. & YAMAGUCHI, A. 1982. Late Pliocene to Holocene benthic foraminifers of the Guaymas Basin, Gulf of California: Sites 477 through 481. *In*: CURRAY, J. R. & MOORE, D. G. (eds) Init. Reports, DSDP Washington, U.S. Govt. Printing Office, 64; 1027–1056.

MULLINS, H. T., THOMPSON, J. B., MCDOUGDALL, K. & VERCOUTERE, T. L. 1985. Oxygen-minimum zone edge effects: Evidence from the central California coastal upwelling system. *Geology*, 13, 491–494.

OBERHÄNSLI, H., HEINZE, P.-M., DIESTER-HAASS, L. & WEFER, G. 1990. Upwelling off Peru during the last 430 000 years and its relationship to the bottom water environment as deduced from coarse grain size distributions and analyses of benthic foraminifers at Holes 679D, 680B, and 681B (ODP LEG 112). *Proceedings of the Ocean Drilling Program, Scientific Results*. Ocean Drilling Program, College Station, TX, 112, 369–390.

PAK, H., CODISPOTI, L. A. & ZANEVELD, V. 1980. On the intermediate particle maxima associated with oxygen-poor water off western South America. *Deep-Sea Research*, 27, 783–797.

PHLEGER, F. B. & SOUTAR, A. 1973. Production of benthic foraminifera in three East Pacific oxygen minima. *Micropaleontology*, 19, 110–115.

PISIAS, N. G., MARTINSON, D. G., MOORE, T. C. (jr.), SHACKLETON, N. J., PRELL, W., HAYS, J. & BODEN, G. 1984. High resolution stratigraphic correlation of benthic oxygen isotopic records spanning the last 300 000 years. *Marine Geology*, **56**, 119–136.

PRELL, W. L., IMBRIE, J., MARTINSON, D. G., MORLEY, J. J., PISIAS, N. G., SHACKLETON, N. J. & STREETER, H. F. 1986. Graphic correlation of oxygen isotope stratigraphy application to late quaternary. *Paleoceanography*, **1**, 37–162.

QUINN, W. H., NEAL, V. T. & ANTUNEZ, DE MAYOLO, S. E. 1987. El Niño occurrences over the last four and a half centuries. *Journal of Geophysical Research*, **92** (C13), 14 449–14 461.

QUINTERNO, P. J. & GARDNER, J. V. 1987. Benthic foraminifers on the continental shelf and upper slope, Russian River area, northern California. *Journal of Foraminiferal Research*, **17**, 132–152.

REIMERS, C. E. & SUESS, E. 1983. Spatial and temporal patterns of organic matter accumulation on the Peru continental margin. *In*: THIEDE, J. & SUESS, E. (eds) *Coastal Upwelling, Its sediment record* (Part B) Plenum, New York. 311–346.

RESIG, J. M. 1981. Biogeography of benthic foraminifera of the northern Nazca Plate and adjacent continental margin. *Geological Society of America Memoir*, **154**, 619–665.

—— 1990. Benthic foraminiferal stratigraphy and paleoenvironments off Peru. *In*: *Proceedings of the Ocean Drilling Program, Scientific Results*, Ocean Drilling Program, College Station, TX, **112**, 263–296.

ROSENBERG, R., ARNTZ, W. E., CHUMAN DEN FLORES, E., FLORES, L. A., CARABAJAL, G., FINGER, I. & TARAZONA, J. 1983. Benthos biomass and oxygen deficiency in the upwelling system off Peru. *Journal of Marine Research*, **41**, 263–279.

SALZWEDEL, H., FLORES, L. A., CARABAJAL, G., CANAHUIRE, E., ZAFRA, A. & ARANDA, C. 1987. Información basica sobre muestras de benthos, sedimentos y factores abioticos en la plataforma continental del Peru entre 1976 y 1987. *In*: *Instituto del mar del Peru, Callao, Procopa*, **90**, 1–41.

SARNTHEIN, M. 1971. Oberflächensedimente im persischen Golf und Golf von Oman II. Quantitative Komponentenanalyse der Grobfraktion. 'Meteor' Forschungsergebn., **5** (C), 1–113.

SCHRADER, H. & SORKNES, R. 1990a. Spatial and temporal variation of Peruvian coastal upwelling during the latest Quaternary. *Proceedings of the Ocean Drilling Program, Scientific Results*, Ocean Drilling Program, College Station, TX, **112**, 391–406.

—— & —— 1990b. Peruvian coastal upwelling: Late Quaternary productivity changes revealed by diatoms. *Marine Geology*, **97**, 233–249.

SHAFFER, G. 1982. On the upwelling circulation over the wide shelf off Peru: 1. Circulation. *Journal of Marine Research*, **40**, 293–314.

SMITH, P. B. 1963. Quantitative and qualitative analysis of the family *Bolivinidae* (Recent foraminifera off Central America). *Geological Survey Professional Paper* **429-A**. 1–49; United States Gov. Printing Office, Washington.

—— 1964. Ecology of benthonic species (Recent foraminifera off Central America). Geological Survey Professional Paper **429-B**, 1–60; United States Gov. Printing Office, Washington.

SMITH, R. L. 1983. Peru coastal currents during El Niño: 1976 und 1982. *Science*, **221**, 1397–1398.

SUESS, E., KULM, L. D. & KILLINGLEY, J. S. 1986. Coastal upwelling and a history of organic-rich mudstone deposition off Peru. *In*: BROOKS, J. & FLEET, A. (eds) *Marine Petroleum Source Rocks* Geological Society, London, Special Publication, **24**, 181–197.

——, HUENE, R. v. *et al.* 1988. *Proceedings of the Ocean Drilling Program, Initial Reports* Ocean Drilling Program, College Station. TX, **112**.

TARAZONA, J., SALZWEDEL, H. & ARNTZ, W. 1988. Oscillations of macrobenthos in shallow waters of the Peruvian central coast induced by El Niño 1982–83. *Journal of Marine Research*, **46**, 593–611.

UCHIO, T. 1960. Ecology of living benthonic foraminifera from the San Diego, California, Area. *Cush. Found. Spec. Publ.*, **5**, 1–72.

VERCOUTERE, T., MULLINS, H. T., McDOUGALL, K. & THOMPSON, J. B. 1987. Sedimentation across the central California oxygen upwelling zone: An alternative coastal upwelling sequence. *Journal of Sedimentary Petrology*, **57**, 709–722.

WEFER, G., DUNBAR, R. B. & SUESS, E. 1983. Stable isotopes of foraminifers off Peru recording high fertility and changes in upwelling history. *In*: THIEDE, J. & SUESS, E. (eds) *Coastal Upwelling, Its Sedimentary Record* (Part B.) Plenum, New York, 295–308.

——, HEINZE, P.-M. & SUESS, E. 1990. Stratigraphy and sedimentation rates from oxygen isotope composition, organic carbon content, and grain size distribution at the Peru upwelling region: Holes 680B and 686B. *Proceedings of the Ocean Drilling Program, Scientific Results*, **112**, 355–367.

WILLIAMS, C. B. 1964. Patterns in the balance of nature and related problems in quantitative ecology. Academic, London.

WYRTKI, K. 1964. Upwelling in the Costa Rica Dome. *Fisheries Bulletin*, **63**, 355–372.

—— 1966. Oceanography of the eastern equatorial Pacific Ocean. *Oceanography & Marine Biology Annual Review*, **4**, 33–68.

—— 1967. Circulation and water masses in the eastern equatorial Pacific Ocean. *Journal of Oceanography and Limnology*, **1**, 117–147.

Temporal variation in intensity of upwelling off southwest Africa

WILLIAM W. HAY[1,2] & JOHN C. BROCK[1]

[1] *Department of Geology and CIRES (Cooperative Institute for Research in Environmental Sciences), Campus Box 216, University of Colorado, Boulder, CO 80309, USA*
[2] *GEOMAR, Wischhofstr. 1−3, D-2300 Kiel 14, Germany*

Abstract: Sediments recovered at DSDP Sites 362 and 532 on Walvis Ridge Abutment Plateau and 530 in the southeastern Angola Basin record long-term waxing and waning of upwelling. The amounts of opaline silica and organic carbon in the sediments increase from latest Miocene to latest Pliocene then decline to present. During the late Pliocene, opaline silica accumulated ten times faster than during the late Pleistocene. If the area of accumulation also expanded to include the Abutment Plateau, this region would have been the global silica sink, consuming the equivalent of the entire silica output of the present ocean. The sediments contain light−dark cycles; the dark cycles contain more terrigenous material and on this basis have been interpreted as representing glacials. Before the Pliocene the maximum biological productivity in this region occurred during the glacials, but since then it has occurred during the interglacials, an effect of sea-level change on productivity opposite to that in most parts of the world. The most important factors causing the changes in sedimentation are judged to be threefold.

(1) Closing of the Central American Isthmus resulted in salinization of the North Atlantic and caused increased production of NADW, AAIW and AABW. The increased rate of production of these water masses resulted in differentiation of nutrients among them and may have resulted in a shallower pycnocline facilitating upwelling of nutrient-rich water. The production of relatively nutrient-rich AAIW was a prerequisite for the long term increase in productive upwelling recorded by the late Miocene to latest Pliocene sediments.

(2) During the Late Miocene northward migration of the subtropical high and ITCZ in response to growth of the Antarctic ice cap may have initiated productive upwelling over the Abutment Plateau. Subsequent southward migration of the ITCZ as the Earth changed from unipolar to bipolar glaciation would have enhanced the Angola Coastal Current and upwelling from the Angola Thermal Dome. A stronger Angola Coastal Current may have carried productive waters from the Angola Dome and focussed advection of productive coastal waters upwelled along the Namibian shelf over the Walvis Ridge Abutment Plateau. The decline in strength of upwelling since 1.7 Ma recorded by the sediments on the Abutment Plateau may reflect southward shift of the upwelling center to its present location near Lüderitz in response to the growth of northern hemisphere ice caps.

(3) The desiccation of the Mediterranean drew the ITCZ to its maximum northern position and the reflooding corresponded to the time of change from maximum upwelling productivity coinciding with glacials to its coinciding with interglacials. During glacials, when NADW production was reduced, AAIW was replaced by nutrient-poor NAIW, so that the upwelled water did not become productive. Another possible cause of the general decline in productivity since 1.7 Ma is the that increased Mediterranean saline outflow has resulted in progressive expansion of NAIW into the South Atlantic during glacials.

Site 362, drilled during Leg 40, of the Deep Sea Drilling Project (DSDP) is on the plateau where Walvis Ridge abuts the continental margin (referred to as the Abutment Plateau or Continental Terrace). It yielded late Neogene sediments with an enrichment of organic carbon and abundant diatoms. At that time all sections were rotary drilled, and the cores from the upper 200 metres of the hole were badly disturbed, so that a detailed interpretation of the record was impossible. Nevertheless, the shipboard scientists

(Bolli, Ryan *et al.* 1978) and subsequent investigators (Diester-Haass & Schrader 1979; Siesser 1980) recognized that the increased abundances of diatoms and organic carbon were linked to upwelling and suggested that they reflected the onset and development of the Benguela upwelling system, the term being used loosely for upwelling off southwest Africa.

During Leg 75 of the Deep Sea Drilling Project, two other sites were drilled in the same region, and the upper 200 metres of the sedi-

From SUMMERHAYES, C. P., PRELL, W. L. & EMEIS, K. C. (eds), 1992, *Upwelling Systems: Evolution Since the Early Miocene.* Geological Society Special Publication No 63, pp 463−497.

463

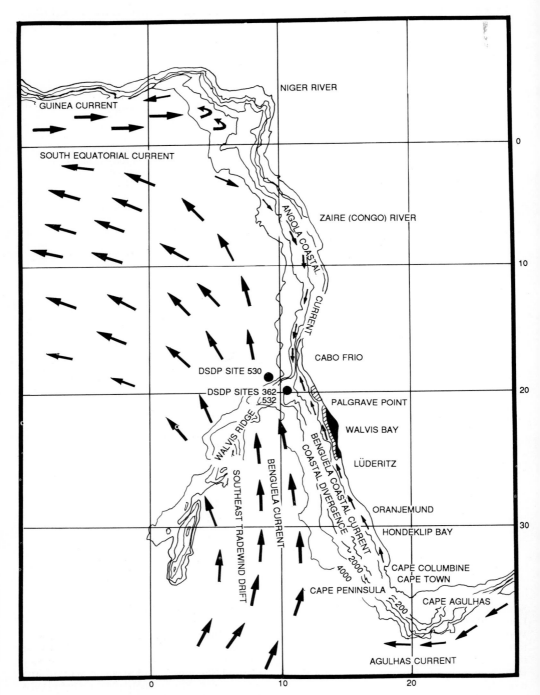

Fig. 1. Map of the margin of southwest Africa, showing the geographical features mentioned in the text, the locations of DSDP Sites 530, 362 and 532, the named ocean currents, and the present extent of sediments having >5% organic carbon (diagonal lines) and diatom muds having >10% opal (black).

Table 1. Accumulation rates of latest Miocene–Recent sediment components at DSDP Site 532 (after Hay, Sibuet *et al.* 1984*c*, Table 3).

Age (Ma)	Depth bsf (m)	Accumulation rates (g/cm²kyr)				
		Opal	C_{org}	$CaCO_3$	Terrigenous	Total
0–0.45	0–19.4	0.101	0.123	1.802	1.124	3.150
0.45–1.7	19.4–76.6	0.719	0.110	1.428	1.304	3.561
1.7–2.0	76.6–94.2	1.807	0.190	1.206	1.151	3.634
2.0–3.0	94.2–148.6	0.474	0.180	1.571	2.009	4.234
3.0–5.8	148.6–256.2	0.088	0.094	2.176	2.037	4.395

ment were piston cored. DSDP Site 530 in the southeastern corner of the Angola Basin also recovered a sequence of late Miocene, Pliocene and Pleistocene hemipelagic sediments rich in organic matter and opaline silica, but interrupted by several massive debris flows and a number of turbidites. Site 532 on Walvis Ridge Abutment Plateau, essentially a reoccupation of Site 362, recovered the Pliocene–Pleistocene sequence in detail. Again, these sediments were interpreted by the Leg 75 Shipboard Scientific Party (Hay, Sibuet *et al.* 1982; 1984*a*) to be the result of an expanded or displaced Benguela Upwelling System. Figure 1 shows the location of the DSDP Sites, and the extent of the modern coastal upwelling system as outlined by Bremner (1983) and Calvert & Price (1983), with the area of >5% C_{org} shown in diagonal lines and the area with >10% opal shown in black.

The data

Table 1 and Fig. 2a,c,e show the average accumulation rates for opaline silica, organic carbon, and calcium carbonate at DSDP Site 532 for five time intervals defined by nannofossil biostratigraphy, with three intervals, 5.8–3.0 Ma, 3.0–2.0 Ma, and 2.0–1.7 Ma in the latest Miocene and Pliocene, and two, 1.7–0.45 Ma and <0.45 Ma, for the Pleistocene (Hay, Sibuet *et al.* 1984*c*; Steinmetz *et al.* 1984; Steinmetz & Stradner 1984). These intervals do not correspond to recognized subdivisions of the epochs, so the terms early middle and late are used in an informal sense in the discussion below. Finer subdivision of the section has not been possible because some of the most useful index species are not present. Diester-Haass *et al.* (1990) have suggested that the Miocene–Pliocene boundary may be about 10 metres higher than placed by the shipboard scientific party. This change is not followed here, and does not materially affect the outcome of the analysis made using the older age interpretation.

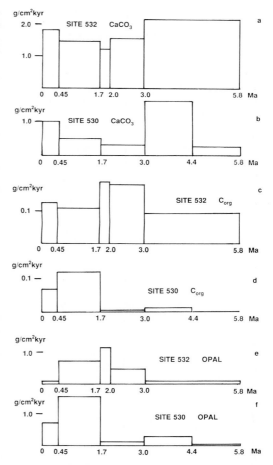

Fig. 2. Mass/age distributions for the three major biogenic components (CaCO₃, C_{org}, Opal) in latest Miocene (5.8 Ma) to Recent sediments recovered at DSDP Sites 530 and 532. Vertical axis is accumulation rate (mass/area × time). Mass is proportional to the area of each bar. (a) CaCO₃ at DSDP Site 532; (b) CaCO₃ at DSDP Site 530; (c) C_{org} at DSDP Site 532; (d) C_{org} at DSDP Site 530; (e) opaline silica at DSDP Site 532; (f) opaline silica at DSDP Site 530.

Table 2. Proportions of latest Miocene−Recent sediment components at DSDP Site 532 (after Hay, Sibuet et al. 1984c, Table 3).

Age (Ma)	Depth bsf (m)	Opal	Proportions (Weight percent)		
			C_{org}	CaCO₃	Terrigenous
0−0.45	0−19.4	3.2	3.9	57.2	35.7
0.45−1.7	19.4−76.6	20.2	3.1	40.1	36.6
1.7−2.0	76.6−94.2	29.9	5.2	33.2	31.7
2.0−3.0	94.2−148.6	11.2	4.2	37.1	47.5
3.0−5.8	148.6−256.2	20.0	2.2	49.5	28.3

Hay et al. (1984c) reported that at DSDP Site 532 the accumulation rate of opaline silica increased from less than 0.080 g cm^{-2} ka^{-1} in the late Miocene to reach an average rate of 1.087 g cm^{-1} ka^{-1} in the latest Pliocene and then declined to 0.101 g cm^{-2} ka^{-1} in the late Pleistocene. Table 2 shows the changes in proportions of biogenic and terrigenous components of the sediments with time. Opaline silica also increases in terms of its proportion of the total sediment, measured in weight percent (see figure 26 in Hay, Sibuet et al. 1984c and fig. 17 in Dean et al. 1984). It rises from 1.0% in the late Miocene to 29.9% in the latest Pliocene to 3.2% in the late Pleistocene. The accumulation rate of C_{org} rose from 0.094 g cm^{-2} ka^{-2} in the early Pliocene to 0.190 g cm^{-2} ka^{-1} in the latest Pliocene and then declined to 0.123 g cm^{-2} ka^{-1} in the late Pleistocene. The proportion of organic carbon in the sediment shows the same trend as opal, increasing from 2.2% in the late Miocene to an average of 5.2% in the latest Pliocene and then declining to 3.9% in the late Pleistocene. The changes in the calcium carbonate accumulation rates show the inverse trend, declining from an average of 2.176 g cm^{-2} ka^{-1} in the early Pliocene, to 1.206 g cm^{-2} ka^{-1} in the latest Pliocene and then increasing to 1.802 g cm^{-2} ka^{-1} in the late Pleistocene. The proportion of carbonate declined from 59.5% in the late Miocene to 33.2% in the latest Pliocene and increased to 57.2% in the late Pleistocene. Diester-Haass et al. (1986), Diester-Haass and Rothe (1987), and Diester-Haass (1988) have suggested that diagenetic dissolution of carbonate may be significant in the layers enriched in organic carbon, causing an apparent reduction in carbonate accumulation rates.

The average accumulation rates for the total sediment show a monotonic decline, from 4.935 g cm^{-2} ka^{-1} in the early Pliocene to 3.150 g cm^{-2} ka^{-1} in the late Pleistocene. The average accumulation rates of non-biogenous components of the sediment show a step function decrease, from about 2.0 g cm^{-2} ka^{-1} in the

early and middle Pliocene to about 1.2 g cm^{-2} ka^{-1} in the latest Pliocene and Pleistocene.

Superimposed on this long-term trend are shorter-term cyclic variations in the carbonate, organic carbon and opal content of the sediments, commonly referred to in the literature as dark−light cycles. The light cycles are relatively carbonate-rich (Dean et al. 1984; Gardner et al. 1984; Dean & Gardner 1985). Dean & Gardner (1985) found a less consistent correlation between the dark cycles and increased organic carbon content, and no clear correlation between the cycles and opal content. The darker parts of the cycles have a higher content of terrigenous material, and have been interpreted as representing low stands of sea level (Gardner et al. 1984). The carbonate cycles have periodicities ranging from 26 to 49 ka, the colour cycles have periodicities ranging from 28 to 83 ka and the carbon cycles have periodicities ranging from 28 to 43 ka. These are in the range of, but not exactly corresponding to, Milankovitch orbital forcing (Gardner et al. 1984). Because of the way the ages were determined and uncertainty of the periodicities, we decided that the use of the cycles to establish a fine stratigraphy for short-term variations in accumulation rates would be questionable.

Although the sediments are rich in C_{org} most of the sequence is bioturbated. The light−dark cycles grade into one another. There is no evidence of lamination that might suggest the complete absence of benthos.

Subsequent studies by Diester-Haass (1985a, b; 1988), Diester-Haass et al. (1986, 1990), and Diester-Haass and Rothe (1987) revealed that in sediments older than Pliocene (5.2 Ma) the glacial (dark) cycles are enriched in opaline silica, whereas there is a negative correlation of the dark cycles and opaline silica content in the younger sediments.

Site 530 was drilled on Leg 75 of the DSDP, in a water depth of 4629 metres in the southeastern corner of the Angola Basin. The sediments were deposited below the lysocline but above the calcite compensation depth during

Table 3. Accumulation rates of latest Miocene–Recent sediment components at DSDP Site 530 (after Hay, Sibuet *et al.* 1984*b*, Table 7, corrected by removal of turbdites and debris-flow deposits).

Age (Ma)	Depth bsf (m)	Accumulation rates (g/cm^2kyr)				
		Opal	C_{org}	$CaCO_3$	Terrigenous	Total
0–0.45	0–30.00	0.671	0.072	1.036	0.884	2.663
0.45–1.7	30.0–117.2	1.444	0.120	0.493	1.250	3.301
1.7–3.0	117.2–129.8	0.103	0.020	0.331	0.604	1.058
3.0–4.4	129.8–196.3	0.317	0.089	1.674	2.717	4.797
4.4–5.8	196.3–205.8	0.023	0.001	0.272	0.438	0.734
5.8–10.0	205.8–262.8	0.070	0.011	0.502	0.820	1.403
10.0–10.6	262.8–287.3	0.000	0.019	0.921	3.117	4.057

the late Miocene, Pliocene and Pleistocene. Again, the biostratigraphy was based on nannofossils but more of the index species were present so that again three intervals, 5.8–4.4 Ma, 4.4–3.0 Ma, and 3.0–1.7 Ma, could be recognized for the latest Miocene and Pliocene, but they differ from those recognized at Site 532. The thickness of material of latest Pliocene age (3.0–1.7 Ma) was determined by combining depth of datums in Holes 530A and 530B. This interval corresponds to the time of maximum accumulation of opaline silica at Site 532, but the accumulation rates calculated for Site 530 are much lower, suggesting a hiatus. Calcareous nannoplankton diagnostic for Zone NN18 were found at Site 532 but not at Site 530. The Pleistocene was divided into two units, 1.7–0.45 Ma and <0.45 Ma, as at Site 532. About 25% of the Pleistocene section consists of debris flow deposits and turbidites. The rest of the section appears to be normal hemipelagic sediment although some of it may be redeposited. Planktonic foraminifers and other shallow water fossils occur in the turbidites and debris flows, but the remainder of the sediment consists of nannofossil and diatom ooze. Again, the sediments are bioturbated and there is no evidence for anoxic bottom conditions.

Table 3 and Fig. 2b,d,f show the accumulation rates for opaline silica, C_{org}, and calcium carbonate at DSDP Site 530. The rates have been corrected from those reported by Hay, Sibuet *et al.* (1984*b*), eliminating debris flows and turbidites. The accumulation rate of opaline silica rose from 0.07 g cm^{-2} ka^{-1} in the late Miocene to 0.317 g cm^{-2} ka^{-1} in the middle Pliocene, then apparently declined to 0.103 g cm^{-2} ka^{-1} in the later Pliocene. It rose sharply to 1.444 g cm^{-2} ka^{-1} in the early Pleistocene and declined to 0.671 g cm^{-2} ka^{-1} in the late Pleistocene. As seen in Table 4, opaline silica also increases in terms of its proportion of the total sediment (see figure 71 in Hay, Sibuet *et al.* 1984*b*). It rose from 0.5% in the late Miocene to 43.6% in the early Pleistocene to 25.2% in the late Pleistocene. The organic carbon accumulation rate rose from 0.001 g cm^{-2} ka^{-1} in the early Pliocene to 0.089 g cm^{-2} ka^{-1} in the middle Pliocene, apparently declining to 0.020 g cm^{-2} ka^{-1} in the late Pliocene. It then rose sharply to 0.120 g cm^{-2} ka^{-1} in the late Pliocene and to 0.072 g cm^{-2} ka^{-1} in the late Pleistocene. The proportion of organic carbon in the sediment, measured in weight percent, shows the same trend, increasing from 2.0% in the late Miocene to an average of 3.6% in the early Pleistocene, declining to 2.7% in the late Pleistocene. Carbonate average accumulation rates are variable ranging from a minimum of 0.272 g cm^{-2} ka^{-1} in the early Pliocene to a maximum of 1.674 g

Table 4. Proportions of latest Miocene–Recent sediment components at DSDP Site 530 (after Hay, Sibuet *et al.* 1984*b*, Table 7).

Age (Ma)	Depth bsf (m)	Proportions (Weight percent)			
		Opal	C_{org}	$CaCO_3$	Terrigenous
0–0.45	0–30.00	25.2	2.7	38.9	33.2
0.45–1.7	30.0–117.2	43.6	3.6	14.9	37.9
1.7–3.0	117.2–129.8	9.7	1.9	31.3	57.1
3.0–4.4	129.8–196.3	6.6	1.9	34.9	56.6
4.4–5.8	196.3–205.8	3.2	2.0	37.0	57.8
5.8–10.0	205.8–262.8	0.5	0.8	35.8	62.9
10.0–10.6	262.8–287.3	0.0	0.5	22.7	76.8

cm^{-2} ka^{-1} in the middle Pliocene. The proportion of carbonate remains almost constant,
about 33%, in the Pliocene, decreases to 15%
in the early Pleistocene and returns to 39% in
the late Pleistocene. Site 530 was strongly affected by fluctuations of the calcite compensation
depth (see figure 13 in Dean et al. 1984).

The average total sediment accumulation
rates for these intervals are variable, from a
minimum of 0.734 g cm^{-2} ka^{-1} in the early
Pliocene to a maximum of 4.797 g cm^{-2} ka^{-1} in
the middle Pliocene. They are always less than
at Site 532, reflecting the effect of nearly complete dissolution of planktonic foraminifera
from the sediments. The average accumulation
rates of non-biogenous components of the sediment were low, 0.438 g cm^{-2} ka^{-1}, in the early
Pliocene, reach a maximum of 2.717 g cm^{-2}
ka^{-1} in the middle Pliocene and decrease to
0.884 g cm^{-2} ka^{-1} in the late Pleistocene.

Even after eliminating contributions from
turbidites and debris flows, the highest concentrations and accumulation rates of opaline silica
are not at the shallower Site 532 on Walvis
Ridge, but are at Site 530 in the Angola Basin.
This is not merely the effect of dilution by
calcium carbonate at the shallower site; the
absolute rate of opal accumulation is almost
50% higher at the deeper site. Site 530 is located
on the gently sloping floor of the southeastern
Angola Basin 20 km north of the Walvis Ridge
escarpment where the ridge rises abruptly from
4500 to 3500 metres. Between 3500 and 3000
metres there is a 50 km broad terrace before
another escarpment rises to the 1500 metre
deep edge of the Walvis Abutment Plateau. It is
possible that there are additional turbidity current deposits that were not recognized by the
shipboard scientific party.

Assuming that the opaline silica accumulation
rates are the best reflection of high biological
productivity in the overlying surface waters, the
sediments indicate a long-term cycle of increasing then decreasing biological productivity over
the Walvis Ridge Abutment Plateau and the
southeastern Angola Basin. The increase in
productivity started about 10 Ma (Bolli, Ryan
et al. 1978; Diester-Haass et al. 1990) and accelerated at 5 Ma to reach a maximum between 1.7
and 3 Ma, followed by a decline in productivity
until present. Superimposed on this long-term
trend are short-term light–dark cycles having
approximate Milankovitch frequencies.

In their investigation of the dark and light
layers at Site 532, Gardner et al. (1984) found
that the dark layers contain more clay and
organic carbon, and less carbonate than the
light layers. They did not find a clear relation

between content of opaline silica and the light
and dark layers. Nevertheless, the correlation
of increased abundance of clay and organic
carbon led them to suggest that the dark layers
represent times of lowered sea level, with enhanced terrigenous supply from land. Subsequent studies have assumed that the darker
cycles represent glacials because they contain
more terrigenous material. There has not yet
been independent confirmation of this hypothesis by oxygen isotopes or other data.

From studies of material from DSDP Sites
362 and 532 and piston cores, Diester-Haass
(1985a, b, 1988), Diester-Haass et al. (1986,
1990), and Diester-Haass & Rothe (1987) have
noted that in sediments older than 5.2 Ma
(Miocene) the glacial (dark) cycles are enriched
in opaline silica. In the younger sediments there
is a negative correlation, with the glacial (dark)
cycles containing less opaline silica than the
interglacial (light) cycles. This suggests that sea
level change per se is not a major factor controlling intensity of the upwelling signal recorded in
the sediments of the Walvis Ridge Abutment
Plateau. The dark cycles have been interpreted
by all investigators as glacials because the dark
colour is imparted by a greater admixture of
terrigenous material and not by the organic
material. The light cycles have a higher proportion of calcium carbonate and represent
interglacials. Before the Pliocene the increased
biological productivity occurred during the
glacial cycles; since then maximum biological
productivity has occurred during the interglacial
cycles.

The varying accumulation rates of opaline
silica, carbonate and organic carbon on both
long and short term must reflect changes in both
the composition and productivity of the plankton in the surface waters over these sites. As
fertility increases, siliceous plankton replace
calcareous plankton, productivity increases and
burial of organic carbon increases. Changes in
productivity of the magnitude recorded by these
sediments must reflect a varying nutrient supply
which could be either introduction from land or
upwelling of nutrient-rich deeper waters. Introduction from land is precluded by the distance
of the DSDP Sites offshore and by the lack of
any major rivers in the immediate area. The
Leg 75 Shipboard Scientific Party (Hay, Sibuet
et al. 1982) assumed that these sediments reflected modulation of the regime of the modern
Benguela Coastal Upwelling System, either as
increased or displaced upwelling. Subsequent
investigators (Meyers et al. 1983; Diester-Haass
1985a, b, 1988; Diester-Haass et al. 1986, 1990;
Diester-Haass & Rothe 1987) have suggested

that enhanced upwelling and offshore advection of the upwelled waters to Walvis Ridge might also be due to formation of eddies where the northward flowing Benguela and southward flowing Angola Coastal currents meet.

The problem

The long-term change in opal accumulation rates at Sites 532 and 530, from latest Pliocene to late Pleistocene is an order of magnitude. If this increase at Sites 532 and 530 is due to intensification and expansion of the present coastal upwelling system, it implies significantly higher rates of accumulation of opaline silica over a much larger area. If the upwelling centre has always been at Lüderitz as it is today, and the increase in accumulation rates were everywhere an order of magnitude, it implies that the rates of accumulation on the shelf south of Walvis Ridge should be an order of magnitude greater than the Holocene rate of 40 g cm^{-2} a^{-1} (calculated from the data of Bremner 1983), or 400 g cm^{-2} a^{-1}, equal to a thickness of about 10 m ka^{-1}. The area over which the opal sedimentation occurred must have been much larger also, at least 700 × 300 km^2, or an order of magnitude larger than the present area of deposition of diatom muds on the Namibian shelf (Bremner 1983). The order of magnitude increase in deposition rate and the order of magnitude increase in the area of deposition imply two orders of magnitude increase in the amount of silica fixed as opal, from the present rate of 1 × 10^{13} g a^{-1} (Bremner 1983) to 1 × 10^{15} g a^{-1}. This would be a sustained output in the southeast Atlantic well in excess of the 6.1 ± 1.8 × 10^{14} g/yr estimated by DeMaster (1981) to be the present global silica input to the ocean.

At DSDP Sites 532 and 530 the latest Pliocene rates of accumulation of C_{org} are double those of the late Pleistocene, but the area over which the C_{org}-rich sediments were deposited must have been about an order of magnitude larger, so that the burial of C_{org} in this region must have been about twenty times higher than at present, or 30 × 10^{12} g a^{-1}. Although this would make a significant regional sink, it is not a major perturbation of the global carbon cycle since the global rate of C_{org} burial on the continental shelves is in the order 120 × 10^{12} g a^{-1} (Holser et al. 1988).

The sediments that accumulate beneath upwelling waters may or may not differ from those of the surrounding area, depending on whether the upwelled waters contain some or all of the nutrients necessary for growth of different kinds of phytoplankton. The sedimentary signal on the Walvis Ridge Abutment Plateau, diatom muds, is a classic example of that expected from late Cenozoic upwelling of waters with a complete complement of nutrients (PO_4, NO_3, H_4SiO_4) from the ocean interior (Calvert 1974; Diester-Haass 1978, 1983; Calvert & Price 1983).

These changes in mass budgets of opal and C_{org} are so large that it seems unlikely that the sediments at DSDP Sites 530, 362/532 are simply a reflection of intensification and expansion of the present coastal upwelling system and offshore-downstream advection of the nutrient-rich waters as proposed by Hay, Sibuet et al. 1982, 1984a). If this were the case they would imply upwelling volumes of water a hundred times larger than at present, or somewhat lesser volumes of water having nutrient concentrations much higher than at present.

The hypothesis of Diester-Haass (1985a, 1985b; 1988), Diester-Haass et al. (1986, 1990), and Diester-Haass & Rothe (1987) that the weakening of productivity during glacials is due to a shift of the latitude at which the Benguela Current leaves the coast is not constrained by observational data.

Expansion and intensification of the present coastal upwelling system is not a viable explanation of either the long-term waxing and waning of the upwelling signal at DSDP Sites 532 and 530 or of the shift of cyclic changes of upwelling intensity from maximum during Miocene glacials to minimum during Pliocene and Pleistocene glacials. The lack of data from pre-Holocene sediments of the Namibian shelf and surrounding areas precludes certain explanations of these changes. To evaluate possible causes we first describe the present oceanographic conditions, the coastal upwelling system, and the sedimentary record of Holocene upwelling in the region. Then we consider the different modes of upwelling and evaluate the effects of changing palaeogeography, palaeoclimatology and palaeoceanography on them. Finally we suggest the most likely explanations of the observed changes and suggest the kinds of data needed to constrain the possibilities.

Oceanographic conditions off southwest Africa at present

Detailed descriptions of the physical oceanography of the upwelling region off southwest Africa have been presented by Bang (1971) and more recently by Nelson & Hutchings (1983), Shannon (1985a, b). The chemical oceanography of the region has been reviewed by Chapman & Shannon (1985).

Figure 1 shows the currents, upwelling sites, and other oceanographic features along the coast of southwestern Africa. The term Benguela Current is ambiguous, being used in several different ways. In general descriptions of circulation in the South Atlantic it is used for the broad, diffuse equatorward flow of the eastern side of the South Atlantic Gyre (Moroshkin et al. 1970). In this sense, the Benguela Current is a weak, thin surface current, less than 80 metres thick, overlying a poleward flowing countercurrent (Sverdrup et al. 1942; Fuglister 1960; Gorshkov 1977; Tchernia 1980; Shannon 1985a). However, in the regional specialist literature, the term Benguela Current is used for the coastal current flowing northward over the Namibian shelf. It is separated from the general northerly flow of the eastern side of the South Atlantic Gyre, referred to as the Southeast Trade Wind Drift, by an offshore divergence associated with the shelf break. This distinction was first made by Hart & Currie (1960, p 287): 'we have restricted the use of the name Benguela Current to the coastal circulation in which upwelling movements occur and have referred to the oceanic circulation as the southeast trade drift.' The upwelling along the Namibian margin occurs both along the coast in response to offshore Ekman transport and over the shelf break where the offshore divergence develops. Accordingly, Bang (1971, p 222), further restricted the definition, stating that 'the Benguela Current is that area east of the off-

shore divergence within which oceanic processes are dominated by short-term atmospheric interactions.' This distinction was also followed by Summerhayes (1983), but the usage of the term Benguela Current by the DSDP Leg 40 (Bolli, Ryan et al. 1978) and Leg 75 Shipboard Scientists (Hay, Sibuet et al. 1982, 1984a; Meyers et al. 1983; Dean et al. 1984) was in the general sense of the northward flowing eastern limb of the South Atlantic anticyclonic gyre. In this paper we shall refer to the coastal current east of the offshore divergence over the shelf break as the Benguela Coastal Current, and the region in which active wind-driven upwelling occurs over the shelf as the Benguela Coastal Upwelling System. Figure 3 is a schematic view of the general oceanography of the region.

Along the tropical coast of southern west Africa there is a southward flowing coastal current; it was named the Angola Current by Moroshkin et al. (1970). This current is the southward-flowing extension of the South Equatorial Countercurrent; because it is restricted to the coast, it will be referred to here as the Angola Coastal Current.

The northward flowing Benguela Coastal Current usually meets the southward flowing Angola Coastal Current in the vicinity of Cabo Frio at 18°S, but the Angola Coastal Current may penetrate as far as 23°S, the latitude of Walvis Bay (Moroshkin et al. 1970). Shannon (1985a) has noted that the data analyzed by Moroshkin et al. (1970) were collected during autumn, a season when current conditions may differ from those encountered during most of

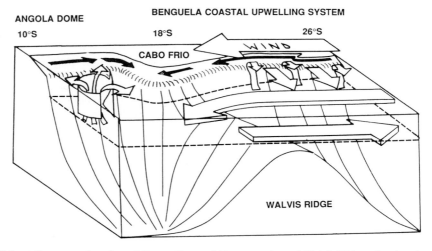

Fig. 3. Schematic perspective view of the southwest African margin and Walvis Ridge, showing the major currents, the coastal upwelling system, and the Angola Dome. Not to scale.

the rest of the year. Where the Benguela and Angola Coastal Currents meet eddies are generated. Eddies containing upwelled water with diatoms and radiolarians drift offshore, and more sterile eddies of tropical water drift inshore (Hart & Currie 1960; Hagen *et al.* 1981). The offshore drifting eddies are thought to be the source of the biogenic silica presently being deposited on the Walvis Ridge Abutment Plateau (Diester-Haass (1985a, b, 1988), Diester-Haass *et al.* (1986, 1990) and Diester-Haass & Rothe (1987).

An oceanic divergence has been shown between the Benguela Coastal Current and Southeast Trade Wind Drift offshore of South Africa by Dietrich (1957; after Schott, 1943), but is not mentioned in the more recent literature. Shannon (1985a) shows this as an area of mesoscale gyres. Moroshkin *et al.* (1970) suggested the existence of a 'Benguela divergence' between the main (westerly) and lesser (easterly) branches of the Benguela Current north of 20°N, starting over the Walvis Ridge Abutment Plateau. The splitting of the Benguela into western and eastern arms suggested by Moroshkin *et al.* (1970) may also be related to interference with the Angola Coastal Current.

Beneath the equatorward surface flow is a poleward flowing countercurrent. It is the east side of a cyclonic subsurface gyre that upwells nutrient-rich Antarctic Intermediate Water immediately beneath the pycnocline (Bogorov *et al.* 1973; Gorshkov 1977; Bainbridge, no date). The longshore winds of southwest Africa are among the most stable on the planet because the steep slope from the shore to the 2 km high western Kalahari restricts the anticyclonic flow around the southeastern Atlantic high. The winds increase during the southern hemisphere summer in response to the intensification of the low that develops over the Kalahari, so that the upwelling maximum occurs from December to April (Schell 1968; Shannon 1985a).

Along the margin of southwest Africa, the strong coastal upwelling occurs over the inner shelf and over the shelf break (Bang 1971; Summerhayes 1983). The maximum upwelling sometimes results in red tides and massive fish kills near Walvis Bay (Brongersma-Sanders 1948, 1957). At present the upwelling along the coast of Namibia takes place within a narrow band, less than 100 km wide and mostly within the 300 m isobath (Bang 1971). Upwelling occurs from Cabo Frio (18.4°S) to Cape Agulhas (34.5°S), but the centre and site of strongest upwelling occurs off Lüderitz (27°S) with secondary sites of strong upwelling off Namaqua at Hondeklip Bay (30°S), off Cape Columbine (32.5°S) and along the Cape Peninsula (34°S) (Nelson & Hutchings 1983; Shannon 1985a). The two northerly sites are just north of the two narrow segments of the shelf (Nelson & Hutchings 1983); the two southerly sites are at the narrowest points of the shelf. There are lesser centres of upwelling at Conception Bay (24°S), Palgrave Point (20–21°S) and south of Cabo Frio (18–19°S) (Shannon 1985a).

From Lüderitz to Cabo Frio the upwelled waters include an admixture of relatively nutrient-rich Antarctic Intermediate Water. The pycnocline marking the top of the Antarctic Intermediate Water lies at a depth of only about 250 metres off Walvis Bay, although the core of the nutrient-rich water is at a depth of 600 metres (Bainbridge, no date). Hart & Currie (1960), Calvert & Price (1971a) and Shannon (1985a) have estimated or cited estimates by others of the depth from which waters are upwelled. Their estimates range from 200 to 330 metres.

South of Lüderitz to Cape Agulhas the upwelled water appears to contain less Antarctic Intermediate Water, and silica may be the limiting nutrient (Chapman & Shannon 1985). Off Cape Columbine and the Cape Peninsula the pycnocline marking the top of the Antarctic Intermediate Water lies at a depth of 550 m (Bainbridge, no date).

Nutrient concentrations in the water upwelled along the Namibian margin are very high, with PO_4 commonly 2.5 micromoles/l and ranging up to 8 micromoles/l (Chapman & Shannon 1985). These concentrations generally exceed those of PO_4 in the core of Antarctic Intermediate Water (Bainbridge, no date). The higher concentrations are attributed to recycling of nutrients on the shelf. Nutrient concentrations in the upwelled waters on the shelf off South Africa are lower, with PO_4 ranging between 1 and 2 micromoles/l (Chapman & Shannon 1985). Here the more rapid flow of water and narrower shelf are thought to inhibit recycling of nutrients.

The western margin of the upwelling region is not well defined in term of sea-surface temperature anomalies. Satellite imagery has shown large scale frontal features, resembling 'giant ripcurrents,' extending up to 500 km offshore (van Foreest *et al.* 1984). Eight of these features, distinguished by a ±1°C depression of the sea surface temperature indicated by NOAA1 enhanced infrared (Channel 4 AVHRR) imagery, were observed in June (1979). The three southernmost features, formed off the southern part of the coast, between Cape Town and

Hondeklip Bay, resembled eddies and did not extend far beyond the shelf break. The three largest features formed between Oranjemund and Palgrave Point, and extended 500 km NE to SW across the outer shelf and over the continental slope. The two northernmost features were weaker and had a different orientation, WNW to ESE. The more southerly extended from Palgrave Point over the Walvis Abutment Plateau, and the northerly one from the north side of Cabo Frio across the Angolan continental slope. They were about 100 km wide and spaced 200 to 400 km apart, the distance between them increasing equatorwards. They were observed to be stationary over the period of their life, about three weeks. The speed of their formation ruled out the possibility that they were advected shelf water, and the fact that they did not drift northward with the current suggested to van Foreest et al. (1984) that they might be caused by some sort of shelf wave. However, analytical attempts to explain them failed. Those over the Namibian shelf had the same orientation as the NE–SW katabatic winds (Berg winds) that affect this region in the late fall and early winter (Shannon 1985a). The Berg winds appear to be responsible for the palaeowind directions suggested by ventifacts (Selby 1977) and oriented wind erosion landforms described from the Namibian region (Sweeting & Lancaster 1982; Besler 1980; Diester-Haass et al. 1988).

A cool 50 km wide upwelling filament extending off the shelf west of Lüderitz has been described by Shillington et al. (1990). They suggest that formation of the filament was forced by an anticyclonic Agulhas ring which then formed the southern border of the filament. The life of the filament was in the order of a month.

The western frontal features off the southern part of the margin have been described in Shannon (1985b) as part of the South African Ocean Colour and Upwelling Experiment.

Distribution of sediments beneath the present upwelling regime

The sedimentary signal of the modern coastal upwelling system is strongly developed on the Namibian shelf; the rate of deposition of diatomaceous mud is highest off Walvis Bay, and the siliceous deposits are restricted to the inner shelf (Bremner 1983). The region of the enhanced organic carbon accumulation (>5%) extends over 600 km along the Namibian coast, but rarely extends more than 150 km offshore (Calvert & Price 1983; Bremner 1983). These deposits, clearly reflecting upwelling of nutrient-rich waters, are attributed to the Benguela Upwelling System. In some of the geological literature this has been taken as implying a relation between upwelling and the offshore Benguela Current (Southeast Trade Wind Drift), but as noted above the Benguela Upwelling System is associated with the Benguela Coastal Current.

The upwelling centres at 30°, 32.5°, and 34°S are reflected by iron-enrichment of the sediments on the South African shelf, but do not contain large concentrations of opal (Gorshkov 1977). In contrast, the sediments on the Namibian shelf, reflecting the upwelling off Lüderitz, are rich in amorphous silica. The strongest phytoplankton bloom, and greatest enrichment of opal in the sediments, occurs off Walvis Bay, some 400 km downstream from the upwelling centre off Lüderitz.

Amounts of opal (diatoms) greater than a trace are restricted to a band 100 km wide along the coast between 19° and 25°S. The sediment is a diatom ooze forming a green mud containing H_2S and devoid of benthos (Calvert & Price 1983). The area covered by the mud was termed the 'azoic zone' by Copenhagen (1953). Bremner (1983) has determined that the siliceous mud belt has an area of 24 400 km^2, a mean thickness of 5.1 m, and averages 54.3% opal by weight. It is Holocene, and has accumulated in about 5000 years, so that total annual accumulation of opal is 1×10^{13} g a^{-1}, about a third of the amount of opal deposited in the Gulf of California during the Holocene (Bremner 1983). Normalized to unit area, this is equivalent to an accumulation rate of 40.95 g cm^{-2} ka^{-1}.

Organic carbon occurs over a wider area than does opaline silica. At present sediments with more than 5% C_{org} (= 7% organic matter) occur in three narrow bands parallel to the coast from 19° to 27°S. The inner band, with patches of $C_{org} > 15\%$ lies within 80 km of the coast and is widest at Walvis Bay. The second band is centred about 100 km offshore, just seaward of the 200 m isobath. The third band is about 150 km offshore and lies roughly along the 1000 m isobath (Bremner 1983). The two inner bands, on the upper and lower shelf, are associated with zones of oxygen deficient (>0.5 ml/l) bottom water. Elsewhere on the shelf the waters are oxic, with dissolved O_2 ranging between 0.5 and 0.75 ml/l (Chapman & Shannon 1985). The total rate of burial of C_{org} in the region is about 1.5×10^{12} g a^{-1} (Bremner (1983) cited 2×10^{12} g a^{-1} of organic matter).

Sediments with C_{org} concentrations less than

5% but greater than 2% occur along the remainder of the entire shelf between the Zaire (Congo) River and Cape Agulhas (Calvert & Price 1983; Bremner 1983; Gorshkov 1977). As noted by Calvert & Price (1983) and Pedersen & Calvert (1990), the C_{org} concentrations on the southwest African margin are highest beneath the region of highest productivity.

Although the frontal features extending west from the shelf upwelling system are spectacular on satellite imagery and, at least in some cases, stationary, none has left a recognizable record in the bottom sediments.

DSDP Sites 362/532 and 530 are 220 and 275 km from the coast, respectively; they are 190 and 230 km seaward of the 200 m isobath, over 500 km downstream from the present site of maximal opal deposition off Walvis Bay and 800 km downstream of the northern upwelling centre off Lüderitz.

No cores have penetrated sediments older than latest Pleistocene on the Namibian shelf, so the history of the coastal upwelling system there is unknown. Thus the evidence for the oceanographic changes that may have occurred on Walvis Ridge and in the Angola Basin is limited to those areas; a regional context is lacking.

Modes of upwelling

Geologists are most familiar with the three modes of upwelling that imprint the global sedimentary record: (1) equatorial upwelling, (2) upwelling at oceanic divergences driven by atmospheric convergences, and (3) wind-driven coastal upwelling. There are at least seven other modes of upwelling that are also important: (4) Kelvin wave-driven coastal upwelling, (5) upward Ekman pumping, (6) bathymetry-driven upwelling, (7) upwelling through mesoscale and submesoscale cyclonic vortices, (8) upwelling from thermal domes, (9) current-induced upwelling and (10) upwelling from divergence within ocean currents.

Equatorial upwelling

Equatorial upwelling occurs along the equator in response to the change in sign of the Coriolis force (CorF). The CorF is equal to the Coriolis parameter f ($= 2\Omega \sin\phi$ where Ω is the angular velocity of the earth in radians and ϕ is the latitude) times the velocity of the water; the Coriolis force is directed *cum sole*, i.e. to the right in the northern hemisphere and to the left in the southern hemisphere. Waters in a west-flowing equatorial current are deflected to the right in the northern hemisphere and to the left in the southern hemisphere, creating a divergence at the equator and causing upwelling. This mode of upwelling is tied to the equator and has no effect at Walvis Ridge.

Upwelling at oceanic divergences driven by atmospheric convergences

Because of the rotation of the Earth, convergences in the atmosphere drive divergences in the ocean. The shear between the wind and the water and between successively deeper layers of water and the CorF combine to produce a net transport of the water 90° *cum sole* of the downwind direction (to the right in the northern hemisphere, to the left in the southern hemisphere). The movement of water 90° *cum sole*, proposed by Ekman (1905), is termed Ekman transport. The northeasterly and southeasterly trade winds converge at the Intertropical Convergence Zone (ITCZ) causing oceanic divergence. At present the thermal equator marking the mean annual position of the ITCZ averages 6°N so that the oceanic divergence associated with it generally occurs north of the equator. If the ITCZ were located over the equator, the divergence associated with it would coincide with the equator. The higher latitude convergences of the Polar and Ferrel Cells induce the Antarctic Divergence (Dietrich 1957), which upwells nutrient-rich water into the seas around the Antarctic, and the smaller, less stable Arctic Divergence, which upwells water in the northeast Pacific. These oceanic divergences are far from the Walvis Ridge Abutment and could have at most an indirect influence on biogenic sedimentation there.

Wind-driven coastal upwelling

Smith (1968, 1983) has summarized the physical oceanography of wind-driven coastal upwelling systems. O'Brien (1975) discussed models of coastal upwelling, noting that there are still major aspects of the phenomenon that are not well understood from a theoretical point of view. In its classic form, originally suggested by Thorade (1909) and subsequently modified by Sverdrup (1938), coastal upwelling is driven by offshore transport of the water under the influence of longshore winds blowing equatorward. The offshore Ekman transport of water is directly proportional to the wind stress (which is in turn proportional to the square of the wind speed) and inversely proportional to the Coriolis parameter (Pond & Pickard 1983; Apel 1987). When the net transport of water is offshore, the sea surface near the shore is depressed and the water being driven away from the shore is replaced by upwelled deeper water. The general pattern of currents in a wind-driven upwelling system is illustrated schematically in Fig. 3.

At the present time conditions favorable to coastal upwelling are best met along N—S trending coasts on the eastern sides of the ocean basins in the latitudes of the subtropical highs. There, the high pressure systems over the ocean and low pressure systems that develop over the continents generate the winds that blow equatorward along the coasts, resulting in offshore Ekman transport and upwelling. The equatorward boundary of wind-driven coastal upwelling is usually a promontory; in the eastern Atlantic, these are Cap Blanc in the north and Cabo Frio in the south (Picaut 1985). In the southern hemisphere, the regular longitudinal alternation of land and ocean results in the stable Walker circulation, with persistent highs developed over the ocean and lows over the continents. These vary less with the seasons than the atmospheric pressure systems over the northern hemisphere continents and oceans, most of which reverse with the seasons. Consequently, wind-driven upwelling in the southern hemisphere tends to have less seasonal variability than that in the northern hemisphere.

Upwelled water is not necessarily nutrient-rich, hence wind-driven coastal upwelling does not always result in increased productivity. Coastal upwelling is ineffective at bringing water from great depths to the surface. The directly upwelled water generally comes from depths of 50 to 200 metres, but this directly upwelled water may in turn be replaced by a mixture of deeper and intermediate water. The degree to which deeper water can be mixed upward is a function of the density gradient and difference between the water masses. Only where the pycnocline separating the surface mixed layer from nutrient-rich deeper waters is shallow can nutrients be introduced into the surface waters in quantities large enough to increase productivity.

A poleward undercurrent beneath the equatorward surface flow is characteristic of all major coastal upwelling regimes (Smith 1983). The undercurrent is usually the coastal side of a subsurface cyclonic gyre that introduces deeper nutrient-rich waters into the shallower levels where they can be readily upwelled under the influence of the wind (Bogorov et al. 1973). Opaline silica-secreting plankton can flourish only if the upwelled water is enriched in dissolved silica as well as phosphate and nitrate. The upwelled water may be advected offshore

by the Ekman transport, but the source of the upwelled water remains tied to the coast.

In the classic description, the rate at which water can be upwelled depends on the rate of offshore transport of water in response to the wind. Because the wind stress is proportional to the square of the wind speed, a hundredfold increase in upwelling indicated by the increased rate of deposition of opal over the Walvis Ridge Abutment Plateau would require an order of magnitude increase in the regionally averaged wind speed, which may be unrealistic.

Kelvin wave-driven coastal upwelling

Coastal upwelling also occurs on the eastern sides of the oceans in the tropics, but is seasonal and is in response to the passage of Kelvin waves trapped by the coast. Picaut (1985) and Brown et al. (1989) have summarized the cause and nature of the phenomenon.

Kelvin waves are long-wavelength gravity waves; they are acted upon by the CorF. The most familiar example of Kelvin waves are the tides. As a wave moves poleward along a coast to its east, the CorF acts on it, causing water to pile up on the coast and increasing the amplitude of the wave along the coast. The Kelvin wave thus appears to be trapped along the coast; its amplitude decays away from the coast, so that at a distance known as the Rossby radius of deformation it is hardly discernable. The Rossby radius of deformation is equal to the wave speed divided by the Coriolis parameter, f. Typically the Rossby radius of deformation, infinite at the equator, decreases to the order of 100 km, 10° away from the equator and to 25 km in the mid-latitudes.

The equatorial region acts as a wave guide for Kelvin waves. Long waves traveling from west to east in the northern and southern hemisphere in the equatorial region experience the CorF to the right and left respectively, tending to make them pile up along the equator where the CorF goes to 0. The result is that a perturbation of the atmospheric forcing can generate west to east propagating Kelvin waves trapped by the equator.

The trade winds produce an east to west upward slope of the sea surface in the equatorial region. In the Pacific, rapid relaxation of the trade winds removes the force supporting the sea surface slope and induces an internal equatorial Kelvin wave that depresses the thermocline and moves from west to east across the Pacific. Upon reaching the eastern side of the ocean, the equatorial Kelvin wave splits into two poleward moving Kelvin waves trapped by the coast. The depression of the thermocline prevents upwelling of nutrient-rich water to the surface, causing the reduction of biological productivity known as El Niño. In the Pacific, this phenomenon occurs on a interannual time scale.

In the Atlantic, seasonal variation of the trade winds results in the production of equatorial Kelvin waves that cause the thermocline to move up and down causing variations in the intensity of equatorial upwelling. On reaching the African margin, the Kelvin waves split and move poleward, bringing the thermocline near the surface as they move along the coast and resulting in productive upwelling in the Gulf of Guinea and along the coast of Gabon (Moore *et al.* 1978; Adamec & O'Brien 1978; Busalacchi & Picaut 1983; McCreary *et al.* 1984; Picaut 1985).

Because they are generated in the equatorial region, the Kelvin waves that can drive coastal upwelling are restricted to low latitudes; in the Atlantic the phenomenon occurs between Cap Blanc in the north and Cabo Frio in the south (Picaut 1985). This process is unlikely to have contributed significantly to productivity over the Walvis Ridge Abutment Plateau.

Upward Ekman pumping

Ekman pumping is vertical motion of the water in response to curl of the wind stress. It is well documented in the Arabian Sea (Luther & O'Brien 1985). Although the onset of the summer monsoon, with winds blowing across the Arabian Sea from southwest to northeast, is marked by coastal upwelling along the southern margin of Arabia, the later development of intense oceanic upwelling depends on another oceanographic phenomenon, Ekman pumping. As the monsoon develops a strong SW−NE wind jet forms over the central Arabian Sea (Findlater 1969). Winds along the axis of the jet are strong but decline sharply to the NW and SE. The resultant differential wind shear over the water, the curl of the wind stress, is positive NE of the axis of the jet and negative to the SE of the jet. The increase in positive vorticity (tendency of the water to move counterclockwise, or cyclonically in the northern hemisphere) to the northeast of the axis creates divergence and results in oceanic upwelling throughout a broad region of the NW Arabian Sea whilst the increase in negative vorticity (tendency of the water to move clockwise) to the southeast of the axis results in convergence and promotes downwelling in the SE Arabian Sea (for a succinct discussion of vorticity as it relates to oceanic upwelling, see Pond & Pickard

1983). The resultant overall effect — oceanic upwelling and downwelling induced by curl of the wind stress — is known as Ekman pumping. Ekman pumping can result from cyclonic and anticyclonic wind circulation associated with weather systems, but because of their rapid drift their effects on the ocean are usually short-lived.

Ekman pumping may also affect upwelling along the southwest African coast. If the axis of the equatorward wind jet were exactly along the shoreline, and the wind speeds decreased offshore, the effect would be to cause downward Ekman pumping over the shelf. The result would be that upwelling would be concentrated along the shore. At present the axis of the equatorward wind jet lies offshore (Hastenrath & Lamb 1977; Shannon 1985a). Because the wind speed decreases toward the shore, a region of upward Ekman pumping develops between the axis of the wind jet and the shore. This helps explain why the upwelling currently occurs both along the shore and near the shelf break. The axis of the wind jet is offshore because the coast is bordered by desert, which creates a thermal front, and by the high edge of the Kalahari Plateau, which forms an orographic boundary and causes frictional drag.

Bathymetry-driven upwelling

Bathymetric control of upwelling results from the differential motion of a current across shallower and deeper features. The magnitude of the CorF acting on the current increases as the current velocity increases (Defant 1961). The zonal (east−west) component of the flow is also affected by the change in potential vorticity, which will cause the current to deviate equatorward as the water depth becomes shallower.

In order for a given volume of water in an ocean current to pass over a shallow ridge, it must speed up. Because the CorF acting on the current is proportional to the velocity of the water, the acceleration of the current as it crosses the ridge causes it to deviate *cum sole*. On entering the deeper water on the other side of the ridge it will deviate *contra solem*, or turn to the left in the northern hemisphere and to the right in the southern hemisphere. This will induce clockwise (cyclonic in the southern hemisphere) circulation on the right side of the current, and the cyclonic circulation will be accompanied by upwelling. This upwelling between the current and the coast need not be confined to the shallow depths to which wind-induced upwelling is restricted. It is presumably this effect that localizes the major upwelling centers at sites where the shelf is narrowest. The wider shelf just north of these sites causes the current to accelerate and produces cyclonic circulation and causes upwelling inshore.

Potential vorticity of the moving water is conserved. The potential vorticity is the sum of the planetary vorticity f (i.e. the vorticity associated with the rotation of the Earth, which is identical with the Coriolis parameter $2\Omega\sin\phi$) and the relative vorticity of the water mass divided by the depth, D. Because planetary vorticity is always much larger than the relative vorticity of the moving water, the potential vorticity is closely approximated by f/D. As D decreases over a shallow bank, f must also decrease to conserve potential vorticity. Hence as water flows zonally across a shallow bank it will move equatorward, toward lower values of planetary vorticity. Succinct discussions of this effect have been presented by Pond & Pickard (1983) and Brown *et al.* (1989). Along the southwest African margin, the flow of the water is almost meridional, so that the effects of changes in potential vorticity are minimal.

The coincidence of upwelling centres with the narrowest parts of the southwest African shelf suggests that bathymetric control is as important in localizing upwelling along this margin as it is along the Peruvian margin (Preller & O'Brien 1980).

Although the Walvis Ridge Abutment is the major bathymetric feature along this margin, there is no upwelling centre currently associated with it. This is probably because is does not appreciably affect the shape of the margin above depths of 1 km. If the Benguela Current were thick enough to be accelerated as it crossed Walvis Ridge, it would be deflected to the left. Fig. 4 shows the hypothetical case of a thick Benguela Current deviating over Walvis Ridge. We also show a cyclonic eddy inshore of and driven by the deviating current. This phenomenon might explain why the maximum accumulation rate for opaline silica appears to have occurred at the Angola Basin site rather than over the shallower Walvis Ridge. At the latitude of Walvis Ridge, the Benguela Current is beginning to leave the coast, and the situation for bathymetrically induced upwelling would be ideal if the ridge were shallower. Although it is difficult to imagine conditions that would so thicken the mixed layer that the Benguela Current could be steered directly by Walvis Ridge, it might 'feel' the ridge indirectly through upward displacement of the pycnocline as the poleward flowing side of the subthermocline cyclonic gyre off southwest Africa crosses the ridge.

Mesoscale and submesoscale vortices

Mesoscale eddies are vortices a few hundred kilometres in diameter; submesoscale vortices are in the order of 100 km or less. Both may be significant in mixing the surface and deeper layers of the ocean on a global scale (McWilliams 1985; Kerr 1985). Mesoscale eddies are a form of turbulence, and are best developed downstream from the western boundary currents after they have left the coasts. Although most mixing in the ocean takes place along isopycnals, the mesoscale and submesoscale

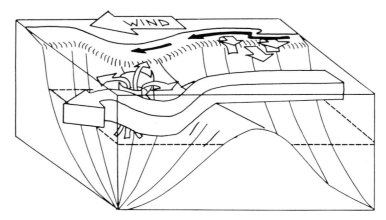

Fig. 4. Schematic perspective view of the southwest African margin and Walvis Ridge, showing the major currents, the coastal upwelling system, and the Angola Dome as they might appear if the surface mixed layer were thick enough to allow Walvis Ridge to interfere with the flow of the Benguela Current (Southeast Trade Wind Drift). The hypothetical cyclonic eddy shown inshore of the current is not the Angola Dome, but is a smaller vortex driven by the deviation of the Benguela Current. Not to scale.

vortices juxtapose waters of different densities at the same horizontal level, so that other turbulent processes may induce them to mix. Cyclonic vortices (counterclockwise in the northern, clockwise in the southern hemisphere) may bring deeper water upward into the mixed layer on a global scale. Cyclonic vortices are sites of divergence at the sea surface and convergence at depth. In the North Atlantic, mesoscale eddies associated with the Gulf Stream commonly extend to depths of 1 km and some raise or depress isohalines all the way to the sea floor (see salinity profiles in Fuglister 1960). Mesoscale eddies that do not extend to the bottom may drive deeper eddies. Submesoscale vortices of Mediterranean water ('Meddies') are introduced into the eastern North Atlantic (McWilliams 1985). The Brazil Current produces much smaller eddies than the Gulf Stream. The largest mesoscale eddies in the South Atlantic are introduced from the Indian Ocean where the Agulhas Current rounds South Africa. They are among the world's most energetic eddies (Olson & Evans 1986) and can be seen on Fuglister's (1960) salinity profiles. Shillington *et al.* (1990) investigated the effects of an Agulhas eddy on the Benguela Current off Lüderitz using coordinated satellite and field observation. The eddies spun off the north side of the Agulhas Current are anticyclonic and hence do not upwell. However, it was found that the edges of these energetic counterclockwise eddies may entrain upwelled shelf water and advect it offshore as filaments of phytoplankton-rich water.

Hart & Currie (1960) reported small eddies being formed south of Cabo Frio by mixing between the Benguela Current and the coastal current flowing southward along the coast of Angola. These have been cited by Diester-Haass (1985a, b, 1988), Diester-Haass *et al.* (1986, 1990), and Diester-Haass & Rothe (1987) as the source of upwelled water containing the siliceous plankton supplying opaline silica to Walvis Ridge.

On a larger scale are subsurface cyclonic gyres that develop in parts of the ocean basins in response to internal pressure gradients in the ocean. Bogorov *et al.* (1973) suggested that these play a major role in bringing nutrients to the surface, and are especially important in the enhancing the effectiveness of upwelling along the eastern sides of the ocean basins in the subtropics. One such subsurface cyclonic gyre occurs off southwest Africa (Moroshkin *et al.* 1970; Gorshkov 1977) bringing nutrient-rich water to shallow depths immediately beneath the thin Benguela Current.

Thermal domes

The term 'thermal dome' is applied by physical oceanographers to subcircular domes of the thermocline that bring cold deep waters closer to the surface. They form in the tropics, centered at 10°N and S, several hundred km off the eastern margins of the ocean basins. The term 'thermocline dome' would be more appropriate because the domes are filled with cold rather than warm water, but we follow the practice in the literature and refer to them as thermal domes. These features have been best described in the northern hemisphere, as the Costa Rica Dome in the Pacific at 10°N off Central America (Wyrtki 1964) and the Guinea Dome at the same latitude of Africa in the Atlantic (Mazeika 1967; Voituriez 1981). In the southern hemisphere these features are less well developed. Voituriez (1981) could find no evidence for the existence of a Peru Dome as suggested by Mazeika (1967). However, the Angola Dome is a perennial feature of the eastern South Atlantic at 10°S, and is shown in Fig. 3. Although recent observations indicate it to be weaker than its northern counterpart, it is the only one of the thermal domes to leave a distinct signature, in the form of enrichment of amorphous silica, in the underlying sediments (Gorshkov 1977). The opal enrichment of the sediments beneath the Angola Dome (5–10% opal) is not as high as on the Namibian shelf, but is higher than anywhere else in the eastern South Atlantic.

The physical oceanography of the tropical thermal domes has been reviewed by Picaut (1985). They were originally thought to form in response to the poleward deflection of the North and South Equatorial Countercurrents as they meet the eastern margins of the ocean basins. The cyclonic flow of the currents causes deep water to be brought close to the surface but an additional impetus is required to cause the waters of the dome to upwell to the surface.

Voiturez (1981) suggested that when the ITCZ becomes located over a thermal dome the winds are weak and variable, the atmospheric pressure is low and the curl of the wind stress becomes favourable for upwelling, pulling the deeper water to the surface. Hofmann *et al.* (1981), using the model of Busalacchi & O'Brien (1980), found the location of the Costa Rica Dome to be fixed by the curl of the wind stress. Busalacchi & Picaut (1983), using the same model to investigate the Guinea and Angola Domes found that the simulated Guinea Dome could be driven by Ekman pumping alone. Picaut reports that maps prepared by Bakun & Nelson (1984) show the Guinea Dome is also located in a region of cyclonic wind stress curl from May to October and that the Angola Dome is also located in a region where the wind stress curl is favourable most of the year. The Guinea Dome plays a major role in offshore upwelling off northwestern Africa. According to the literature, the Angola Dome plays a much lesser role in upwelling off southern Africa but the accumulation of amorphous silica in the sediments beneath it suggests that it may have been a more prominent feature in the immediate past.

The Angola Dome lies 1200 km north of the Walvis Ridge Abutment Plateau. The east side of the Angola Dome is bordered by the Angola Coastal Current, so that it lies upstream from Cabo Frio and the Walvis Ridge Abutment. The most intense oxygen minimum in the Atlantic extends from beneath the dome to the Congo−Angola margin north of Cabo Frio. Associated with this oxygen minimum is the most intense shallow phosphate maximum in the Atlantic except for that developed over the Namibian shelf. The temperature of the low-oxygen, high-phosphate water is 15°C. Chemical oceanographic conditions are ripe for upwelling of nutrient-rich waters. If upwelling from the Angola Dome were more intense than at present it could be a major centre of offshore upwelling and phytoplankton production. If the Angola Coastal Current were stronger, it could carry productive waters south in larger quantities.

Current-induced upwelling

A geostrophic ocean current impinging on a shelf may cause bottom Ekman transport onto the shelf, forcing weak upwelling on the shelf. Hsueh and O'Brien (1971) have suggested that this phenomenon occurs in response to the strong flow of the loop current in the Gulf of Mexico. O'Brien (1975) suggested that Bang's (1971) description of upwelling on the southwest African margin may indicate that current-induced upwelling occurs there also. The possible significance of this process to upwelling over the Walvis Ridge Abutment is difficult to evaluate.

Upwelling from divergence within ocean currents

In addition to upwelling in response to the CorF at the equator, the curl of the wind stress, and bathymetric features, divergence resulting in productive upwelling may occur within ocean currents because of the shape of coasts and changes in wind stress. Divergence within the Benguela Current system has been indicated by Schott (1943), Dietrich (1957) and Moroshkin et al. (1970). The causes of these divergences vary, but many are related to the wind stress at the time the observations were made.

Changes in the production of intermediate and deep waters

The water masses in the interior of the ocean play a critical role in determining whether upwelled waters are productive or sterile. A shallow or weak pycnocline may allow more nutrients to be introduced into the upwelled water. The pycnocline represents the balance between processes acting to mix the surface waters and the processes that produce deep and intermediate waters. Assuming a constant rate of deep and intermediate water production, the thickness of the surface mixed layer depends on the air−sea temperature difference, on internal mixing by wave action that is in turn a function of the strength and constancy of the wind, and on the density difference between the surface and underlying waters. A shallower pycnocline implies less wave action and hence lessened wind strength, but slower winds imply less upwelling. A less intense pycnocline also implies less mixing as well as lower nutrient content of the waters beneath the pycnocline. Assuming the processes mixing the surface layer to be constant, the position of the pycnocline will depend on the rate of production of deep and intermediate water. If the rate of production of deep and intermediate water is high, i.e. the thermohaline circulation is vigorous, the pycnocline will be shallow and intense.

Off southwest Africa the pycnocline separating the mixed surface layer from nutrient-rich Antarctic Intermediate Water is less than 100 metres below the surface. The Benguela Current is thin, less than 80 metres thick, and overlies a countercurrent that is the eastern side of a subsurface clockwise (cyclonic in the southern hemisphere) gyre (Gorshkov 1977). The subsurface cyclonic gyre induces divergence, causing subsurface upwelling that brings nutrient-rich water from the interior of the AAIW into contact with the base of the Benguela Current. It is this special set of circumstances that makes the present Benguela Coastal Upwelling System productive along the coast of Namibia. However, the origin of AAIW on which the productivity ultimately depends is quite complex and depends on the production of other water masses elsewhere.

The Mediterranean outflow is the densest water entering a major ocean basin (Kraus et al.

1978). However, as it flows down the slope from the Straits of Gibraltar it entrains Atlantic interior water and the mixture spreads out at a depth of about 1.5 km as sterile North Atlantic Intermediate Water (NAIW). Some of this relatively warm saline water contributes to the formation of NADW in the Norwegian–Greenland Sea, Labrador Sea and off southeastern Greenland (Reid 1979; Peterson & Rooth 1976; Broecker & Takahashi 1980).

Thunell *et al.* (1987) suggested that the balance between Mediterranean outflow and NADW production may be delicate. They note that during the Messinian, when the Mediterranean desiccated and there was no outflow to the Atlantic, production of NADW did not cease. During the early Pliocene, when the Mediterranean had estuarine circulation and produced no saline outflow, NADW production also continued. They suggested that during the last glacial the Mediterranean outflow was more saline than it is today. Their argument assumed that the fresh water balance of the Mediterranean was the same as today and that the in- and outflows through the Straits of Gibraltar would be restricted due to lowered sea level. They suggested that NADW production slowed during the last glacial because the outflow was more dense and sank to a level where it could no longer participate in formation of NADW. However, in our view it is more likely that the fresh water balance during glacials was much more positive than it is today, reducing the saline outflow.

The NADW, mixing with other waters along the way, returns to the surface in the region of the Antarctic Polar Front and Antarctic Divergence. The fraction that goes north becomes slightly freshened by the excess of precipitation over evaporation but remains cold. At the Subtropical Convergence it sinks beneath warmer subtropical waters of the South Atlantic gyre to form Antarctic Intermediate Water (AAIW). This South Atlantic AAIW is the ultimate source of the nutrients upwelled along the Namibian margin.

It is interesting to speculate on what would happen if the formation of NADW were to cease. The global deep water conveyor belt exporting nutrients from the North Atlantic to the Northeast Pacific would cease (Broecker *et al.* 1985; Broecker *et al.* 1990; Birchfield & Broecker 1990). The production of AAIW and AABW would slow, and the depth of the pycnocline, i.e. thickness of the mixed layer, would increase. Because of the diversion of equatorial flow into the North Atlantic, the surface of the North Atlantic would rise until a new dynamic

equilibrium became established. This equilibrium would require that the Equatorial System divide the waters equally between the northern and southern hemispheres. Because of the asymmetry of the westward flow, the balance would have to be made up by a larger flow in South Equatorial Countercurrent. A strengthened South Equatorial Countercurrent would drive a more pronounced Angola thermal dome and Angola Coastal Current, enhancing the potential for oceanic upwelling over the Angola Basin and off Cabo Frio.

Woodruff & Savin (1989), considering a wide variety of data, have developed a scenario for the development of global deep water masses during the Miocene. They suggest that until the late Miocene the Tethys was a major source of warm saline deep ocean water, which they termed Tethyan–Indian Saline Water (TISW). They found no evidence to contradict the idea that North Atlantic Deep Water production may have begun during the Middle Miocene in response to subsidence of the Scotland–Faroes–Iceland–Greenland Ridge, allowing better exchange between the Norwegian-Greenland Sea and the North Atlantic (Schnitker 1980; Blanc & Duplessy 1982). The late Miocene growth of the Antarctic ice cap may have been in response to the upwelling of relatively warm NADW around Antarctica. NADW production increased during the late Miocene as a result of the incipient salinization of the North Atlantic in response to restriction of the Central American Isthmus.

Wise *et al.* (1985) described the development of conditions in the southwestern Atlantic since the Middle Miocene. The polar front migrated north to about 48°S during the late Miocene, reflecting the build-up of ice on the Antarctic continent. It reached its maximum northerly position, north of 46°S from 2.5 Ma to 1.0 Ma, and has since returned south toward its present position near 50°S.

McKenzie & Oberhänsli (1985) have discussed the late Miocene section at DSDP Site 519, beneath the South Atlantic gyre centre. They found that the oxygen isotopic record indicates cooling from 6.1 to 5.7 Ma, the time of build-up of Antarctic glaciation and restricted circulation in the Mediterranean. This was followed by two discrete cooling phases, between 5.7 and 5.1 Ma, corresponding to the times of formation of the lower and upper evaporite series in the Mediterranean. Finally, between 5.1 and 4.9 Ma, the record is chaotic, reflecting unstable climatic conditions.

Hodell *et al.* (1985) and Weissert & Oberhänsli (1985) have described conditions during the Pliocene near the southern margins of the Brazil and Angola basins respectively. Hodell *et al.* (1985) suggested that there was reorganization of the deep ocean circulation reflected by a pulse-like increase of AABW at 3.2 Ma. Weissert & Oberhänsli (1985) found that the production of NADW and AABW increased at about 3.35 Ma. Both groups of authors attributed the changes in deep circulation to closing of the Central American Isthmus.

Winter & Martin (1990) have discussed changes of the Agulhas Current during the late Quaternary. The Agulhas Current plays a major role in the global heat balance, carrying 8 to 18 Sv (1 Svedrup = 10^6 m^3 S^{-1}) of warm Indian Ocean water into the South Atlantic (Gordon 1985, 1986). At about 38°S, south of South Africa, the Agulhas Current approaches the Subtropical Convergence (40°S) and reverses its course, turning to the east ('Agulhas retroflection'). Winter & Martin note that if the Subtropical Convergence migrated 4°N it would force the retroflection to occur in the Indian Ocean, interrupting the supply of warm water from the Indian Ocean and altering the global heat balance. Their studies of cores suggest that the Subtropical Convergence did not migrate north of 38°S during the past 150 000 years.

The position of the Subtropical Convergence south of South Africa is important in confirming the hypothesis of Diester-Haass (1985*a*, *b*, 1988), Diester-Haass *et al.* (1986, 1990) and Diester-Haass & Rothe (1987) that during glacials the Benguela Current (Southeast Trade Wind Drift) turned from the coast at 17°S rather than at 20°S as it does today. Winter & Martin (1990) found that the northward migration of the Subtropical Convergence, and hence the atmospheric Subtropical High inducing it, was slight, casting doubt on the hypothesis of northward migration of the location where the Benguela Current leaves the coast.

Changes in palaeogeography, palaeoclimatology and palaeoceanography

Global and regional palaeogeographic, palaeoclimatologic and palaeoceanographic factors that may have changed during the past 15 million years include: (1) the northward drift of South America and Africa; (2) changes in topographic relief; (3) Late Cenozoic sea-level changes; (4) growth of the Antarctic ice cap and onset of northern hemisphere glaciation; (5) closing of the Central American isthmus; (6) desiccation and reflooding of the Mediterranean.

The northward drift of South America and Africa

Plate tectonic reconstructions (Briden *et al.* 1974; Barron *et al.* 1981; Ziegler *et al.* 1982) indicate that Africa and South America have drifted 5° north during the past 15 million years. This will have affected both atmospheric and oceanic circulation.

The primary effect of the northward drift of the continents on atmospheric circulation would be to carry the Intertropical Convergence Zone (ITCZ) northward, so that it remains over the land areas having the broadest zonal extent in the subtropics. The general effect is shown in wind vector diagrams of the Cenozoic atmospheric circulation models of Barron & Peterson (1991). Migration of the ITCZ with the drift of the continents is slow and of a magnitude much smaller than that associated with changes from unipolar to bipolar glaciation.

The effect on oceanic circulation is more complex and possibly much more important because the northward drift has caused both the eastern tip of South America (Cabo San Roque) and the re-entrant in Africa (Gulf of Guinea) to be displaced with reference to the Equatorial Current System.

The history of circulation in the South Atlantic is intimately related to changes in the symmetry of the Atlantic Equatorial Current system, and to the interchange of water between the northern and southern hemispheres, as shown in Fig. 4a. At present the Equatorial Current System in the Atlantic is strongly asymmetrical. Maps depicting the flow may appear to differ greatly (Schott 1942; Dietrich 1963; Gorshkov 1977; Tchernia 1980) because of the seasonal and interannual variability. At present the eastern tip of South America at Cabo San Roque diverts part of the flow of the southern limb of the west-flowing Equatorial Current into the northern hemisphere as the Brazilian Coastal Current. It then enters the Caribbean and flows on into the Gulf of Mexico. It leaves the Gulf of Mexico as the Florida Current and on entering the North Atlantic becomes the Gulf Stream. The amount of this diversion of equatorial surface water into the North Atlantic is not exactly known, but model studies by Philander and Pacanowski (1986) suggest that it is about 8.5 Sv. The diversion into the North Atlantic is balanced by export of water to the Pacific and Indian Oceans through net evaporation (0.2 Sv, Baumgartner & Reichel 1975) and return flow to the South Atlantic (8.3 Sv) as a major part of the volume of North Atlantic

Intermediate and Deep Waters. The remainder of the volume of North Atlantic Intermediate and Deep Waters leaving the North Atlantic entered as Antarctic Bottom and Intermediate Waters. Kier (1988, 1989), from box modelling of the present global ocean circulation, has suggested that the surface water input into Northern Component Water is 10 Sv, and an additional 12 Sv of interior water are entrained for a net production of 22 Sv of North Atlantic Intermediate and Deep Water.

Because of the average location of the thermal equator at about 6°N, a surface Equatorial Countercurrent, often termed the Guinea Current at its eastern end, develops north of the equator, driven chiefly by cross-equatorial flow of the southeast trade winds during the northern hemisphere summer (for a discussion of the dynamics of the wind-driven Equatorial Current System, see Neumann & Pierson (1966) or the excellent brief account in Brown et al. (1989)). At a shallow depth (c. 100 m) beneath the surface currents flow the more symmetrical North and South Equatorial Countercurrents, centred at 4−5°N and S of the equator (Voituriez 1981). These subsurface currents are not under the direct influence of the wind, and hence respond more directly to the rotation of the Earth. On reaching the eastern margin of the ocean, they turn poleward and form the cyclonic subthermocline gyres enclosing the Guinea and Angola Domes. If the location of the thermal domes is determined by the position where the North and South Equatorial Undercurrents turn poleward, the northward drift of Africa has brought the Walvis Ridge Abutment Plateau 100 km closer to the Angola Dome every million years.

The gradual northward drift of South America has displaced Cabo San Roque. It is located at 5°S at present; at 5 Ma it was about 7°S, at 10 Ma about 8°S and at 15 Ma it was at about 9°S. In the late Miocene it would have diverted the entire westward flowing Equatorial Current System into the northern hemisphere. Only in the late Pliocene and Quaternary has it has been located far enough north to divide the flow so that a significant part of it returns to the South Atlantic.

On the east side of the Atlantic, the E−W trending Guinea Coast of west Africa is at 5°N at present, but at 5 Ma it was at 2.5°N, at 10 Ma at 1°N and at 15 Ma it lay along the equator. At that time the dynamics of the seasonal upwelling forced by coastal Kelvin waves propagating poleward must have been very different from the process as observed today.

Although the changes in the equatorial current system in response to the northward drift of the continents must have been of great significance in the equatorial region, the upwelling signal in the sediment on Walvis Ridge Abutment Plateau does not directly reflect them.

Changes in topographic relief

Many mountain ranges and plateau areas appear to have had substantial increases in elevation in the past few million years affecting the global climate. This is particularly true of the northern hemisphere where uplift of broad regions of Asia and North America have disrupted the zonal circulation of the atmosphere, causing onset of glaciation (Ruddiman et al. 1986; Ruddiman & Raymo 1988; Hay et al. 1989; Ruddiman & Kutzbach 1989). The interpretation of the sedimentary and palaeontological record as reflecting uplift in young geological times has been questioned by Molnar & England (1990), who believe that late Cenozoic climate change is responsible for creating the appearance of uplift.

Although classically interpreted as having been a high area throughout most the Mesozoic and Cenozoic (King 1967), the uplift of the Kalahari may also be young (Ronov et al. 1989). If it had been eroding to its present elevation during the entire Cenozoic, it would have delivered much more sediment to the southern African margin than it has.

Late Cenozoic increase of the elevation of Southern Africa would have reduced the seasonal variability of the winds and increased the land-ocean pressure contrast, strengthening the winds. The rise of the edge of the plateau just inshore of the present coast would cause friction and displace the axis of the equatorward wind jet to the west.

Wind-driven coastal upwelling is enhanced where the winds are strong and constant in direction over long periods of time and part of the increased upwelling recorded by the sediments might be due to lesser seasonal variation and less vigorous winds when the Kalahari Plateau was lower. Displacement of the axis of the wind jet to the west would increase the region of cyclonic wind stress curl over the shelf, also promoting upwelling.

The effect of uplift of Southern Africa would be to enhance both wind-driven coastal upwelling and upward Ekman pumping on the shelf. If uplift progressed along the margin of the continent from Cabo Frio to Cape Agulhas it could cause the coastal upwelling system to migrate meridionally from north to south. It is doubtful that uplift would affect upwelling over the Walvis Ridge Abutment Plateau.

Closing of the Central American isthmus

The separation of the Atlantic from the Pacific took place gradually from about 13 Ma to 2.5 Ma. Keller & Barron (1983), McDougall (1985) and Duque-Caro (1990) suggest that a sill with a depth of about 1 km had formed during the Middle Miocene, 12 Ma. By 6 Ma, during the late Miocene, the sill depth had shallowed to about 200 metres (McDougall 1985; Savin & Douglas 1985; Duque-Caro 1990). Final closure occurred about 2.5 Ma (Keigwin 1978, 1982a, b; Gartner et al. 1987; Lundelius 1987; Marshall 1988). The details of the closure are still not known, but work is in progress that should clarify the sequence of events (Jung 1990; Coates et al. in press).

Maier-Reimer et al. (1990) have used an ocean general circulation model driven by present winds to examine the effect of closure of the Central American Isthmus on global ocean circulation. They did not take drift of the continents into account.

Comparison of the control and open isthmus models suggests that with an open isthmus the present slope of the sea surface, a difference of 0.8 m between the Caribbean and the Norwegian−Greenland Sea, would disappear. The strength of the Gulf Stream would be much reduced. The east−west slope of the ocean in the Pacific would also be reduced, but there would still be a strong North Equatorial Countercurrent beneath the surface that would carry 10 Sv into the Atlantic whereas only 1 Sv would pass from Atlantic to Pacific on the surface. The effect of the large scale mixing of Atlantic and Pacific waters would be to reduce the salinity of the Atlantic so that there would be no production of North Atlantic Deep Water. In the South Atlantic, the flow of the Brazil Current (the west side of the South Atlantic anticyclonic gyre) would be enhanced. The result is that the northern and southern Western Boundary Currents of the Atlantic, the Gulf Stream and the Brazil Current would be nearly equal in strength. The strength of the Benguela Current did not change.

Taking the drift of the continents and migration of the ITCZ in response to buildup of ice in the northern hemisphere into account, the oceanographic response must have been more complex. It is likely that during the Middle Miocene the west-flowing North and South Equatorial Currents were both deflected into the northern hemisphere. The large flow of water did not pile up against Central America because of the open passage to the Pacific but would have been larger than indicated by the Maier-Reimer et al. (1990) model. Although the tendency to become part of the North Atlantic anticyclonic subtropical gyre would have existed, most of the excess water would have exited to the Pacific.

The South Equatorial Countercurrent was bounded on the north by the E−W trending Guinea margin so that its entire flow was deflected south on meeting the African margin. It was freshened by the outflow of the Niger, the tropical African river of the time. A weak 'Congo' thermal dome may have existed, but it would have been capped by relative fresh, light water inhibiting upwelling to the surface. The ITCZ did not penetrate this far south so that a major impetus for upwelling was lacking.

At the beginning of the late Miocene the west-flowing North and South Equatorial Currents were both still deflected largely into the northern hemisphere, but again this large flow of water did not pile up against Central America because of the passage to the Pacific (Fig. 5). Restriction of the passage would have caused some of the excess water to enter the North Atlantic. Differentiation of the salinities of the Atlantic and Pacific would allow initiation of NADW production at the end of the Middle Miocene (Woodruff & Savin 1989). The excess water diverted into the North Atlantic could thus be returned to the South Atlantic at depth as part of the North Atlantic Deep Water (NADW).

By the end of the Miocene (Fig. 5) the northward drift of South America had begun to divert a larger part of the South Equatorial Current into the South Atlantic anticyclonic gyre but by then the restriction at the Central American Isthmus was more complete so that the condition of nearly equal Gulf Stream and Brazil Current flows suggested by the Maier-Reimer et al. (1990) model may never have occurred.

During the Pliocene the connection between the Atlantic through Central America closed (Fig. 6). According to Gartner et al. (1987) the final connection was across the Isthmus of Tehuantepec, and was severed at about 2.5 Ma. The closing of the passages to the Pacific across Panama and Costa Rica had occurred earlier, and with them went the Pacific to Atlantic flow that kept the salinities of the two oceans more nearly equal. As the salinity difference increased, the production of North Atlantic Deep Water would have increased.

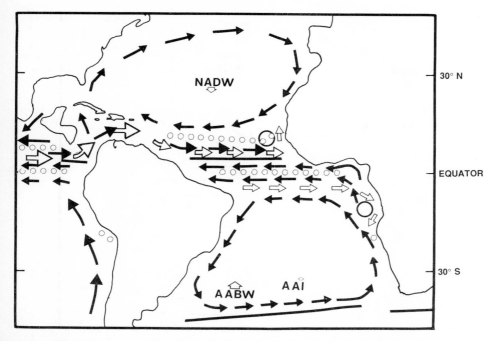

Fig. 5. Speculative palaeogeography and oceanic circulation in the Atlantic during the latest Miocene (6 Ma). Small open circles = divergence (upwelling); large open circles = thermal domes [Guinea and Angola]; heavy solid lines = convergence; open arrows = major subthermocline and deeper currents; solid arrows = surface currents. Europe and Africa form a single landmass joined by the dry Mediterranean basin. The Central American isthmi are closing, but are still deep enough to allow passage of large volumes of subthermocline water from the Pacific to the Atlantic. An ITCZ at an extreme northerly position over Africa causes the convergence between the South Equatorial Current and the Equatorial Countercurrent and the divergence between the latter and the North Equatorial Current to be much further north than they are today. Because the ITCZ is in the northern hemisphere in both seasons there is no upwelling from the Angola Dome.

The transport of warm equatorial waters to the northern North Atlantic seas has important effects on the climate. The heat is released to the atmosphere over the Norwegian–Greenland Sea as both sensible and latent heat providing the mild winter temperatures and large volumes of precipitation required for the development of continental ice caps.

The coincidence of gradual closure of the Central American Isthmus and the increase of upwelling intensity on Walvis Ridge Abutment Plateau suggests cause and effect, but the relation is obviously not direct. The indirect connection is probably through increasing production of North Atlantic Deep Water as salinization of the North Atlantic took place. The increased production of NADW in turn increased the production of AAIW and AABW. The long-term trend of increasing productivity over Walvis Ridge Abutment Plateau until 2.0–1.7 Ma could be the result of an increasing supply of nutrient-rich AAIW beneath a shallowing pycnocline.

Growth of the Antarctic ice cap and onset of northern hemisphere glaciation

Flohn (1979, 1981, 1983, 1984) has discussed the changes in atmospheric circulation that might be expected from the transition of the Earth having a single ice covered pole in the Miocene to bipolar glaciation in the Pliocene and Pleistocene. He noted that at the present time there is a difference between the meridional temperature gradients in the two hemispheres. Although both are snow covered, the difference in elevation between the Arctic sea ice (0 km) and the Antarctic (3 km) causes a stronger temperature gradient in middle of the troposphere and is a major factor contributing to the displacement of the thermal equator to the north of the geographic equator. The

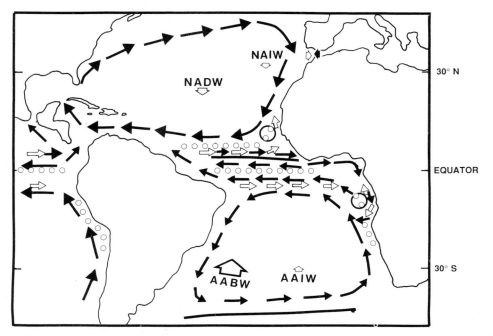

Fig. 6. Speculative palaeogeography and oceanic circulation in the Atlantic during the middle Pliocene (3 Ma). Symbols as in Fig. 5. Mediterranean basin is flooded but has estuarine circulation. The Central American isthmi have closed to subthermocline waters, but still allow exchange of surface water between the Atlantic and Pacific. The ITCZ having migrated to about 10°N, the convergence between the South Equatorial Current and the Equatorial Countercurrent and the divergence between the latter and the North Equatorial Current are only slightly north of their present positions. The ITCZ can now migrate into the southern hemisphere during the northern winter, so that upwelling from the Angola Dome may occur.

seasonal latitudinal variation of the subtropical highs is greater in the southern than in the northern hemisphere. Flohn suggested that when the planet had a single ice-covered pole, the contrast between the meridional temperature gradients of the two hemispheres would be even greater, and the thermal equator and latitudes of the subtropical highs would have been displaced even further northward.

Prior to about 3.4 Ma, the Earth had unipolar glaciation centred on the South Pole and the thermal equator, the mean annual position of the Intertropical Convergence Zone (ITCZ), lay further north than it does today (6°N), perhaps at about 10°N (Flohn 1979, 1981, 1983, 1984). This implies that during the Miocene and early Pliocene the ITCZ would have been unlikely to penetrate far, if at all, into the southern hemisphere.

The East Antarctic Ice Cap formed during the Middle and early Late Miocene (14 to 10 Ma), reaching its maximum extent during the Late Miocene (Shackleton & Kennett 1975). The West Antarctic Ice Sheet formed during

the Late Miocene (Ciesielski *et al.* 1982). The formation of these major ice masses on Antarctica lowered sea level, and would have altered atmospheric circulation. If Flohn's ideas are correct, the growth of the Antarctic Ice Caps would have gradually displaced the subtropical highs and ITCZ northward creating asymmetric atmospheric circulation. It can be speculated that the southeast trade winds, between the subtropical high and the ITCZ, would have migrated northward along the coast of southwest Africa, and that the centre of Middle and Late Miocene upwelling might have been along the southern part of the southwest African margin.

The onset of northern hemisphere glaciaton at 3.4 Ma, with periodic formation of ice caps over eastern North America, Scandinavia and Siberia, changed the configuration of the Earth to one having bipolar ice. Since 2.5 Ma the northern hemisphere has alternated between glacial conditions with three 2 km thick ice caps centred on 60°N and interglacials during which only Greenland has an ice cap but sea-ice covers

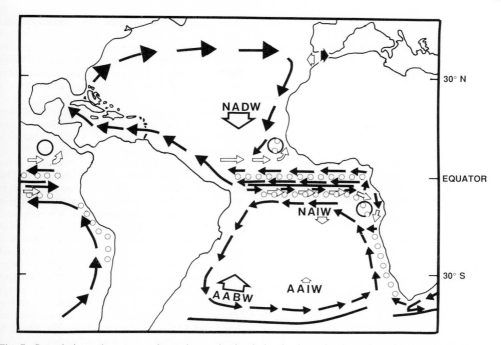

Fig. 7. Speculative palaeogeography and oceanic circulation in the Atlantic during a low stand of sea-level (glacial) during the late Pleistocene (0.5 Ma). Symbols as in Fig. 5. Mediterranean basin has reduced anti-estuarine circulation. The Central American isthmi have closed, separating the Atlantic and Pacific. Exposure of banks and shelves in many areas (particularly in the West Indies and Bahamas and off South Africa) restricts flow. The ITCZ is shown as having migrated to about 6°S. The pattern of the equatorial current is the inverse of that today. There is convergence between the wider North Equatorial Current and the Equatorial Countercurrent and the divergence between the latter and the restricted South Equatorial Current. The Agulhas retroflection is shown schematically. The subtropical convergence remains far enough south of Africa to allow warm Indian Ocean water to enter the South Atlantic.

the Arctic Ocean. Flohn (1979, 1981, 1983, 1984) has suggested that these changes would result in a change of the meridional temperature gradients, causing a shift of the ITCZ from its more northerly position during the time of unipolar glaciation to its present average position of 6°N. Assuming that Flohn is correct in believing that the position of the ITCZ is determined by the meridional temperature gradient in the middle of the troposphere, it can be suggested that during times of northern hemisphere glaciation the ITCZ may have migrated to a mean position south of the equator as suggested in Fig. 7.

For the southwest African coast, the expected effect of the transition from unipolar to bipolar glaciation would be southward migration of the subtropical high over the South Atlantic, strengthening of the longshore wind, and enhanced upwelling. Siesser (1980) concluded that the increased organic carbon and opaline silica content of the sediments since the Miocene

reflected the development of a strong southeast trade wind system. This essentially corresponds to Flohn's analysis of what could be expected from the unipolar–bipolar transition.

Unfortunately, these suggested changes in atmospheric circulation in response to unipolar and bipolar glaciation have not been adequately tested by atmospheric circulation models. No model for unipolar glaciation has been published. Barron & Peterson (1991) show the atmospheric circulation for 20 Ma (Miocene) palaeogeography, but did not include ice on Antarctica. The results of several atmospheric general circulation models (GCMs) comparing ice age and modern circulation have, however, been published. Williams et al. (1974) used the NCAR (National Center for Atmospheric Research) Community Climate model to simulate atmospheric circulation on Earth with ice-age boundary conditions (topography and albedo). Their ice age maps indicate southward displacement of the belts of subtropical highs by 5°

(southern hemisphere) to 10° (northern hemisphere). Subsequent experiments by Gates (1976) and Manabe & Hahn (1977) used boundary conditions (elevation, sea surface temperatures and albedo) prescribed by CLIMAP (1976) with the Oregon State and NOAA Princeton Geophysical Fluid Dynamics Laboratory (GFDL) models respectively. These model runs showed no difference in the position of the ITCZ between ice age and present conditions. More recently, an atmosphere—ocean mixed layer version of the GFDL model run by Manabe & Broccoli (1985) predicts sea surface temperatures rather than using prescribed SSTs as a boundary condition input. Their December—February wind vector map for the ice age run shows the ITCZ displaced into the southern hemisphere everywhere except over the Gulf of Guinea. Its average position during the southern hemisphere summer appears to be about 10°S during ice age conditions whereas at present its average position during the southern hemisphere winter is about the equator.

According to Hart & Currie (1960) the southward flowing Angola Coastal Current meets the Benguela Current at Cabo Frio (Figs 1 & 3), causing eddies and upwelling. Diester-Haass (1985a, b, 1988), Diester-Haass et al. (1986, 1990), and Diester-Haass & Rothe (1987) have suggested that it is the advection of these eddies of upwelled water over Walvis Ridge that results in the occurrences of opaline silica in the biogenic sediment there.

Van Zinderen-Bakker (1976), Diester-Haass (1985a, b, 1988), Diester-Haass et al. (1986, 1990), and Dieter-Haass & Rothe (1987) stated that between glacials and interglacials the winds change in such a way as to shift the position where the Benguela Current leaves the coast northward. They suggest that during interglacial times, the Benguela Current begins to turn westward at the latitude of Walvis Ridge, whereas during a glacial it flows along the coast to a lower latitude (17°N), turning west well north of Walvis Ridge. They believe that the eddy production is suppressed by northward displacement of the juncture of the Benguela and Angola Coastal Currents during glacials, but southward displacement would have the same effect.

Northward shift of the position where the Benguela Current leaves the coast implies that the subtropical highs and ITCZ move northward during glacials. However, because the northern hemisphere ice caps were centred at 60°N, closer to the equator than the Antarctic ice cap, it seems likely that the thermal equator would be displaced to the south, not the north. Winter &

Martin (1990) found that the northward displacement of the Subtropical Convergence south of South Africa was no more than 2°. We suggest that the winds at the latitude of Walvis Ridge Abutment Plateau may have increased in intensity, but that their pattern probably did not change.

A possible explanation for the late Pliocene—Pleistocene waning of the upwelling signal in the sediments on Walvis Ridge Abutment Plateau and in the adjacent Angola Basin is that during the Pliocene an upwelling centre existed just south of the Walvis Ridge Abutment. This upwelling centre might have been similar to that near Lüderitz today, perhaps replacing it in importance as a site of upwelling of waters with a complete suite of nutrients. The location of the upwelling centre would have been fixed by the local changes in bathymetry associated with the Abutment. The size of the upwelling system would not have been appreciably different from that of today, but it would have been located 5° further north than the Lüderitz centre is today. This implies southward shift of the subtropical high and ITCZ of about 5° since the onset of major northern hemisphere glaciation.

Neumann & Pierson (1966) have noted that the equatorial circulation system is very sensitive to changes in the average position of the ITCZ, and have described the organization of the Equatorial Current System under different positions of the ITCZ. The changes occur because both the cross equatorial flow of air and the Ekman transport in the ocean mixed layer respond to the change in sign of the CorF at the equator.

If the ITCZ is centred on the equator, the equatorial current system will be symmetrical, with a vigorous equatorial divergence and North and South Equatorial currents flowing east to west bordered poleward by convergences between 10° and 20°N and S.

If the ITCZ is displaced north of the equator, as it is today (Fig. 8), the southeast trade winds cross the equator and begin to be turned toward the northeast. There is a less vigorous equatorial divergence, which now occurs within the South Equatorial Current. As the southeast trade winds turn toward the northeast after crossing the equator they drive a west to east flowing Equatorial Countercurrent separated from the broad South Equatorial Current by a convergence north of the equator. A second divergence develops beneath the ITCZ. North of the ITCZ the Northeast Trade Winds drive a narrow east to west flowing North Equatorial Current. The South and the North Equatorial Currents are bordered poleward by convergences.

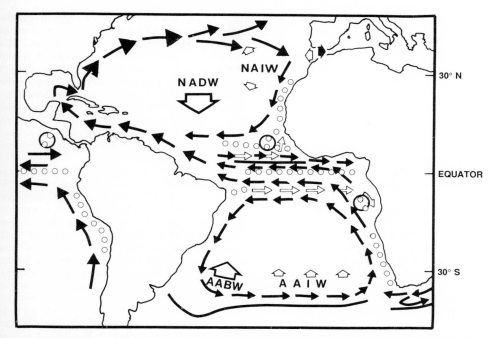

Fig. 8. Present-day geography and currents shown schematically, after sources discussed in the text. Symbols as in Fig. 5. The average position of the ITCZ is about 6°N, and the Guinea and Costa Rica Domes are sites of active seasonal upwelling. The convergence between the broad South Equatorial Current and the Equatorial Countercurrent and the divergence between the latter and the narrower North Equatorial Current are north of the equator. The ITCZ migrates into the southern hemisphere during the northern winter, inducing upwelling from the Angola Dome during northern hemisphere winter.

If the ITCZ is located in the southern hemisphere the asymmetry is reversed (Fig. 7).

We can speculate that the effect of the change from unipolar ice cover to the present condition with an ice cap on Antarctica and an ice-covered Arctic Ocean would be to move the mean position of the ITCZ from 10°N or further north (Fig. 5) to 6°N (Fig. ?). This would reduce the asymmetry of the Equatorial Current System, reducing the width of the South Equatorial Current and expanding the width of the North Equatorial Current. This would allow the Equatorial Countercurrent to enter the Gulf of Guinea more directly, enhancing the flow of the Angola Coastal Current. It would also reduce the vigour of the divergence at the northern boundary of the Equatorial Countercurrent.

The effect of appearance and disappearance of ice caps but maintenance of an ice-covered Arctic Ocean during glacials and interglacials in the northern hemisphere may be to cause the mean position of the ITCZ to migrate back and forth across the equator (Figs 7 & 8). This would cause reversals of the asymmetry of the Equatorial Current System which would thus

change from having a broad South Equatorial Current extending to about 4°N during interglacials to having a broad North Equatorial Current extending to about 4°S during glacials. There would be a South Equatorial Countercurrent which would enhance the flow of the Angola Coastal Current. This might be the mechanism for greater production of eddies and upwelling where the Angola and Benguela Coastal Currents meet.

These changes in the Equatorial Current System are especially significant in the context of northward drift of South America and Africa and the closing of the Central American Isthmus.

The desiccation and reflooding of the Mediterranean

During the late Miocene the Mediterranean Basin was desiccated (Fig. 5), and during the Pliocene it again filled with water (Hsü *et al.* 1977; Cita & McKenzie 1986). While the Mediterranean basins were dry, the ITCZ moved to its most extreme northern position, north of the present Sahara at 30°N palaeolatitude (Thiedemann et al. 1989; Ruddiman et al. 1989).

Re-evaluation of the timescale indicates that the reflooding of the Mediterranean took place at about 4.9 Ma (McKenzie et al. 1988) although 5.2 Ma is the age given in most older studies. For a brief (70 ka) period shortly after reflooding, the Mediterranean basins became filled with cold deep Atlantic water (McKenzie & Sprovieri 1990) and clearly had estuarine circulation. According to Rio et al. (1990) the Mediterranean had a positive fresh water balance and estuarine circulation until 2.5 Ma, as shown in our Fig. 6. Then the fresh water balance became negative and the present lagoonal circulation was established (Rio et al. 1990). Once the Mediterranean became a major source of saline water for the North Atlantic the production of North Atlantic Deep Water was enhanced.

It was at the end of the Messinian, at '5.2 Ma' that upwelling at the Walvis Ridge Abutment Plateau shifted from a maximum during glacial to a maximum during interglacial cycles (Diester-Haass, 1985a, b, 1988; Diester-Haass et al. 1986, 1990; Diester–Haass & Rothe 1987). The coincidence between reflooding of the Mediterranean and the change to maximally productive upwelling during interglacials suggest cause and effect but, again, not directly.

In most regions where upwelling occurs, biological productivity is increased during glacials (Pedersen & Calvert 1990), probably as a direct result of the increased wind stress. Increased upwelling off southwest Africa during the glacials was assumed by CLIMAP (1976), Morley & Hays (1979) and van Zinderen-Bakker (1980). That the upwelling during glacials is less productive in the southeast Atlantic, as documented by Diester-Haass (1985a, b, 1988), Diester-Haass et al. (1986, 1990) and Diester-Haass & Rothe (1987) may indicate that the water being upwelled there was nutrient-poor. The indirect connection between re-flooding of the Mediterranean and lesser productivity during glacials may be through the expansion of nutrient-poor intermediate water into the South Atlantic during the glacials.

The nutrient-rich Antarctic Intermediate Water presently upwelled is characterized by low salinities (34.2) and cold temperatures (2−4°C). Its formation involves dilution of upwelling NADW by the large excess of precipitation over evaporation between 40° and 50°S. If the production of NADW is reduced, the dilution can become more extreme and the production of AAIW could also cease. If the production of AAIW ceases also, this may allow nutrient-poor NAIW formed from entrainment of saline Mediterranean water to become the dominant water mass in the northern South Atlantic during glacials. Thus even though upwelling might become more intense at the Angola Thermal Dome and along the Namibian margin as a result of greater wind stress, the upwelled water would contain fewer nutrients and hence there would be less of an 'upwelling signal' i.e. record of enhanced biological productivity, in the sediments.

The reduction or cessation of NADW production during glacials is indicated by Boyle and Keigwin (1982, 1987). Although there are no data from the South Atlantic to demonstrate that the Antarctic Intermediate Water was depleted in nutrients during glacials, Boyle & Keigwin (1987) have noted that the Cd/Ca ratio in the Caribbean Sea was significantly less during the last glacial than it is today. The Antillean barrier prevents North Atlantic Deep Water and Antarctic Bottom Water from entering the Caribbean, so that it is filled by Antarctic Intermediate Water and North Atlantic Intermediate Water. Hence, the data of Boyle & Keigwin (1987) provide indirect evidence that Antarctic Intermediate Water in the South Atlantic was nutrient-depleted during the last glacial.

If the circulation of the Mediterranean has been lagoonal since the brief episode of estuarine circulation after flooding described by McKenzie & Sprovieri (1990), the alternation of AAIW during interglacials and NAIW during glacials can explain the change at '5.2 Ma'.

According to Rio et al. (1990) the Mediterranean has been supplying saline water to the Atlantic only during the past 2.5 Ma. If this is true, then between 4.6 and 2.5 Ma nutrient-poor intermediate waters would have required a source other than the Mediterranean. Enhanced production of cold North Atlantic Intermediate Water near the polar front is a possibility. However, the evidence for a shift from estuarine to lagoonal state of the Mediterranean is not wholly compelling, being based on increased aridity in Europe documented by pollen and spores (Zagwin 1974; Suc 1984) and on interpretation of oxygen isotopes (Loubere 1987). While the evidence clearly indicates that lagoonal flow should have strengthened since 2.5 Ma, it does not necessarily require that there be estuarine flow between 4.6 and 2.5 Ma.

Late Cenozoic sea-level changes

At low stands of sea level during the Pleistocene, the configuration of the shorelines of the world changes markedly (Fig. 7). Along Namibia the coastal plain (land from sea-level to 200 m elevation) would expand from its present width of about 20 km to about 100 km. Lowering of sea level would cause the shoreline to move westward exposing a broad coastal plain and reducing the orographic effect of the Kalahari Plateau. The axis of the wind jet would be closer to the shore, reducing upward Ekman pumping over the shelf.

Off southwest Africa a lower sea level would significantly reduce the width of the shelf and enhance coastal upwelling by forcing the same volume of upwelled water to come from a narrower band in order to maintain continuity of volume. Lower sea level, by bringing the shelf break closer to the sea surface, would also enhance the likelihood of upwelling the nutrient-rich oceanic waters that overlie the slope below the shelf break.

The present oceanographic conditions observed during a high stand of sea level are probably anomalous for most of the Pliocene and Pleistocene. Although the sea-level curve of Haq et al. (1987) indicates that sea level has been at or above its present level for most of the past 5 Ma, the $\delta^{18}O$ record suggests that during the past 2.5 Ma sea level was intermediate between the late Pleistocene high and low stands (Raymo et al. 1990), and thus a generally more enhanced upwelling might be expected. The correlation of less productivity with the glacial (dark) cycles in the southeast Atlantic suggests that sea level change per se is not responsible for the upwelling signal recorded in the sediments on the Walvis Ridge Abutment Plateau.

Discussion

Two questions are raised by the study of the sediments reflecting upwelling at DSDP Site 532 on the Walvis Ridge Abutment Plateau and at Site 530 in the Angola Basin: what is the cause of the long-term trend of increase in biological productivity from late Miocene to latest Pliocene followed by declining productivity to present; and what is the cause of the change from association of highest biological productivity with glacials before 5.2 Ma to highest productivity during interglacials since? The anwers to these questions are important not only to understanding the evolution of upwelling off southwestern Africa, but to gaining insight into the relative importance of different oceanographic processes in nutrient cycling and the global carbon budget.

The information on distribution of sediments reflecting upwelling of southwestern Africa is too sparse to permit conclusive answers, but possible causes can be identified and the work required to falsify specific hypotheses can be defined.

Several upwelling processes, specifically equatorial upwelling, upwelling at oceanic divergences associated with atmospheric convergences, and Kelvin wave-driven coastal upwelling can be eliminated as possibilities. We consider the other processes in terms of how they may have been affected by palaeogeographical changes.

The northward drift of the continents would slowly displace the ITCZ, gradually divert more South Equatorial Current water into the South Atlantic gyre and affect the Kelvin wave-driven coastal upwelling of the tropics. The timescales of changes in sedimentation do not correspond with those of the drift of the continents.

Changes in the topographic relief of southern Africa and uplift of the Kalahari region would enhance wind-driven coastal upwelling and upward Ekman pumping on the Namibian shelf but, again, does not seem to be directly reflected by the sediments.

The closing of the Central American Isthmus had major indirect effects (Maier-Reimer et al. 1990). It resulted in salinization of the North Atlantic and caused an increase in production of NADW, AAIW and AABW, as shown schematically in Figs 5–8. The increased rate of production of these water masses resulted in differentiation of nutrients among them, and may have resulted in a shallower pycnocline. The production of relatively nutrient-rich AAIW was a prerequisite for the long-term increase in productive upwelling recorded by the late Miocene to latest Pliocene sediments.

The desiccation and reflooding of the Mediterranean also had a major indirect effect on the upwelling off southwest Africa (Figs 5 & 6). The desiccation corresponds to the time of appearance of an upwelling signal in the sediments on the Abutment Plateau. The desiccation of the Mediterranean and the growth of the Antarctic ice cap during the late Miocene combined to force the ITCZ to an extreme northerly position over Africa. The apparent onset of upwelling may reflect both the northward shift of the southern hemisphere subtropical high and the availability of nutrient-rich waters. The time of reflooding of the Mediterranean corresponds to the time of change from maximum upwelling productivity coinciding with glacials to its coinciding with interglacials. A simple explanation for this change is that during glacials, when NADW production is reduced, AAIW is replaced by nutrient-poor NAIW, so that the water upwelled does not become productive. The effect is shown schematically in Fig. 7. Another possible cause of the decline in productivity since 2.5 Ma is the possibility that increased Mediterranean saline outflow has resulted in progressive expansion of NAIW into the South Atlantic during glacials.

The growth of the Antarctic and northern hemisphere ice caps was important in changing the atmospheric circulation patterns driving ocean currents and upwelling. As noted above, the subtropical high and ITCZ would have migrated north as the Antarctic ice cap grew during the late Miocene, reaching an extreme northern position as the Mediterranean desiccated. This could have displaced the Benguela Coastal Upwelling System northward to an upwelling centre associated with the Walvis Ridge Abutment. However, the flow of the gyre would advect the upwelled waters to the northwest, not to the west over the Abutment Plateau. Subsequent southward migration of the ITCZ as the Earth changed from unipolar to bipolar glaciation would have enhanced the Angola Coastal Current and upwelling from the Angola Thermal Dome. A stronger Angola Coastal Current may have both carried productive waters from the Angola Dome and focussed advection of productive coastal waters over the Walvis Ridge Abutment Plateau resulting in the increased upwelling signal in the sediments. The decline in strength of upwelling since 1.7 Ma recorded by the sediments on the Abutment Plateau may reflect southward shift of the upwelling centre to its present location near Lüderitz in response to growth of larger northern hemisphere ice caps during the glacials.

Changes in sea level associated with the growth and decay of ice caps has had a major effect. The light and dark cycles in the sediments caused by lesser and greater amounts of terrigenous material are thought to correspond to high and low stands of sea level (Dean & Gardner 1985). The effect of sea-level change on productivity is opposite to that found in most of the world; instead of the highest productivity occurring during glacials (Pedersen & Calvert 1990), it occurs during the interglacials (Diester-Haass 1985a, b, 1988; Diester-Haass et al. 1986, 1990; Diester-Haass & Rothe 1987). Wind stress and hence upwelling should increase during glacials. The simplest explanation for the lessened productivity in this region during glacials is that the upwelled waters are nutrient-poor, reflecting replacement of AAIW by NAIW.

To distinguish among these possibilities, more data are needed. Most importantly, the history of the Benguela Coastal Upwelling System should be investigated by deeper coring on the Namibian shelf and adjacent deeper offshore. Does the diatom mud always accumulate off Walvis Bay during interglacials, or has its site of accumulation migrated on the shelf with time? Where is the major site of accumulation of siliceous sediment off southwest Africa during the glacials, and has it migrated with time? Has high productivity on the shelf always been to the south of Cabo Frio? Is there a long term history of productivity beneath the Angola Thermal Dome?

Summary and conclusions

Sediments recovered at DSDP Sites 362 and 532 on Walvis Ridge and 530 in the southeastern Angola Basin record long-term waxing and waning of upwelling and a shift from maximum productivity during glacials to during interglacials. The organic carbon and opaline silica content of the sediments both increase from latest Miocene to latest Pliocene, then decline to the present. The average late Pliocene accumulation rate of opaline silica is greater than that of the late Pleistocene by a factor of ten. The late Pliocene rate of accumulation of organic carbon content is almost double that of the late Pleistocene.

The sediments contain light–dark cycles; the dark cycles contain more terrigenous material and on this basis have been interpreted as representing glacials. Before the Pliocene the maximum biological productivity in this region occurred during the glacials, but since then it has occurred during the interglacials. Thus the effect of sea-level change on productivity since the Miocene is opposite to that found in most of the world.

The most important causative factors resulting in the changes in sedimentation observed at these sites were as follows.

The closing of the Central American Isthmus had major indirect effects. It resulted in salinization of the North Atlantic and caused increased production of NADW, AAIW and AABW. The increased rate of production of these water masses resulted in differentiation of nutrients among them, and may have resulted in a shallower pycnocline, enhancing the likelihood of upwelling nutrient-rich water. The production of relatively nutrient-rich AAIW was a prerequisite for the long-term increase in productive upwelling recorded by the late Miocene to latest Pliocene sediments.

The growth of the Antarctic and northern hemisphere ice caps was important in changing the atmospheric circulation patterns driving ocean currents and upwelling. The sub-tropical high and ITCZ would have migrated north as the Antarctic ice cap grew and the Mediterranean desiccated during the late Miocene. This may have displaced the Benguela Coastal Upwelling System northward initiating productive upwelling near the Abutment Plateau, but the upwelled waters would have been advected mostly to the northwest. Subsequent southward migration of the ITCZ as the Earth changed from unipolar to bipolar glaciation would have enhanced the Angola Coastal Current and upwelling from the Angola Thermal Dome. A stronger Angola Coastal Current may have both carried productive waters from the Angola Dome and focussed advection of productive coastal waters from the south and north over the Walvis Ridge Abutment Plateau. The decline in strength of upwelling since 1.7 Ma recorded by the sediments on the Abutment Plateau may reflect the southward shift of the upwelling centre to its present location near Lüderitz in response to more intense northern hemisphere glaciations.

The reflooding of the Mediterranean corresponds to the time of change from maximum upwelling productivity coinciding with glacials to its coinciding with interglacials. During glacials, when NADW production was reduced, AAIW was replaced by nutrient-poor NAIW, so that the upwelled water did not become productive. Another possible cause of the decline in productivity since 1.7 Ma is the that increased Mediterranean saline outflow during the Pleistocene has resulted in an increase in the volume of NAIW generally so that during glacials it has progressively expanded further and further into the Southeastern Atlantic.

Acknowledgement is made to the Donors of The Petroleum Research Fund, administered by the American Chemical Society, for the support of this research. John Brock has been supported by the NASA Graduate Student Researchers Program. The authors have benefitted from discussions with many colleagues, including L. Diester-Haass, E. Suess, C. R. McClain, M. E. Luther, J. J. O'Brien, C. R. McClain, P. A. Meyers, C. N. Wold, G. W. Brass, and G. Wefer. We especially appreciated constructive comments on the manuscript by L. Diester-Haass, R. Stewart and W. Prell.

References

ADAMEC, D. & O'BRIEN, J. J. 1978. The seasonal upwelling in the Gulf of Guinea due to remote forcing. *Journal of Physical Oceanography*, **8**, 1050–1060.

APEL, J. 1987. *Principles of Ocean Physics*. Academic, London.

BAINBRIDGE, A. E. No date. *GEOSECS Atlantic Expedition, Volume 2, Sections and Profiles*. National Science Foundation, Washington, D.C.

BAKUN, A. & NELSON, C. S. 1984. Wind stress curl in the California, Peru, Canary, and Benguela Current systems (Poster) *In*: *CalCOFI Conference, Idyllwild, California, October 29–31, 1984. (cited by Picaut 1985).*

BANG, N. D. 1971. The southern Benguela Current region in February 1966: Part II: Bathythermography and air-sea interactions. *Deep-Sea Research, Part A*, **18**, 209–224.

BARRON, E. J., HARRISON, C. G. A., SLOAN, J. L. I. & HAY, W. W. 1981. Paleogeography, 180 million years ago to the present. *Eclogae Geologicae Helvetiae*, **74**, 443–470.

—— & PETERSON, W. H. 1991. The Cenozoic ocean circulation based on ocean General Circulation Model results. *Palaeogeography, Palaeoclimatology, Palaeoecology*, **83**, 1–28.

BAUMGARTNER, A. & REICHEL, E. 1975. *The World Water Balance: Mean Annual Global Continental and Maritime Precipitation, Evaporation and Runoff*, Elsevier, Amsterdam.

BESLER, H. 1980. *Die Dünen-Namib: Entstehung und Dynamik Eines Ergs, Stuttgarter Geographische Studien* **96**.

BIRCHFIELD, G. E. & BROECKER, W. S. 1990. A salt oscillator in the glacial Atlantic? 2. A 'scale analysis' model. *Paleoceanography*, **5**, 835–843.

BLANC, P.-L. & DUPLESSY, J.-C. 1982. The deep-water circulation during the Neogene and the impact of the Messinian salinity crisis. *Deep-Sea Research, Part A*, **29**, 1391–1414.

BOGOROV, V. G., VINOGRADOV, M. E., STEPANOV, V. N., MOROSHKIN, K. V. & BULATOV, R. P. 1973. Tropical cyclonic macrocirculation systems and their role in the formation of ocean structure (in Russian). Formation of Biological Productivity and Bottom Sediments as Related to Ocean Circulation in the South-eastern Atlantic. *Transactions of the P.P. Shirshov Institute of Oceanology*, **95**, 1–13.

BOLLI, H. M., RYAN, W. B. F. *et al.* 1978. *Initial Reports of the Deep Sea Drilling Project*, **40**, U.S. Government Printing Office, Washington.

BOYLE, E. A. & KEIGWIN, L. D. 1982. Deep circulation of the North Atlantic over the last 200 000 years: Geological evidence. *Science*, **218**, 784–787.

—— 1987. North Atlantic thermohaline circulation during the past 20 000 years linked to high-latitude surface temperature. *Nature*, **330**, 35–40.

BREMNER, J. M. 1983. Biogenic sediments on the south west African (Namibian) continental margin. *In*: THIEDE, J. & SUESS, E. (eds) *Coastal Upwelling, Its Sediment Record, Part B: Sedimentary Records of Ancient Coastal Upwelling*. NATO Conference Series, Series IV: Marine Sciences 10b, Plenum, New York, 73–103.

BRIDEN, J. C., DREWRY, G. E. & SMITH, A. G. 1974. Phanerozoic equal-area world maps. *Journal of Geophysical Research*, **82**, 555–574.

BROECKER, W. S., BOND, G., KLAS, M., BONANI, G. & WOLFLI, W. 1990. A salt oscillator in the glacial Atlantic? 1. The concept. *Paleoceanography*, **5**, 469–477.

——, PETEET, D. & RIND, D. 1985. Does the ocean-atmosphere have more than one stable mode of operation. *Nature*, **315**, 21–25.

—— & TAKAHASHI, T. 1980. Hydrography of the Central Atlantic III, The North Atlantic deep water complex. *Deep-Sea Research, Part A*, **27**, 591–613.

BRONGERSMA-SANDERS, M. 1948. The importance of upwelling water to vertebrate paleontology and oil geology. *Verhandlingen Koninklijke Nederlanse Akademie van Wetenschappen (Afdeeling Natuurkunde, 2 Sect.)*, **45**(4), 1–112.

—— 1957. Mass mortality in the sea. *In*: HEDGPETH, J. W. (ed.) *Geological Society of America Memoir 67: Treatise on Marine Ecology and Paleo-ecology, 1, Ecology*, 941–1010.

BROWN, J., COLLING, A., PARK, D., PHILLIPS, J., ROTHERY, D. & WRIGHT, J. 1989. *Ocean Circulation*. Open University/Pergamon, Oxford.

BUSALACCHI, A. J. & O'BRIEN, J. J. 1980. The seasonal variability of the tropical Pacific. *Journal of Physical Oceanography*, **10**, 1929–1950.

—— & PICAUT, J. 1983. Seasonal variation from a model of the tropical Atlantic. *Journal of Physical Oceanography*, **13**, 1564–1588.

CALVERT, S. 1974. Deposition and diagenesis of silica in marine sediment. *In*: HSÜ, K. J. & JENKYNS, H. C. (eds) *Pelagic Sediments: On Land and Under the Sea*, International Association of Sedimentology Special Publication 1, 273–299.

—— & PRICE, N. B. 1971a. Recent sediments of the South West African shelf. *In*: DELANY, F. M. (ed.) *ICSU/SCOR Institute Geological Sciences Report 70/16, The Geology of the East Atlantic Continental Margin*, 171–185.

—— 1983. Geochemistry in Namibian shelf sediments. *In*: SUESS, E. & THIEDE, J. (eds) *Coastal Upwelling, Its Sediment Record. Part A. Responses of the Sedimentary Regime to Present Coastal Upwelling*. NATO Conference Series, Series IV: Marine Sciences 10a Plenum, New York, 337–375.

CHAPMAN, P. & SHANNON, L. V. 1985. The Benguela ecosystem: Part II. Chemistry and related processes. *Annual Review of Oceanography and Marine Biology*, **25**, 183–251.

CIESIELSKI, P. F., LEDBETTER, M. F. & ELLWOOD, B. B. 1982. The development of Antarctic glaciation and the Neogene paleoenvironment of the Maurice Ewing Bank. *Marine Geology*, **46**, 1–51.

CITA, M. B. & McKENZIE, J. A. 1986. The terminal Miocene event. *In*: HSÜ, K. J. (ed.) *Mesozoic and Cenozoic Oceans*. Geodynamics Series, 15 American Geophysical Union, Washington, D.C., 123–140.

CLIMAP Project Members. 1976. The surface of the ice-age earth. *Science*, **191**, 1131–1137.

COATES, A. G., JACKSON, J. B. C., COLLINS, L. S., CRONIN, T. M., DOWSETT, H. J., BYBELL, L. M.,

JUNG, P. & OBANDO, J. A. in press. Closure of the Isthmus of Panama: The near shore record of Costa Rica and Panama. *Geological Society of America Bulletin*.

COPENHAGEN, W. J. 1953. The periodic mortality of fish in the Walvis Bay region, in *Division of Fisheries, Union of South Africa, Investigational Report*, **14**.

DEAN, W. & GARDNER, J. 1985. Cyclic variations in calcium carbonate and organic carbon in Miocene to Holocene sediments, Walvis Ridge, South Atlantic Ocean. *In*: HSÜ, K. J. & WEISSERT, H. J. (eds) *South Atlantic Paleoceanography*. Cambridge University Press, 61–78.

DEAN, W. E., HAY, W. W. & SIBUET, J.-C. 1984. Geologic evolution, sedimentation and paleo-environments of the Angola Basin and adjacent Walvis Ridge: Synthesis of results of Deep Sea Drilling Project Leg 75. *In*: HAY, W. W. & SIBUET, J.-C. *et al.* (eds) *Initial Reports of the Deep Sea Drilling Project*, **75**. U.S. Government Printing Office, Washington, D.C., 509–544.

DEFANT, A. 1961. *Physical Oceanography*. Pergamon, New York.

DEMASTER, D. J. 1981. The supply and accumulation of silica in the marine environment. *Geochimica et Cosmochimica Acta*, **45**, 1715–1732.

DIESTER-HAASS, L. 1978. Sediments as indicators of upwelling. *In*: BOJE, R. & TOMCZAK, M. (eds) *Upwelling Ecosystems*. Springer, Berlin, 261–281.

—— 1983. Differentiation of high oceanic fertility in marine sediments caused by coastal upwelling and/or river discharge off northwest Africa during the Late Quaternary. *In*: THIEDE, J. & SUESS, E. (eds) *Coastal Upwelling, Its Sedimentary Record; Part B: Sedimentary Records of Ancient Coastal Upwelling*. NATO Conference Series IV, Marine Sciences, **10b**, Plenum, New York, 399–419.

—— 1985a. Late Quaternary sedimentation on the eastern Walvis Ridge, SE Atlantic (HPC 532 and four piston cores). *Marine Geology*, **65**, 145–189.

—— 1985b. Late Quaternary upwelling history off southwest Africa (DSDP Leg 75, HPC 532). *In*: HSÜ, K. J. & WEISSERT, H. J. (eds) *South Atlantic Paleoceanography*. Cambridge University Press, 47–55.

—— 1988. Sea level changes, carbonate dissolution and history of the Benguela Current in the Oligocene-Miocene off southwest Africa. *Marine Geology*, **79**, 213–242.

DIESTER-HAASS, L., HEINE, K., ROTHE, P. & SCHRADER, H. 1988. Late Quaternary history of continental climate and the Benguela Current off South West Africa. *Palaeogeography, Palaeoclimatology, Palaeoecology*, **65**, 81–91.

——, MEYERS, P. A. & ROTHE, P. 1986. Light-dark cycles in opal-rich sediments near the Plio-Pleistocene boundary, DSDP Site 532, Walvis Ridge continental terrace. *Marine Geology*, 1–23.

—— 1990. Miocene history of the Benguela Current and Antarctic ice volumes: Evidence from rhythmic sedimentation and current growth across the Walvis Ridge (Deep Sea Drilling Project Sites 362 and 532). *Paleoceanography*, **5**, 685−707.

—— & ROTHE, P. 1987. Plio-Pleistocene sedimentation on the Walvis Ridge, southeast Atlantic (DSDP Leg 75, Site 532) − Influence of surface currents, carbonate dissolution and climate. *Marine Geology*, **77**, 53−85.

DIESTER-HAASS, L. & SCHRADER, H. J. 1979. Neogene coastal upwelling history off northwest and southwest Africa. *Marine Geology*, **29**, 39−53.

DIETRICH, G. 1963. *General Oceanography*. Wiley, New York.

DUQUE-CARO, H. 1990. Neogene stratigraphy, paleoceanography and paleobiogeography in northwest South America and the evolution of the Panama Seaway. *Palaeogeography, Palaeoclimatology, Palaeoecology*, **77**, 203−234.

EKMAN, V. W. 1905. On the influence of the earth's rotation on ocean currents. *Arkiv for Matematik Astronomi och Fysik*, **12**, 1−52.

FINDLATER, J. 1969. A major low level air current near the Indian Ocean during the northern summer. *Quarterly Journal of the Royal Meterological Society*, **95**, 362−380.

FLOHN, H. 1979. Possible climatic consequences of a man-made global warming: Energy systems analysis. *In: International Conference on Energy Systems Analysis, Proceedings*, Dublin, 558−568.

—— 1981. A hemispheric circulation asymmetry during Late Tertiar (sic). *Geologische Rundschau*, **70**, 725−736.

—— 1983. Actual palaeoclimatic problems from a climatologist's viewpoint. *In*: Ghazi, A. (ed.) *Paleoclimatic Research and Models*. Reidel, Dordrecht, 17−33.

—— 1984. Climatic belts in the case of a unipolar glaciation. *In*: MÖRNER, N. A. & KARLEN, J. (eds) *Climatic Changes on a Yearly to Millenial Basis, Proceedings of the Second NATO Symposium on Climatic Changes and Related Problems*. D. Reidel, Dordrecht, 609−620.

FUGLISTER, F. C. 1960. *Atlantic Ocean Atlas, Temperature and Salinity Profiles and Data from the International Geophysical Year of 1957−1958*. Woods Hole Oceanographic Institution, Woods Hole.

GARDNER, J. V., DEAN, W. E. & WILSON, C. R. 1984. Carbonate and organic carbon cycles and the history of upwelling at Deep Sea Drilling Project Site 532, Walvis Ridge, South Atlantic Ocean. *In*: HAY, W. W., SIBUET, J.-C. *et al*. (eds) *Initial Reports of the Deep Sea Drilling Project*, **75**, U.S. Government Printing Office, Washington, 905−921.

GARTNER, S., CHOW, J. & STANTON, R. J. J. 1987. Late Neogene paleooceanography of the eastern Caribbean, Gulf of Mexico and the eastern equatorial Pacific. *Marine Micropaleontology*, **12**, 255−304.

GATES, W. L. 1976. The numerical simulation of ice-age climate with a general circulation model. *Journal of Atmospheric Sciences*, **33**, 1844−1873.

GORDON, A. L. J. 1985. Indian-Atlantic transfer for thermocline water at the Agulhas Retroflection. *Science*, **227**, 1030−1033.

—— 1986. Interocean exchange of thermocline water. *Journal of Geophysical Research*, **91**, 5037−5046.

GORSHKOV, S. G. 1977. *Atlas Okeanov, Atlanticheskiy I Indiyskiy Okean'i*. Ministerstvo Oboronyi SSSR, Voenno-Morskoe Flot, Leningrad.

HAGEN, E., SCHEMAINDA, R., MICHELSEN, N., POSTEL, L., SCHULZ, S. & BELOW, M. 1981. Zur Küstensenkrechten Struktur des Kaltwasserauftriebs vor der Küste Namibias. *Geodätische und geophysikalische Veröffentlichungen*, **36**, 1−99.

HAQ, B. U., HARDENBOL, J. & VAIL, P. R. 1987. Chronology of fluctuating sea levels since the Triassic. *Science*, **235**, 1156−1167.

HART, T. J. & CURRIE, R. T. 1960. The Benguela Current. *Discovery Reports*, **31**, 123−298.

HASTENRATH, S. & LAMB, P. 1977. *Climatic Atlas of the Tropical Atlantic and Eastern Pacific Oceans*. University of Wisconsin Press, Madison, WI.

HAY, W. W., SHAW, C. A. & WOLD, C. N. 1989. Mass-balanced paleogeographic reconstructions. *Geologische Rundschau*, **78**, 207−242.

——, SIBUET, J.-C. & Leg 75 Shipboard Party. 1982. Sedimentation and accumulation of organic carbon in the Angola Basin and on Walvis Ridge: Preliminary results of Deep Sea Drilling Project Leg 75. *Geological Society of America Bulletin*, **93**, 1038−1055.

——, —— *et al*. 1984a. *Initial Reports of the Deep Sea Drilling Project*, **75**.

—— 1984b Site 530: Southeastern corner of the Angola Basin. *In*: HAY, W. W., SIBUET, J.-C. *et al*. (eds) *Initial Reports of the Deep Sea Drilling Project*, **75**, U.S. Government Printing Office, Washington, 29−285.

—— 1984c. Site 532: Walvis Ridge. *In*: HAY, W. W. & SIBUET, J.-C. *et al*. (eds) *Initial Reports of the Deep Sea Drilling Project*, **75**, U.S. Government Printing Office, Washington, 295−445.

HODELL, D. A., WILLIAMS, D. F. & KENNETT, J. P. 1985. Late Pliocene reorganization of deep vertical water-mass structure in the western South Atlantic: Faunal and isotopic evidence. *Geological Society of America Bulletin*, **96**, 495−503.

HOFMANN, E. E., BUSALACCHI, A. J. & O'BRIEN, J. J. 1981. Wind generation of the Costa Rica Dome. *Science*, **214**, 552−554.

HOLSER, W. T., SCHIDLOWSKI, M., MACKENZIE, F. T. & MAYNARD, J. B. 1988. Geochemical cycles of carbon and sulfur. *In*: GREGOR, C. B. & GARRELS, R. M. M. F. T. M. J. B. (eds) *Chemical Cycles in the Evolution of the Earth*. Wiley, New York, 105−173.

HSUEH, Y. & O'BRIEN, J. J. 1971. Steady coastal upwelling induced by an alongshore current. *Journal of Physical Oceanography*, **1**, 180−186.

HSÜ, K. J., MONTADERT, L., BERNOULLI, D., CITA, M. B., ERICKSON, A., GARRISON, R. B., KIDD, R. B., MELIERES, F., MULLER, C. & WRIGHT, R. 1977. History of Mediterranean salinity crisis. *Nature*, **267**, 399−403.

JUNG, P. 1990. Paleontologic field work between Atlantic and Pacific. *Bulletin Swiss Association of Petroleum Geologists and Engineers*, **55**, 17−20.

KEIGWIN, L. D. J. 1978. Pliocene closing of the Isthmus of Panama, based on biostratigraphic evidence from nearby Pacific Ocean and Caribbean Sea cores. *Geology*, **6**, 630−634.

—— 1982a. Isotopic paleoceanography of the Caribbean and east Pacific: Role of Panama uplift in late Neogene time. *Science*, **217**, 350−353.

—— 1982b. Stable isotope stratigraphy and paleoceanography of Sites 502 and 503. *In*: PRELL, W. L., GARDNER, J. V. *et al.* (eds) *Initial Reports of the Deep Sea Drilling Project*, **68**, U.S. Government Printing Office, Washington, D.C., 269−288.

KELLER, G. & BARRON, J. A. 1983. Paleoceanographic implications of Miocene deep-sea hiatuses. *Geological Society of America Bulletin*, **94**, 590−613.

KERR, R. A. 1985. Small eddies are mixing the oceans. *Science*, **230**, 793.

KIER, R. S. 1988. On the late Pleistocene ocean geochemistry and circulation. *Paleoceanography*, **3**, 443−445.

—— 1989. Paleoproduction and atmospheric CO_2 based on ocean modeling. *In*: BERGER, W. H., SMETACEK, V. S. & WEFER, G. (eds) *Productivity of the Ocean: Present and Past*. Wiley, New York.

KING, L. C. 1967. *The Morphology of the Earth*. Oliver and Boyd, Edinburgh.

KRAUS, E. B., PETERSEN, W. H. & ROOTH, C. G. 1978. The thermal evolution of the ocean. *In*: *International Conference, Evolution of Planetary Atmospheres and Climatology of the Earth*, Centre national d'études spatiales (France), 201−211.

LOUBERE, P. 1987. Changes in mid-depth North Atlantic and Mediterranean circulation during the late Pliocene. Isotopic and sedimentological evidence. *Marine Geology*, **77**, 15−38.

LUNDELIUS, E. L. J. 1987. The North American Quaternary sequence. *In*: WOODBURNE, M. O. (ed.) *Cenozoic Mammals of North America*. University of California Press, Berkeley, CA, 211−235.

LUTHER, M. E. & O'BRIEN, J. J. 1985. A model of the seasonal circulation in the Arabian Sea forced by observed winds. *Progress in Oceanography*, **14**, 353−385.

MAIER-REIMER, E., MIKOLAJEWICZ, U. & CROWLEY, T. 1990. Ocean general circulation model sensitivity experiment with an open Central American isthmus. *Paleoceanography*, **5**, 349−366.

MANABE, S. & BROCCOLI, A. J. 1985. The influence of continental ice sheets on the climate of an ice age. *Journal of Geophysical Research*, **90**, 2167−2190.

—— & HAHN, D. G. 1977. Simulation of the tropical climate of an ice age. *Journal of Geophysical Research*, **82**, 3889−3911.

MARSHALL, L. G. 1988. Land mammals and the great American interchange. *American Scientist*, **76**, 380−388.

MAZEIKA, P. A. 1967. Thermal domes in the eastern tropical Atlantic Ocean. *Limnology and Oceanography*, **12**, 537−539.

MCCREARY, J. P., PICAUT, J. & MOORE, D. W. 1984. Effect of annual remote forcing in the eastern tropical Atlantic. *Journal of Marine Research*, **42**, 45−81.

MCDOUGALL, K. 1985. Miocene to Pliocene benthonic foraminifers and paleoceanography of the Middle America slope, Deep Sea Drilling Project, Leg 84. *In*: VON HUENE, R., AUBOIN, J. *et al.* (eds) *Initial Reports of the Deep Sea Drilling Project*, **84**, U.S. Government Printing Office, Washington, D.C., 363−418.

MCKENZIE, J. A., HODELL, D. A., MUELLER, P. A. & MULLER, D. W. 1988. Application of strontium isotopes to late Miocene-early Pliocene stratigraphy. *Geology*, **16**, 1022−1025.

—— & OBERHÄNSLI, H. 1985. Paleoceanographic expressions of the Messian salinity crisis. *In*: HSÜ, K. J. (ed.) *South Atlantic Paleoceanograhy*. Cambridge University Press, 99−123.

MCKENZIE, J. A. & SPROVIERI, R. 1990. Paleoceanographic conditions following the earliest Pliocene flooding of the Tyrrhenian sea. *In*: KASTENS, K. A., MASCLE, J. *et al.* (eds) *Proceedings of the Ocean Drilling Program, Scientific Results*, **107**, Ocean Drilling Program, College Station, TX, 405−414.

MEYERS, P. A., BRASSELL, S. C., HUC, A. Y., BARRON, E. J., BOYCE, R. E., DEAN, W. E., HAY, W. W., KEATING, B. H., MCNULTY, C. L., NOHARA, M., SCHALLREUTER, R. E., SIBUET, J.-C., STEINMETZ, J. C., STOW, D. & STRADNER, H. 1983. Organic geochemistry of sediments recovered by DSDP/IPOD Leg 75 from under the Benguela Current. *In*: THIEDE, J. & SUESS, E. (eds) *Coastal Upwelling, Its Sedimentary Record, Part B: Sedimentary Records of Ancient Coastal Upwelling*. NATO Conference Series, Series IV: Marine Sciences, Plenum Press, New York, **10b**, 453−466.

MOLNAR, P. & ENGLAND, P. 1990. Late Cenozoic uplift of mountain ranges and global climate change: Chicken or egg. *Nature*, **346**, 29−34.

MOORE, D. W., HISARD, P., MCCREARY, J. P., MERLE, J., O'BRIEN, J. J., PICAUT, J., VERSTRAETE, J. M. & WUNSCH, C. 1978. Equatorial adjustment in the eastern Atlantic. *Geophysical Research Letters*, **5**, 637−640.

MORLEY, J. J. & HAYES, J. D. 1979. Comparison of glacial and interglacial oceanographic conditions in the South Atlantic from variations in calcium carbonate and radiolarian distributions. *Quaternary Research*, **12**, 396−408.

MOROSHKIN, K. V., BUBNOV, V. A. & BULATOV, R. P. 1970. Water circulation in the eastern South Atlantic Ocean. *Oceanology*, **10**, 27−37.

NELSON, G. & HUTCHINGS, L. 1983. The Benguela upwelling area. *Progress in Oceanography*, **12**, 333−356.

NEUMANN, G. & PIERSON, W. J. J. 1966. *Principles of Physical Oceanography*. Prentice-Hall, Englewood Cliffs, N.J.

O'BRIEN, J. J. 1975. Models of Coastal Upwelling. *In: Numerical Models of Ocean Circulation.* National Academy of Sciences, Washington, D.C., 204–215.

OLSON, D. B. & EVANS, R. H. 1986. Rings of the Agulhas Current. *Deep-Sea Research*, **33**, 27–42.

PEDERSEN, T. F. & CALVERT, S. 1990. Anoxia vs. productivity: What controls the formation of organic-carbon-rich sediments and sedimentary rocks? *American Association of Petroleum Geologists Bulletin*, **74**, 454–466.

PETERSON, W. H. & ROOTH, C. G. H. 1976. Formation and exchange of deep water in the Norwegian Greenland Seas. *Deep-Sea Research, Part A*, **23**, 273–283.

PHILANDER, S. G. H. & PACANOWSKI, R. C. 1986. The mass and heat budget in a model of the tropical Atlantic Ocean. *Journal of Geophysical Research*, **91**, 14212–14220.

PICAUT, J. 1985. Major dynamics affecting the eastern tropical Atlantic and Pacific oceans. *CalCOFI Reports*, **26**, 41–49.

POND, S. & PICKARD, G. L. 1983. *Introductory Dynamical Oceanography*, Pergamon, Oxford.

PRELLER, R. & O'BRIEN, J. J. 1980. The influence of bottom topography on upwelling off Peru. *Journal of Physical Oceanography*, **10**, 1377–1398.

RAYMO, M. E., RIND, D. & RUDDIMAN, W. F. 1990. Climatic effects of reduced Arctic sea ice limits in the GISS II general circulation model. *Paleoceanography*, **5**, 367–382.

REID, J. L. 1979. On the contribution of the Mediterranean Sea outflow to the Norwegian-Greenland Sea. *Deep-Sea Research, Part A*, **26**, 1199–1223.

RIO, D., SPROVIERI, R., THUNELL, R., VERGNAUD GRAZZINI, C. & GLACON, G. 1990. Pliocene-Pleistocene paleoenvironmental history of the western Mediterranean: A synthesis of ODP Site 653 results. *In: KASTENS, K. A., MASCLE, J. et al.* (eds) *Proceedings of the Ocean Drilling Program, Scientific Results*, **107**, Ocean Drilling Program, College Station, TX, 695–704.

RONOV, A. B., KHAIN, V. & BALUKHOVSKY, A. 1989. *Atlas of Lithological-Paleogeographical Maps of the World. The Mesozoic and Cenozoic of Continents and Oceans.* Editorial Publishing Group VNII Zarubezhgeologia, Moscow, 24 maps with explanatory notes and bibliography.

RUDDIMAN, W. F. & KUTZBACH, J. E. 1989. Forcing of late Cenozoic northern hemisphere climate by plateau uplift in southeast Asia and the American Southwest. *Journal of Geophysical Research*, **94**, 18409–18427.

—— & RAYMO, M. E. 1988. Northern hemisphere climatic regimes during the past 3 Ma: Possible tectonic connnections. *In: SHACKLETON, N. I., WEST, R. G. & BOWEN, D. Q.* (eds) *The Past Three Million Years: Evolution of Climatic Variability in the North Atlantic Region.* Cambridge University Press, 227–234.

——, —— & MCINTYRE, A. 1986. Matuyama 41000-year cycles: North Atlantic Ocean and northern hemisphere ice sheets. *Earth and Planetary Science Letters*, **80**, 117–129.

RUDDIMAN, W. F., SARNTHEIN, M., BACKMAN, J., BALDAUF, J. G., CURRY, W., DUPONT, L. M., JANECEK, T., POKRAS, E. M., RAYMO, M. E., STABELL, B., STEIN, R. & THIEDEMANN, R. 1989. Late Miocene to Pleistocene evolution of climate in Africa and the low-latitude Atlantic: Overview of Leg 108 results. *In: RUDDIMAN, W. F., SARNTHEIN, M. et al.* (eds) *Proceedings of the Ocean Drilling Program, Scientific Results*, **108**, Ocean Drilling Program, College Station, TX, 463–484.

SAVIN, S. M. & DOUGLAS, R. G. 1985. Sea level, climate and the Central American land bridge. *In: STEHLI, F. G. & WEBB, S. D.* (eds) *The Great American Biotic Interchange.* Plenum, New York, 303–324.

SCHELL, I. I. 1968. On the relation between winds off south west Africa and the Benguela Current, and Aghulas Current penetration in the South Atlantic. *Deutsche Hydrographische Zeitschrift*, **21**, 109–117.

SCHNITKER, D. 1980. North Atlantic oceanography as possible cause of Antarctic glaciation and eutrophication. *Nature*, **284**, 615–616.

SCHOTT, G. 1942. *Geographie des Atlantischen Ozeans*, 3rd edition. C. Boysen, Hamburg.

—— 1943. Weltkarte zur Übersicht der Meeresströmungen. *Annalen der Hydrographie und maritimen Meterologie*.

SELBY, M. J. 1977. Paleowind directions in the Central Namib Desert as indicated by ventifacts. *Madoqua*, **10**, 195–198.

SHACKLETON, N. J. & KENNETT, J. P. 1975. Paleotemperature history of the Cenozoic and the initiation of Antarctic glaciation: Oxygen and carbon isotope analyses in DSDP Sites 277, 279, and 281. *In: KENNETT, J. P., HOUTZ, R. E. et al.* (eds) *Initial Reports of the Deep Sea Drilling Project*, **29**, U.S. Government Printing Office, Washington, D.C., 743–755.

SHANNON, L. V. 1985a. The Benguela ecosystem: Part I. Evolution of the Benguela, physical features and processes. *Annual Review of Oceanography and Marine Biology*, **23**, 105–182.

—— 1985b. *South African Ocean Colour and Upwelling Experiment.* Sea Fisheries Research Institute, Cape Town, S.A.

SHILLINGTON, F. A., PETERSON, W. A., HUTCHINGS, L., PROBYN, T. A., WALDRON, H. N. & AGENBAG, J. J. 1990. A cool upwelling filament off Namibia, southwest Africa: Preliminary measurements of physical and biological features. *Deep-Sea Research, Part A*, **37**, 1753–1772.

SIESSER, W. G. 1980. Late Miocene origin of the Benguela upwelling system off northern Namibia. *Science*, **208**, 283–285.

SMITH, R. L. 1968. Upwelling. *Annual Review of Oceanography and Marine Biology*, **6**, 11–47.

—— 1983. Circulation patterns in upwelling regimes. *In: SUESS, E. & THIEDE, J.* (eds) *Coastal Upwelling, Its Sedimentary Record. Part A: Responses of the Sedimentary Regime to Present*

Coastal Upwelling. NATO Conference Series IV: Marine Sciences, **10a**, Plenum, New York, 13–35.

STEINMETZ, J. C. & STRADNER, H. 1984. Cenozoic calcareous nannofossils from Deep Sea Drilling Project Leg 75, southeast Atlantic Ocean. *In*: HAY, W. W., SIBUET, J. C. *et al.* (eds) *Initial Reports of the Deep Sea Drilling Project*, **75**, U.S. Government Printing Office, Washington, D.C., 671–754.

——, BARRON, E. J., BOERSMA, A., KEATING, B., MCNULTY, C., SANCETTA, C. & STRADNER, H. 1984. Summary of biostratigraphy and magnetostratigraphy of Deep Sea Drilling Project Leg 75. *In*: HAY, W. W., SIBUET, J.-C. *et al.* (eds) *Initial Reports of the Deep Sea Drilling Project*, **75**, U.S. Government Printing Office, Washington, D.C., 449–458.

SUC, J. P. 1984. Origin and evolution of the Mediterranean vegetation and climate in Europe. *Nature*, **307**, 429–432.

SUMMERHAYES, C. 1983. Sedimentation of organic matter in upwelling regimes. *In*: THIEDE, J. & SUESS, E. (eds) *Coastal Upwelling, Its Sediment Record, Part B: Sedimentary Records of Ancient Coastal Upwelling*, Plenum, New York, 29–72.

SVERDRUP, H. U. 1938. On the process of upwelling. *Journal of Marine Research*, **1**, 155–164.

SVERDRUP, H. U., JOHNSON, M. W. & FLEMING, R. H. 1942. *The Oceans: Their Physics, Chemistry, and General Biology*. Prentice-Hall, Englewood Cliffs, New Jersey.

SWEETING, M. M. & LANCASTER, N. 1982. Solution and wind erosion forms on limestone in the Central Namib Desert. *Zeitschrift für Geomorphologie, N. F.*, **26**, 197–207.

TCHERNIA, P. 1980. *Descriptive Regional Oceanography*. Pergamon, Oxford.

THIEDEMANN, R., SARNTHEIN, M. & STEIN, R. 1989. Climatic changes in the western Sahara: Aeolomarine sediment record of the last 8 million years (Sites 657–661). *In*: RUDDIMAN, W. F., SARNTHEIN, M. *et al.* (eds) *Proceedings of the Ocean Drilling Program, Scientific Results*, **108**, Ocean Drilling Program, College Station, TX, 241–277.

THORADE, H. 1909. Über die Kalifornische Meeresströmung. *Annalen der Hydrographie und maritimen Meteorologie*, **37**, 17–34, 63–76.

THUNELL, R. C., WILLIAMS, D. F. & HOWELL, M. 1987. Atlantic-Mediterranean water exchange during the Late Neogene. *Paleoceanography*, **2**, 661–678.

VAN FOREEST, D., SHILLINGTON, F. A. & LEGECKIS, R. 1984. Large scale stationary frontal features in the Benguela Current system. *Continental Shelf Research*, **3**, 465–474.

VAN ZINDEREN-BAKKER, E. M. 1976. The evolution of late Quaternary paleoclimates of southern Africa. *In*: VAN ZINDEREN-BAKKER, E. M. & COETZEE, J. A. (eds) *Paleoecology of Africa*, **8**, Balkema, Cape Town, 160–202.

—— 1980. Comparison of Late Quaternary climatic evolutions in the Sahara and the Namib-Kalahari

region. *In*: VAN ZINDEREN-BAKKER, E. M. & COETZEE, J. A. (eds) *Paleoecology of Africa*, **12**, Balkema, Rotterdam, 381–394.

VOITURIEZ, B. 1981. Le sous-courants equatoriaux nord et sud et la formation des dômes thermiques tropicaux. *Oceanologica Acta*, **4**, 497–506.

WEISSERT, H. J. & OBERHÄNSLI, H. 1985. Pliocene oceanography and climate: An isotope record from the southwestern Angola Basin. *In*: HSÜ, K. J. & WEISSERT, H. J. (eds) *South Atlantic Paleoceanography*. Cambridge University Press, Cambridge, 79–97.

WILLIAMS, J., BARRY, R. G. & WASHINGTON, W. M. 1974. Simulation of the atmospheric circulation using the NCAR global circulation model with ice age conditions. *Journal of Applied Meterology*, **13**, 305–317.

WINTER, A. & MARTIN, K. 1990. Late Quaternary history of the Agulhas Current. *Paleoceanography*, **5**, 479–486.

WISE, S. W., GOMBOS, A. M. & MUZA, J. P. 1985. Cenozoic evolution of polar water masses, southwest Atlantic Ocean. *In*: HSÜ, K. J. (ed.) *South Atlantic Paleoceanography*. Cambridge University Press, 283–324.

WOODRUFF, F. & SAVIN, S. M. 1989. Miocene deepwater oceanography. *Paleoceanography*, 87–140.

WYRTKI, K. 1964. Upwelling in the Costa Rica Dome. *Fishery Bulletin*, **63**, 355–372.

ZAGWIN, W. H. 1974. The Plio-Pleistocene boundary in western and southern Europe. *Boreas*, **3**, 75–97.

ZIEGLER, A. M., SCOTESE, C. R. & BARRETT, S. F. 1982. Mesozoic and Cenozoic paleogeographic maps. *In*: BROSCHE, P. & SUNDERMAN, J. (eds) *Tidal Friction and the Earth's Rotation*. Springer, New York, 240–252.

Note added in proof

While this paper was in press, several works have appeared, significantly revising ideas of the surface circulation of the South Atlantic. It has now been shown that the general surface circulation is not the rectangular gyre shown on classic current diagrams, but the anticyclonic gyre is triangular, confined to the southwestern South Atlantic. Its northeastern limb is the Benguela Current ('Southeast Trade Wind Drift') which extends diagonally across the ocean from South Africa toward Cabo San Roque, crossing the Greenwich meridian at 20°S (Peterson & Stramma 1991; Stramma 1991). The northeastern South Atlantic circulates as a cyclonic gyre (Gordon & Bosley 1992; Wacongne & Piton in press). The implication for the deposition of opal and organic carbon on the Walvis Ridge Abutment Plateau and southeastern Angola Basin is that the contribution of productive waters advected from the north may be more significant than had been assumed. DSDP Sites 530 and 362/532 lie downstream from both the Namibian coastal upwelling system and the Angola Dome.

Additional references

GORDON, A. L. & BOSLEY, K. T. 1992. Cyclonic gyre in the tropical South Atlantic. *Deep-Sea Research*, in press.

PETERSON, R. G. & STRAMMA, L. 1991. Upper-level circulation in the South Atlantic Ocean. *Progress in Oceanography*, **26**, 1–73.

STRAMMA, L. 1991. Geostrophic transport of the South Equatorial Current in the Atlantic. *Journal of Marine Research*, **49**, 281–294.

WACONGNE, S. & PITON, B. 1992. The near-surface circulation in the northeastern corner of the South Atlantic ocean. *Deep-Sea Research* in press.

Palaeoproductivity oscillations during the last 130 ka along the Portuguese and NW African margins

FATIMA ABRANTES

Graduate School of Oceanography, University of Rhode Island, Narragansett, RI 02882, USA

and

Serviços Geológicos de Portugal, Rua Academia das Ciências, 19 2°, 1200 Lisboa, Portugal

Abstract: Diatom abundance and taxonomic changes were quantitatively studied in the latest Quaternary (~130 ka to present day) sequences of the upwelling zones associated with the continental margins of Portugal and northwest Africa. Marked oscillations in diatom abundances accompanied by changes in the assemblage composition are evident during the late Quaternary and reflect changes in primary productivity related to upwelling intensity. Upwelling increased during glacial episodes (Isotopic Stages 2 and 6) relative to interglacial intervals (Isotopic Stages 1, 3 and 5). During the late Holocene, primary productivity levels are similar to those for Stage 5, and, lower than today in the early Holocene.

The palaeoproductivity reconstruction based on the diatom record is supported by independent estimates of palaeoproductivity based on the organic carbon content of the sediments.

Background

On the western boundaries of the continents, where winds blow nearly parallel to the coast (such as the NW coast of the United States, Peru, SW Africa, NW Africa and Portugal), surface waters are transported away from the coast, due to the Coriolis effect and replaced by subsurficial waters usually colder and richer in nutrients than the surface waters. This is generally called coastal upwelling.

In upwelling zones, primary production is very high, because the input of inorganic nutrients into the system produces energy (Margalef 1981) that is transformed mainly by diatoms (Margalef 1978, 1979, 1985; Margalef *et al.* 1979; Blasco *et al.* 1980, 1981) into the 'new production' of Dugdale & Goering (1976). It is this new production that is of interest for palaeoproductivity studies, because it determines the supply of organic material to the sea floor and the sediments, thus it determines the export production. Since diatoms dominate the phytoplankton of such regions, their abundance in coastal sediments should be correlated to high primary production generated by upwelling. Such a correlation was shown for the southern Portuguese coast by Monteiro *et al.* (1983) and Abrantes & Sancetta (1985) and, for NW Africa, in studies by Diester-Haass *et al.* (1976*a*, *b*) and Richert (1977).

These studies provided significant information toward our interpretation of palaeoupwelling along these margins. However, several important questions remained.

(1) Would it be possible to identify not only the loci of high productivity but also the dynamic characteristics of the system that generated a specific geological record?

(2) Does the distribution of diatom assemblages, as recorded in the sediments reflect the dynamics of the upwelling system?

(3) If so, are we be able to use those results to infer variations in productivity resultant from changes in the upwelling system throughout the Quaternary?

This paper addresses these questions using surficial sediments and late Quaternary sequences from the Portuguese and NW African continental margins.

The record from the surface sediments off Portugal

Upwelling patterns

Along the Portuguese and NW African coasts, coastal upwelling is the result of the interaction of the trade winds and the Canary Current. The upwelling is variable both in space and time: It occurs year-round from 20°N to 25°N, being most intensive off Cape Blanc. During the

From SUMMERHAYES, C. P., PRELL, W. L. & EMEIS, K. C. (eds), 1992, *Upwelling Systems: Evolution Since the Early Miocene*. Geological Society Special Publication No 64, pp 499–510.

winter it occurs south of Sierra Leone and during
the summer (from May to September) it extends
further north up to Portugal (Barton *et al.* 1977;
Fiuza 1983; Jones & Halpern 1981; Smith 1968).
Off Portugal, distinct upwelling patterns related
to characteristic topographic constrains have
been recognized by Fiuza (1983, 1984) (Fig. 1).

To the north of Nazaré, the upwelling is
homogeneous alongshore, intense and consistent, with an inner front located near the mid
shelf (Fiuza 1983, 1984). South of Lisbon the
upwelling has a more pulse-like situation and
the inner front is closest to the shore. Along the
Algarve coast, upwelling only takes place
occasionally, when westerly winds blow locally.
During such periods, the Algarve coast becomes
covered with upwelled water which extends
offshore from the Guadiana River as a plume.
However, the westernmost area, immediately to
the east of Cape S. Vicente, is generally covered

Fig. 1. Tiros-N thermal infrared image obtained
during the summer of 1979 (courtesy of A. Fiuza,
University of Lisbon).

by western upwelled waters carried along the
shelf break around Cape S. Vicente (Fiuza
1983, 1984).

This coastal upwelling brings waters from
depths of 60–120 m to the surface. South of
Lisbon the upwelled water has thermohaline
characteristics corresponding to Eastern North
Atlantic Central Water (ENACW) as defined
by Fiuza (1984). To the north of Nazaré the
upwelled water is ENACW with subpolar
characteristics (Fiuza 1984). Little data is available on the chemical characteristics of these
water masses. Boto (1945) states that the
phosphate concentrations vary from total
depletion during the winter to concentrations as
high as 170 mg/m^3 off Porto and 40 mg/m^3 off
the eastern Algarve coast during the summer.
A study by Coste *et al.* (1986) shows that off
Cape Sines, and during a period of weak upwelling activity the deep layers of central waters
are richer in nutrients (4 μm_{at} N–NO$_3$/l) and
poorer in dissolved oxygen (0.5 ml/l) nearer the
coast than offshore.

Methods

A quantitative analysis was made of opaline
microfossils and diatom assemblages preserved
in surficial shelf sediments from the Portuguese
margin and in Quaternary sequences retrieved
from the continental margin of Portugal: cores
1326 KS11 and 1327 KS12 (Fig. 4; Abrantes,
1991*a*) and, from the continental margin of NW
Africa, cores 12392–1 and 16030–1 (Fig. 5;
Abrantes, 1991*b*). Each sample was quantitatively evaluated for the number of whole
diatoms, diatom fragments, silicoflagellates and
radiolarians per cubic centimetre of fresh sediment (/cm^3 f.s.) and per gram of dry sediment
(/g d.s.). For the core samples, accumulation
rates were also calculated for each group, as
a number of valves per cm^2/ka. Quantitative
microfossil slides were prepared using the
procedures described by Abrantes (1988*a*).
Diatom counts were made at 1000 × following
the counting procedures and definitions of
counting units of Abrantes & Sancetta (1985).
The per cent abundance of diatom species was
determined for specimen counts of 200–300
individuals per sample.

Age control is based upon oxygen isotope
record of the planktonic foraminifer *Globigerina
bulloides* and the benthic foraminifer
Cibicidoides wuellerstorfi. Graphic correlation
(Miller 1977) of these records with the standard
curve (SPECMAP $\delta^{18}O$) provided the chrono-
logic framework. For the NW African cores,
age control for the most recent 30 ka is based

Table 1. Depth, age and sedimentation rates used as the chronological framework for core 12392−1.

Depth (cm)	Age (ka)	Sed. rate (cm/ka)	Conventional ^{14}C ages (ka) δ ^{18}O-events
0.00	2.00	4.46	AMS ^{14}C-analogue
31.25	9.00	5.29	^{14}C age*
40.25	10.70	6.47	AMS ^{14}C-analogue*
51.25	12.40	8.47	AMS ^{14}C-analogue*
101.25	18.30	13.39	AMS ^{14}C-analogue*
251.25	29.50	10.77	δ ^{18}O-event 3.31
474.25	50.21	3.82	δ ^{18}O-event 3.33
494.25	55.45	4.01	δ ^{18}O-event 4.22
514.25	60.44	6.72	δ ^{18}O-event 5.1 top
634.25	78.30	7.35	δ ^{18}O-event 5.1 base
644.25	76.66	3.91	δ ^{18}O-event 5.31
709.00	96.21	4.80	δ ^{18}O-event 5.33
744.25	103.55	4.22	δ ^{18}O-event 5.51
824.25	122.50	3.72	δ ^{18}O-event 5.53
834.25	125.19	4.24	δ ^{18}O-event 6.22
876.25	135.10		

* corrected after Bard *et al.* (1990).

upon Th-age corrections of AMS^{14}C ages (Bard *et al.* 1990). Ages and resulting sedimentation rates for core 12392−1 are listed in Table 1. The oxygen and carbon isotope data of the NW African cores is from Zhan (1986). Organic carbon data for core 12392−1 is from Muller *et al.* (1983).

Total diatom and diatom assemblages distribution patterns

To address the first two questions, Abrantes (1988*b*) conducted a quantitative analyses, in the sediments, of diatoms in the upwelling associated with the Portuguese continental margin. The distribution of the diatom abundance (number/cm^3) in the 169 sediment samples distributed on the Portuguese margin (Fig. 2) shows a generalized high abundance of diatoms on the northern part of the shelf, a band-like distribution in the southern region and high abundances immediately to the east of Cape S. Vicente.

This distribution pattern suggests that absolute diatom abundance in the sediments off Portugal reflect the fairly homogeneous upwelling regime north of the Nazaré Canyon. The patterns also reflect the closeness to the shore of the inner upwelling front on the southwestern coast and the eastward progression of western upwelled waters along the Algarve coast.

The most abundant and persistent taxa are the genera *Chaetoceros* Ehrenberg, and *Thalassiosira* Cleve and the species *Paralia sulcata* (Ehr.) Cleve and *Thalassionema nitzschioides* (Grunow) Hustedt (Fig. 3). The resting spores mainly of the genus *Chaetoceros* indicate the location of the inner upwelling fronts (Fig. 3a). *Thalassiosira*, and especially very small forms of *T. binata* Fryxell, *T. decipiens* (Grunow ex Van Heurck) Jorgensen, *T. delicatula* (Ostenfeld) Hasle and *T. diporocyclus* Hasle, being more abundant in the north, also appear to reflect the higher nutrient availability in this region (Fig. 3b). *Paralia sulcata* present in all the sediments underlying upwelling waters can be considered an upwelling related species (Fig. 3c) and its cell size shows significant variations. It increases with the decrease of available nutrients both offshore and southwards (Fig. 3d). In contrast, *T. nitzschioides*, records a weaker upwelling situation (Fig. 3e).

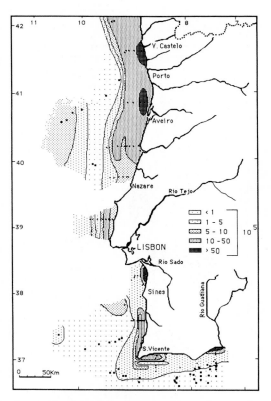

Fig. 2. Number of diatoms per cubic centimetre of fresh sediment.

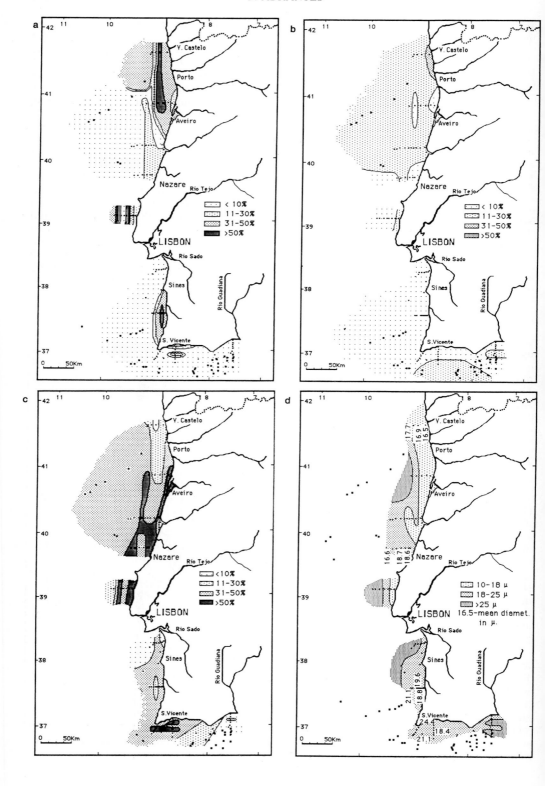

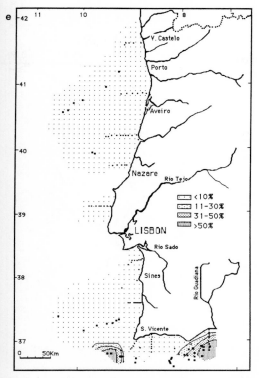

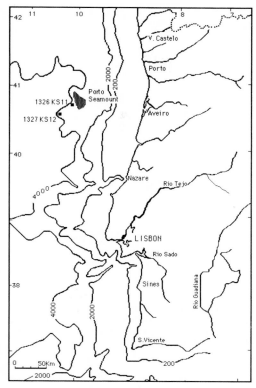

Fig. 3. (a) Distribution pattern of the resting spores of the genus *Chaetoceros* (b) Distribution pattern of *Thalassiosira*. (c) Distribution pattern of *Paralia sulcata*. (d) Size variation in *Paralia sulcata*. (e) Distribution pattern of *Thalassionema nitzschioides*.

Fig. 4. Position of investigated sediment cores off Portugal.

Latest Quaternary history of upwelling

The diatom record

The relationships between upwelling centers and diatom distribution in the underlying sediments obtained for the modern setting of the Portuguese margin (Fig. 4) are used to try to interpret changes in upwelling intensity and related surface productivity during the latest Quaternary recorded in sediment cores.

Core 12392–1 was collected off Cape Blanc (NW Africa), a region where high productivity results from the occurrence of upwelling favourable winds throughout the year (Fig. 5) and is the core that contains the best stratigraphic control for the last 130 ka (Fig. 6). The downcore distribution of both total numbers and accumulation rates of diatoms show the same general pattern (Fig. 7). For a better

assessment of the rates of change with the time, as well as easier comparison between cores, accumulation rates are used for discussion and are plotted against age in all figures.

High diatom accumulation rates (5 × 10^8 valves/cm^2 ka) (Fig. 9) are observed immediately above the oxygen isotope Stages 6/5 boundary, followed by an important and sharp decrease (at ~120 ka) to values of 10^5 valves/cm^2 ka that are maintained throughout Stage 5. Within Stage 4, the low values observed in the early part of this stage are followed by a rapid increase with values of 1–2 × 10^8 valves/cm^2 ka during late Stage 4 and the 4/3 boundary. High values also occur in oxygen isotope Stage 3. During glacial Stage 2, from 20 to 12 ka, very high diatom accumulation rates (5–7 × 10^8 valves/cm^2 ka) are again observed. This peak is also followed by a continuous and rapid decrease with disappearance of diatoms from 7 to 5 ka. At 3 ka diatoms reappear with accumulation rates of the same order of magnitude of the ones observed for Stage 5.

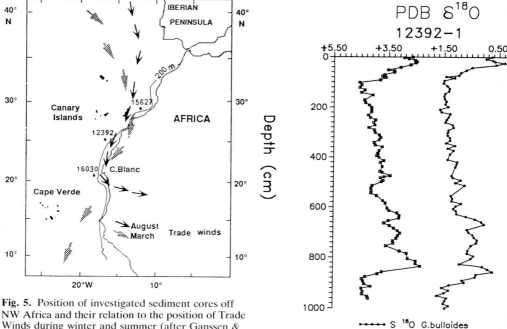

Fig. 5. Position of investigated sediment cores off NW Africa and their relation to the position of Trade Winds during winter and summer (after Ganssen & Sarnthein 1983).

Fig. 6. Oxygen isotope distribution along core 12392–1.

Productivity versus Preservation

Differential dissolution must be considered before the diatom distribution pattern can be used to monitor fluctuations in production caused by changes in upwelling intensity. Opal skeletons readily dissolve due to under-saturation of pore and seawater with respect to silica. Among the siliceous microfossil groups, radiolarians are generally more resistant to dissolution than diatoms and silicoflagellates are less resistant than diatoms (Schrader 1972). The downcore abundances of other opaline microfossils within this core (Fig. 8) provide important information on the preservation state of the whole siliceous assemblage. In general the accumulation rates of the other opaline microfossils agree well with the diatom distri-bution. Dissolution is also selective within the diatom group itself. It destroys valves of some species more readily than others, increasing the relative abundance in the sediments of solution-resistant forms. In this core, the resistant group (*Azpetia nodulifer*, *Paralia sulcata*, *Stepha-nopyxis*; Fig. 9) shows no important variation throughout the core, except for the increase in abundance observed during the Holocene. Both the opaline microfossils and resistant

group downcore abundances indicate that productivity is the determinant factor of the biogenic opal record. Within the Recent sedi-ments of the Portuguese margin, high abun-dances of the genus *Chaetoceros* were associated with the position of the upwelling fronts. In this core, the genus *Chaetoceros* (Fig. 10) clearly increases at about 76 ka and contributes up to 90% of the assemblage at the diatom peaks with an almost equal contribution of spores and vegetative cells during Stage 2. The preservation of dissolution sensitive cells and even of the delicate bristles of some species of the genus is extraordinary and must bear a relationship to extremely high supply rates and rapid burial at times of diatom maxima. Therefore I assume that the major variations in diatom accumu-lation rates are a reflection of changes in surface productivity over the last 130 ka. Though no absolute estimations of upwelling intensity are possible from the diatom data, it is possible to infer that along the NW African margin:

(i)   glacial Stage 6 was a time of intense pro-ductivity that continued through the 6/5 boundary, decreasing sharply around 120 ka;

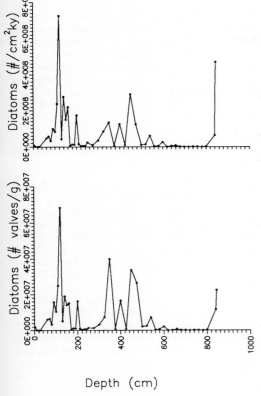

Fig. 7. Total number as number/g and accumulation rate of diatoms versus depth in core 12392–1.

(ii) Stage 5 appears as one of the times of lower production.

(iii) a new increase in production occurs around 76 ka, early Stage 4, but the higher productivity occurs right above the 4/3 boundary;

(iv) throughout the rest of Stage 3, production is lower than at early Stage 3 but it is still important as reflected by the abundance of *Chaetoceros* spores;

(v) on Stage 2 very high productivity conditions prevail for about 8000 years, terminating abruptly slightly earlier than the initiation of the last deglaciation.

These findings are in accordance with previous evidence that productivity off NW Africa was higher during Quaternary glacial Stage 2 (Diester-Haass *et al.* 1973; Labracherie 1980; Labracherie *et al.* 1983; Müller *et al.* 1983; Sarnthein *et al.* 1982; Thiede 1977; Thiede *et al.* 1982). Increased diatom productivity during

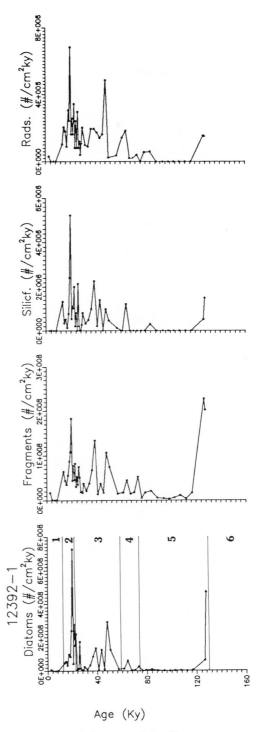

Fig. 8. Accumulation rates of the siliceous microfossil groups.

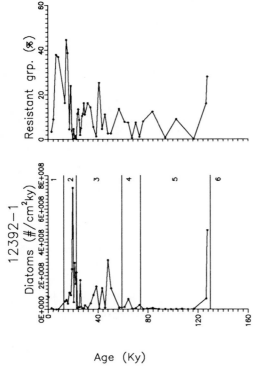

Fig. 9. Distribution pattern as a percentage of the total assemblage of the resistant group.

glacial intervals implies stronger coastal up-welling which is strongly dependent on the intensity of the trade winds. Existing indicators for an increase in atmospheric circulation during the last glacial maximum includes the spreading of dune fields over large parts of north Africa (Sarnthein *et al.* 1982), the distribution and composition of eolian–marine deposits (Hooghiemstra 1989; Sarnthein *et al.* 1982) and the results of the modelling of CLIMAP data (Manabe & Hahn 1977).

Comparison between core 12392–1 and the other cores

When this core is compared to the diatom record of the other three cores (KS11, KS12 and 16030–1; Fig. 11), the distribution patterns are very similar for the last 40 ka. In summary, diatoms are present throughout the cores with an important and rapid increase in diatom accumulation rates during stage 2. This increase is followed by a decrease in the early Holocene and a subsequent increase within the last 3–4 ka. In terms of assemblage composition, *Chaetoceros* dominates the assemblage from 46 to 12 ka, with vegetative cells reaching their highest abundance during Stage 2. The observed agreement between these two regions supports the assumption that increased diatom accumulation rates reflect increased productivity over

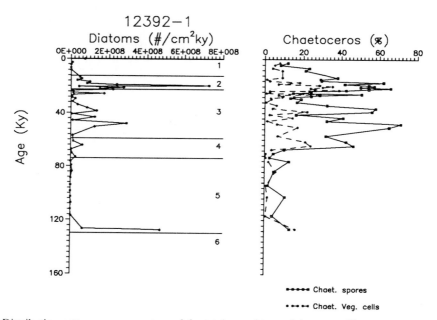

Fig. 10. Distribution pattern as a percentage of the total assemblage of the genus *Chaetoceros*.

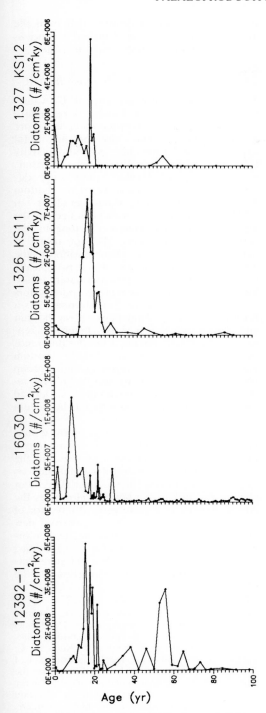

Fig. 11. Comparison of the diatom accumulation rates recorded on NW African cores (12392−1 and 16030−1) and on the Portuguese cores (1326 KS11 and 1327 KS12).

broad areas of the northeast Atlantic margins. A somewhat diminished coherence is observed in the magnitude of the maximum accumulation rates observed for the two regions. Off NW Africa diatom accumulation rates are one order of magnitude higher than in the cores off Portugal throughout the latest Quaternary. According to Broecker & Peng (1982) opal dissolution on the seafloor depends on three major factors: sedimentation rate of the bulk sediment, bottom water dissolved silica concentrations and flux of opal to the sediments.

Bulk sedimentation rates at the Portuguese sites (~7 cm/ka) are 1.5 Xs higher than at the NW African sites (~4 cm/ka) for most of the last 100 ka. For the Stage 2 interval, sedimentation rates are about the same in both locations (14 cm/ka off Portugal and 13 cm/ka off NW Africa). One possible explanation for the observed results may very well reside in the fact that the bottom waters are different at the water depths of the Portuguese and the NW African cores location. In fact, core 16030−1 was collected at 1500 m depth off Cape Blanc (NW Africa), at a depth occupied by the modern Mediterranean outflow water (MOW) (Mittelstaedt *et al.* 1975). However, the present bottom water that flows over the NW African core 12392−1, and the Portuguese cores 1326 KS11 and 1327 KS12 is North Atlantic Deep Water (NADW) that flows in the region at a depth below 2000 m. Neither one of the factors discussed above can then explain the constant one order of magnitude difference observed in diatom accumulation rates between the Portuguese and the NW African margins. Available measurements of mean actual primary production for NW Africa indicate highest values off Cape Blanc (325 g C m^{-2}a^{-1}, coinciding with year round upwelling. To the south, where upwelling is seasonal, values decrease to 250 g C m^{-2}a^{-1}. In the northern region the values are even lower (200 g C m^{-2}a^{-1}. (Schemainda *et al.* 1975). Based on these data, the lower diatom accumulation rates observed off Portugal are interpreted as reflecting the lower seasonal (May to September) production off Portugal compared to the higher year-round production off NW Africa: a situation that has been maintained for the last 100 ka.

Palaeoproductivity from other methods

Carbon derived 'new palaeoproductivity'

An independent estimate of palaeoproductivity is that proposed by Sarnthein *et al.* (1987). This calculation is based on the organic carbon content of the sediments and the values obtained for this core are plotted on Fig. 12. A comparison of this curve with the diatom accumulation rate distribution pattern for the same core (Fig. 12) reveals that, except for the interval between 32 and 24 ka, the diatom accumulation rates and the new palaeoproductivity values not only vary in the same direction but also reach maxima and minima of the same magnitude at the same time. This

seems to be a good indication that both the diatom and the C_{org} reflect the same process, the flux of matter from the euphotic zone.

The bottom-pore water difference in $\delta^{13}C$

The difference between the $\delta^{13}C$ values ($\Delta\delta^{13}C$) of a pair of benthic foraminifera species which record bottom water and pore water conditions, may also be an useful approach for estimating paleoproductivity (McCorkle & Emerson 1988; Michael Arthur, pers. comm.). The bottom–pore water difference in $\delta^{13}C$ is a measure of the bottom water–sediment pore water gradient in $^{12}C/^{13}C$, which in turn may be reflecting the amount of organic matter oxidized in the surficial sediments. Since the net result of oxidative organic matter decomposition in the deep sea is to make the pore waters isotopically lighter than the overlying bottom water, as biological productivity increases, the pore waters of the surficial sediments $\delta^{13}C$ decrease. As a result, the $\delta^{13}C$ gradient between the bottom and pore waters will increase. Figure 12 represents the results obtained for the difference between *Cibicidoides wuellerstorfi* (bottom water indicator) and *Uvigerina peregrina* group (pore water indicator) (Corliss 1985). This record is in good agreement with the C_{org}-derived new palaeoproductivity values and the diatom accumulation record.

In conclusion, both the C_{org} derived new palaeoproductivity and the $\delta^{13}C$ record constitute independent additional evidence that the diatom variations are mainly due to fluctuations in diatom production in the overlying water column and flux to the bottom. However, the $\Delta\delta^{13}C$ appears as a more general indicator of increased productivity. The C_{org} derived new palaeoproductivity gives more detailed information on the palaeoproductivity variations, but it is the diatom record that better reflects the episodic nature of nutrient injection into the photic zone.

Samples from the NW African cores were obtained from the Kiel University core repository. Dr Michael Sarnthein made this study possible through outstanding co-operation. I thank J.P. Kennett, C. Sancetta and M. Arthur for stimulating discussions. I also thank H. Monteiro and my colleagues at the Marine Geology Department of the Geological Survey of Portugal for their assistance during the collection of data from the Portuguese continental margin. Dr Dale Krauss arranged for Unesco contract no SC/RP 267062.9. The French-Portuguese Committee of Oceanographic Cooperation supported visits to the 'IGBA — Université de Bordeaux' for sampling of

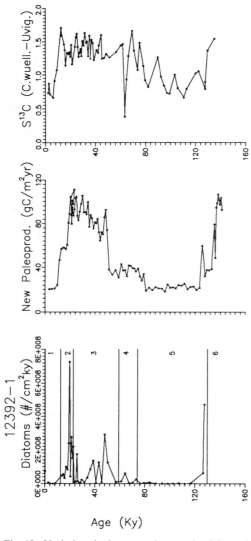

Fig. 12. Variations in the new palaeoproductivity and the carbon isotope difference between bottom and sediment pore waters in core 12392−1.

the Portuguese margin cores. Financial support was received through JNICT ICDE contract no 572.83.92, the Geological Survey of Portugal and by the Comissao permanente INVOTAN fellowship no 50/84.

References

ABRANTES, F. F. 1988a. Diatom productivity peak and increased circulation during latest Quaternary: Alboran Basin (Western Mediterranean). *Marine Micropaleontology*, **13**, 79–96.

—— 1988b. Diatom assemblages as upwelling indicators in surface sediments off Portugal. *Marine Geology*, **85**, 15–39.

—— 1991a. Increased upwelling off Portugal during the last glaciation: diatom evidence, *Marine Micropaleontology*, **17**, 285–310.

—— 1991b. Variability of upwelling off NW Africa during the latest Quaternary: diatom evidence, *Paleoceanography*, **64**, 431–460.

—— & SANCETTA, C. 1985. Diatom assemblages in surface sediments reflect coastal upwelling of southern Portugal, *Oceanologica Acta*, **8.1**, 7–12.

BARD, E., HAMELIN, B., FAIRBANKS, R. & ZINDLER, A. 1990. Calibration of the ^{14}C timescale over the past 30 000 years using mass spectrometric U–Th ages from Barbados corals. *Nature*, **345**, 405–410.

BARTON, E., HUYER, A. & SMITH, R. 1977. Temporal variation observed in the hydrographic regime near Cabo Corveiro in the NW African upwelling region, February to April 1974. *Deep-Sea Research*, **24**, 7–23.

BLASCO, D., ESTRADA, M. & JONES, B. 1980. Relationship between the phytoplankton distribution and composition and the hydrography in the Northwest African upwelling region near Cabo Carvoeiro. *Deep-Sea Research*, **27-A**, 799–821.

BLASCO, D., ESTRADA, M. & JONES, B. 1981. Short time variability of phytoplankton populations in upwelling regions — the example of Northwest Africa. *In: Coastal Upwelling and Estuarine Sciences 1.* American Geophysical Union, 339–347.

BOTO, R. G. 1945. Contribuição para os estudos de oceanografia ao longo da costa de Portugal — fosfatos e nitratos. *Travaux de la Station de Biologie Maritime de Lisbonne*, **49**.

BROECKER, W. S. & PENG, T. H. 1982. *Tracers in the Sea*. Eldigio, New York, 47–94, 1982.

CORLISS, B. H. 1985. Microhabitats of benthic foraminifera within deep-sea sediments. *Nature*, **314**, 435–438.

COSTE, B., FIUZA, A. F. & MINAS, H. J. 1986. Conditions hydrologiques et chimiques associees a l'upwelling cotier du Portugal en fin d'ete. *Oceanologica Acta*, **9.2**, 149–158.

DIESTER-HAASS, L. 1976a. Late Quaternary Climatic Variations in Northwest Africa deduced from East Atlantic Sediment Cores. *Quaternary Research*, **6**, 299–314.

—— 1976b. Quaternary accumulation rates of biogenous and terrigenous components on the east Atlantic continental slope off NW Africa. *Marine Geology*, **21**, 1–24.

DIESTER-HAASS, L., SCHRADER, H.-J. & THIEDE, J. 1973 Sedimentological and paleoclimatological investigations of two pelagic ooze cores off Cape Barbas, Northwest Africa. *'Meteor' Forsch.-Ergebnisse, Reihe C*, **16**, 19–66.

DUGDALE, R. C. & GOERING, J. J. 1976. Uptake of new and regenerated forms of nitrogen in primary productivity. *Limnology and Oceanography*, **12**, 196–206.

FIUZA, A. 1983. Upwelling patterns off Portugal. *In*: SUESS, E. & THIEDE, J. (eds) *Coastal Upwelling: Its Sediment Record. Part A: Responses of the Sedimentary Regime to Present Coastal Upwelling*, Plenum, New York, 85–98.

—— 1986. Hidrologia e Dinamica das Aguas Costeiras de Portugal. Tese doutoramento apresentada a Universidade de Lisboa.

GANSSEN, G. & SARNTHEIN, M. 1983. Stable isotope composition of foraminifers: The surface and bottom water record of coastal upwelling. *In*: SUESS, E. & THIEDE, J. (eds) *Coastal upwelling: its sediment record. Part A: Responses of the Sedimentary Regime to Present Coastal Upwelling*, 99–121.

HOOGHIEMSTRA, H. 1989. Variations of the NW African trade wind regime during the last 140 000 years: changes in pollen flux evidenced by marine sediment records. *In*: LEINEN, M. & SARNTHEIN, M. *Palaeoclimatology and Palaeometeorology: Modern and Past Patterns of Global Atmospheric Transport*. 733–770.

JONES, B. H. & HALPERN, D. 1981. Biological and physical aspects of a coastal upwelling event observed during March-April 1974 off northwest Africa. *Deep-Sea Research*, **28A**, 71–81.

LABRACHERIE, M. 1980. Les radiolaires temoins de l'evolution hydrologique depuis le dernier maximum glaciaire au large de Cap Blanc (Afrique du Nord-Ouest). *Palaeogeography, Palaeoclimatology, Palaeoecology*, **32** (1/2), 163–184.

——, BARDE, J., MOYES, J. & PUJOS-LAMY, A. 1983. Variability of upwelling regimes (northwest Africa, south Arabia) during the latest Pleistocene: A comparison. *In*: SUESS, E. & THIEDE, J. (eds) *Coastal upwelling its sediment record. Part B: Sedimentary Records of Ancient Coastal Upwelling*. Plenum, New York, 347–364.

MANABE, S. & HANH, D.G. 1977. Stimulation of the tropical climate of an Ice Age. *Journal of Geophysical Research*, **82**, 3889–3911.

MARGALEF, R. Life-forms of phytoplankton as survival alternatives in an unstable environment. *Oceanologica Acta*, **1**, 493–509.

—— 1979. Phytoplankton communities in upwelling areas. The example of NW Africa. *Oecologia aquatica*, **3**, 97–132.

—— 1981. Asimetrias introducidas por la operacion de la energia externa en sequencias de sedimentos y de poblaciones. *Acta Geologica Hispanica*, **16**,

1−2, 35−38.

—— 1985. Primary production in upwelling areas. Energy, Global Ecology and Resources. *In*: Bas, C., Margalef, R. & Rubies, P. (eds). *Simposio international sobre las areas de afloramiento mas importantes del oest Africano (Cabo Blanco y Benguela)*. 225−232.

——, Estrada, M. & Blasco, D. 1979. Functional morphology of organisms involved in red tides, as adapted to decaying turbulence. *In*: Taylor & Seliger (eds) *Toxic Dinoflagellate Blooms*. Elsevier, New York, 89−94.

McCorkle, D. C. & Emerson, S. R. 1988. The relationship between pore water carbon isotopic composition and bottom water oxygen concentration. *Geochimica et Cosmochimica Acta*, **52**, 1169−1178.

Miller, F. X. 1977. The Graphic correlation method in biostratigraphy. *In*: Kauffman, E. G. & Hazel, J. E. (eds) *Concepts and Methods of Biostratigraphy*, Strousburg, 165−186.

Mittelstaedt, E., Pillsbury, D. & Smith, R. L. 1975. Flow patterns in the Northwest African Upwelling Area. *Deutsche Hydrographische Zeitschrift*, **28**, 145−167.

Monteiro, J. H., Abrantes, F., Alveirinho-Dias, J. M. & Gaspar, L. 1983. Upwelling records in recent sediments from southern Portugal: a reconnaissence survey. *In*: Suess, E. & Thiede, J. (eds) *Coastal upwelling its sediment record. Part B: Sedimentary Records of Ancient Coastal Upwelling*, Plenum, New York, 145−162.

Muller, P. J., Erlenkeuser, H. & Grafenstein, R. 1983. Glacial — Interglacial cycles in Oceanic Productivity inferred from organic carbon contents in eastern north Atlantic sediment cores. *In*: Suess, E. & Thiede, J. (eds) *Coastal Upwelling: its Sediment Record. Part B: Sedimentary Records of Ancient Coastal Upwelling*, Plenum, New York, 365−398.

Richert, P. 1977. Relationship between diatom biocoenoses and taphocoenoses in upwelling areas off West Africa. *Beih. Nov. Hedw.* **54**, 408.

(abstract).

Sarnthein, M., Thiede, J., Pflaumann, U., Erlenkeuser, H., Futterer, D., Koopmann, B., Lange, H. & Seibold, E. 1982. Atmospheric and Oceanic Circulation patterns off Northwest Africa during the Past 25 million years. In: Von Rad, U., Hinz, K., Sarnthein, M. & Seibold, E. (ed.) Springer, Berlin 584−604.

Sarnthein, M., Winn, K., Duplessy, J. C. & Fontugne, M. R. 1987. Global variations of surface Ocean Productivity in Low and Mid Latitudes: Influence on CO_2 reservoirs of the Deep Ocean and Atmosphere during the last 21 000 years. *Paleoceanography*, **3**, 3, 361−399.

Schemainda, R., Nehring, D. & Schulz, S. 1975. Ozeanologische Untersuchungen zum Produktionspotential der nordwestafrikanischen Wasserauftriebsregion 1970−1973. *Geodatische und Geophysikalische Veroffentlichungen, Reihe IV*, Heft 16.

Schrader, H. 1972. Kieselsaure-Skelette in Sedimenten des ibero-marokkanischen Kontinentalrandes und angrenzender Tiefsee-Ebenen. *Meteor-Forsch.-Ergebnisse, Reihe C.* n. 8, 10−36.

Smith, R. L. 1968. Upwelling. *Oceanogr. Mar. Biol. Ann. Rev.*, n. 6, 11−46.

Thiede, J. 1977. Aspects of the variability of the Glacial and Interglacial North Atlantic eastern boundarÿcurrent (last 150 000 years). *'Meteor' Forsch.-Ergebnisse, Rheihe C*, n°28, 1−36.

——, Suess, E. & Muller, P. J. 1982. Late Quaternary Fluxes of Major Sediment components to the sea floor at the northwest African continental slope. *In*: von Rad, U., Hinz, K., Sarnthein, M. & Seibold, E. (eds) *Geology of the Northwest African Continental Margin*. Springer, Berlin 605−631.

Zahn R. 1986. Spatquartare entwicklung von kustenauftrieb und tiefenwasserzirkulation im nordost-Atlantik. Rekonstruktion anhand stabiler isotope kalkschaliger foraminiferen. *Kiel University Dissertation*.

Index

Modern and Ancient Continental Shelf Anoxia

Edited by R.V. Tyson (Newcastle University, UK) and T.H. Pearson (Scottish Environmental Advisory Services Ltd, UK)

This volume is unique in its consideration of severe oxygen depletion in coastal shelf waters from the perspectives of both marine ecology and geology.

Seasonal anoxia is a serious problem in the coastal waters of Europe, North America and Japan. Its drastic impact on environmental quality and on marine inshore fisheries has stimulated intensive research, in particular into the relative roles of biological and meteorological variables and of anthropogenic eutrophication. However, continental shelf anoxia is not a new phenomenon; at many times in the geological past vast areas of extensive shelf seas experienced episodes of severe oxygen depletion that lasted from thousands to millions of years, depositing most of the source beds for the world's hydrocarbon reserves. This fact has stimulated intensive research into the sedimentology, palaeoecology and organic and inorganic geochemistry of these sediments.

It is hoped that this book will inspire further research into this economically and environmentally important phenomenon.

Principal Authors

R.V. Tyson (Newcastle University, UK)
D.F. Boesch (University of Maryland, USA)
N.N. Rabalais (Louisiana Universities Marine Consortium, USA)
D.E. Harper, Jr. (Texas A&M University, USA)
G.J. van der Zwaan (University of Utrecht, The Netherlands)
T.C. Malone (University of Maryland, USA)
D. Justic (University of Zagreb, Yugoslavia)
J. Faganeli (Marine Biological Station, Yugoslavia)
M. Stachowitsch (University of Vienna, Austria)
W.E. Arntz (Alfred Wegener Institute, Germany)
K.-C. Emeis (Woods Hole Oceanographic Institution, USA)
G.W. Bailey (Sea Fisheries Research Institute, South Africa)
D.C. Rhoads (Science Applications International Corp., USA)
C.E. Savrda (Auburn University, USA)
M.C. Cuomo (Marine Sciences Research Center, SUNY at Stony Brook, USA)
G.C. Baird (Dept of Geosciences, SUNY, College at Fredonia, USA)
P.H. Heckel (University of Iowa, USA)
S. Piasecki (Geological Survey of Greenland)
P.B. Wignall (University of Leeds, UK)
R. Littke (Institute of Petroleum & Organic Geochemistry, KFA Julich, Germany)
M. Prauss (Universitat Gottingen, Germany)
H.-J. Brumsack (Geochemisches Institut, Gottingen, Germany)
J.D. Hudson (University of Leicester, UK)
W. Oschmann (Universitat Wurzburg, Germany)
P. Doyle (British Antarctic Survey, UK)
J.-G. Breheret (Laboratoire de Geologie, Tours, France)
E.A.M. Koutsoukos (Petrobras, Brazil)
I. Veto (Hungarian Geological Survey)

Outline of Contents

Modern and ancient continental shelf anoxia: an overview · **Modern shelf anoxia** · Effects of hypoxia on continental shelf benthos · Hypoxia in the Gulf of Mexico 1985-88 · Recovery responses of benthic assemblages in the Gulf of Mexico · Biofacial patterns in river-induced shelf anoxia · Oxygen depletion in Chesapeake Bay · Hypoxia in the northern Adriatic Sea · Sedimentary biogeochemistry · Anoxia in the northern Adriatic Sea · Benthos communities and oxygen-deficient conditions on the Peru Shelf · Oxygen deficiency on the Benguela continental shelf · **Ancient shelf anoxia** · The dysaerobic zone revisited · Oxygen-related biofacies in marine strata · Pelletal black shale fabrics · Submarine erosion on the anoxic sea floor · Pennsylvanian black shales, N America · Late Permian anoxia in E Greenland · British black shale biofacies · Posidonia Shale, Germany: depositional history · Toarcian palynomorphs, S Germany · Inorganic geochemistry of 'Posidonia Shale' · The Lower Oxford Clay, central England · Kimmeridgian shelf anoxia, western Europe · Nordenskjold Formation palaeoenvironments · Mid-Cretaceous glauconitization, SE France · Mid-Cretaceous of Sergipe Basin, NE Brazil · Sulphur and carbon in dysoxic-anoxic conditions, Central Parathethys

- An improved understanding of shelf anoxia owing to the unique combination of geological and biological approaches
- Assesses palaeo-oxygenation in the marine sedimentary record using palaeontological, sedimentological and geochemical criteria
- Primary audience: Sedimentologists, Palaeoecologists, Palaeontologists, Sedimentary Geochemists, Petroleum Geochemists, Marine Biologists, Marine Geologists and Oceanographers

- *Geological Society Special Publication No. 58*
- 470 pages, 259 illustrations, hardback
  ISBN 0-903317-67-2
  December 1991
- List price £75/US$125*

* Discounts are available to members of the Geological Society and the AAPG
